STUDY GUIDE AND SOLUTIONS MANUAL FOR ORGANIC CHEMISTRY

STUDY GUIDE AND SOLUTIONS MANUAL FOR

ORGANIC CHEMISTRY

Neil E. Schore

University of California, Davis

W. H. Freeman and Company

New York

ISBN 0-7167-1882-0

Printed in the United States of America

2 3 4 5 6 7 8 9 0 RRD 5 4 3 2 1 0 8 9 8

Contents

Preface

From One Organic Chemistry Teacher to Another

"I study all the time, I understand what you're saying in the lecture, and I do all the problems. So how come I got a '12' on the exam?" Ouch! We've all heard this from our students, haven't we? (At least I *assume* I'm not the only one.) Why is it that perfectly reasonable students of perfectly reasonable intelligence sometimes wind up being hopelessly buried by this course? More to the point, what, if anything, can *we* do about it? Clearly, in a perfect world, where students have ample time to do everything they're supposed to do and know everything that they need to know from freshman chemistry, things would be better. Typically, however, that is not the case. Students are pressed to budget their time and divide it among their courses. Because they often can't spend sufficient time studying for each course during the semester, they sometimes lag so far behind in their studying that, come exam time, they fall into the "Big Trap": they try to memorize everything. And then they get those "12"s and wonder what went wrong.

Well, we're the *teachers,* and we ought to know what's gone wrong and how to help the students do better. My experience has taught me that two critical factors almost always contribute to these predicaments: flawed understanding of basic concepts and lack of ability to apply the concepts to new, unfamiliar situations. The first involves an unsure grasp of mostly descriptive, informational material. Students must learn this fundamental material as surely as they learn the grammar and vocabulary of a foreign language. It has to be done, but there is no big trick to it. The basics can usually be mastered by serious study. Continuing emphasis on concepts and mechanisms, including the self-consistent, functional use of color in the Vollhardt text, and reemphasis in terms of relationships among topics in the "Introduction" and "Keys" sections of each chapter of this study guide are intended to make this process as manageable as possible for students.

The second factor is the killer for teachers: how to teach struggling students to (1) sort out the concepts and patterns relevant to a given problem and then (2) apply them in a logical way to the development of an answer. We all recognize that what we are trying to teach is not simply a piece of information, but a thought *process.* How does one go about teaching a thought process? The most successful way for me has been to lead students through a problem step-by-step, so they can experience the process, even if initially only from the outside looking in. They must be shown the choices that need to be made, why some are wrong and can be dismissed immediately, and how to evaluate the others. My goal in the preparation of the solutions to the end-of-chapter problems in the text was precisely this: to illustrate the thought process involved in getting from the problem to a reasonable answer. I've provided the greatest amount of detail in the earlier chapters, and I've *deliberately* omitted details in answers to some problems toward the end of the book. The learning process almost always requires *direct* experience on the students' part. It isn't enough for students to read an answer *even if it is fully understood!* Students must have opportunities to carry out the mental process for themselves. Therefore in many cases I've begun an answer with a hint, asking students to go back and attempt the problem again if they had difficulty the first time. Getting started is often the hard part, and this ploy at least gives serious students a second chance to make the connections required to proceed to a solution. It's a technique I use in helping students during office hours, and it seems to work.

I've also tried to be as rigorous and as complete as possible in the presentation of mechanisms, even to the extent of showing two-electron arrows in simple proton transfer processes. This might seem excessive to some, but remember, here we are dealing with students who may be in a position to derive clarifying insight from even the most insignificant of points. In the end, we must face the fact that our job is not really to "teach students organic chemistry." It may be possible to teach students a collection of facts, but knowing organic chemistry is much more than just knowing facts: it requires the ability to work with them as well. Our goal really has to be to teach students how to *learn* what organic chemistry is all about and how it *works*. Teaching students "how to learn" can be a difficult task. I hope the approach taken in this book is helpful in achieving that end.

Acknowledgments

The true credit for the existence of this volume belongs to Marilee Urban, whose typing, drafting, and endurance stood up throughout the inordinate demands of a project of this size. Thanks also to Ernie and John for their patience during all the nights and weekends Marilee worked on this.

While we're on the subject of patience, I'd like to thank my wife, Carrie, and my kids, Michael and Stefanie, for theirs as well. I wouldn't have gotten very far without it.

Thanks are also due in considerable measure to William Closson, Gene Hiegel, and Steven Zimmerman who reviewed and made many useful comments concerning textual portions of several chapters of the study guide portion of this book, as well as reviewing the end-of-chapter problems in the Vollhardt text, and to Michael Gernon, Raji Iyer, Ramesh Krishnamurti, and Karl Seper who carried out the unenviable task of working every one of those problems to see if my answers made any sense. To the extent they *don't*, I take full responsibility.

Of course, no acknowledgements would be complete without mentioning Mom and Dad, who for the first time get to see their son's name on the front of a real book.

Neil E. Schore
Davis, California

STUDY GUIDE AND SOLUTIONS MANUAL FOR ORGANIC CHEMISTRY

General Introduction

OR

WHOSE "BRILLIANT" IDEA WAS IT FOR ME TO TAKE ORGANIC CHEMISTRY, ANYWAY?

Good question. What is the problem with organic chemistry that causes so many students to view the class with so much anxiety? I think there are at least two good reasons:

1. Very bad experiences in freshman chemistry. Even students *interested* in chemistry find significant stretches of "Chem 1" to be intolerably dull.

2. Comments from students who've just finished taking organic chemistry. For example: "you have to memorize eight hundred million reactions, and then they don't even ask you the ones you've had in class on the tests."

Let's take these one at a time. Freshman chemistry is a little like scrambled eggs with a lot of other ingredients mixed in: a little bit of theoretical chemistry (electronic structure, bonding), physical chemistry (gas laws, equilibria, kinetics), inorganic chemistry (periodic table, descriptive chemistry of the elements, coordination compounds), organic chemistry (hydrocarbons, other types of carbon compounds), and who knows what else. No wonder so many students finish the first year of chemistry without the slightest trace of an overview of what they've sat through, or the faintest hint of an idea of what's supposed to come next. The problem is that "chemistry" is a very big operation that covers a lot of territory. It starts with atoms, but can go in lots of directions, and each of these can get pretty complicated. For now, all you need to know is that only a portion of what you saw in freshman chemistry is necessary as background for organic chemistry. This will be the subject of the first chapter of your textbook.

As for the second reason people are afraid of organic chemistry, all that famous "memorizing" you have to do, like most stories heard over and over again, there is truth to it. You will have to memorize a lot of organic chemistry. However, you *won't* have to memorize eight hundred million reactions. If you try to do that, you will be lucky to pass the course *even if you succeed.* What you really have to memorize are some basic properties of atoms and molecules, a number of principles that describe why and how reactions take place, and a number of reaction *types* that later can be generalized to include the various reactions of organic compounds that you will see throughout the course. From this framework you will be shown how the various details of organic chemistry are derived from some basic principles or "ground rules." You'll be expected to learn about, and *really understand* these ground rules, so that you can apply them in a logical way to completely new kinds of situations, and come up with sensible answers. It's a little like learning arithmetic. You all learned how to add when you were little. So if someone asked you to add $-1845\frac{2}{3}$ to $793\frac{1}{5}$, you would be able to figure out how to do it, even though it's pretty unlikely that you've added $-1845\frac{2}{3}$ to $793\frac{1}{5}$ ever before in your life. This is because you are familiar with some basic ground rules: what + and - signs mean, how to do fractions, the general methodology for adding (carrying numbers and all that). The difference is that you do arithmetic in elementary school and organic chemistry in college. The principles, the ground rules, and the methods of organic chemistry are going to go by quickly, and you're going to have to learn them well enough to make use of them . . . *quickly*.

That is where this study guide enters the picture. A textbook has a *linear* makeup. It starts at the beginning with page 1, and goes on in a straight line until it gets to the end. Now that might be a decent way to present, say, history, where the book could follow a calendar of events as they occur over a period of time. However, it doesn't work quite as cleanly with chemistry, where the same basic principles operating in chapter 2 are also cooking in chapter 12 as well as chapter 20. In a sense, organic chemistry is three-dimensional: there is a network of interrelationships among the various subtopics, *derived from these basic principles*, and hard to bring out clearly within the framework of a linear textbook. But it's a knowledge of these interrelationships that can make learning organic chemistry a much more reasonable job for a student to undertake. So, what you will find in each chapter of this study guide will be several features aimed at tying things together, so that you can see at every stage of the course the realtionship between the new material, what has gone before, and what will be coming up. Each chapter will have at least the following four components:

1. A general introduction to the textbook chapter as a whole in the context of previously covered material.

2. An outline of the chapter, with brief comments on the nature and significance of each chapter section.

3. More detailed comments about those features of the chapters that are of greater importance in terms of the course as a whole.

4. Solutions to problems at the end of the chapter, with explanations.

As this book is a solutions manual, a comment on that aspect of it is also appropriate. The problems in the textbook range from "drill" problems, which require you to apply only a single new idea in a repetitive way to several simple cases, to "think" problems, where several ideas, new and old, have to be applied, often to cases which at first glance may look very different from the examples presented in the textbook chapter. This cross-section of problems is intended to illustrate the thought processes involved in analyzing this kind of subject matter, and to resemble the kinds of problems you might encounter in exams.

Try to do the problems!!! If you can't see how to do a problem at first glance, try to analyze its features: what is involved conceptually and what is its context, *before* looking here for the answer. Then, if you're still stuck, note that in some cases you will often find a short introductory comment in this manual before the actual answer to the problem. This is intended to show you where the problem fits in to the chapter material and, perhaps, give you enough of a hint so that you might be able to go back and work it yourself. Then the answer will follow, plus an explanation. If you get a problem wrong, try to do two things: (1) understand the *process* for arriving at the answer, as illustrated in this guide, well enough so that you could answer a similar problem yourself without help, and (2) understand *why* the problem was asked in the first place - what points does it illustrate and what kinds of analogies, interpolations, or extrapolations of the basic subject matter does it involve. This kind of exercise will put you in a much better position to face the kinds of problems you are likely to encounter in exam situations.

Good luck!

CHAPTER 1

Structure and Bonding in Organic Molecules

General Introduction

The first chapter of the text covers the basic features associated with the bonding together of atoms to make molecules. Although this course will eventually focus on organic molecules, both organic and inorganic molecules are discussed in this chapter to allow a reasonably complete overview of bonding to be presented. Most of the material in this chapter (at least through section 1-8) is really a review of topics with which you should have some familiarity from freshman chemistry. In other words, this chapter is describing just those topics from freshman chemistry that are the most important to know in order to get off to a good start in organic chemistry: bonds, Lewis structures, resonance, atomic and molecular orbitals, and hybrid orbitals. These concepts are so fundamental to the course that the ability to work with them comfortably is really one that you should try to develop as early as possible. Read the chapter, try the problems, read the comments below, and, if necessary, look to other supplementary sources for additional problems and examples. For instance, "Electron Movement: A Guide for Students of Organic Chemistry" by D. Weeks (Saunders, 1976) presents extensive chapters on Lewis structures and resonance, suitable even for students whose chemistry background did not cover these topics at all.

Outline of the Chapter

1-1. Introduction and Overview.

1-2. Coulomb Forces.
The simple *physical* basis for bonding between atoms. *Conceptually* important.

1-3. Ionic and Covalent Bonds.
Review of principles involved.

1-4. Lewis Structures.
Operationally, perhaps the most important section of the chapter. You *have* to learn how to draw correct Lewis structures for molecules.

1-5. Resonance Structures.
Applies to species for which no single Lewis structure is adequate.

1-6. Atomic Orbitals.

Review material.

1-7. Molecular Orbitals.

Review material.

1-8. Hybrid Orbitals.

Simplest way to understand the geometry of molecules in the context of the orbitals involved in bonding.

1-9. Formulas, Structure, and Geometry of Organic Molecules.

General information section on experimental techniques and conventions for drawing formulas.

Keys to the Chapter

1-2 and 1-3. Coulomb Forces; Bonds

"Unlike charges attract" and "like charges repel." These consequences of elementary physics dealing with electrostatics and Coulomb's law are unquestionably the most important conceptual ideas to a basic understanding of chemistry. Not only do they determine whether, and how strongly, atoms will bond to each other (as described in this chapter), but they can also be applied to an even more complicated question: whether two molecules are likely to react with each other. Time and time again we will return to simple electrostatics, in the context of the properties of the individual elements, to explain the reactions of organic chemistry. Most of the bonds in organic molecules are polarized covalent bonds. These are bonds in which one or more pairs of electrons are shared between two atoms but due to an electronegativity difference between the atoms, the bond electrons on the average are closer to the more electronegative atom, creating a partial charge separation. In general, for A more electronegative than B, we have $\overset{\delta-}{A}\!:\ \overset{\delta+}{B}$. See the specific examples in section 1-3. As you will see later on, most of the reactions in organic chemistry follow a general pattern. First, two separate atoms with either unlike charges or polarities are attracted to each other. Then, electrons move from an "electron-rich" atom to an "electron-poor" atom to form a new covalent bond between them. Since bonds are made up of electrons, it's very important to keep track of how many electrons are involved, and where they are located. This is why Lewis structures are of paramount importance.

1-4. Lewis Structures

Whether you've ever done Lewis structures before or not, follow the rules in section 1-4 very closely at first. This will give you an opportunity to become familiar with the number of electrons around common atoms, and the common arrangements of these electrons in the bonds of molecules. This familiarity, brought about by doing *lots* of examples, is the best way to ensure that you will quickly and confidently be able to picture a Lewis structure for any of the types of species we will encounter later on. As you gain confidence through practice, you will be able to use more shorthand notations, replacing bonding electron pairs with lines, and omitting lone pairs that are not important to the chemistry of the atom. For the time being, however, you should include all electrons either as "bond lines" or dots, until you have seen enough reactions to know when the lone pairs are not going to be important.

To be more specific, organic chemistry involves reactions between organic compounds and other organic or inorganic species. These reactions can involve both bond breaking and bond forming processes, and the key to both is the movement of electrons. Speaking simplistically, electrons are much lighter than whole atoms. Therefore, in a reaction it will be the electrons (and specifically, the bonding or lone pair electrons) that will move first from negative places to positive places - the atoms involved will pretty much just follow the electrons around. The result is that our descriptions of reactions (reaction mechanisms) will invariably be in terms of number and location of electrons before, during, and after the reaction. Lewis structures provide the bookkeeping to help us keep track of electrons in reactions.

1-5. Resonance Structures

Two important conventions involving the use of arrows are introduced in section 1-5. The first is the use of double headed arrows to indicate resonance structures. This is a special kind of notation because of the special role resonance structures play in organic chemistry. When the rules for Lewis structures were invented in the early part of the century, it was initially thought that they would provide adequate representations for all known molecules. Mother Nature, however, designs molecules according to her own rules, involving electrostatics, among other things. As it happened, the Lewis structure rules (invented by *people*) were ultimately found to be somewhat inflexible, and incapable of handling a number of molecules. As shown in this section, many species have structures that cannot be represented by a single Lewis structure. They can only be described as intermediate in nature between two or more Lewis structures, each of which *by itself* is an incomplete picture of the molecule's structure. A completely correct description of such a molecule includes the best possible Lewis structures (resonance structures), separated by double-headed arrows, all enclosed in brackets. The result is the resonance hybrid. The only allowable difference between the resonance structures is a different location for the electrons from one structure to the next. All atoms must maintain the same geometrical arrangement in all the resonance forms. Later on, for purposes of brevity, you may find that a molecule which actually exists as a resonance hybrid may be represented by a drawing of only one of its Lewis structures. In cases like this you need to be aware of the fact that this is a shortcut for convenience purposes only, and that the real structure is still the resonance hybrid - the other resonance structures are implied even if they aren't written down.

The second use of arrows in section 1-5 is the use of curved arrows to show the movement of electron pairs. In this section, the only application is in showing how the electron pairs have been moved from one Lewis structure of a resonance hybrid to another (see picture of carbonate dianion). A more important use which will appear shortly is the use of curved arrows in reaction mechanisms to show the movement of electron pairs from one atom to another in the course of a real chemical reaction. You will find that pictorial descriptions of electron movement using these arrows will be very useful tools to help you learn and understand organic reactions.

1-6, 1-7, and 1-8. Orbitals

Atomic orbitals represent a convenient way to describe in detail the arrangement of electrons in atoms. Since this material should be familiar to you from freshman chemistry, the treatment here is brief. Note only that the + and - signs associated with parts of these orbitals *do not* refer to electrical charges *at all*. They refer to mathematical signs of functions (*wave* functions) associated with the distribution of the electrons of the orbital. Molecular orbitals are similar in nature mathematically. They are spread out over more than one atom, and provide an alternative, and somewhat more detailed method for picturing bonds in atoms, compared with Lewis structures. Recall that the number of molecular orbitals involved in describing a molecule is always exactly equal to the number of atomic orbitals that the individual atoms originally contained. However, when atomic orbitals are combined to make molecular orbitals, the result is always a combination of bonding, antibonding, and sometimes also nonbonding molecular orbitals. Bonding orbitals are always lower in energy (more stable) than their original constituent atomic orbitals, and antibonding orbitals are always higher in energy. The logical result is that electrons in bonding molecular orbitals will be more strongly attracted to positive nuclei, and more stable than electrons in atomic orbitals, and will give rise to strong bonds that stabilize their molecules. Electrons in antibonding orbitals will have just the opposite effect. Molecular orbitals will be especially useful aids in understanding the reactions of molecules containing double or triple bonds.

Hybrid orbitals are actually atomic orbitals that have been mathematically modified to permit them to reasonably accurately describe the geometric shapes of simple molecules. Hybrid orbitals have several advantages over ordinary atomic orbitals. Whereas plain atomic orbitals are arranged symmetrically around a single atom, hybrid orbitals can "point" in the direction of the bond towards a second atom. With most of the hybrid orbital located in between the bonded atoms, more electron density is located between the atoms where it can do some good, helping to bond the atoms to one another. By using different numbers of s and p orbitals in the hybridization, a wide range of bond angles are possible. This allows electron pairs to get as far away from each other as possible, minimizing unfavorable electrostatic repulsion.

Keep in mind some points on bookkeeping with hybrid orbitals. If an atom starts with one s orbital and three p orbitals, it will always end up with a total of four orbitals, no matter how the orbitals have hybridized for bonding purposes. In addition, if all the percentages of s and p characters in those orbitals are *added up* around the atom, the result will be just what the atom started with before hybridization: one orbital worth of s character, and three orbitals worth of p character. This is illustrated below.

(a) sp hybridized atom: contains two sp orbitals (each one is $\frac{1}{2}$ s and $\frac{1}{2}$ p character) and two ordinary p orbitals

$$2(\tfrac{1}{2}\,s + \tfrac{1}{2}\,p) \;+\; 2p \;=\; 1s \;+\; 3p$$

(b) sp^2 hybridized atom: contains three sp^2 orbitals (each one is $\frac{1}{3}$ s and $\frac{2}{3}$ p character) and one ordinary p orbital

$$3(\tfrac{1}{3}\,s + \tfrac{2}{3}\,p) \;+\; 1p \;=\; 1s \;+\; 3p$$

(c) sp^3 hybridized atom: contains four sp^3 orbitals (each one is $\frac{1}{4}$ s and $\frac{3}{4}$ p character)

$$4(\tfrac{1}{4}\,s + \tfrac{3}{4}\,p) \;=\; 1s \;+\; 3p$$

So in all cases exactly four orbitals are present, and they add up to the equivalent of one s and three p orbitals, even though each form of hybridization leads to a very different form of bonding and molecular shape from any of the others. As these examples show, the mathematical nature of hybridization is very flexible. The determining factors in the choice of hybridization will be based on electrostatics: the molecule will utilize the arrangement of electrons (that is, type of orbitals) that will maximize favorable bonding attractions and minimize unfavorable electron-electron repulsions.

As noted earlier, much of the material in these sections will be review for you. Nevertheless, you should be prepared to use any aspect of it in any of a number of places coming up in this course: these are the basics, and everything else will build from them.

Solutions to Chapter 1 Problems

1. Remember: ionization potentials represent energy input and electron affinities represent energy released. They are associated with the following processes:

   (1) $\text{Atom} \rightarrow \text{Atom}^+ + e^-$ IP (positive)

   (2) $\text{Atom} + e^- \rightarrow \text{Atom}^-$ EA (usually negative)

   The overall process

   (3) $\text{Atom}_1 + \text{Atom}_2 \rightarrow \text{Atom}_1^+ + \text{Atom}_2^-$

   should have an energy change equal to $IP_1 + EA_2$, since it is just the sum of the equations (1) and (2) for the two individual atoms.

   IP ↓ EA ↓

   (a) 119 + (-83) = 36 kcal/mole of energy required

   (b) 314 + (-83) = 231 kcal/mole of energy required

   (c) 124 + (-80) = 44 kcal/mole of energy required

   (d) $\underbrace{214 + 420}_{2e^- \text{ ionized from Be}} + 2(-77) = 480$ kcal/mole required

   (e) 214 + 420 + 2(-18) = 598 kcal/mole required

   Notice how, even in "favorable" cases, the overall process always requires input of energy. The next problem will illustrate the effect on these values of electrostatic attraction between ions.

****

2. Electrostatic attraction between ions is the only thing that makes ionic compounds feasible at all, as you will see.

(a) $Na^+ Cl^-$ Distance between ions is 1.0 + 1.8 = 2.8 Å. Electrostatic attraction between ions is therefore

$$E = \frac{(332 \text{ kcal/mole})(+1 \text{ charge on } Na^+)(-1 \text{ charge on } Cl^-)}{2.8} = -119 \text{ kcal/mole}$$

The reaction Na + Cl → Na^+Cl^- has an energy change of 36 (answer to Problem 1, part a) - 119 = -83 kcal/mole energy released.

(b) $H^+ Cl^-$ Distance = 1.8Å; E = -332/1.8 = -184 kcal/mole
For H + Cl → H^+Cl^-, 231 (Problem 1, part b) - 184 = +47 kcal/mole input still required. The reaction is still energetically unfavorable! HCl is not an ionic compound!

(c) $Li^+ F^-$ Distance = 0.6 + 1.4 = 2.0Å; E = -332/2.0 = -166 kcal/mole
For Li + F → Li^+F^-, 44 (Problem 1c) - 166 = -122 kcal/mole energy released.

(d) Be^{++} $2Br^-$ Distances = 0.3 + 2.0 = 2.3Å between Be^{++} and each Br^-.
$E = 2\left[\frac{332(+2)(-1)}{2.3}\right]$ = -577 kcal/mole, attraction between Be^{++} and the two Br^- ions. However, to be fair, the repulsion between the two Br^- ions for each other needs to be included, too. Assuming that they are 2 x 2.3Å = 4.6Å apart, E = 332/4.6 = 72 kcal/mole repulsion.
So for Be + 2Br → Be^{++} $2Br^-$, 480 (Prob. 1d) - 577 + 72 = -25 kcal/mole energy released.

(e) Be^{++} $2H^-$ Distances = 0.3 + 2.1 = 2.4Å
$E = 2\left[\frac{332(+2)(-1)}{2.4}\right]$ = -553 kcal/mole, attraction between Be^{++} and the two H^- ions. This is not enough to overcome the 598 kcal/mole input needed to make the ions in the first place (Problem 1e). Even without considering repulsion between the H^- ions, BeH_2 cannot be ionic.

****

3 (and 5 - see below).

(a) 

(b) :B̈r:C:::N: Triple bond is needed to give C and N atoms octets.

(c) H:Ö:C̈l:

(d) :C̈l:S̈:C̈l: ⟷ :C̈l:S̈:C̈l: Note that the availability of d
         :Ö: :Ö: orbitals allows S to be surrounded
          ‾   by a *fifth* electron pair.

      major (octets)

      H H   H   H
(e) H:C:N:H   (f) H:C:O:C:H
      H   H   H

(g) H:N::N:H   Double bond between nitrogens.

      H
(h) H:C::C::Ö: A molecule with two double bonds.

         + ‾   ‾ +
(i) H:N::N::N: ⟷ H:N:N:::N:

      ‾ +   + ‾
(j) :N::N::O: ⟷ :N:::N:O:
                    major (O more electronegative than N)
                    ****

4. (a) H:⁻   Hydride ion. Contrast H⁺ (a proton) and H· (H atom).

         H
    (b) H:C:⁻   A carbanion: C has an octet and a -1 formal charge.
         H

         H
    (c) H:C:⁺   A carbocation: C has only a sextet and a +1 charge.
         H

         H
    (d) H:C·   A carbon "free radical": C is neutral, bonded to only three
         H   other atoms, and surrounded by 7 electrons.

         H H
    (e) H:C:N:H   The methylammonium cation. The product of $CH_3NH_2 + H^+$.
         H H   Compare $NH_3 + H^+ \rightarrow NH_4^+$.

         H
    (f) H:C:O: Methoxide ion. The product of ionization of methanol:
         H $CH_3OH \rightleftharpoons CH_3O^- + H^+$. Compare $H_2O \rightleftharpoons HO^- + H^+$.

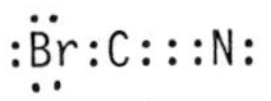

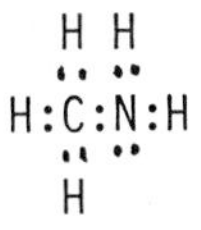

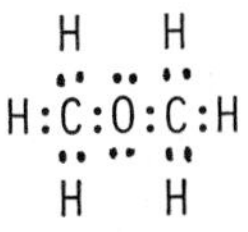

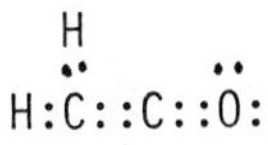

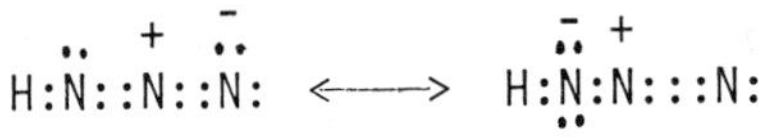

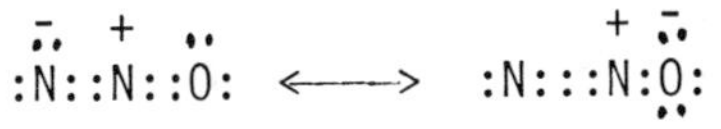

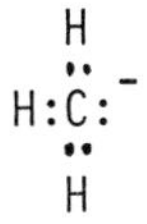

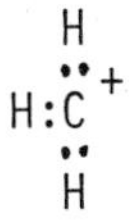

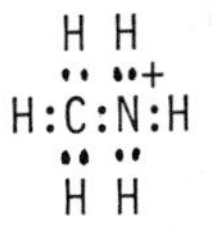

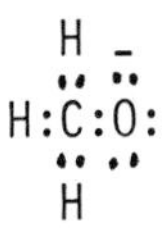

(g) 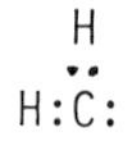 A "carbene": a neutral carbon, bonded to two other atoms, with only a sextet of electrons.

(h) H:C:::C:⁻ Another carbanion.

Carbanions (b and h), carbocations (c), free radicals (d), and carbenes (g) are high energy, reactive species that generally can't be "put into a bottle" due to their instability. They can, however, briefly appear as reaction "intermediates."

(i)  Hydrogen peroxide.

(j) 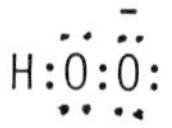 The conjugate base of hydrogen peroxide.

****

5. Resonance forms for answers 3(d), (i), and (j) have already been shown. A couple of other structures have resonance forms, too, as shown below. In each case the form below is not nearly as good as the one shown in the answer to problem 3, for the reasons given.

(b) 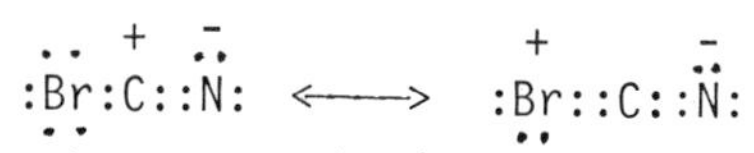
(carbon sextet) (separation of charge)

(h) 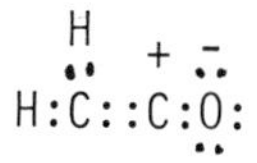
(carbon sextet)

****

6. (a) 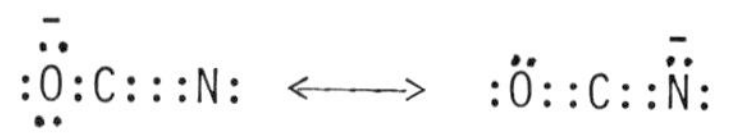
major (negative charge prefers the more electronegative atom - oxygen)

(b) 
major (negative charge prefers the more electronegative atom - nitrogen)

(c) 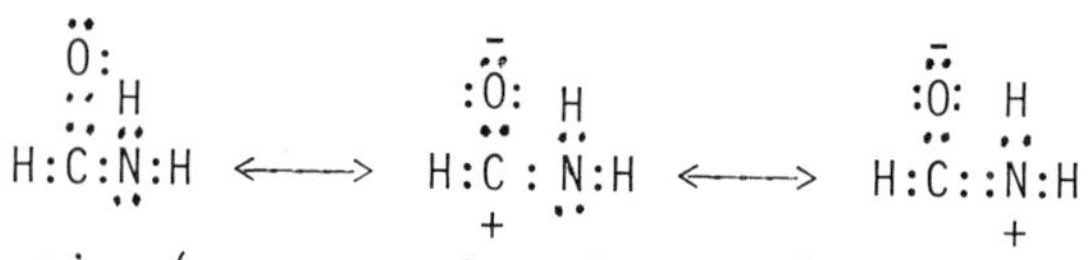
major (no separation of charge)

(d) 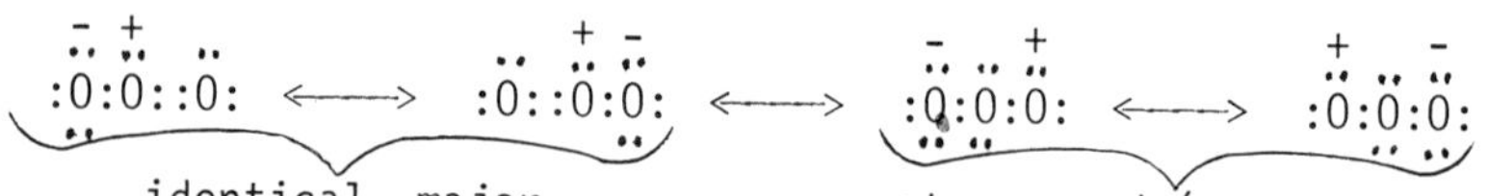
identical, major — not as good (oxygen sextet)

(e)  identical

(f) 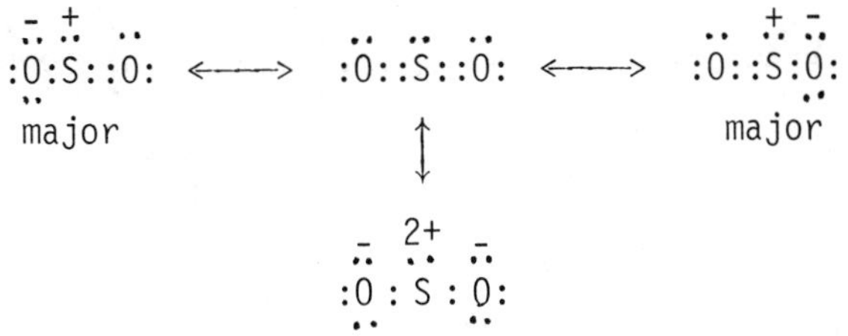

(g) 

major (octets) (carbon has sextet here)

(h) 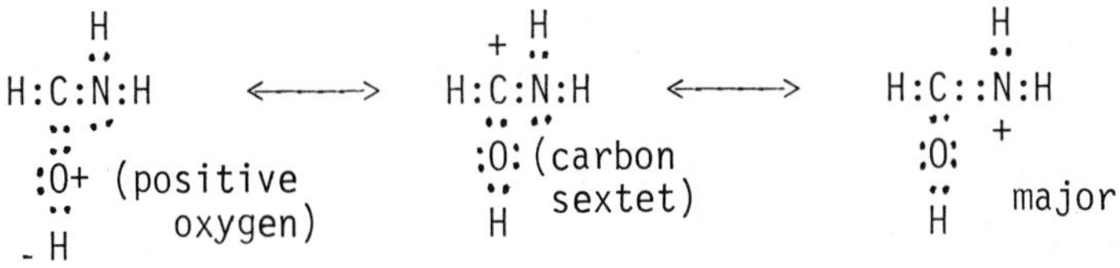

(i) 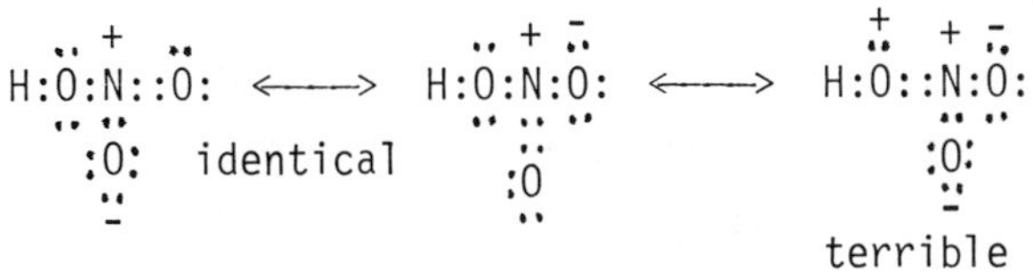

(j) 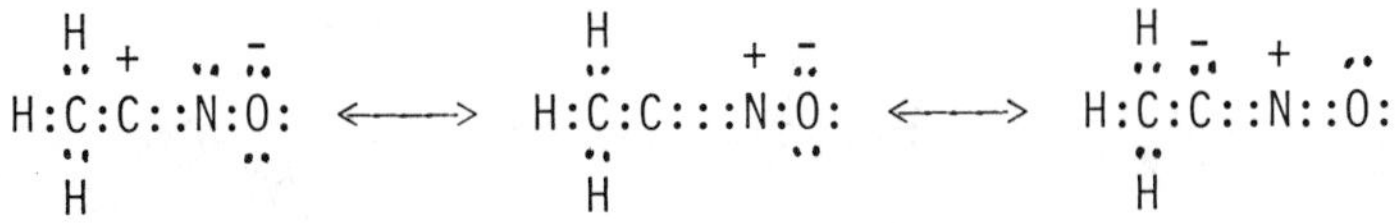

(carbon sextet) major (oxygen more electronegative than carbon)

****

7. (a) (i) 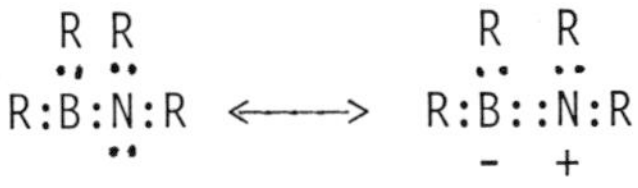 (ii) 

(iii) 

(b) The octet guideline takes precedence over the electronegativity guideline, so the doubly-bond structures are preferred for all three compounds.

(c) Due to the electronegativity order F > O > N, the doubly bonded structure in R_2BF, which puts a positive charge on the most electronegative element (F), will be preferred by the smallest margin. This preference will increase for R_2BOR and be the greatest for R_2BNR_2, as the electronegativity of the positively charged element in the doubly-bonded structure decreases.

(d) The doubly-bonded resonance forms in (i) and (ii) require sp^2 hybridization for N and O.

****

8. Each marked carbon is attached to three others in a trigonal planar manner, with a fourth carbon (the other marked carbon) above the plane, connected by a bond perpendicular to it:

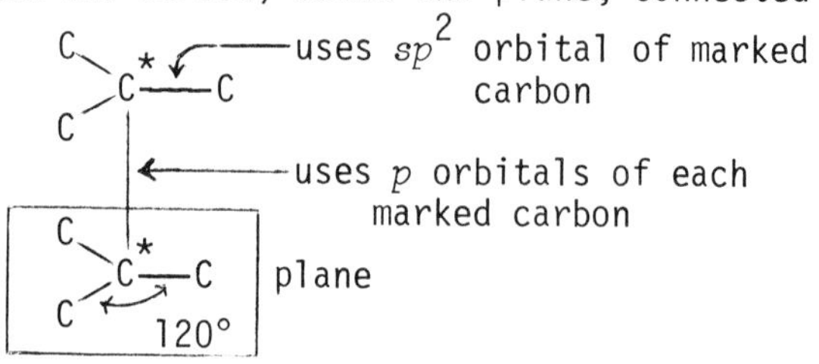

This is most consistent with sp^2 hybridization, where sp^2 orbitals are used in bonds to the other three carbons in the plane, and a *pure p orbital* bonds to the fourth carbon.

The bond between the two marked carbons involves end-to-end (σ) overlap of two unhybridized p orbitals, and consequently is longer and weaker than normal sp^3-sp^3 C-C single bonds.

****

9. (Compare Exercise 1-11.) (a) The molecular orbitals are obtained as follows:

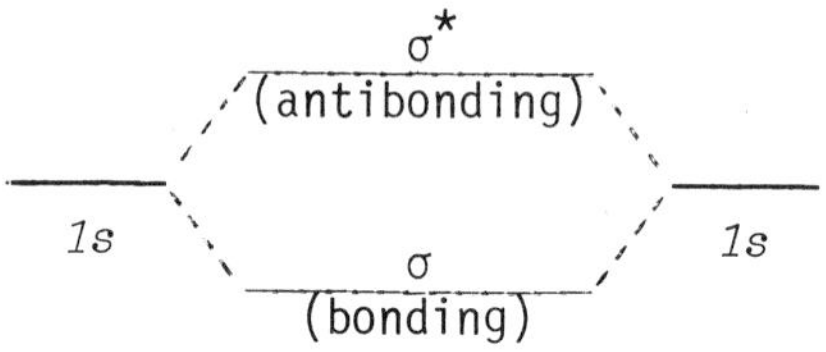

Therefore, the resulting electronic configurations are H_2, $(\sigma)^2$, with 2 bonding electrons vs. H_2^+, $(\sigma)^1$, with 1 bonding electron. So H_2 possesses the stronger bond.

(b) and (c) The relevant orbitals are:

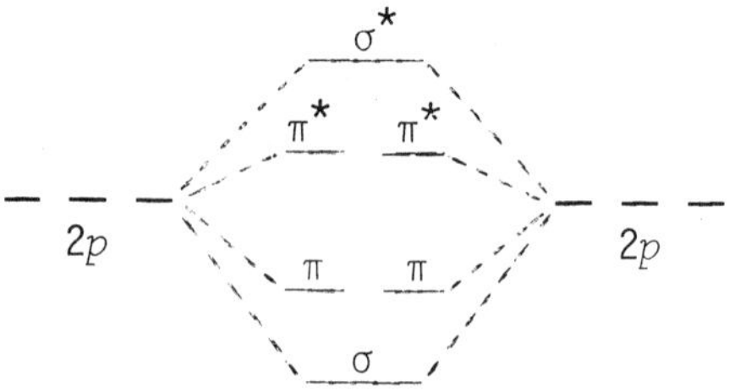

For (b), O_2, $(\sigma)^2(\pi)^2(\pi)^2(\pi^*)^1(\pi^*)^1$, 4 <u>net</u> bonding electrons vs.

$O_2{}^+$, $(\sigma)^2(\pi)^2(\pi)^2(\pi^*)^1$, 5 <u>net</u> bonding electrons. So $O_2{}^+$ has the stronger bond.

For (c), N_2, $(\sigma)^2(\pi)^2(\pi)^2$, 6 <u>net</u> bonding electrons vs.

$N_2{}^+$, $(\sigma)^2(\pi)^2(\pi)^1$, 5 <u>net</u> bonding electrons. So N_2 is better.

****

10. (a), (b), and (c). Each carbon is bonded to four other atoms and, there-fore, will possess approximate tetrahedral geometry. Each carbon in these molecules is sp^3 hybridized.

(d) Each carbon is attached to three other atoms (two hydrogens, and the other carbon). The bonds to hydrogen are σ bonds. One of the carbon-carbon bonds is a σ bond and the other carbon-carbon bond is a π bond. The result is that each carbon has approximately trigonal planar geometry (like boron in BH_3) and is sp^2 hybridized. In other words, each carbon uses sp^2 orbitals in three σ bonds, and the left-over p orbital in a π bond.

(e) Each carbon is attached to two other atoms (one hydrogen and the other carbon). The C-H bonds are σ bonds, as is one of the C-C bonds. The other two C-C bonds (of the "triple" bond) are π bonds. Geometry about carbon is linear (like beryllium in BeH_2) and each is sp hybri-dized. Each carbon uses two sp orbitals for σ bonds and two p orbitals for π bonds.

(f)
$$CH_3-\overset{\overset{\displaystyle O}{\|}}{C}-H$$
$$\underset{sp^3}{\uparrow}\quad\underset{sp^2}{\uparrow}$$

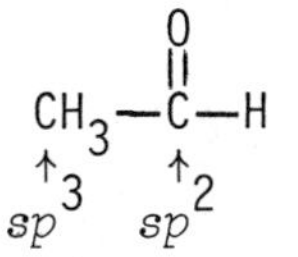

(g) Hybridization must allow both carbons to be doubly bonded (resonance form on the right). Both, therefore are sp^2.

****

11. (a)(i) The negatively charged carbon is bonded to three other atoms, and has a lone pair, similar to N in NH_3: sp^3.

(ii) Compare 10d: carbon will be sp^2 (double bond requires a p orbital).

(iii) Compare 10e: carbon will be sp (triple bond requires two p orbitals).

(b) Since s orbitals are smaller than p orbitals, s electrons are closer to the nucleus than *p* electrons. Thus electrons in orbitals with high *s* character (e.g. *sp*, which is ½*s*) will be closer to the nucleus than electrons in orbitals with less *s* character (sp^2, ⅓*s*, or sp^3, ¼*s*). Stability of negative charge therefore is $sp > sp^2 > sp^3$, or $HC_2^- > CH_2CH^- > CH_3CH_2^-$.

(c) $HC{\equiv}CH > CH_2{=}CH_2 > CH_3CH_3$, with acid strength paralleling stability of the conjugate base.

****

12. Assume a total weight of 100 g in each case, and divide each percent by the atom's atomic weight, to get the relative number of moles of the atom in the molecule (remember?).

(a) C, 92.31/12 = 7.69 and H, 7.69/1 = 7.69. So empirical formula is CH (equal numbers of C and H). Real molecules with this analysis include ethyne, C_2H_2, and benzene, C_6H_6.

(b) C, 62.07/12 = 5.17; H, 10.34/1 = 10.34. Assume O present is 100 - (62.07 + 10.34) = 27.59%, so O, 27.59/16 = 1.72. Using 1.72 as a common factor, there are 5.17/1.72 = 3 atoms C for each O, and 10.34/1.72 = 6 atoms H for each O. Answer is C_3H_6O.

(c) C, 71.11/12 = 5.92; H, 6.67/1 = 6.67; N, 10.37/14 = 0.74; O, 11.85/16 = 0.74. Answer: C_8H_9NO.

(d) C, 48.70/12 = 4.06; H, 2.90/1 = 2.90; Cl, 20.58/35.5 = 0.58; O, 27.82/16 = 1.74. Answer: $C_7H_5ClO_3$

(e) C_7H_{16} (f) C_2H_2O

****

13. (a) 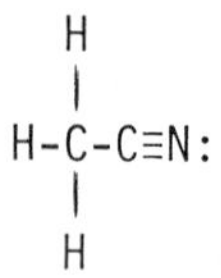 (b) 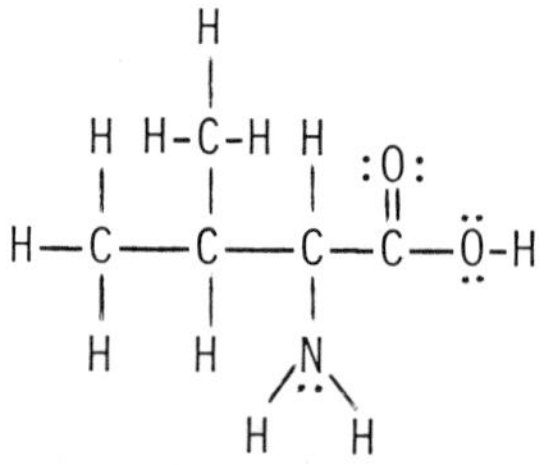 (c) 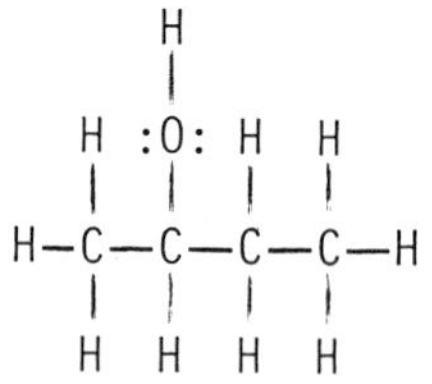

(d) 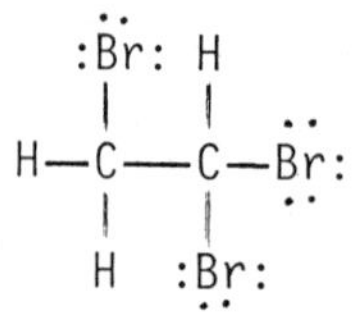 (e) 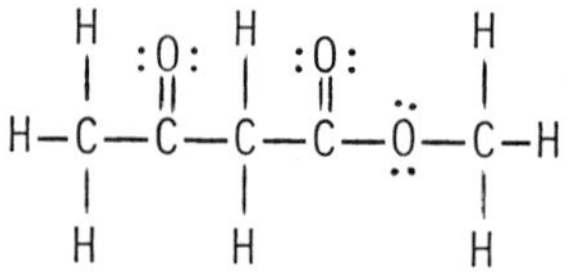 (f) 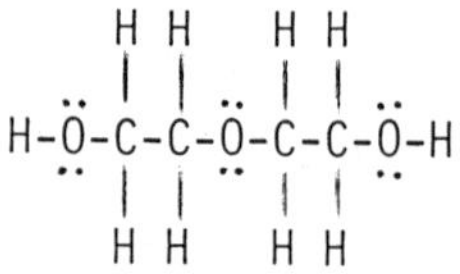

Line formulas do *not* as a rule show true bond angles.

****

14. (a) $H_2NCH_2CH_2NH_2$ (b) $CH_3CH_2OCH_2CN$ (c) $CHBr_3$

****

15. (a) $(CH_3)_2NH$ (b) $CH_3\overset{\overset{O}{\|}}{C}NHCH_2CH_3$ (c) $CH_3CHOHCH_2CH_2SH$

(d) CF_3CH_2OH (e) $CH_3CH{=}C(CH_3)_2$ (f) $CH_2{=}CH\underset{\underset{O}{\|}}{C}CH_3$

****

16. (a) 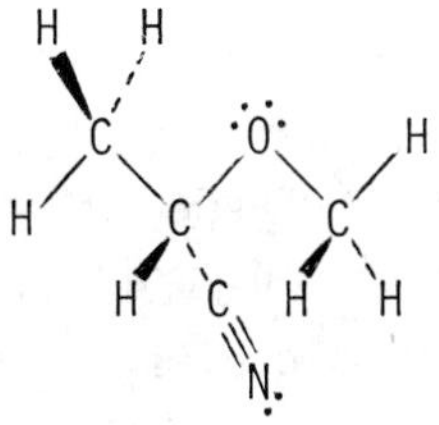   (b) 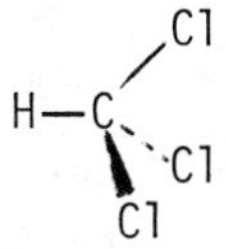   (c) 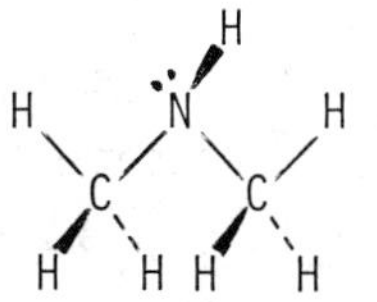

(d) 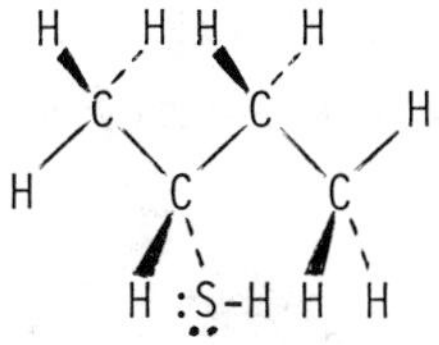

****

17. In each case calculate the molecular weight first.

(a) MW = 180.15; $C = \frac{9(12.011)}{180.15} = 60.00\%$; $H = \frac{8(1.0079)}{180.15} = 4.48\%$;

$O = \frac{4(15.9994)}{180.15} = 35.53\%$.

(b) MW = 151.15; C = 63.56%; H = 6.00%; N = 9.27%; O = 21.17%.

(c) MW = 206.27; C = 75.69%; H = 8.80%; O = 15.51%.

(d) MW = 183.18; C = 45.89%; H = 2.75%; N = 7.65%; O = 26.20%; S = 17.50%.

(e) MW = 179.24; C = 40.20%; H = 7.31%; N = 7.82%; O = 26.78%; S = 17.89%.

(f) MW = 294.30; C = 57.14%; H = 6.16%; N = 9.52%; O = 27.18%.

****

18. e > c > d > a > b   After the cation, positive character on carbon is related to number of (polarized) bonds to electronegative atoms.

****

19. (a) C-O, O-H   (b) any C-C   (c) $\underset{\uparrow}{C}\equiv\underset{\uparrow}{C}$ (d) $\underset{\uparrow}{C}{=}\underset{\uparrow}{C}$

(e) any C with 4 single bonds   (f) $C\underset{\uparrow}{-}C{=}C$ or $C\underset{\uparrow}{-}C\equiv C$

****

CHAPTER 2

Alkanes: Molecules Lacking Functional Groups

General Introduction

Alkanes are the simplest class of organic compounds. For this reason, it is convenient to use alkanes to illustrate several new topics that will later be found to be generally applicable to the other compound classes, too. These topics, as presented in this chapter, are (1) how to name organic molecules (nomenclature), (2) the relation of the physical properties of molecules to their molecular structure, (3) flexibility and shape of molecules (conformations), and (4) energy in organic chemistry. In chapter 3 we will cover chemical reactions of alkanes.

First, however, it is useful to put alkanes in a perspective as to their relationship towards other organic molecules. This is done through an introductory section on "functional groups."

Outline of the Chapter

2-1. Functional Groups.

The "business ends" of molecules: where reactions are likely to occur.

2-2. Straight-Chain and Branched Alkanes.

Alkanes of various structures. Isomers.

2-3. Nomenclature.

The first of a group of rules necessary to unambiguously name any organic compound.

2-4. Physical Properties.

A topic that is usually not emphasized very much, but which does reveal several useful, generalizable points about molecules.

2-5. Conformational Isomers.

A discussion of the actual three-dimensional shapes a molecule may possess.

2-6. Thermodynamics and Kinetics.

The energetic factors that determine whether or not a molecule is likely to "do anything," like change its shape, or undergo a chemical reaction.

Keys to the Chapter

2-1. Functional Groups.

One look at the fourteen classes of organic compounds in Table 2-1 (and these are only some of the most common ones!) will immediately tell you how complicated organic chemistry can become. At the same time, however, closer inspection reveals features of these compound classes that can greatly simplify learning in this course. Each compound class is characterized by a specific atom grouping called a functional group. Notice that only nine different elements are represented in these 14 classes: the four halogens, C, H, S, N, and O. In fact, ten of these classes only contain carbon, hydrogen, and oxygen! Knowledge of the characteristics of these atoms and the bonds between them, as we will see, will tell us the properties of the functional groups in which they appear. The functional groups will, in turn, provide the key to understanding the chemistry of *all* the members of the compound class. Thus, *all* members of the "alcohol" class of compounds, for instance, have certain common physical and chemical properties, resulting from the presence of the -OH group in *all* of them. This kind of generalizable, qualitative similarity between compounds in any given class allows organic chemistry to be learned in a structured, organized, and, above all, logical way.

Functional groups consist either of polarized bonds, whose atoms can attract other polarized or charged species, leading to reactions, or multiple (double or triple) bonds which also show reactivity for reasons we'll explore later. Functional groups are the parts of molecules that are most often involved in chemical reactions of those molecules. They are the "centers of reactivity" of molecules - where the action is.

The most fundamental feature of alkanes relates to this concept of functional groups: alkanes don't have any. We'll see the consequences of this in the next chapter.

2-2 and 2-3. Structures and Names for Alkanes.

There are a *lot* of organic compounds. Table 2-2 lists the numbers of isomers of just alkanes, and only goes up to 20 carbons, and already over half a million structures are possible! Imagine how many more structures can be manufactured when functional groups are present, or when the molecules get larger. Obviously not all of these possible structures exist in nature or have been prepared in laboratories. Nonetheless, a good five million different compounds are known at present, and nomenclature is the language that allows anyone interested in any of these materials to communicate about them in a clear and sensible way.

The text presents brief descriptions of the problems associated with naming compounds before the systematic procedures of the I.U.P.A.C. were developed. It then goes on to introduce just the rules necessary for naming simple alkanes: molecules containing only carbon and hydrogen atoms, and using only single bonds for holding the atoms together. Only four rules are needed at this stage:

(1) Identify the longest carbon chain (the "parent" chain) in the molecule.

(2) Name all groups attached to this chain as "substituents."

(3) Number the carbon atoms of the parent chain from the end that gives the ones containing substituents the lowest possible numbers.

(4) Assemble the name using the proper format.

Although examples are given in the text and there are lots of problems for you to practice on, here are a couple of additional worked-out examples to further clarify some fine points of the procedure.

$$
\begin{array}{c}
3 \, \overset{CH_3}{\underset{|}{}} \, 2 \, {}^{1} \\
CHCH_2CH_3 \quad \leftarrow \quad \text{chain 'b'} \\
|
\end{array}
$$

Example 1: name $CH_3CH_2CH_2CHCH_2CH_2CH_3$ ← chain 'a'

7 6 5 4 3 2 1

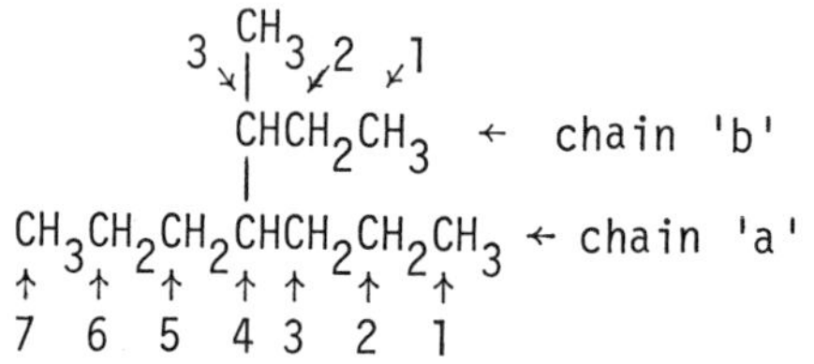

Analysis: the longest chain contains seven carbons, so this is a "heptane". However, there are *two* ways to find a seven-carbon chain (see numbering). Which one is the parent? The rules specify that, in case of a tie for longest chain, the one with the *most* substituents is chosen as the parent. The seven-carbon chain labeled 'a' has one substituent (a *sec*-butyl group on carbon 4). The seven-carbon chain labeled 'b' has *two* substituents (a methyl on carbon 3 and a propyl on carbon 4), so it wins. The molecule is called 3-methyl-4-propyl-heptane.

Example 2: name 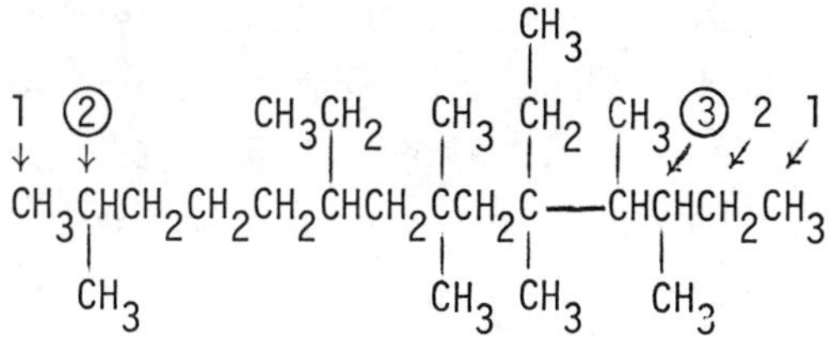

Analysis: the main chain here is unambiguous and 14 carbons long - the "parent" is "tetradecane". Which is the correct numbering direction, however? Most of the groups are close to the right-hand end, and will have low numbers if we number right-to-left. But that is *not* the criterion for determining which way to number the chain. The rule says to number in the direction that makes the lowest substituent number as low as possible. Numbering right-to-left gives a lowest substituent number of 3; left-to-right gives a lowest substituent number of 2. So, left-to-right is correct and the molecule's name is 6,10-diethyl-2,8,8,10,11,12-hexamethyltetradecane. Even though the name that comes from numbering the other way has mostly low numbers, (5,9-diethyl-3,4,5,7,7,13-hexamethyltetradecane) it is wrong - its lowest number is a '3', and the correct name's lowest number is a '2'.

Example 3: name 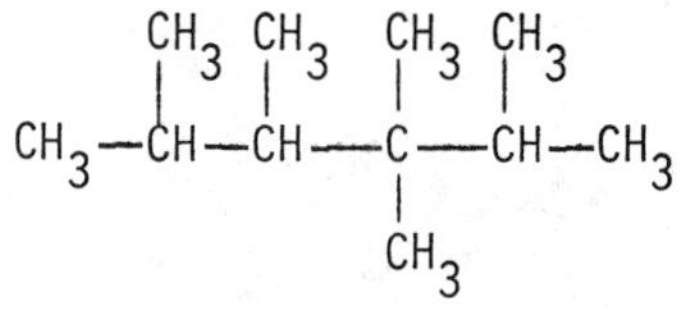

Analysis: a "hexane." Numbering left-to-right gives 2,3,4,4,5-pentamethylhexane; right-to-left gives 2,3,3,4,5-pentamethylhexane. The choice is made by looking at substituent numbers in order of lowest first. The name with the lower number *at the first point of difference* is the winner. So 2,3,3,4,5 is the winner over 2,3,4,4,5.

Example 4: name 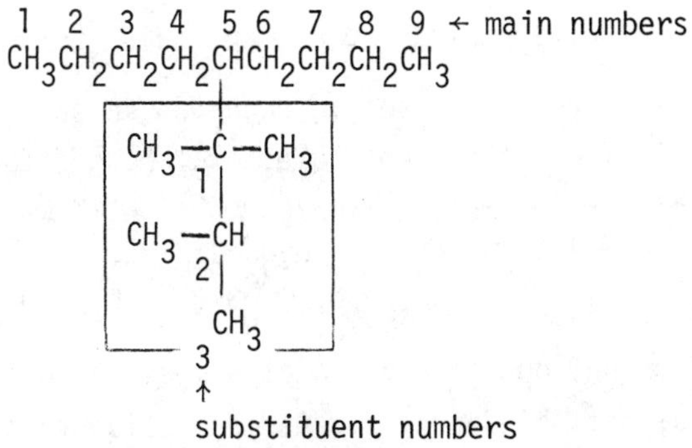

Analysis: a "nonane" with a complicated substituent on carbon 5. Rule 3 illustrates what to do. Number the substituent carbons from the point of attachment to the main chain, outward along the *substituent's* longest chain. This is three carbons, so the substituent has a name based on "propyl." Then add appropriate numbers and names for groups attached to the substituent chain. This gives "1,1,2-trimethylpropyl" as the final name *of the substituent.* Now, attach it to the name of the main chain to give the whole name of the molecule: 5-(1,1,2-trimethylpropyl)nonane. Note punctuation. It's not hard, but it does take some care.

The notes above refer to the systematic nomenclature method as it is currently used. Please note, however, that there are many nonsystematic names in common use that are holdovers from the olden days and are still used by force of habit. In addition, a number of compounds whose systematic names are very complicated have been given names that are well-understood by people in the business, but may seem pretty random to the uninitiated. Several of these are mentioned in the text. Perhaps one more example may help provide some perspective in this area. Some years back the research group of Professor Thomas Katz at Columbia University encountered the hydrocarbon pictured below as the product of a new chemical reaction.

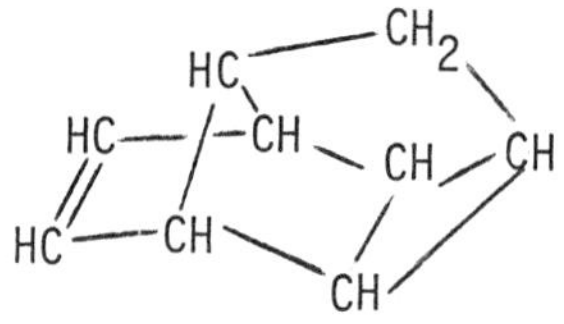

George

When student James Carnahan approached with the question "What shall we call it?", Prof. Katz *could* have sat down with his I.U.P.A.C. handbook of rules and come up with the correct name tetracyclo[4.3.0.0^{2,4}.0^{3,7}]non-8-ene. But, like most of us, he had better things to do, and said "Let's call it 'George'".

Several days later, the same student succeeded in carrying out a reaction that resulted in the linking of two molecules of "George" together. He again approached his boss with the same question: "What shall we call it?" The good Professor never even hinted that the real name of this dimeric compound might be exo,trans,exo-nonacyclo[9.7.0.0^{2,10}.0^{3,8}.0^{4,5}.0^{5,9}.0^{12,16}.0^{13,18}.-0^{15,17}]octadecane. No, not one to ever be at a loss in such a situation, he was ready: "Let's call it 'bi-George'". And so it is, to this day.

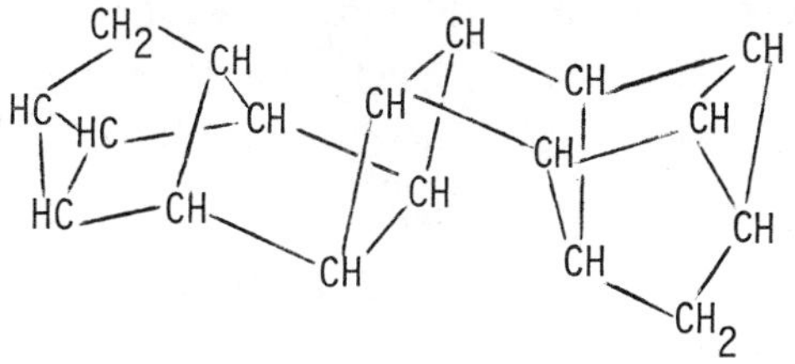

bi-George

Fear not, odds are you will never, ever, have to give an I.U.P.A.C. name to a molecule like this. *I* never did, at least until I had to write this study guide.

2-4. Physical Properties

Every time we encounter a new class of compounds we will briefly discuss common "physical properties" of members of that compound class. These will include general comments on the nature of the compound under ordinary conditions (e.g. diethylamine, colorless liquid, smells like something died, or, 2-hydroperoxy-2-isopropoxypropane, colorless crystalline solid, blows up like an A-bomb if you look at it cross-eyed). The purpose of these comments is to give you a "feeling" for what these materials are really like (as well as alerting you to the fact that some organic molecules may not be your friends). For the record, alkanes are colorless gases or liquids, with rather light odors, or white, waxy solids (candle wax is mainly alkanes).

More specific discussion will focus on relationships between molecular structure and physical properties for the class of compounds as a whole. In this chapter a brief summary of the kinds of forces that attract molecules to each other is presented. Alkanes, lacking charged atoms or highly polarized bonds, do not exhibit either ionic or dipolar forces. As *nonpolar* molecules, alkane molecules are attracted to each other by only the rather weak van der Waals forces. These can be understood fairly simply. In even a totally unpolarized bond, the electrons are always moving. Even though, on the average, the electron pair is exactly half-way between the atoms, at any instant in time, the electrons may be closer to one atom or the other:

"fleeting dipole" →	$\delta-$ $\delta+$ A: A	vs.	o o A : A	vs.	$\delta+$ $\delta-$ A :A	← "fleeting dipole"
			↑ average situation			

At these instants, the bond becomes polarized. Since this polarization is not permanent, the partial charges associated with it are only transient, or fleeting in nature, thus the name "fleeting dipoles." If two non-polar molecules are close to each other, and a bond in one of them exhibits a fleeting dipole for an instant, the electrons in a nearby bond of the *other* molecule will be pushed away from the fleeting dipole's '-' end and towards its '+' end. The positions and movements of all the electrons are said to be "correlated":

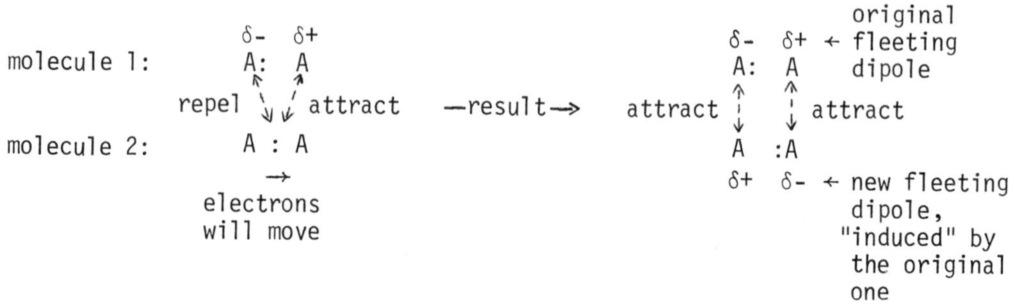

The result will be a new dipole in the second molecule's bond, "induced" by the original fleeting dipole in the first molecule. As the diagram shows, the polarizations that result lead to an attractive force between the molecules - the so-called van der Waal's force. Even though the dipoles involved have only transient existence and all the bonds are, on the average, non-polar, it turns out that the odds always favor the presence of some fleeting dipoles in a molecule, and the net result is this weak, but real van der Waal's attraction.

The weakness of this attraction results in relatively low melting points and boiling points, compared with more polar, or charged molecules. The non-polar nature of alkanes results in other physical consequences, such as rather limited ability to serve as solvents for polar compounds (remember "like dissolves like" from freshman chemistry?). Lack of polarized bonds also very much limits the chemistry that alkanes can display. This will be taken up in the next chapter.

2-5. Conformational Isomers

Although we generally draw pictures of molecules in a single geometrical representation, the fact is that no molecule has a single rigid geometry. The electrons in bonds can be viewed as sort of an elastic glue holding the atoms together. The bonds are therefore somewhat flexible and are subject to some degree of bending or stretching. So, even in the simplest molecules like H_2 the atoms are capable of some degree of motion with respect to each other. In more complicated molecules additional forms of internal motion become possible. The *conformations* of ethane and larger alkanes are a result of rotation about carbon-carbon single bonds, a relatively easy motion for atoms to undergo. The major features in this chapter section include the energetics associated with this rotation, and the names associated with the various shapes of the molecules as this rotation occurs. Using Newman projections, which view the molecule by sighting down the bond in question, the names can be summarized:

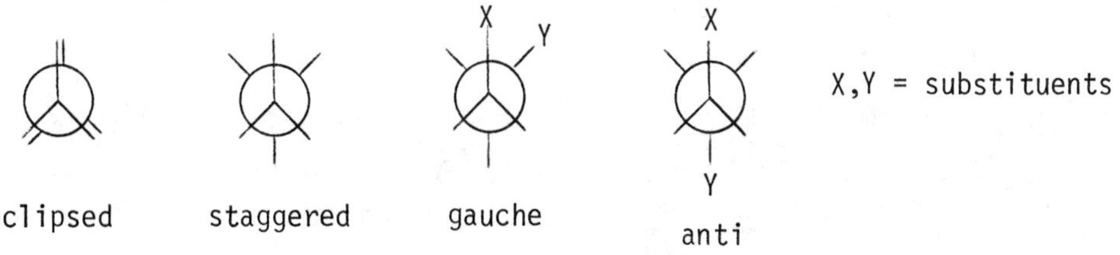

At this point you should take a look at a set of molecular models so that you can become familiar with these conformations in three dimensions.

Conformational energetics can be summarized for alkanes as follows:

a. Eclipsed is 3.0 kcal/mole higher in energy (less stable) than staggered for ethane.

b. Each CH_3-H eclipsing is 0.4 kcal/mole worse than an H-H eclipsing (relative to corresponding changes in staggered conformation energies).

c. Each CH_3-CH_3 eclipsing is 1.5 kcal/mole worse than an H-H eclipsing.

d. Each CH_3-CH_3 gauche is 0.9 kcal/mole worse than CH_3-CH_3 anti.

With these individual estimates the graph of energy vs. rotational angle can be readily sketched for simple alkanes. *Note*: these "energy" values are actually enthalpies (heat content, or $\Delta H°$ values).

2-6. Thermodynamics and Kinetics

This section introduces ideas associated with energy changes in organic chemistry. Even though some of the terminology may be somewhat familiar to you from freshman chemistry, a few comments may be useful for orientation purposes. In this course you are going to encounter a lot of discussion concerning the *energy content* of molecules or other species. This term will refer in general to what is called "potential energy" in physics: energy that is stored in some way and can *potentially* be released in some process later on. Discussions involving energy will often refer to the *stability* or *instability* of various substances or systems. Energy and stability are related in the following way: a species with high energy content will tend to want to get rid of some of its energy somehow. So, relatively speaking, high energy species are generally *unstable*. Heat and energy are also related, so a simple example of an unstable, high energy species is a hot oven. After the cooking is finished and the flame turned off, the hot oven will tend to lose energy by radiating heat to its cooler surroundings. This process of heat or energy transfer is an example of *thermodynamics*. Eventually, the oven will cool off to the point where it is the same temperature as the kitchen, and no more net heat transfer takes place. At this point, the situation is said to have reached *equilibrium*. If we were to take the temperatures of the oven and the kitchen as this occurred, we might observe a result such as that shown on the graph below.

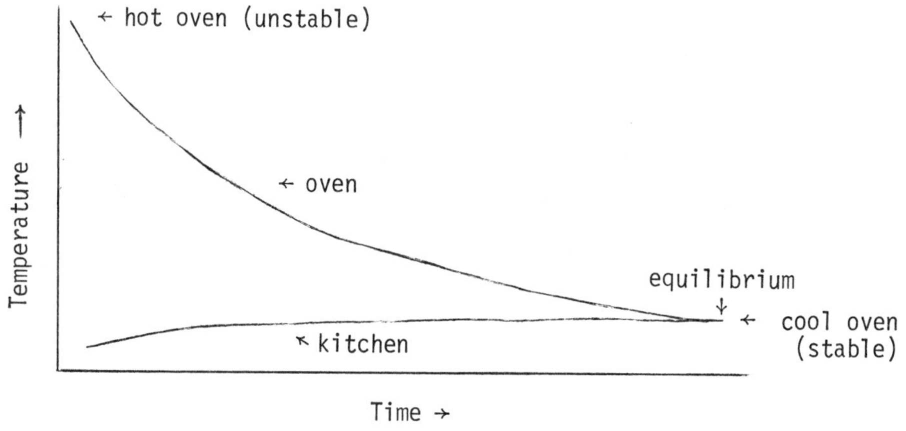

The time it takes for the oven to cool off will depend on, for instance, whether the door is open or closed. This question is one of *kinetics*. A well-insulated oven with a tightly sealed door might cool off only very slowly, even if it starts out very hot. The point here is that the *rate* of a process is the subject of *kinetics*, while the *energetic favorability* is one of *thermodynamics*, and the two are very different. Energetically favorable processes can take place at fast rates, slow rates, or in some cases, hardly seem to take place at all. A wooden match in the presence of air is a good chemical example of the latter. The reactions of the compounds in the wood as well as the head of the match with oxygen are all extremely energetically favorable (*thermodynamics*), but nothing perceptible happens at room temperature. Why not? The *rate* of the reaction is too small: the number of molecules actually reacting with the oxygen at room temperature is so small that nothing seems to be happening at all (*kinetics*). However, if we strike the match - heat the match head with friction - it starts burning, and continues until the whole thing has burned up. The reaction of most organic molecules with oxygen requires energy *input* to get started even though it ultimately results in net energy *output* after it has finished. The reason is as follows: in most reactions, old bonds are broken and new ones are formed, but not exactly simultaneously. Some partial breaking of old bonds has to take place before anything else, and that requires an input of energy. Once this process has started, it can lead to new bonds being formed, resulting in energy being released - enough to make more old bonds break plus extra in the form of the flame and heat of burning. This initial energy input is the *activation energy* of the reaction, and it is the primary factor in understanding *kinetics*:*rates* of reactions.

This chapter section provides a brief mathematical description of each of the main factors involved in *thermodynamics* and *kinetics* as applied to organic chemistry. The equations are generally fairly straightforward in their application. The problems will give you several chances to use them.

Solutions to Chapter 2 Problems

1. Refer to any table of electronegativities to determine bond polarities. Butane, 2-methylpropene, 2-butyne, and methylbenzene lack polarized bonds. The other structures have the polarized bonds shown.

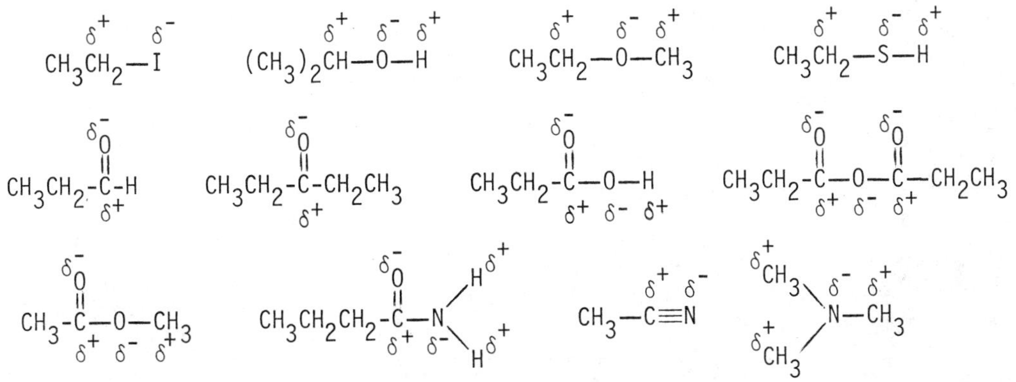

$$\overset{\delta^+}{CH_3}CH_2 \overset{\delta^-}{-} I \qquad (CH_3)_2\overset{\delta^+}{CH}\overset{\delta^-}{-}O\overset{\delta^+}{-}H \qquad CH_3\overset{\delta^+}{CH_2}\overset{\delta^-}{-}O\overset{\delta^+}{-}CH_3 \qquad CH_3\overset{\delta^+}{CH_2}\overset{\delta^-}{-}S\overset{\delta^+}{-}H$$

$$CH_3CH_2\overset{\overset{\delta^-}{O}}{\underset{\delta^+}{-C}}-H \qquad CH_3CH_2\overset{\overset{\delta^-}{O}}{\underset{\delta^+}{-C}}-CH_2CH_3 \qquad CH_3CH_2\overset{\overset{\delta^-}{O}}{-C}\overset{}{\underset{\delta^+\ \delta^-\ \delta^+}{-O-H}} \qquad CH_3CH_2\overset{\overset{\delta^-}{O}}{-C}\overset{\overset{\delta^-}{O}}{\underset{\delta^+\ \delta^-\ \delta^+}{-O-C}}-CH_2CH_3$$

$$CH_3\overset{\overset{\delta^-}{O}}{-C}\underset{\delta^+\ \delta^-\ \delta^+3}{-O-CH_3} \qquad CH_3CH_2CH_2\overset{\overset{\delta^-}{O}}{\underset{\delta^+\ \delta^-}{-C}}\overset{H\delta^+}{\underset{H\delta^+}{-N}} \qquad CH_3\overset{\delta^+}{-}\overset{\delta^-}{C}\equiv N \qquad \overset{\overset{\delta^+}{CH_3}}{\underset{\delta^+}{CH_3}}N\overset{\delta^-\ \delta^+}{-CH_3}$$

****

2. (a) $CH_3\text{-}\overset{\delta^+}{CH_2}\text{-}\overset{\delta^-}{I}$ The δ^+ carbon will attract the negatively charged oxygen atom of hydroxide ion.

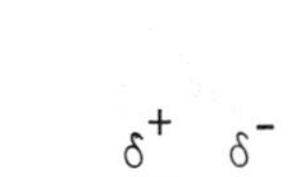

(b) 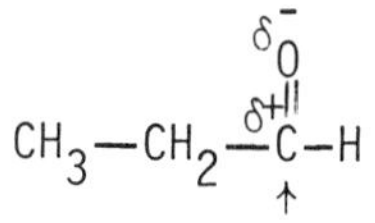

The δ^+ carbon will attract the lone pair on the δ^- nitrogen of ammonia. At the same time, the δ^- oxygen will attract a δ^+ hydrogen of ammonia.

(c) 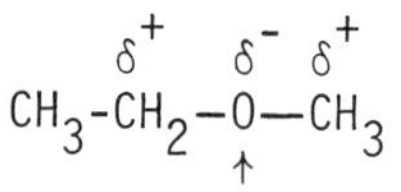

A δ^- oxygen lone pair will bond to H^+.

(d) 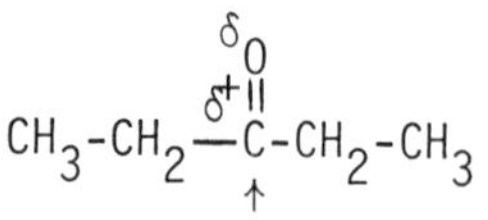

The ketone's δ^+ carbon will attract to the negatively charged carbon of the carbanion.

(e) 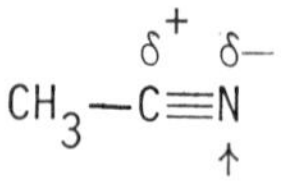

The lone pair on nitrogen should be attracted to the positively charged carbon.

(f) No reaction. Butane has no polarized atoms, so should not be reactive towards charged or polarized species.

****

3. Recall that condensed formulas only tell you what atoms are connected to what other atoms, <u>not</u> the real 3-D shape of a molecule. The longest chain is the chain with the most atoms, not necessarily the one drawn on a single horizontal line in these formulas.

(a) 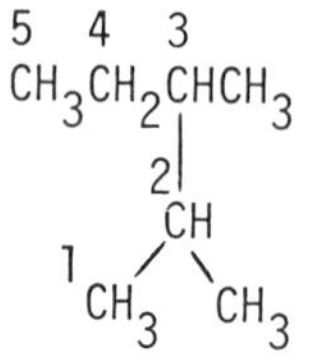 ∴ 2,3-dimethylpentane

(b) Parent chain is already horizontal; number left-to-right (nonane): 2-methyl-5(1-methylethyl)-5(1-methylpropyl)nonane.

(c) 3,3-diethylpentane, any way you look at it.

(d) Redraw: 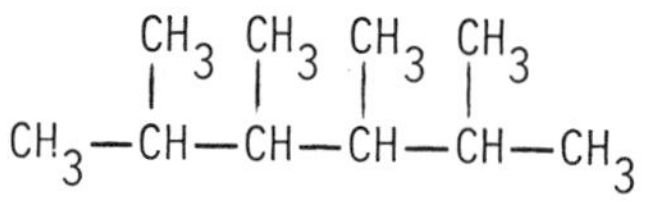 ∴ 2,3,4,5-tetramethylhexane

(e) Parent: 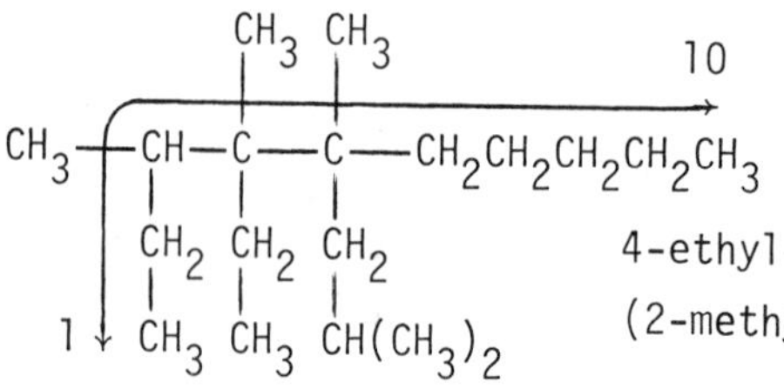 (10 carbons), ∴ 4-ethyl-3,4,5-trimethyl-5-(2-methylpropyl)decane.

(f) hexane (don't be fooled by the way it's drawn).

(g) 2-methylpropane. For this one as well as the next three, redraw to show all the atoms, if you need to.

(h) 2,2-dimethylbutane   (i) 2-methylpentane

(j) 2,5-dimethyl-4-(1-methylethyl)heptane

****

4. (a)

$$CH_3\overset{1}{-}\overset{2}{CH}\overset{\overset{\displaystyle CH_3}{|}\,3}{-}\overset{3}{CH}-CH_2-CH_3$$

with $\overset{4|}{CH_2}-\overset{5}{CH_2}-\overset{6}{CH_3}$

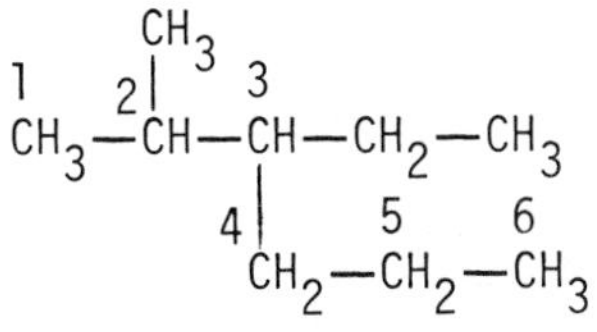

"Pentane" is an incorrect parent name. Correct name is 3-ethyl-2-methylhexane.

(b) $CH_3CH_2CH_2CH_2CHCH_2CH_2CH_2CH_3$

$CH_3\text{-}C\text{-}CH_2\text{-}CH_3$

CH_3

Name is correct.

(c)

$\overset{1}{CH_3}-\overset{\overset{CH_3}{|}\,\overset{2}{}}{CH}-\overset{\overset{CH_3}{|}\,\overset{3}{}}{CH}-\overset{\overset{CH_3}{|}\,\overset{4}{}}{C}-CH_2CH_2CH_3$

$\overset{5|}{CH_2}CH_2CH_2\overset{8}{CH_3}$

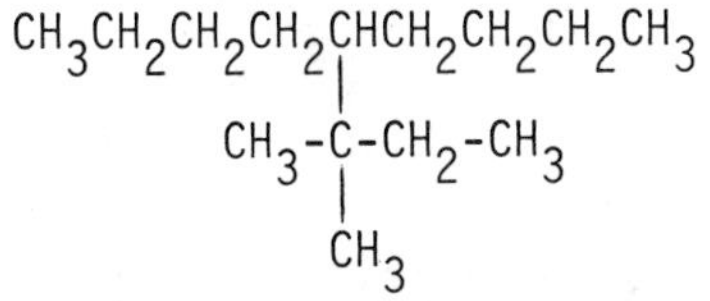

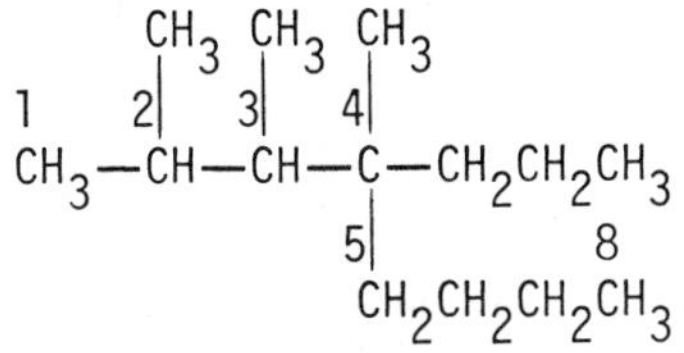

Not a "heptane." Should be 2,3,4-trimethyl-4-propyloctane.

(d)

$\overset{2}{CH_3}\text{-}\overset{1}{CH}\text{-}CH_3$

$\overset{7}{CH_3}\overset{6}{CH_2}\overset{5}{CH_2}\overset{4}{C}--\overset{3}{CH}-CH_3$

$CH_3\text{-}C\text{-}CH_3$

CH_3

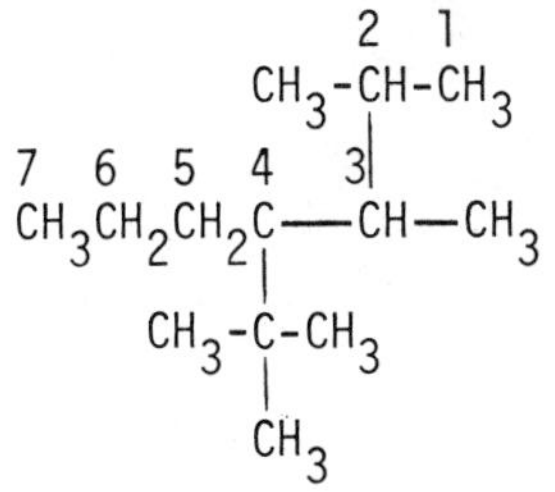

Parent and numbering are both wrong. Rename as 2,3-dimethyl-4-(1,1-dimethylethyl)heptane.

(e)

$\overset{5}{CH_3}CH_2CH_2CHCH_2CH_2CH_2CH_2CH_2\overset{11}{CH_3}$

$\overset{4}{}CH_2$

$\overset{1}{CH_3}\overset{2}{CH_2}\overset{3|}{CH}CH_2CH_3$

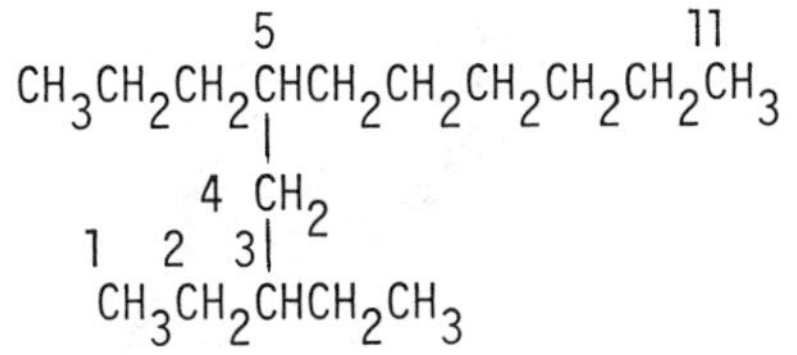

Wrong parent chain. This is 3-ethyl-5-propylundecane.

(f)

$\overset{5}{CH_3}-\overset{4}{CH}-\overset{3}{CH_2}-\overset{\overset{CH_3}{|}\,\overset{2}{}}{C}-\overset{1}{CH_3}$

$CH_3 \qquad CH_3$

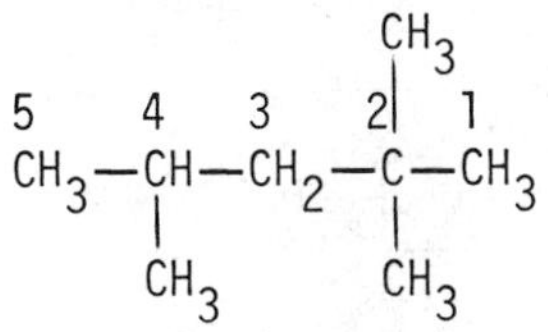

The numbering is backwards. It should be 2,2,4-trimethylpentane.

(g)

$\overset{7}{CH_3}\overset{6}{CH_2}\overset{5}{CH_2}\overset{4}{CH}CH_2\overset{}{CH_2}CH_3$

$\overset{3|}{CH_3}\overset{2}{CH}CH_2\overset{1}{CH_3}$

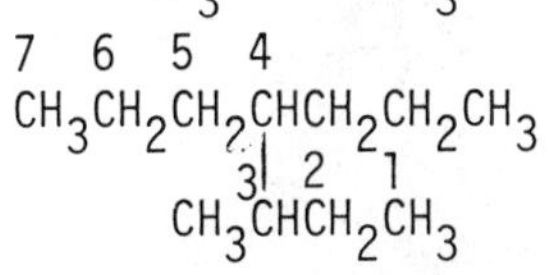

The parent chain is wrong based on the "maximum number of substituents" rule. Call it 3-methyl-4-propylheptane.

****

5. Do not answer questions like this by haphazardly writing down possible structures. You will almost certainly write some molecules down more than once. Do the problem systematically: write down answers with successively shorter parent chains as shown here.

(a) $CH_3CH_2CH_2CH_2CH_2CH_2CH_3$, heptane (7 carbon parent)

(b) $CH_3\overset{\underset{\displaystyle CH_3}{|}}{C}HCH_2CH_2CH_2CH_3$, 2-methylhexane

(c) $CH_3CH_2\overset{\underset{\displaystyle CH_3}{|}}{C}HCH_2CH_2CH_3$, 3-methylhexane

(6 carbon parents)

(d) $CH_3\overset{\underset{\displaystyle CH_3}{|}}{\overset{\displaystyle CH_3}{\underset{}{C}}}CH_2CH_2CH_3$, 2,2-dimethylpentane

(e) $CH_3\overset{\underset{\displaystyle CH_3}{|}}{C}HCH_2\overset{\underset{\displaystyle CH_3}{|}}{C}HCH_3$, 2,4-dimethylpentane

(f) $CH_3\overset{\underset{\displaystyle CH_3}{|}}{C}H\overset{\underset{\displaystyle CH_3}{|}}{C}HCH_2CH_3$, 2,3-dimethylpentane

(g) $CH_3CH_2\overset{\underset{\displaystyle CH_2CH_3}{|}}{C}HCH_2CH_3$, 3-ethylpentane

(h) $CH_3CH_2\overset{\underset{\displaystyle CH_3}{|}}{\overset{\displaystyle CH_3}{\underset{}{C}}}CH_2CH_3$, 3,3-dimethylpentane

(5 carbon parents)

(i) $CH_3\overset{\underset{\displaystyle CH_3}{|}}{\overset{\displaystyle CH_3}{\underset{}{C}}}\!\!-\!\!CHCH_3$, 2,2,3-trimethylbutane (4 carbon parent)

These are all the possible C_7H_{16} isomers.

****

6. (a) CH_3-CH_3 Both carbons and all hydrogens are primary.

(b) (CH_3)—CH_2-CH_2-CH_2—(CH_3)

primary   secondary   primary

(c) (CH_3)—CH—[CH_2]—(CH_3) ← primary

primary   tertiary   secondary

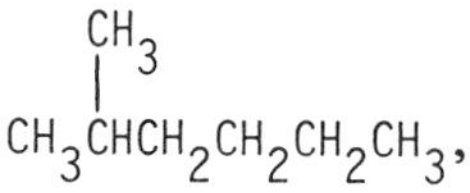

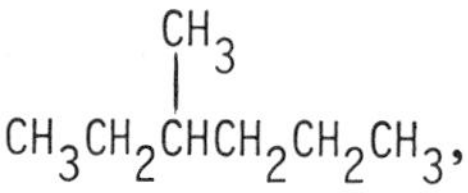

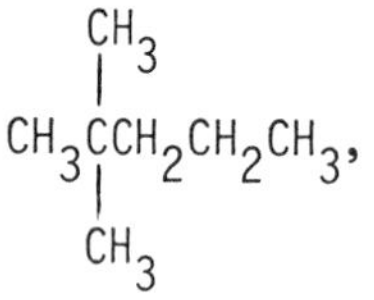

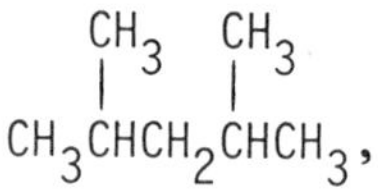

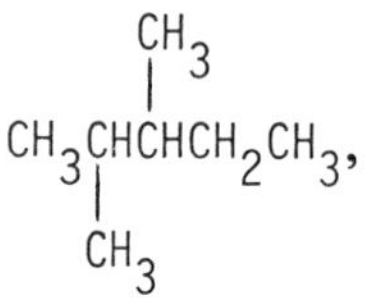

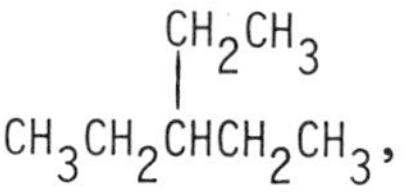

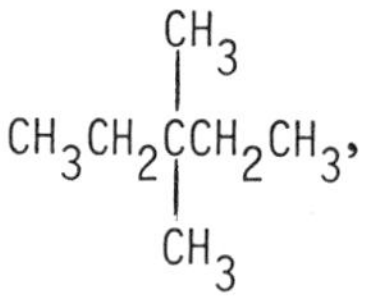

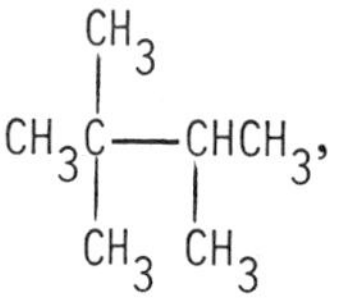

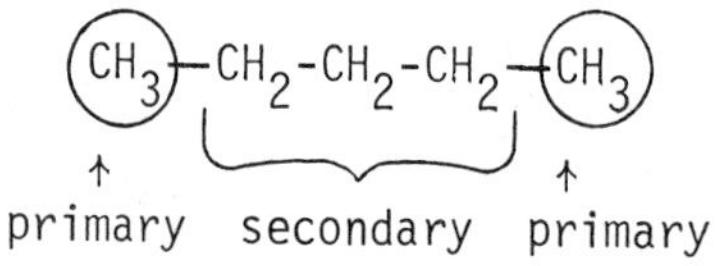

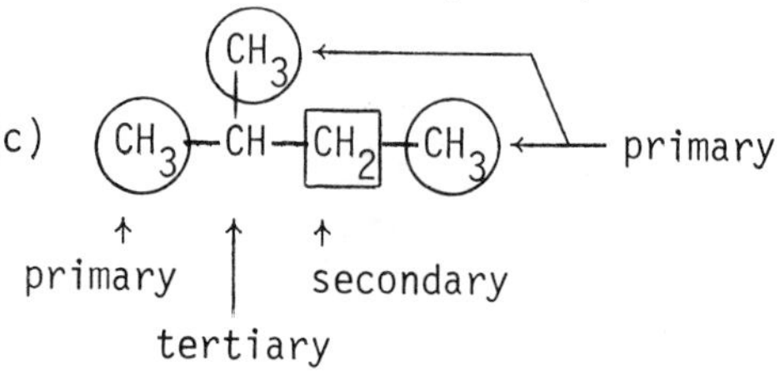

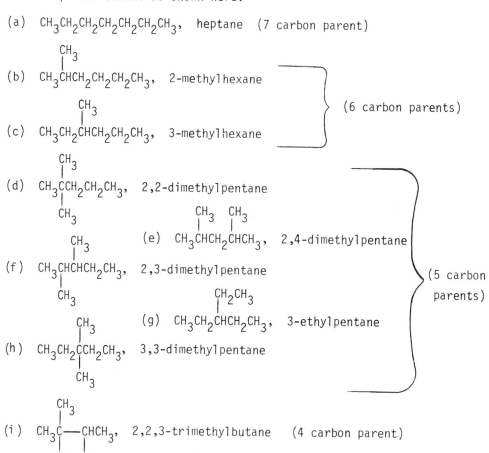

(d) 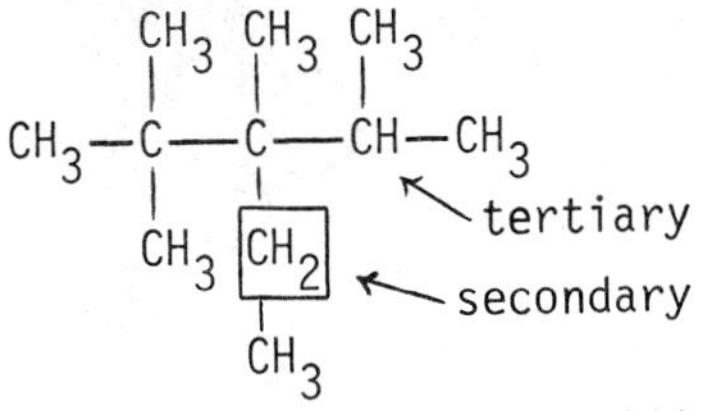

All CH_3- groups are primary.

****

7. The designation is assigned according to the type of carbon at position number 1 (the "point of connection" position).

(a) 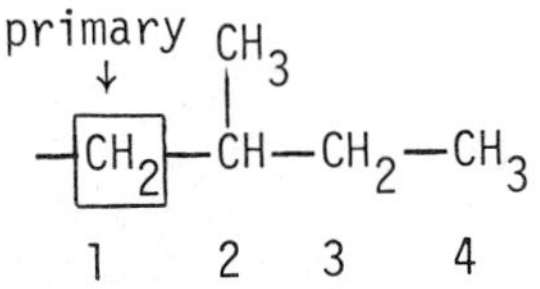

primary; 2-methylbutyl

(b) primary; 3-methylbutyl

(c) secondary; 1,2-dimethylpropyl

(d) primary; 2-ethylbutyl

(e) secondary; 1,2-dimethylbutyl

(f) tertiary; 1-ethyl-1-methylpropyl

****

8. Draw out the structures first. Boiling points increase as the molecule becomes less branched and starts resembling a straight chain structure. (Straight chains have more surface area for more effective van der Waals' interactions.) So, boiling points increase in the order d < c < a < b.

****

9. (a) 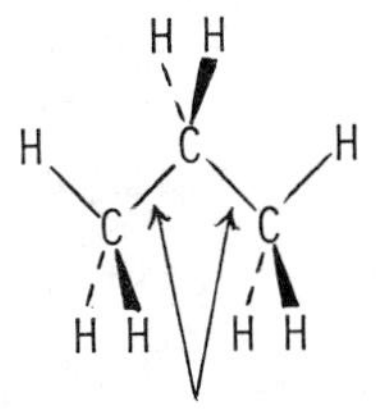

both staggered

(b) 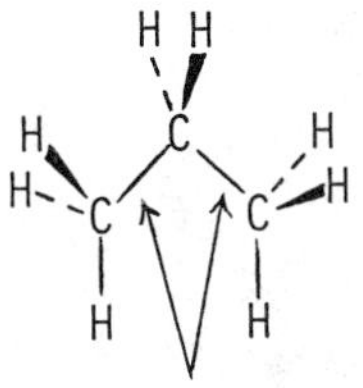

both eclipsed

For (c) and (d) note that *anti* and *gauche* refer to conformations around C-C bonds where each carbon has one non-hydrogen group attached. Therefore, consider only the C2-C3 bond.

(c) 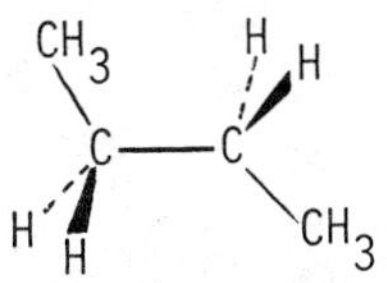

anti

(d) 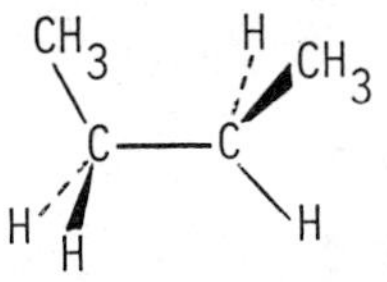

gauche

****

10. The problem deals with conformations about the C2-C3 bond of $(CH_3)_2\underset{2}{C}H{-}\underset{3}{C}H_2CH_3$.

(a) Use $\Delta G° = -RT\ell nK = -2.303RT\ell og\, K$. $T = 298°K$, $K = 90\%/10\% = 9$, and $R = 1.986$ Cal $deg^{-1} mole^{-1}$. So, $\Delta G° = -2.303(1.986)(298)\ell og\ 9 = -(1.360)\ell og\ 9 = -(1.360)(0.954) = -1297$ cal/mole = -1.30 kcal/mole.

Do parts (b) and (c) together: you can't draw the diagram until you know what all the conformations look like! It doesn't matter where you start (what you define as the 0° conformation). Here are four Newman projections showing 180° rotation of C-3:

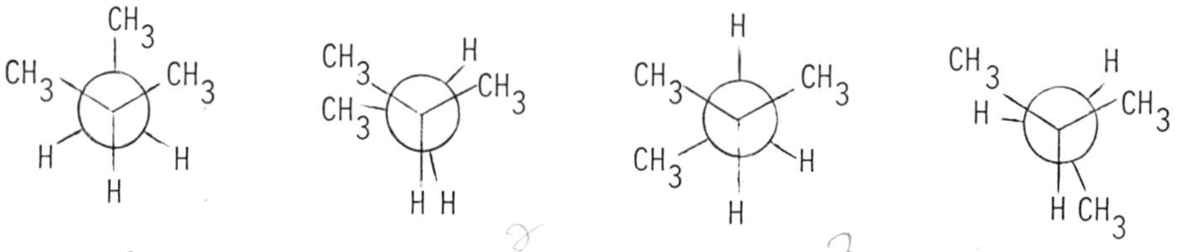

0° 60° 120° 180°

The 240° conformation is like the 120° one, and the 300° conformation is like the 60° one (make a model). Next, calculate relative energies for the diagram. Note that these will be <u>enthalpies</u> ($\Delta H°$), not free energies ($\Delta G°$).

Of the staggered conformations, the 120°/240° ones are best, with one *anti* CH_3/CH_3 pair and one *gauche* CH_3/CH_3 pair. Set these at 0 kcal/mole.

The 0° conformation has two *gauche* CH_3/CH_3 interactions, and will be 0.9 kcal/mole higher.

The 60°/300° conformations are eclipsed (+3.0 kcal/mole), with one CH_3/H eclipsing (+0.4 kcal/mole) and one CH_3/CH_3 eclipsing (+1.5 kcal/mole), for a total of 4.9 kcal/mole.

The 180° conformation is eclipsed (+3.0) with three CH_3/H eclipsings (3 x 0.4 = +1.2) for a total of 4.2 kcal/mole.

So the graph (on the following page) looks like this:

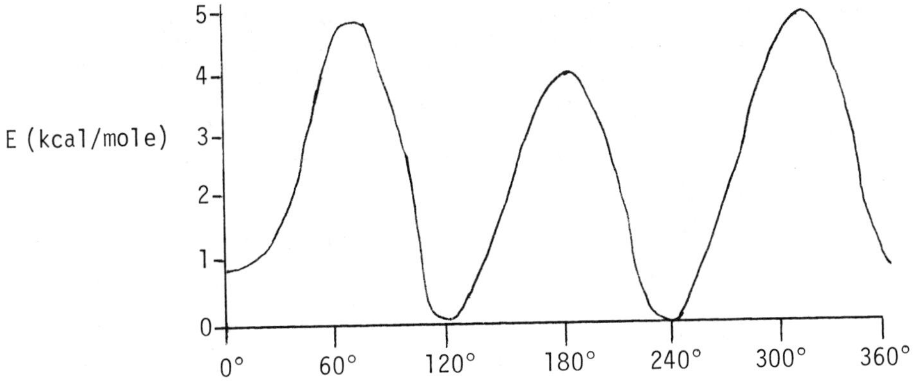

****

11. (a) From 10(a), we have $\Delta G° = -1.30$ kcal/mole. $T = 298K$ and $\Delta S° = +1.4$ cal/deg mole $= +1.4 \times 10^{-3}$ kcal/deg mole. So, $\Delta G° = \Delta H° - T\Delta S°$ needs to be rearranged to solve for $\Delta H°$: $\Delta H° = \Delta G° + T\Delta S° = -1.30 + 298(+1.4 \times 10^{-3}) = -1.30 + 0.42$. $\Delta H° = -0.88$ kcal/mole.

This agrees very nicely with the $\Delta H° = -0.9$ kcal/mole calculated in problem 10(b)/(c) above from the number of gauche interactions in the 0° conformation relative to the 120° conformation.

(b) Don't forget to change °C to K by adding 273°!

(i) $\Delta G° (-250°C) = \Delta H° - T\Delta S° = -0.88 - (23K)(1.4 \times 10^{-3}) = -0.91$ kcal/mole

(ii) $\Delta G° (-100°C) = \Delta H° - T\Delta S° = -0.88 - (173K)(1.4 \times 10^{-3}) = -1.12$ kcal/mole

(iii) $\Delta G° (500°C) = \Delta H° - T\Delta S° = -0.88 - (773K)(1.4 \times 10^{-3}) = -1.96$ kcal/mole

(c) Use $\Delta G° = -RT\ell nK = -2.303\ RT\ell ogK$. This rearranges to $-\frac{\Delta G°}{2.303RT} = \ell og\,K$, or $K = 10^{(-\Delta G°/2.303RT)}$ = antilog($-\Delta G°/2.303RT$)

(i) At $T = -250°C = 23K$, $\Delta G° = -0.91$ kcal/mole $= -910$ cal/mole;
$-\frac{\Delta G°}{2.303RT} = \frac{-910}{2.303(1.986)(23)} = 8.65 = \ell og\ K$, so $K = 4.5 \times 10^{8}$.

(ii) At $T = -100°C = 173K$, $\Delta G° = -1.12$ kcal/mole $= -1120$ cal/mole;
$-\frac{\Delta G°}{2.303RT} = -\frac{-1120}{2.303(1.986)(173)} = 1.42 = \ell og\ K$, so $K = 26$.

(iii) At $T = 500°C = 773K$, $\Delta G° = -1.96$ kcal/mole $= -1960$ cal/mole;
$-\frac{\Delta G°}{2.303RT} = -\frac{-1960}{2.303(1.986)(773)} = 0.55 = \ell og\ K$, so $K = 3.5$.

We can summarize the results of problems 10 and 11 in a little table:

T	23°K	173°K	298°K	773°K
ΔG°	-0.91	-1.12	-1.30	-1.96
K	4.5×10^8	26	9	3.5

These data illustrate two points. The most obvious is the huge effect of temperature on *K*. At 23° only 2 2-methylbutane molecules out of a billion are in the higher energy (0°) conformation. There is very little thermal energy around to cause bond rotation to occur. In contrast, at higher temperatures *K* drops as the increased thermal energy allows more and more molecules to be in less stable conformations.

Note also that the ΔS° value does cause ΔG° to vary with temperature, too, but the effect is small, since ΔS° is small. By the way, the source of ΔS° here is statistical: there are <u>two</u> lowest energy conformations (120° and 240°). This statistical ΔS° factor was neglected in Exercise 2-7.

****

12. Here is the situation:

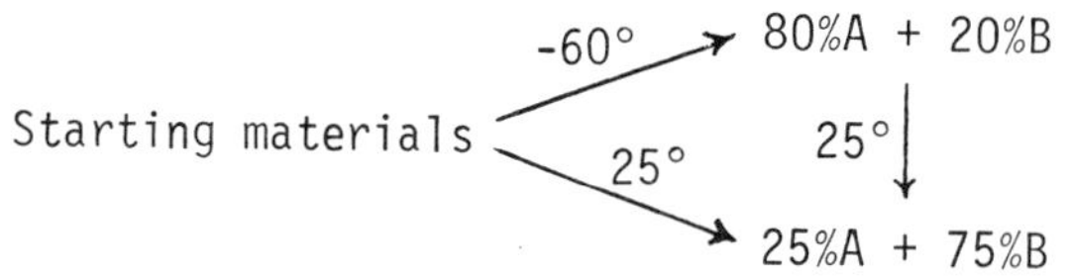

The result at -60° implies that A forms *faster* than B: E_a to form A is lower than E_a to form B. The change in product ratio on warming implies that A can be converted into B, giving an equilibrium mixture of the two (25% A and 75% B). B is, apparently, the *more stable* of the two products. Pictorially, we have this situation:

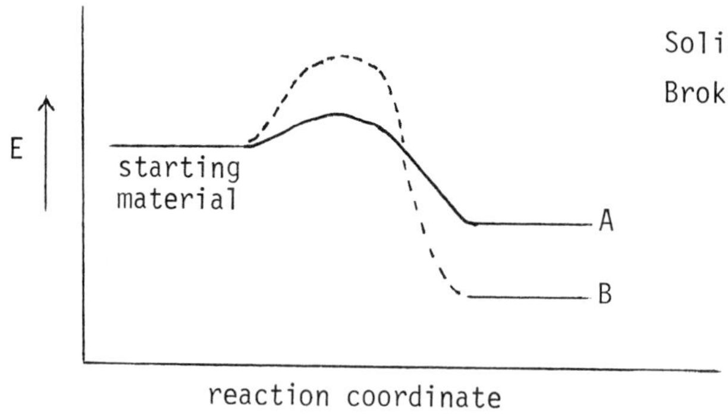

Solid line: pathway to A.
Broken line: pathway to B.

Formation of A has a lower E_a and occurs quickly and essentially irreversibly at low temperature. At higher temperature A can revert back to starting material, which now can go over the higher E_a barrier to form the more stable product B as the major component in the final equilibrium mixture.

****

13. (a) Remember, $\Delta H°$ (reaction) = $\Delta H°$ (bonds broken) - $\Delta H°$ (bonds formed).

(i) In order to figure out the $\Delta H°$ associated with breaking one of the two bonds in the carbon-carbon double bond, use $\Delta H°$ (C=C) as a bond breaking contribution and $\Delta H°$ (C-C) as a bond forming contribution:

$$\Delta H° = \underset{\substack{\text{break}\\ \text{C=C}}}{146} + \underset{\substack{\text{break}\\ \text{Br-Br}}}{46} - \underset{\substack{\text{form}\\ \text{C-C}}}{83} - \underset{\substack{\text{form}\\ \text{2C-Br}}}{2(68)} = -27 \text{ kcal/mole}$$

(ii) $$\Delta H° = \underset{\substack{\text{break}\\ \text{C-H}}}{99} + \underset{\substack{\text{break}\\ \text{Br-Br}}}{46} - \underset{\substack{\text{form}\\ \text{C-Br}}}{68} - \underset{\substack{\text{form}\\ \text{H-Br}}}{87} = -10 \text{ kcal/mole}$$

(b) In reaction (i), two molecules combine to make one. This greatly increases the "order" in the system. Since $\Delta S°$ measures "randomness" or "disorder", it is reasonable that it has a large negative value for reaction (i). In reaction (ii), two molecules react to make two new molecules. No major change in disorder is occurring, so $\Delta S°$ is small.

For (i) at 25°C,

$$\Delta G° = \Delta H° - T\Delta S° = -27 - 298(-35 \times 10^{-3}) = -17 \text{ kcal/mole}$$

For (i) at 600°C,

$$\Delta G° = \Delta H° - T\Delta S° = -27 - 873(-35 \times 10^{-3}) = +4 \text{ kcal/mole}$$

For (ii) at either 25°C or 600°, $\Delta G° \simeq \Delta H° = -10$ kcal/mole since $\Delta S° \simeq 0$.

(c) At 25°C, only reaction (i) will occur to give 1,2-dibromopropane since it has a lower E_a than reaction (ii).

At 600°C, the $\Delta S°$ for reaction (i) has made its $\Delta G°$ value positive: the reaction is therefore energetically unfavorable. Reaction (ii) is still just as good as it was at 25°C, so it now is preferred energetically, and thus the products obtained are 3-bromopropene and hydrogen bromide.

****

14. Before starting, you must understand quantitatively just what this question is asking. By "effect on k" of a change in temperature, we mean "how much bigger is k at a higher temperature than at a lower temperature," or, the ratio "$k_{\text{higher temp}}/k_{\text{lower temp}}$." You can't answer a question before you know just what the question is asking.

(a) E_a = 15 kcal/mole $\qquad\qquad k = Ae^{-E_a/RT}$

Set up: it has to be assumed that A is constant at the different temperatures, so that it will divide out, giving the general solution

$$\frac{k_{T_2}}{k_{T_1}} = \frac{e^{-E_a/RT_2}}{e^{-E_a/RT_2}} \qquad \text{or} \qquad k_{T_2} = \left(\frac{e^{-E_a/RT_2}}{e^{-E_a/RT_1}}\right) k_{T_1}$$

Then, remember that R = 1.986 cal/deg mole, so E_a must be changed from kcal/mole to cal/mole:

(i) For a 10° rise, $k_{310°} = \dfrac{e^{-15000/(1.986)(310)}}{e^{-15000/(1.986)(300)}} k_{300°}$

$$= \frac{e^{-24.36}}{e^{-25.18}} = \frac{2.62 \times 10^{-11}}{1.16 \times 10^{-11}} = 2.26\ k_{300°}$$

(ii) For a 30° rise, $k_{330°} = \dfrac{e^{-15000/(1.986)(330)}}{1.16 \times 10^{-11}} = \dfrac{e^{-22.89}}{1.16 \times 10^{-11}}$

$$= \frac{1.15 \times 10^{-10}}{1.16 \times 10^{-11}} = 9.91\ k_{300°}$$

(iii) For a 50° rise, $k_{350°} = 36.6\ k_{300°}$

(b) E_a = 30 kcal/mole = 30,000 cal/mole

(i) For a 10° rise, $k_{310°} = \dfrac{e^{-30000/(1.986)(310)}}{e^{-30000/(1.986)(300)}} = \dfrac{6.88 \times 10^{-22}}{1.36 \times 10^{-22}}$

$= 5.06\ k_{300°}$

(ii) For a 30° rise, $k_{330°} = 96.9\ k_{300°}$

(iii) For a 50° rise, $k_{350°} = 1320\ k_{300°}$

(c) E_a = 45 kcal/mole = 45,000 cal/mole

(i) For a 10° rise, $k_{310°} = \dfrac{e^{-45000/(1.986)(310)}}{e^{-45000/(1.986)(300)}} = \dfrac{1.80 \times 10^{-32}}{1.58 \times 10^{-33}}$

$= 11.4\ k_{300°}$

(ii) For a 30° rise, $k_{330°}$ = 958.6 $k_{300°}$

(iii) For a 50° rise, $k_{350°}$ = 48,480 $k_{300°}$

Let's summarize in tabular form, rounding off the above answers:

E_a =	15 kcal/mole	30 kcal/mole	45 kcal/mole
$k_{310°}/k_{300°}$	2	5	10
$k_{330°}/k_{300°}$	10	100	1,000
$k_{350°}/k_{300°}$	40	1,300	50,000

This problem illustrates the effect of temperature change on rate constants of reactions with three different activation energies. Notice the following:

1. Reactions with high activation energies are the most sensitive to temperature changes.

2. Even reactions with lower activation energies show rather significant responses to fairly modest temperature increases. This is relevant because many reactions in organic chemistry have E_a values in the 15-30 kcal/mole range.

****

15.

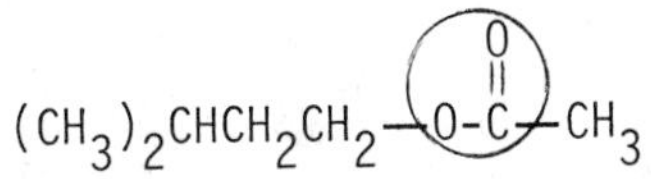

ester

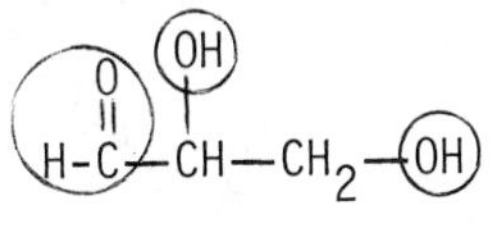

aldehyde, alcohol

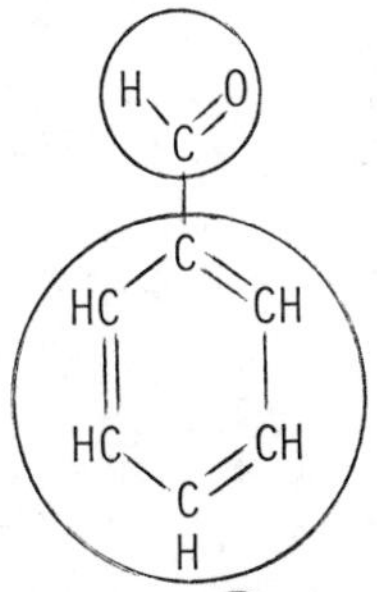

aldehyde,

aromatic compound

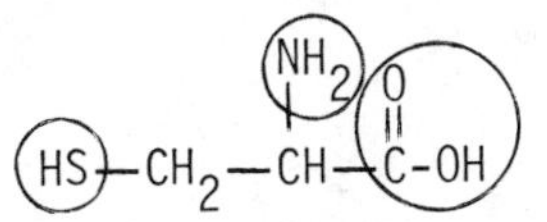

thiol amine

carboxylic acid

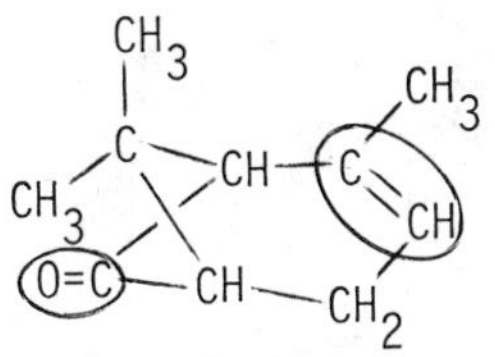

ketone, alkene

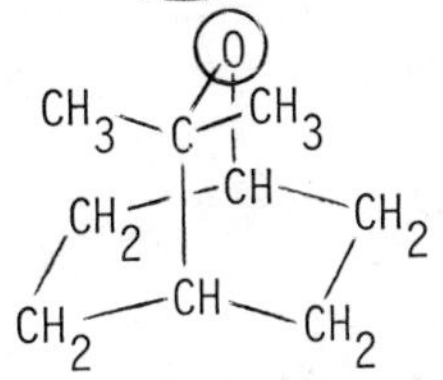

ether

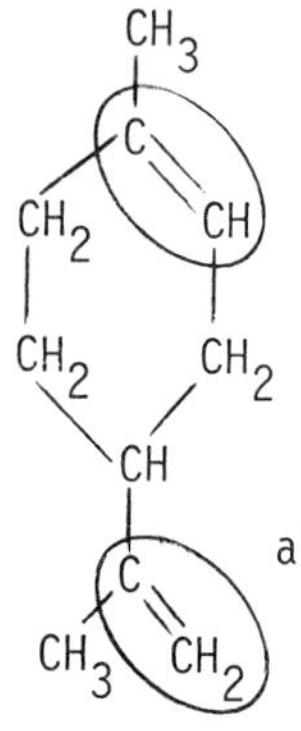

alkene

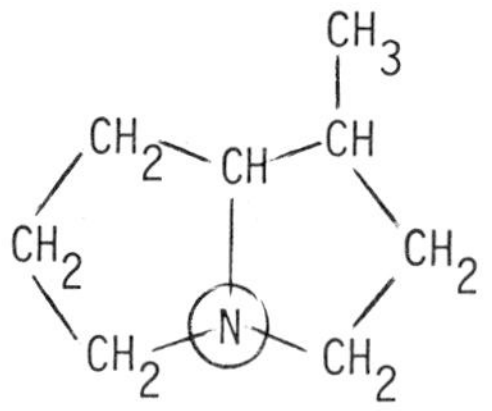

amine

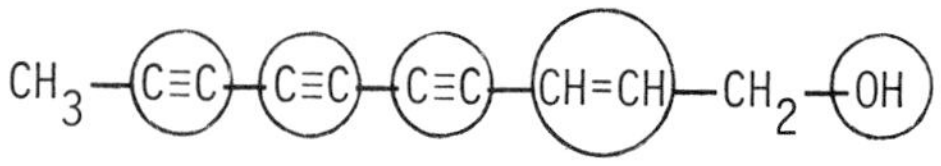

alkyne, alkene, alcohol

****

16. Top line, left to right: 1-methylethyl (secondary), 2-methylpropyl (primary), and 1-methylpropyl (secondary). In vitamin D_4: 1,4,5-trimethylhexyl (secondary). In cholesterol: 1,5-dimethylhexyl (secondary). In vitamin E: 4,8,12-trimethyltridecyl (primary).

****

CHAPTER 3

The Reactions of Alkanes: Pyrolysis and Dissociation Energies, Combustion and Heat Content, Free-Radical Halogenation, and Relative Reactivity

General Introduction

Discussing reactions of alkanes at the start of an organic chemistry course has advantages and disadvantages. The main advantage is that alkanes are the simplest class of organic compounds. The main disadvantage is that the reactions that alkanes undergo are *not* typical organic reactions and are qualitatively *very different* from most of the reactions you will see in this course. Most organic compounds contain functional groups: combinations of atoms that favor reactions with *charged* or *polar* atoms. The great majority of organic reactions are therefore *polar reactions*, involving functional groups. Alkanes do not contain any functional groups, however: they are made up of non-polar C-C and C-H bonds, and nothing else. So alkanes are essentially unreactive toward ionic or polar materials; indeed, alkanes are just about the least reactive of *all* organic compound classes because of this lack of a functional group. What does it take to make an alkane react chemically? Anything that can cause cleavage of one of the bonds in the alkane molecule. Since alkanes do not contain polarized bonds, the only reasonable way for an alkane bond to cleave is *homolytically*, leaving one electron with each of the formerly bonded atoms: C-C → C• + •C or C-H → C• + •H. This kind of bond cleavage is difficult, and only occurs at high temperature or in the presence of certain especially reactive species like halogen atoms.

This chapter will cover three major ways alkane bonds can be cleaved: pyrolysis (high temperature), combustion (high temperature and oxygen), and halogenation reactions. You will note a strong emphasis on discussions involving bond energies. This should not be surprising since the prerequisite for alkane reaction is cleavage of a bond, which requires input of energy. The discussions will also introduce the concept of a *reaction mechanism*. In most reactions, including those of alkanes, more than one bond will ultimately be involved (either broken or formed) before the reaction is finished. The *mechanism* will present the reaction in terms of a step-by-step, bond-by-bond analysis that will, in general, be a helpful way to spot trends and analogies in organic reactivity.

Outline of the Chapter

3-1. The Strength of Alkane Bonds: Pyrolysis.

Exactly what *does* it take to cleave bonds in alkanes?

3-2. Alkyl Radicals and Hyperconjugation.

The nature of the species obtained upon alkane bond cleavage.

3-3. Cracking: An Example of Pyrolysis.

Practical considerations.

3-4. Combustion of Alkanes.

Included is a detailed introduction to the evaluation of the energetics associated with a chemical reaction.

3-5. Halogenation of Methane.

Mechanism and energetics of free-radical substitution of halogen for hydrogen: formation of the halomethanes.

3-6. Chlorination of Higher Alkanes.

What happens when substitution for different hydrogens in an alkane can give different products.

3-7. Halogenation with Other Halogens.

Energetic comparisons of the reactions involving F_2, Br_2, and I_2.

3-8. Synthetic Aspects.

More practical considerations.

Keys to the Chapter

3-1. The Strength of Alkane Bonds: Pyrolysis.

A minor but annoying point of confusion is often encountered when one discusses bond strengths. A bond's strength, or more properly, bond dissociation energy (DH°), is defined as the energy *released* when a bond *forms* or, equivalently, the energy *input* required to *break* a bond:

$$A\cdot + B\cdot \longrightarrow A\text{-}B \qquad \Delta H° = -DH° \qquad \text{(energy is released)}$$

$$A\text{-}B \longrightarrow A\cdot + B\cdot \qquad \Delta H° = DH° \qquad \text{(energy is put in)}$$

Inspection of these two equations shows that the *bonded* molecule A-B is *more stable* — *lower* in energy — than the separated atoms A and B by an amount equal to DH°. When the bonds in a molecule are strong (high DH°), the molecule is usually relatively low in energy content (e.g., stable). As long as you always remember that DH° is the energy that *has to be put in* to *break* a bond, you won't fall into the common trap of associating large DH° values with high-energy species. Large DH° values imply *low* energy, strongly bonded, *stable* species. The tables and figures in this section should further help you develop a comfortable understanding of the meaning of DH° values, in preparation for their use later on.

3-2. Alkyl Radicals and Hyperconjugation.

Homolytic cleavage of any bond in an alkane generates "radicals": species with a single unpaired electron where an attached group used to be. The section illustrates four such examples: methyl, $\cdot CH_3$; ethyl, $\cdot CH_2CH_3$; isopropyl, $\cdot CH(CH_3)_2$; and *tert*-butyl, $\cdot C(CH_3)_3$. The term "radical" also applies to non-organic entities containing a single unpaired electron, such as the hydrogen atom, H•, and any of the halogen atoms, e.g. :C̈l̤• or :B̈r̤•.

Several points are made in the section. First, radical carbons are sp^2 hybridized (planar), not sp^3 hybridized (tetrahedral, as in alkanes). Why should this be? A partial reason goes back to basic electrostatics. Using methyl radical as an example, we can compare sp^3 vs. sp^2 hybridization in terms of distances between the carbon atom's seven valence electrons, and the carbon atom's nucleus. In the actual sp^2 structure, six of these electrons are in sp^2 orbitals ($\frac{1}{3}$ s character), and are closer to the carbon nucleus than electrons in sp^3 orbitals ($\frac{1}{4}$ s character) would be. (Remember: s orbitals are smaller and closer to the nucleus than the comparable p orbitals.) Electrons like to be close to oppositely charged nuclei, so this feature favors the sp^2 structure. One of the electrons in the sp^2 structure is stuck in a p orbital, which is worse than being in an sp^3 orbital. So, on balance, in the sp^2 form of the radical, six electrons are better off and one is worse off, relative to sp^3 hybridization.

The second main point in the chapter is the stabilization of a radical center by the presence of alkyl groups attached to the radical carbon, in place of hydrogens. So, *tert*-butyl radical is more stable than isopropyl, which is better than ethyl; methyl radical is the least stable. *Hyperconjugation* is one concept often used to explain this stabilization, and it is described in terms of a simple molecular orbital picture (Fig. 3-4). Physically, and electrostatically, the radical carbon can be viewed as somewhat *electron-deficient* (7 valence electrons instead of an octet). Hyperconjugation provides a means for bonds in neighboring alkyl groups to "lend" a little electron density to the free-radical center, thereby making it feel a little less electron deficient. In doing so, the alkyl groups effectively take some of the electron deficiency onto themselves. Thus the deficiency is spread out, or "delocalized" somewhat. Delocalization of an electron deficiency or an electron excess over more than just the atom on which it was originally located is often an energetically favorable, stabilizing process. It effectively allows the "problem" to be diluted over a larger area, rather than being the concentrated burden of a single atom.

The ability of alkyl groups to stabilize electron-deficient centers like radicals is often taken to imply that alkyl groups are better *donors* of electrons than are hydrogen atoms. Alkyl groups are often referred to as *electron donating* groups.

3-3 and 3-4. Pyrolysis and Combustion.

Although these two chemical processes are obviously important in the larger scheme of things, neither will be emphasized much in this course, since we will be more concerned with reactions that give just one or two major products via well defined (usually polar) pathways. So, the material in section 3-3 should be taken as illustrative of a process that is intrinsically important, but not conceptually related to much of anything that will follow in the rest of the course. Don't dwell on it.

Much more important is the coverage of the energetic interrelationships between heats of combustion, heats of formation, and bond energies in section 3-4. Remembering that all these actually refer to heats of specific types of reactions will help to keep them straight. So, for methane:

$$CH_4 + 2\,O_2 \longrightarrow CO_2 + 2\,H_2O \qquad \Delta H° = \text{heat of combustion}$$

$$C_{(graphite)} + 2H_2 \longrightarrow CH_4 \qquad \Delta H° = \text{heat of formation } (\Delta H_f)$$

$$CH_4 \longrightarrow \cdot CH_3 + H\cdot \qquad \Delta H° = \text{bond dissociation energy } (DH°)$$

Heats of reaction may be calculated in several ways, depending on the data available. Without going into a lot of detail, here are the two most common:

(1) $\Delta H^\circ_{reaction}$ from heats of formation (ΔH_f)

$$\Delta H^\circ_{reaction} = \sum \Delta H_f \text{(products)} - \sum \Delta H_f \text{(reactants)}$$

Example: calculate $\Delta H^\circ_{combustion}$ of CH_4 from ΔH_f values

	CH_4	+ $2\ O_2$	$\longrightarrow$	CO_2	+ $2\ H_2O$	
ΔH_f =	-17.9	0.0		-94.1	-68.3	kcal/mole

$$\Delta H^\circ_{reaction} = [-94.1 + 2(-68.3)] - [-17.9 + 0.0] = -212.8 \text{ kcal/mole}$$

↑ note 2 moles water (cf. Table 3-4)

(2) $\Delta H^\circ_{reaction}$ from bond dissociation energies (DH°)

$$\Delta H^\circ_{reaction} = \sum DH^\circ \text{(bonds broken)} - \sum DH^\circ \text{(bonds formed)}$$

(energy input) (energy output)

Example: calculate ΔH° for the process $C_2H_6 + H_2 \longrightarrow 2\ CH_4$

	$CH_3\text{-}CH_3$	+ H-H	$\longrightarrow$	$2\ CH_3\text{-}H$	
DH° =	90	104		105	kcal/mole

$$\Delta H^\circ_{reaction} = [90 + 104] - [2(105)] = -16 \text{ kcal/mole}$$

↑ note 2 methane C-H bonds

Comment: this is a "hydrocracking" process which, although exothermic, requires very high temperatures to occur (cleavage of C-C bond is necessary).

Note in these two calculation methods a source of potential confusion. Starting with ΔH_f, the formula involves "products - reactants." Starting with DH°, the formula is the other way around: "bonds broken (reactants) - bonds formed (products)." This difference is a result of the ways ΔH_f and DH° are defined: ΔH_f is the heat of a reaction that puts a molecule together, while DH° is the heat of a reaction that takes a molecule apart. The typical stable molecule has a large *negative* ΔH_f value, but large *positive* DH° values. This natural sign difference results in the different forms for the two formulas. For example, we just did $C_2H_6 + H_2 \rightarrow 2\ CH_4$ using DH°'s. Let's now use ΔH_f's:

$$C_2H_6 \quad + \quad H_2 \quad \longrightarrow \quad 2\ CH_4$$

$$\Delta H_f \quad = \quad -20.2 \qquad 0.0 \qquad\qquad -17.9$$

$$\Delta H^\circ_{reaction} = [\underset{\substack{\uparrow \\ \underline{2}\text{ moles methane}}}{2}(-17.9)] - [-20.2] = -15.6 \text{ kcal/mole}$$

Another way to analyze these calculations is to separate them into individual contributions of the simple processes defined by the DH°'s or ΔH_f's, respectively. Then the contributing processes are added algebraically, cancelling out species that appear on both sides of the equations as required:

For DH°'s:

$CH_3\text{-}CH_3 \longrightarrow 2\ CH_3\cdot$	$\Delta H^\circ = DH^\circ(CH_3\text{-}CH_3) = 90$
$H\text{—}H \longrightarrow 2\ H\cdot$	$\Delta H^\circ = DH^\circ(H\text{-}H) = 104$
$2(CH_3\cdot + H\cdot \longrightarrow CH_4)$	$2\,\Delta H^\circ = -2\ DH^\circ(CH_3\text{-}H) = -210$
$CH_3\text{-}CH_3 + H\text{-}H = 2\ CH_4$	$\Delta H^\circ = -16$ kcal/mole

For ΔH_f's:

$C_2H_6 \longrightarrow 2\,C_{(graphite)} + 3\,H_2$	$\Delta H^\circ = -\Delta H_f(C_2H_6) = 20.2$
$H_2 \rightleftharpoons H_2$	$\Delta H^\circ = \Delta H_f(H_2) = 0.0$
$2(C_{(graphite)} + 2\,H_2 \longrightarrow CH_4)$	$2\,\Delta H^\circ = 2\,\Delta H_f(CH_4) = -35.8$
$C_2H_6 + H_2 \longrightarrow 2\ CH_4$	$\Delta H^\circ = -15.6$ kcal/mole

Manipulations of these sorts will be required from time to time, so be sure to practice this kind of thing.

3-5. Halogenation of Methane.

In this section the reaction of methane with halogen molecules (and chlorine in particular) is discussed. The reaction

$$CH_4 \quad + \quad Cl_2 \quad \longrightarrow \quad HCl \quad + \quad CH_3Cl$$

is conceptually important because it converts a non-functionalized molecule (an alkane) into a molecule containing a functional group (a haloalkane). Once the functional group is present, many more kinds of chemical reactions will become possible. This section also presents the *mechanism* of this reaction in full detail. (Briefer mechanisms were presented in the previous two sections, but this is the first really important presentation of this type.) Pay close attention not only to the steps of the reaction (initiation, propagation, and termination), but also to the finer details relating $\Delta H°$, E_a, and transition state structure for each step. Although much of the terminology introduced here is appropriate only for free-radical mechanisms and not for the majority of reactions to come later, the type of *information* that the mechanism contains is critical to an understanding of how and why organic reactions occur. Take some time in this section to study each reaction step. What are its energetic circumstances, under what conditions does it occur, how does it fit into the total reaction. Try to establish a feeling for the species involved as "stable" or "unstable", "reactive" or "unreactive", relatively speaking. Reaction mechanisms are intended to allow one to make sense out of organic chemistry. Give this one the time to do that for you.

Note on energetics: the overall enthalpy of a radical chain reaction is the sum of the $\Delta H°$ values for *only* the *propagation steps*. The $\Delta H°$ terms associated with initiation and termination steps do not contribute because (1) for the most part they cancel each other out and (2) they don't occur frequently relative to the propagation steps, anyway.

3-6. Chlorination of Higher Alkanes.

One of the best features of organic chemistry is the fact that one mechanism can hold for many individual reactions. Thus, the mechanism for chlorination of methane is qualitatively applicable to methane's reactions with the other halogens (previous section). It turns out that it also holds for chlorination of other alkanes. The only difference is in the nature of the C-H bonds available in the alkane to be broken. They are generally less strong than the bonds in methane, following a DH° order of CH_4 > 1° > 2° > 3°. (Note: 1° = primary, 2° = secondary, and 3° = tertiary. Commonly used symbols.) The weakest (3°) bonds are the most readily broken; thus alkanes with different types of C-H bonds display a built-in *selectivity* of 3° > 2° > 1° in their reactions with chlorine. This section describes this selectivity quantitatively, illustrating how both reactivity differences and statistical factors combine to produce the observed ratios of products in several selected systesm.

3-7. Halogenation with Other Halogens.

An extension of the previous two sections. The most significant point is that reactivity and selectivity are inversely related. Simply put, the more reactive halogens are less picky and show less preference for 3° vs. 2° vs. 1° C-H bonds relative to less reactive halogens. The reason lies in the different activation energies associated with the C-H bond-breaking step. The values for fluorine are all very small, and very close to one another. Fluorine thus reacts very rapidly with any C-H bond in a molecule. The reactions for bromine have large activation energies, with significant differences associated with the different types of C-H bonds involved. The result is that bromine is much much slower than fluorine to react with any alkane, and bromine is much more discriminating (selective) in its reactions, too, greatly preferring 3° over 2° or 1° C-H bonds due to the corresponding E_a differences.

3-8. Synthetic Aspects.

Synthesis is one primary function associated with organic chemistry. For a reaction to be useful synthetically, it must be able to change a starting material into the desired product molecule in reasonable yield. Poor yields, or mixtures of products necessitate inconvenient procedures for separation and purification. In this chapter we have seen a large number of possible permutations of a single reaction: alkane halogenation. For *practical* purposes, however, many of the reactions in this chapter are synthetically useless because of the hard-to-separate product mixtures they produce. The best synthetic reactions start with an alkane in which all hydrogens are chemically indistinguishable (methane, ethane, neopentane), because they can only produce one monohalogenation product. In the case of most alkanes, synthetic utility will be determined by the number of different types of hydrogens present, and whether the desired product involves substitution of a more reactive or a less reactive hydrogen in the molecule.

Taking isobutane as an example, there are one 3° and nine 1° hydrogens. If one desires to halogenate at the 3° center, the natural selectivity of bromine makes it the obvious halogen to choose. If one desires to halogenate a 1° carbon, a less selective, more reactive halogen would allow one to take best advantage of the statistical factor of nine possible 1° hydrogens available to be replaced in each molecule. Thus:

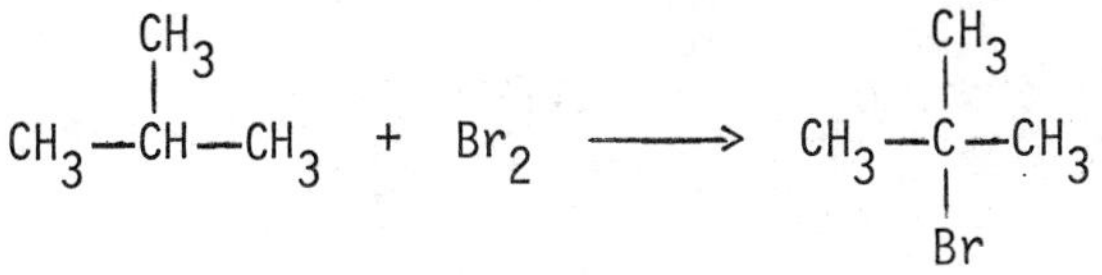 major product

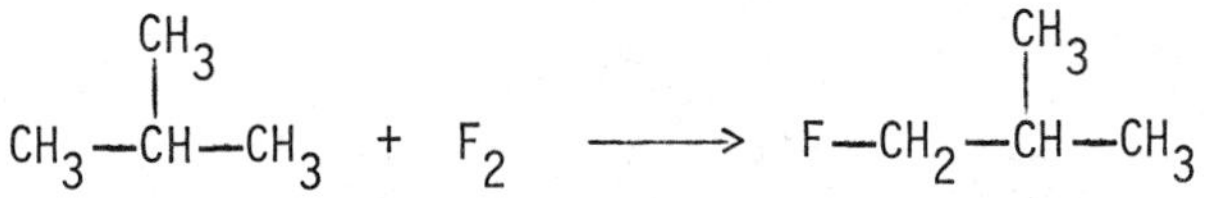 major product

Solutions to Chapter 3 Problems

1. This problem is really a reminder of material from the previous chapter. For shorthand purposes, we use the symbols 1° = primary, 2° = secondary, and 3° = tertiary.

(a) $CH_3CH_2CH_3$ (↑ 1° ↑ 2° ↑ 1°)

(b) $CH_3CH_2CH_2CH_3$ (↑ 1° ↖↗ 2° ↑ 1°)

(c) 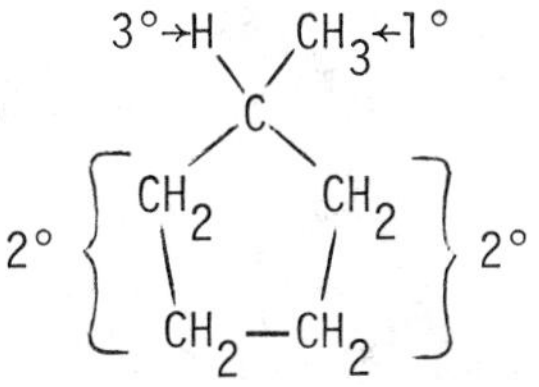

As you will see in Chapter 4, most "ring" compounds can be treated just the same as molecules without rings.

(d) All are 1°.

(e) 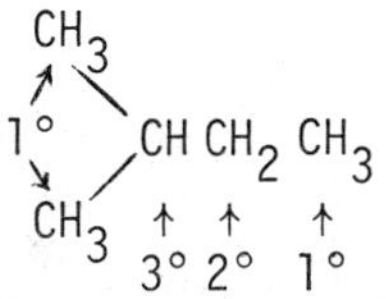

****

2. Work problems like this "mechanistically": proceed via general reaction steps as you have previously seen illustrated in the text, until you reach stable molecules. Pyrolysis of propane starts as follows:

(1) $CH_3CH_2\text{-}CH_3 \longrightarrow CH_3CH_2\cdot + \cdot CH_3$ C-C bond cleavage

Then there are three possible recombinations:

(2) $2\,CH_3\cdot \longrightarrow CH_3CH_3$ ethane

(3) $2\,CH_3CH_2\cdot \longrightarrow CH_3CH_2CH_2CH_3$ butane

(4) $CH_3\cdot + CH_3CH_2\cdot \longrightarrow CH_3CH_2CH_3$ propane (reverse of first step)

Two possible hydrgoen abstractions can occur:

(5) $CH_3\cdot + \overset{H}{|}CH_2CH_2\cdot \longrightarrow CH_4 + CH_2{=}CH_2$

methane ethene

(6) $CH_3CH_2\cdot + \overset{H}{|}CH_2CH_2\cdot \longrightarrow CH_3CH_3 + CH_2{=}CH_2$

ethane ethene

Abstraction only occurs from the carbon next to a free-radical carbon. Methyl radical, $\cdot CH_3$, doesn't have another carbon next to its free radical center, so it cannot give up a hydrogen in an abstraction. It can still *accept* a hydrogen, though (reaction 5, above).

So there are four new products formed from cracking of propane: methane, ethane, butane, and ethene (ethylene).

****

3. (a) The weakest bond in butane is the C2-C3 bond, DH° = 82 kcal/mole. Pyrolysis should therefore proceed as follows:

(1) $CH_3CH_2\text{-}CH_2CH_3 \longrightarrow 2\ CH_3CH_2\cdot$ C-C bond cleavage

(2) $2\ CH_3CH_2\cdot \longrightarrow CH_3CH_2CH_2CH_3$ reverse of (1)

(3) $CH_3CH_2\cdot + H\text{-}CH_2CH_2\cdot \longrightarrow CH_3CH_3 + CH_2{=}CH_2$ hydrogen abstraction

ethane ethene

These are the only available processes.

(b) The weakest bonds are the three equivalent C-C bonds, DH° = 86 kcal/mole. Therefore:

(1) $(CH_3)_2CH\text{-}CH_3 \longrightarrow (CH_3)_2CH\cdot + \cdot CH_3$ (cleavage)

(2) $2\ CH_3\cdot \longrightarrow CH_3CH_3$ ethane

(3) $2\ (CH_3)_2CH\cdot \longrightarrow (CH_3)_2CHCH(CH_3)_2$ 2,3-dimethylbutane

(4) $CH_3\cdot + \cdot CH(CH_3)_2 \longrightarrow (CH_3)_3CH$ reverse of (1) (recombinations)

(5) $CH_3\cdot + H\text{-}CH_2\dot{C}HCH_3 \longrightarrow CH_4 + CH_2{=}CHCH_3$

methane propene (hydrogen abstractions)

(6) $(CH_3)_2CH\cdot + H\text{-}CH_2\dot{C}HCH_3 \longrightarrow CH_3CH_2CH_3 + CH_2{=}CHCH_3$

propane propene

****

4. Hyperconjugation is π-type (sideways) overlap of a bonding orbital with a non-bonding orbital on a neighboring atom. The chapter example (free radical stabilization) is presented in a molecular orbital framework. That is, $CH_3CH_2\cdot$ is more stable than $CH_3\cdot$ due to the overlap between a C-H bonding orbital of the CH_3 group in CH_3CH_2 and the half-filled *p* orbital on the radical carbon:

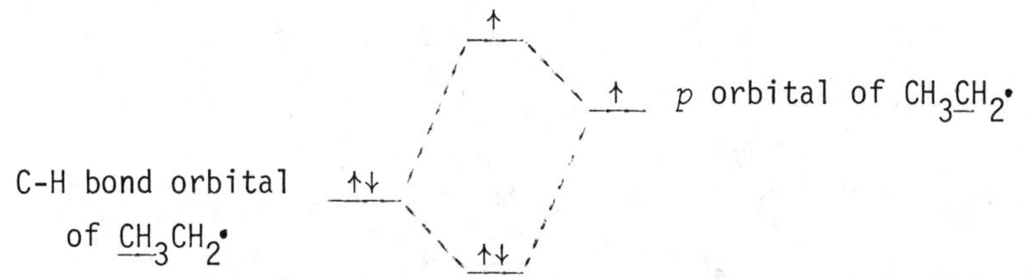

The result is a *net* energy lowering of the three electrons, so, hyperconjugation here is a stabilizing effect.

(a) Applied to $CH_3CH_2^+$ vs. CH_3^+, the only difference is that the *p* orbital of a carbocation is <u>empty</u> instead of half filled. We have, therefore, for $CH_3CH_2^+$:

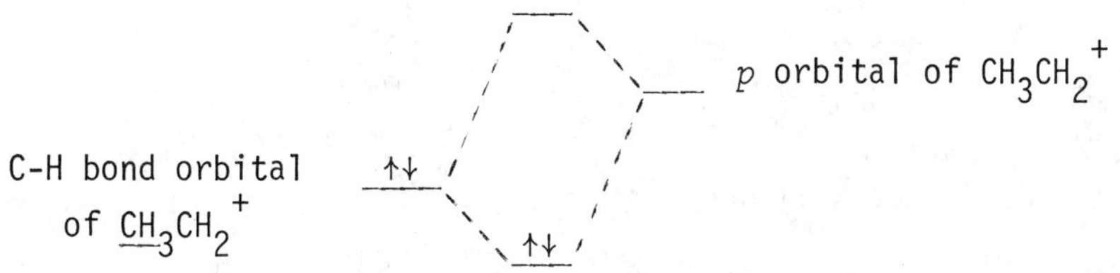

The result of hyperconjugation is, again, a net energy lowering. Hyperconjugation stabilizes $CH_3CH_2^+$ substantially, relative to CH_3^+.

(b) Applied to $CH_3CH_2^-$ vs. CH_3^-: hyperconjugation would require sp^2 hybridization for the negative carbanionic carbon. The *p* orbital is now <u>filled</u>, so the M.O. picture is

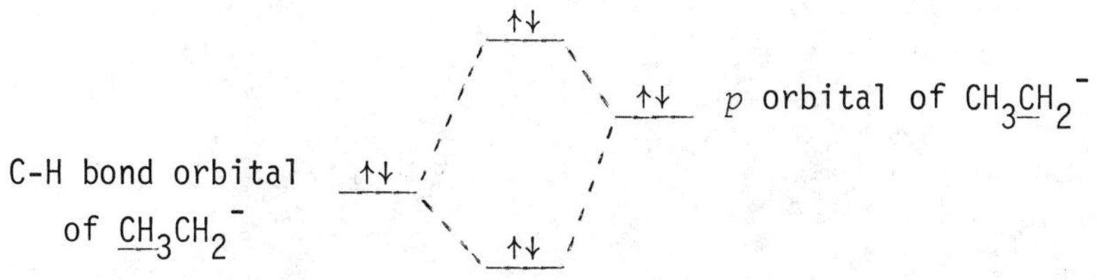

<u>No</u> net stabilization results from this overlap! Two electrons come down in energy, but two others go up. Hyperconjugation does <u>not</u> stabilize $CH_3CH_2^-$ relative to CH_3^-

****

5. Heats of combustion (Table 3-4) may be used together with ΔH_f° values for H_2O and CO_2 to calculate the ΔH_f° value of any compound.

Given:

(1) $C + O_2 \longrightarrow CO_2 \quad \Delta H_f^\circ(CO_2)$

(2) $H_2 + \frac{1}{2}O_2 \longrightarrow H_2O \quad \Delta H_f^\circ(H_2O)$

(3) $C_xH_yO_z + (x + \frac{y}{4} - \frac{z}{2})\,O_2 \longrightarrow xCO_2 + \frac{y}{2}H_2O \quad \Delta H^\circ_{combustion}$

Want:

(4) $xC + \frac{y}{2}H_2 + \frac{z}{2}O_2 \longrightarrow C_xH_yO_z \quad \Delta H_f^\circ$

If we multiply equation (1) by x, multiply equation (2) by $\frac{y}{2}$, add them together, and then subtract equation (3) by turning it around backwards, we should get equation (4):

x(1)	$xC + \cancel{xO_2} \longrightarrow \cancel{xCO_2}$	$x[\Delta H_f^\circ(CO_2)]$
$\frac{y}{2}$(2)	$\frac{y}{2}H_2 + \cancel{\frac{y}{4}O_2} \longrightarrow \cancel{\frac{y}{2}H_2O}$	$\frac{y}{2}[\Delta H_f^\circ(H_2O)]$
-(3)	$\cancel{xCO_2} + \cancel{\frac{y}{2}H_2O} \longrightarrow C_xH_yO_z + (x + \cancel{\frac{y}{4}} - \frac{z}{2})O_2$	$-\Delta H^\circ_{combustion}$
	$xC + \frac{y}{2}H_2 + \frac{z}{2}O_2 \longrightarrow C_xH_yO_z$	ΔH_f°

Their ΔH° values will add accordingly:

$$x[\Delta H_f^\circ(CO_2)] + \frac{y}{2}[\Delta H_f^\circ(H_2O)] - \Delta H^\circ_{combustion} = \Delta H_f^\circ$$

Try it first on a simple compound for which you can check the answer, like methane:

CH_4: x = 1, y = 4

$\Delta H_f^\circ(CO)_2 = -94.1$ kcal/mole

$\Delta H_f^\circ(\text{liquid } H_2O) = -68.3$ kcal/mole

$\Delta H^\circ_{combustion} = -212.8$ kcal/mole

$$\Delta H_f^\circ = (-94.1) + \frac{4}{2}(-68.3) - (-212.8) = -17.9 \text{ kcal/mole}$$

Perfect! Note: ΔH_f° for liquid H_2O is the correct one to use.

Cyclohexane (liquid)

C_6H_{12}: x = 6, y = 12 $\quad \Delta H^\circ_{combustion} = -936.9$ kcal/mole

$$\Delta H_f^\circ = 6(-94.1) + \frac{12}{2}(-68.3) - (-936.9) = -37.5 \text{ kcal/mole}$$

Ethanol (gas)

C_2H_6O: x = 2, y = 6 $\Delta H^\circ_{combustion}$ = -336.4 kcal/mole

$\Delta H^\circ_f = 2(-94.1) + \frac{6}{2}(-68.3) - (-336.4) = -56.7$ kcal/mole

Ethanol (liquid)

C_2H_6O: x = 2, y = 6 $\Delta H^\circ_{combustion}$ = -326.7 kcal/mole

$\Delta H^\circ_f = 2(-94.1) + \frac{6}{2}(-68.3) - (-326.7) = -66.4$ kcal/mole

Sucrose (solid)

$C_{12}H_{22}O_{11}$: x = 12, y = 22 $\Delta H^\circ_{combustion}$ = -1348.2 kcal/mole

$\Delta H^\circ_f = 12(-94.1) + \frac{22}{2}(-68.3) - (-1348.2) = -532.3$ kcal/mole

****

6. More of the same.

(a) benzene (liquid), C_6H_6: x = 6, y = 6 $\Delta H^\circ_{combustion}$ = -781.0 kcal/mole

$\Delta H^\circ_f = 6(-94.1) + \frac{6}{2}(-68.3) - (-781.0) = 11.5$ kcal/mole

(b) propanone (liquid), C_3H_6: x = 3, y = 6 $\Delta H^\circ_{combustion}$ = -427.9 kcal/mole

$\Delta H^\circ_f = 3(-94.1) + \frac{6}{2}(-68.3) - (-427.9) = -59.3$ kcal/mole

(c) propanal (liquid) ΔH°_f = -53.1 kcal/mole

****

7. Propanone, with the *more negative* ΔH°_f, is more stable.

****

8. Calculation of ΔH° for a reaction from ΔH°_f values utilizes the equation

$$\Delta H^\circ = \sum \Delta H^\circ_f(\text{products}) - \sum \Delta H^\circ_f(\text{reactants})$$

ΔH°_f(cyclopropane) = +12.7 kcal/mole (gas)   from Exercise 3-3

ΔH°_f(cyclohexane) = -37.5 kcal/mole (liquid)

So, for 2 cyclopropane (C_3H_6, gas) → cyclohexane (C_6H_{12}, liquid), $\Delta H^\circ = -37.5 - \underline{2}(+12.7) = -62.9$ kcal/mole. Note the factor of 2 due to the involvement of 2 moles of cyclopropane.

****

9. Again, $\Delta H° = \sum \Delta H_f^\circ(\text{products}) - \sum \Delta H_f^\circ(\text{reactants})$.

$$\underset{\Delta H_f^\circ = +54.2}{HC{\equiv}CH} + \underset{0}{2\,H_2} \longrightarrow \underset{-20.2}{CH_3CH_3} \qquad \Delta H° = -20.2 - (+54.2) = -74.4 \text{ kcal/mole}$$

****

10. (a) $HC{\equiv}CH + \frac{5}{2}O_2 \longrightarrow 2\,CO_2 + H_2O$ is balanced.

Section 3-4 presents ΔH_f° data for ethyne in Table 3-5. Turning around the equation used first in Problem 5, for any molecule with x carbons and y hydrogens, we have

$$x[\Delta H_f^\circ(CO_2)] + \frac{y}{2}[\Delta H_f^\circ(H_2O)] - \Delta H_f^\circ = \Delta H^\circ_{combustion}$$

For acetylene x = 2, and y = 2, so

$$\Delta H^\circ_{combustion} = 2(-94.1) + \frac{2}{2}(-68.3) - (+54.2) = -310.7 \text{ kcal/mole}$$

(b) Propane has a $\Delta H^\circ_{combustion}$ = -530.6 kcal/mole, larger than that of ethyne. However, propane has a molecular weight of 44 and ethyne, 26. So propane has $\Delta H^\circ_{combustion}$ = -12.0 kcal/gram and ethyne has $\Delta H^\circ_{combustion}$ = -12.0 kcal/gram. Obviously this does not explain the hotter flame of ethyne since these values come out to be the same. However, the total quantity of product gases from combustion of ethyne is smaller than that from combustion of propane. When this smaller quantity of product gas from ethyne absorbs the combustion heat, it gets heated to a much hotter temperature (ca. 2700°C, vs. 2100°C for propane). This is the reason for the hotter flame.

****

11. The derivation of ΔH_f° would be exactly the same because the heats of combustion for carbon and hydrogen are identical to the ΔH_f° values for CO_2 and H_2O:

$$C + O_2 \longrightarrow CO_2 \qquad \Delta H° = \Delta H^\circ_{combustion}(C) = \Delta H_f^\circ(CO_2)$$

$$H_2 + \tfrac{1}{2}O_2 \longrightarrow H_2O \qquad \Delta H° = \Delta H^\circ_{combustion}(H_2) = \Delta H_f^\circ(H_2O)$$

****

12. All necessary DH° values are in Table 3-1, except for X-X, which are given in Section 3-5. (You would need to go to other sources of data for all the necessary ΔH_f° values.)

(a) The answers (kcal/mole), using $\Delta H° = DH°$ (bond broken) - $DH°$ (bond formed), are:

Reaction			ΔH° for X =	F	Cl	Br	I
(1)	$X\cdot + CH_4$	$\longrightarrow CH_3X + H\cdot$		-5	+20	+34	+48
(2)	$H\cdot + X_2$	$\longrightarrow HX + X\cdot$		-98	-45	-41	-35
	$CH_4 + X_2$	$\longrightarrow CH_3X + HX$	ΔH° =	-103	-25	-7	+13

(b) In every case the ΔH° for the hypothetical first propagation step above is much less favorable than the ΔH° for the generally accepted, correct step (Table 3-6). Therefore, the E_a values for the first steps above will, in all probability, be much larger than the E_a values for the correct steps. Relative to the correct propagation steps, then, the reaction $X\cdot + CH_4 \rightarrow CH_3X + H\cdot$ will probably by very, very slow, and unlikely to compete kinetically.

****

13. Initiation $\quad Br_2 \longrightarrow 2Br\cdot \quad \Delta H° = +46$ kcal/mole

Propagation

(1) $Br\cdot + C_6H_6 \longrightarrow HBr + C_6H_5\cdot \quad \Delta H° = +24$ kcal/mole

(2) $C_6H_5\cdot + Br_2 \longrightarrow C_6H_5Br + Br\cdot \quad \Delta H° = -35$ kcal/mole

Overall $\Delta H° = -11$ kcal/mole

The overall ΔH° is not very different from those of typical alkane C-H bonds: methane, ΔH° = -7 kcal/mole; 1° C-H, ΔH° = -11; 2° C-H, ΔH° = -14.5; 3° C-H, ΔH° = -16. However, the rate determining first propagation step in the reaction of benzene is much more endothermic than any of the alkane reactions, due to the exceptional strength of the C-H bonds in benzene. The result is that bromination of benzene by this mechanism is exceedingly difficult (very slow), and does not complete kinetically with bromination reactions of typical alkanes.

****

14. Inhibition usually comes about by reaction of the inhibitor with one of the reactive "chain-carrying" species in a propagation step. In the case of free-radical halogenation, the alkyl radical is susceptible to reaction with inhibitors. The products of the inhibition process are not reactive enough to continue on to another propagation step, so the propagation "chain" is broken in much the same way that termination steps break the

propagation chain process. We have the following:

$Cl_2 \longrightarrow 2Cl\cdot$ Initiation

$Cl\cdot + CH_4 \longrightarrow HCl + CH_3\cdot$ Propagation step 1 ($\Delta H° = +1$ kcal/mole)

Then, however, in the presence of I_2:

$CH_3\cdot + I_2 \longrightarrow CH_3I + I\cdot$ Inhibition step, $\Delta H° = -20$ kcal/mole.

The chain started by propagation step 1 is now broken because I· cannot react with CH_4 ($\Delta H° = +34$ kcal/mole, from Table 3-6). A chain carrying $CH_3\cdot$ radical has been permanently lost from the reaction system.

****

15. Either DH° or ΔH_f° values may be used, although the DH° data are more readily found (Table 3-1 and Section 3-5). Values in kcal/mole.

(a) 104 + 37 - 2(135) = -129
(b) 104 + 58 - 2(103) = -44
(c) 104 + 46 - 2(87) = -24
(d) 104 + 36 - 2(71) = -2
(e) 93 + 37 - (110 + 135) = -115
(f) 93 + 58 - (81 + 103) = -33
(g) 93 + 46 - (67 + 87) = -15
(h) 93 + 36 - (52 + 71) = +6

****

16. Unless otherwise stated, assume that no more than one halogen atom attaches to each alkane molecule.

(a) No reaction. Iodination of alkanes is endothermic.

(b) $CH_3CHFCH_3 + CH_3CH_2CH_2F$ F_2 is not very selective.

(c) 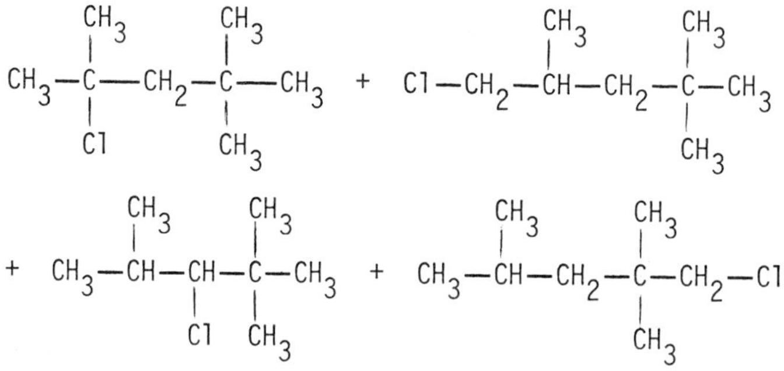

A complex mixture is obtained. Cl_2 is more selective than F_2, but still only prefers 3° to 1° positions by a factor of about 5 to 1.

(d) 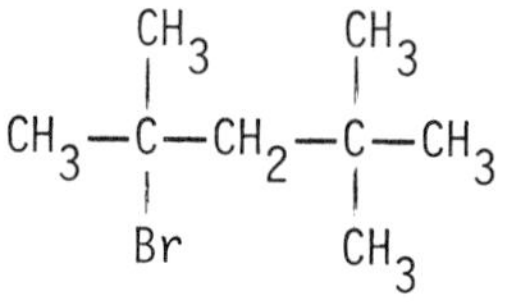 Br_2 is very selective for 3° C-H bonds.

(e) 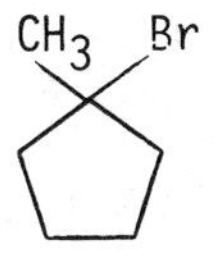 Again, bromination goes 3°, whenever possible. See note in answer to Problem 1(c).

****

17. How the calculations are done: (Number of hydrogens of a given type in the starting alkane) x (Relative Reactivity) = Relative Yield

$$\frac{\text{Relative yield of one product}}{\text{Sum of Relative Yields of all products}} \times 100\% = \%\text{ Yield of That Product}$$

	Product	Hydrogen Type	Number of Hydrogens	Relative Reactivity	Relative Yield	% Yield
(b)	CH_3CHFCH_3	2°	2	1.2	2.4	29
	$CH_3CH_2CH_2F$	1°	6	1	6	71
(c)	$(CH_3)_2CClCH_2C(CH_3)_3$	3°	1	5	5	18
	$ClCH_2CH(CH_3)CH_2C(CH_3)_3$	1°	6	1	6	21
	$(CH_3)_2CHCHClC(CH_3)_3$	2°	2	4	8	29
	$(CH_3)_2CHCH_2C(CH_3)_2CH_2Cl$	1°	9	1	9	32

(d) and (e) 3° substitution by Br_2 is at least 90% selective.

****

18. Only the bromination reactions (d) and (e) are really acceptible as synthetic methods. The other reactions, giving several products in comparable yields, are not synthetically useful. The fluorination (b) might look good on paper, but use of F_2 as a reagent in practice is very difficult.

****

19. How to begin: look for the weakest bond in either CH_3I or HI, and then try to design a free radical chain reaction. The weakest bond is CH_3-I (DH° = 56 kcal/mole), so use it as an initiation step:

<u>Initiation</u>: $CH_3\text{-I} \xrightarrow{\Delta} CH_3\cdot + I\cdot$ $\Delta H° = +57$ kcal/mole

Now what? Use either $CH_3\cdot$ or I• in the best propagation step you can come up with. It turns out to be:

<u>Propagation 1</u>: $CH_3\cdot + \text{H-I} \longrightarrow CH_3\text{-H} + I\cdot$ $\Delta H° = -34$ kcal/mole

DH° 71 105

The only thing left to do is to finish the chain reaction with I· + CH_3I:

Propagation 2: $I\cdot + CH_3{-}I \longrightarrow I{-}I + CH_3\cdot$ $\quad \Delta H^\circ = +21$ kcal/mole

DH° 57 36

Not very good, but the sum of both propagation steps together is fine:

$$HI + CH_3I \longrightarrow I_2 + CH_4 \qquad \Delta H^\circ = -13 \text{ kcal/mole}$$

See what you wound up with? The reverse of an iodination reaction (in the direction it actually goes)!

****

20. (a) Three tertiary hydrogens are present to be readily brominated:

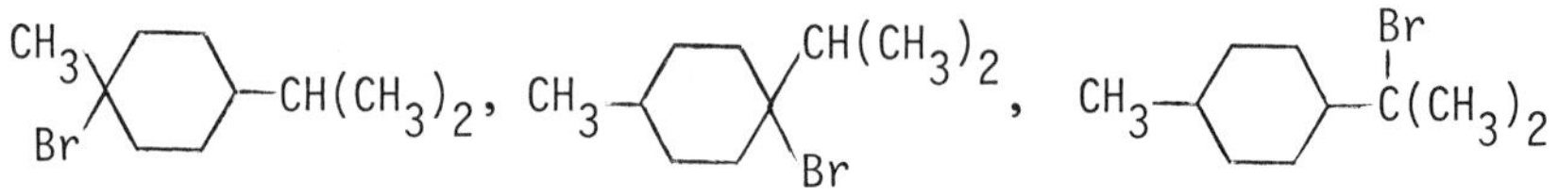

(b) Even worse, with four 3° positions:

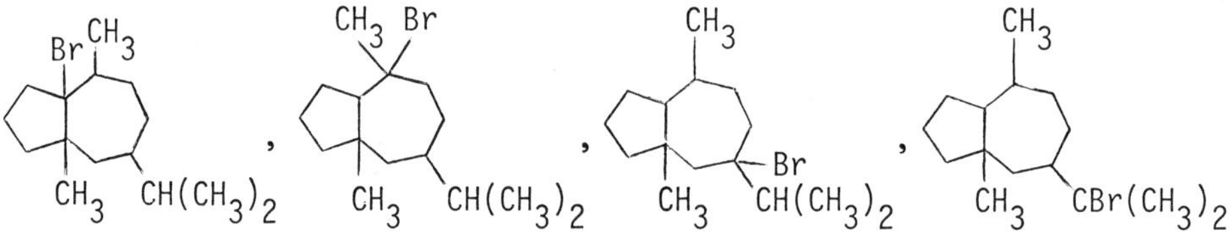

(c) Only one 3° hydrogen; this reaction might be reasonably selective:

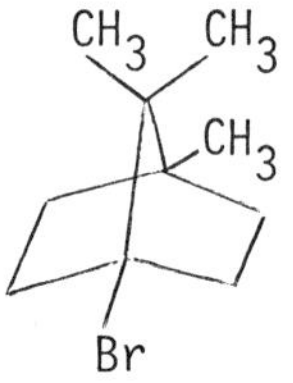

(d) Four, again:

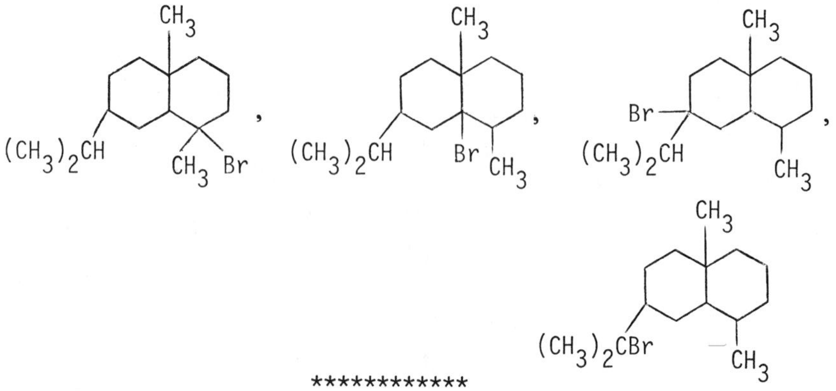

****

21. (a) Benzene hydrogens are not readily halogenated. Consider only hydrogens on alkyl groups.

   (i) Due to low selectivity a mixture of monochlorination products will be obtained: $ClCH_2$-⟨benzene⟩-$CH(CH_3)_2$, CH_3-⟨benzene⟩-$CCl(CH_3)_2$, and CH_3-⟨benzene⟩-$CH(CH_3)CH_2Cl$.

   (ii) Selective for 3° hydrogen: major product is CH_3-⟨benzene⟩-$CBr(CH_3)_2$.

   (b) <u>Initiation</u>

   Init· + ⟨succinimide⟩N-Br ⟶ Init—Br + ⟨succinimide⟩N·

   <u>Propagation</u>

   ⟨succinimide⟩N· + CH_3-⟨benzene⟩-$CH(CH_3)_2$ ⟶ ⟨succinimide⟩NH + CH_3-⟨benzene⟩-$\dot{C}(CH_3)_2$

   CH_3-⟨benzene⟩-$\dot{C}(CH_3)_2$ + ⟨succinimide⟩N-Br ⟶ CH_3-⟨benzene⟩-$CBr(CH_3)_2$ + ⟨succinimide⟩N·

   <u>Termination</u>

   (one possibility) CH_3-⟨benzene⟩-$\dot{C}(CH_3)_2$ + ⟨succinimide⟩N· ⟶ CH_3-⟨benzene⟩-$C(CH_3)_2$N⟨succinimide⟩

   ****

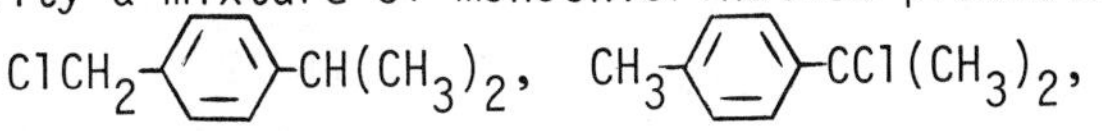

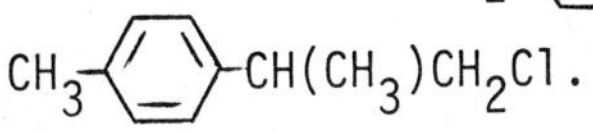

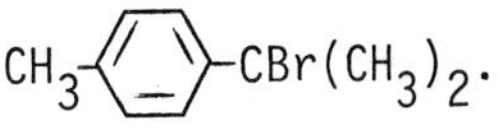

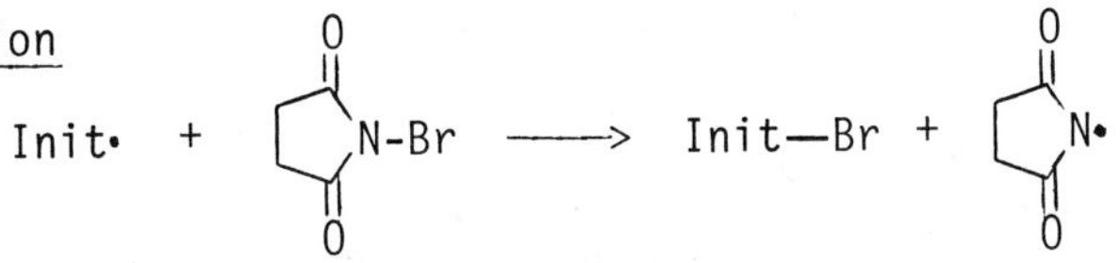

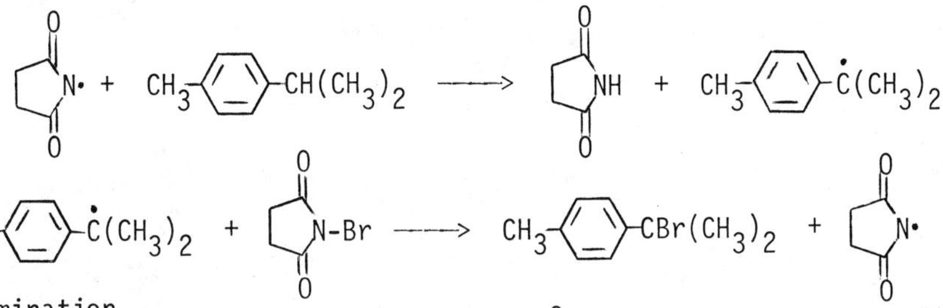

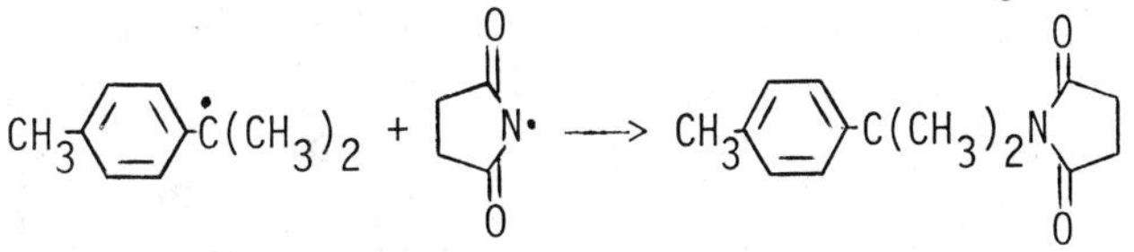

22. (a) $2CH_3OH + 3O_2 \longrightarrow 2CO_2 + 4H_2O$

   $2(CH_3)_3COCH_3 + 15O_2 \longrightarrow 10 CO_2 + 12 H_2O$

   Except for liquid H_2O, all substances in gas phase.

   (b) $\Delta H^\circ_{rxn} = \Delta H^\circ_{comb} = \sum \Delta H^\circ_f \text{(products)} - \sum \Delta H^\circ_f \text{(reactants)}$

   For CH_3OH, $\Delta H^\circ_{comb} = \Delta H^\circ_f(CO_2) + 2 \Delta H^\circ_f(H_2O) - \Delta H^\circ_f(CH_3OH) = (-94.1) + 2(-68.3) - (-48.1) = -182.6$ kcal/mole of CH_3OH.

   For $(CH_3)_3COCH_3$, $\Delta H^\circ_{comb} = 5\Delta H^\circ_f(CO)_2 + 6\Delta H^\circ_f(H_2O) - \Delta H^\circ_f[(CH_3)_3COCH_3] = 5(-94.1) + 6(-68.3) - (-70.6) = -809.7$ kcal/mole of $(CH_3)_3COCH_3$

   Did you miss these by a factor of two? Notice the equations in part (a): to get whole number coefficients it was necessary to start with two moles of starting compound. In entering the number of moles of each substance in the equations in part (b), this factor of two must be divided out, to give an answer in kcal/<u>mole</u> of <u>compound burned</u>.

(c) ΔH°_{comb} for ethane = -372.8 kcal/mole and ΔH°_{comb} for hexane = -995.0 kcal/mole. Combustion of hydrocarbons liberates much more heat than combustion of oxygenated organic compounds.

****

23. (a) Divide ΔH°_{comb} by the molecular weight: (kcal/mole) ÷ (grams/mole) = kcal/gram

Methane: $\Delta H^\circ_{comb} = \dfrac{-212.8 \text{ kcal/mole}}{16 \text{ g/mole (MW of } CH_4)} = -13.3$ kcal/g

Ethane: ΔH°_{comb} = -12.4 kcal/g Propane: ΔH°_{comb} = -12.0 kcal/g

Pentane: ΔH°_{comb} = -11.7 kcal/g

(b) Ethanol (gas): ΔH°_{comb} = -7.3 kcal/g

Methanol: ΔH°_{comb} = -5.7 kcal/g

$(CH_3)_3COCH_3$: ΔH°_{comb} = -9.2 kcal/g

(c) Qualitatively, the observation is quite consistent with the much lower heat production by weight from the combustion of ethanol vs. alkanes; oxygen-containing molecules are indeed poorer sources of energy as fuels.

****

24. You need to do part (a) before drawing the diagram.

(a) Primary: ΔH° = (+23) + (-8.7) - (-24.8) - (+26.7) = +12.4 kcal/mole

Secondary: ΔH° = (+18) + (-8.7) - (-24.8) - (+26.7) = +7.4 kcal/mole

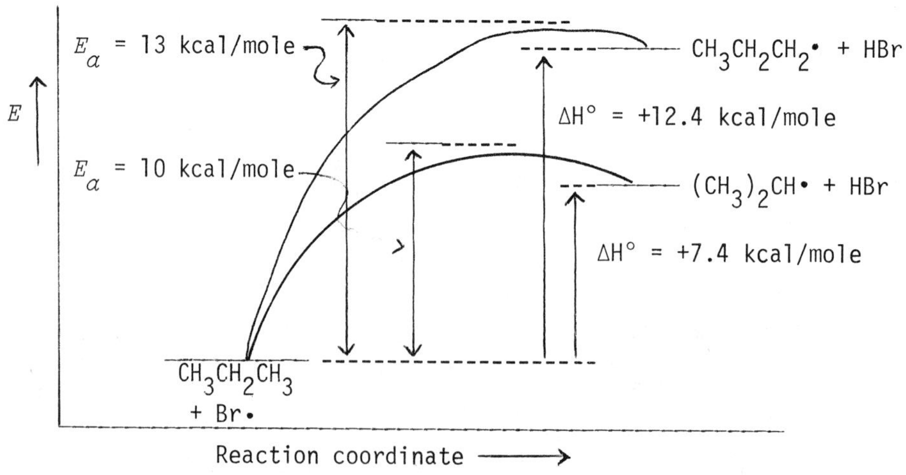

(b) These are "late" transition states, most resembling the products in energy. (Contrast the very "early" transition states in chlorination.)

(c) These transition states closely resemble the product radicals in structures, and therefore have considerable free-radical character. By comparison, those in Figure 3-12 (for chlorination) show much less radical character, being much "earlier," and much less product-like.

(d) Yes. For bromination the radical-like transition states for primary vs. secondary reaction differ in energy by an amount (3 kcal/mole) that closely reflects the difference in energy of the radicals themselves (5 kcal/mole). For chlorination, the much less radical-like transition states do not reflect the energies of the product radicals nearly as much, so the difference between them is much less (1 kcal/mole). Selectivity here is totally determined by the energy difference between transition states of competing pathways; therefore, bromination is much more selective than chlorination.

****

CHAPTER 4

Cyclic Alkanes

General Introduction

The fact that ordinary alkanes and cyclic alkanes are covered in separate chapters of organic chemistry textbooks is more a matter of tradition and convenience rather than a matter of fundamental importance. In most cases, the presence or absence of a ring in a molecule makes only a little difference to its physical properties or its chemical behaviour. What you have learned in chapters 2 and 3 can be applied virtually without change to the molecules presented in chapter 4. Cyclic alkanes are non-polar, lacking in any functional groups, and therefore are relatively unreactive, like acyclic alkanes. For most of them, the only important reactions are free-radical reactions, just as is the case with ordinary alkanes. The major topics of concern are those dealing with the shapes (conformations) of the types of ring systems, and effects of these shapes on the bonding and stability of each size ring. Some new points of nomenclature are presented. On the whole, however, the chapter contains only one new topic that is not a direct extrapolation of what has gone before: the concept of bond angle strain in compounds containing small rings.

Outline of the Chapter

4-1. Nomenclature and Physical Properties.

Basic material.

4-2. Ring Strain and Structure.

The bonding consequences of closing a chain of atoms into a ring of 3, 4, or 5 carbons.

4-3. Cyclohexane.

The most common and most important ring size (6 carbons). Its shapes, and their consequences.

4-4. Substituted Cyclohexanes.

More of the same.

4-5. Larger Cycloalkanes.

Very brief overview.

4-6. Polycyclic Alkanes.

Ditto.

4-7. Carbocyclic Natural Products.

Common ring-containing molecules of biological importance.

Keys to the Chapter

4-1. Nomenclature and Physical Properties.

The naming of ring compounds requires two new procedures in addition to those associated with acyclic compounds. First, since rings have no "ends", numbering starts at whichever carbon around the ring that gives the lowest numbers for substituent groups, using the same criteria for "lowest numbers" presented earlier. Second, rings have a "top" and a "bottom" face, relatively speaking. Therefore, substituents on different ring carbons may either be on the same side or on different sides, necessitating the "cis" or "trans" denotation in the name. All other principles of nomenclature follow unchanged.

4-2. Ring Strain and Structure.

Electron pairs repel each other, and try to be as far apart as possible. Rings with only 3 or 4 atoms force the electron pairs of the C-C bonds to be closer together than is normal for carbon atoms in molecules. The repulsion that results is the major cause of the "high energy" nature of small ring compounds and is the physical cause of the "ring strain" referred to in the text.

In order to examine the structural aspects of these molecules you will find your set of models to be indispensible. Cyclopropane is the only flat cycloalkane ring. *All* larger cycloalkanes are non-planar. Ring distortion away from a planar structure reduces eclipsing interactions involving carbon-hydrogen bonds.

4-3 and 4-4. Cyclohexanes.

Before you do *anything* else, make a model of cyclohexane. Be sure to use the correct atoms and bonds from your kit. The completed model should not be too floppy and should be easily capable of holding the shape shown in Figure 4-5(b). This is the "chair" conformation, with 3 C-H bonds pointing straight up and 3 C-H bonds pointing straight down (the "axial" C-H bonds). Starting from this point you should be able to easily construct the other important cyclohexane conformations by moving an "end" carbon through the plane of the "middle" four carbons of the ring; that is,

move up

boat and boat-like conformations (rather floppy, too)

Learn to recognize "axial" and "equatorial" positions and their cis/trans interrelationships around the ring. Again, use your model in conjunction with the chapter text and illustrations. In your model, note the congestion associated with large groups in axial positions, a result of "1,3-diaxial" interactions, the main effect that causes differences in energy between the two possible chair conformations of a substituted cyclohexane. Be sure to use your models when trying to do the problems at the end of the chapter.

4-5 and 4-6. Larger Rings; Polycyclic Molecules.

The material in these sections is intended only to give a very brief introduction to areas of organic chemistry that are important in current research but are generally beyond the scope of a course at this level. Only a small number of selected molecules are mentioned with relevant points of structure and nomenclature presented where appropriate.

Solutions to Chapter 4 Problems

1. Start with the largest ring, and systematically go through successively smaller rings:

cyclopentane

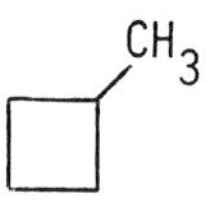

methylcyclobutane

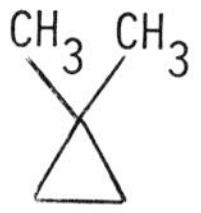

1,1-dimethylcyclopropane

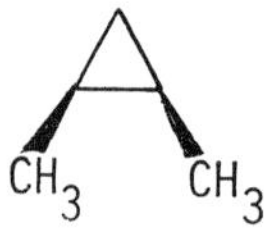

cis-1,2-dimethyl-cyclopropane

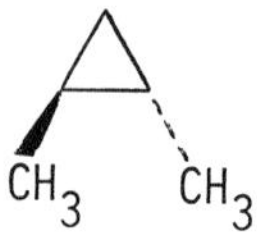

trans-1,2-dimethyl-cyclopropane

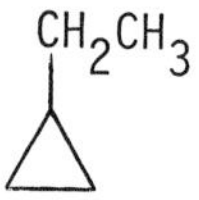

ethylcyclopropane (Did you forget this one? Lots of students miss it.)

****

2. (a) iodocyclopropane

   (b) *trans*-1-methyl-3-(1-methylethyl)cyclopentane

   (c) *cis*-1,2-dichlorocyclobutane

   (d) *cis*-1-cyclohexyl-5-methylcyclodecane

   (e) To tell whether this is *cis* or *trans*, draw in the hydrogens on the substituted carbons:

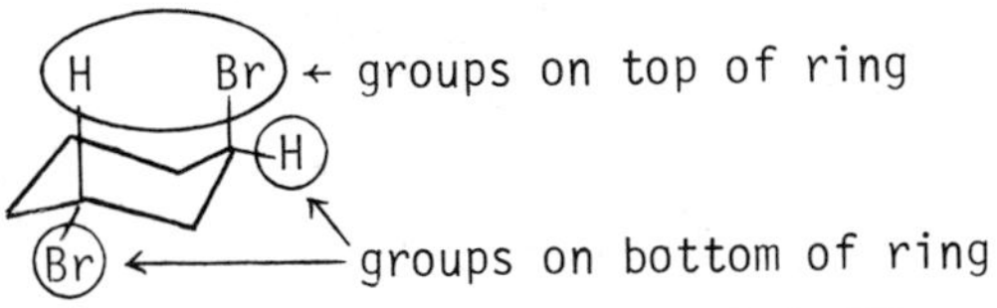

   One Br on top, one on bottom ∴ *trans*-1,3-dibromocyclohexane.

   (f) Similarly,

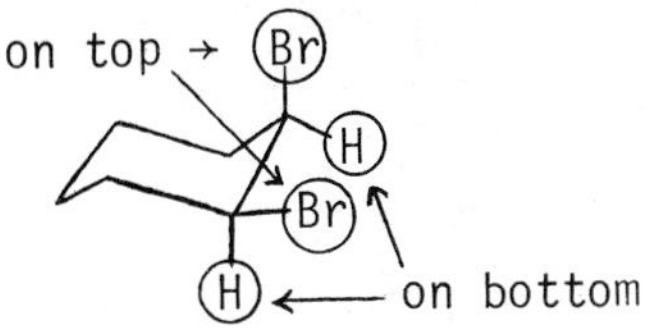

   ∴ *cis*-1,2-dibromocyclohexane

   (g) Identify the "bridgehead" carbons and count carbons in the "bridges" of this nine-carbon bicyclic compound. Note *trans* ring fusion.

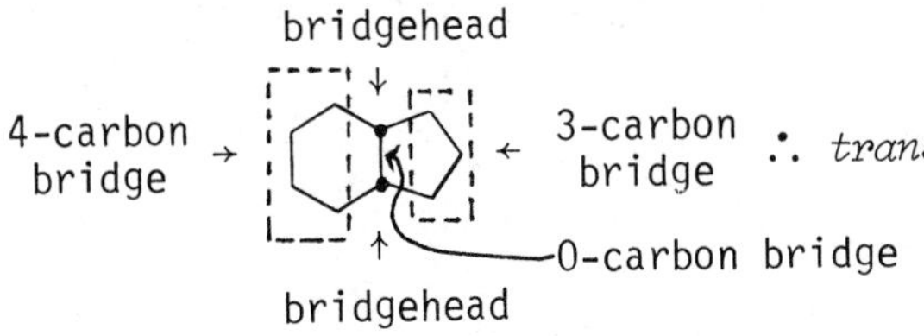

   ∴ *trans*-bicyclo[4.3.0]nonane

   (h) Similarly, 3, 0, and 3-atom bridges, a *cis* ring fusion, and eight carbons total. So, *cis*-bicyclo[3.3.0]octane.

   (i) 1,7,7-trimethylbicyclo[2.2.1]heptane (see text, p. 132).

****

3. (a) The very low relative reactivity of cyclopropane implies (i) abnormally strong C-H bonds and (ii) an abnormally unstable cyclopropyl radical.

   (b) Radicals prefer sp^2 hybridization, with 120° bond angles. So in cyclopropyl radical the bond-angle strain at the radical carbon is greater (120° - 60° = 60° bond angle compression) than at a carbon in cyclopropane itself (109.5° - 60° = 49.5° bond angle compression).

   (c) The enhanced reactivity of 1,1-dimethylcyclopropane relative to cyclopropane itself must result from reaction of the methyl hydrogens.

So,

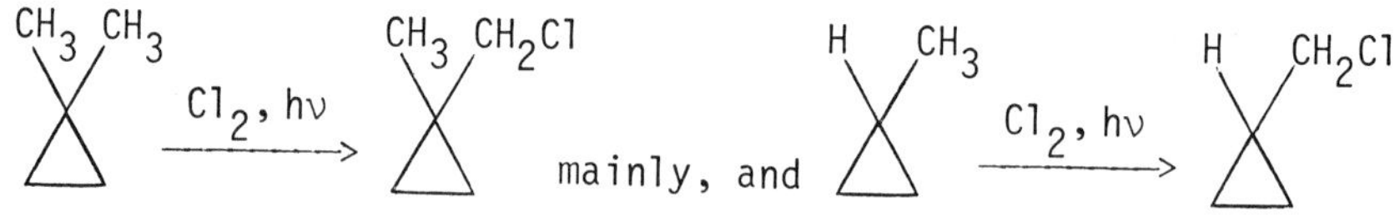

The 3° hydrogen in methylcyclopropane is not that much more reactive towards Cl• than the 2° hydrogens (recall Section 3-6).

****

4. In all cases the reference value to begin with is the DH° for the C-C bond between CH_2 (2°) groups, i.e. DH° for $CH_3CH_2—CH_2CH_3$, 82 kcal/mole (Table 3-2).

(a) Cleavage of a C-C bond in cyclopropane requires a smaller net energy input because ring strain is relieved in the process.

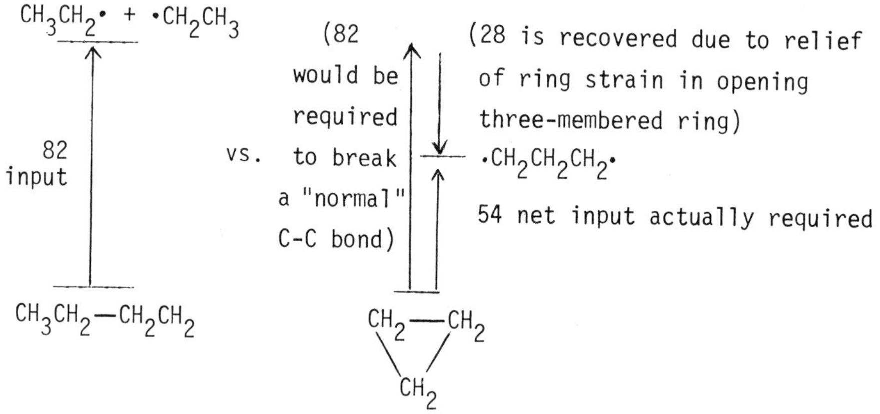

So DH° = 82 - 28 = 54 kcal/mole. Note that this is consistent with the E_a of 65 kcal/mole for ring opening (section 4-2).

(b) For cyclobutane, our estimated DH° = 82-27 = 55 kcal/mole. Both the cyclopropane and cyclobutane values calculated in this manner are estimates only (experimental data actually put the cyclobutane DH° value slightly higher).

(c) DH° = 82 - 7 = 75 kcal/mole (d) DH° = 82 - 1 = 81 kcal/mole

Thus the unusual ring-opening reactions of cyclopropane and cyclobutane (relative to other alkanes and cycloalkanes) are thermodynamically reasonable.

****

5. The first step must be cleavage of the weakest bond, a ring C-C bond, forming the trimethylene diradical:

$$CH_2\!\!-\!\!CH_2 \diagdown CH_2 \quad \xrightarrow{\Delta} \quad \cdot CH_2\!-\!CH_2\!-\!CH_2 \cdot$$

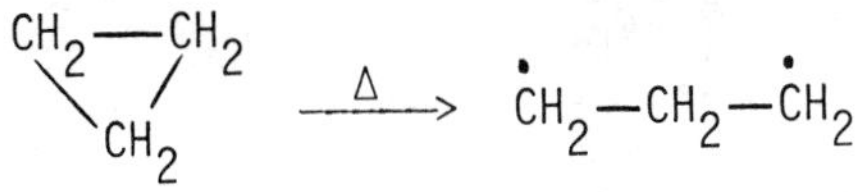

The simplest possible process that can occur to convert this to the more stable molecule propene would be a hydrogen atom shift from the middle CH_2 group to either end. (This is an intramolecular version of the hydrogen abstraction reaction presented in Chapter 3-3, and Problems 2 and 3 of Chapter 3.)

$$\cdot CH_2\!-\!\overset{\overset{\textstyle H}{|}}{CH}\!-\!CH_2 \cdot \quad \longrightarrow \quad CH_2\!\!=\!\!\overset{\overset{\textstyle H}{|}}{CH}\!-\!CH_2$$

It is also possible to write an intermolecular mechanism for this hydrogen abstraction:

$$\cdot CH_2\text{-}\overset{H}{CH}\text{-}CH_2 \cdot \ + \ \cdot CH_2\text{-}CH_2\text{-}CH_2 \cdot \ \longrightarrow \ CH_2\!=\!CH\text{-}\dot{C}H_2 \ + \ CH_3\text{-}\overset{H}{CH}\text{-}\dot{C}H_2 \ \longrightarrow \ 2\ CH_2\!=\!CH\text{-}CH_3$$

****

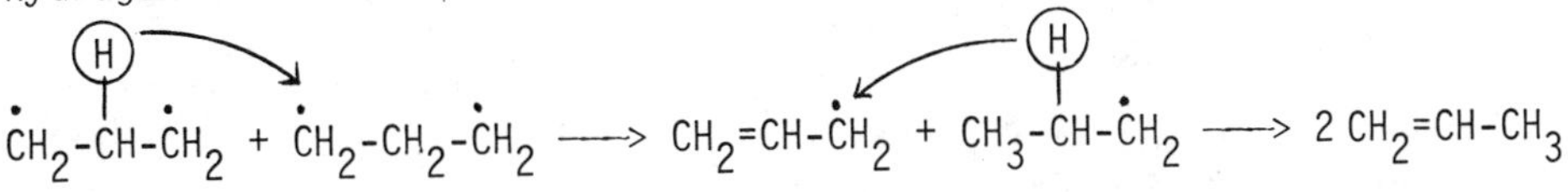

6. Using $DH°$ values (cf. problem 4):

(a) ⬡ ← + H—H ⟶ H—$CH_2(CH_2)_4CH_2$—H

    $DH° = 81$ 104   98   98

$\Delta H° = $ (energy in) $-$ (energy out) $= \Sigma DH°$ (bonds broken) $- \Sigma DH°$ (bonds formed)
$\Delta H° = 185 - 196 = -11$ kcal/mole

(b) ⬡ ← + H—Cl ⟶ H—$CH_2(CH_2)_4CH_2$—Cl

    $DH° = 81$ 103   98   81

$\Delta H° = 184 - 179 = +5$ kcal/mole

(c) △ + H—H ⟶ H—$CH_2CH_2CH_2$—H

    $DH° = 54$ 104   98   98

$\Delta H° = 158 - 196 = -38$ kcal/mole

(d) △ + H—Cl ⟶ H—$CH_2CH_2CH_2$—Cl

    $DH° = 54$ 103   98   81

$\Delta H° = 157 - 179 = -22$ kcal/mole

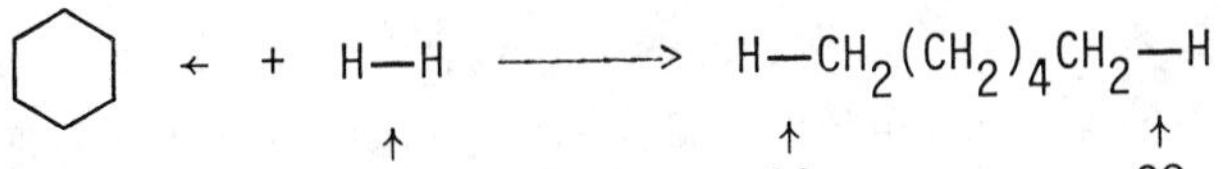

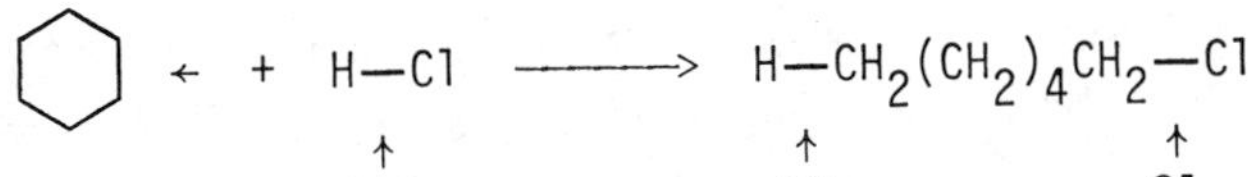

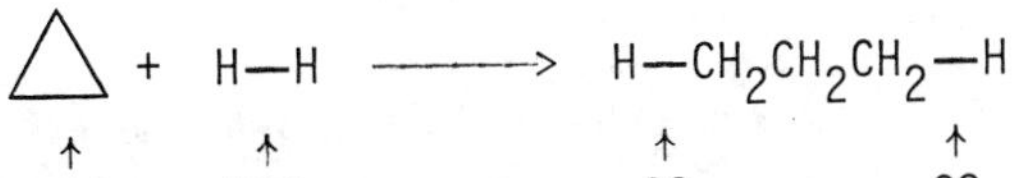

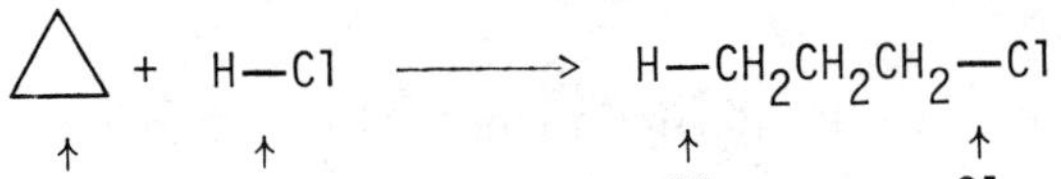

Reactions c and d can be made to occur readily. Reaction b is endothermic and cannot be done. Reaction a, although exothermic, has a very high E_a and cannot be carried out under ordinary conditions. (However, under pyrolytic conditions it can occur: "hydrocracking").

****

7. If pure *p* orbitals were used for the C-C bonds of cyclobutane, then each carbon could be *sp* hybridized:

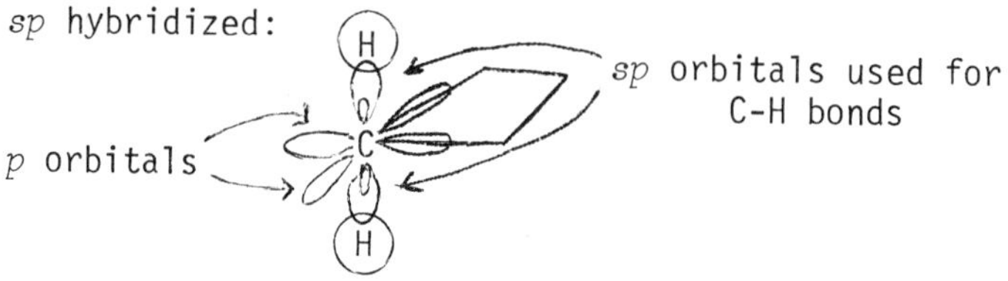

The H-C-H bond angle would be 180° and cyclobutane would look like this:

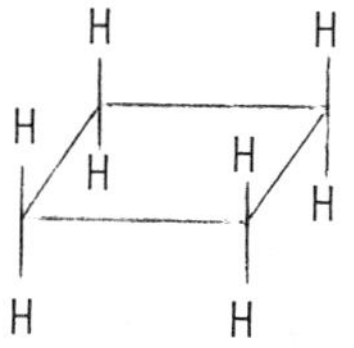

In reality, cyclobutane uses "bent" bonds just like cyclopropane, and all four bonds to each carbon involve hybridized orbitals. In addition, cyclobutane is not flat at all, and the H-C-H bond angle is not much different from the normal tetrahedral value of 109° (see Figure 4-3).

****

8. Compare eclipsing interactions in the two forms.

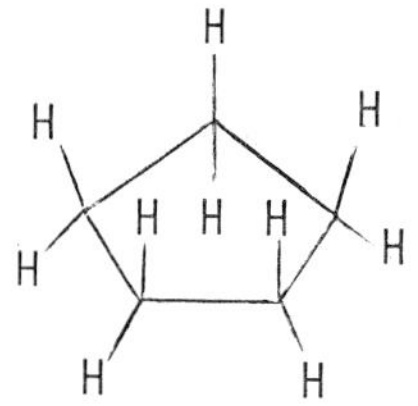

Planar - all C-H bonds on top and bottom are eclipsed for a total of 10 interactions.

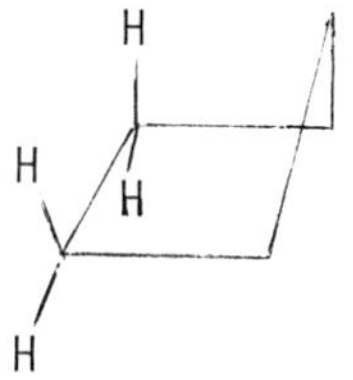

Envelope - only the C-H bonds shown are eclipsed, for a total of 2 interactions.

From ethane, we estimate each eclipsing interaction to cost 1 kcal/mole. Therefore ΔH_f° for planar cyclopentane will be 10 - 2 or 8 kcal/mole more positive (i.e., less stable) than ΔH_f° for envelope cyclopentane. ΔH_f° for the equilibrium shown is then -8 kcal/mole.

****

9. Refer to answers to problems 2(e) and 2(f) for quidelines.

(a) *Trans*! (Surprise!) Note positions of hydrogens:

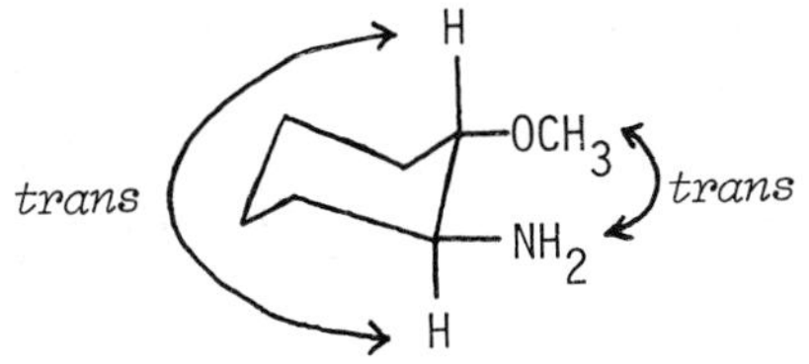

The two hydrogens are *trans*, so obviously the NH_2 and OCH_3 groups must be *trans*, also. The NH_2 is *cis* to the top H, and the OCH_3 is *cis* to the bottom H.

Both groups are equatorial, so this is the most stable conformation.

(b) *Cis*:

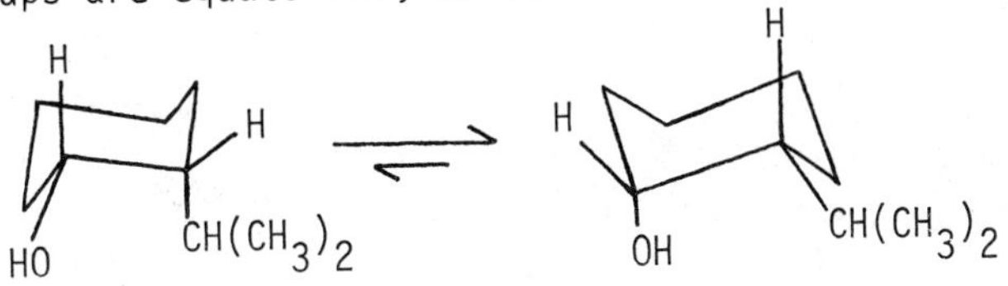

From Table 4-3, $CH(CH_3)_2$ prefers an equatorial position by more (2.2 kcal/mole) than does OH (0.94 kcal/mole). In the structure drawn, $CH(CH_3)_2$ is axial and OH is equatorial. This is not the most stable conformation since the ring can flip to the form on the right, in which $CH(CH_3)_2$ is equatorial and OH axial.

(c) *Trans*:

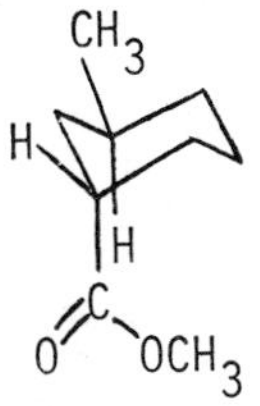

Most stable conformation (CH_3 equatorial).

(d) *Trans*: Not most stable form. Ring flip gives diequatorial conformation:

(e) *Cis*:

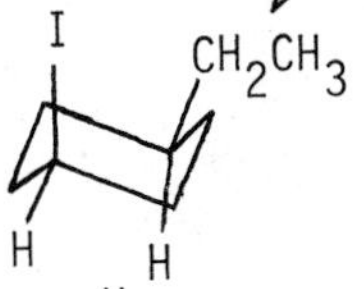

Most stable form (CH_3CH_2 equatorial).

(f) *Trans*:

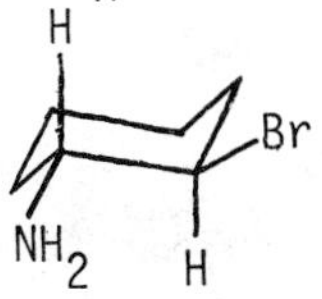

Most stable form (both groups equatorial).

(g) *Cis*: 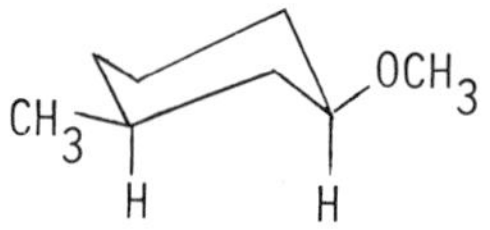

Most stable form (both groups equatorial).

(h) *Cis*. Not most stable form. Ring flip makes it diequatorial:

(i) *Cis*: 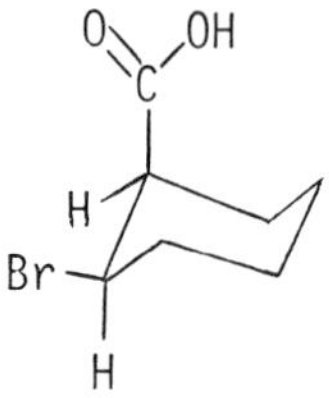

Not most stable form. Ring flip makes HO-C(=O) group equatorial, which is preferable (Table 4-3).

(j) *Trans*. Most stable form [compare part (a), above].

****

	Best	Next Best
10. (a)	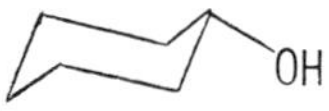	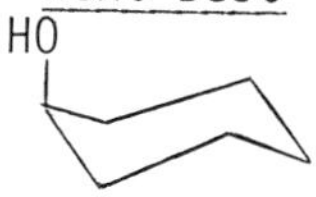
(b)	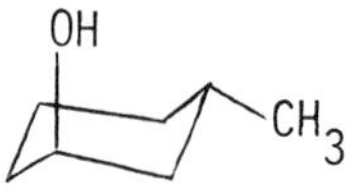	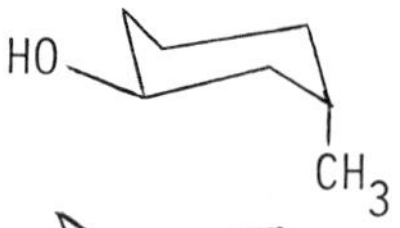
(c)	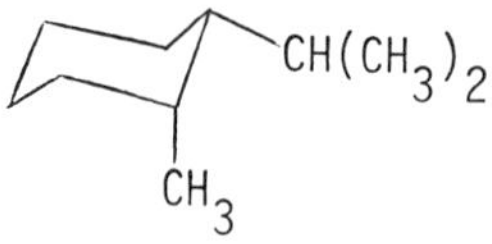	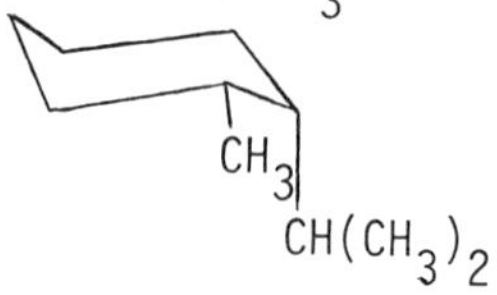
(d)	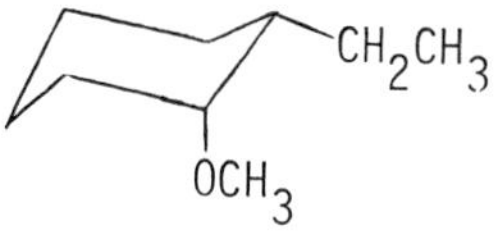	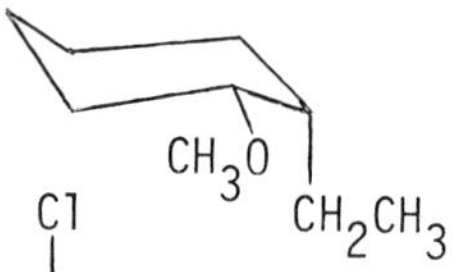
(e)	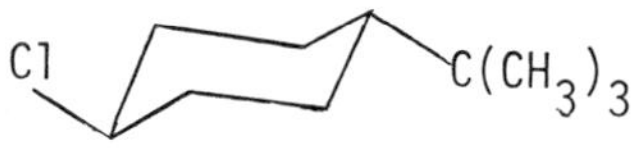	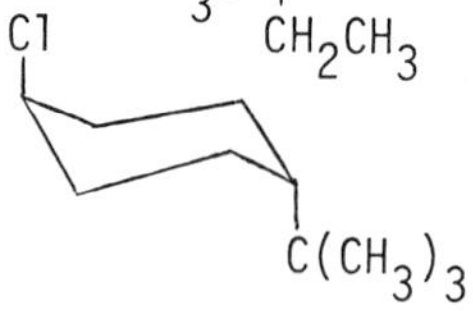

****

11. From Table 4-3:

Ratios, using $\Delta G° = -RT \ln K_{eq}$:

(a) 0.94 kcal/mole (less stable conformation is higher in energy)

$K_{eq} = 4.8$; $\frac{4.8}{4.8+1} = .83$; ∴ 83/17 ratio (in favor of more stable conformation)

(b) $1.7 - 0.94 = 0.8$ kcal/mole

$K_{eq} = 3.8$; $\frac{3.8}{3.8+1} = .79$; ∴ 79/21 ratio

(c) 2.2 - 1.7 = 0.5 kcal/mole K_{eq} = 2.3; 70/30 ratio

(d) 1.75 - 0.75 = 1.00 kcal/mole K_{eq} = 5.3; 84/16 ratio

(e) 5 + 0.52 = 5.5 kcal/mole $K_{eq} \simeq 10^4$; >> 99.9/0.1 ratio

In each case the more stable conformation is the one in which the group with largest ΔG° value from Table 4-3 is equatorial.

****

12. Only a boat-related conformation permits both bulky groups to avoid axial positions. Notice how some positions around a boat conformation of cyclohexane are axial-like ("pseudoaxial") and some are equatorial-like ("pseudo-equatorial"):

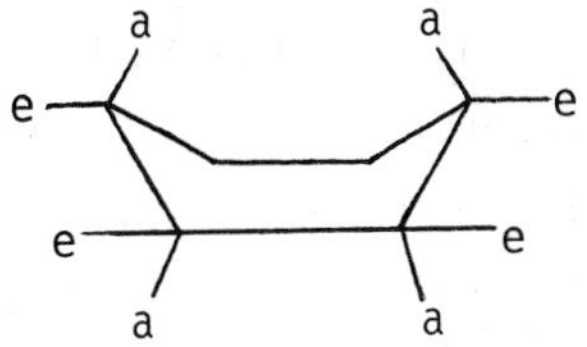

a = pseudoaxial
e = pseudoequatorial

This molecule will adopt a conformation in which both groups are "pseudo-equatorial." The true shape will be based on the twist-boat of cyclohexane in order to minimize eclipsing interactions of the true boat conformation (Section 4-3) (make a model!):

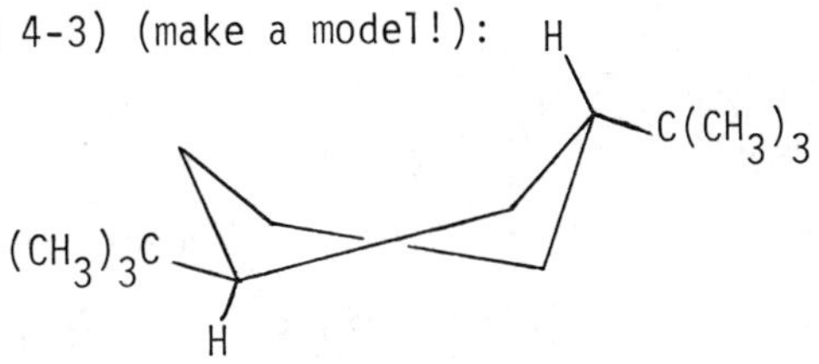

****

13. Make another model! Notice that making "all-chair" cyclodecane is essentially the same as removing the "zero bridge" bond from *trans*-decalin and replacing it with two hydrogens - on on each former bridge-head carbon:

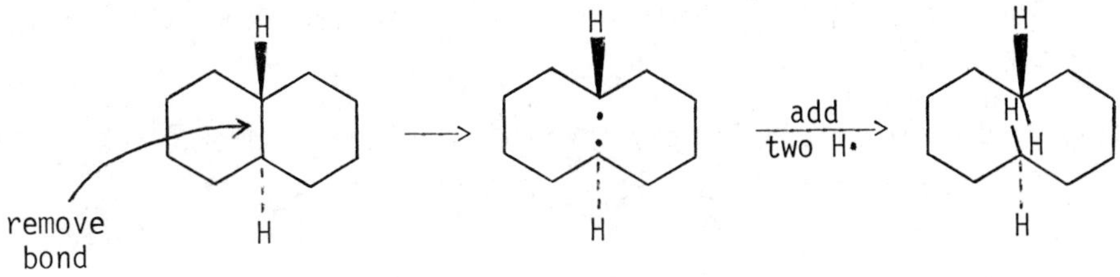

The resulting molecule has these two new hydrogens pointing into the ring, in prohibitively close contact with the carbon and hydrogens on the opposite side of the ring. The steric strain of this transannular interaction makes this a very high energy conformation.

****

14. The *trans* isomer is a more rigid, regularly shaped molecule than the *cis*, and it therefore crystallizes in a more regular arrangement, giving a higher melting point (see Section 4-1).

****

15. (a) Notice (Figure 4.15 or models) that all ring carbon-carbon bonds are equatorial with respect to either ring in the *trans* isomer, while in the *cis* compound two carbon-carbon bonds are forced to be axial in the molecule. This results in a net total of three more gauche interactions in the *cis* isomer relative to the *trans* (see Figure 4-6, and below).

vs.
arrows are gauche interactions between rings

trans
(no gauche interactions between rings)

cis

Trans-bicyclo[4.4.0]decane is therefore more stable than *cis*. This result holds even though *cis*-decalin is more flexible, and therefore has a higher entropy than the rigid *trans* isomer (Exercise 4-7).

(b) Contracting one ring from six to five carbons introduces some bond angle strain and partial eclipsing into both the *cis*- and *trans*-bicyclo[4.3.0]nonane structures. It also reduces the importance of gauche interactions between rings in the *cis* isomer (make a model). The result is that the *cis* and *trans* isomers are very close in energy.

(c) Bond angle strain is very large in the *trans* isomer. *Cis*-bicyclo-[4.2.0]octane is much more stable:

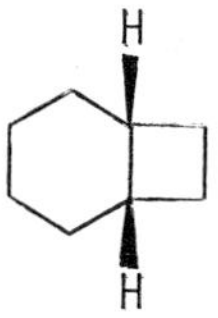

****

16. Count carbons in the "skeleton" of the molecule. If there are 10, the molecule is a monoterpene; if 15, a sesquiterpene; if 20, a diterpene.

(a) 10 carbons, monoterpene

(b), (c), and (d) 15 carbons, sesquiterpene

(e) 11 carbons, but only 10 in the molecular "skeleton"; monoterpene

(f) 15, sesquiterpene (g) 10, monoterpene (h) 20, diterpene

****

17. Each isoprene unit may be set off by dotted lines:

(a)

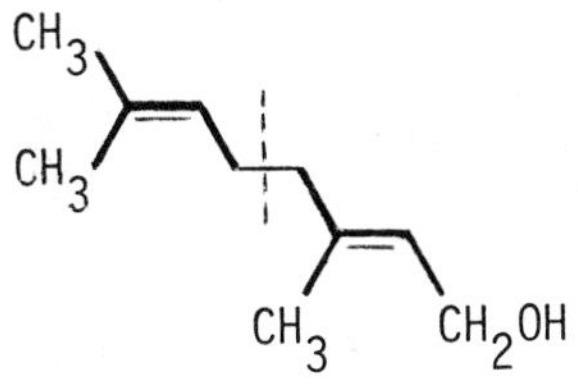

(b)

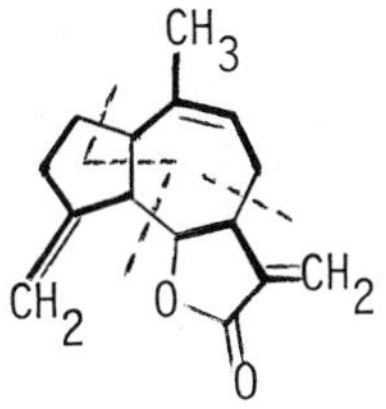

or

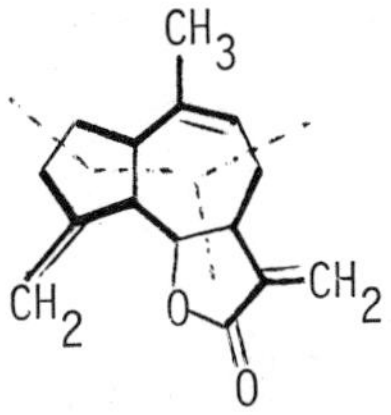

(c)

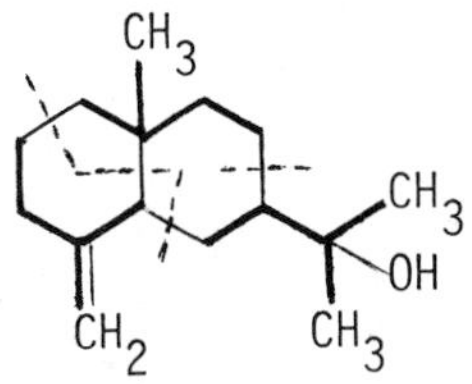

or

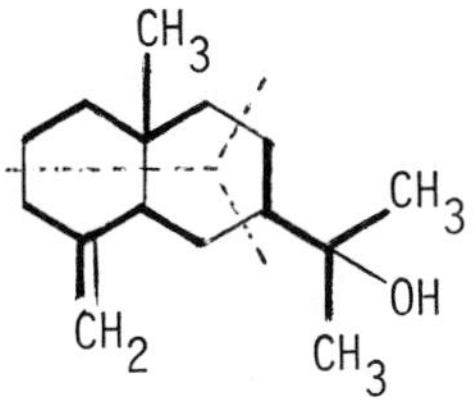

(d)

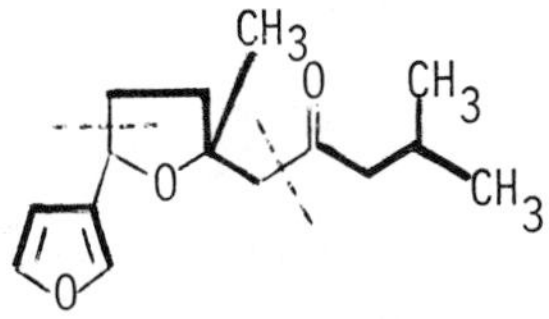

(e)

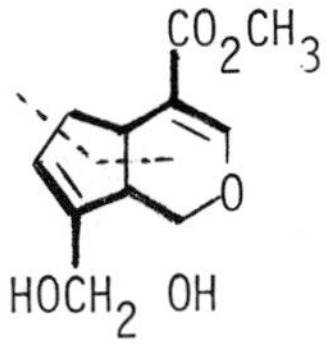

(f)

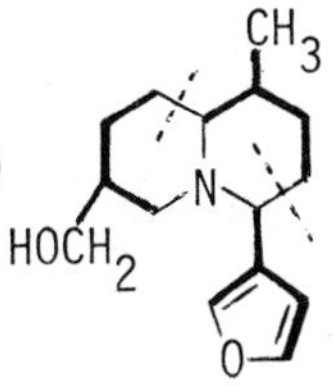

(g)

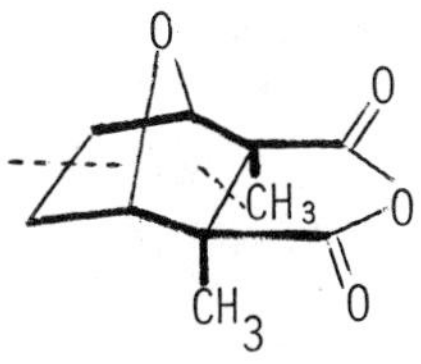

(h)

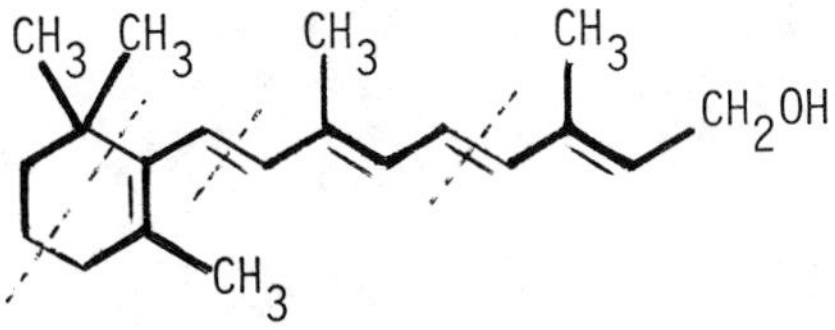

****

18. Cortisone provides a good example for this exercise:

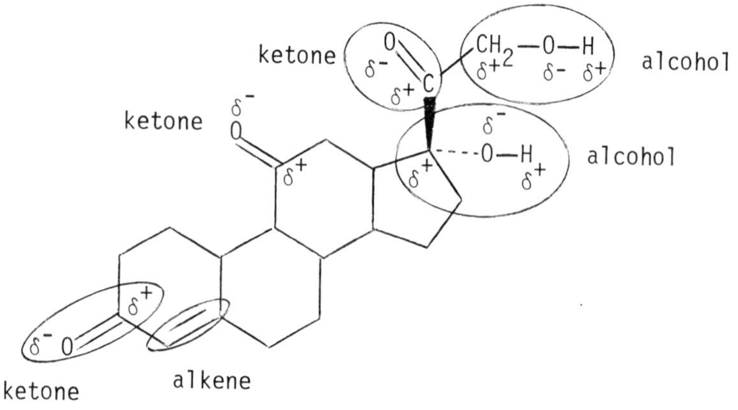

Other functional groups shown in this section include the following:

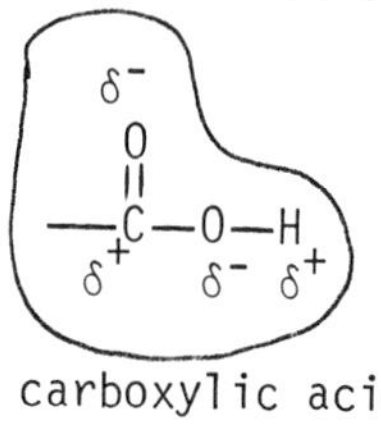

in cholic acid;

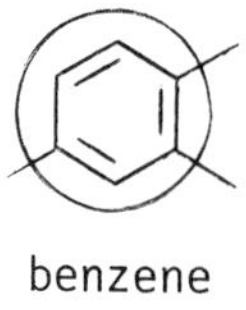

in estradiol;

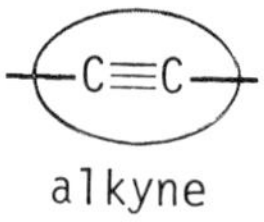

in norethynodrel and mestranol; and

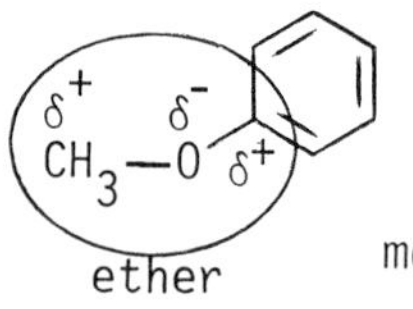

in mestranol.

****

19. (a) α-pinene is a monoterpene:

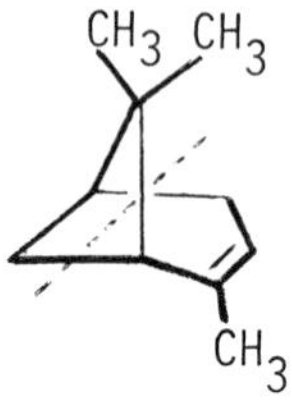

10 carbons

Africanone is a sesquiterpene:

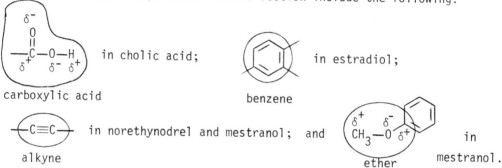

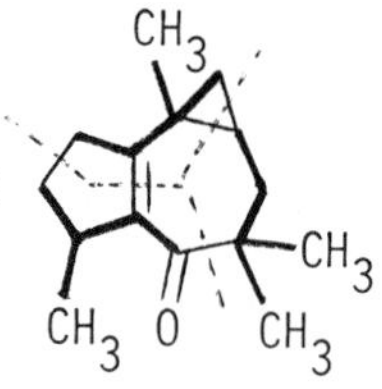

(b) (i) Bicyclo[3.1.1]heptane (ii) *cis*-bicyclo[5.1.0]octane

****

20. (a) From left to right: chair cyclohexane, boat (or twist-boat) cyclohexane, chair cyclohexane, envelope cyclopentane.

(b) All are *trans*.

(c) $\underline{\alpha}$ means below and $\underline{\beta}$ means above. Therfore: $3\underline{\alpha}$-OH, $4\underline{\alpha}$-CH$_3$, $8\underline{\alpha}$-CH$_3$, $11\underline{\alpha}$-OH, $14\underline{\beta}$-CH$_3$, $16\underline{\beta}$-OCCH$_3$.
  $\qquad\qquad\qquad\qquad\qquad\qquad\qquad\qquad\quad$ ‖
  $\qquad\qquad\qquad\qquad\qquad\qquad\qquad\qquad\quad$ O

(d) The boat-like cyclohexane ring is the most unusual feature; most steroids have only chair cyclohexanes. The boat shape is a result of the unusual *cis* relationship of the groups at positions 9 and 10, and also at positions 5 and 8. Note also the unusual number and location of methyl groups: at positions 4, 8, and 14, instead of the more common pair of methyl groups at 10 and 13.

****

21.

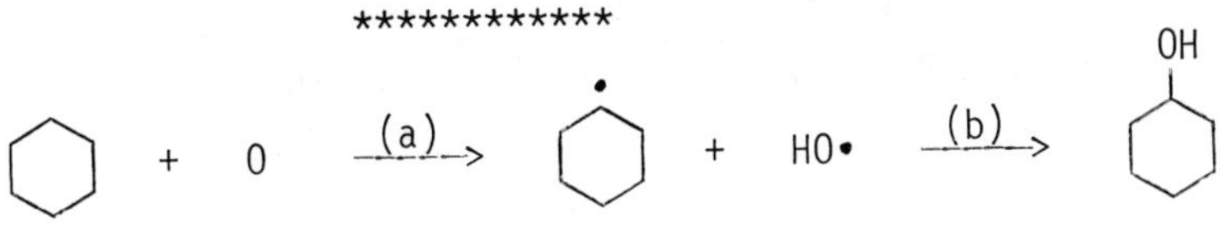

ΔH_f° =	-29.5 $+59.6$	$+15$ $+9.4$	-68.4
sums =	$+30.1$	$+24.4$	-68.4

For (a), ΔH° = $+24.4 - 30.1 = -5.7$ kcal/mole; For (b), ΔH° = $-68.4 - 24.4 =$ -92.8 kcal/mole. Overall, ΔH° = -98.5 kcal/mole.

****

22. (a) <u>Propagation</u>

$\qquad$ Cl• + RH $\longrightarrow$ HCl + R•   can happen initially

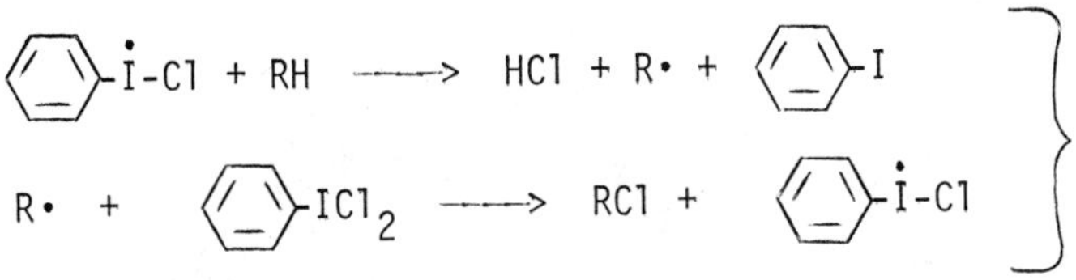

$\qquad$ $\overset{\bullet}{\text{I}}$-Cl + RH $\longrightarrow$ HCl + R• + I $\Big\}$ main steps of chain reaction

$\qquad$ R• + ICl_2 $\longrightarrow$ RCl + $\overset{\bullet}{\text{I}}$-Cl

<u>Termination</u> (one possibility)

$\qquad$ R• + $\overset{\bullet}{\text{I}}$-Cl $\longrightarrow$ RCl + I

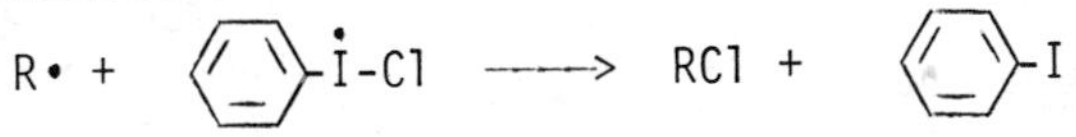

(b) There are four tertiary hydrogens, but the one that is β (up) is too hindered to be chlorinated, due to its 1,3-diaxial interactions with the two β methyl groups. So the sites of chlorination are the three tertiary α (down) hydrogens:

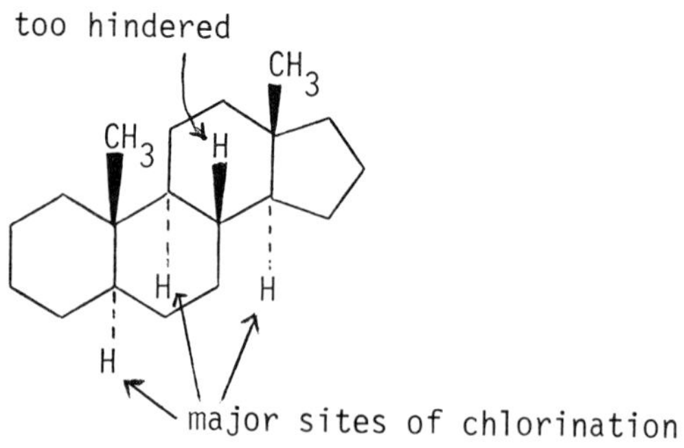

****

23. Addition of Cl_2 in each case generates a substituted 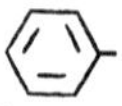-ICl_2 unit. Then, in the presence of light, these become 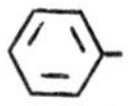-İ-Cl groups, which can chlorinate nearby C-H bonds according the propagation steps shown in the answer to problem 22(a). The selectivity comes from the fact that in reaction (i), the 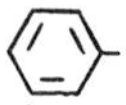-İ-Cl group can reach the H at position 9 most easily, while in (ii) it most easily reaches the H at position 14. Your models should look something like these:

(a)

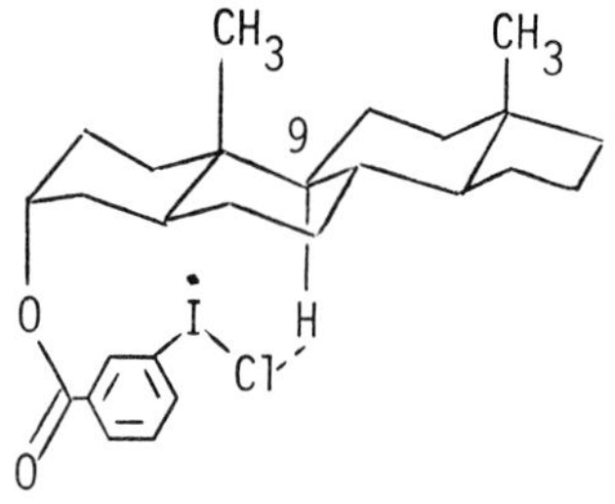

vs.

(b)

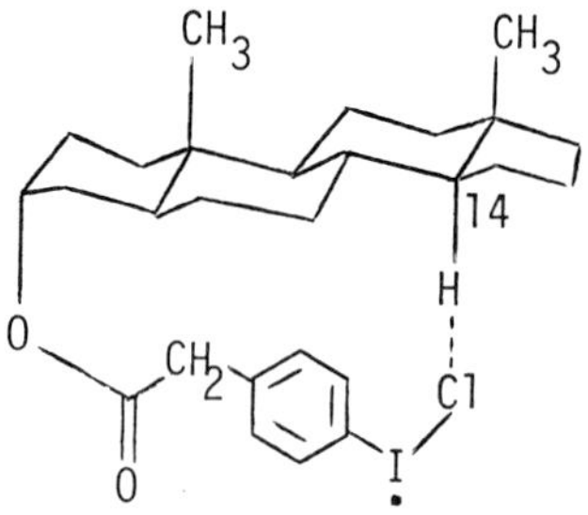

****

CHAPTER 5

Stereoisomerism

General Introduction

By now you are well aware that molecules are three-dimensional objects. This chapter explores some of the more subtle, but extremely critical consequences of this fact. If you have not done so as yet, make a point of obtaining a set of models to aid you in visualizing the structures described in this chapter. For many students, the isomeric relationships to be discussed here will be the most difficult ones to be encountered in organic chemistry, and they will become important later on in descriptions of several types of compounds and reactions. The implications toward biological chemistry are especially significant.

Outline of the Chapter

5-1. Chiral Molecules.

The key definitions: what makes an object different from its mirror image.

5-2. Optical Activity.

Physical properties of chiral molecules.

5-3. The R-S Sequence Rules.

How to name chiral molecules.

5-4. Fischer Projections.

How to draw chiral molecules.

5-5. Molecules Incorporating Several Stereocenters: Diastereomers.

Further elaboration, proceeding in the general direction of biological chemistry.

5-6. Stereochemistry in Chemical Reactions.

Ground rules.

5-7. Resolution of Enantiomers.

Practical techniques.

Keys to the Chapter

5-1. Chiral Molecules.

In this chapter you will be introduced to more new terms than anywhere else in organic chemistry. Follow their definitions along with the structures given as examples. This guide will direct your attention to the more important or more widely used terms. The first key is derived from the chapter title: *stereoisomer*. In brief, stereoisomers are molecules whose atoms are linked in the same order (i.e., identical connectivity), but do not have identical three-dimensional shapes. Except for conformational isomers, stereoisomers cannot be readily interconverted by simple motions like bond rotation under ordinary conditions. The first example in the text section, 2-bromobutane, is one of a vast number of molecules that are *chiral*. Chiral molecules can exist as either of two stereoisomeric shapes, which are related as an object is to its mirror image. Before going on any further, let's make one point clear: every molecule has a mirror image, obviously. What makes a chiral molecule special is that it is *not identical to its mirror image*. Methane is identical to its mirror image; it is not chiral. The two possible shapes of a chiral molecule differ in the same way that a right-handed object differs from a left-handed object, as in gloves, shoes, hands, etc. Chirality, therefore, is essentially "handedness" on a molecular level. The two mirror image-shapes of a chiral molecule are called *enantiomers* of each other.

What makes a molecule chiral? The simplest of several types of structural features that can make a molecule chiral is the presence of a carbon atom attached to four different atoms or groups (an *asymmetric carbon atom*, an example of what is called a *stereocenter*). At this point it is worthwhile to dust off your set of models and start manufacturing chiral molecules. Begin with simple models of carbon stereocenters, and demonstrate to yourself that the model of the mirror image of a stereocenter cannot be made to superimpose on the original. This is the first step towards developing the ability to visualize this relationship clearly.

5-2. Optical Activity.

The physical difference between enantiomers is so subtle that they wind up for the most part displaying identical physical and chemical properties. They can be distinguished from each other only upon interaction with something else that is, itself, already "handed." By analogy, a right and a left glove will have the same weight, color, and texture. However, interaction with, for instance a right hand will immediately tell them apart. The fact that one can tell them apart just by looking at them reflects the fact that our brain's interpretation of the signals from our binocular visual system is "handed" in its ability to perceive depth as well as left-right relationships. For chiral molecules, the counterpart to this is their interaction with plane polarized light. Polarized light is "handed" by virtue of the relationship of the vectors defining its electric and magnetic fields. This handedness results in the plane of polarization of plane polarized light being rotated when it passes through a solution of one enantiomer of a chiral molecule. This phenomenon, labeled optical rotation, is the most common way of detecting chiral molecules, and is described in considerable detail in this chapter section. Molecules possessing the ability to rotate the plane of polarized light are often described as being optically active, or displaying optical activity, and another term for enantiomers is optical isomers. One further term of importance is the one given to a mixture of equal amounts of the two enantiomers of a chiral molecule: racemic mixture. Since the two enantiomers of a chiral molecule each rotate light by equal amounts, but in opposite directions, the racemic mixture displays no optical activity at all as the two optical isomers exactly cancel out each other's optical properties.

Again, due to the large number of new terms and ideas associated with this material, it merits careful consideation, with a good set of models close at hand.

5-3. The *R-S* Sequence Rules.

Like all the rules of nomenclature, the *R-S* system for molecules containing stereocenters has one purpose: the concise, unambiguous description of a single chemical structure. In most cases the system is not particularly difficult to apply as the assignment of priorities to the groups on an asymmetric carbon is usually straightforward, and use of models to view the stereocenter properly takes care of the rest. Models should be made of the examples in the chapter so that you can confirm the *R* or *S* designations in the text.

Priority rule 2 is an occasional source of trouble until the concept of "first point of difference" is well-understood. If this gives you trouble, take it stepwise as follows:

(a) Write the substituent groups to be compared side-by-side, with the bond of attachment to the asymmetric atom to the left.

(b) Starting at the left, look at the first atom in each substituent chain, and identify the atoms attached to it in descending order of priority. If the highest priority atoms in each are the same, work your way along (down) in priority, looking for the first non-identical atoms (first point of difference). If no differences are found at this stage, move out from the first to the second atom in the chain from the stereocenter, and repeat the process. If there is branching here, the direction of this move should be chosen to examine the highest priority atom for a point of difference. If no difference is found, then examine the second highest priority group, and so on. It is actually easier to *do* than it is to describe, so lets try a couple of examples:

Example - determine *R/S* designation for

$$\begin{array}{c} CCl_3 \\ | \\ H\text{---}C \\ \diagup \quad \diagdown CH_2Br \\ CH_3 \end{array}$$

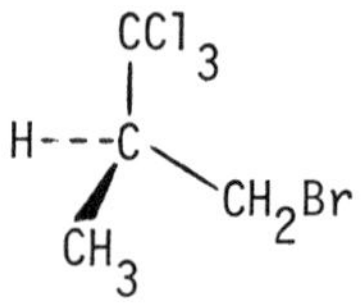

Procedure - H is obviously lowest priority; the other three need to be compared. Write them out side-by-side:

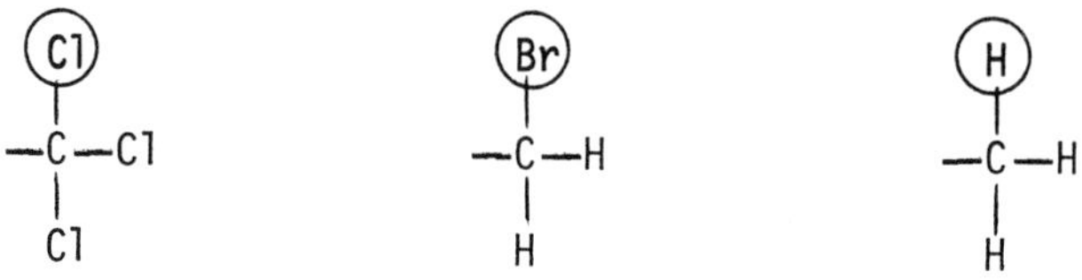

$$\begin{array}{ccc} \boxed{Cl} & \boxed{Br} & \boxed{H} \\ | & | & | \\ -C-Cl & -C-H & -C-H \\ | & | & | \\ Cl & H & H \\ \\ -CCl_3 & -CH_2Br & -CH_3 \end{array}$$

Identify the highest priority atom according to atomic number on each carbon. In -CCl$_3$ it is Cl, in -CH$_2$Br it is Br, and in -CH$_3$ it is H. All three are different, therefore priorities can be assigned immediately. Br > Cl > H, therefore -CH$_2$Br > -CCl$_3$ > -CH$_3$. The fact that there are <u>three</u> Cl's on -CCl$_3$ and only <u>one</u> Br on -CH$_2$Br is <u>irrelevant!</u> The <u>first</u> point of difference is the Br on -CH$_2$Br vs. the <u>first</u> Cl on -CCl$_3$, and Br is "bigger" than Cl. Once the first point of difference is identified, <u>nothing else matters</u>.

With priorities now assigned, we can redraw the molecule with the highest priority group designated 'a', the second 'b', the third 'c', and the lowest 'd':

$$\begin{array}{c} CCl_3 \\ | \\ H\text{--}C \\ \diagup \quad \diagdown CH_2Br \\ CH_3 \end{array} \quad \text{becomes} \quad \begin{array}{c} b \\ | \\ d\text{--}C \\ \diagup \quad \diagdown a \\ c \end{array} \equiv \begin{array}{c} b \\ | \\ C \\ \diagup \quad \diagdown \\ c \quad a \end{array} \text{(d in back)}$$

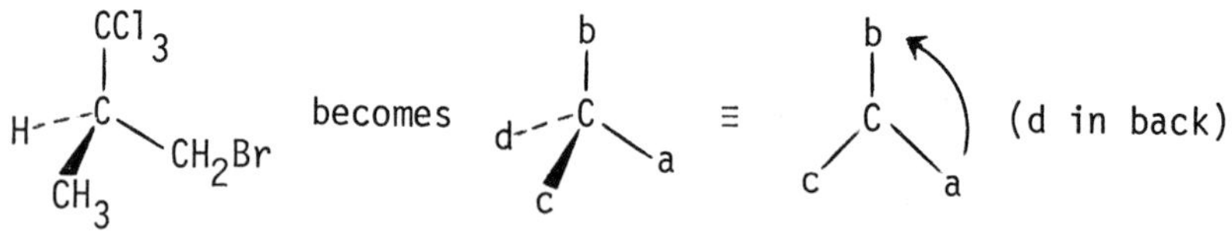

Counterclockwise = *S*

Example - determine *R/S* designation for

$$\begin{array}{c} H \\ | \\ H_2C\text{--}C \\ \diagup \quad \diagdown CH_2CH_3 \\ (CH_3)_2C \end{array}$$

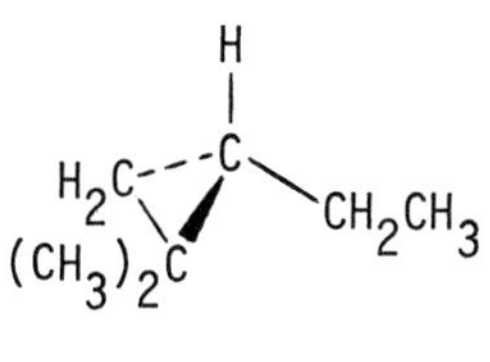

Procedure - the stereocenter is in a ring, but the procedure is not really different. The H is lowest priority, and the other three groups have to be compared. The problem is interpreting what that means with the stereocenter in a ring. One group is ethyl; that's obvious. The other two "groups" are really just the sequence of *ring atoms* attached to the stereocenter. For one group, start at the ring CH_2 and move around the ring; for the other, start at the ring $C(CH_3)_2$, and move around the ring in the other direction. So, we compare the "groups"

$$-CH_2-CH_3, \quad -CH_2-C(CH_3)_2\text{-etc.,} \quad \text{and} \quad -C(CH_3)_2-CH_2\text{-etc.,}$$

where the left hand bond goes to the stereocenter and "etc." means "continuing aroung the ring." Priorities are assigned in accordance with rule 2 again, since in all three groups the first atom in the "chain" attached to the asymmetric carbon is identical (carbon). We move out to the atoms attached to each of these carbons for comparison (circled):

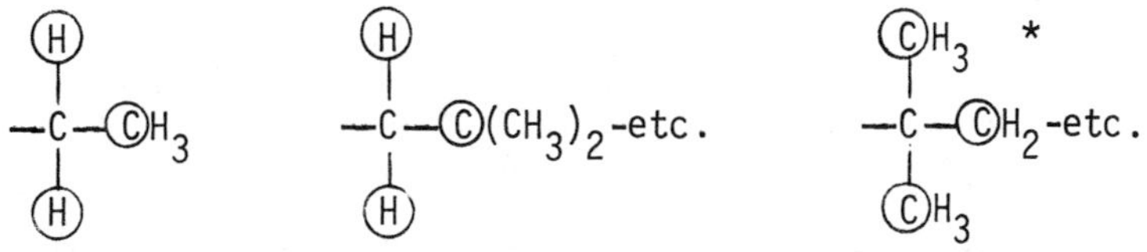

In each case the largest of these atoms is carbon. No difference. However, in the case of the group marked by the asterisk, the second largest is also carbon, while the second largest for the other two groups is hydrogen. The highest priority of these three groups is therefore the ring-contained "$-C(CH_3)_2-CH_2$-etc." Second and third priorities are determined by moving one atom further out as shown (circled):

Comparison here is straightforward. The CH_2 in the ethyl is connected only to a simple $C\underline{H}_3$ group, while the CH_2 of the ring is attached to a "$C(\underline{C}H_3)_2$-etc." group. So the latter one is higher in priority ($\underline{C}$ larger than $\underline{H}$). Therefore we have:

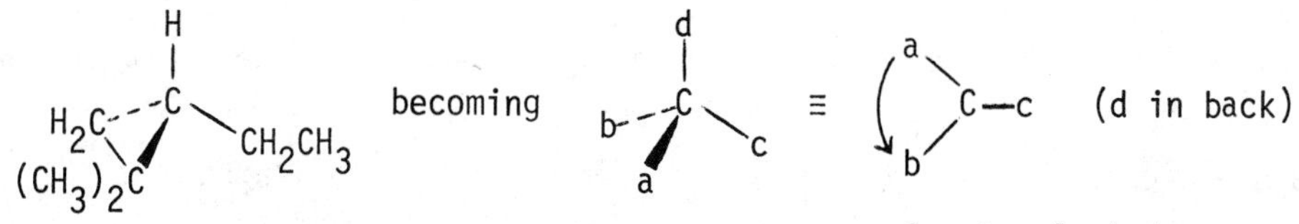

Counterclockwise = *S*

<u>Example</u> - determine *R/S* designation for the starred carbon in

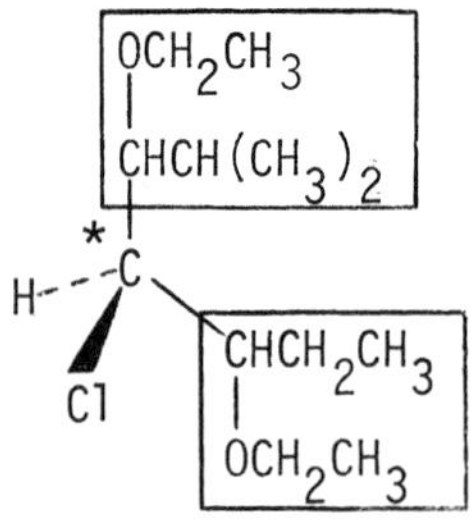

<u>Procedure</u> - highest priority is Cl, and lowest is H. A priority choice between the two outlined groups needs to be made, however. We write the groups out side-by-side:

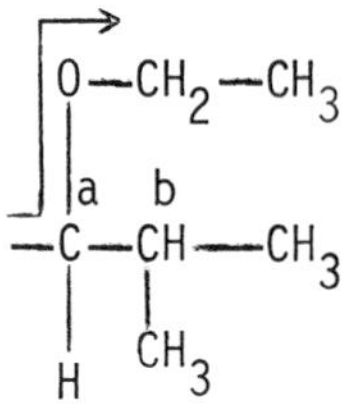

vs.

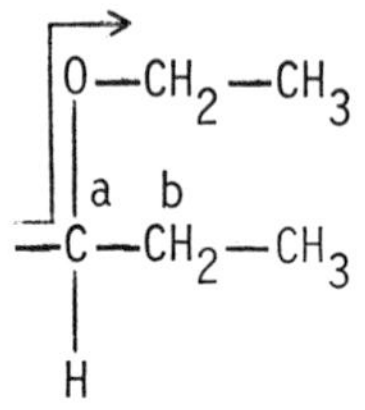

<u>Group 1</u> <u>Group 2</u>

Start at carbon atom labeled 'a' in each group. In both groups, the highest priority atom attached to carbon 'a' is oxygen, the second highest is carbon, and the last is hydrogen. No difference is found, so move out to the <u>highest priority atom</u> on carbon 'a' for the next comparison: follow the arrow and move to the <u>oxygen</u> (<u>not</u> carbon atom 'b' - <u>oxygen is higher priority</u>, so it is evaluated <u>first</u>). Both groups 1 and 2 have identical CH_2's attached directly to O, so there is still a tie. Turning to the second largest group attached to 'a', we look to carbon 'b', and see that here the tie can be broken: in <u>group 1</u>, this atom is attached to two carbons and one hydrogen, while in <u>group 2</u>, it is attached to just one carbon and two hydrogens. <u>Group 1</u> therefore is higher in priority than <u>group 2</u>, at atom 'b', the first point of difference.

With priorities done, the groups can all be labeled and *R* or *S* assigned:

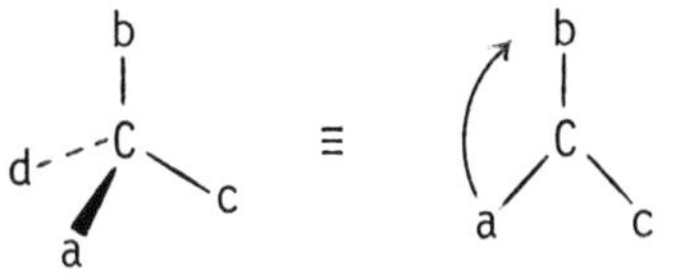

(d in back); clockwise = *R*.

If, on the other hand, the oxygen in <u>group 1</u> were attached to an H instead of a C, that would become the first point of difference, and <u>group 2</u> would be the higher in priority. The differences at the 'b' carbons would become irrelevant. See?

The above three examples have each been chosen to deliberately contain a "trick" - an unusual feature that is not often encountered, but which illustrates the application of the rules in detail. Most chapter and exam problems you see will not be "tricky". However, by understanding the toughies, proper application of the procedure becomes quicker and simpler in *all* cases, since you've now seen what to do when things get complicated.

Before leaving this section, note also there is a bit of a trick to Rule 3 as well. For priority determination purposes, double and triple bonds are changed so that both atoms involved are doubled or tripled. For example, a carbon doubly bonded to another carbon is changed to a carbon singly bonded to two carbons. One is the carbon actually present, and the other is invented:

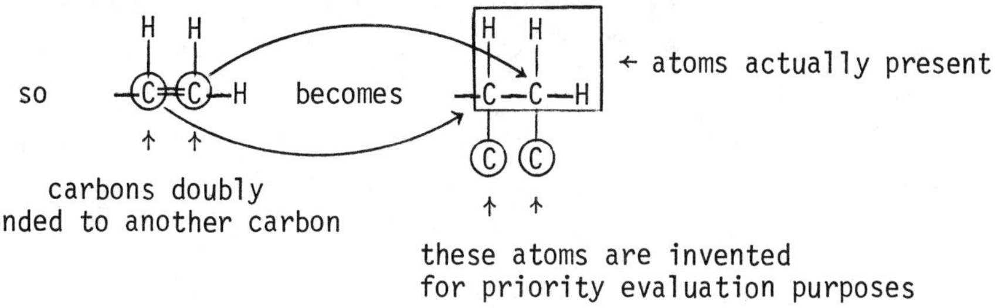

Similarly for a carbon-oxygen double bond, the carbon is changed to be singly bonded to two oxygens (one real, one invented), and likewise the oxygen is changed to be singly bonded to two carbons (one real, one invented):

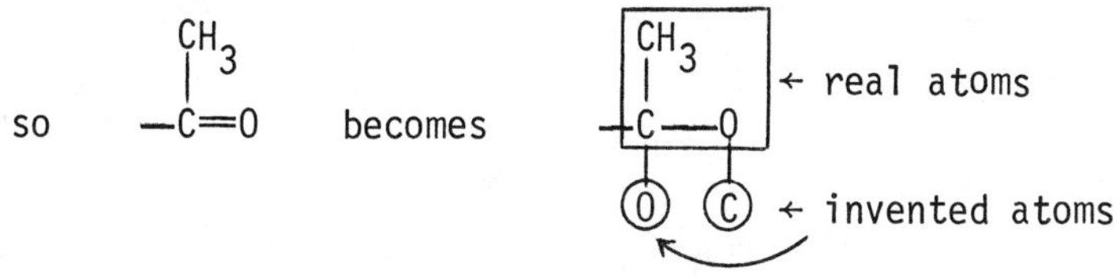

5-4. Fischer Projections.

The purpose of Fischer projections is to simplify the on-paper drawing of asymmetric carbons by using a simple convention to represent the three-dimensional structural details. The rules are simple, but again, following the text with a set of models handy will help you master this material a lot more readily.

5-5. Molecules Incorporating Several Stereocenters: Diastereomers.

When a molecule has more than one stereocenter, like 2,3-bromochlorobutane, it may have considerably more than just the 2 stereoisomers possible for a molecule with just one stereocenter. Since an object can never have more than one mirror image, any one of the many stereoisomers for such a compound can only have one enantiomer. Suppose we have a molecule with, say, 8 stereoisomers. If we pick any one of these (stereoisomer 'A'), it may have no more than one enantiomer (stereoisomer 'B'). What about the other 6 isomers? They are also stereoisomers of 'A', but they can't be its mirror image. The relationship of any of these other 6 molecules with 'A' is described by a new term: *diastereomer*. Diastereomers are stereoisomers that are *not mirror images of each other*. Since diastereomers are *not* mirror images of each other, they have *different physical properties, and may therefore be separated by standard laboratory techniques. This is very important.* This feature distinguishes diastereomers from enantiomers, which cannot readily be separated from one another.

Diastereomer is a very important term, as important as "enantiomer," and one which you should make a point of understanding well before you leave this section. Notice that both "enantiomer" and "diastereomer" really describe *relationships* between structures. As described above, 'A' is the enantiomer of 'B'; 'A' is also a diastereomer of any of the other 6 isomers we talked about. It may seem odd at first that a single molecule can be called both an enantiomer and a diastereomer at the same time. However, if you remember that these terms really describe relationships between *pairs* of structures, it makes more sense. The following illustration is not a perfect analogy, but it might help you get the idea. Your right and left hands are enantiomers of each other. Your right and left feet are enantiomers of each other. If you make believe that hands and feet are stereoisomers of each other (don't all groan at once), then your right hand is a diastereomer of your right foot and also a diastereomer of your left foot, and the same goes for your left hand:

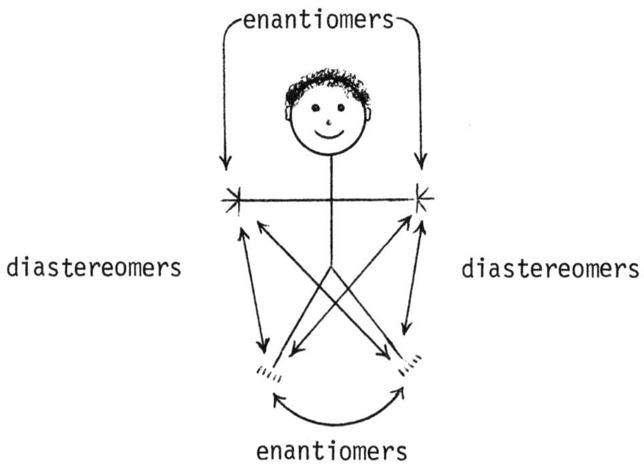

As the figures in this section show, molecules work similarly. Actually the real trouble in, for instance, determining whether two structures are enantiomers or diastereomers of each other stems from difficulty in drawing and orienting the pictures of the molecules *so that the stereocenters can be compared in the first place.* An example:

Anyone can look at

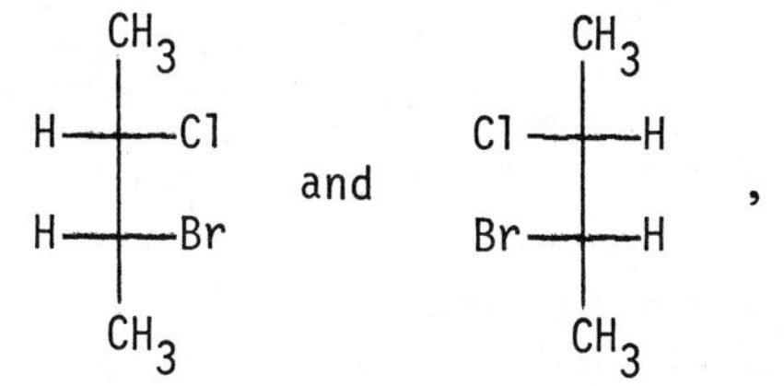

immediately visualize the mirror plane between them, and recognize them as enantiomers. Similarly,

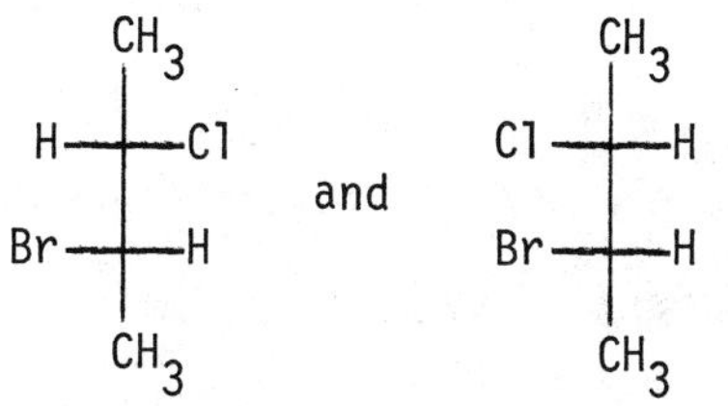

obviously lack a mirror-image relationship, and must be diastereomers.

The hard part is determining, for example, the relationship between

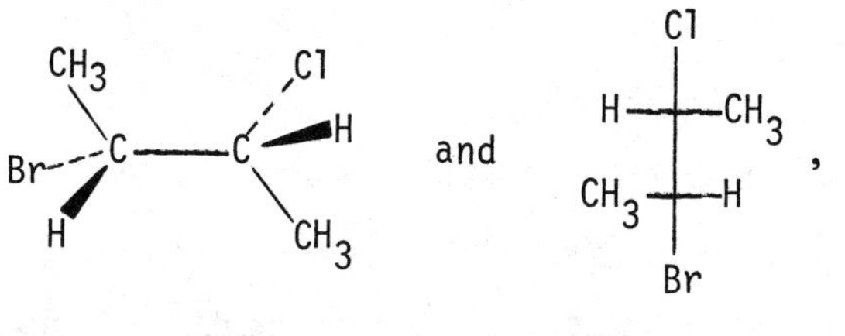

without getting all messed up (or taking forever to do it, and *then* getting all messed up). In short, you need to be able to quickly and accurately move among sawhorse, Newman, dashed-wedged line, and Fischer structures. This takes practice at visualizing three-dimensional structures from flat drawings, and requires application of a couple of specific techniques. The text covers *comparison and interconversion of Fischer projections* very thoroughly. The one important precaution here is *never* operate on more than one stereocenter at a time when interconverting Fischer projections.

Example - What is the relationship between the following structures: identical, enantiomers, or diastereomers?

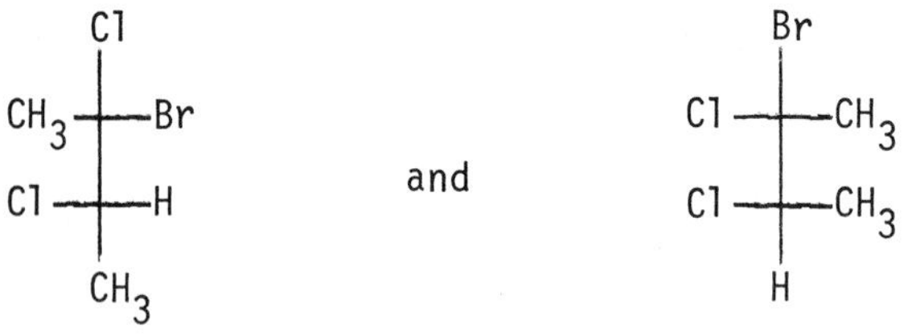

Structure 1 and Structure 2

(a) Operate on top stereocenter:

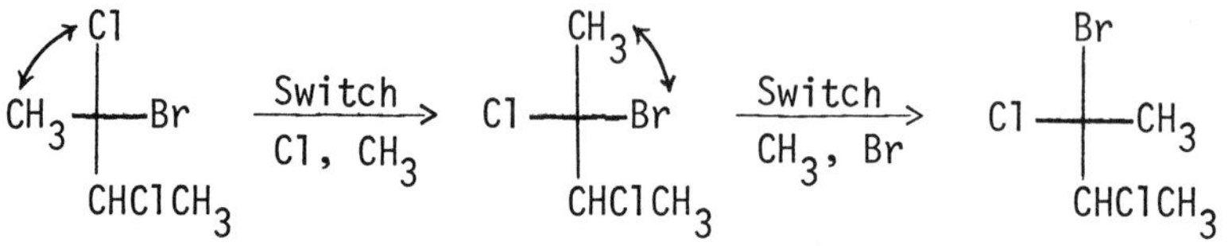

Structure 1 same as Structure 2

Two switches made the top stereocenter of 1 identical to that of 2; therefore these carbons are *identical* in configuration.

(b) Then do bottom stereocenter:

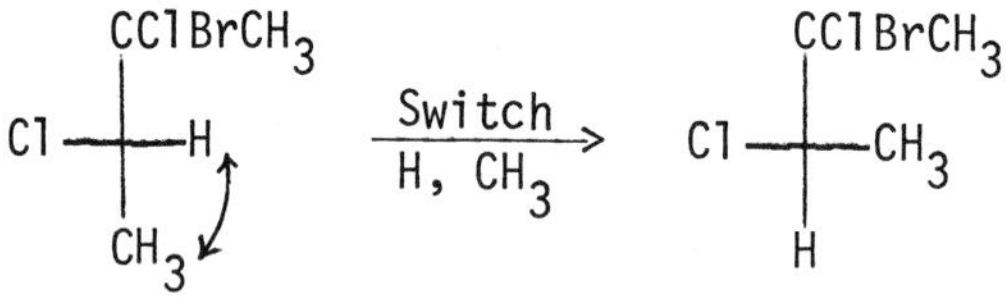

Structure 1 same as Structure 2

One switch made the bottom stereocenter of 1 identical to that of 2; therefore these carbons are *opposite* in configuration.

Answer: the two structures are *diastereomers* (not completely identical, and not mirror image).

Let's now examine our problem of comparing a dashed-wedged line formula with a Fischer projection. The actual problem is how to interconvert dashed-wedged line and Fischer formulas. The key to this is recognizing that Fischer projections are pictures of a molecule *in an eclipsed conformation.* Very important. So the first step in comparison is to get the dashed-wedged line formula into an eclipsed conformation. Any 60° rotation will do, such as rotation of the left-hand methyl group up out of the page, towards you:

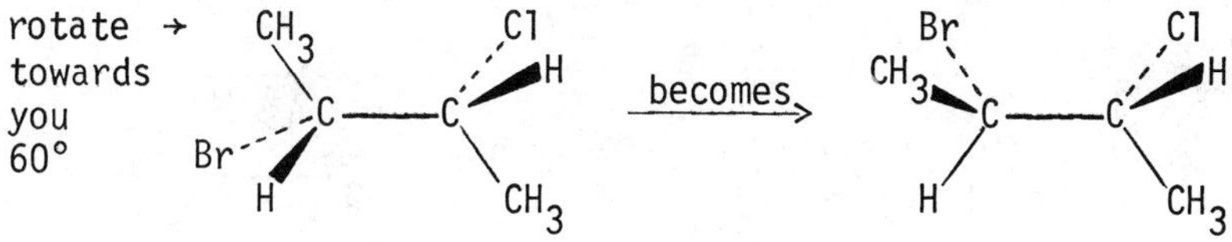

Look at these two conformations of the same identical molecule *carefully* - with the help of a model, if necessary - to convince yourself that the pictures on the page are what I've said they are.

We can now convert the eclipsed formula, above, into a Fischer projection. Imagine looking at it from a direction such that the carbon-carbon bond is vertical, and the groups horizontal to it point towards us, for example:

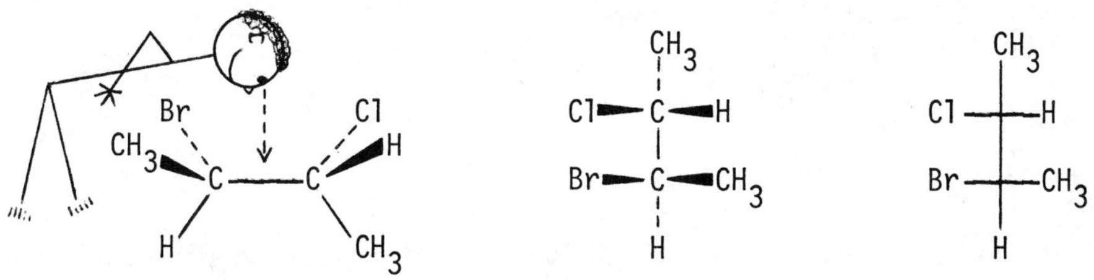

If you look at it like this.......this is what you see.....which is this.

Now you can compare the Fischer projection above with the one we wrote earlier:

Structure 1 Structure 2

(a) Top stereocenter:

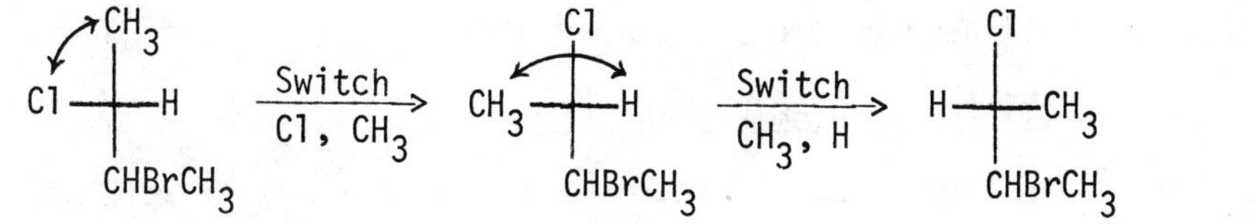

Structure 1 same as Structure 2

Two switches; therefore identical.

(b) Bottom stereocenter:

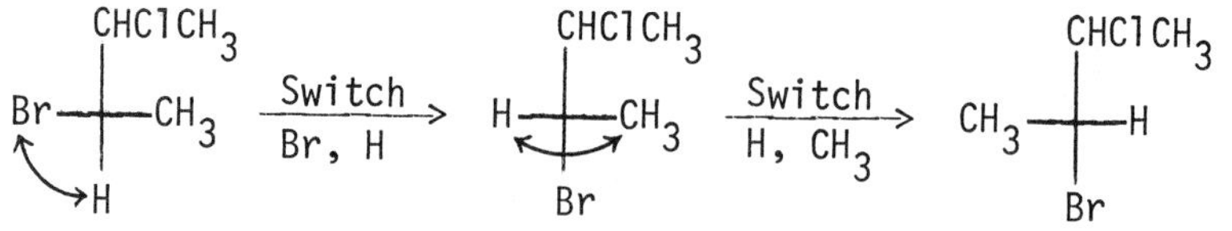

Structure 1 same as Structure 2

Two switches; therefore also identical.

So the two structures shown earlier were identical to each other:

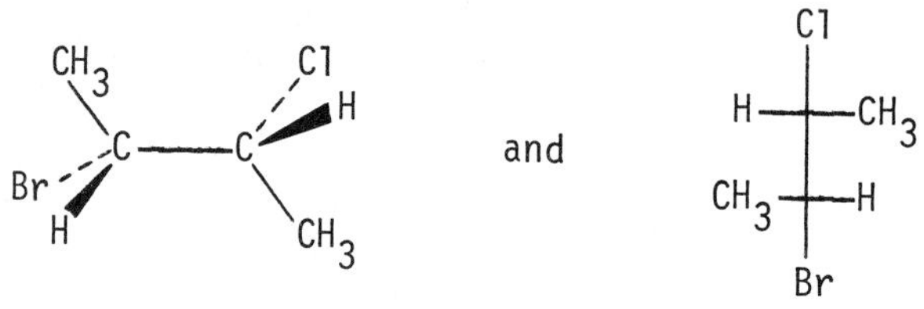

are exactly the same molecule.

It is useful to recognize at this point that comparing pictorial formulas is just one of several ways to determine the relationship between possible stereoisomeric structures. If you have the time, making models is always useful, especially for visualization purposes. An even better way is to apply the rules of nomenclature to each structure and to determine the *R* or *S* configuration of each stereocenter. Once you have become comfortable with this technique as it applies to the different types of structural pictures, you may find that this is the quickest method of all: once *R*/*S* assignments have been made to structures under consideration, their stereochemical relationship is obvious. (I.e., for two stereocenters, *R*,*R* and *S*,*S* are enantiomers of each other, *R*,*S* and *S*,*R* are enantiomers of each other, and any other combination is a pair of diastereomers.)

Notice that I never said this was easy. It takes practice to do, and to extend to other common ways of drawing molecules that imply three-dimensional structure. With practice, however, comes experience and confidence, just what you will need come exam time.

5-6. Stereochemistry in Chemical Reactions.

Some newer terminology is introduced here which is of more specialized usage and less frequently encountered than what has been presented earlier in the chapter. However, the material develops very naturally with no special pitfalls.

5-7. Resolution of Enantiomers.

The most common laboratory method to separate enantiomers is presented. What is required is a pure enantiomer of a molecule that reacts with the molecules of your racemic mixture. The procedure outlined is a straightforward application of the ideas in sections 5-2 (properties of chiral molecules) and 5-5 (molecules with more than one stereocenter).

Solutions to Chapter 5 Problems

1. Chiral: b*, c (fan blades are always twisted!), d, e, h. Achiral: a, f, g, i, j, k, l. All the achiral objects contain a plane of symmetry:

spoon

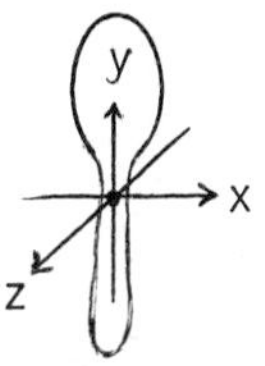

yz symmetry plane

knife

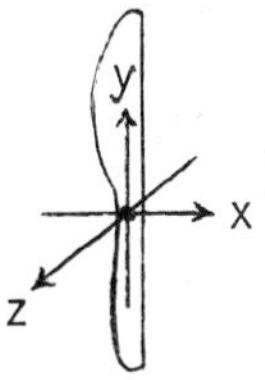

xy symmetry plane

*A door is chiral unless the mounting hinges and doorknob are arranged symmetrically or bisected by a horizontal plane that bisects the door. Thus a very plain door (lacking knocker, peephole, etc.) could conceivably be achiral.

****

2. (a) enantiomers (b) enantiomers (c) diastereomers

   (d) identical (if one pair is flipped over intact, it becomes superimposable with the other pair)

****

3. (a) structural isomers

   (b) identical (superimposable after a 180° rotation of either one)

   (c) stereoisomers (enantiomers), but interconvertible

   (d) stereoisomers (enantiomers), not interconvertible

   (e) stereoisomers (enantiomers), not interconvertible

   (f) structural isomers

   (g) stereoisomers, but interconvertible

   (h) structural isomers

****

4. The stereocenter has been labeled with a star (*) in each chiral molecule.

(a) 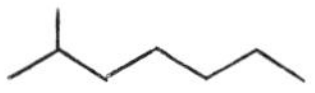 not chiral (achiral) (2 CH_3's on the tertiary carbon!)

(b) 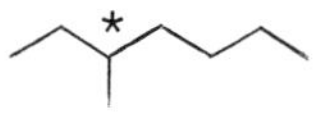 chiral

(c)  not chiral

(d) 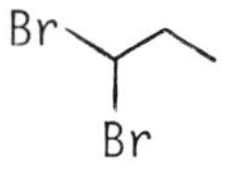 not chiral

(e) 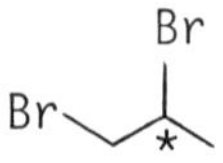 chiral

(f)  not chiral

(g), (h), (i) not chiral (all are planar molecules)

(j) 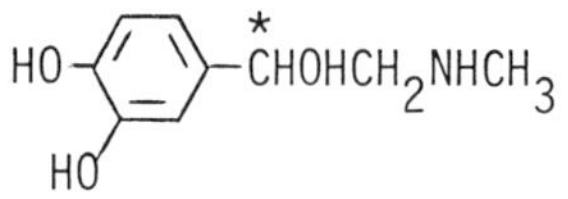 chiral

(k) not chiral

(l) not chiral

(m) 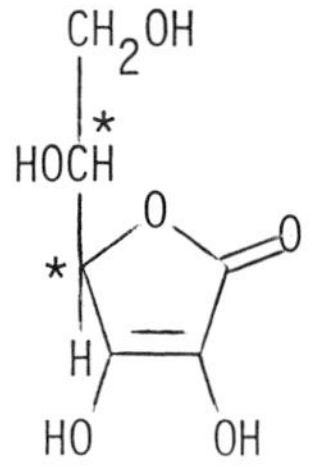 chiral (has 2 stereocenters)

(n) and (o) not chiral- both molecules have vertical planes of symmetry bisecting the rings. Make models!

****

5. (a) 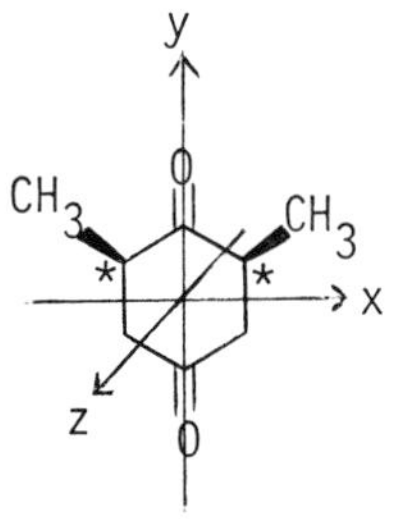 not chiral (yz plane of symmetry) (two stereo-centers, but compound is *meso* - Section 5-5)

(b) chiral

(c) chiral

(d) 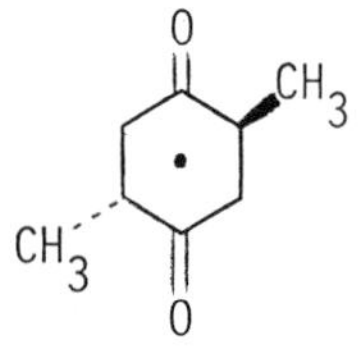 not chiral (molecule contains a center of symmetry)

****

6. (a) not chiral (*meso*: contains a plane of symmetry - see Section 5-5)

(b) chiral

(c) chiral

(d) not chiral (contains plane of symmetry - note that substituted carbons <u>are not stereocenters</u>)

****

7. (a) 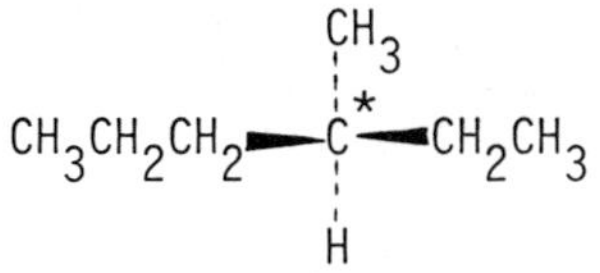

1 stereocenter (*), 2 stereoisomers
(*S*)-3-methylhexane

(In all of these the *R*-enantiomer would be the mirror image of the structure shown.)

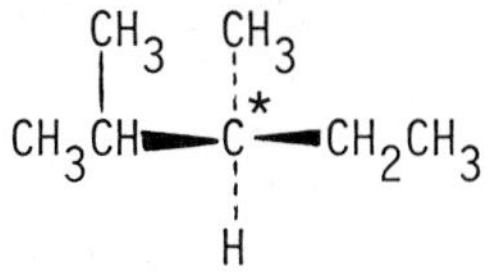

1 stereocenter (*), 2 stereoisomers
(*S*)-2,3-dimethylpentane

Note that there is no need to say '3*S*' in the name - only carbon 3 is chiral, so '*S*' is sufficient. Carbon 2 is not a stereocenter since it contains two identical methyl groups.

These are the only two chiral isomers of heptane.

(b) 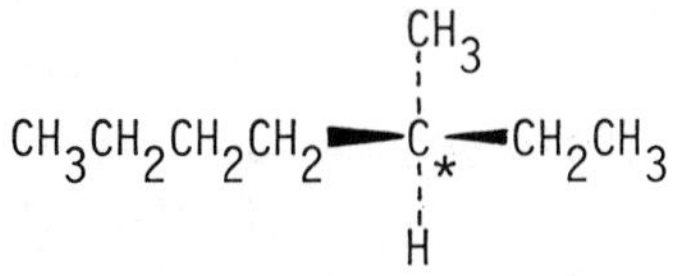

1 stereocenter (*), 2 stereoisomers
(*S*)-3-methylheptane

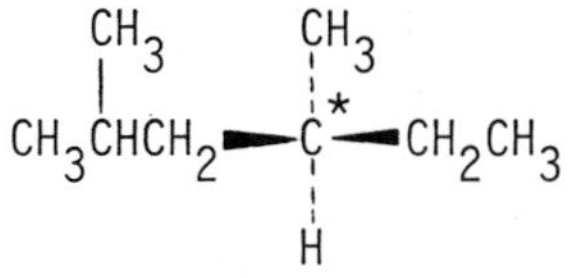

1 stereocenter (*), 2 stereoisomers
(*S*)-2,4-dimethylhexane

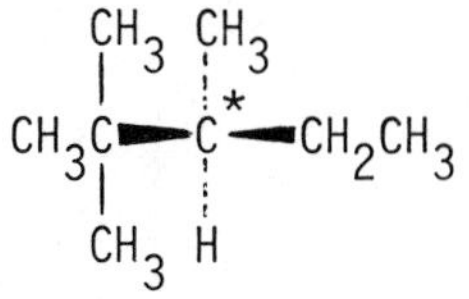

1 stereocenter (*), 2 stereoisomers
(*S*)-2,2,3-trimethylpentane

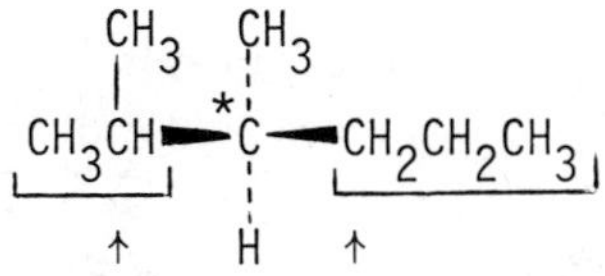

1 stereocenter (*), 2 stereoisomers
(*S*)-2,3-dimethylhexane

Note how the isopropyl group has priority over n-propyl: at the first point of difference (arrows) the isopropyl carbon is connected to C,<u>C</u>,H while the n-propyl carbon is connected to C,<u>H</u>,H. The underlined atoms (2d C for isopropyl vs. 1st H for n-propyl) set the priority.

The structures on the previous page are the only ones with exactly one stereocenter. Following is the single isomer with more than one stereocenter.

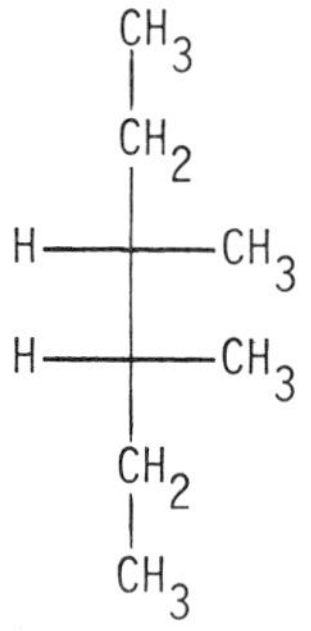

2 stereocenters, 3 stereoisomers
meso or (3*R*,4*S*)-3,4-dimethylhexane is shown.

(c)

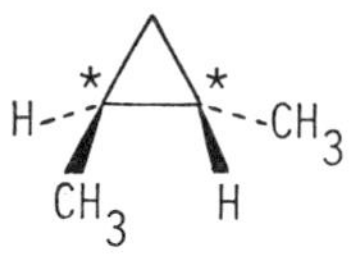

2 stereocenters, 3 stereoisomers
(1*S*,2*S*)-1,2-dimethylcyclopropane is shown.

("*Trans*" is implied by the (*S*,*S*) designation.) The other two stereoisomers are the (*R*,*R*), its enantiomer (obviously also *trans*), and the *cis* isomer, a diastereomer, which is a *meso* (*R*,*S*) compound (Section 5-5). This is the only possible chiral molecule with the formula C_5H_{10} and one ring.

****

8. Letters correspond to parts of problem 4.

(b) See answer to problem 7(b).

(e)

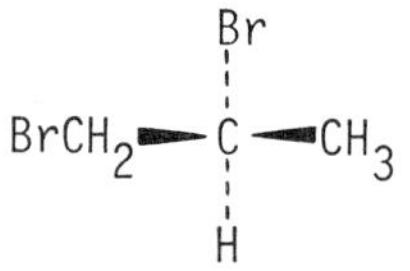

(*S*)-1,2-dibromopropane

(j)

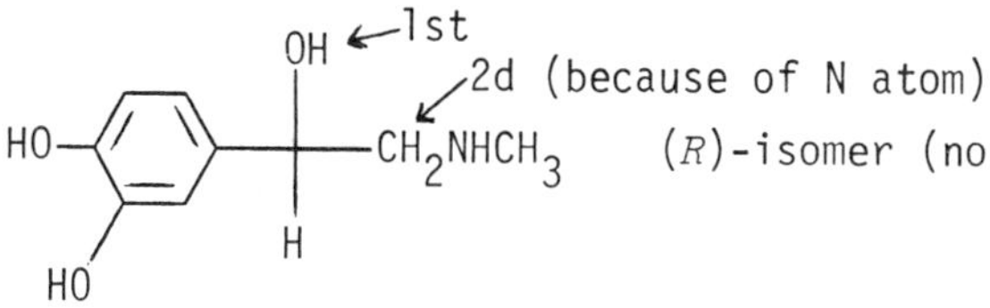

(*R*)-isomer (note priorities)

(m) 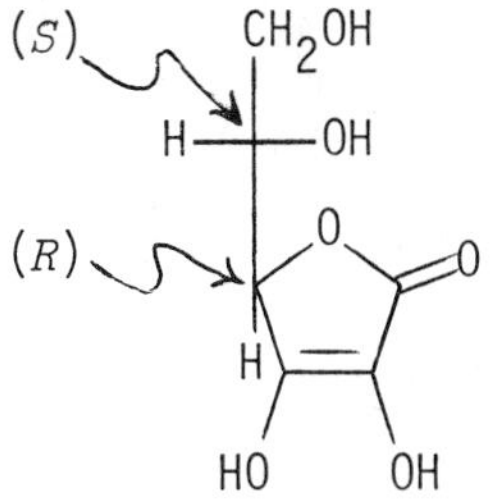

Redraw the top stereocenter:

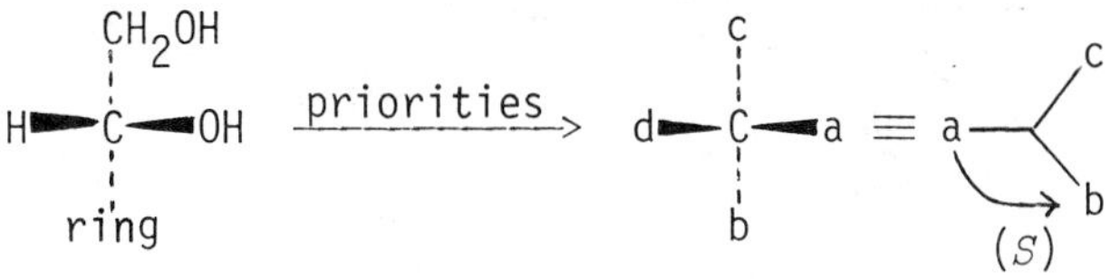

The bottom stereocenter:

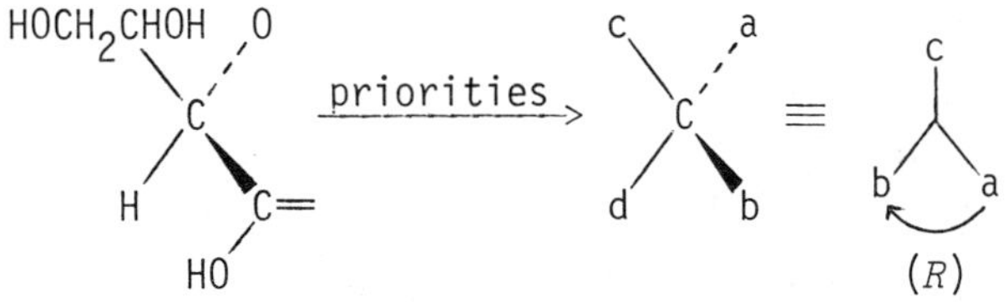

****

9. 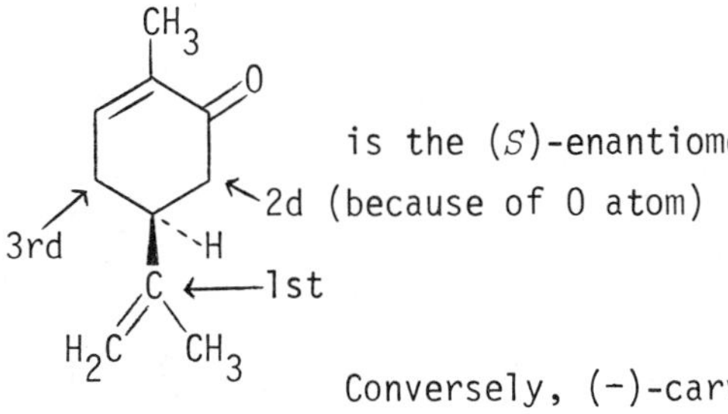

is the (S)-enantiomer (note priorities) ⇛

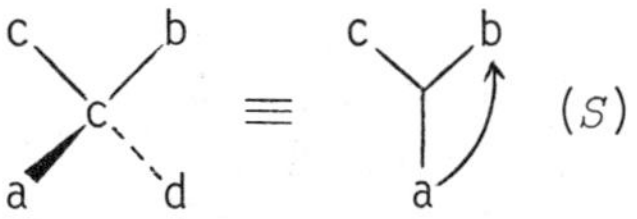

Conversely, (−)-carvone has the *R* configuration.

****

10. (a) 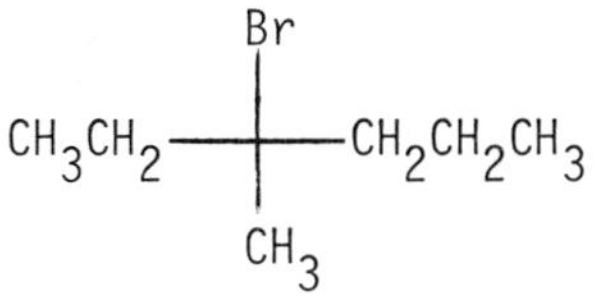

,
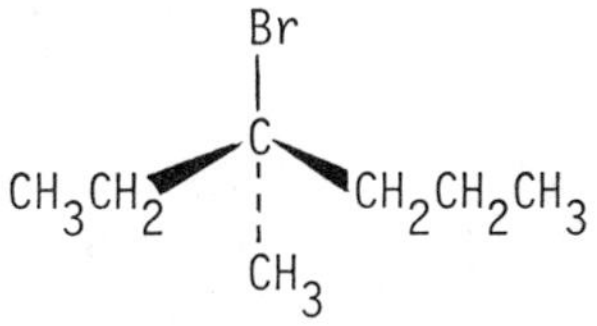

(b) 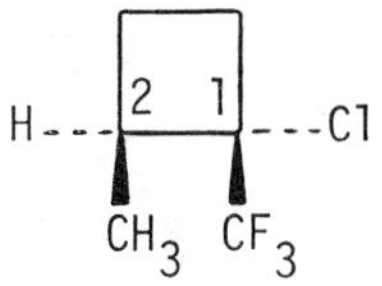

Note priorities on C-1: $Cl > CF_3 >$ ring $CHCH_3 >$ ring CH_2

(c) 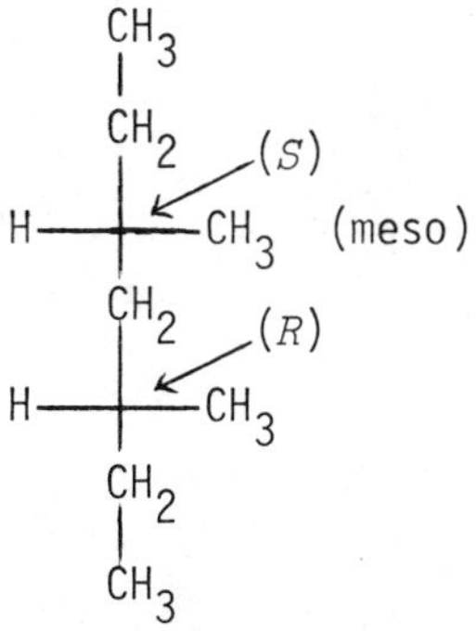

(d) 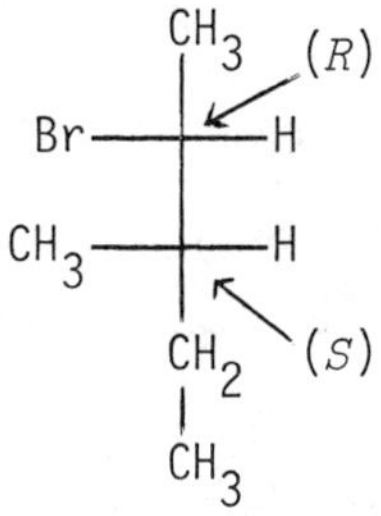

(e) 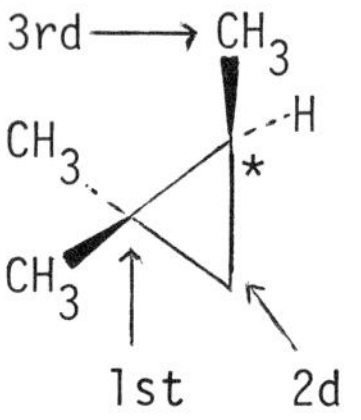

Note priorities. (f) 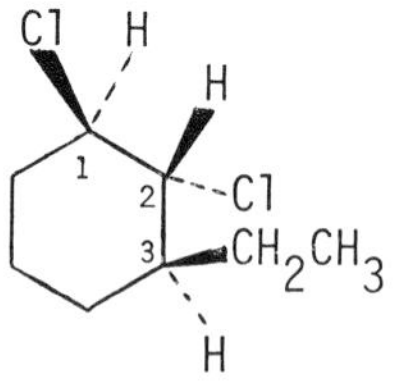

****

11. Use $[\alpha]_D$ (specific rotation) $= \dfrac{\alpha \text{ (observed rotation)}}{\text{conc. (g/mL) x path length (dm)}}$

(a) $C = \dfrac{0.4 \text{ g}}{10 \text{ mL}} = 0.04 \dfrac{\text{g}}{\text{mL}}$, $\alpha = -0.56°$, and $\ell = 10$ cm $= 1$ dm.

So $[\alpha]_D = -14.0°$

(b) $[\alpha]_D = +66.4°$, $C = 0.3 \dfrac{\text{g}}{\text{mL}}$, $\ell = 1$ dm. $\therefore \alpha = +19.9°$

(c) Rearranging gives $C = \dfrac{\alpha}{[\alpha]_D} = \dfrac{57.3°}{23.1°} = 2.48$ g/mL

****

12. $C = \dfrac{1\text{g}}{20 \text{ mL}} = .05$ g/mL, so $\dfrac{\alpha}{C \times \ell} = \dfrac{-2.5°}{.05} = -50°$, which is identical to the the actual $[\alpha]_D$. Therefore the epinephrine is optically pure and, presumably, safe to use.

****

13. (a) 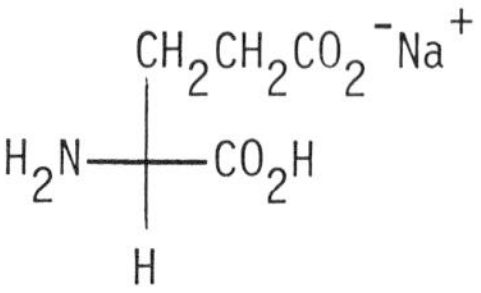

(priorities: 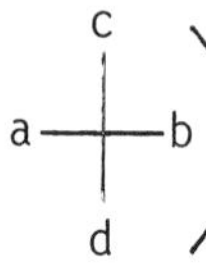

)

(b) $\dfrac{8°}{24°} = 0.33$ or 33% optically pure, corresponding to a mixture of 33% pure *S* + 67% racemate, or 67% *S* and 33% *R*.

(c) $\dfrac{16°}{24°} = 0.67$ or 67% optical purity, which equals 67% pure *S* + 33% racemate. That's the same as 83% *S* and 17% *R*.

****

14. For brevity, only the enantiomer of each molecule in this problem is shown below. Stereocenters are starred.

(a) Enantiomer is 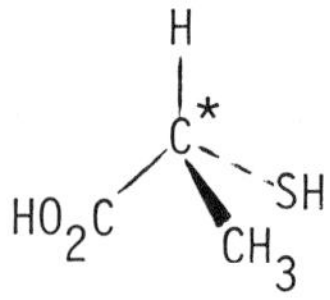

, which is *R* (original molecule was *S*).

(b) Enantiomer: 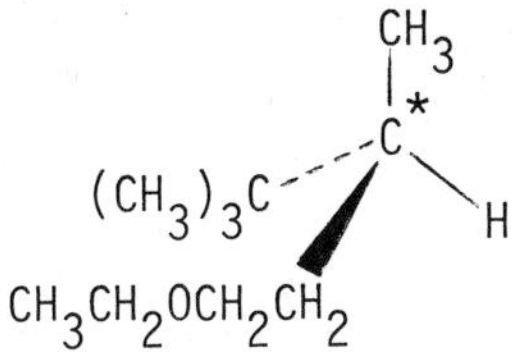 (*S*). Original molecule was *R*. Careful here - $(CH_3)_3C$ has priority over $CH_3CH_2OCH_2CH_2$!

(c) Enantiomer: 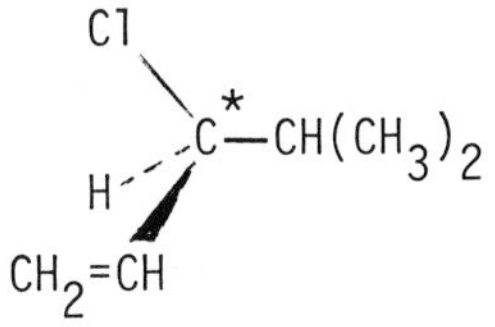 (*S*). Original was *R*. Careful again - CH_2=CH- counts as

```
 C    C
 |    |
ⒸH2-CH-,
```

and therefore has priority over

```
     CH3
     |
ⒸH3-CH-.
```

The circled carbons show the first point of difference. In the vinyl group the circled carbon counts as having another C on it, while in the isopropyl group, that carbon is attached to 3 H's.

(d) 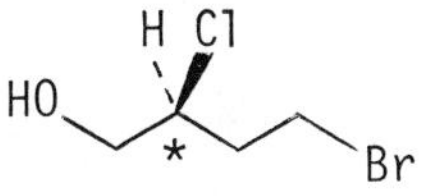 (*S*) Original = *R*.

(e) 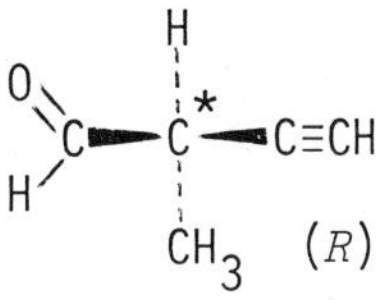 (*R*) Original = *S*.

(f) 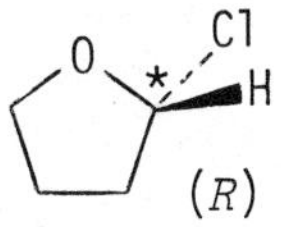 (*R*) Original = *S*.

(g) 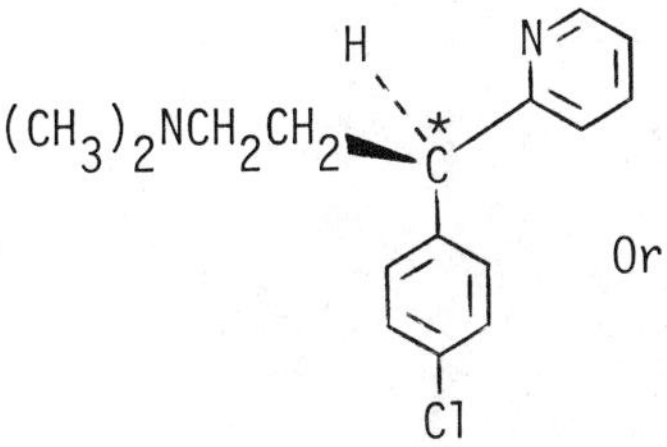 (*R*) Original = *S*.

(h) 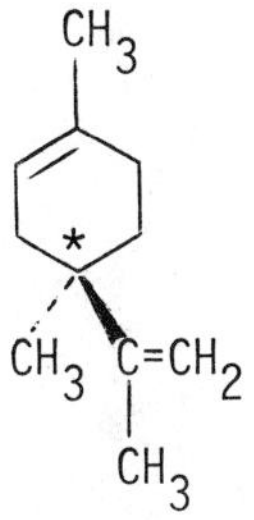 (*R*) Original = *S*.

****

15. (a) Identical (the carbon in the middle is not a stereocenter - it has two ethyl groups on it).

(b) Enantiomers: 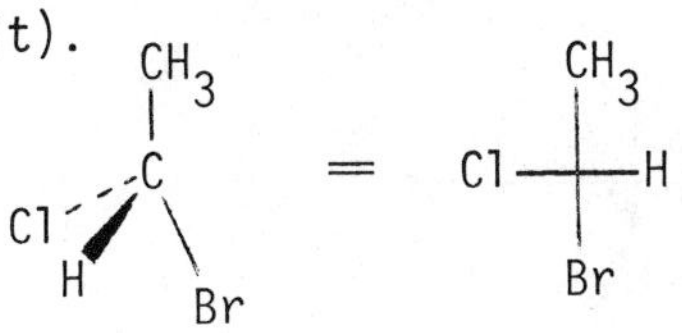

(c) Carry out pairwise switches on one to compare it with the other:

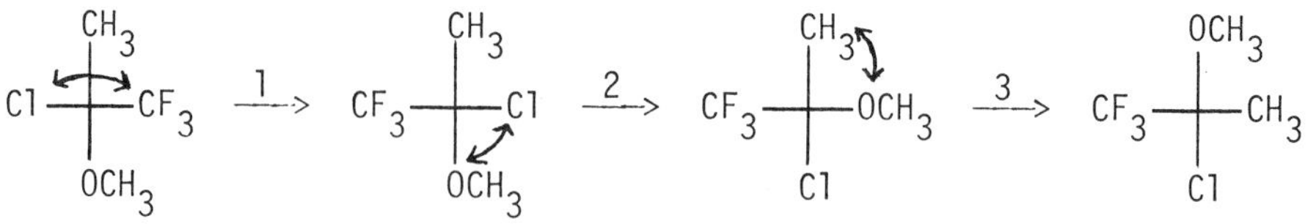

Three pairwise switches make the structures identical. The odd number of switches means that the structures were enantiomers of each other.

(d) Similarly:

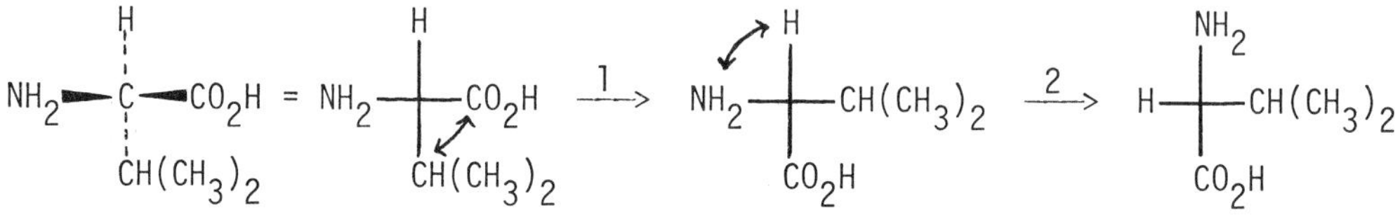

Two pairwise switches, so the structures are identical.

****

16. (a) No asymmetric carbons. (b) 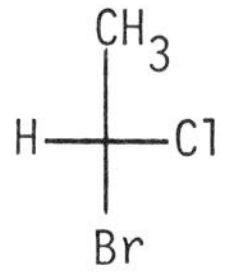 is *R*. Other is *S*.

(c) 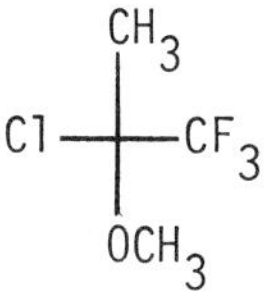 is *S*. Other is *R*. (d) Both are *R*.

****

17. (a) 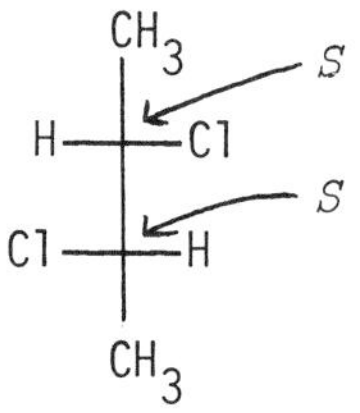

(b) 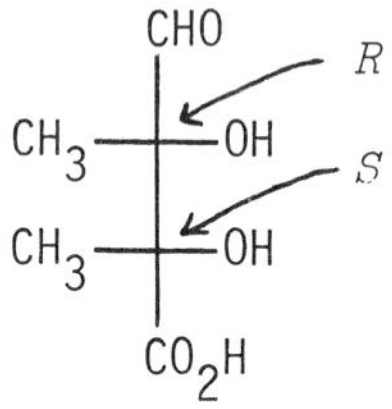

(c) 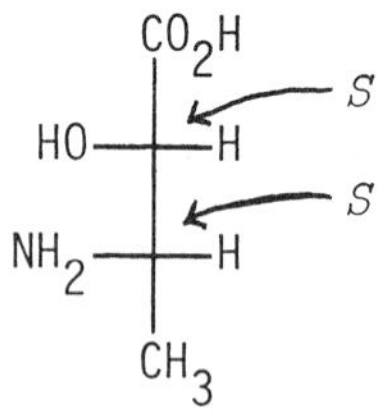

(d) 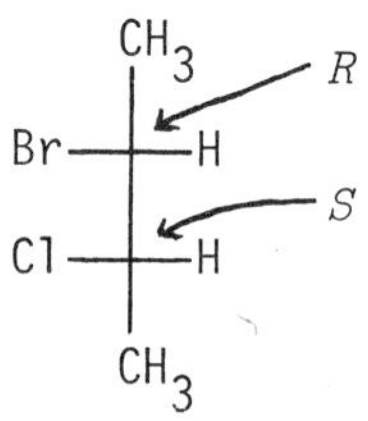

Problems? Refer back to pages 84 and 85 of this Study Guide. Remember: there is free rotation about all carbon-carbon bonds. So your picture might *look* different, but your R and S answers should be the same.

****

18. (a) 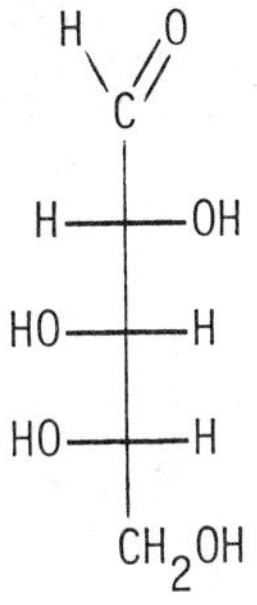

(b) No. An object can only have one mirror image.

(c) There are several. Here's one: 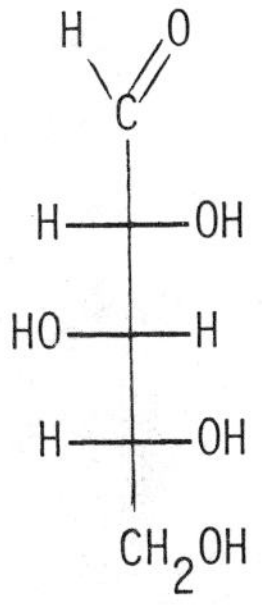

(d) Yes.

(e) +105°

(f) There is no way to predict the optical rotation of a diastereomer of a compound whose optical rotation you know. Diastereomeric compounds usually have very different physical properties.

(g) No. Since the groups on the two end carbons are different, there is no way to have the plane of symmetry that would be required for a meso compound.

****

19. *S*-1,3-dichloropentane is the compound's name.

(a) A single achiral product is formed: $ClCH_2CH_2CCl_2CH_2CH_3$.

(b) Two diastereomers are formed in unequal amounts:

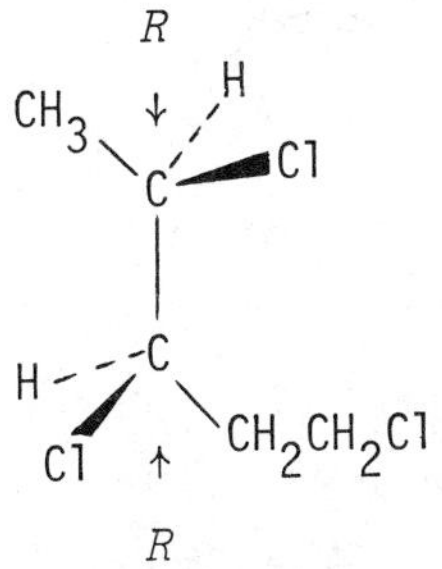

and

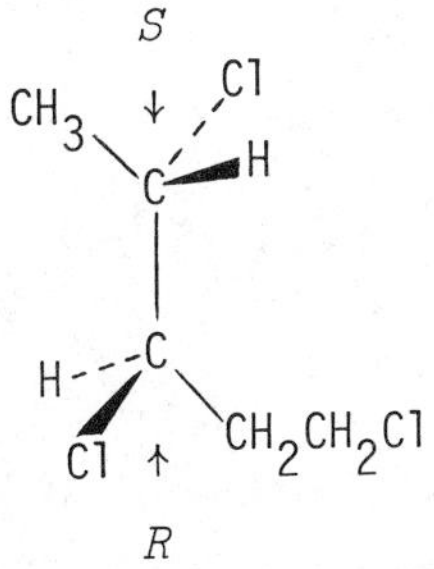

Notice that the designation for C-3 has changed to *R* because the priority of the $CHClCH_3$ group is higher than the CH_2CH_2Cl group.

(c) A single achiral product is formed: $ClCH_2CH_2CHClCH_2CH_2Cl$.

Notice that in (a) and (c) the chirality at C-3 has been eliminated in two slightly different ways. In (a), a bond to C-3 has been broken and a second Cl attached. In (b), no bond to C-3 has been affected, but a remote change has made two groups on C-3 identical.

****

20. (a) A single achiral product is formed: 1-chloro-1-methylcyclopentane.

(b) Four stereoisomers are formed as shown below:

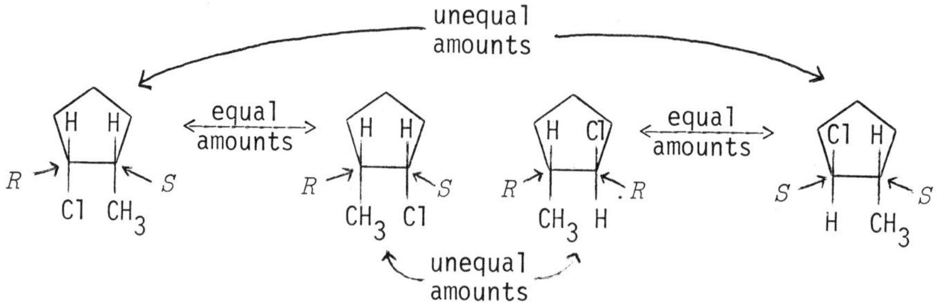

(1*R*,2*S*) (1*S*,2*R*) (1*R*,2*R*) (1*S*,2*S*)

1-chloro-2-methylcyclopentane

(c) Four stereoisomers are again formed:

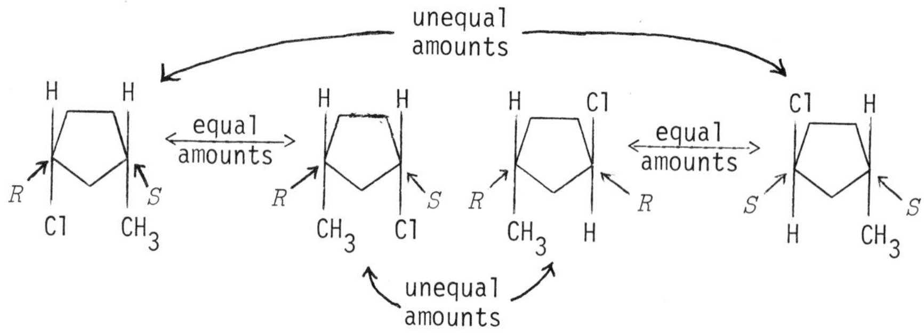

(1*R*,3*S*) (1*S*,3*R*) (1*R*,3*R*) (1*S*,3*S*)

1-chloro-3-methylcyclopentane

****

21. In steps:

(1) Racemic amine is neutralized with an equimolar amount of an optically pure acid, such as naturally occurring (*S*)-lactic acid, $CH_3CHOHCOOH$. This would form two diastereomeric salts: (*R*)-amine/(*S*)-acid salt, and (*S*)-amine/(*S*)-acid salt.

(2) The salt mixture is separated into its two diastereomeric components by recrystallization, typically from an alcohol-water solvent mixture.

(3) The two diastereomeric salts are separately treated with strong base such as aqueous NaOH, removing the lactic acid and freeing the individual enantiomers of the amine, which can be isolated in pure form.

****

22. Reversing the procedure of problem 21:

racemic lactic acid

(*R*) + (*S*)

↓ Treat with the optically pure, basic (*S*)-amine

(*S*)-amine/(*R*)-acid salt + (*S*)-amine/(*S*)-acid salt

diastereomeric salts

↓ Recrystallize

(*S*)-amine/(*R*)-acid salt → HCl (removes amine) → (*R*)-lactic acid

(*S*)-amine/(*S*)-acid salt → HCl (removes amine) → (*S*)-lactic acid

****

23. Bromination is highly selective, so consider reacting only at the tertiary carbons!

(a) Four stereoisomeric products:

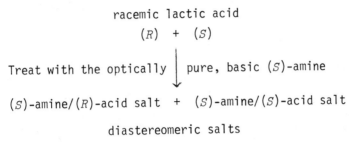

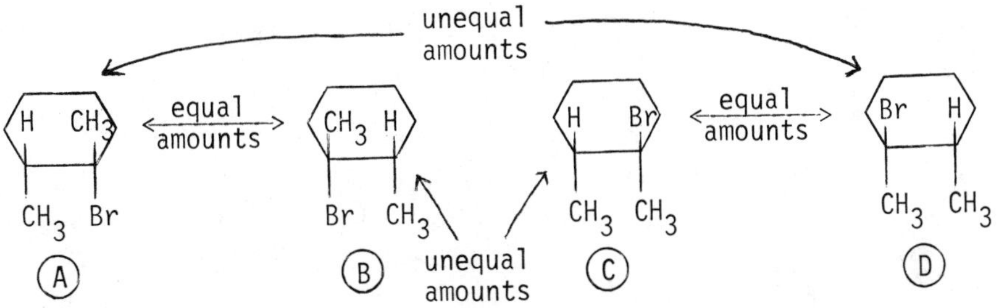

A racemic mixture of (A) and (B) can be separated from a racemic mixture of (C) and (D), but no net optical activity will be observed in the isolated products.

(b) *R,R*-1,2-dimethylcyclohexane is 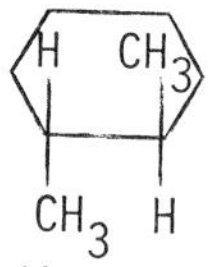

. Only two of the four products in part (a) are possible: Ⓐ and Ⓒ. They are diastereomers of each other, they are formed in unequal amounts, they can be physically separated, and both are formed optically pure.

Don't forget, free-radical halogenation gives both possible stereochem cal configurations at the *reacting* carbon, but it does not change the configuration of carbons that do not react.

****

24. Review the definitions of these lesser used terms before proceeding.

(a) 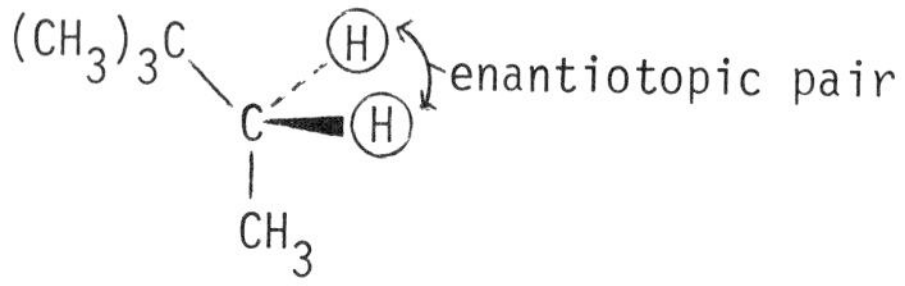

Substitution of either hydrogen by a new group creates an asymmetric carbon (a stereocenter). Substitution of one of them gives the enantiomer of the substitution product of the other.

(b) 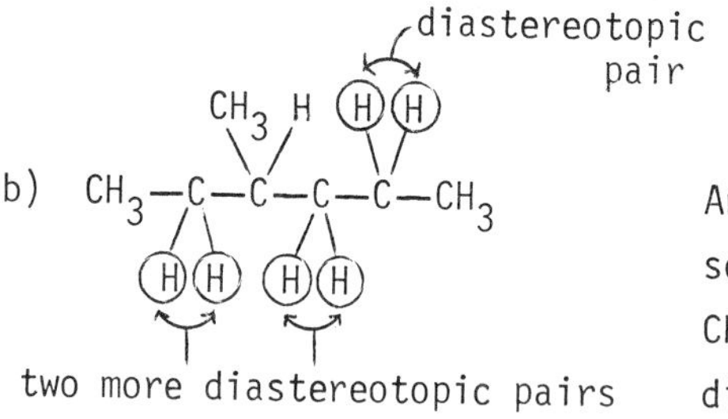

An asymmetric carbon is already present, so further substitution at <u>any</u> of the CH_2 groups will give either of two diastereomers.

(c) 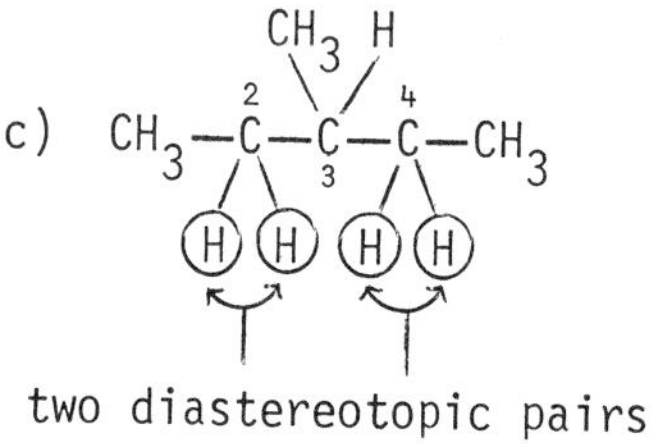

Careful! Carbon-3 is not a stereocenter, but it becomes one if either carbon-2 or carbon-4 is substituted. So the hydrogen pairs on C-2 and C-4, respectively, are actually diastereotopic pairs, not enantiotopic pairs. Look at the example given here of chlorination at C-2:

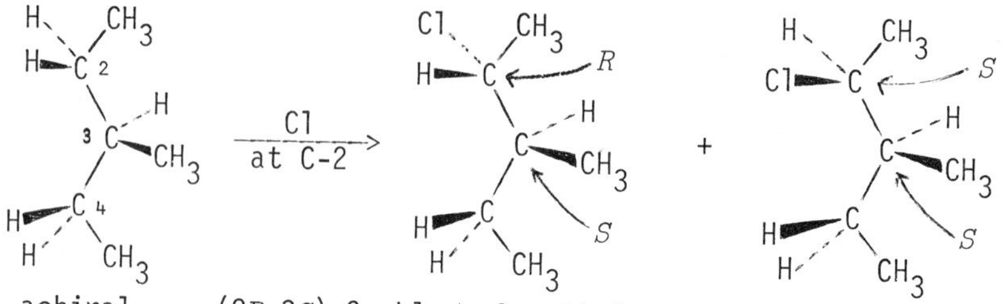

achiral (2*R*,3*S*)-2-chloro-3-methylpentane

(2*S*,3*S*)-2-chloro-3-methylpentane

Products are diastereomers. Note (important!): each one is formed as a racemate with its enantiomer (from chlorinations at C-4). Notice how the special nature of the molecule also gives rise to two enantiotopic pairs of hydrogens as well:

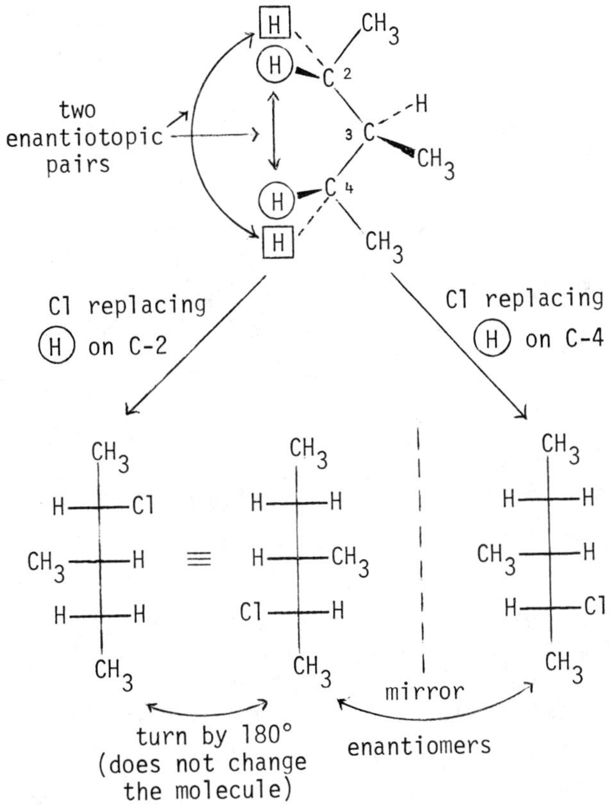

(d) Redraw structure:

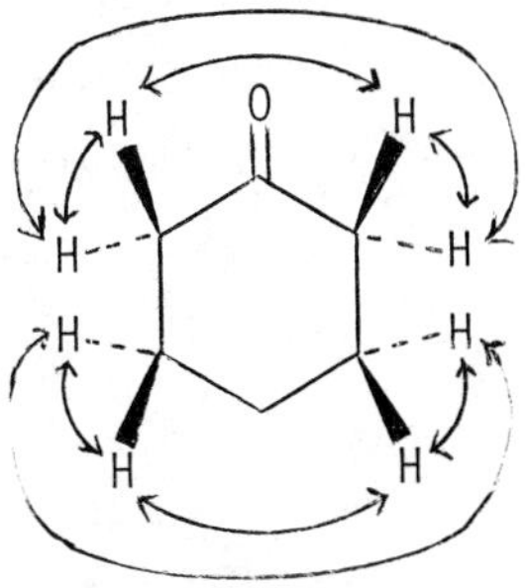

eight enantiotopic pairs

Substitution of any one of the eight hydrogens gives one of the two enantiomers. See example on the following page.

and

(These are enantiomers)

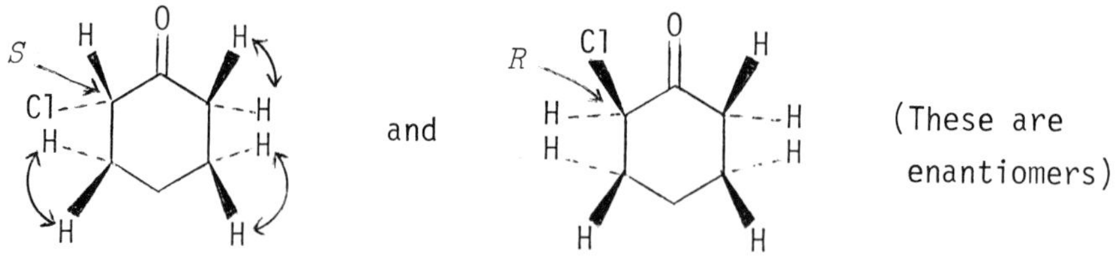

This sequence gives 4 pairs of enantiotopic hydrogens.

Also, we can have 4 more enantiotopic pairs as seen from the following example:

and

mirror images

(These are enantiomers)

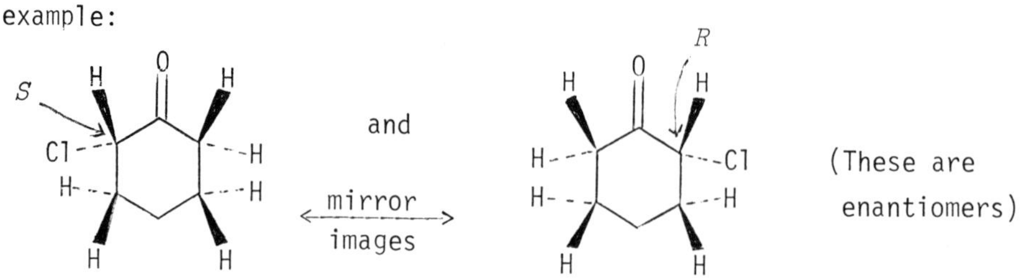

This sequence also gives 4 pairs of enantiotopic hydrogens to make a total of eight pairs of enantiotopic hydrogens.

****

25. has neither a plane nor a center of symmetry: it is chiral when locked in this conformation. A ring flip leads to the *mirror image* (enantiomer) of the above conformation, however (try it!). Therefore, *cis*-1,2-dimethylcyclohexane is actually a mixture of enantiomeric chairs rapidly interconverting via ring flips. This leads to the compound displaying no optical activity, just like any ordinary *meso* compound. Although neither chair has a plane of symmetry, notice that one of the boat transition states for chair-chair interconversion does, just like a true *meso* structure:

mirror plane

****

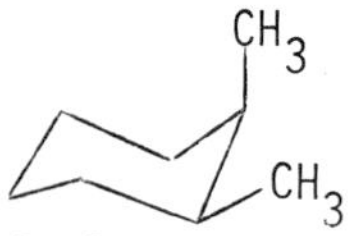

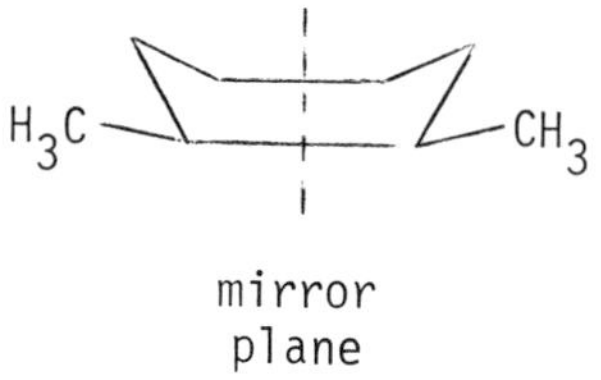

26. (a) There are three (C-9, 13, 14):

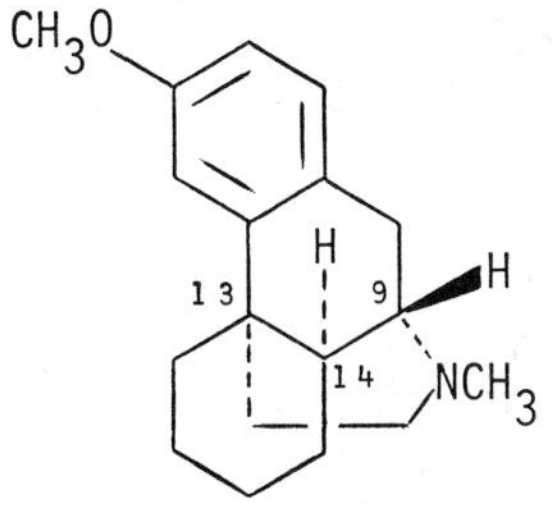

(b)

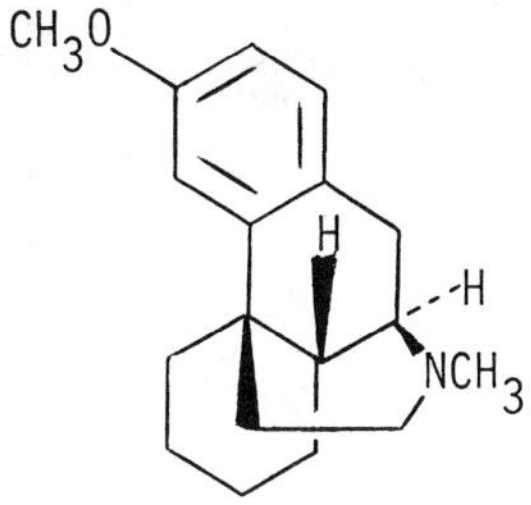

(c) For each of these stereocenters the groups are drawn out as far as needed to reach the first point of difference.

C-9:

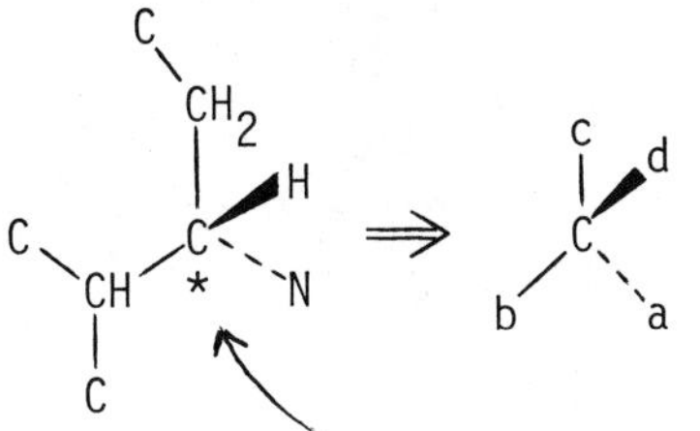

; flip so lowest priority group d (the H) is in the back:

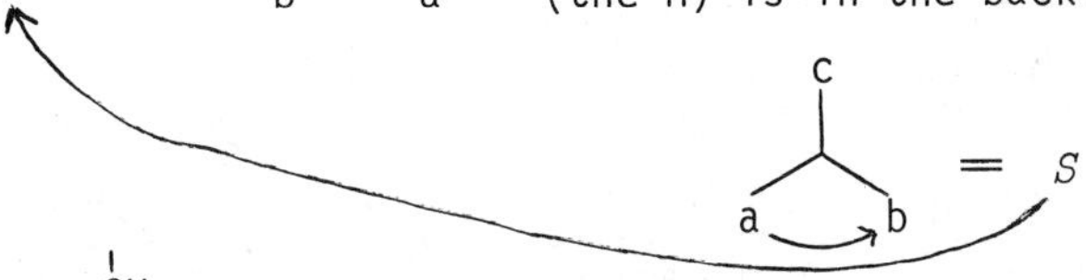

C-13:

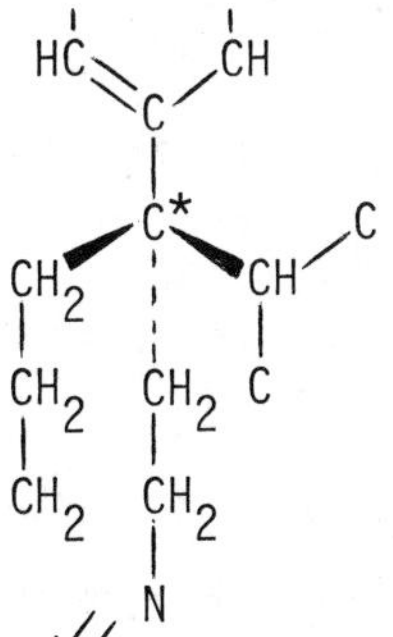

Treat the benzene carbon as any carbon with a double bond: 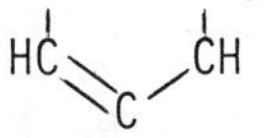 becomes 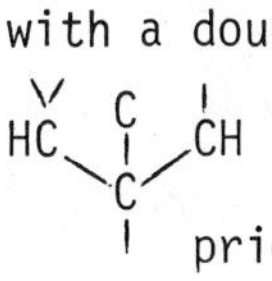 , and is therefore highest in priority over all the other groups.

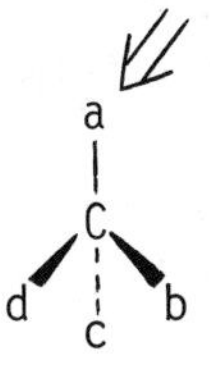

; rotate d in back:

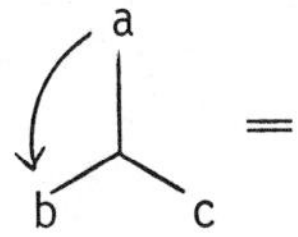

= *S* again

C-14:

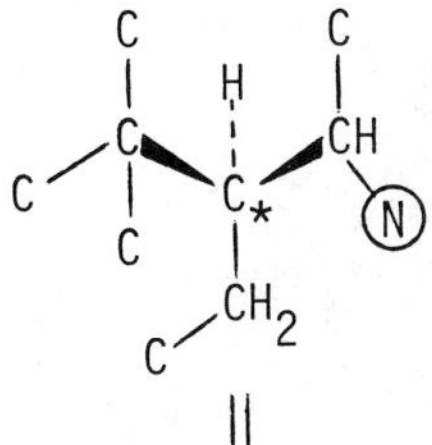

Careful! The C on right (attached to N, C, H) takes precedence over the C on the left (attached to 3 C's): at the first point of difference, N (circled) > C.

(see next page)

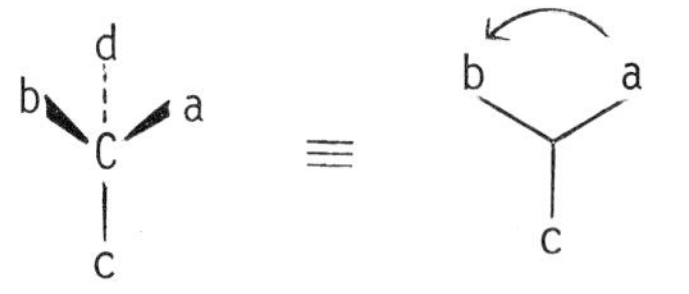

S again!

Dextromethorphan therefore has the (9*S*, 13*S*, 14*S*) configuration.

****

27. (a)

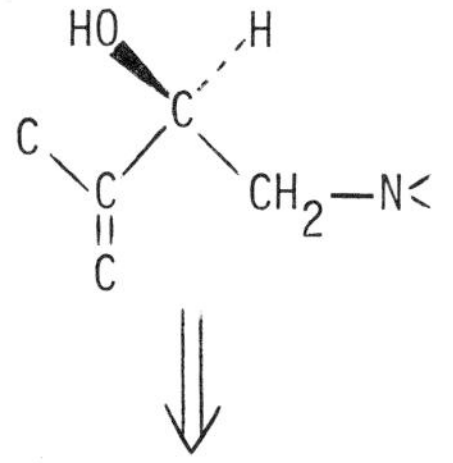

Careful! The $-CH_2N<$ group is higher priority than the benzene ring, even though the latter translates into 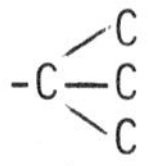 . The first point of difference is N > C!

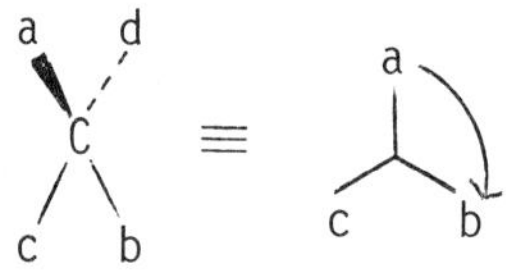

R is the answer.

(b) Enantiotopic (replacement of one with any group 'G' produces the enantiomer of the compound produced by replacement of the other).

(c) Equal energy: the transition states are mirror images of each other (they are *enantiomeric*).

(d) The enzyme must be lowering the energy of the transition state that leads to the (-) isomer, relative to the one that leads to the (+) isomer. To do this, the enzyme must be chiral, and optically pure as well, so that the two transition states in the presence of the enzyme become diastereomeric and, therefore, different in energy from each other.

****

CHAPTER 6

The Properties and Reactions of Haloalkanes: Bimolecular Nucleophilic Substitution

General Introduction

Referring all the way back to chapter 1, recall that polarized covalent bonds are at the heart of most of organic reaction chemistry. In this chapter, for the first time, the properties and chemical behaviour of molecules containing a polarized covalent bond will be presented in full detail. The molecules are alkyl halides or haloalkanes (the terms are interchangeable), containing the polarized carbon(δ+)-halogen(δ-) bond as their functional group. As a model for many subsequent chapters on the chemistry of the various functional groups, this chapter should be examined particularly closely. Many concepts presented in detail here will be fully applicable later on, even though later presentations may not be as comprehensive. With this chapter, we really start covering *typical* organic chemistry. Together with chapter 7, you will get your first opportunity to see the "big picture" with respect to one portion of organic chemistry: much of what has been presented in the first five chapters will play a role in the behavior of haloalkanes. Comprehending the material in chapters 6 and 7 in a *general overall* sense will in the long run actually be more important than remembering every last detail.

Outline of the Chapter

6-1. Nomenclature.

6-2. Physical Properties of Haloalkanes.

6-3. Nucleophilic Substitution.

The nature of a functional group, and an introduction to its most important reaction.

6-4. Mechanism of Nucleophilic Substitution: Kinetics.

The first section in the text to cover the mechanism (i.e. complete detailed course) of a polar reaction. As such, a very important section.

6-5. Stereochemistry.

Tying together this reaction with material in chapter 5.

6-6. Consequences of Inversion in S_N2 Reactions.

Further implications of material in chapters 4 and 5.

6-7. The Leaving Group.

6-8. The Nucleophile.

6-9. The Structure of the Substrate.

6-10. The Solvent.

The roles of four major variables on the favorability of the single reaction type under discussion.

Keys to the Chapter

6-1 and 6-2. Nomenclature and Physical Properties.

The carbon-halogen bond is the focal point of this chapter. Its polarization is the major feature governing the physical and chemical behaviour of these molecules. Differences among the four halogens will affect the *degree* to which a haloalkane exhibits any given physical or chemical characteristic. In a qualitative sense, however, any statement describing any one of the types of haloalkanes will be applicable to some extent to any of the others.

6-3. Nucleophilic Substitution.

At this stage we begin the discussion of our first major class of polar reactions. Note the following features:

(1) All nucleophilic substitutions have a similar general appearance, with a similar cast of characters, so to speak. Using the first example in the text table, we have

$$\underset{\text{nucleophile}}{\underset{\uparrow}{HO^-}} + \underset{\text{substrate}}{\underset{\uparrow}{CH_3Cl}} \longrightarrow \underset{\text{product}}{\underset{\uparrow}{CH_3OH}} + \underset{\text{leaving group}}{\underset{\uparrow}{Cl^-}}$$

Whenever a new reaction class is presented, analyze the various examples presented from the point of view of the common roles played by the chemical species involved. You should do this now for all the examples in the table in this text section. That is, in each case identify the nucleophile, substrate, product, and leaving group. Start getting used to the variety of species that belong to each category.

(2) All nucleophilic substitutions are *electrostatically sensible*. In every case an *electron rich* atom in the nucleophile ultimately becomes attached via a new bond to an *electrophilic* (positively polarized) carbon atom in the substrate. Opposite charges attract!!

$$H\text{-}O^- \quad + \quad \overset{\displaystyle H}{\underset{\displaystyle H}{H\text{---}\overset{}{C}}}\text{---}Cl \longrightarrow HO\text{---}CH_3 \quad + \quad Cl^-$$

electron rich   new bond

electrophilic

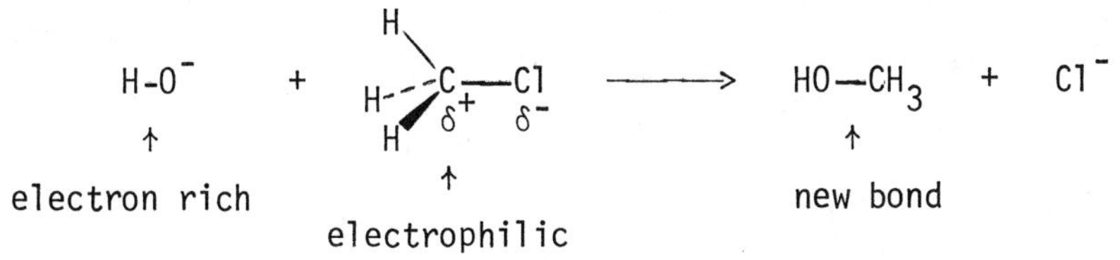

Again, whenever a new reaction class is presented, analyze the examples given on the basis of electrostatics. Focus on the logical consequences of oppositely charged or polarized atoms attracting each other. Do this now for the examples in the reaction table in the text section.

By doing these two analyses, you will have taken the first step towards learning organic chemistry by understanding, instead of by memorizing.

6-4, 6-5, and 6-6. Mechanism of the Reaction.

Knowing which old bonds break and which new bonds form is the first step in understanding a reaction. The *mechanism* describes it in more detail. When complete, it tells us when and how the bonding changes occur, and to as great an extent as possible, why these changes occur in just this particular way. The result is a description of the reaction that is hopefully complete enough to be of *predictive* value: good enough to tell us whether an unknown new example of the reaction is likely to work or not. This is important in *synthesis*: the preparation of new molecules from old ones for, e.g., medicinal purposes, theoretical study, etc. Thorough knowledge of a reaction's mechanism allows a chemist to estimate ahead of time how likely the reaction is to succeed if tried on a totally new molecule.

Section 6-4 describes one of the more common methods of deriving mechanistic information: kinetics experiments. Section 6-5 describes another common method: experiments involving the observation of stereochemical changes. By combining information from these and other types of experiments, the overall mechanistic picture of the bimolecular nucleophilic displacement, or S_N2 reaction, was developed over the first 30-odd years of this century. The key features, second-order kinetics and inversion of configuration at the substrate carbon, are common to all the reactions in this chapter. These mechanistic features are enough to allow predictions to be made concerning the effects of changing any of a number of variables in the S_N2 reaction. The last four sections of the chapter explore the most important of these. It should be pointed out that many of the observations described in these sections *were predicted ahead of time* based on the logical implications of the S_N2 mechanism. Part of your job as a student in organic chemistry will be to develop the ability to predict the result of a reaction of molecules *you may never have seen before*, on the basis of your knowledge of reaction mechanisms associated with the functional groups the molecules contain.

One final comment on mechanisms in general: there exists a common sort of shorthand way of writing organic reaction mechanisms. First of all, each step is written separately. Second, bonding changes in each step are indicated by *arrows* that represent the movement of *pairs of electrons*. For the S_N2 mechanism, a one-step process, we have:

$$HO^- \; + \; CH_3-Cl \longrightarrow HO-CH_3 \; + \; Cl^-$$

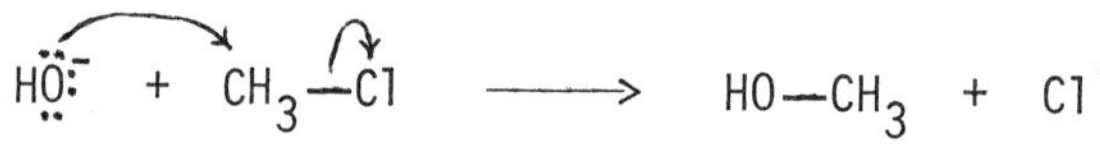

The two arrows show (1) movement of a pair of electrons from oxygen to carbon to form the new C-O bond and (2) movement of a pair of electrons from the C-Cl bond to chlorine to form the chloride ion. Mechanism arrows depict the movement of pairs of electrons, *not the movement of atoms*. This is a logical result of the fact that chemical reactions are due to changes in *bonds*, and bonds are made out of electrons. Practice using "arrow pushing" in mechanisms as frequently as you can so that you can get used to the technique. Note that proper use of electron-pair arrows *automatically* results in the correct Lewis structures for the products of a reaction, including formal charges if any. An example of this is the application of arrows to an even simpler reaction, the reaction of an acid and a base:

$$HO^- \; + \; H-Cl \longrightarrow HO-H \; (H_2O) \; + \; Cl^-$$

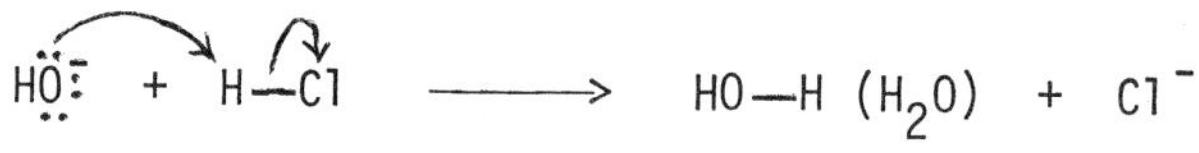

6-7, 6-8, 6-9, and 6-10. The S_N2 Reaction in Depth.

These sections explore the effects of changing four variables on the S_N2 reaction rate: leaving group, nucleophile, substrate structure, and solvent. All of the material in these sections derives logically from a knowledge of the mechanism and an awareness of the role each of the four variables can play. In each of these sections the effect of the variable on the *rate* of reaction is considered. This should tell you that the point of each discussion will be: "How does changing this variable affect the activation energy - the energy of the transition state relative to that of the starting materials?" We may not say it in so many words every time, but *that's what we mean*. Even if the discussion is *totally qualitative*, and no actual rate data is given, the focus of such a discussion will still be the effect of the variable in question on relative transition state energy.

Consideration of the *leaving group* is fairly simple. Since the leaving group is "beginning to leave" in the S_N2 transition state, the energy of the transition state will reflect to some extent the stability of the leaving group. Stable leaving groups are therefore better (interpret: "faster") leaving groups. The parallel between leaving group ability and non-basic character drawn in the chapter section is the easiest one to work with and is fairly good. "Good" leaving groups are usually the conjugate bases of strong acids (top six entries in Table 6-3). "Bad" leaving groups are strong bases, i.e., they are the conjugate bases of weak acids (bottom entries in Table 6-3). The section also describes ways to manufacture good leaving groups out of bad ones. Thus protonation of an alcohol changes the leaving group from hydroxide (a strong base, and therefore a "bad" leaving group) to water (the weak conjugate base of the strong acid H_3O^+, and therefore a "good" leaving group). This re-emphasis of the chapter material is intended to remind you of the important role fundamental concepts such as acid/base strength can play in many aspects of organic chemistry.

Consideration of the *nucleophile* is a bit more complicated. The section discusses *two* characteristics that can give rise to high nucleophilicity: high *basicity*, as in hydroxide ion, and large size of the nucleophilic atom, as in iodide ion. The reasons behind this are explored in detail and are relatively straightforward. In attempting to understand these, consider, again, how the characteristics in question influence the relative stability of the *transition state* of the reaction. Get into the habit of doing this whenever you are faced with totally new concepts relating to reactions and their kinetic favorability.

Consideration of *substrate structure* is much simpler, as the major consideration for an S_N2 reaction is, simply, "How crowded is the 'back-side' of the atom being attacked?" The less crowded, then the less *steric hindrance* to approach of the nucleophile, so the better will be the situation for an S_N2 reaction. The extreme importance of steric hindrance is emphasized by the fact that *t*-butyl and neopentyl halides are virtually totally incapable of reacting by the S_N2 mechanism.

Finally, consideration of *solvent* encompasses several effects associated with the roles that a solvent molecule can play in a reaction. The most important involves hydrogen bonding between *protic* solvents and nucleophiles, a process that effectively "ties up" the nucleophile, reducing its reactivity. The emergence of polar but *nonprotic* or *aprotic* solvents, incapable of hydrogen bonding, for S_N2 reactions is a recent development in organic chemistry.

Solutions to Chapter 6 Problems

1. (a) chloroethane
   (b) 1,2-dibromoethane
   (c) 3-(fluoromethyl)pentane
   (d) 1-iodo-2,2-dimethylpropane
   (e) (trichloromethyl)cyclohexane
   (f) tribromomethane

****

2. (a) $CH_3CHICHCH_2CH_3$ (with CH_2CH_3 on the third carbon)

   (b) $CHCl_2CH_2CHBrCH_3$

   (c) 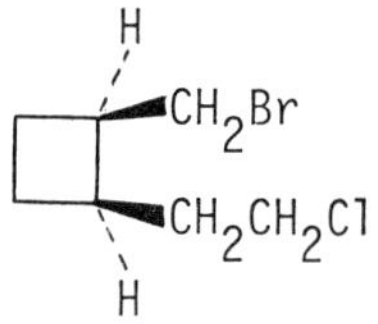

   (d) 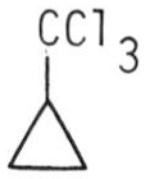

   (e) CH_2ClCCH_2Cl (with Cl above and CH_3 below the central carbon)

****

3. Answers for problem 5 are also given. Stereocenters are starred and numbers of stereoisomers given in parentheses.

   $BrCl\overset{*}{C}HCH_2CH_3$
   1-bromo-1-chloropropane (2)

   $BrCH_2\overset{*}{C}HClCH_3$
   1-bromo-2-chloropropane (2)

   $ClCH_2\overset{*}{C}HBrCH_3$
   2-bromo-1-chloropropane (2)

   $CH_3CBrClCH_3$
   2-bromo-2-chloropropane

   $BrCH_2CH_2CH_2Cl$
   1-bromo-3-chloropropane

****

4. Stereocenters are starred and numbers of stereoisomers given in parentheses.

$BrCH_2CH_2CH_2CH_2CH_3$ $CH_3\overset{*}{C}HBrCH_2CH_2CH_3$ $CH_3CH_2CHBrCH_2CH_3$

1-bromopentane   2-bromopentane (2)   3-bromopentane

$BrCH_2CH_2CHCH_3$
            |
           CH_3

$CH_3\overset{*}{C}HBrCHCH_3$
              |
             CH_3

$CH_3CH_2CBrCH_3$
              |
             CH_3

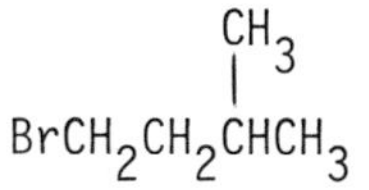

1-bromo-3-methylbutane   2-bromo-3-methylbutane (2)   2-bromo-2-methylbutane

$CH_3CH_2\underset{*}{C}HCH_2Br$
            |
           CH_3

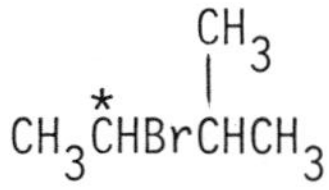

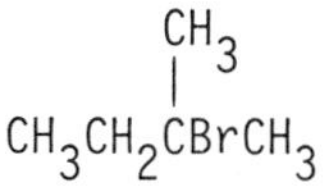

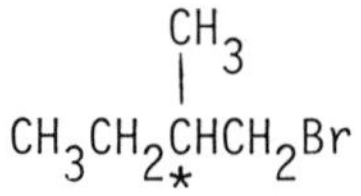

1-bromo-2-methylbutane (2)

$BrCH_2CCH_3$
            |
           CH_3

and
           CH_3

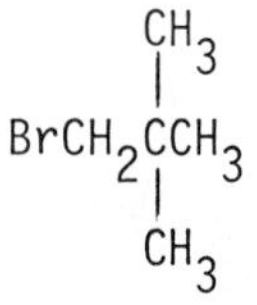

1-bromo-2,2-dimethylpropane

****

5. See 3 and 4.

****

6. In the answers below, the nuclephilic atom in the nucleophile, and the electrophilic atom in the substrate are both <u>underlined</u>.

Reaction	Nucleophile	Substrate	Leaving Group
1.	$H\underline{O}:^-$	$\underline{C}H_3Cl$	Cl^-
2.	$CH_3\underline{O}:^-$	$CH_3\underline{C}H_2I$	I^-
3.	$:\underline{I}:^-$	$CH_3\underline{C}HBrCH_2CH_3$	Br^-
4.	$:N{\equiv}\underline{C}:^-$	$(CH_3)_2CH\underline{C}H_2I$	I^-
5.	$CH_3\underline{S}:^-$	⬡$\underline{C}HBr$	Br^-
6.	$:\underline{N}H_3$	$CH_3\underline{C}H_2I$	I^-
7.	$:\underline{P}(CH_3)_3$	$\underline{C}H_3Br$	Br^-

****

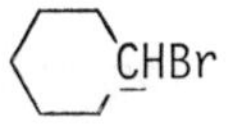

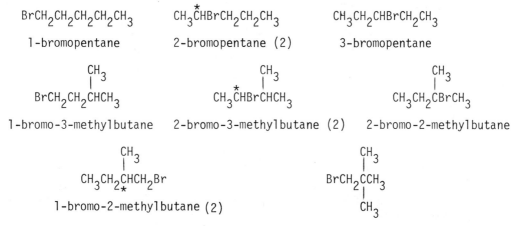

7. (a) $:N{\equiv}C: \longleftrightarrow :\ddot{N}{=}C:$ in reaction 4.

   (b) The N may act as a nucleophilic atom in cyanide (CN^-). The reaction would then proceed as follows:

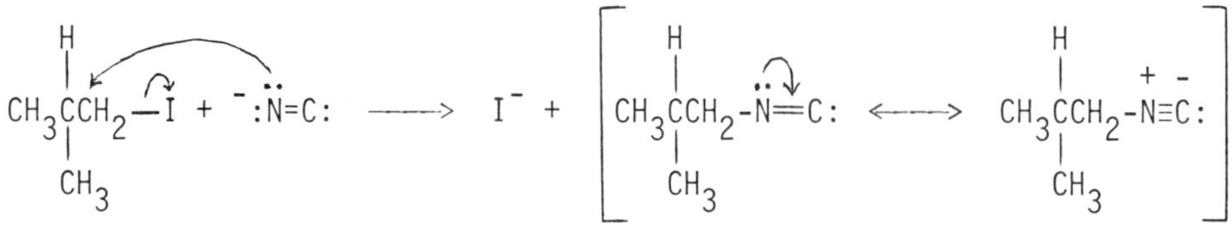

An organic "isonitrile".

****

8. (1) heterolytic dissociation/combination: assume the first step is slow and rate-determining

   (a) I^- a better leaving group than Cl^-, so reaction will be faster

   (b) nucleophile not involved in slow step, so little change if any

   (c) a more crowded starting molecule, so slow step may be sterically speeded up (in the next chapter you will see that the intermediate cation is also strongly stabilized by hyperconjugation, resulting in considerable additional acceleration)

   (d) both solvents will solvate cation well, but aprotic $(CH_3)_2SO$ cannot hydrogen bond to leaving group, so slow step will slow down.

   (2) homolytic dissociation (the slow step)

   (a) C-I bond weaker than C-Cl, so reaction will be faster

   (b) little change (nucleophile not involved in slow step)

   (c) secondary C-Cl bond weaker than CH_3-Cl, so reaction will be faster

   (d) solvent will have little effect on the rate of a radical reaction

   (3) single step front-side displacement

   (a) I^- a better leaving group, so reaction will be faster

   (b) $^-SCH_3$ a better nucelophile, so reaction will be faster

   (c) front side of reacting carbon somewhat harder to attack due to steric crowding, so reaction will be slower

   (d) aprotic solvent will not hydrogen bond to nucleophile, so reaction will be greatly speeded up

(4) single step back-side displacement

(a), (b), (d) same as (3)

(c) back side of reacting carbon is strongly sterically hindered to attack, so reaction will be slowed down greatly

****

9. Bimolecular displacement is first order in each component.

(a) Rate = k[CH_3Cl][KSCN]

2×10^{-8} mole ℓ^{-1}sec^{-1} = k (0.1 M)(0.1 M), so k = 2×10^{-6} ℓ mole^{-1}sec^{-1}

(b) Reading down the table, the three missing rates will be 4×10^{-8}, 1.2×10^{-7}, and 3.2×10^{-7} mole ℓ^{-1}sec^{-1}, respectively.

****

10. (a) Starting material is *R*. Product, 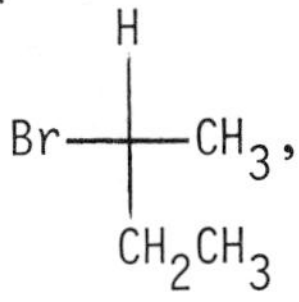

, is *S*.

(b) Starting material is (2*S*,3*S*)-2-bromo-3-chlorobutane. Product will be

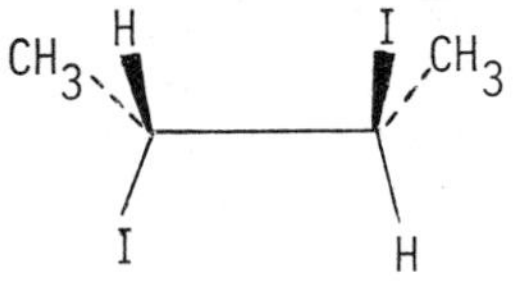

, (2*R*,3*R*)-2,3-diiodobutane.

(c) Starting material is (1*S*,3*R*)-3-chlorocyclohexanol (the position of the OH group is understood to be C-1). Product will be (1*S*,3*S*)-1,3-cyclohexanediol monoethanoate.

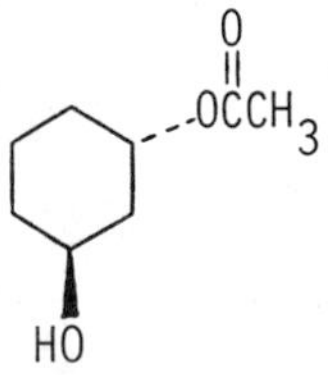

,

(d) Starting material is (1*S*,3*S*)-3-chlorocyclohexanol. Product will be

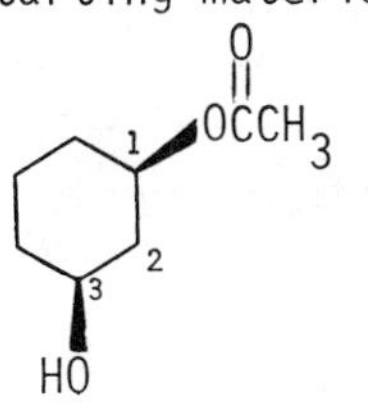

, (1*R*,3*S*)-1,3-cyclohexanediol monoethanoate

Notice that in the product for part (c), exchanging the OH and $O\overset{O}{\overset{\|}{C}}CH_3$ groups does not change the molecule. However, in the product for part (d), such an exchange turns the molecule into its enantiomer.

****

11. In the S_N2 transition state the angles for the three bonds not directly involved in the reaction <u>expand</u> from 109.5° to 120°. When a small ring with strained and compressed angles is involved, the structure resists the bond angle expansion, and the S_N2 transition state energy becomes very high. The result is a high activation energy and a very slow reaction. (See Section 6-6.)

****

12. (a) No reaction, although $CH_3CH_2CH_2OH$ would eventually form after a few centuries. H_2O is a very poor nucleophile.

(b) No reaction. (c) $CH_3CH_2CH_2OH$ (d) $CH_3CH_2CH_2I$

(e) $CH_3CH_2CH_2CN$ (f) No reaction. (g) $CH_3CH_2CH_2\underset{CH_3}{\overset{+}{S}}CH_3\ Br^-$

(h) $CH_3CH_2CH_2\overset{+}{N}H_3\ Br^-$

(i) No reaction. However, in the presence of heat or light free radical chlorination will occur, giving a mixture of products.

(j) No reaction; F^- is a poor nucleophile.

****

13. (a) $CH_3CH_2CH_2CH_2OH$ (b) CH_3CH_2Cl (c) 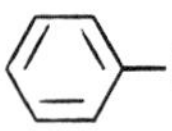$-CH_2OCH_2CH_3$

(d) $(CH_3)_2CHCH_2I$ (<u>very</u> slowly!) (e) $CH_3CH_2CH_2SCN$

(f) No reaction (F^- is a very poor leaving group).

(g) No reaction (OH^- is an even worse leaving group).

(h) CH_3SCH_3

(i) No reaction ($^-OCH_2CH_3$ is not a reasonable leaving group).

(j) $CH_3CH_2O\overset{O}{\overset{\|}{C}}CH_3$

****

14. These are representative answers.

(a) ![piperidine with N-CH3] + $CH_3OSO_2OCH_3$ ——————> ![N,N-dimethyl piperidinium] $^-OSO_2OCH_3$

dimethyl sulfate

(b) $(R)-CH_3CHOHCH_2CH_3$ + CH_3SO_2Cl ————> $(R)-CH_3\overset{\displaystyle OSO_2CH_3}{\underset{|}{C}}HCH_2CH_3$

"mesyl chloride"   "mesylate"

Then, $(R)-CH_3\overset{\displaystyle OSO_2CH_3}{\underset{|}{C}}HCH_2CH_3$ + $Na^+\,^-SH$ ————> $(S)-CH_3CHSHCH_2CH_3$ + $Na^+\,^-OSO_2CH_3$

(c)

	CH₃	
HO—	—H	
CH₃O—	—H	
	CH₃	

+ CH_3—⟨benzene⟩—SO_2Cl ————>

	CH₃	
CH_3—⟨benzene⟩—SO_2O—	—H	
CH₃O—	—H	
	CH₃	

"tosyl chloride"   "tosylate"

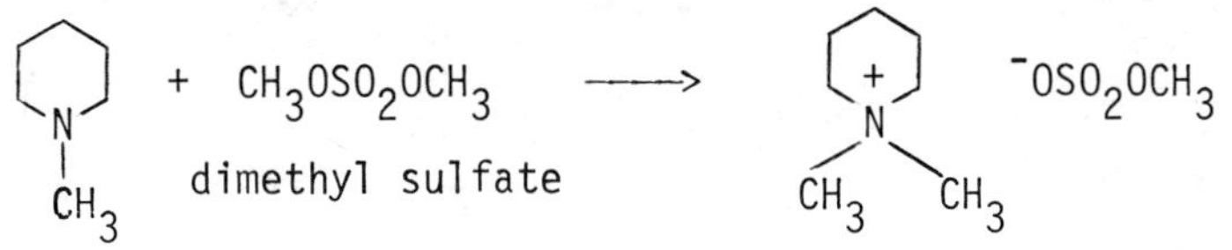

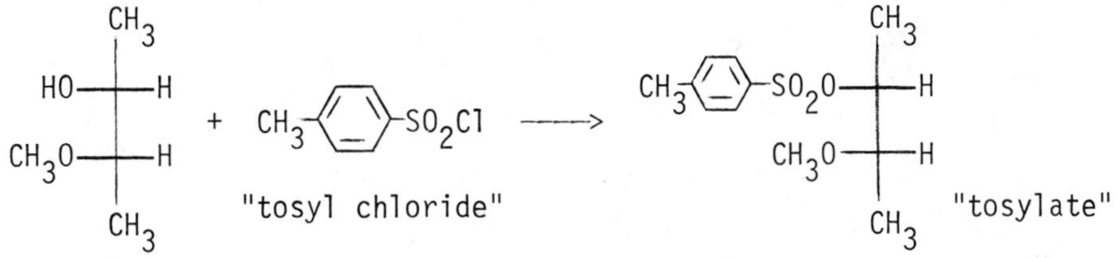

Then, reaction with $K^+\,^-CN$ ————>

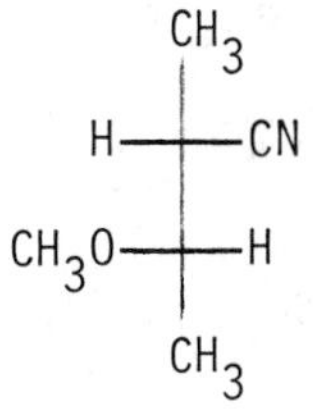

	CH₃	
H—	—CN	
CH₃O—	—H	
	CH₃	

(d) ![bicyclic structure with H and ---OH] $\xrightarrow{\text{HBr}}$![bicyclic structure with H and Br]

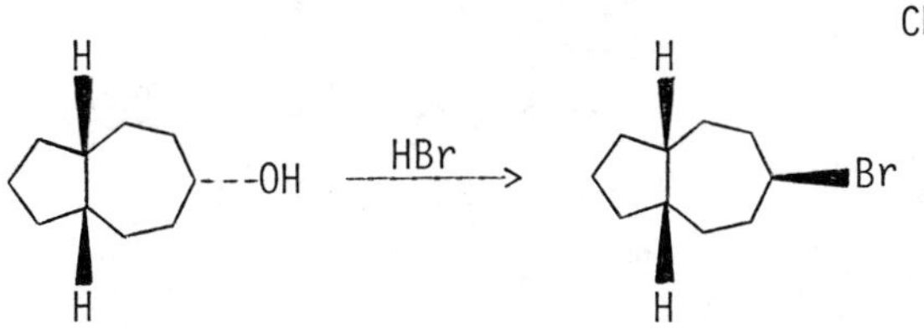

(An acceptable answer for now, but for reasons discussed in the next two chapters this is not quite as good as alternatives like reaction first with tosyl chloride and then with K^+ Br^-, similar to part c.)

****

15. The reaction involves two steps:

(1) $CH_3CH_2CH_2\ddot{O}H$ + $H-\overset{\displaystyle O}{\underset{\displaystyle O}{OSOH}}$ ————> $CH_3CH_2CH_2\overset{+}{O}H_2$ + $^-OSO_3H$

(protonation)

(2) Br^- + $CH_3CH_2CH_2-\overset{+}{O}H_2$ ————> $CH_3CH_2CH_2Br$ + H_2O

(S_N2 displacement)

****

16. (a) $ClCH_2CH_2CH_2CH_2O-H$ + ^-OH $\xrightarrow{\text{(proton transfer)}}$ H_2O + $Cl-CH_2CH_2CH_2CH_2O^-$

$\xrightarrow{\text{(intramolecular displacement)}}$ [tetrahydrofuran ring] + Cl^-

(b) $BrCH_2CH_2S-H$ + ^-OH $\longrightarrow$ $Br-CH_2CH_2S^-$ $\longrightarrow$ CH_2-CH_2 (thiirane, S) + Br^-

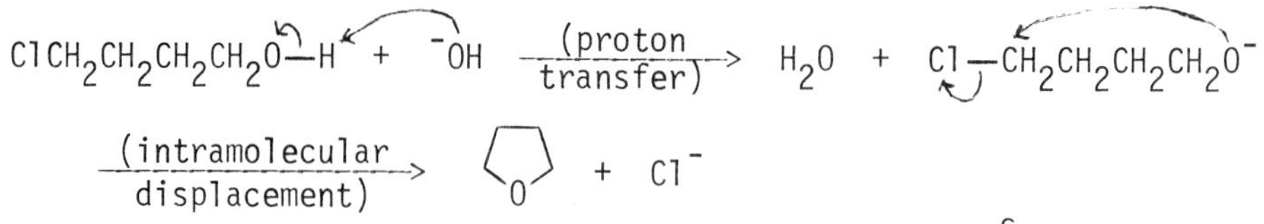

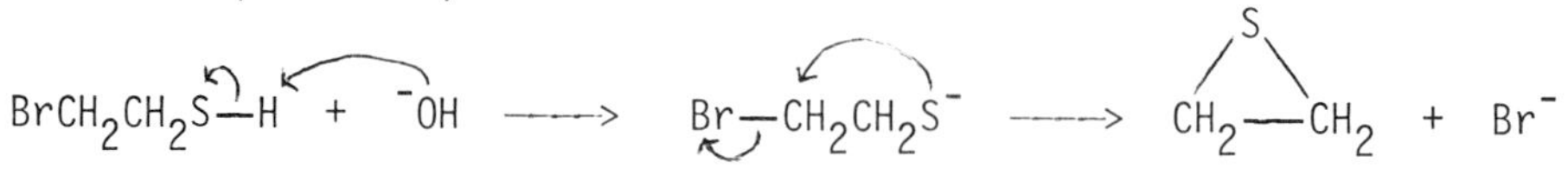

Alternatively, sulfur is such a good nucleophile that a slightly different mechanism may also occur:

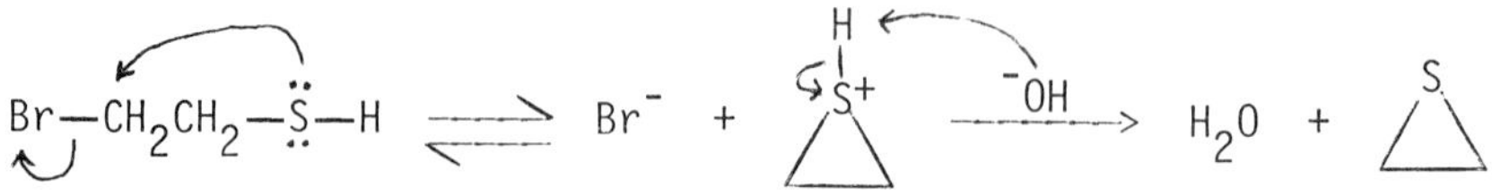

$Br-CH_2CH_2-\ddot{S}-H$ $\rightleftharpoons$ Br^- + [3-membered ring S^+ with H] $\xrightarrow{^-OH}$ H_2O + [thiirane ring, S]

(c) $BrCH_2CH_2CH_2CH_2CH_2-Br$ + ^-OH $\longrightarrow$ Br^- +

$BrCH_2CH_2CH_2CH_2CH_2O-H$ $\xrightarrow{^-OH}$ H_2O +

$Br-CH_2CH_2CH_2CH_2CH_2O^-$ $\longrightarrow$ Br^- + [tetrahydropyran ring, O]

(d) $BrCH_2CH_2CH_2CH_2CH_2-Br$ + $\ddot{N}H_3$ $\longrightarrow$ Br^- +

$BrCH_2CH_2CH_2CH_2CH_2\overset{+}{N}H_2$ (with H) $\underset{:NH_3}{\rightleftharpoons}$ NH_4^+ +

$Br-CH_2CH_2CH_2CH_2CH_2\ddot{N}H_2$ $\longrightarrow$ [piperidinium ring, N^+ with H, H] $\underset{\ddot{N}H_3}{\rightleftharpoons}$ NH_4^+ + [piperidine ring, N–H]

****

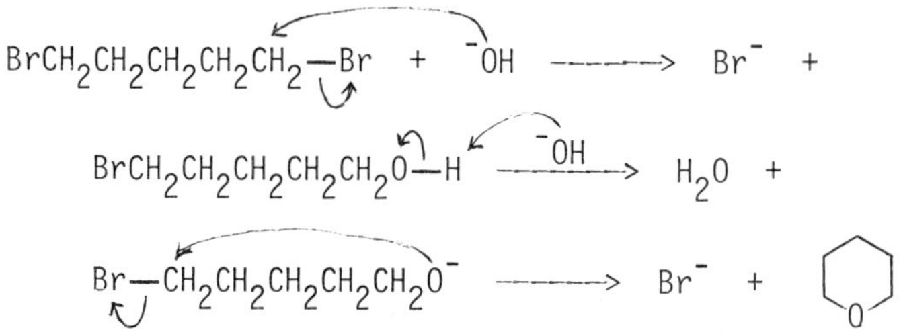

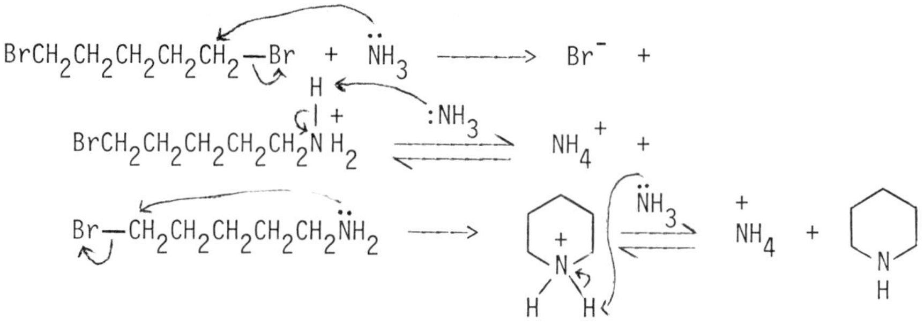

17. (a) (1) HO^- > $CH_3CO_2^-$ > H_2O Basicity increases with charge and decreases with charge stabilization.

(2) HO^- > $CH_3CO_2^-$ > H_2O For a single atom nucleophilicity parallels basicity.

(3) H_2O > $CH_3CO_2^-$ > HO^- Leaving group ability is inversely related to basicity.

(b) (1) F^- > Cl^- > Br^- > I^- Larger size stabilizes negative charge, making base weaker.

(2) I^- > Br^- > Cl^- > F^- Larger size decreases solvation and

			increases polarizability, increasing nucleophilicity.
	(3)	$I^- > Br^- > Cl^- > F^-$	Reverse order of (1).
(c)	(1)	$^-NH_2 > {}^-PH_2 > NH_3$	Larger size makes $^-PH_2$ weaker base than $^-NH_2$; lack of charge makes NH_3 the weakest.
	(2)	$^-PH_2 > {}^-NH_2 > NH_3$	Size puts $^-PH_2$ first; lack of charge puts NH_3 last.
	(3)	$NH_3 > {}^-PH_2 > {}^-NH_2$	Reverse of (1).
(d)	(1)	$^-OCN > {}^-SCN$	Size (smaller atom is more basic)
	(2)	$^-SCN > {}^-OCN$	Size (larger atom is more nucleophilic)
	(3)	$^-SCN > {}^-OCN$	Reverse of (1)
(e)	(1)	$HO^- > CH_3S^- > F^-$	HO^- stronger than CH_3S^- due to size, and stronger than F^- due to electronegativity difference. Comparison between CH_3S^- and F^- hard to make as small size favors F^-, while lower electronegativity favors CH_3S^-.
	(2)	$CH_3S^- > HO^- > F^-$	Large size of CH_3S^- takes precedence for nucleophilicity.
	(3)	$F^- > CH_3S^- > HO^-$	They're all bad. Order is reverse of (1).
(f)	(1)	$NH_3 > H_2O > H_2S$	Electronegativity, then size.
	(2)	$H_2S > NH_3 > H_2O$	Size, then electronegativity.
	(3)	$H_2S > H_2O > NH_3$	Reverse of (1).

****

18\. (a) No reaction. (Starting material is an alkane. Alkanes don't react with nucleophiles.)

(b) $CH_3CH_2OCH_3$

(c) 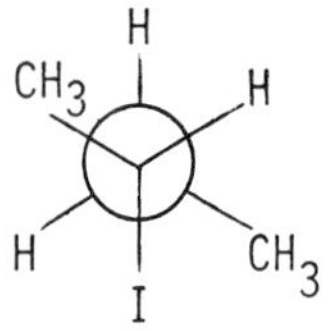 would be a good conformation of the product after inversion of the reacting carbon.

(d) 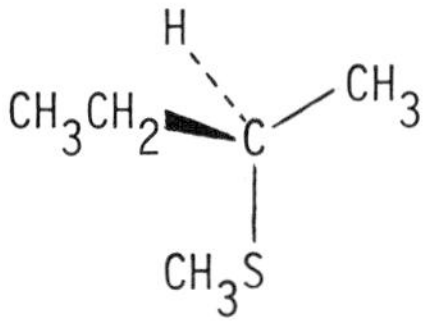

(e) No reaction (no good leaving group)

(f) No reaction (Same reason, and HCN is too weak an acid to protonate the alcohol oxygen to help.)

(g) $CH_3CHBrCH_3$ (HBr is a strong acid, so it can protonate the OH group and form H_2O, a good leaving group, in the reaction).

(h) $(CH_3)_2CHCH_2CH_2SCN$ (leaving group is 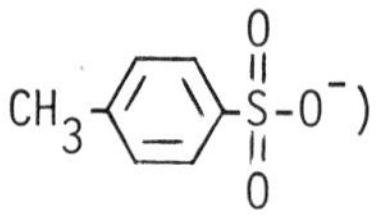).

(i) No reaction (NH_2^- is a bad leaving group).

(j) CH_3NH_2

(k) $(CH_3)_2\overset{+}{N}H_2 \;\; I^-$

(l) 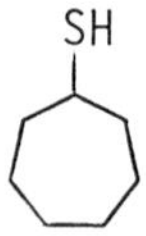

(m) 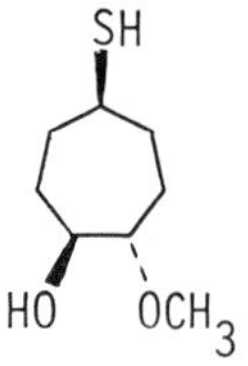

(n) 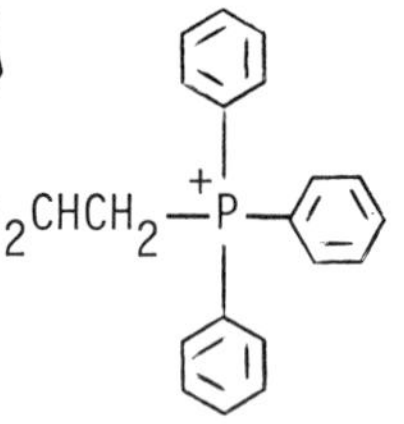 Br^-

****

19. (a) $CH_3CH_2CH_3 \xrightarrow{Cl_2,\ 100°C} CH_3CH_2CH_2Cl + CH_3CHClCH_3$ (Table 3-7)

60%   40%

This is the best way you know, even though a mixture is formed.

(b) Making use of the selectivity of bromination for secondary C-H bonds leads to the best route:

$$CH_3CH_2CH_2 \xrightarrow{Br_2,\ h\nu} CH_3CHBrCH_3 \xrightarrow{KCl,\ DMSO} CH_3CHClCH_3$$

(c) $CH_3CH_2CH_2Cl$ [from part (a)] $\xrightarrow{NaBr,\ propanone} CH_3CH_2CH_2Br$

(d) See part (b).

(e) $CH_3CH_2CH_2Cl$ [from part (a)] $\xrightarrow{\text{NaI, propanone}}$ $CH_3CH_2CH_2I$

(f) $CH_3CHBrCH_3$ [from part (b)] $\xrightarrow{\text{NaI, propanone}}$ CH_3CHICH_3

****

20. Don't forget: each S_N2 reaction <u>inverts</u> the stereochemistry at the site of reaction.

(a)

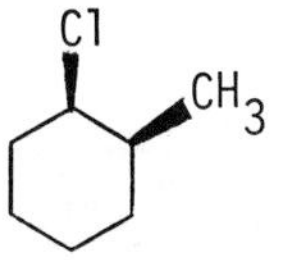

$\xrightarrow{\text{CH}_3\text{S}^- \text{ Na}^+}$ *trans* product from one S_N2 inversion

(b) The starting material is already *trans*. Direct S_N2 reaction with CH_3S^- will give a *cis* product, which you don't want. Instead, plan out a synthesis involving <u>two successive</u> S_N2 inversions: go from *trans* to *cis* first, and then back to *trans*. The first S_N2 reaction should use a nucleophile which can later function as a leaving group as well, such as Br^-; CH_3S^- can then be the nucleophile in the second S_N2 step:

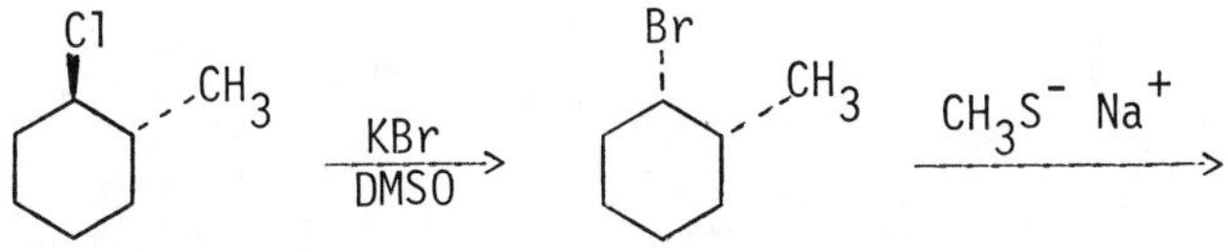

$\xrightarrow[\text{DMSO}]{\text{KBr}}$

$\xrightarrow{\text{CH}_3\text{S}^- \text{ Na}^+}$ *trans* product

(c)

$\xrightarrow[(-\text{HCl})]{\text{CH}_3\text{SO}_2\text{Cl}}$

$\xrightarrow{\text{CH}_3\text{S}^- \text{ Na}^+}$ *trans* product

cis
but poor leaving group

still *cis*,
but leaving group is better

(d)

$\xrightarrow[(-\text{HCl})]{\text{CH}_3\text{SO}_2\text{Cl}}$

$\xrightarrow[\text{DMSO}]{\text{KBr}}$

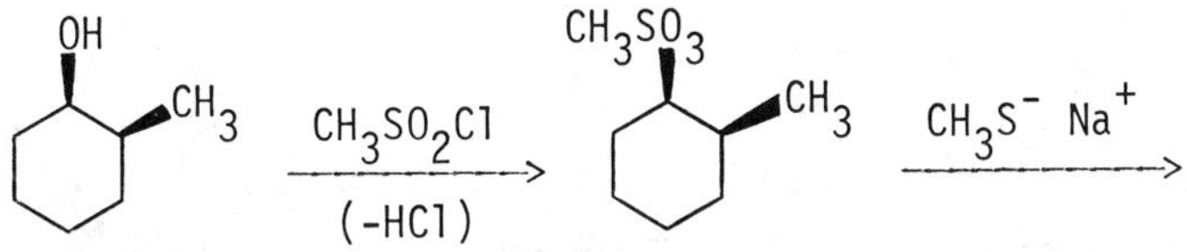

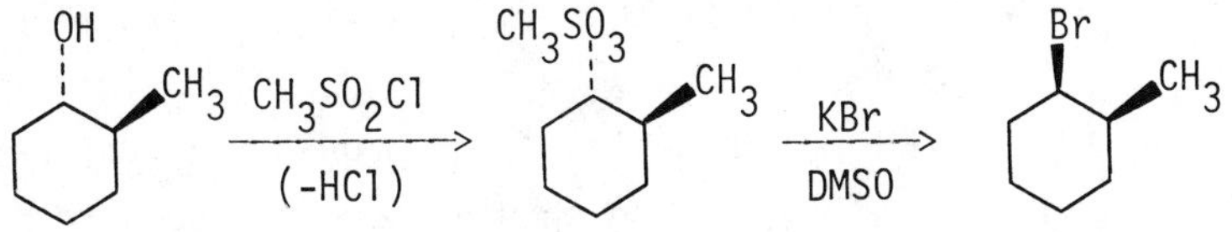

trans

still *trans*

cis

$\xrightarrow{\text{CH}_3\text{S}^- \text{ Na}^+}$ *trans* product

****

21. (a) CH_3Br > CH_3CH_2Br > $(CH_3)_2CHBr$

(b) $(CH_3)_2CHCH_2CH_2Cl$ > $(CH_3)_2CHCH_2Cl$ > $(CH_3)_2CHCl$

(c) CH_3CH_2I > CH_3CH_2Cl > 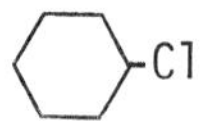

(d) $(CH_3)_2CHCH_2Br$ > $(CH_3CH_2)_2CHCH_2Br$ > $CH_3CH_2CH_2CHBrCH_3$

****

22. The nucleophilicity of the three unsolvated anions is reflected by the rate constants in DMF: Cl^- > Br^- = ^-SeCN. This probably reflects slightly higher basicity for Cl^-. Hydrogen bonding to CH_3OH reduces the reactivity of all three differently. Cl^-, the smallest ion, is solvated most, and becomes the poorest nucleophile in methanol. Solvation is a little less for Br^-, and much less for ^-SeCN, due to the delocalized charge in the latter.

****

23. (a) Yes!

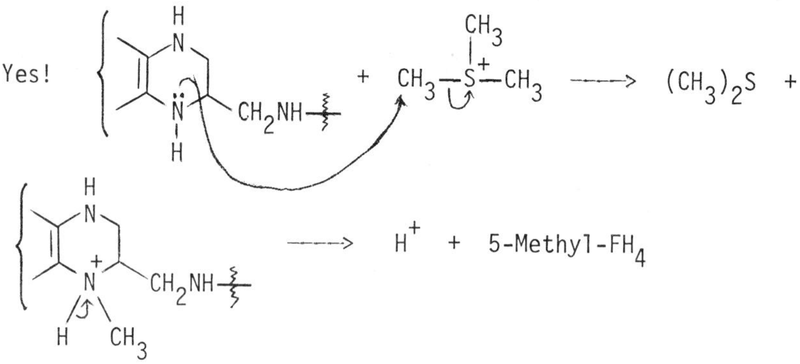

(b) Nucleophile: FH_4. Nucleophilic atom: N-5. Electrophilic atom: C in methyl group on $(CH_3)_3S^+$. Leaving group: $(CH_3)_2S$.

(c) Yes! N-5 in FH_4 resembles the N in ammonia, and is therefore a Lewis base and a reasonable candidate for a nucleophile. The methyls in $(CH_3)_3S^+$ should be polarized δ^+ due to electron attraction from them by positively charged sulfur. Their carbon atoms should be reasonable electrophiles. $(CH_3)_2S$ is neutral, and probably a very weak base by analogy with H_2S and CH_3SH, and should therefore be a very good leaving group.

****

24. (a) Yes! A possible mechanism:

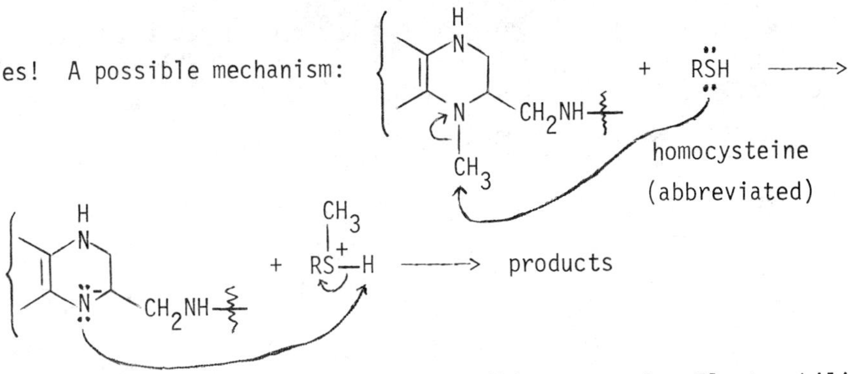

(b) Nucleophile: homocysteine. Nucleophilic atom: S. Electrophilic atom: C of N-5 methyl group in 5-methyl-FH_4. Leaving group: conjugate base of FH_4.

(c) Everything is fine except for the leaving group. As the conjugate base of a rather weak acid, it will be a moderately strong base, and therefore not a very good leaving group. However, just as protonation of oxygen in alcohols leads to a better leaving group (water), protonation of N-5 by acid in 5-methyl-FH_4 *before* nucleophilic displacement should lead to a better leaving group (FH_4 itself) for the reaction in this problem:

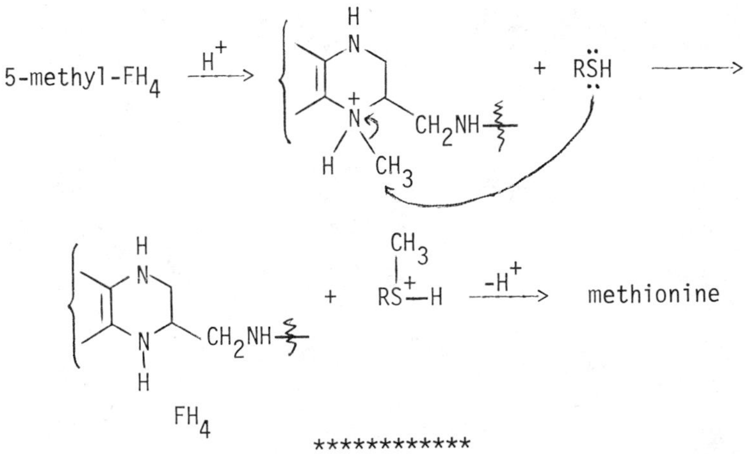

****

25. (a) Reaction 1 is an S_N2 process. The S of methionine displaces triphosphate from the CH_2 group in ATP. Reaction 2 is an S_N2 process. The N of norepinephrine displaces *S*-adenosyl homocysteine from a CH_3 group, making the key CH_3-N bond in adrenalin. The ATP makes the second S_N2 reaction possible by turning everything that's attached to the CH_3 of methionine into one great big leaving group. In other

words, *S*-adenosyl methionine is a fancy biological equivalent of CH_3I.

(b) No. S_N2 reaction on the CH_3 doesn't occur because the leaving group (essentially RS^-) is not a good one.

(c) Simple! React it with one equivalent of CH_3I! (Actually, it's not quite so simple - care is necessary to prevent extensive reaction of the adrenalin nitrogen, which is still nucleophilic, with additional CH_3I.)

****

CHAPTER 7

Further Reactions of Haloalkanes: Unimolecular Substitution and Pathways of Elimination

General Introduction

In Chapter 7 we continue, and complete a discussion of major reaction types and mechanisms for haloalkanes. Three new reaction types will be discussed. Pay close attention how each of these mechanisms makes electrostatic sense: just as the S_N2 mechanism in the last chapter, each of these new reactions provides a means for an electron pair to move towards the electrophilic haloalkane carbon, forming a new bond. As we emphasized before, this mechanistic understanding is the first step to real comprehension of this material.

Of more practical importance, and the real focal point of this chapter, is the fact that similar compounds can undergo several different types of reactions. Both the text and this guide will attempt to provide you with the means to decide just what reaction is likely to occur under any given set of conditions on the basis of logical reasoning, based on a few relatively simple criteria. As complicated as this might look the first time through, there is logic to it, and you don't have to be any sort of genius to learn it and apply it!

Outline of the Chapter

7-1. Solvolysis of Tertiary Haloalkanes.

A surprising reaction of compounds that do not undergo the S_N2 reaction.

7-2. Mechanism of Solvolysis: Unimolecular Nucleophilic Substitution.

The explanation.

7-3. Substrate Structure: The Stability of Carbocations.

A new kind of reactive intermediate in organic chemistry. Also, a summary of nucleophilic displacement reactions.

7-4. Unimolecular Elimination: E1.

7-5. Bimolecular Elimination: E2.

Two mechanisms for a new reaction of haloalkanes.

Keys to the Chapter

7-1 and 7-2. Solvolysis: Unimolecular Nucleophilic Substitution.

Tertiary haloalkanes, although they do not react at all via the S_N2 mechanism (chapter 6), still undergo very rapid nucleophilic displacement under certain reaction conditions. This is due to the appearance of a *completely new mechanism* for displacement for which *tertiary* halides are the best suited substrate molecules: unimolecular nucleophilic substitution, or the S_N1 mechanism. Section 7-2 presents the kinetic and stereochemical details of experiments that led to the formulation of this mechanism. Note that this is typically a two- or three-step reaction, in contrast to the single step S_N2 process, and it requires a rate-determining *ionization* of the carbon-halogen (or carbon-leaving group) bond, leading to a new reactive species called a *carbocation* (pronounced car-bo-cat-ion). You may occasionally encounter the term "carbonium ion," an older name for these species. Another name currently in use is "carbenium ion." Note carefully how the various features of this reaction as described in this section (e.g., rate, stereochemistry, sensitivity to solvent polarity and leaving group) are closely and logically derived from the nature of this rate-determining reaction step.

7-3. Substrate Structure: The Stability of Carbocations.

The chief requirement for an S_N1 mechanism is ease of ionization of the bond between the carbon atom and the leaving group. Since the initial result of this is formation of a positively charged (cationic) carbon species (carbocation), it is logical that the ease of the S_N1 mechanism will reflect the ease of generation of the corresponding carbocation. Carbon is not a very electropositive atom, and a carbon with a full positive charge is, in general, not going to be a very stable species, and, so, it will be difficult to generate. As explained here, however, alkyl groups (as opposed to hydrogen atoms) stabilize cationic carbon centers. Thus cations in which the positive charge is on a *tertiary* carbon atom will be the most stable, and the easiest to generate, since *three* alkyl groups are present to help alleviate the electron deficiency of the cationic carbon. Thus, the reactivity of tertiary substrates in S_N1 reactions boils down to the ease of their ionization to form the *relatively* stable tertiary carbocation intermediate. Table 7-3 summarizes the distinct modes of substitution for methyl and primary halides (S_N2 only) vs. tertiary halides (S_N1 only). The obvious omission of secondary substrates is due to the fact that their behaviour is more complicated. Depending on the specific situation either S_N1 or S_N2 behaviour, or both, may occur.

Prediction of the pathway a secondary substrate will follow is another direct application of the logical consequences of the two competing mechanisms. Read the last portion of section 7-3 particularly carefully as it presents a classic example of the use of mechanistic information to explain (and predict) the effects of reaction variables on possible reaction pathways.

7-4 and 7-5. Elimination Reactions.

The positively charged carbon atom in a carbocation represents, in a sense, the ultimate electron-deficient (electrophilic) carbon. As such, its behaviour is dominated by a need to obtain an electron pair from any available source, whether inter- or intramolecular. The S_N1 reaction illustrates the most obvious fate of a carbocation: combination with an external Lewis base, forming a new bond to carbon. However, the electron deficiency of cationic carbon is so great that even under typical S_N1 solvolysis conditions, surrounded by nucleophilic solvent molecules, some of the cations won't wait to combine with external electron-pair sources. Instead, they will seek available electron pairs in bonds elsewhere in their own molecular structures. The most available of these are electrons in carbon-hydrogen bonds one carbon removed from the cationic center (at the so-called "β" carbon):

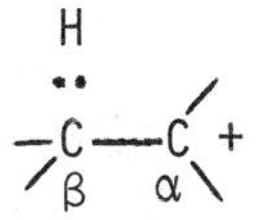

Attraction of this electron pair towards the positively charged carbon leads naturally to two reasonable products: an alkene and a proton, the products of El elimination. As mentioned in the text, the proton doesn't just "fall off." Actually, it is removed by any Lewis base available in the reaction system, such as solvent or nucleophile molecules.

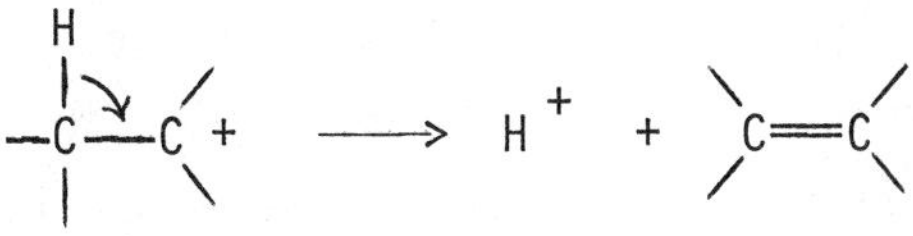

Note that only the "β"-carbon-hydrogen bond (the one next to the positive carbon) is normally susceptible to cleavage in this manner. Other C-H bonds would not give such stable products if they were to be broken:

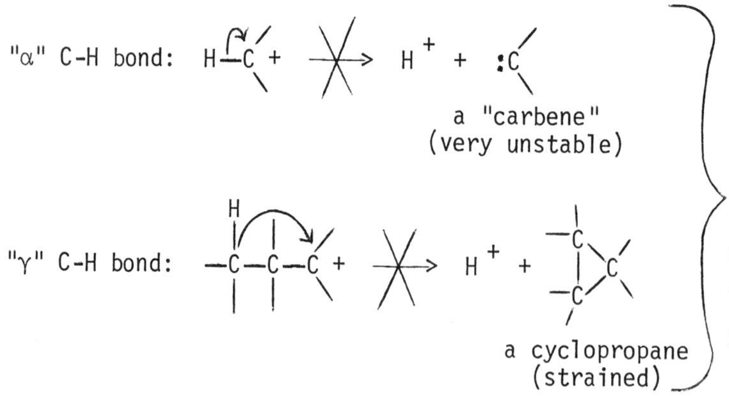

Both of these are very uncommon processes. Their occurrence is limited to situations where normal "β" elimination cannot take place.

As the E1 process has the same rate determining step as the S_N1 reaction, it too is unimolecular kinetically. E1 elimination almost always accompanies S_N1 substitution. Not much can be done to control the ratio of the two processes. The choice is between the nucleophile attaching to a cationic carbon (S_N1), or to a proton (lost via E1). Thus, weakly basic nucleophiles will favor S_N1, while stronger bases will favor elimination. Other effects are discussed in section 7-4, but the real consequence is that S_N1 reactions of tertiary halides rarely occur without some simultaneous elimination, and are therefore not usually efficient ways to make new molecules.

By contrast, addition of base can lead to complete elimination reaction from a tertiary halide. At high concentrations, in fact, a second elimination mechanism with bimolecular kinetic behaviour begins to appear (E2 reaction). Section 7-5 describes the details of this process pictorially. Note that the same electrons (those in a β C-H bond) move towards the electrophilic carbon; the difference is that this electron movement occurs *simultaneously* with loss of the leaving group, instead of *after* the leaving group leaves, as was the case in the E1 process. The role of the base in the E2 reaction is to begin pulling off the β proton, to allow all these bonding changes to begin to occur. Figure 7-8 should be examined closely. Note the electron motion towards the chlorine-bearing carbon: it is actually quite similar to the electron motion of an S_N2 process! The tertiary halide cannot undergo S_N2 displacement, but the E2 mechanism is a way for it to move electrons in a similar way, getting them from a β C-H bond instead of an external nucleophile.

As the rest of this section shows, *any* haloalkane with a β C-H bond can undergo E2 elimination. In the case of 1° and 2° halides, E2 and S_N2 reactions compete. However, as the summary sections in the text and below will show, it is very easy to control this competition and predict the favored products in these cases.

General Guidelines

The text summarizes the preferences for E1, E2, S_N1 and S_N2 reactions for 1°, 2°, and 3° haloalkanes, as a function of reaction conditions, in quite a bit of detail. The chart which follows presents the same material in graphical form, although somewhat oversimplified for clarity (solvent effects are not included, for instance). The key consideration for synthetic purposes is elimination vs. substitution, and it turns out that the preference in most cases can be determined by answering the following three questions:

1. Is the nucleophile a strong base?
2. Is the nucleophile sterically very bulky?
3. Is the substrate sterically hindered (i.e. 3°, 2°, or 1° with branching)?

If the answer to at least two out of these three questions is "yes," elimination will be favored. Otherwise substitution will predominate. Check the reactions in the chapter to see how these guidelines work!

SUMMARY CHART

Major reactions of haloalkanes with nucleophiles

Type of nucleophile

Type of halide	Poor nucleophile like H_2O	Weakly basic good nucleophile like I^-	Strongly basic unhindered nucleophile like HO^-	Strongly basic hindered nucleophile like $(CH_3)_3CO^-$
methyl	no reaction	S_N2	S_N2	S_N2
1°	no reaction	S_N2	S_N2	E 2
2°	slow S_N1	S_N2	E 2	E 2
3°	S_N1 and E 1	S_N1 and E 1	E 1 and E 2	E 1 and E 2

Solutions to Chapter 7 Problems

1. (a) $(CH_3)_3COCH_2CH_3$

(b) 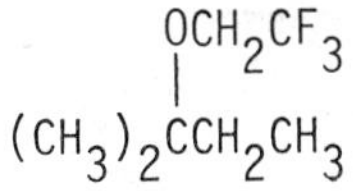

(c) 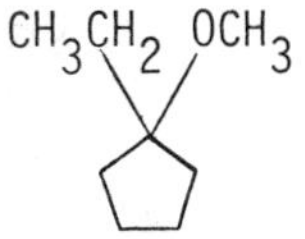

(d) 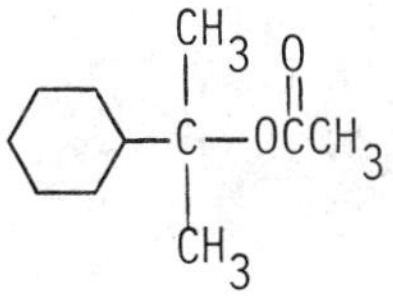

(e) $(CH_3)_3COD$

(f) 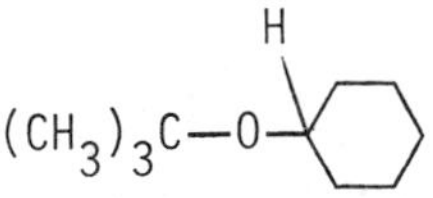

****

2. 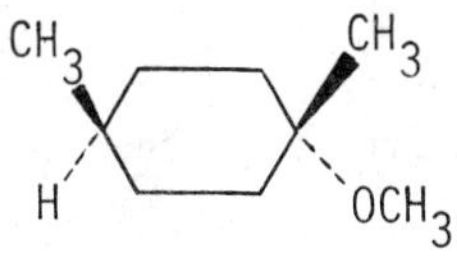 and 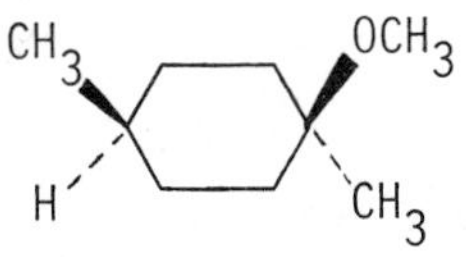

(a) two steps:

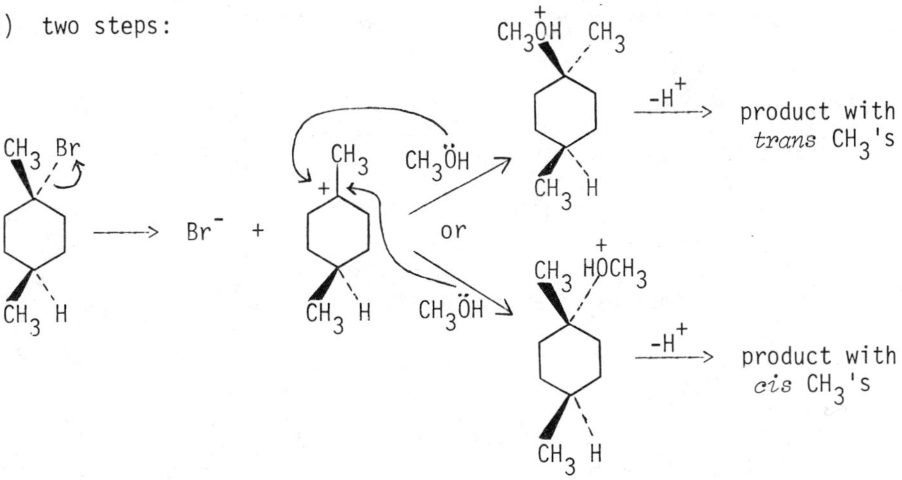

The nucleophile can attach to either face of the planar cationic carbon, resulting in the two products shown.

(b)  , by attachment of Br^- to opposite side of cationic carbon

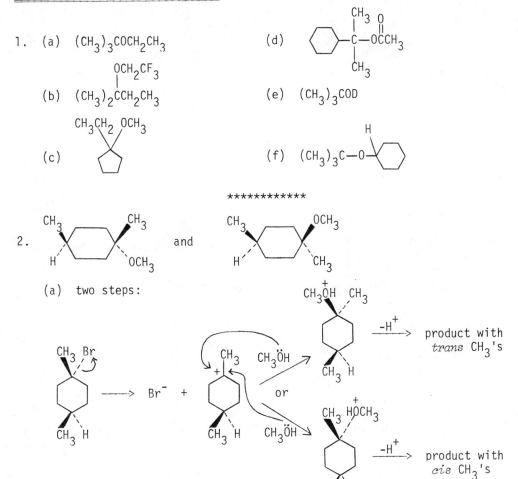

3. Two products: 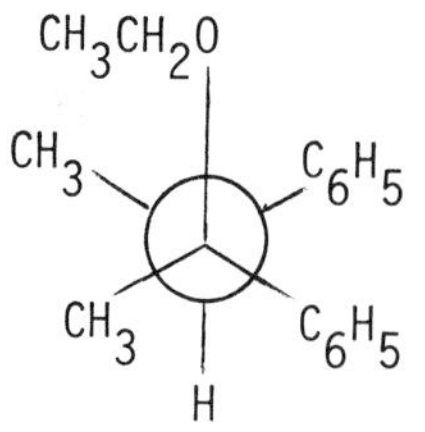

and 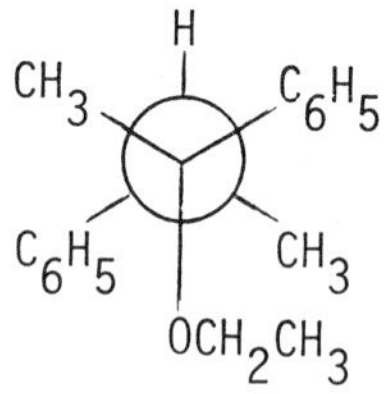

****

4. (a) H_2O will speed up all of the reactions except for 1(d) since it is more polar than any of the other solvolysis solvents. It will also compete for the carbocations, forming alcohols as products.

(b) Similar to (a), H_2S will increase the polarity of most of the solvent systems and speed up solvolysis. It will also react with the carbocations in preference to the less nucleophilic solvent molecules, making thiols as products (R-SH).

(c) Ionic salts strongly increase polarity and accelerate S_N1 reactions (see problem 6, however). The main products will be iodoalkanes.

(d) Same as (c); azide ion is a strong nucleophile and products will be azidoalkanes (alkyl azides, $R\text{-}N_3$).

(e) This should reduce polarity somewhat and slow down all the solvolyses.

(f) Same as (e), but to a greater extent as ethers are even less polar than ketones.

****

5. 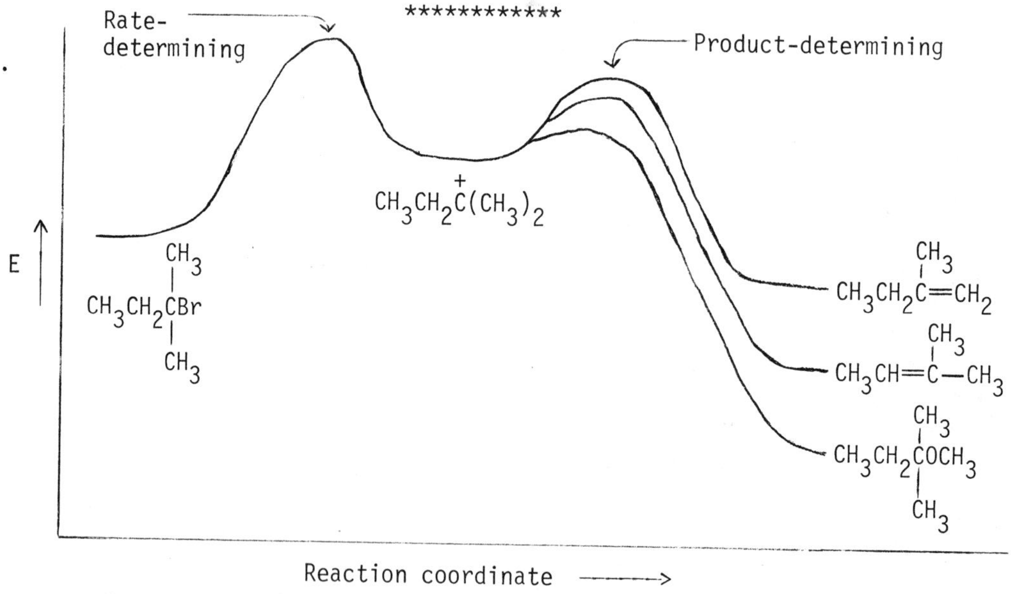

The first step (ionization) is the slow (rate-determining) one. The product is determined by what the carbocation chooses to do after it is formed. Thus the *second* step is product determining.

****

6. (a) Rate = k[RBr] so $2 \times 10^{-4} = k(0.1)$, and therefore $k = 2 \times 10^{-3} s^{-1}$.
Product is $-C(CH_3)_2-OH$ (ROH).

(b) New "k_{LiCl}" = $4 \times 10^{-3} s^{-1}$. Addition of LiCl increases the polarity of the solution by adding ions, and this speeds up the rate determining ionization step in the solvolysis process.

(c) In this case the added salt contains Br^-, *which is also the leaving group in the solvolysis reaction.* This leads to a decrease in rate because the first step in solvolysis is reversible, and recombination of R^+ and Br^- is occurring in competition with reaction of R^+ with H_2O:

$$RBr \underset{\text{recombination}}{\overset{\text{ionization}}{\rightleftharpoons}} Br^- + R^+ \xrightarrow{H_2O} ROH$$

****

7. 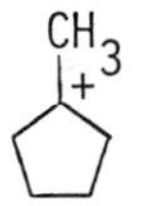 > $CH_3\overset{+}{C}HCH_2CH_3$ > 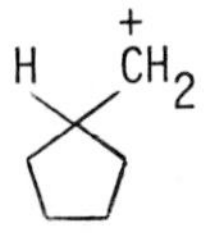

(tertiary) (secondary) (primary)

****

8. 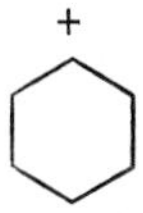 > 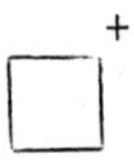 > 

Carbocations prefer sp^2 hybridization and 120° bond angles. As the ring gets smaller, the deviation from 120° increases, destabilizing the carbocation.

****

9. (a) $(CH_3)_2CClCH_2CH_3$ > $(CH_3)_2CHCHClCH_3$ > $(CH_3)_2CHCH_2CH_2Cl$ (3° > 2° > 1°)

(b) RCl > $RO\overset{O}{\overset{\|}{C}}CH_3$ > ROH (order of leaving group ability)

(c) [structure: cyclohexane with Cl and CH₃] > [benzene-Br] -Br > [benzene-Cl] -Cl   (both of the previous)

****

10. (a) A secondary system with an excellent leaving group and a poor
    nucleophile ⟹ S_N1 reaction.

$(CH_3)_2CH-OSO_2CF_3 \longrightarrow {}^-OSO_2CF_3 + (CH_3)_2\overset{+}{CH} \xleftarrow{CH_3CH_2-\overset{..}{O}H} \longrightarrow$

$(CH_3)_2\overset{+}{CH}\overset{H}{\underset{+}{O}}CH_2CH_3 \longrightarrow H^+ + (CH_3)_2CHOCH_2CH_3$

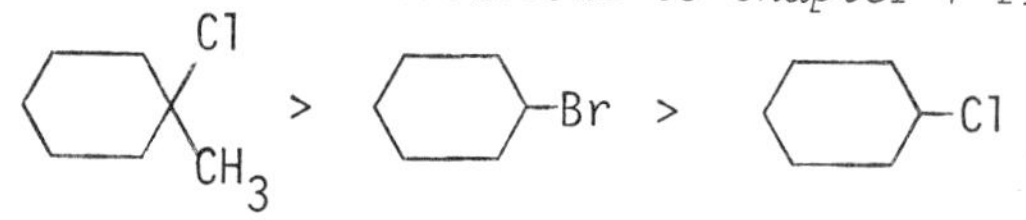

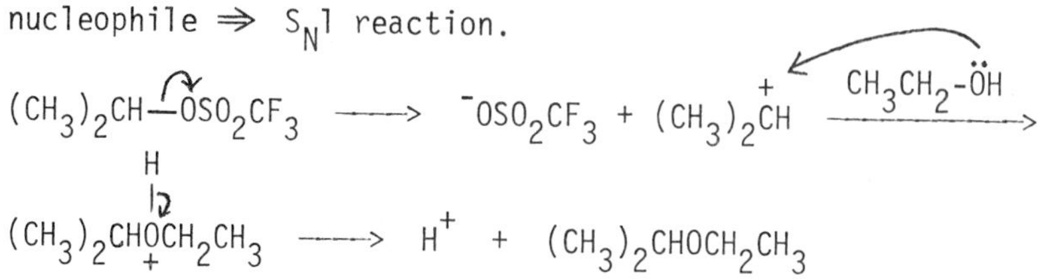

(b) A tertiary alcohol in strong aqueous acid ⟹ S_N1 reaction.

[cyclopentane-C(CH₃)(OH)] + $H-\overset{+}{\underset{|}{O}}-H$ over H ⟶ H_2O + [cyclopentane-C(CH₃)(OH₂⁺)] ⟶ H_2O +

[cyclopentane cation with +CH₃] $\xrightarrow{Cl^-}$ [cyclopentane-C(CH₃)(Cl)]

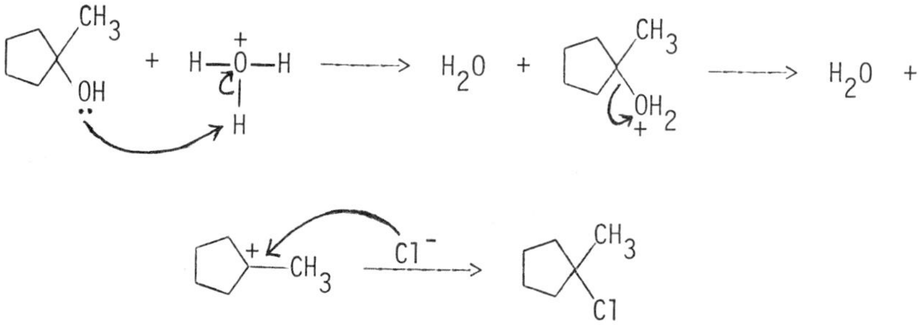

(c) A primary halide with a good nucleophile in an aprotic solvent
    ⟹ S_N2 reaction.

$CH_3CH_2CH_2CH_2-Br + (C_6H_5)_3\overset{..}{P} \longrightarrow CH_3CH_2CH_2CH_2\overset{+}{P}(C_6H_5)_3 \quad Br^-$

(d) Similar to (c), except a secondary halide ⟹ still an S_N2 reaction.

$CH_3CH_2\overset{\overset{Cl}{|}}{C}HCH_2CH_3 + I^- \longrightarrow CH_3CH_2CHICH_2CH_3$

****

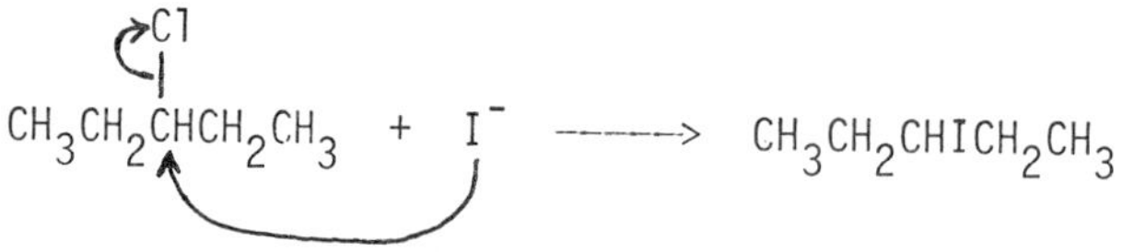

11. <u>Two</u> <u>successive</u> S_N2 inversion steps are necessary to give the desired net
    result of stereochemical retention:

    (R)-2-bromobutane $\xrightarrow{\text{KI, DMSO}}$ (S)-2-iodobutane $\xrightarrow{\text{NaN}_3, \text{ DMSO}}$

    (R)-2-azidobutane

****

12. (a) A tertiary halide $\Rightarrow$ S_N1 reaction, which will be two simple steps as in reaction profile (3).

$E = (CH_3)_3\overset{\delta+}{C}\cdots\overset{\delta-}{Cl}$

$F = (CH_3)_3C+$

$G = (CH_3)_3\overset{\delta+}{C}\cdots\overset{\delta+}{P}(C_6H_5)_3$

$H = (CH_3)_3C\overset{+}{P}(C_6H_5)_3$

(b) A secondary halide being displaced by another halide $\Rightarrow$ S_N2 reaction. The product and starting material are comparable in stability: reaction profile (2).

$C = \overset{\delta-}{Br}\cdots\overset{H}{\underset{CH_3\ CH_3}{C}}\cdots\overset{\delta-}{I}$

$D = (CH_3)_2CHBr$

(c) A tertiary alcohol with strong aqueous acid $\Rightarrow$ S_N1, with several steps along the way: reaction profile (4).

$I = (CH_3)_3C\text{-}\overset{H}{\underset{\delta+}{O}}\cdots\underset{\delta+}{H}$

$J = (CH_3)_3C\overset{+}{O}H_2$

$K = (CH_3)_3\underset{\delta+}{C}\cdots\underset{\delta+}{OH_2}$

$L = (CH_3)_3C+$

$M = (CH_3)_3\underset{\delta+}{C}\cdots\underset{\delta-}{Br}$

$N = (CH_3)_3CBr$

(d) A primary halide and a good nucleophile $\Rightarrow$ S_N2 reaction, but the product is much more stable than the starting material (C-O bonds are stronger than C-Br bonds): reaction profile (1).

$A = CH_3CH_2\overset{\delta-}{O}\cdots\overset{H\ \ H}{\underset{CH_3}{C}}\cdots\overset{\delta-}{Br}$

$B = CH_3CH_2OCH_2CH_3$

****

13. (1) Racemic $CH_3CH_2CH(O\overset{O}{\overset{\|}{C}}H)CH_3$ will be formed via an S_N1 process (a solvolysis).

(2) $(R)\text{-}CH_3CH_2CH(O\overset{O}{\overset{\|}{C}}H)CH_3$ will be formed via an S_N2 process (good nucleophile, aprotic solvent). Note the very different conditions.

****

14. (1a) $(CH_3)_2C=CH_2$

(1b) $CH_2=C(CH_3)CH_2CH_3$, $CH_3CH=C(CH_3)_2$

(1c) $CH_3CH=\!\bigcirc$, $CH_3CH_2-\!\bigcirc$

(1d) $(CH_3)_2C=\!\bigcirc$, $CH_2=C(CH_3)-\!\bigcirc$

(1e), (1f) same as (1a)

(2) $CH_2=\!\bigcirc\!-CH_3$, $CH_3-\!\bigcirc\!-CH_3$

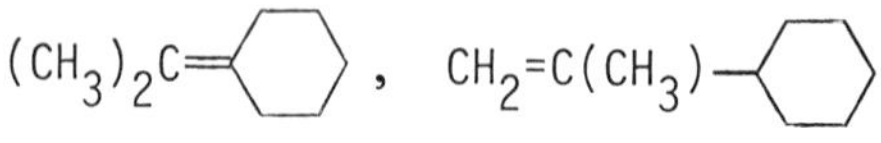

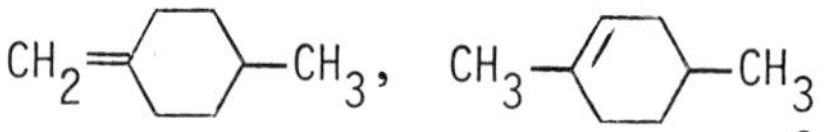

(3) $C_6H_5(CH_3)C=C(CH_3)C_6H_5$, $CH_3\overset{\overset{C_6H_5}{|}}{\underset{\underset{H}{|}}{C}}\!\!-\!\!\overset{\overset{C_6H_5}{|}}{C}=CH_2$

****

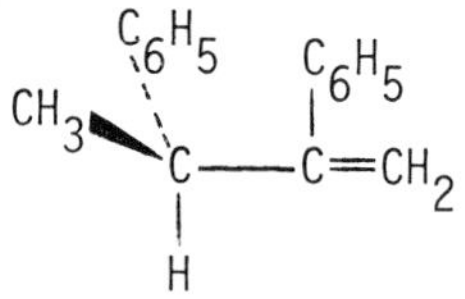

15. Neutral polar conditions are ideal for an *intra*molecular S_N1 reaction:

$(CH_3)_2\overset{\overset{Cl}{|}}{C}CH_2CH_2CH_2OH \longrightarrow (CH_3)_2\overset{+}{C}CH_2CH_2CH_2\overset{..}{O}H \longrightarrow$

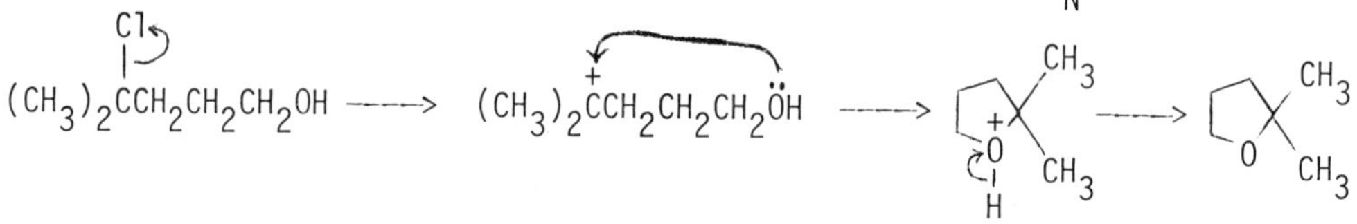

Basic conditions promote elimination leading to alkenes. Two isomeric alkenes are actually possible: $CH_2=C(CH_3)CH_2CH_2CH_2OH$ and $(CH_3)_2C=CHCH_2CH_2OH$.

****

16.

	H_2O	$NaSCH_3$	$NaOCH_3$	$KOC(CH_3)_3$
CH_3Cl	no reaction	CH_3SCH_3	CH_3OCH_3	$CH_3OC(CH_3)_3 \vert S_N2$
CH_3CH_2Cl	no reaction	$CH_3CH_2SCH_3$ $\left.\vphantom{\begin{array}{c}a\\b\end{array}}\right\}S_N2$	$CH_3CH_2OCH_3$ $\left.\vphantom{\begin{array}{c}a\\b\end{array}}\right\}S_N2$	$CH_2=CH_2$
$(CH_3)_2CHCl$	$(CH_3)_2CHOH$ $\left.\vphantom{\begin{array}{c}a\\b\end{array}}\right\}S_N1$	$(CH_3)_2CHSCH_3$	$CH_3CH=CH_2$ $\left.\vphantom{\begin{array}{c}a\\b\end{array}}\right\}E2$	$CH_3CH=CH_2$ $\left.\vphantom{\begin{array}{c}a\\b\end{array}}\right\}E2$
$(CH_3)_3CCl$	$(CH_3)_3COH$	$(CH_3)_3CSCH_3 \vert S_N1$	$(CH_3)_2C=CH_2$	$(CH_3)_2C=CH_2$
	and	and	(also E1 for last two entries)	
	$(CH_3)_2C=CH_2 \vert E1$	$(CH_3)_2C=CH_2 \vert E1$		

****

17. See 16 on previous page. Secondary halides give higher E2/E1 ratios than do tertiary halides.

****

18. (a) E1 rate = $(1.4 \times 10^{-4} \text{sec}^{-1})(2 \times 10^{-2}\text{M}) = 2.8 \times 10^{-6} \text{moles } \ell^{-1}\text{sec}^{-1}$

E2 rate = $(1.9 \times 10^{-4} \ell \text{ mole}^{-1}\text{sec}^{-1})(2 \times 10^{-2}\text{M})(5 \times 10^{-1}\text{M}) = 1.9 \times 10^{-6} \text{ moles } \ell^{-1}\text{sec}^{-1}$

E1 rate is faster, so E1 reaction predominates.

(b) E1 rate = 2.8×10^{-6} moles $\ell^{-1}\text{sec}^{-1}$ (no change)

E2 rate = $(1.9 \times 10^{-4} \ell \text{ mol}^{-1}\text{sec}^{-1})(2 \times 10^{-2}\text{M})(2\text{M}) = 7.6 \times 10^{-6} \text{ moles } \ell^{-1}\text{sec}^{-1}$

E2 rate is now faster, so E2 reaction predominates.

(c) Solve for $[NaOCH_3]$ when E1 rate = E2 rate:

$$2.8 \times 10^{-6} \text{ moles } \ell^{-1}\text{sec}^{-1} = (1.9 \times 10^{-4} \ \ell \text{ mol}^{-1}\text{sec}^{-1})(2 \times 10^{-2}\text{M})[NaOCH_3]$$

$[NaOCH_3] = 0.74\text{M}$

****

19. (a) E1:
(CH3)3C-OH + H-OSO3H ⟶ -OSO3H + (CH3)3C-OH2+ ⟶
(CH3)2C+-CH2-H ⟶ H+ + (CH3)2C=CH2

(b) E2:
CH3CH2CH(H)-CH2-Cl + [(CH3)2CH]2N- Li+ ⟶ [(CH3)2CH]2NH + CH3CH2CH=CH2
(LDA, "lithium diisopropylamide")

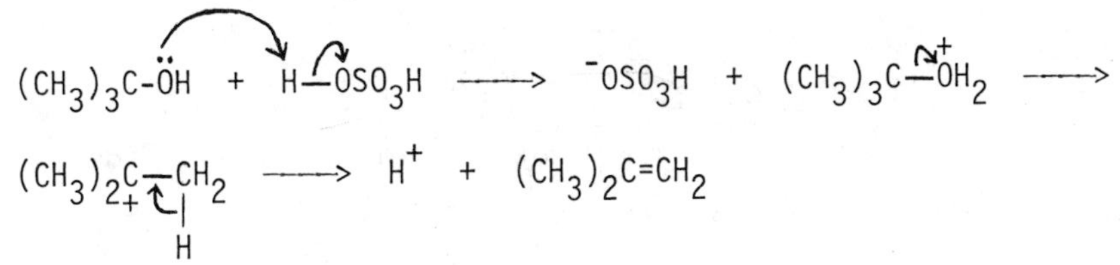

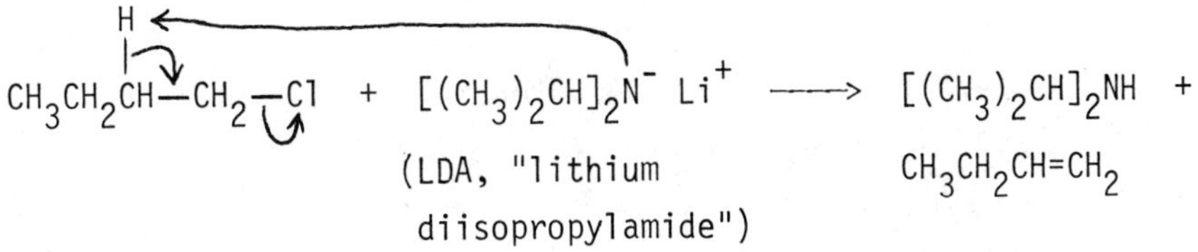

(c) E2:
Br
H
CH
+ HO- ⟶ H2O +
CH=

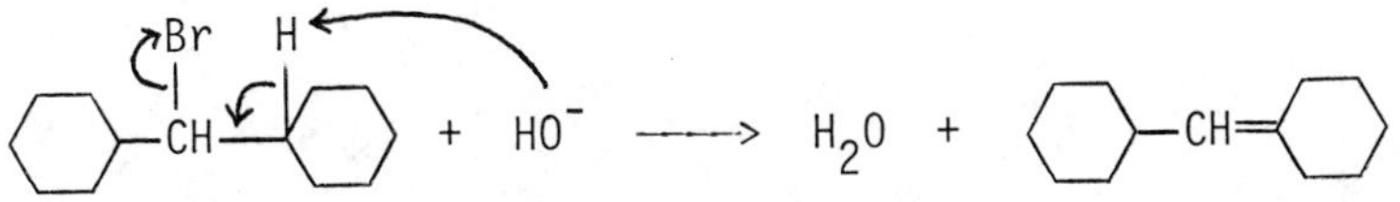

(d) Either E1 or E2 can occur, and two products can form from either:

CH3
and
=CH2.

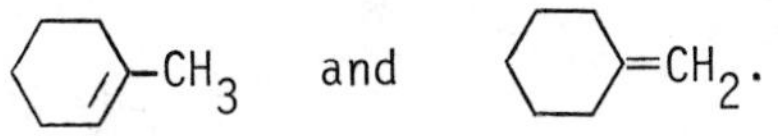

Example of E1 mechanism:

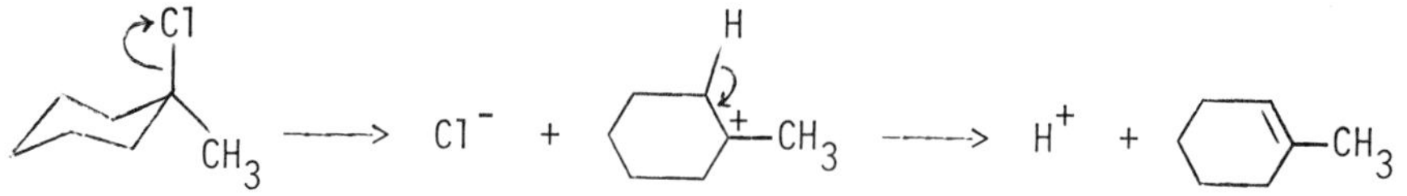

Example of E2 mechanism:

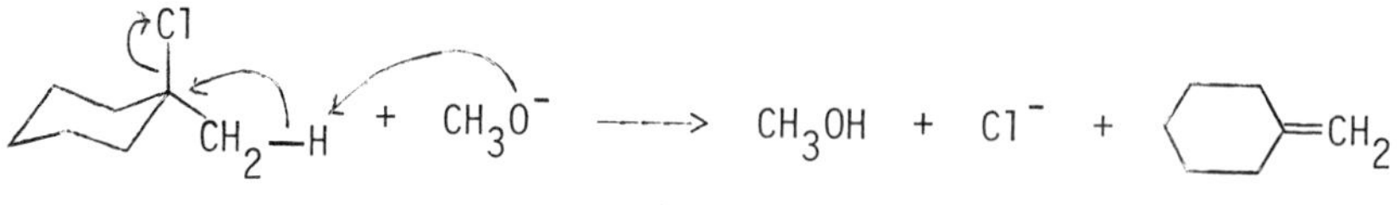

****

20. Mainly S_N2: (a), (d), (f), (h), (i), (j) (these nucleophiles are all weak bases, so elimination is not favored)

Mixture of S_N2 and E2: (c), (g)

Mainly E2: (b), (e) (strong bases favor elimination, although certain hydride-containing reagents are capable of S_N2 displacement on secondary halides)

****

21. (a) (1) $(CH_3)_3CSH$

(2) $(CH_3)_2C{=}CH_2$ ($CH_3\overset{O}{\overset{\|}{C}}O^-\ K^+$ is basic enough to give preferential elimination from tertiary halides)

(3) $(CH_3)_2C{=}CH_2$

(b) Rates of (1) and (2) will be the same. (1) is S_N1 and (2) is E1, and they have the same rate determining ionization step. Rate of (3) will be higher because the stronger base causes E2 reaction to occur in addition to E1.

(c)

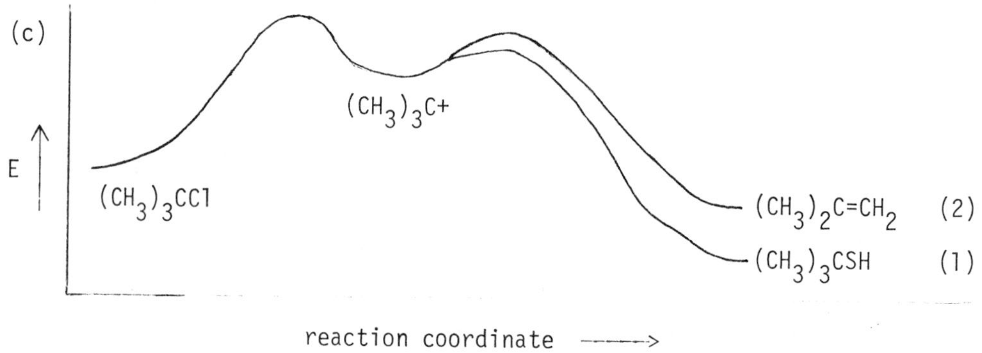

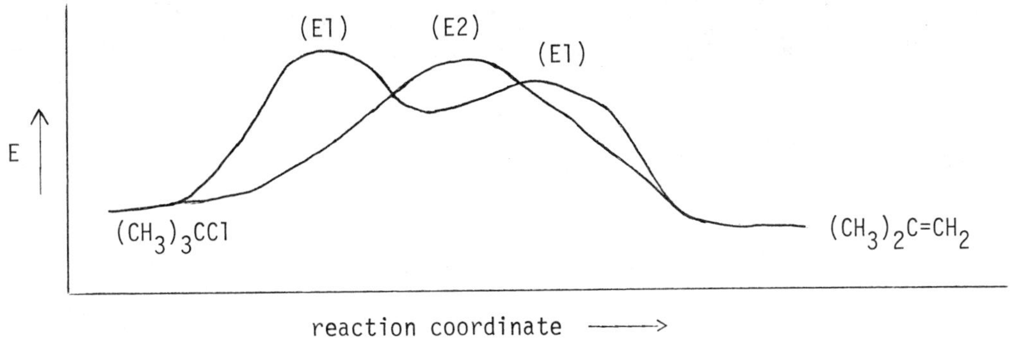

****

22. (a) 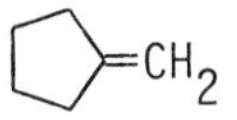 (E2)

(b) No reaction (poor leaving group)

(c) Racemic $CH_3CH_2CHOHCH_3$ (S_N1)

(d)  (E2)

(e) $(CH_3)_2CHCH_2CH_2CH_2OCH_2CH_3$ (S_N2)

(f) Racemic $CH_3CH_2C(I)(CH_3)CH_2CH_2CH_3$ (S_N1)

(g) No reaction (except for reversible proton transfer)

(h) 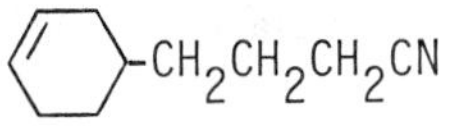 and 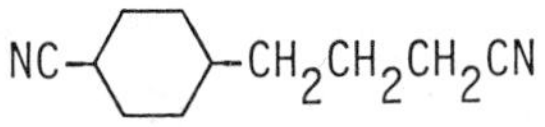 (E2 and S_N2)

(i) (S)-$CH_3CH_2CHSHCH_3$ (S_N2)

(j) $(CH_3CH_2)_3CCl$ (S_N1)

(k) $CH_2{=}C(CH_3)_2$ (E2)

(l) 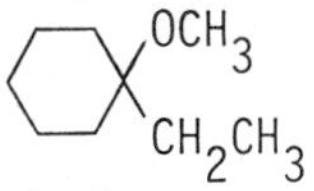 (S_N1)

(m) $(CH)_3CCH{=}CH_2$ (E2)

(n) No reaction (poor nucleophile)

****

23. (a) Poorly: $CH_3CH{=}CHCH_3$ and $CH_3CH_2CH{=}CH_3$ are important products.

(b) Not at all: no reaction (poor nucleophile).

(c) Not at all: no appreciable reaction.

(d) Well: an "intramolecular" (internal) S_N1 reaction.

(e) Well, eventually, but very, very slowly. (f) Well.

(g) Well, although some elimination also occurs and the reaction is very slow (see text, p. 239).

(h) Not at all: no reaction due to very poor nucelophile.

(i) Not at all: no reaction

(j) Poorly: good nucleophile gives mainly $CH_3CH_2CH_2CH_2OCH_2CH_3$.

(k) Poorly, but better than (j); $(CH_3)_2CHCH_2CH_2OCH_2CH_3$ forms.

(l) Not at all: no reaction, due to very poor leaving group.

****

24. (a) $CH_3CH_2CH_2CH_3$ $\xrightarrow{Br_2, \; \Delta}$ $CH_3CH_2CHBrCH_3$ $\xrightarrow{KI, \; DMSO}$ $CH_3CH_2CHICH_3$

(b) $CH_3CH_2CH_2CH_3$ $\xrightarrow{Cl_2, \; 100°C}$ some $CH_3CH_2CH_2CH_2Cl$ $\xrightarrow{NaI, \; propanone}$

$CH_3CH_2CH_2CH_2I$

(c) CH_4 $\xrightarrow{Cl_2, \; h\nu}$ CH_3Cl $\xrightarrow{KOH, \; H_2O}$ CH_3OH;

then $(CH_3)_3CH$ $\xrightarrow{Br_2, \; \Delta}$ $(CH_3)_3CBr$ $\xrightarrow{CH_3OH}$ $(CH_3)_3COCH_3$

(d) $\xrightarrow{Br_2, \; h\nu}$ Br $\xrightarrow{KOCH_2CH_3, \; CH_3CH_2OH}$

(e) From (d), Br $\xrightarrow{H_2O \; (S_N1)}$ OH (a better method will be presented in Chapter 8-4)

(f) Conc. H_2SO_4, heat (one step, an intramolecular S_N2-type reaction)

(g) Na_2S in alcohol (one step!)

****

25. In both <u>A</u> and <u>B</u> the necessary *anti* alignment between H and Cl (both of which are in axial positions) is present across the required carbon-carbon bond, so E2 elimination will give the desired alkene. In <u>C</u> the Cl is equatorial and no *anti*-elimination can occur at all (make a model). Instead, very slow eliminations will proceed via *syn* geometries to give a mixture containing the desired alkene together with the isomer shown below.

****

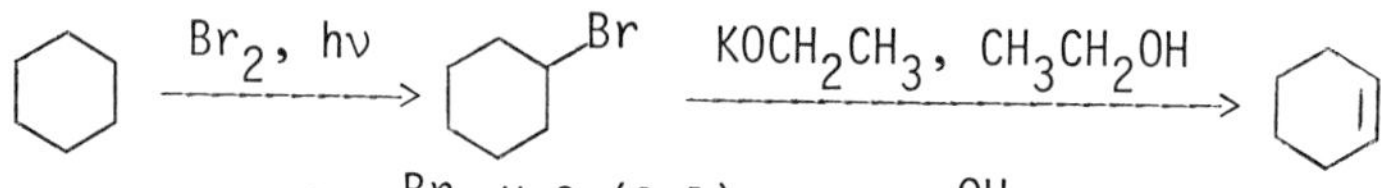

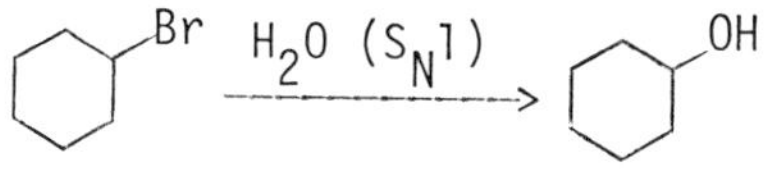

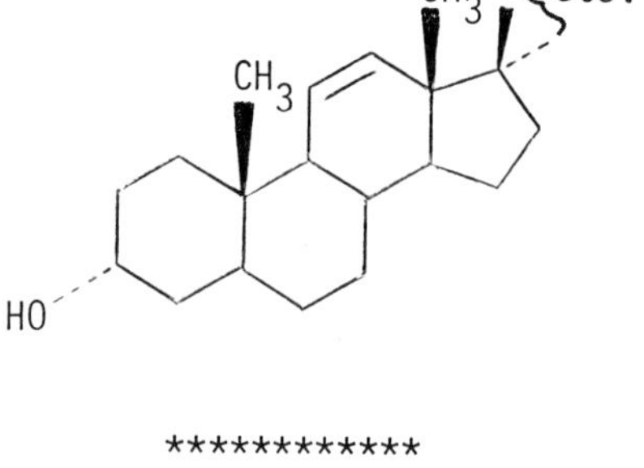

26. Look at the conformations first (the deuterium atoms for part b are also written in):

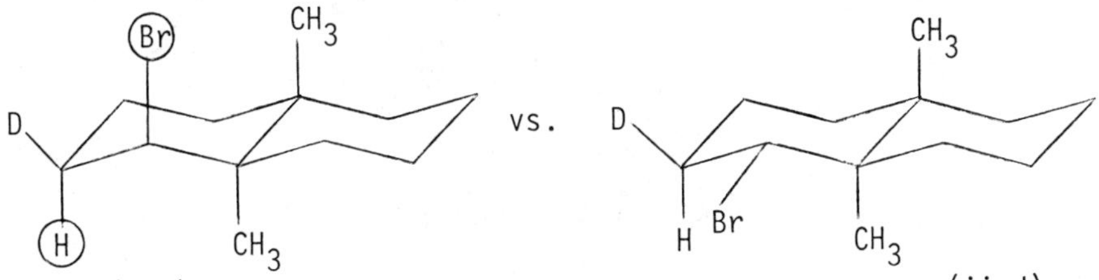

(i-d) (ii-d)

(a) and (b) Compound i reacts much faster since it already possesses the necessary *anti* alignment of Br and H (on the neighboring carbon, circled). In the deuterated example shown, the E2 reaction results in loss of HBr only; all the D is retained since the D atom is not capable of adopting an *anti* alignment relative to bromine. The conformation shown is the reactive one.

Compound ii possesses no hydrogen *anti* to Br in the conformation shown. However, if the left-hand ring adopts a boat-like conformation resembling that shown below, E2-elimination via an *anti* transition state can readily occur:

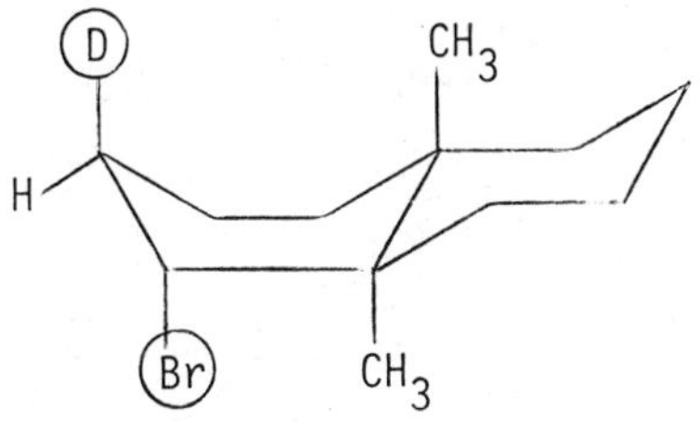

As indicated, all the D should be lost, according to this mechanism, and that is the result observed.

(c) The reaction of ii-d should exhibit an isotope effect since a C-D bond is broken in the rate determining step. Thus E2 reaction of ii-d should be slower than E2 reaction of ii. The E2 reactions of i and i-d should be virtually the same in rate, since the C-D bond in i-d is not directly involved in the reaction.

****

27. Two methods for converting -OH into a leaving group have been presented: protonation by strong acid, and conversion to a sulfonate. We can take advantage of either method to achieve elimination to an alkene.

(a) For E1, a reasonable approach would be protonation by a strong acid which *lacks* a nucleophilic counterion; H_2SO_4, for example:

$$RCH_2\overset{\underset{|}{OH}}{C}HCH_2\overset{\underset{\|}{O}}{C}OH \quad \xrightarrow{H_2SO_4} \quad RCH_2\overset{\underset{|}{\overset{+}{O}H_2}}{C}HCH_2\overset{\underset{\|}{O}}{C}OH \quad \xrightarrow{E1}$$

$$RCH_2\overset{+}{C}H\overset{\underset{|}{H}}{\underset{}{\curvearrowleft}}CH\overset{\underset{\|}{O}}{C}OH \quad \longrightarrow \quad RCH_2CH=CHCOH$$

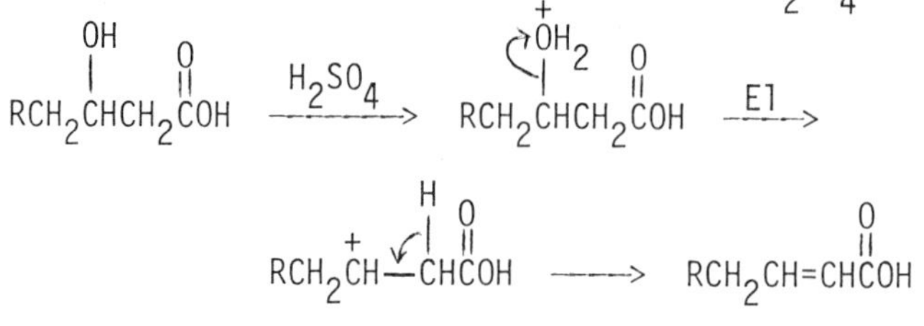

(b) For E2, a reasonable choice would be tosylate formation, followed by treatment with a strong, bulky base:

$$RCH_2\overset{\underset{|}{OH}}{C}HCH_2\overset{\underset{\|}{O}}{C}OH \quad \xrightarrow{CH_3-\langle\rangle-SO_2Cl} \quad RCH_2\overset{\underset{|}{OSO_2-\langle\rangle-CH_3}}{C}HCH_2\overset{\underset{\|}{O}}{C}OH \quad \xrightarrow[\text{LDA (E2)}]{\text{excess}} \quad RCH_2CH=CHCOH$$

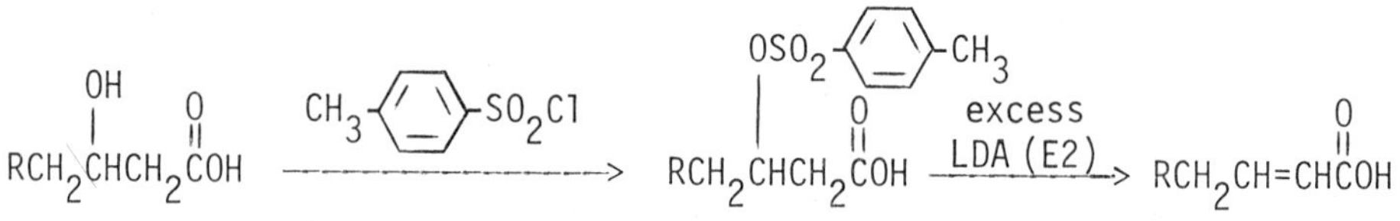

(Only one of the two possible alkene isomers has been shown in the answers above; the other is $RCH=CHCH_2\overset{\underset{\|}{O}}{C}OH$.)

****

CHAPTER 8

The Formation of the Hydroxy Functional Group: Properties of the Alcohols and Synthetic Strategy in Their Preparation

General Introduction

With this chapter we begin the first in depth examination of alcohols, molecules containing the hydroxy functional group. Together with carbonyl compounds, alcohols represent one of the two most important classes of compounds in organic chemistry. Alcohols can be prepared from many different types of compounds, and, in turn, they can be converted into many different types of compounds. They therefore play a central role in organic chemistry, and, moreover, their preparation, properties, and reactions all serve as classic representative illustrations of the underlying logic behind all of organic chemistry.

The approach to chapters 8 and 9 will be similar to that used in chapters 6 and 7. However, and this is very important, alcohols have much more potential for chemical conversion to and from other molecules, compared with haloalkanes. This means that a full examination of alcohol chemistry will involve much more new descriptive material. You must be prepared even more than before to focus on the functional groups and their polar bonds as sites of possible reactivity. A comparison of, first, the bonds and, second, the possible bonding changes available in alcohols *vs* haloalkanes is useful. Haloalkane chemistry mostly involves three bonds:

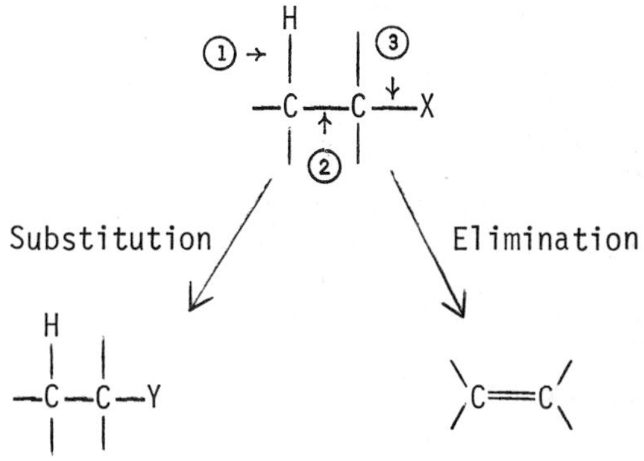

Substitution breaks bond #3. Elimination breaks bonds 1 and 3, and "doubles" bond 2.

By comparison, five bonds may be chemically active in alcohols:

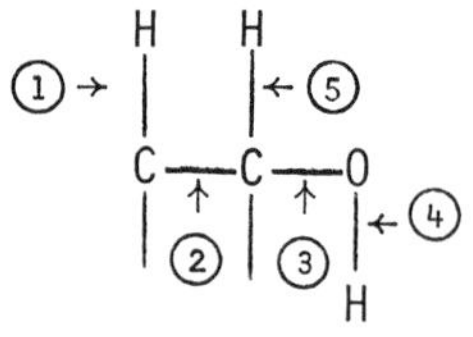

We will see in the next chapter how this situation leads to a much wider variety of reactions from this functional group, and a much greater fundamental importance for alcohols in general.

For the present, we will focus first on properties of alcohols, then their preparation, and finally examine the general problem of synthesis: how to plan a logical and practical sequence of chemical steps that will allow the conversion of an available starting material into a needed final organic product molecule.

Outline of the Chapter

8-1. Nomenclature.

A description of both systematic and "common" naming systems for these very common molecules.

8-2. Physical Properties.

A new factor is introduced: hydrogen bonding.

8-3. Acidity and Basicity of Alcohols.

Similarities and differences with water, the simplest inorganic relative.

8-4. The Synthesis of Alcohols.

Methods of preparation of alcohols by either displacement or reduction reactions.

8-5. Organometallic Reagents.

A detour, introducing compounds containing *negatively polarized, nucleophilic* carbon atoms.

8-6. Organometallic Reagents in the Synthesis of Alcohols.

The most important general alcohol syntheses: addition of nucleophilic carbon compounds to carbonyl groups.

An Introduction to Synthetic Strategy.

How to look at a "target" molecule and logically "plan" its synthesis using sequences of several individual reactions.

Keys to the Chapter

8-1 and 8-2. Nomenclature and Physical Properties.

Two points need to be made concerning nomenclature. First, alcohols have been around for a long time, and the "common" names given in this section are still in widespread use, and need to be learned and understood. Second, there is an order of preference among functional groups that is to be used when two or more functional groups of different kinds are in a molecule. This preference order is used for determining a direction for numbering, if there is more than one obvious choice. The alcohol group is of fairly high ranking on this list, while halogens are at the bottom. So:

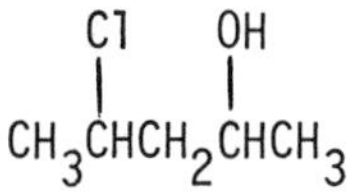

$$\begin{array}{cc} Cl & OH \\ | & | \\ CH_3CHCH_2CHCH_3 \end{array}$$ is 4-chloro-2-pentanol (not 2-chloro-4-pentanol)

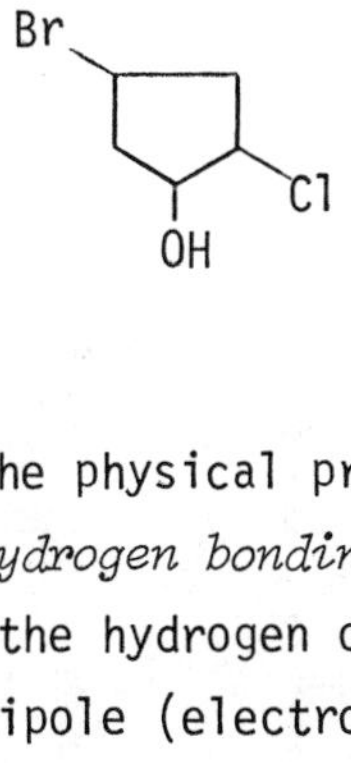

is 4-bromo-2-chlorocyclopentanol
(note that the position of the OH is understood
to be carbon 1 in the ring compound, and need
not be stated explicitly)

The physical properties of alcohols are highlighted by the consequences of the *hydrogen bonding ability* of the -OH group. Just as is the case in water itself, the hydrogen of the -OH group in an alcohol may be attracted by the dipole-dipole (electrostatic) force towards a lone pair on an electronegative atom in a second molecule. Hydrogen bonding is the strongest kind of dipole-dipole attraction known. It can be as strong as several kcal/mole, while most ordinary dipole-dipole attractions are much weaker. The strength of this attraction is what merits it its own special name of "hydrogen bonding":

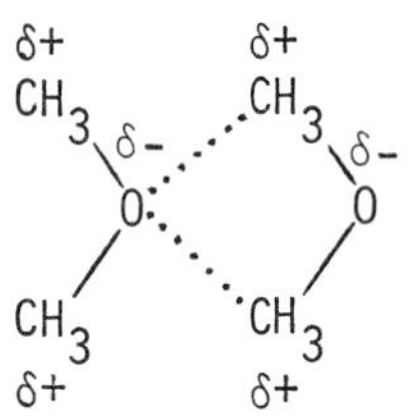

weak dipole-dipole attractions in dimethyl ether

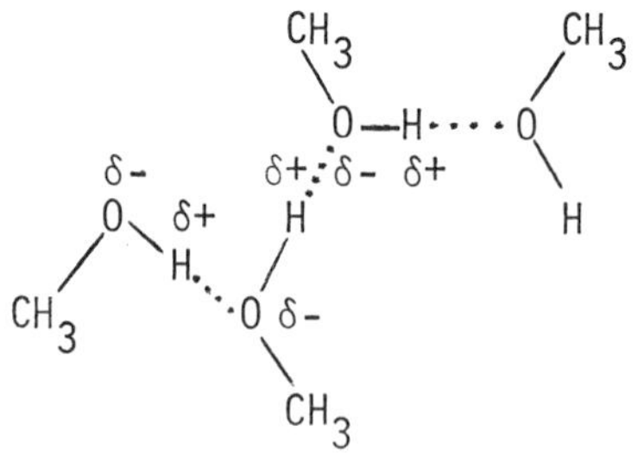

strong "hydrogen bonding" type dipole-dipole attractions in methanol

Remember, for hydrogen bonding to occur, the molecules involved must have very δ^+ hydrogens, such as those attached to very electronegative atoms (e.g. N, O, F), as well as electronegative atoms with lone pairs to attract these δ^+ hydrogens (again, mainly N, O, and F).

8-3. Acidity and Basicity of Alcohols.

If you understand the acidic and basic nature of water, then you will need to learn only a little bit that is new here with alcohols. The equilibrium processes are qualitatively identical:

$$H_3O^+ \rightleftharpoons H_2O \rightleftharpoons HO^-$$

$$\xleftarrow[\text{(adds } H^+)]{\text{as a base}} \qquad \xrightarrow[\text{(loses } H^+)]{\text{as an acid}}$$

$$ROH_2^+ \rightleftharpoons ROH \rightleftharpoons RO^-$$

The differences will involve the effect of having an R group present (instead of an H), which can affect the relative stabilities of the three species involved. Simple alkyl groups, for a variety of reasons, generally destabilize both ROH_2^+ and RO^- relative to ROH, as compared with water. So most ordinary alcohols are both weaker acids and weaker bases than water. Electron withdrawing substituents in R (such as halogens) will *stabilize* RO^-, however, making ROH a stronger acid (see entries in Table 8-2).

The acidic and basic properties of alcohols will play major roles in some of their reactions. When an alcohol acts like a base and is protonated by a strong acid, becoming ROH_2^+, it then contains a good leaving group and is thus capable of both substitution and elimination reactions (chapter 6, section 7 and chapter 9, section 3). When an alcohol acts like an acid, and loses a proton to a strong base, it becomes RO^-, a good nucleophile capable of doing

S_N2 reactions with appropriate molecules (chapter 6, section 3 and chapter 9, section 2), among other things. So this reaction really serves as a general entry to the more extensive survey of reactions of alcohols coming up in the next chapter.

8-4. The Synthesis of Alcohols.

Part of the importance of alcohols lies in the fact that they can be synthesized from many other kinds of organic molecules. Two types of general methods are presented here: nucleophilic displacement methods and reduction methods. Primary alcohols may be prepared by S_N2 displacement reactions of HO^- with appropriate substrates (e.g. 1° haloalkanes). To a limited extent, 2° and 3° alcohols are also available via displacement reactions (S_N2 and S_N1, respectively). These displacement methods are rarely used in alcohol synthesis, though, because the methods described in the rest of the chapter utilize much more readily available starting materials, and employ much more generally reliable reactions.

Four types of useful reduction processes are presented in this section. Carbonyl compounds, including ketones, aldehydes, carboxylic acids, and carboxylic acid derivatives, are the most practical *precursors* (starting materials) for the synthesis of alcohols. Either catalytic H_2 addition, or reaction with certain metal hydrides ($NaBH_4$ of $LiAlH_4$) converts aldehydes to 1° alcohols. The same reactions convert ketones to 2° alcohols. Carboxylic acids and their esters are converted by $LiAlH_4$ (but not $NaBH_4$) to 1° alcohols, too. The hydride reactions are members of a class of reactions involving nucleophilic addition to the electrophilic carbon of a carbonyl group. This is one of the most important classes of reactions in organic chemistry. A related reaction is the reduction of *oxacyclopropanes* (three-membered ring ethers) with $LiAlH_4$ to make 1° alcohols, the last reaction of this section. This is an S_N2 process which displaces an alkoxide, which is a very bad leaving group. Normally alkoxides cannot be displaced in S_N2 reactions. In oxacyclopropanes, however, ring strain raises the energy content such that suitably reactive nucleophiles can displace negatively charged oxygen leaving groups in an exothermic process. This is what is going on here (see graph, below).

$$E \uparrow$$

Reaction coordinate

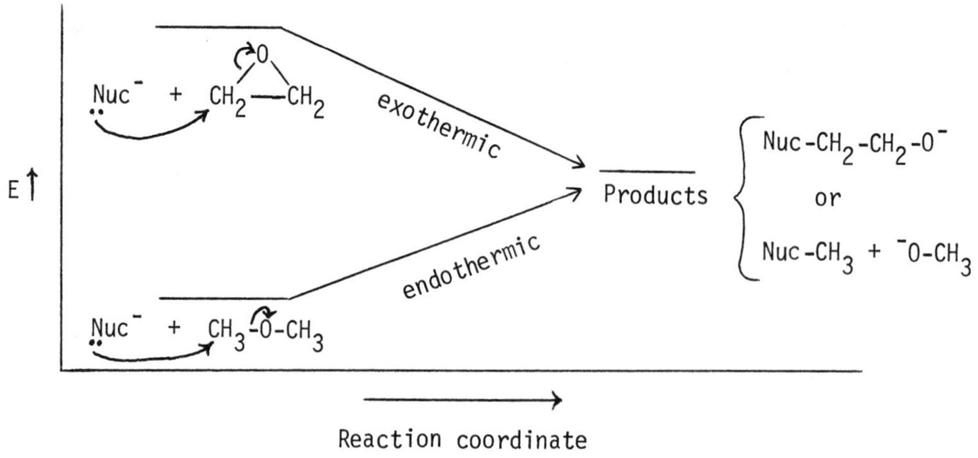

Further syntheses of alcohols are deferred until after an introduction to organometallic compounds (sections 5 and 6).

8-5. Organometallic Compounds.

So far the only kind of polarized carbon we've looked at in any detail is the δ^+ (electrophilic) carbon that results from its attachment to a very electronegative atom. Referring way back to table 2-1, we've seen quite a few of these:

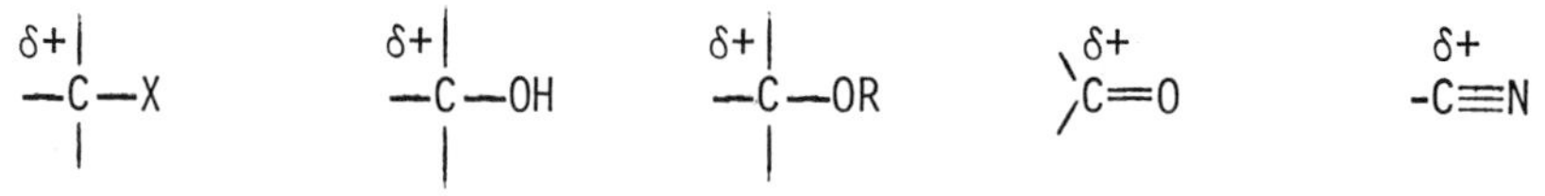

δ^+ $\overset{\mid}{-}\overset{\mid}{\underset{\mid}{C}}-X$	δ^+ $\overset{\mid}{-}\overset{\mid}{\underset{\mid}{C}}-OH$	δ^+ $\overset{\mid}{-}\overset{\mid}{\underset{\mid}{C}}-OR$	$\overset{\delta^+}{\underset{/}{\diagdown}}C{=}0$	$\overset{\delta^+}{-C{\equiv}N}$
haloalkane	alcohol	ether	carbonyl	nitrile

If one were to seek a *logical* way to attach two carbon atoms of different molecules together in a synthetic process, thereby making a new carbon-carbon bond, one would try to take advantage of electrostatics, and find molecules with δ^- carbons, which could combine with the δ^+ carbons above. That's very nice, but how does anyone go about looking for δ^- carbon atoms? *Logically*, if δ^+ carbons result from attachment to electronegative atoms, *then δ^- carbons should result from attachment to electropositive atoms.* Metals are the most electropositive elements, and, so, the way to get δ^- (nucleophilic) carbon would be to attach it to a metal. Compounds with carbon-metal bonds are called organometallic compounds, and are important sources of nucleophilic carbons. This section details preparation methods of several types of organometallic compounds. These are mostly oxidation-reduction processes that proceed via complicated mechanisms. They are easy to do, though, and the reagents you get are very useful in synthesis. They all contain δ^- carbon atoms bonded to metals, and some of their simple reactions as nucleophiles are given as well. Like all nucleophiles, these molecules can act as bases as well, and, in fact, the R groups in RLi, RMgX, and R_2CuLi act as very strong bases. They are protonated by even weak acids like water or ammonia, giving the hydrocarbon RH as the product. Essentially we have

"R^-"	+	"H^+"	⟶	RH
strong base (as in R-M)		from even weakly acidic molecules (e.g. H_2O, ROH, NH_3)		weak acid

One reaction in this section that is of use in organic synthesis is the S_N2 reaction of the R groups in cuprates (R_2CuLi) with 1° haloalkanes to make larger alkanes. For reasons we won't go into R_2CuLi is much better for this reaction than either RMgX or RLi.

8-6. Organometallic Reagents in the Synthesis of Alcohols.

We now come to the real, primary value of these reagents: their ability to react as nucleophiles towards the electrophilic carbon in carbonyl compounds ($>\overset{\delta+}{C}=O$). In a reaction mechanistically analogous to the hydride additions of section 8-4, organometallic reagents add nucleophilic carbon to carbonyl compounds, resulting in alcohols, and making a new carbon-carbon bond in the process. These reagents also add to oxacyclopropanes. The last page in this section contains a summary chart of the major types of reactions that convert carbonyl compounds to alcohols.

8-7. An Introduction to Synthetic Strategy.

In order to be able to come up with sensible ways to make large organic molecules from small ones (a typical sort of problem), you need to be able to approach the problem logically. First, note that the reactions that you are learning can be classified in two categories:

1. Reactions that exchange one functional group for another, but do not make or break any carbon-carbon bonds. These are called "functional group interconversions" and a simple example is

$$CH_3OH + HI \longrightarrow CH_3I + H_2O.$$

2. Reactions that make or break carbon-carbon bonds. In the chapter section just completed you saw several very typical examples of this kind of reaction.

One very useful thing we can do at this stage is begin a chart of general functional group interconversions that we've seen so far. This is how it would look at the moment:

Functional Group Interconversions

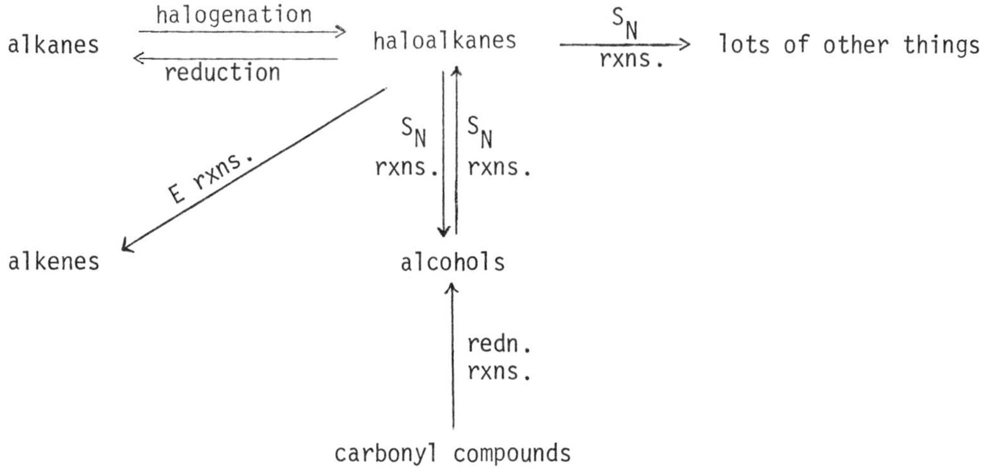

It is absolutely necessary to know these interconversion patterns, because they provide the framework for designing synthetic strategy. Suppose we wish to synthesize an alcohol starting with an alkane. From this chart we see immediately that we have no direct method for converting alkanes to alcohols. We must first make a haloalkane, and then use it in another reaction to make an alcohol. We set up the proposed synthesis in just that way, and insert the specific reagents necessary to carry out the two synthetic steps:

$$CH_4 \not\longrightarrow CH_3OH \quad \text{(no direct method)}$$

$$CH_4 \xrightarrow{Cl_2,\ h\nu} CH_3Cl \xrightarrow{HO^-} CH_3OH \quad \text{(a sensible synthesis)}$$

Note that it is not enough to use the general labels "free-radical halogenation" or "S_N2 reaction" in the synthesis equations; the actual reagents have to be given.

All right. What about carbon-carbon bond forming reactions? Syntheses requiring the formation of new bonds are best approached via the retrosynthetic analysis described in the text. One works *backwards* on paper, imagining disconnecting bonds in the desired product molecule, looking for methods that can put together the necessary bonds in an efficient way from reasonable starting molecules. Functional group interconversions are applied as necessary. Take some time to look over the examples in the text. Note the comments concerning the preferability of some routes over others, based on efficient incorporation of small molecules into large ones. Finally, apply the techniques to the problems that follow. The practice will not only help you develop and improve your ability to analyze synthesis problems, it will also help you become more and more familiar with all the reactions and reagents. You will have to know them in the end.

SUMMARY CHART

Synthesis of alcohols from carbonyl compounds

Reagent

Carbonyl compounds	H_2 + catalyst or $NaBH_4$	$LiAlH_4$	R"Li or R"MgX
methanal (HCHO)	methanol (CH_3OH)	methanol (CH_3OH)	1° alcohol (R"CH_2OH)
aldehyde (RCHO)	1° alcohol (RCH_2OH)	1° alcohol (RCH_2OH)	2° alcohol (RR"CHOH)
ketone (RR'CO)	2° alcohol (RR'CHOH)	2° alcohol (RR'CHOH)	3° alcohol (RR'R"COH)
methanoate ester (HCOOR)	usually no reaction	methanol (CH_3OH)	2° alcohol (R''_2CHOH)
carboxylic ester (RCOOR')	usually no reaction	1° alcohol (RCH_2OH)	3° alcohol (RR''_2COH)

Product

Note: $LiAlH_4$ also reduces carboxylic acids to 1° alcohols ($RCOOH \rightarrow RCH_2OH$) and oxacyclopropanes to alcohols as well. RLi and RMgX convert oxacyclopropanes to alcohols, too.

Solutions to Chapter 8 Problems

1. (a) 2-butanol, secondary (2°) (b) 5-bromo-3-hexanol, 2°

   (c) 2-propyl-1-pentanol, primary (1°)

   (d) (*S*)-1-chloro-2-propanol, 2°

   (e) 1-ethylcyclobutanol, tertiary (3°)

   (f) *trans*-(1*R*,2*R*)-2-bromocyclodecanol, 2°

   (g) 2,2-bis(hydroxymethyl)-1,3-propanediol, 1° ["bis" is used as the prefix instead of "di" when the name that follows is complicated enough to be in parentheses]

   (h) *meso*-1,2,3,4-butanetetraol, 1° on C-1 and 4, 2° on C-2 and 3

   (i) *cis*-(1*R*,2*R*)-2-(2-hydroxyethyl)cyclopentanol, 2° on ring, 1° on side chain

   (j) (*R*)-2-chloro-2-methyl-1-butanol, 1°

****

2. (a) $(CH_3)_3SiCH_2CH_2OH$

   (b) 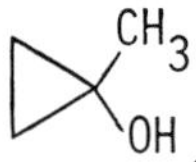

   (c)
$$\begin{array}{c} \quad\quad CH(CH_3)_2 \\ \quad | \\ CH_3CHOHCHCH_2CH_2CH_3 \end{array}$$

   (d) 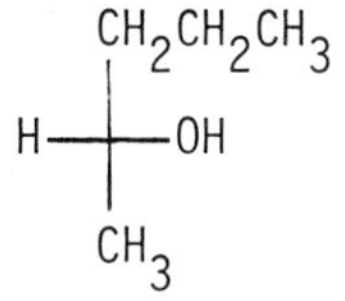

   (e) 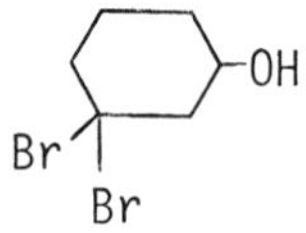

****

3. (a) cyclohexanol > chlorocyclohexane > cyclohexane (polarity)

   (b) 2-heptanol > 2-methyl-2-hexanol > 2,3-dimethyl-2-pentanol (branching)

****

4. (a) Ethanol hydrogen bonds to water. Chloroethane is attracted to water by dipole attraction. Ethane is non-polar, and attracted least to water.

   (b) Solubility decreases as the non-polar portion of a molecule gets larger relative to the polar position.

****

5. Intramolecular hydrogen bonding can occur in the *gauche* conformation:

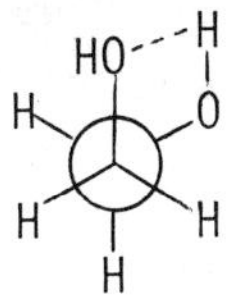

, but not in the *anti* form. This stabilizes the *gauche* conformation relative to the *anti*.

In 2-chloroethanol a similar, but weaker hydrogen bonding can also occur:

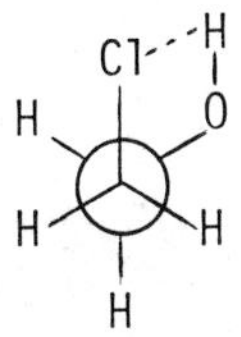

. So the conformation ratio of 2-chloroethanol should be more like that of 1,2-ethanediol than 1,2-dichloroethane, where no hydrogen bonding is possible at all.

****

6. Three factors are involved: the electronegativity of the electron-withdrawing atom, how many there are, and their distance from the hydroxy group.

(a) $CH_3CHClCH_2OH > CH_3CHBrCH_2OH > ClCH_2CH_2CH_2OH$

(b) $CCl_3CH_2OH > CH_3CCl_2CH_2OH > (CH_3)_2CClCH_2OH$

(c) $(CF_3)_2CHOH > (CCl_3)_2CHOH > (CH_3)_2CHOH$

****

7. (a) $(CH_3)_2CH\overset{+}{O}H_2 \xleftarrow{\text{as a base, } H^+} (CH_3)_2CHOH \xrightarrow{\text{as an acid, } HO^-} (CH_3)_2CHO^-$

This is both a weaker acid and a weaker base than methanol (Tables 8-2 and 8-3).

(b) $CH_3CHFCH_2\overset{+}{O}H_2 \xleftarrow{H^+} CH_3CHFCH_2OH \xrightarrow{HO^-,\ (-H^+)} CH_3CHFCH_2O^-$

(c) $CCl_3CH_2\overset{+}{O}H_2 \xleftarrow{H^+} CCl_3CH_2OH \xrightarrow{HO^-,\ (-H^+)} CCl_3CH_2O^-$

The last two are both stronger acids and weaker bases than methanol. In each the alkoxide is stabilized and the oxonium ion destabilized by the electronegative halogens.

****

8. (a) Halfway between the two pK_a values: pH 6.7. (Compare H_2O - at pH 7 equal amounts of H_3O^+ and HO^- are present.)

(b) pH -2.2 (c) pH +15.5

****

9. No. There are no empty p orbitals on oxygen in these ions, in contrast to carbocations. Hyperconjugation requires π overlap of a bonding orbital with an empty p orbital. No such overlap is possible here, so no hyperconjugative stabilization is possible.

****

10. (a) (i) S_N1; (ii) E2; (iii) S_N1; (iv) S_N2

(b) HO^- (c) $CH_3CO_2^-$

****

11. (a) worthless (H_2O is a very poor nucleophile in S_N2 reactions)

(b) good (excellent S_N2 reaction)

(c) not so good (bases give much elimination with 2° haloalkanes)

(d) good (but slow, via an S_N1 mechanism)

(e) worthless (^-CN is a bad leaving group)

(f) worthless ($^-OCH_3$ is a bad leaving group)

(g) good (S_N1 first step)

(h) not so good (branching reduces S_N2 reactivity, and E2 occurs)

****

12. (a) $CH_3CH_2CHOHCH_3$

(b) (*R*)-$CH_3(CH_2)_5CH(\overset{O}{\overset{\|}{C}}CH_3)CH_3$ — printed as (*R*)-$CH_3(CH_2)_5CH(OCCH_3)CH_3$ with C=O

(c) (*R*)-$CH_3(CH_2)_5CHOHCH_3$

(d) $CH_3CHOHCH_2CH_2CHOHCH_3$

(e) 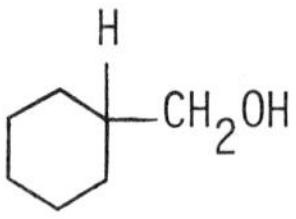

(f) 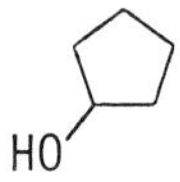

(g) 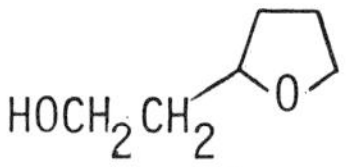

(h) 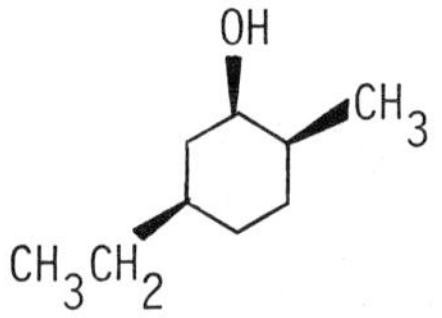

****

13. To the right (H_2 is a weaker acid than H_2O and HO^- is a weaker base than H^-).

****

14. (a) CH_3CHDOH

(b) CH_2DCH_2OH

(c) 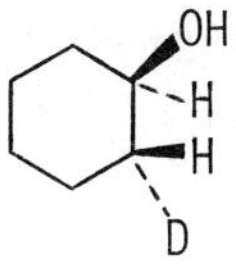

Notice that the S_N2 mechanism gives a *trans* product.

(d) $CH_2DCH_2CH_2OH$

****

15. (a)
MgCl
|
$CH_3(CH_2)_5CHCH_3$

(b) $CH_3(CH_2)_5CHDCH_3$

(c) 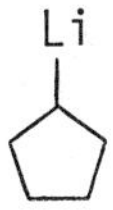

(d) 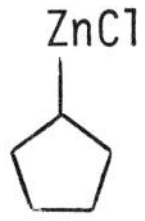

****

16. (a) $(CH_3)_3CSi(CH_3)_2Cl$

(b) $(CH_3)_2CHLi$

(c) $[(CH_3)_2CH]_2CuLi$

(d) $(CH_3)_2CHCH_2CH_2CH(CH_3)_2$

(e) $CH_3CH_2CH_2MgCl$

(f) 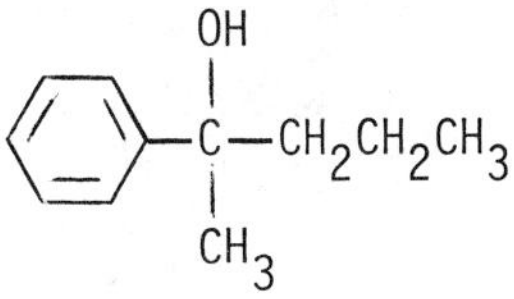

(g) 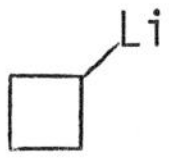

(h) 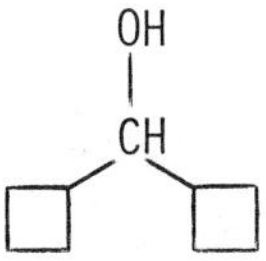

****

17. There was no way to control the reaction to prevent coupling of two "like" alkyl groups while attempting to couple two different ones. In other words, the reaction between chloroethane and 1-chloropropane gives a statistical mixture of butane (from two ethyls), pentane (from an ethyl and a propyl), and hexane (from two propyls).

****

18. Products after hydrolysis are given.

(a) 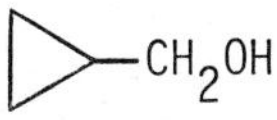

(b) $(CH_3)_2CHCH_2CHOHCH_3$

(c) $C_6H_5CH_2CHOHC_6H_5$

(d) 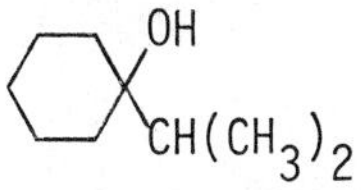

(e) $C_6H_5COH(CH_3)_2$

(f) $(CH_3CH_2)_2CHOH$

(g) 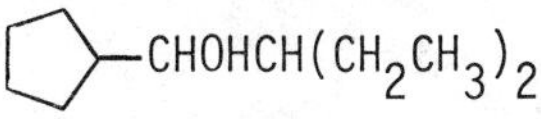

(h) $C_6H_5CH_2CH_2OH$

****

19. A = $BrMgCH_2CH_2CH_2CH_2MgBr$ (a "bis-Grignard" reagent)

B = $CH_3CHOHCH_2CH_2CH_2CH_2CHOHCH_3$

****

20. C = $CH_3CHICH_2CH_2CH_2CH_2CHICH_3$

D = $CH_3\underset{MgI}{\underset{|}{C}}HCH_2CH_2CH_2CH_2\underset{MgI}{\underset{|}{C}}HCH_3$ E = $CH_3\underset{CH_2OH}{\underset{|}{C}}HCH_2CH_2CH_2CH_2\underset{CH_2OH}{\underset{|}{C}}HCH_3$

****

21. Esters react with two moles of Grignard reagent. The first mole yields a ketone (or aldehyde), which goes on to react with the second mole. Here, the two "moles" of Grignard reagent are contained in a single molecule:

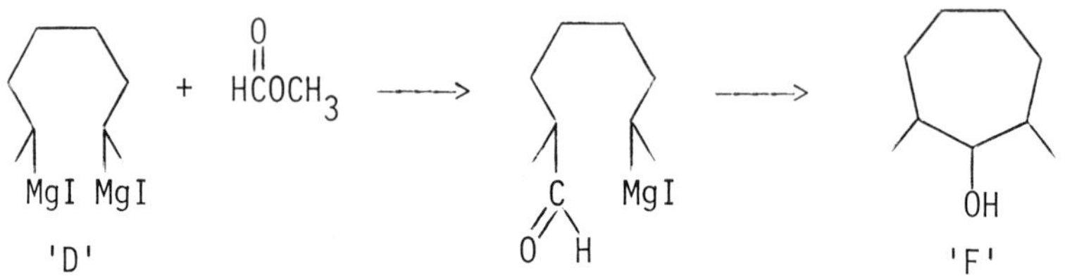

'D' 'F'

****

22. (a) $CH_4 \xrightarrow{Cl_2,\ h\nu} CH_3Cl \xrightarrow{HO^-,\ H_2O} CH_3OH$

(b) Same as (a), starting with ethane.

(c) Same as (a), starting with propane (not very good).

(d) $CH_3CH_2CH_3 \xrightarrow{Br_2,\ \Delta} CH_3CHBrCH_3 \xrightarrow[2.\ HO^-,\ H_2O]{1.\ K^+\ {}^-O\overset{O}{\overset{\|}{C}}CH_3} CH_3CHOHCH_3$

(e) Same as (a), starting with butane (not very good).

(f) Same as (d), starting with butane (much better).

(g) $(CH_3)_3CH \xrightarrow{Br_2,\ \Delta} (CH_3)_3CBr \xrightarrow{H_2O} (CH_3)_3COH$

Beginning with alkanes, the only possible first step is halogenation, which is a poor way to functionalize 1° carbons even if chlorination is utilized. Also, monochlorination is difficult in a practical sense.

****

23. Note: the halide (X) in all Grignard reagents may be Cl, Br, or I.

(i) From aldehydes, use RCHO $\xrightarrow{\text{H}_2, \text{ Pd-C or NaBH}_4 \text{ or LiAlH}_4}$ RCH$_2$OH for

(a) R = H, (b) R = CH$_3$, (c) R = CH$_3$CH$_2$, and (e) R = CH$_3$CH$_2$CH$_2$.

Alternatively, for all but the first one, use

$\qquad$ HCHO $\xrightarrow{\text{RMgX or RLi}}$ RCH$_2$OH with (b) R = CH$_3$, (c) R = CH$_3$CH$_2$,

and (e) R = CH$_3$CH$_2$CH$_2$.

$\qquad$ Finally, (d) CH$_3$CHO $\xrightarrow{\text{CH}_3\text{MgX or CH}_3\text{Li}}$ CH$_3$CHOHCH$_3$ and

$\qquad$ (f) either CH$_3$CHO $\xrightarrow{\text{CH}_3\text{CH}_2\text{MgX or CH}_3\text{CH}_2\text{Li}}$ CH$_3$CHOHCH$_2$CH$_3$ or

$\qquad$ CH$_3$CH$_2$CHO $\xrightarrow{\text{CH}_3\text{MgX or CH}_3\text{Li}}$ CH$_3$CH$_2$CHOHCH$_3$.

(ii) From ketones, use $\overset{\text{O}}{\overset{\|}{\text{RCR'}}}$ $\xrightarrow{\text{H}_2, \text{ Pd-C or NaBH}_4 \text{ or LiAlH}_4}$ RCHOHR' for

(d) both R and R' = CH$_3$ and (f) R = CH$_3$, R' = CH$_3$CH$_2$.

Also, (g) $\overset{\text{O}}{\overset{\|}{\text{CH}_3\text{CCH}_3}}$ $\xrightarrow{\text{CH}_3\text{MgX or CH}_3\text{Li}}$ (CH$_3$)$_3$COH

(iii) From oxacyclopropanes:

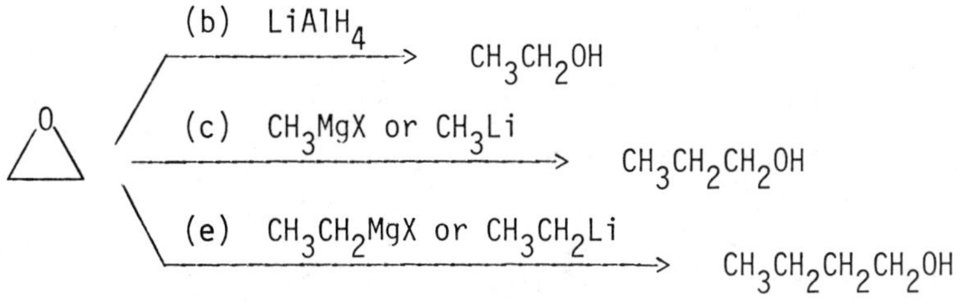

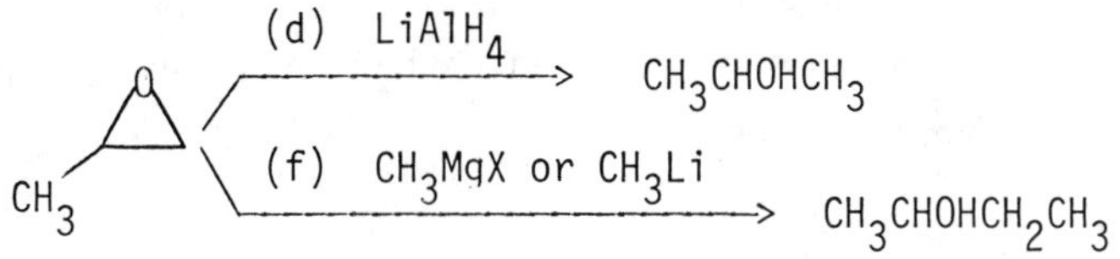

(b) LiAlH$_4$ $\longrightarrow$ CH$_3$CH$_2$OH

(c) CH$_3$MgX or CH$_3$Li $\longrightarrow$ CH$_3$CH$_2$CH$_2$OH

(e) CH$_3$CH$_2$MgX or CH$_3$CH$_2$Li $\longrightarrow$ CH$_3$CH$_2$CH$_2$CH$_2$OH

(d) LiAlH$_4$ $\longrightarrow$ CH$_3$CHOHCH$_3$

(f) CH$_3$MgX or CH$_3$Li $\longrightarrow$ CH$_3$CHOHCH$_2$CH$_3$

Also, for (f) CH$_3$ —(oxacyclopropane)— CH$_3$ $\xrightarrow{\text{LiAlH}_4}$ CH$_3$CHOHCH$_2$CH$_3$

Finally (g) CH$_3$ —(oxacyclopropane) CH$_3$ $\xrightarrow{\text{LiAlH}_4}$ (CH$_3$)$_3$COH

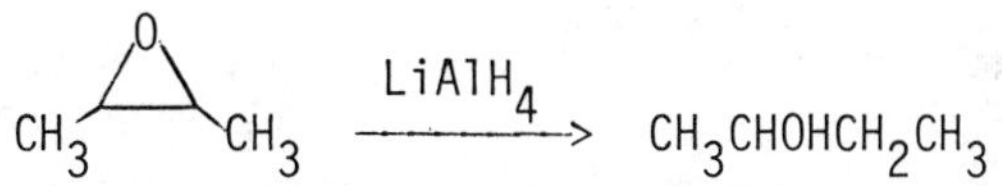

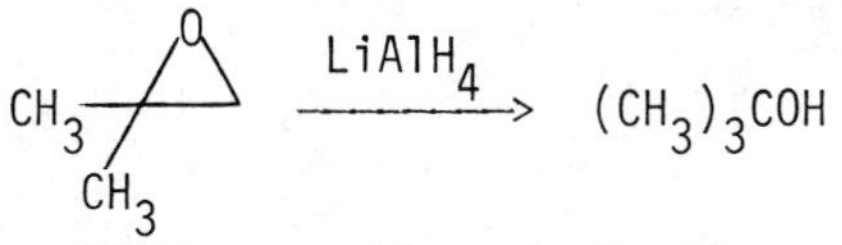

A suitable solvent for all the reactions in Problems 23 through 29 is (CH$_3$CH$_2$)$_2$O, and protonation of all alkoxide products with aqueous acid is required to produce each final alcohol.

$$************$$

24. (a) HCOOH or HCOOR $\xrightarrow{\text{LiAlH}_4}$ CH$_3$OH   R = any group

    (b) CH$_3$COOH or CH$_3$COOR $\xrightarrow{\text{LiAlH}_4}$ CH$_3$CH$_2$OH

    (c) CH$_3$CH$_2$COOH or CH$_3$CH$_2$COOR $\xrightarrow{\text{LiAlH}_4}$ CH$_3$CH$_2$CH$_2$OH

    (d) HCOOR $\xrightarrow{\text{CH}_3\text{Li or CH}_3\text{MgBr}}$ (CH$_3$)$_2$CHOH

    (e) CH$_3$CH$_2$CH$_2$COOH or CH$_3$CH$_2$CH$_2$COOR $\xrightarrow{\text{LiAlH}_4}$ CH$_3$CH$_2$CH$_2$CH$_2$OH

    (f) Not possible: does not have two identical groups on alcohol carbon.

    (g) CH$_3$COOR $\xrightarrow{\text{CH}_3\text{Li or CH}_3\text{MgBr}}$ (CH$_3$)$_3$COH

****

25. Target molecule is CH$_3$—$\overset{\displaystyle \text{OH}}{\underset{\displaystyle \text{CH}_3}{\text{C}}}$—CH$_2CH_2CH_2CH_3$:

    (a) CH$_3\overset{\text{O}}{\overset{\|}{\text{C}}}CH_3$ + CH$_3$CH$_2$CH$_2$CH$_2$Li

    (b) CH$_3\overset{\text{O}}{\overset{\|}{\text{C}}}CH_2CH_2CH_2CH_3$ + CH$_3$Li

    (c) CH$_3$CH$_2$CH$_2$CH$_2$COOCH$_3$ + 2 CH$_3$Li

All of the above are comparable although (c) is best since it combines <u>three</u> smaller molecules instead of two. Grignards may be used in place of alkyllithiums in any of these.

    (d) More involved, since the carbon that will contain an -OH at the end starts out unfunctionalized. It is 3°, however, which will allow functionalization after the needed carbon framework of the molecule is put together. First:

(CH$_3$)$_2$CHCH$_2$CH$_2$Br $\xrightarrow[\text{2. } \triangle\!\!\!\!\overset{\text{O}}{~}]{\text{1. Mg}}$ (CH$_3$)$_2$CHCH$_2$CH$_2$CH$_2$CH$_2$OH

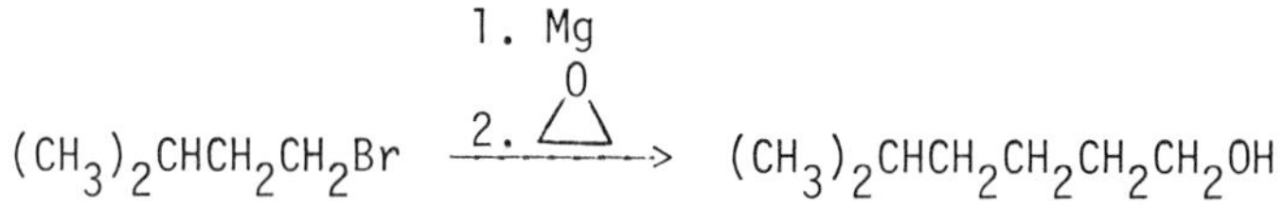

Next, the 1° -OH is unnecessary. Get rid of it.

$\xrightarrow{\text{conc. HBr}}$ (CH$_3$)$_2$CHCH$_2$CH$_2$CH$_2$CH$_2$Br $\xrightarrow{\text{LiAlH}_4}$ (CH$_3$)$_2$CHCH$_2$CH$_2$CH$_2$CH$_3$

Now functionalize the 3° carbon.

$$\xrightarrow{\text{Br}_2, \Delta} \quad (CH_3)_2CBrCH_2CH_2CH_2CH_3 \quad \xrightarrow{H_2O} \quad (CH_3)_2COHCH_2CH_2CH_2CH_3$$

You have no doubt already noticed that this is an indirect and rather poor method, retrosynthetically speaking.

****

26. Try using an oxacyclopropane:

   (a) Either $\overset{O}{\triangle}$-CH$_2$CH$_2$CH$_2$CH$_3$ or CH$_3$-$\overset{O}{\triangle}$-CH$_2$CH$_2$CH$_3$ + LiAlH$_4$ works,
   CH$_3$ CH$_3$

   but each is a poor practical synthesis since the starting material is not simpler than the desired product.

   (b) But CH$_3$-$\overset{O}{\triangle}$-CH$_3$ + CH$_3$CH$_2$CH$_2$MgBr is an excellent way to make the molecule since it starts with two materials that are each about half the size of the ultimate product.

****

27. (a) CH$_3$CH$_2$COCH$_2$CH$_2$CH$_2$CH$_2$CH$_3$ + LiAlH$_4$ or NaBH$_4$ or H$_2$, Pd-C

   (b) CH$_3$CH$_2$CHO + CH$_3$CH$_2$CH$_2$CH$_2$CH$_2$MgBr (lithium reagent O.K. too)

   (c) CH$_3$CH$_2$CH$_2$CH$_2$CH$_2$CHO + CH$_3$CH$_2$MgBr (lithium reagent O.K. too)

****

28. To get the most benefit from the answers below, do retrosynthetic analyses of the disconnections in each case. This is done for you in part (a).

   (a) Analyze the target molecule. Focus on the bonds near the functional groups. Look for bonds that can be made by reactions you know. For example:

$$
\begin{array}{ccc}
CH_3 & & CH_3 \\
| & & | \\
CH_3-C-CH_2-CH_2-OH & \Rightarrow & CH_3-C-CH_2MgCl + H_2C=O \\
| & & | \\
CH_3 & & CH_3
\end{array}
$$

   This implies the following overall synthesis.

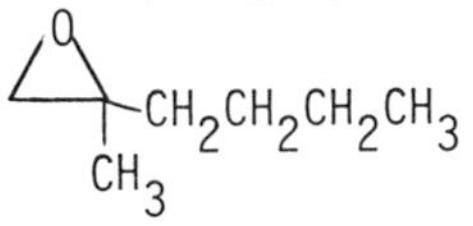

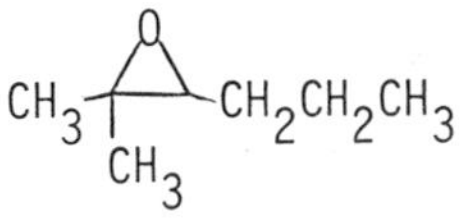

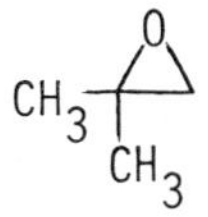

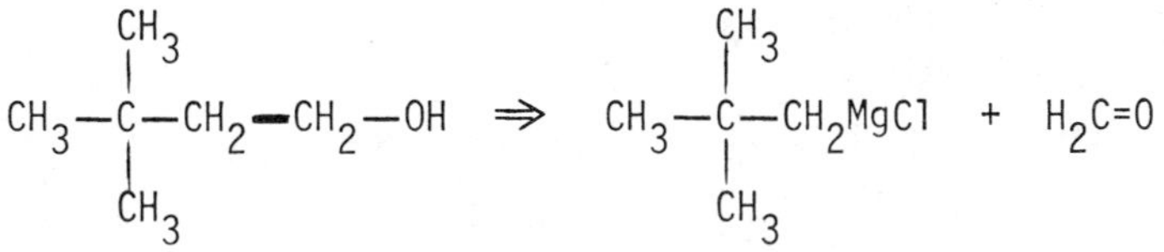

$$CH_3-\underset{\underset{CH_3}{|}}{\overset{\overset{CH_3}{|}}{C}}-CH_3 \xrightarrow{Cl_2,\ h\nu} CH_3-\underset{\underset{CH_3}{|}}{\overset{\overset{CH_3}{|}}{C}}-CH_2Cl \xrightarrow{Mg} CH_3-\underset{\underset{CH_3}{|}}{\overset{\overset{CH_3}{|}}{C}}-CH_2MgCl$$

$$\xrightarrow[\begin{array}{l}1.\ HCHO\\ 2.\ H^+,\ H_2O\end{array}]{} (CH_3)_3CCH_2CH_2OH$$

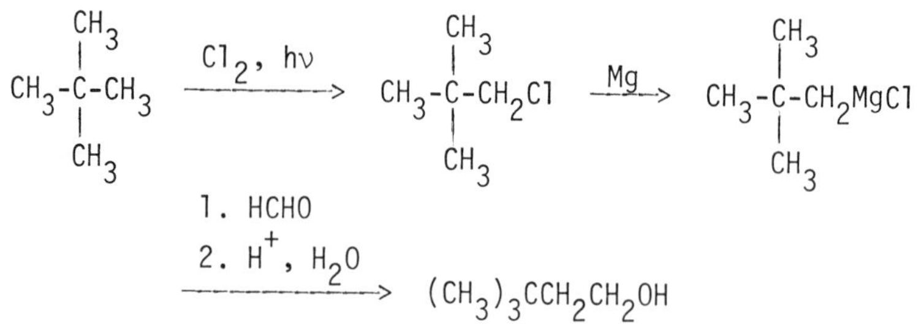

Is there a better way? Look for a more symmetrical retrosynthetic disconnection, if possible. How about:

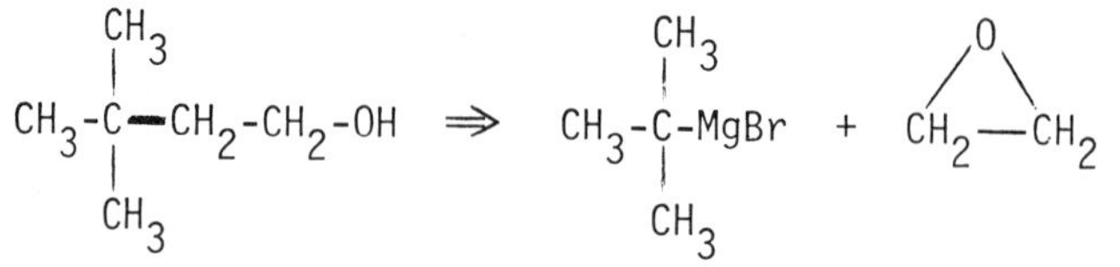

$$CH_3-\underset{\underset{CH_3}{|}}{\overset{\overset{CH_3}{|}}{C}}-CH_2-CH_2-OH \Rightarrow CH_3-\underset{\underset{CH_3}{|}}{\overset{\overset{CH_3}{|}}{C}}-MgBr \ + \ \overset{O}{\overset{\triangle}{CH_2-CH_2}} \qquad \text{Better!}$$

So the synthesis is

$$(CH_3)_3CH \xrightarrow{Br_2,\ h\nu} (CH_3)_3CBr \xrightarrow{Mg} (CH_3)_3CMgBr$$

$$\xrightarrow[\begin{array}{l}1.\ \triangle^O\\ 2.\ H^+,\ H_2O\end{array}]{} (CH_3)_3CCH_2CH_2OH$$

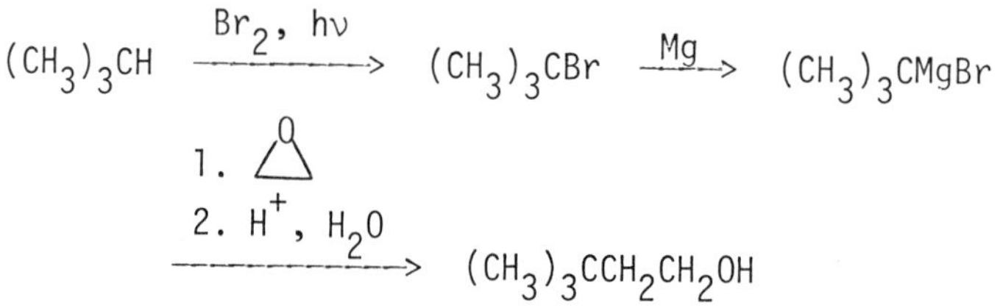

(b) Three routes will be shown, but the last step in each is the same:

$$CH_3CH_2\underset{\underset{CH_3CH_2}{|}}{\overset{\overset{CH_3}{|}}{C}}-CH_2OH \Rightarrow CH_3CH_2\underset{\underset{CH_3CH_2}{|}}{\overset{\overset{CH_3}{|}}{C}}MgBr \ + \ H_2C=O$$

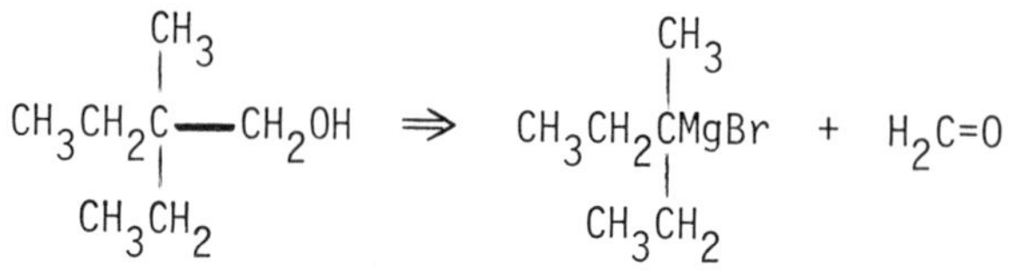

The Grignard comes from a bromide, which can come from either bromination of an alkane, 3-methylpentane, or nucleophilic displacement on an alcohol, 3-methyl-3-pentanol. Alcohols are easy to make; let's look at this one:

Method 1 -

$$CH_3CH_2\underset{\underset{OH}{|}}{\overset{\overset{CH_3}{|}}{C}}CH_2CH_3 \Rightarrow CH_3CH_2\overset{\overset{O}{||}}{C}CH_2CH_3 \ + \ CH_3MgCl$$

Method 2 -

$$CH_3CH_2-\underset{\underset{OH}{|}}{\overset{\overset{CH_3}{|}}{C}}CH_2CH_3 \Rightarrow CH_3\overset{\overset{O}{||}}{C}CH_2CH_3 \ + \ CH_3CH_2MgBr$$

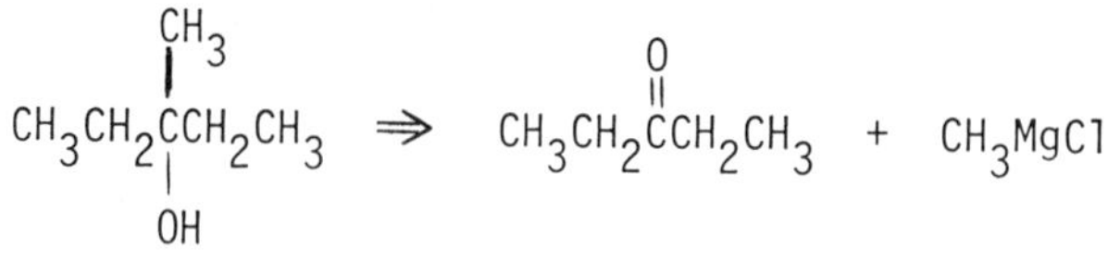

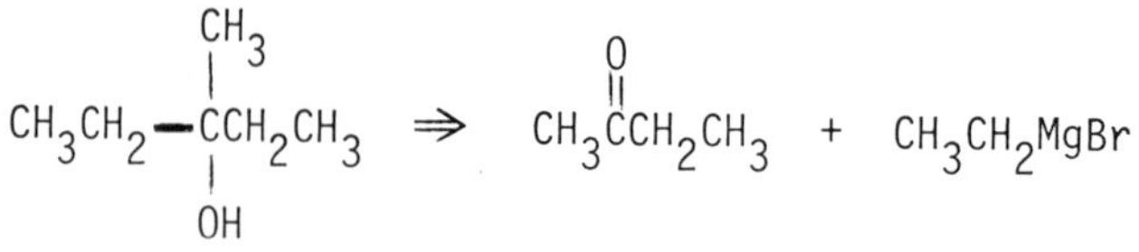

These both manufacture one bond, from rather unequal sized compounds. But notice that the desired alcohol has two identical groups on the alcohol carbon. So you can do this:

Method 3 -

$$\boxed{CH_3CH_2}{-}\underset{\underset{OH}{|}}{\overset{\overset{CH_3}{|}}{C}}{-}\boxed{CH_2CH_3} \implies CH_3COOR + 2\ CH_3CH_2MgBr$$

(R = any alkyl group)

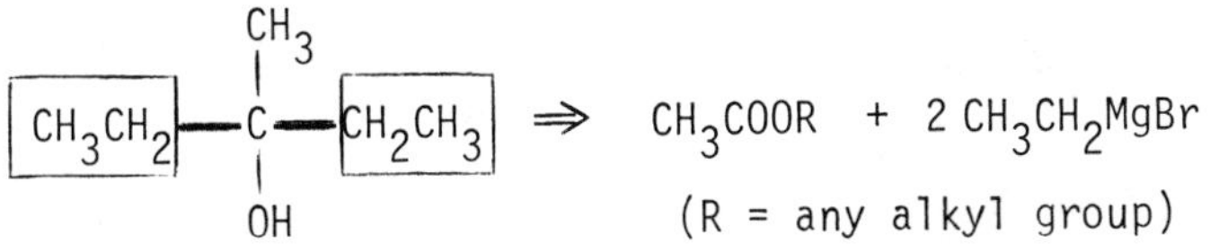

This last disconnection provides the best synthesis, which follows in full.

$$CH_3COOCH_2CH_3 \xrightarrow[\quad 2.\ H^+,\ H_2O \quad]{1.\ 2CH_3CH_2MgBr} CH_3CH_2\underset{\underset{OH}{|}}{\overset{\overset{CH_3}{|}}{C}}CH_2CH_3 \xrightarrow{\text{conc. HBr}}$$

$$CH_3CH_2\underset{\underset{Br}{|}}{\overset{\overset{CH_3}{|}}{C}}CH_2CH_3 \xrightarrow{Mg} CH_3CH_2\underset{\underset{MgBr}{|}}{\overset{\overset{CH_3}{|}}{C}}CH_2CH_3 \xrightarrow[\quad 2.\ H^+,\ H_2O \quad]{1.\ HCHO} CH_3CH_2\underset{\underset{CH_2OH}{|}}{\overset{\overset{CH_3}{|}}{C}}CH_2CH_3$$

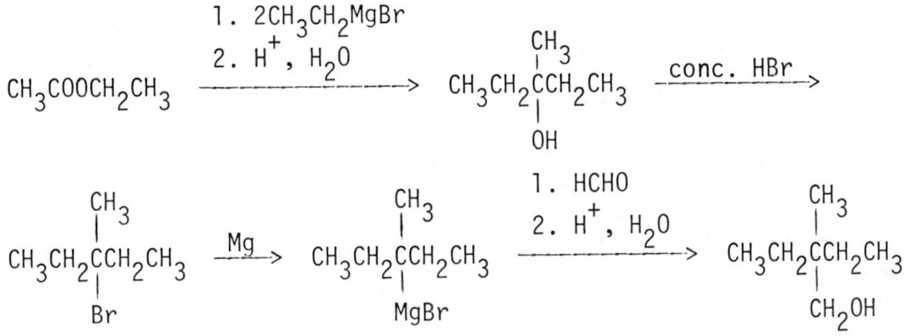

Notice how the molecule has been built up: its seven carbons came from 4 molecules, each donating either one or two carbons to it. The synthesis required three "real" steps: two Grignard reactions to make bonds, and one functional group interconversion.

(c) Method 1 -

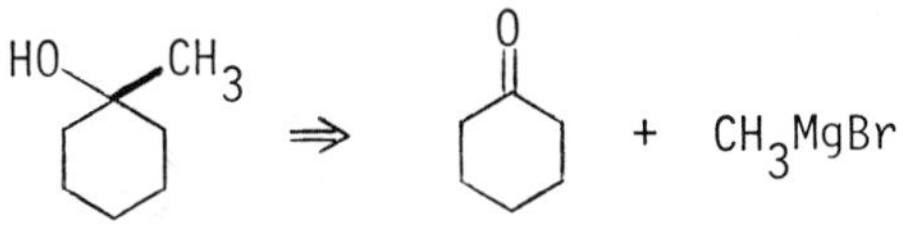

Method 2 -

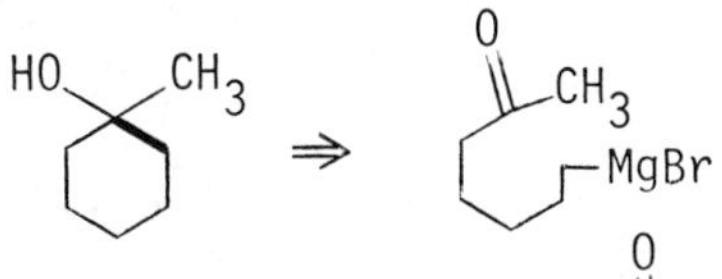

Method 3 -

Last one involves less unequal-sized pieces, so

$$Br(CH_2)_5Br \xrightarrow{Mg} BrMg(CH_2)_5MgBr \xrightarrow[\quad 2.\ H^+,\ H_2O \quad]{1.\ CH_3COOCH_2CH_3}$$

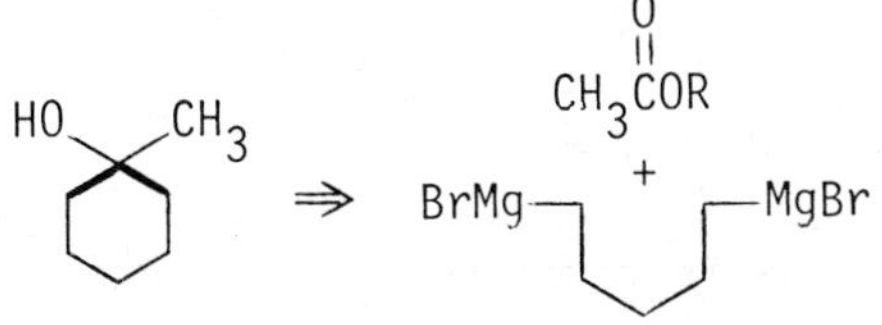

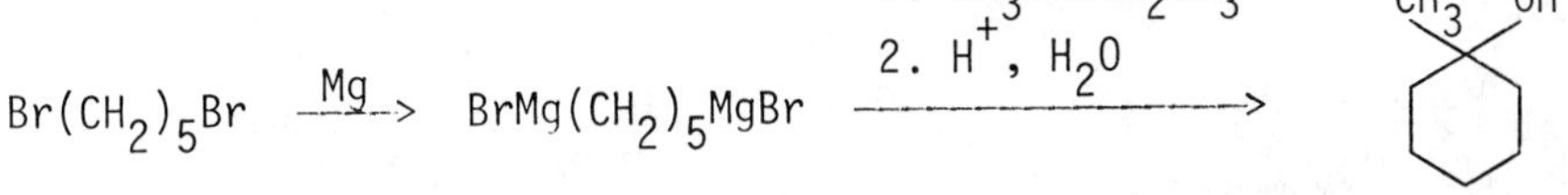

In practice, the most "retrosynthetically elegant" synthesis may not be the one everyone uses. In this case, cyclohexanone is so readily available that Method 1 would be the method chosen in real life.

(d) Method 1 - $C_6H_5CH_2C(OH)(H)CH_2C_6H_5 \Rightarrow C_6H_5CH_2C(=O)CH_2C_6H_5 + NaBH_4$

Method 2 - $C_6H_5CH_2{-}CH(OH)CH_2C_6H_5 \Rightarrow C_6H_5CH_2CH(=O) + C_6H_5CH_2MgCl$

Method 3 - $C_6H_5CH_2{-}CH(OH){-}CH_2C_6H_5 \Rightarrow HCOOR + 2\,C_6H_5CH_2MgCl$

The obvious best choice:

$$C_6H_5CH_3 \xrightarrow{Cl_2,\ h\nu} C_6H_5CH_2Cl \xrightarrow{Mg} C_6H_5CH_2MgCl$$

$$\xrightarrow[2.\ H^+,\ H_2O]{1.\ HCOOCH_2CH_3} C_6H_5CH_2CH(OH)CH_2C_6H_5$$

(e) Method 1 - 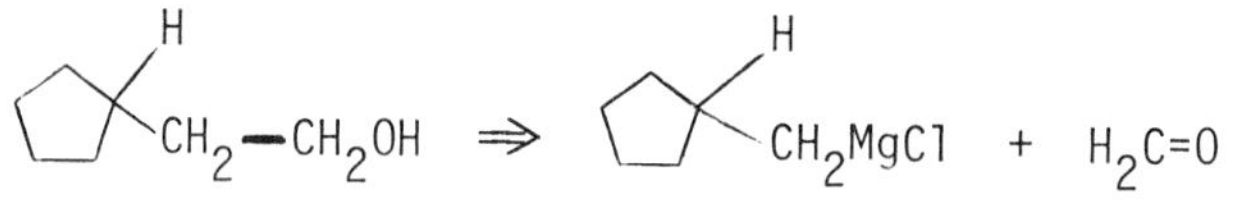

Method 2 - 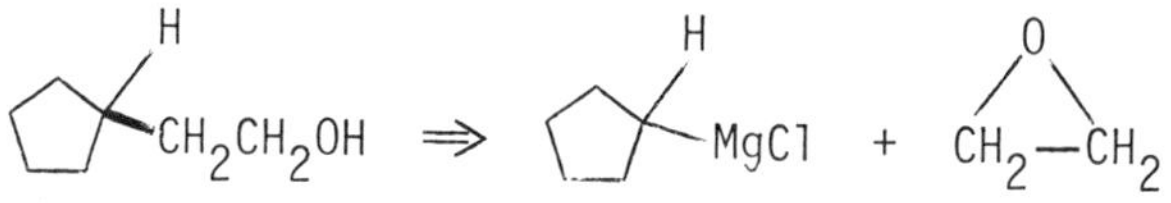

Second method involves a better disconnection, and also involves readily prepared starting materials:

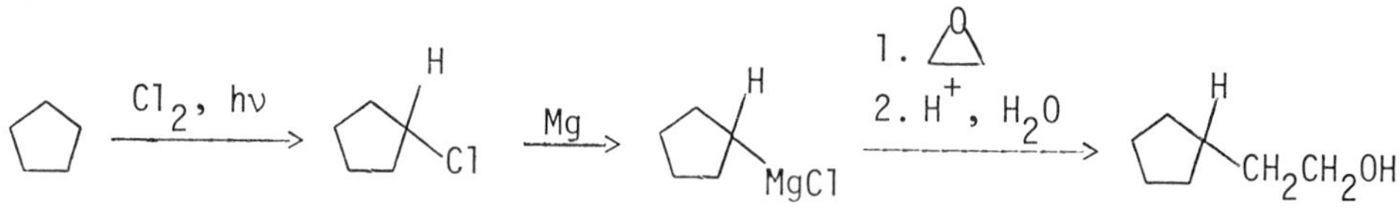

Note the similarity to part (a).

****

29. Divide the alcohols up into the following categories:

(i) - simple primary: (a) and (e)

(ii) - hindered primary, and secondary: (b) and (d), respectively

(iii) - tertiary: (c)

(1) (i) NaBr + conc. H_2SO_4 is simplest for ordinary 1° alcohols

(ii) Hindered 1° and many 2° alcohols are prone to rearrangement. Use PBr_3 to reduce this risk.

(iii) Conc. HBr is simplest for 3° alcohols.

(2) Start with the bromides that were formed in part (1). Then, reaction with Mg to make a Grignard, followed by treatment with water, will work for all of them. $LiAlH_4$ will also directly replace Br by H in category (i).

(3) Again, start with the bromides from part (1): Reaction with first Li and then CuI forms an organocuprate. Reaction with CH_3I will yield the desired product in every case.

(4) and (5) The 1° bromides from part (1) will form the desired products upon reaction with $[(CH_3)_2CH]_2CuLi$ and $[(CH_3)_3]_2CuLi$, respectively. Cuprates do <u>not</u> react well with 2° or 3° halides, so the others need to be made by indirect routes, e.g.

For (4), $RBr \xrightarrow{\text{1. Mg; 2. } CH_3CHO} RCHOHCH_3 \xrightarrow{\text{1. } CH_3SO_2Cl \text{ ("mesyl chloride"); 2. } K^+\,Br^-} RCHBrCH_3$

$\xrightarrow{\text{1. Li; 2. CuI; 3. } CH_3I} RCH(CH_3)_2$

and for (5), $RBr \xrightarrow{\text{1. Mg; 2. } CH_3COCH_3} RCOH(CH_3)_2 \xrightarrow{HBr} RCBr(CH_3)_2$

$\xrightarrow{\text{1. Li; 2. CuI; 3. } CH_3I} RC(CH_3)_3.$

****

30. (a) $CH_3(CH_2)_{14}\overset{O}{\overset{\|}{C}}O^- \quad + \quad I(CH_2)_{15}CH_3$

(b) $CH_3(CH_2)_{14}\overset{O}{\overset{\|}{C}}O^-\ Na^+ \quad + \quad HO(CH_2)_{15}CH_3$

****

31. (a) CH_3CH_2OH

(b) $CH_3CHOH\overset{O}{\overset{\|}{C}}OH$

(c) $HO\overset{O}{\overset{\|}{C}}CH_2CHOH\overset{O}{\overset{\|}{C}}OH$

(b) and (c): only the ketone carbonyl is reduced in these

****

32. 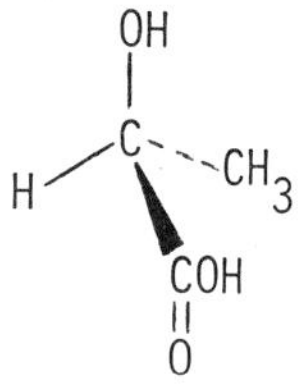 and 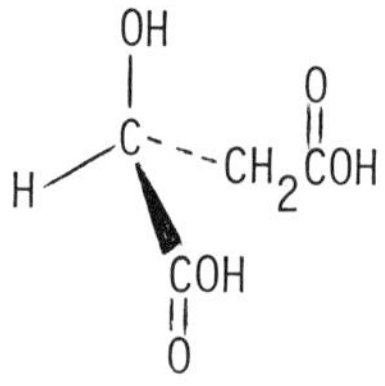

****

33. The bottom face of the steroid is less hindered.

(a) 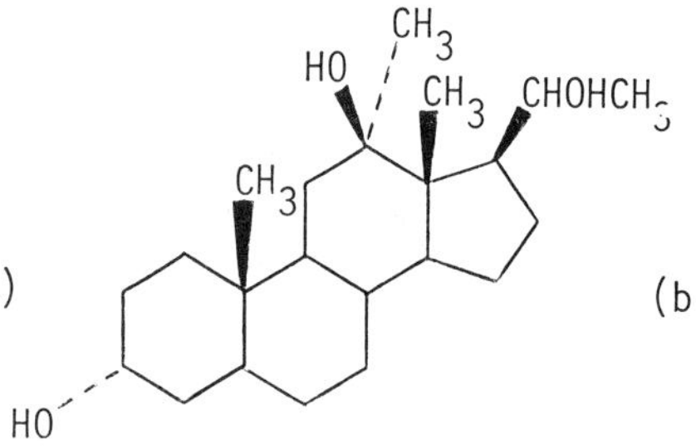

(b) 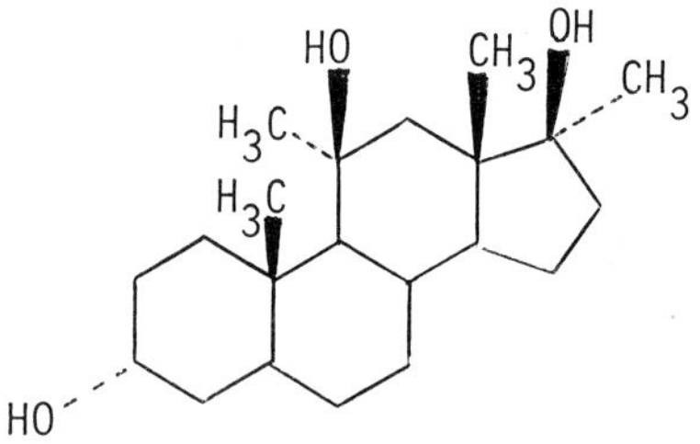

(c) 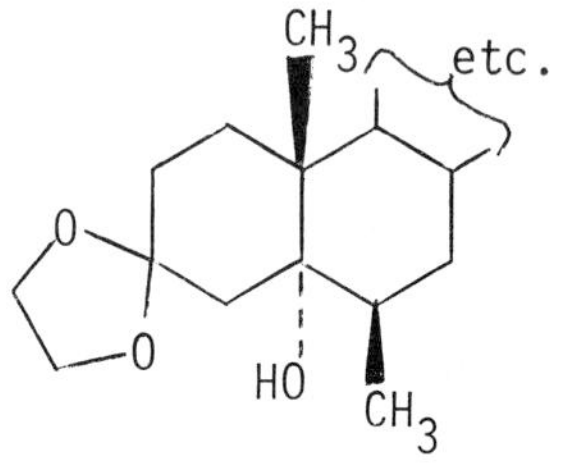

In (c) attack can only occur from the top, since nucleophilic ring-opening of oxacyclopropanes (epoxides) is an S_N2 (backside) displacement process.

****

CHAPTER 9

The Reactions of Alcohols and the Chemistry of Ethers

General Introduction

In this chapter we will explore the reactions of alcohols in detail. Note the three general reaction modes in Figure 9-1. Referring to the comparison with haloalkanes in the introduction to the previous chapter in this study guide, we see that a more detailed analysis might look like this:

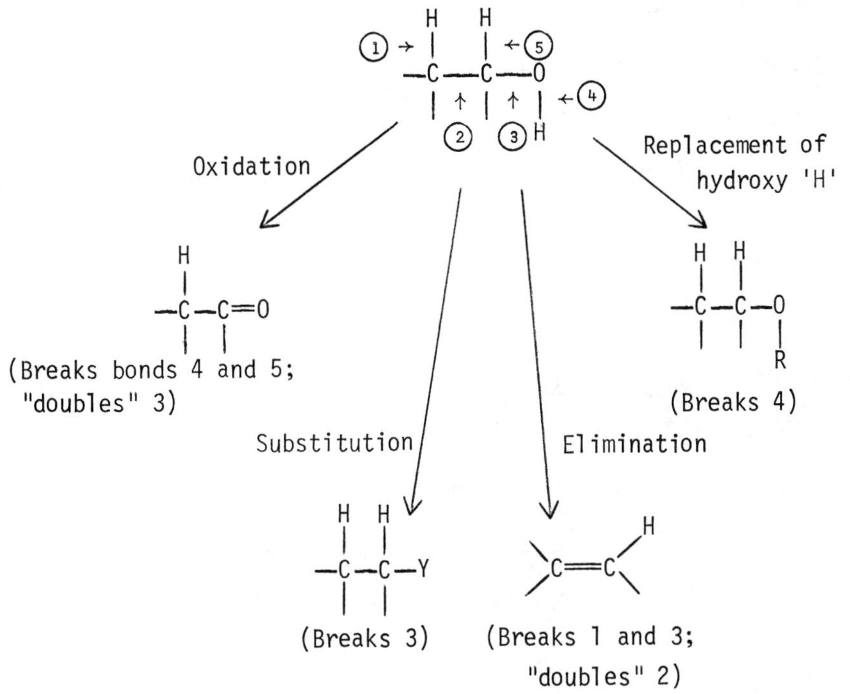

In fact, any of five bonds may be involved in alcohol chemistry, and if we treat substitution and elimination separately, a total of four types of reactions are possible, as shown. A related class of compounds, ethers, will also be presented. Since these lack an oxygen-hydrogen bond, the two reactions of alcohols that involve the O-H bond will not be available to ethers. In fact, only substitution reactions will turn out to be important in the chemistry of ethers, and those only will occur under certain sets of conditions, depending on the nature of the ether. By and large, ethers, in contrast to alcohols, will be found to be very unreactive molecules, a property that results in their usefulness as solvents for a wide variety of other reactions in organic chemistry.

Outline of the Chapter

9-1. The Preparation of Alkoxides and Carbocations.

A selection of methods for deprotonation and protonation of alcohols, and use of the latter in carbon-oxygen bond cleavage.

9-2. Carbocation Rearrangements.

A new reaction pathway for carbocations.

9-3. Esters from Alcohols.

A brief overview of organic and inorganic esters.

9-4. Oxidation of Alcohols.

Preparation of aldehydes and ketones: a key to opening up many synthetic possibilities.

9-5. Synthesis of Ethers.

The alcohol oxygen as a nucleophile.

9-6. Reactions of Oxacyclopropanes.

Putting an unreactive functional group into a strained ring.

9-7. Sulfur Analogs of Alcohols and Ethers.

The parallels between oxygen and sulfur compounds.

9-8. Physiological and Other Properties and Uses of Some Alcohols and Ethers.

Keys to the Chapter

9-1. The Preparation of Alkoxides and Carbocations.

We have already seen how the acidity of alcohols resembles the acidity of water. Here two general approaches are presented for the removal of a proton from an alcohol, to form an alkoxide ion: reaction with strong bases (such as $(CH_3)_3CO^-$, $[(CH_3)_2CH]_2N^-$, or hydride) and reaction with active metals (especially alkali metals). All are commonly used, with current preferences leaning towards the very convenient hydride reagents (NaH, KH). Alkoxides are therefore readily available species whose reactions will be explored at several places in this chapter.

The other side of the acid-base story for alcohols is their basicity: just like water, they can be protonated by strong acid, making oxonium ions. These turn out to be very important in the chemistry of alcohols, because they allow reactions to occur that involve cleavage of the carbon-oxygen bond. This bond is hard to break under neutral or basic conditions, and a comparison with haloalkanes shows why: haloalkanes already possess a good leaving group (halide ion), while alcohols do not. For instance, compare:

$$Nuc^- + R\text{-}X \longrightarrow R\text{-}Nuc + X^- \quad \text{(good leaving group)}$$

vs.

$$Nuc^- + R\text{-}OH \longrightarrow R\text{-}Nuc + HO^- \quad \text{(bad leaving group)}$$

Alcohols require improvement of their potential leaving group before they can become substrates in substitution reactions. The most common way to do this is protonation of the oxygen atom with strong acid. This converts a bad potential leaving group (HO^-) into a good one (H_2O, about as good as Br^-). Then, 1° alcohols can undergo S_N2 reactions, and 2° and 3° alcohols can undergo S_N1 reactions. Common nucleophiles in these reactions are halide ions, which form haloalkanes, and other molecules of alcohol, which form ethers. As always, elimination reactions can compete with these substitutions, especially at high temperatures, and alkenes are the products of the very important acid-catalyzed dehydration reaction of alcohols. Fuller descriptions of all these processes will be presented later in this chapter, too.

9-2. Carbocation Rearrangements.

So far you have seen two reactions of carbocations: combination with a nucleophile (the second step of the S_N1 process) and loss of a proton (the second step of the E1 process). There are more, as you might expect. After all, carbocations are very reactive species, and they will do just about anything to find sources of electrons. They can even attack unsuspecting atoms or groups in their own molecule, moving the atom or group, together with its bonding electrons, from its original location to the positively charged carbon. Such shifts of atoms or groups from one place in a molecule to another are called rearrangements. The most common kind of rearrangement is the kind shown in this chapter section: shift of a hydrogen atom or an alkyl group from one atom to another, with the electrons of the breaking bond, to generate a more stable carbocation from a less stable one. The most typical example is a rearrangement that changes a 2° carbocation into a 3° carbocation, a thermodynamically favorable process. Other common types of shifts turn 2° ions into new 2° ions and 3° ions into new 3° ions. All these rearrangements are liable to occur whenever "rearrangeable" carbocations are formed, namely, in the first steps of S_N1 or El reactions of appropriately constructed molecules. In addition, protonated 1° alcohols like 2,2-dimethyl-1-propanol can sometimes change directly to 2° or 3° carbocations via simultaneous ionization and rearrangement, even though they don't undergo simple ionization alone to 1° ions. These rearrangements compete with the other possible reactions (substitution and elimination). A short list of examples of the main types follows.

1. 2° → 2° via H shift

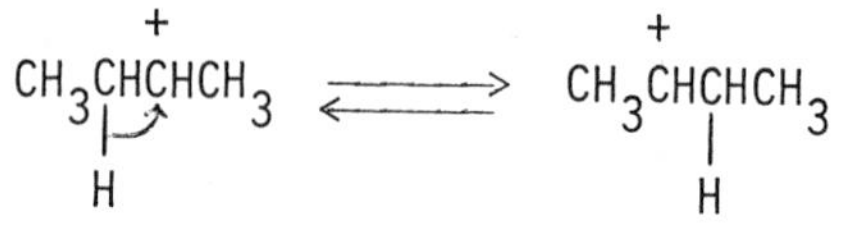

$$CH_3\overset{+}{\underset{\underset{H}{|}}{C}HCHCH_3} \rightleftharpoons CH_3\overset{+}{\underset{\underset{H}{|}}{C}HCHCH_3} \qquad \text{(readily reversible)}$$

2a. 2° → 3° via H shift

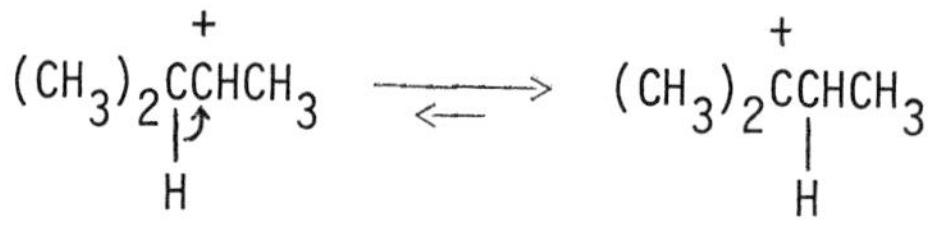

$$(CH_3)_2\overset{+}{\underset{\underset{H}{|}}{C}CHCH_3} \rightleftharpoons (CH_3)_2\overset{+}{\underset{\underset{H}{|}}{C}CHCH_3} \qquad \text{(reversible but favored in direction shown)}$$

2b. 2° → 3° via alkyl shift

$$(CH_3)_2\overset{+}{\underset{\underset{CH_3}{|}}{C}CHCH_3} \longrightarrow (CH_3)_2\overset{+}{\underset{\underset{CH_3}{|}}{C}CHCH_3} \qquad \text{(not reversible; product ion can undergo 3° ⇌ 3° inter-conversion - see next example)}$$

3a. 3° → 3° via H shift

$$(CH_3)_2\overset{+}{\underset{\underset{H}{|}}{C}C(CH_3)_2} \rightleftharpoons (CH_3)_2\overset{+}{\underset{\underset{H}{|}}{C}C(CH_3)_2} \qquad \text{(reversible)}$$

3b. 3° → 3° via alkyl shift

$$(CH_3)_2\overset{+}{\underset{\underset{CH_3}{|}}{C}C(CH_3)_2} \rightleftharpoons (CH_3)_2\overset{+}{\underset{\underset{CH_3}{|}}{C}C(CH_2)_3} \qquad \text{(reversible)}$$

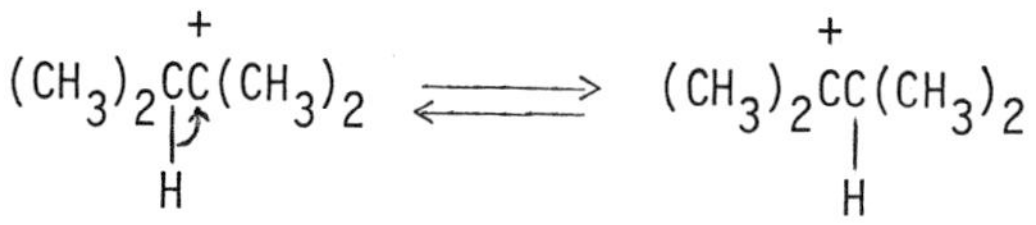

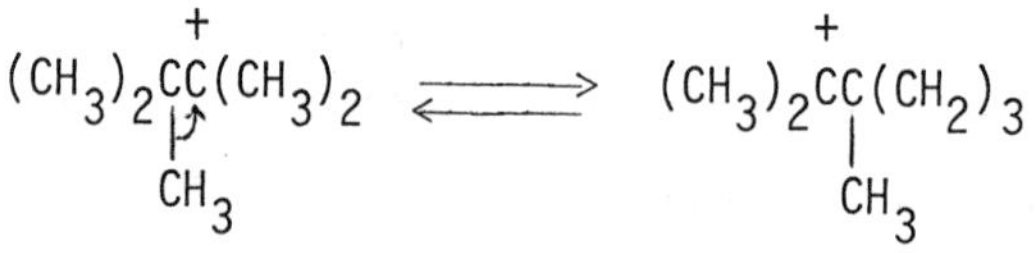

4. <u>"1°" → 2° via H shift</u>

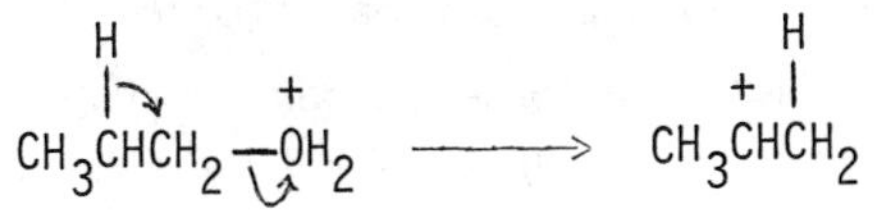

$$CH_3\overset{H}{\underset{\curvearrowleft}{C}}HCH_2 \overset{+}{-}\overset{\curvearrowright}{O}H_2 \longrightarrow CH_3\overset{+}{\underset{}{C}}\overset{H}{\underset{}{|}}HCH_2$$

5a. <u>"1°" → 3° via H shift</u>

$$(CH_3)_2\overset{H}{\underset{\curvearrowleft}{C}}CH_2 \overset{+}{-}\overset{\curvearrowright}{O}H_2 \longrightarrow (CH_3)_2\overset{+}{\underset{}{C}}\overset{H}{\underset{}{|}}CH_2$$

5b. <u>"1°" → 3° via alkyl shift</u>

$$(CH_3)_2\overset{CH_3}{\underset{\curvearrowleft}{C}}CH_2 \overset{+}{-}\overset{\curvearrowright}{O}H_2 \longrightarrow (CH_3)_2\overset{+}{\underset{}{C}}\overset{CH_3}{\underset{}{|}}CH_2$$

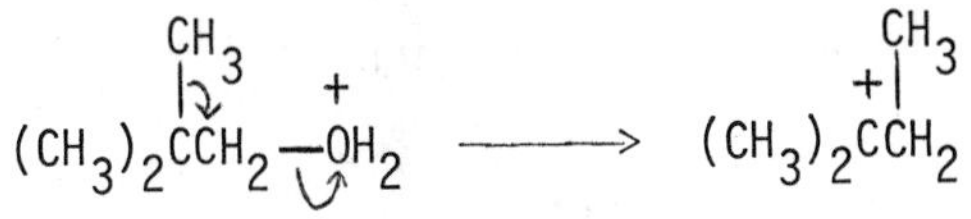

Finally note that all of these rearranged carbocations can either combine with a nucleophile to give a rearranged substitution product, or lose a proton to give an alkene (elimination) *just like any other carbocation*.

<u>9-3.</u> <u>Esters from Alcohols.</u>

The reversible reaction of alcohols and carboxylic acids to make organic esters is presented here only to alert you to the major connection alcohols have with esters. Esters are the most common and most important <u>carboxylic acid derivative</u>, and their chemistry will be explored in detail in several places during the last third of the course.

Inorganic esters are much less important *per se*, but they do serve useful purposes as synthetic intermediates for certain functional group interconversions. Here, alternative ways to transform alcohols into haloalkanes using these compounds are shown to often be superior to the more "classical" method involving acid-catalyzed substitution. Whereas the latter is often susceptible to rearrangement, the phosphorus and sulfur reagents presented here can often allow substitutions to occur without having rearrangements interfere with the course of the reaction. This is most noticeable with 2° alcohols. Protonation of a 2° alcohol generates such a good leaving group that S_N1 reactivity (i.e. carbocation chemistry) predominates. The leaving groups of inorganic esters are not quite as reactive, so those derived from 2° alcohols are not as likely to simply ionize on their own, and therefore a more moderate and well-behaved S_N2 reactivity is obtained. This can be *very* useful.

9-4. Oxidation of Alcohols: Preparation of Aldehydes and Ketones.

Alcohol oxidation is a straightforward reaction of major importance. Since carbonyl compounds are the products, and the carbonyl group is the most important functional group of all, alcohol oxidations are perhaps the most important of all reactions that alcohols undergo. Note the two types of reagents based on Cr(VI): anhydrous CrO_3 + pyridine, which is specifically intended for oxidation of 1° alcohols to aldehydes, and aqueous Cr(VI), which oxidizes 1° alcohols to carboxylic acids, and 2° alcohols to ketones. With these reactions and the other reactions so far described in this chapter, the chart of functional group interconversions first presented in Chapter 8 has grown to look like this:

Functional Group Interconversions

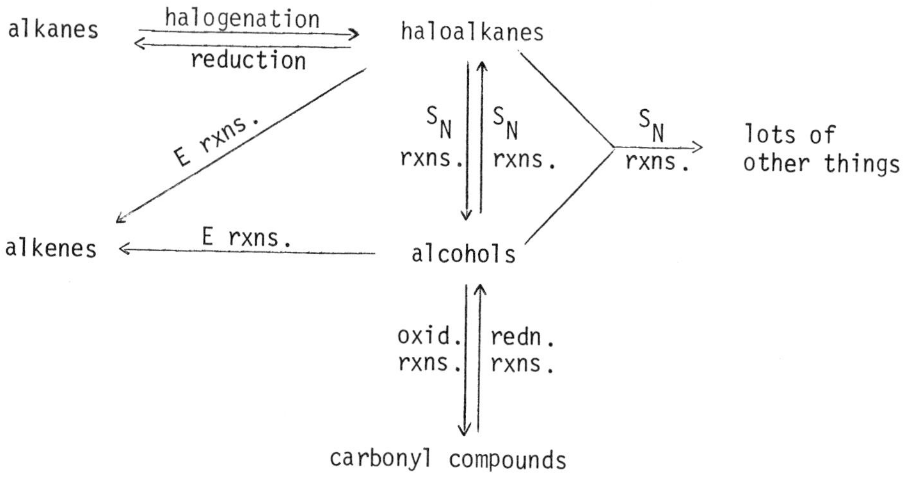

The general principles associated with solving problems in synthesis, first presented in chapter 8, remain applicable and should continue to be used. Notice that by combining the interconversion possibilities above with the one main carbon-carbon bond forming reaction you've had so far, addition of Grignard reagents to carbonyl compounds to make alcohols (chapter 8), you can now put together pretty big molecules via synthetic schemes of many steps. The key is the following sequence, made possible by the capability to oxidize alcohols to carbonyl compounds:

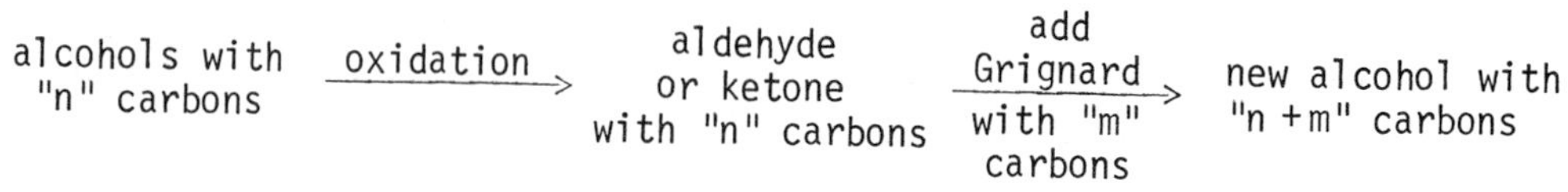
alcohols with "n" carbons
oxidation
aldehyde or ketone with "n" carbons
add Grignard
with "m" carbons
new alcohol with "n +m" carbons

The new alcohol may then be subjected to the whole range of functional group interconversions in the chart to make all kinds of molecules (now, with "n + m" carbons).

The iodoform reaction is included in this section for completeness. It is an oxidation process that is useful as a test for oxidizable methyl-substituted alcohols, but it is not generally used in synthesis.

9-5. Synthesis of Ethers.

In chapters 6 and 7 we saw examples of both substitution and elimination reactions involving alcohols and alkoxides in reactions with haloalkanes and related compounds. For general calibration purposes please refer now to the Summary Chart in the last "Keys to the Chapter" section of chapter 7 of this study guide ("Major reactions of haloalkanes with nucleophiles"). Alkoxides derived from smaller alcohols are comparable to hydroxide: strongly basic and unhindered, and give excellent results in S_N2 reactions with both methyl and 1° halides (third column). These are the prototypical Williamson ether syntheses, and several are illustrated in this chapter section. Increased bulk in either the alkoxide (e.g. $(CH_3)_2CHO^-$ or $(CH_3)_3CO^-$) or the haloalkane (branched, hindered 1°, 2°, etc.) tends to increase the amount of E2 reaction at the expense of S_N2 chemistry (refer to the "three questions" for favoring elimination or substitution, also in chapter 7 of this study guide). Obviously 3° halides are worthless in the Williamson ether synthesis as they will give only elimination products upon reaction with the strongly basic alkoxide reagent. Normal considerations of kinetics and stereochemistry apply, of course, to these substitution and elimination processes.

In contrast to alkoxides, alcohols are poor nucleophiles, like water (see left hand column in "Major reactions of haloalkanes with nucleophiles" chart). However, alcohols can act as nucleophiles to make ethers in either of two ways: strongly acidic conditions when no other nucleophiles are present, and solvolytic (S_N1) conditions with 3° halides. Typical examples of each are presented.

This section begins with a short description of the nomenclature and physical properties of ethers. No particularly new or fundamental points are introduced.

This section also concludes the coverage of alcohol chemistry for now. A summary chart concerning the various conditions for substitution and elimination reactions follows.

SUMMARY CHART

Substitution and elimination reactions of alcohols

Type of conditions

Type of alcohol	Substitution via inorganic ester, e.g. RSO_2Cl then $I^{\ominus}$	Strong acid with good nucleophile, e.g. conc. HI	Strong acid with poor nucleophile, e.g. H_2SO_4 in alcohol as solvent	
			Lower temperatures	Higher temperatures
methyl	S_N2	S_N2	S_N2	S_N2
1°	S_N2	S_N2	S_N2	E2
2°	S_N2	S_N1	S_N1	E1
3°	S_N1	S_N1	S_N1	E1
Rearrangements?	uncommon	common	common	common

9-6. Reactions of Oxacyclopropanes.

As mentioned in the General Introduction to this study guide chapter, the chemistry of ethers is very limited, showing a tendency towards nucleophilic displacement reactivity only under fairly special conditions. As is the case with alcohols, for any kind of nucleophilic displacement to occur to an ether (S_N1 or S_N2), the leaving group (alkoxide in this case) has to be improved. This is again done most simply by protonation with a strong acid. Then reaction can occur with a good nucleophile. <u>Notice that the nucleophile</u>

$$\ddot{\text{Nuc}}^- \quad + \quad \text{R} \overset{\overset{\text{H}}{\underset{|}{}}}{\underset{+}{-\text{O}-}} \text{R} \quad \longrightarrow \quad \text{R-Nuc} \quad + \quad \text{H-O-R} \quad \text{(good leaving group)}$$

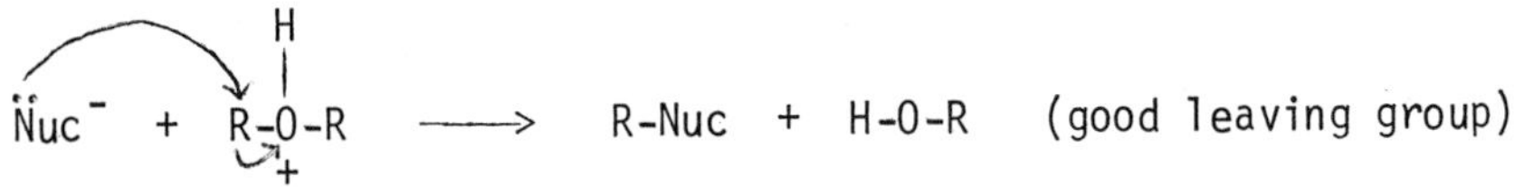

<u>in such a reaction cannot ever be a strong base!</u> A strong base cannot be present together with the strong acid needed to protonate the ether: they would just neutralize each other. Addition of a strongly basic nucleophile to an already protonated ether is also no good. All that would happen would be loss of the proton from the protonated ether to the base; no nucleophilic displacement would occur:

$$\text{CH}_3\text{-O-CH}_3 \quad \underset{\longleftarrow}{\overset{\text{H}_2\text{SO}_4}{\longrightarrow}} \quad \text{CH}_3 \overset{\overset{\text{H}}{\underset{|}{}}}{\underset{+}{-\text{O}-}} \text{CH}_3 \quad \overset{\text{Then add}}{\underset{\text{CH}_3\text{CH}_2\text{O}^-\text{Na}^+}{\longrightarrow}} \quad \text{CH}_3\text{-O-CH}_3 \quad + \quad \text{CH}_3\text{CH}_2\text{OH}$$

$$(\underline{\text{No}} \ \text{CH}_3\text{CH}_2\text{-O-CH}_3)$$

For these reasons nucleophilic ether cleavages are limited to good nucleophiles that are weakly basic like Br^- and I^-, which can exist in the presence of strong acid. (If you look back now at the reactions of alcohols you'll see the same considerations applying there, too.) Methyl and 1° alkyl ethers react via the S_N2 mechanism, while 3° ethers follow an S_N1 pathway. Least reactive are 2° ethers (worse than 1° for S_N2, and worse than 3° for S_N1; the latter mechanism is more typical, though).

Strained cyclic ethers (e.g., oxacyclopropanes) react similarly to ordinary ethers with acids, only faster. Order of reactivity is again 3° > 2° ≲ 1°. At a 1° carbon the reaction is clearly via an S_N2 mechanism to displace the protonated oxygen.

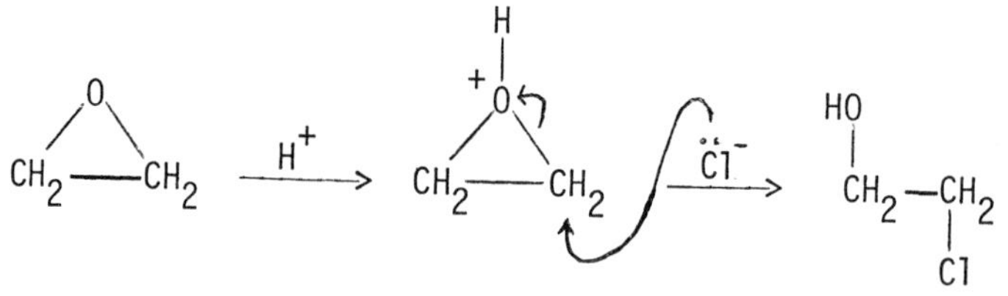

At 2° and 3° carbons the reaction may be described as an "S_N2-like S_N1 reaction". To clarify this, let's look at three ways to draw the Lewis structure of protonated trimethyloxacyclopropane:

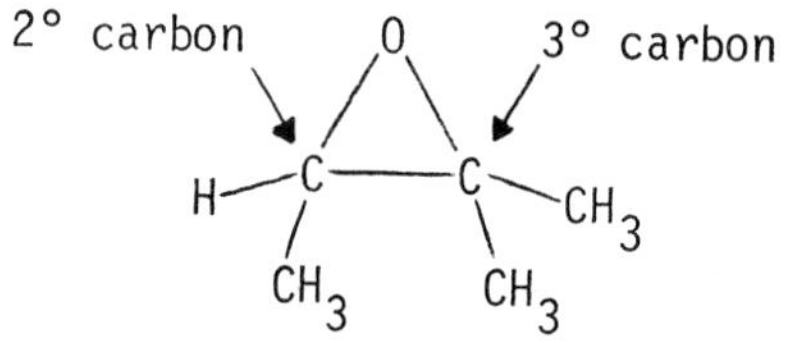

trimethyloxacyclopropane

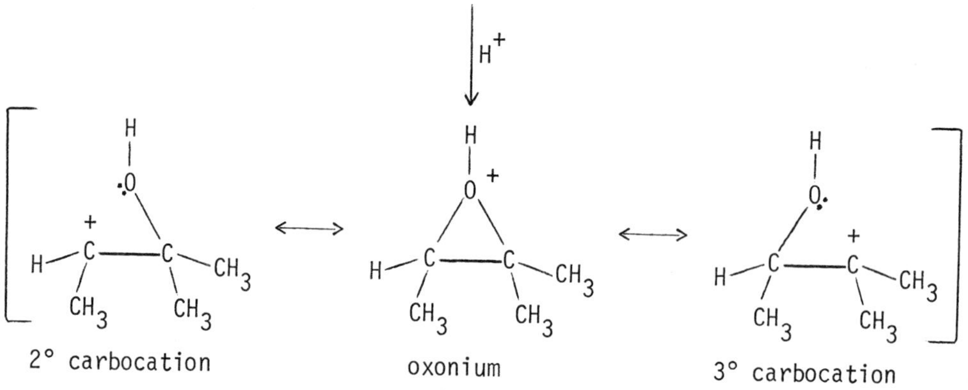

These are actually three resonance forms of the protonated molecule. It may look odd to draw resonance forms where a whole single bond is missing, but such pictures ("no-bond resonance forms") are useful in some cases, provided that you recognize that the individual forms are not real, and only the intermediate resonance hybrid really counts. In the case above the resonance hybrid will probably look more like the oxonium and 3° carbocation structures, than the 2° carbocation structure (since 2° carbocations are worse than 3° carbocations):

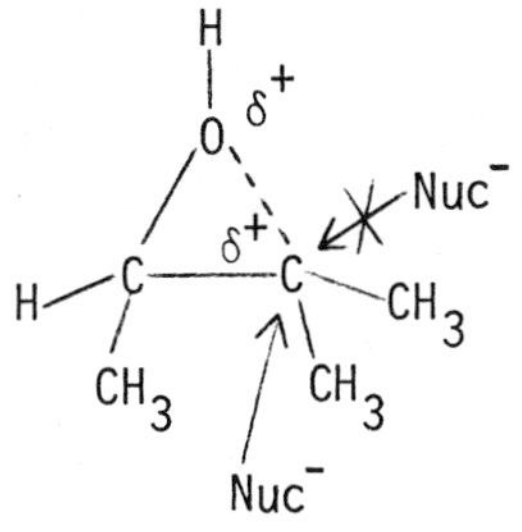

likely resonance hybrid

Reaction of this protonated epoxide with a nucleophile will therefore occur at the 3° carbon, which is the most carbocation-like, as you would expect for an S_N1 reaction. However, because of the position of the oxygen leaving group, which is at least partially bonded to the 3° carbon, the nucleophile can only attach to the 3° carbon from the side opposite the oxygen, resulting in inversion at that carbon atom, as you would epxect for an S_N2 reaction (see illustration above). For these reasons the S_N1 and S_N2 labels really don't apply in a clear-cut way: S_N1 considerations determine which C-O bond *breaks*, but the approach of the *nucleophile* is characteristic of an S_N2 process.

Strained cyclic ethers, as was discussed in chapter 8, also react with basic nucleophiles. The nucleophile has to be a good one because the leaving group (a negatively charged alkoxide ion) is a terrible one. The reaction follows an S_N2 mechanism with a reactivity order of 1° >> 2° >> 3°. The only reason this reaction occurs at all is that the displacement reaction breaks open a small, strained ring. Please note that this is a reaction unique to small-ring ethers. Unstrained ethers are unreactive towards basic nucleophiles.

9-7. Sulfur Analogs of Alcohols and Ethers: Thiols and Thioethers.

This short section expands on the obvious parallels between oxygen and sulfur that arise due to their relationship in the periodic table. As you saw earlier, the larger sized atoms are more nucleophilic, but less basic. Thus comparisons of the chemical properties of pairs of species like HS^- vs. HO^-, H_2S vs. H_2O, CH_3SH vs. CH_3OH, etc., are straight-forward. Larger atoms are also more readily oxidized, and sulfur chemistry includes a variety of oxidized species. Common examples are SO_2 and H_2SO_4. New systems introduced here include sulfonic acid (RSO_3H), sulfoxides (RSOR'), and sulfones (RSO_2R').

Solutions to Chapter 9 Problems

1. Equilibrium always lies on the side with the weaker acid-base pair.
   (a) Left. (b) Left. (c) Right. (d) Right.

****

2. In each case the species are written in an order reflecting a sequence of rearrangement steps. Rearrangements do not occur to an equal extent under all circumstances.

   (a) $CH_3CH_2CH_2\overset{+}{O}H_2$, $CH_3\overset{+}{C}HCH_3$ (similar to rearrangement of 2,2-dimethyl-1-propanol in Section 9-2)

   (b) $CH_3CH\overset{+}{O}H_2CH_3$, $CH_3\overset{+}{C}HCH_3$

   (c) $CH_3CH_2CH_2CH_2\overset{+}{O}H_2$, $CH_3CH_2\overset{+}{C}HCH_3$

   (d) $(CH_3)_2CHCH_2\overset{+}{O}H_2$, $(CH_3)_3C+$

   (e) $(CH_3)_3CCH_2CH_2\overset{+}{O}H_2$, $(CH_3)_3C\overset{+}{C}HCH_3$, $(CH_3)_2\overset{+}{C}CH(CH_3)_2$

   Some mechanism arrows are included below to help you find your way.

   (f) 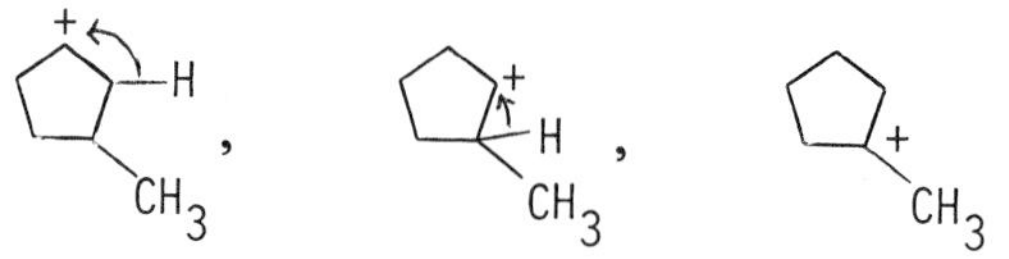

   (g) 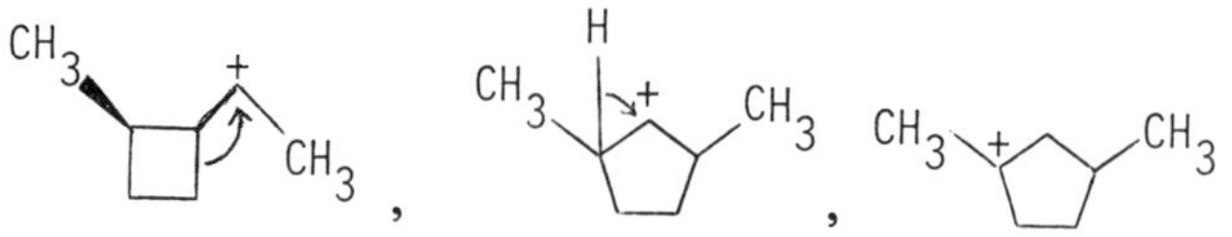

   (h) 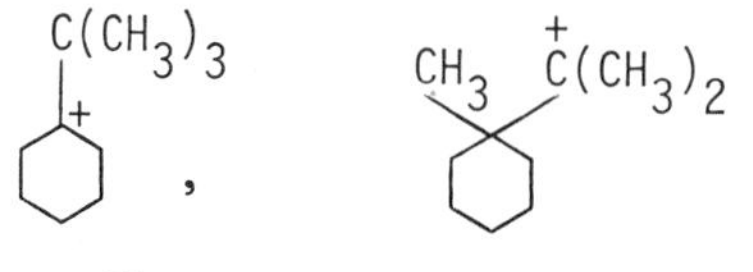

   (i) 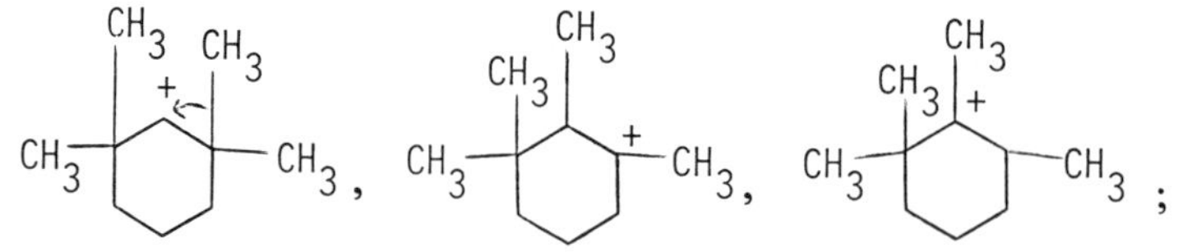

   also 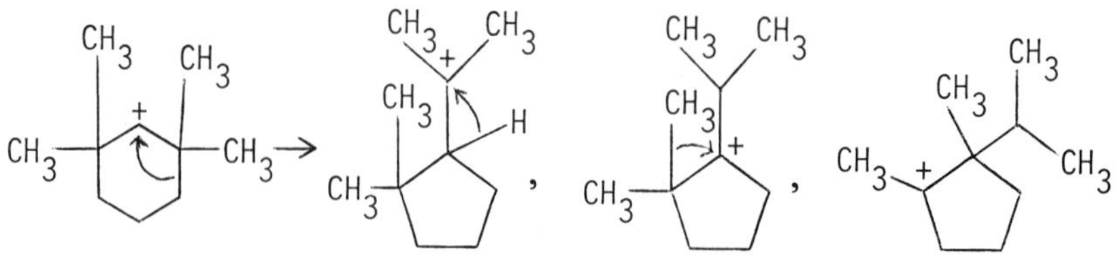

(j) 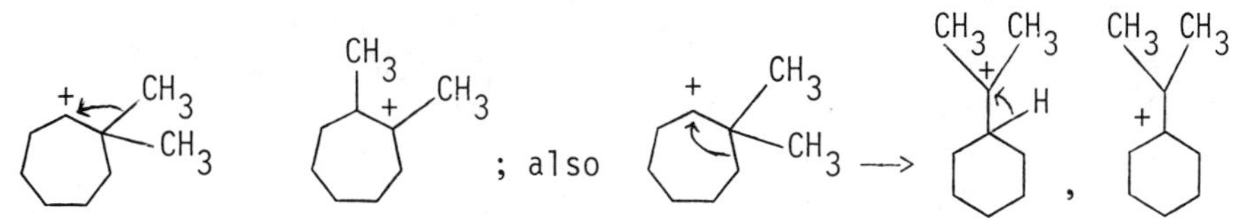

****

3. These conditions favor rearrangements. They allow carbocations to exist for a long time, because they are strongly acidic and lack decent nucleophiles.

   (a) and (b) $CH_3CH{=}CH_2$

   (c) $CH_3CH_2CH{=}CH_2$, $CH_3CH{=}CHCH_3$ (major product)

   (d) $(CH_3)_2C{=}CH_2$

   (e) $(CH_3)_3CCH{=}CH_2$, $(CH_3)_2C{=}C(CH_3)_2$ (major product)

   Line formulas will be used for most of the cyclic structures below. Note that methyl groups are understood to be present at the ends of lines even when "CH_3" is not written in.

   (f) 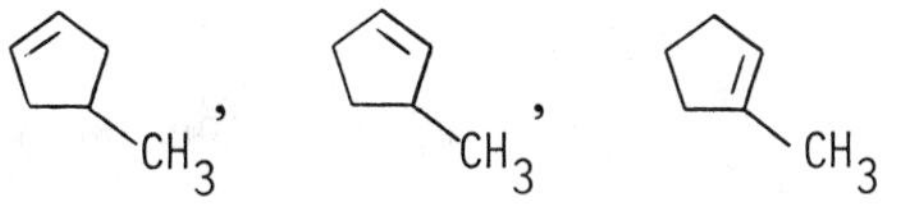 (major product)

   (g) 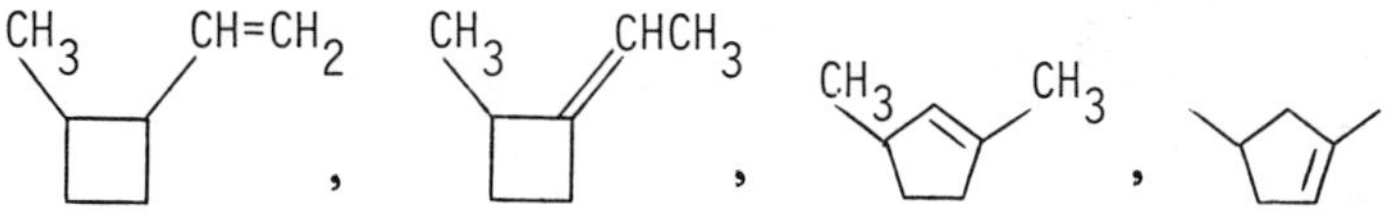

   (last two are major products; the first is the least important one.)

   (h) 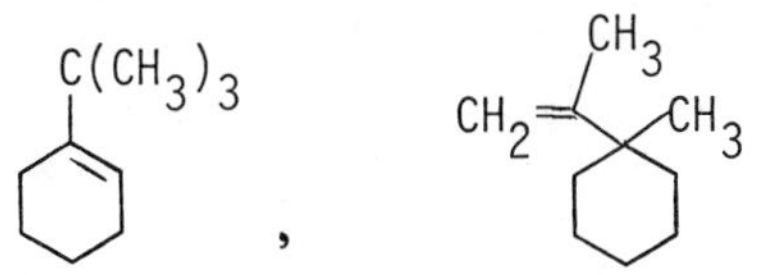

   (i) 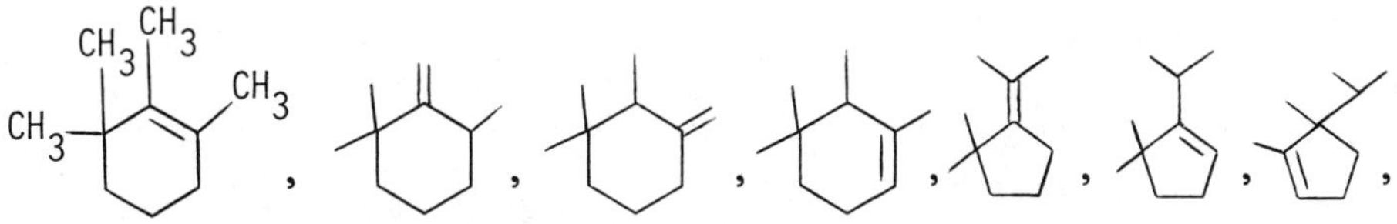

   Each product arises from loss of a proton from a carbon adjacent to the positively-charged carbon of a structure in the previous problem.

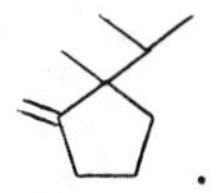

(j) 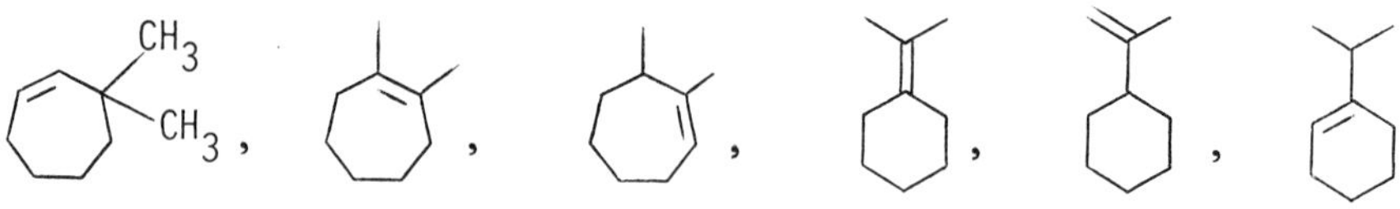

****

4. Rearrangements are much less likely under these conditions, the acid is much weaker (H_3O^+ rather than H_2SO_4), and there is a good nucleophile around. None of the primary alcohols rearrange.

(a) $CH_3CH_2CH_2Br$ (b) $CH_3CHBrCH_3$ (c) $CH_3CH_2CH_2CH_2Br$

(d) $(CH_3)_2CHCH_2Br$ (e) $(CH_3)_3CCH_2CH_2Br$

With secondary or tertiary alcohols rearrangements again become more likely. Products will result from attachment of Br^- to any positively charged carbon in the carbocations present: see answers to question 2, parts (f) through (j).

****

5. We have seen this reaction before. The water-free conditions allow *quantitative* conversion of the alcohol to its oxonium ion form, in the presence of high Br^- concentration:

$$RCH_2OH \underset{\longleftarrow}{\xrightarrow{\text{conc. } H_2SO_4}} RCH_2\overset{+}{O}H_2 \xrightarrow{Br^-\ (S_N2)} RCH_2Br$$

ca. 100%

In concentrated aqueous HBr the main acid present is H_3O^+, which is a *weaker* acid than the oxonium ion. The first equilibrium lies well to the left, and so the overall reaction rate is much slower (there is much less protonated alcohol to react with Br^-):

$$\underset{\text{ca. 99\%}}{RCH_2OH} \underset{\longleftarrow\!\!\!-\!\!\!-\!\!\!-}{\xrightarrow{H_3O^+}} \underset{\text{ca. 1\%}}{RCH_2\overset{+}{O}H_2} \xrightarrow{Br^-\ (S_N2)} RCH_2Br$$

****

6. Everything goes well until the last step. Then - disaster!

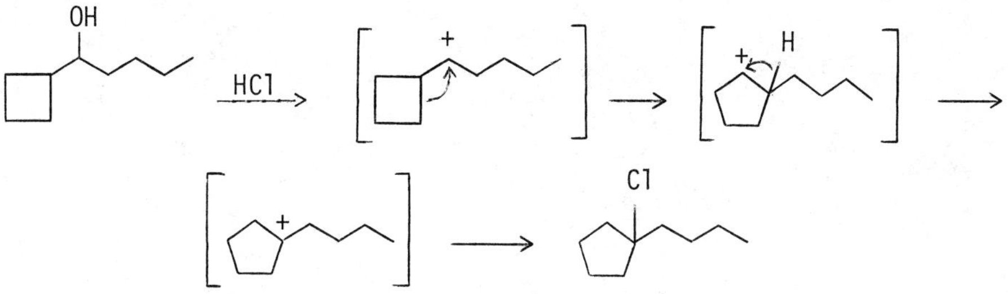

Strained rings are particularly good candidates for carbocation rearrangement if the strain can be relieved in the process.

****

7. Two things to remember: only the __better__ of the two possible carbocations forms first, and rearrangement always follows from the other original alcohol carbon, to give a protonated carbonyl product. Example (a) is fully detailed:

(a) $CH_3-\underset{\underset{CH_3}{|}}{\overset{\overset{OH\ OH}{|\ \ |}}{C}}-CH_2$

$\xrightarrow{H^+}$ or

$CH_3-\underset{\underset{CH_3}{|}}{\overset{\overset{OH\ \overset{+}{O}H_2}{|\ \ \ |}}{C}}-CH_2$ $\xrightarrow{-H_2O}$ ✗ $CH_3-\underset{\underset{CH_3}{|}}{\overset{\overset{OH}{|}}{C}}-\overset{+}{C}H_2$ Does not happen (primary).

$\xrightarrow{H^+}$ $CH_3-\underset{\underset{CH_3}{|}}{\overset{\overset{\overset{+}{O}H_2\ OH}{|\ \ \ |}}{C}}-CH_2$ $\xrightarrow{-H_2O}$ $CH_3-\overset{+}{\underset{\underset{CH_3}{|}}{C}}-\underset{\underset{H}{|}}{\overset{\overset{:OH}{|}}{C}}-H$ Correct initial carbocation (tertiary).

$\longrightarrow$ $(CH_3)_2CH\overset{\overset{+}{O}H}{\overset{||}{C}}H$ $\xrightarrow{-H^+}$ $(CH_3)_2CHCHO$ Only product.

(b) $CH_3CH_2CD_2\overset{\overset{O}{||}}{C}CH_2CH_3$, via $CH_3CH_2\overset{+}{C}D-\underset{\underset{D}{|}}{\overset{\overset{:OH}{|}}{C}}-CH_2CH_3$

(c) Two products:

and

(d) , via

****

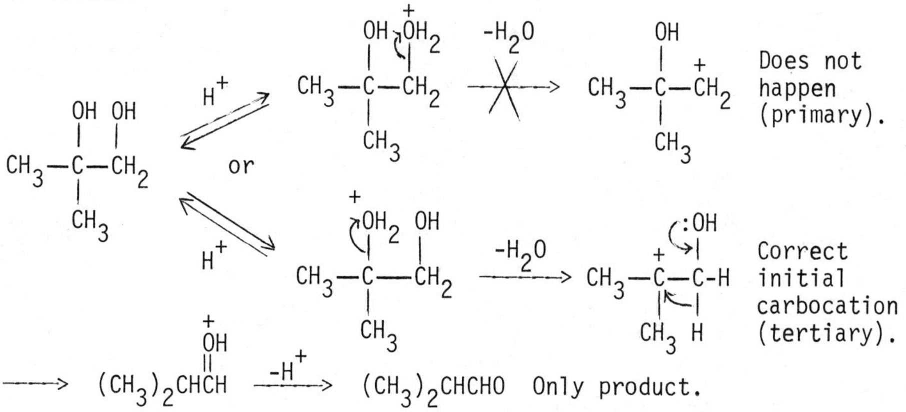

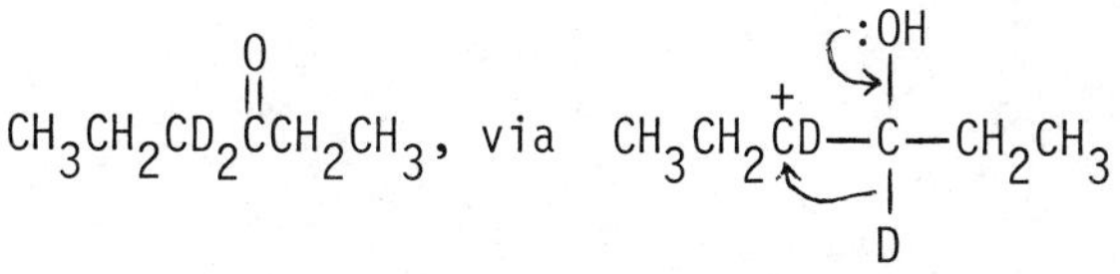

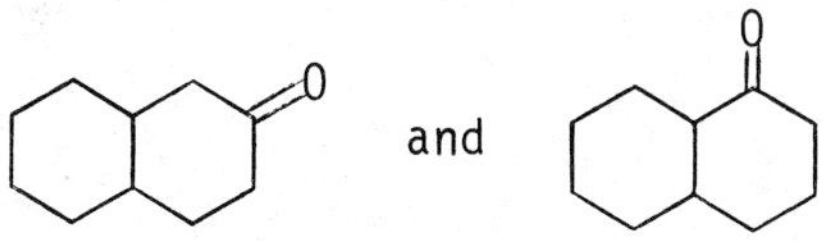

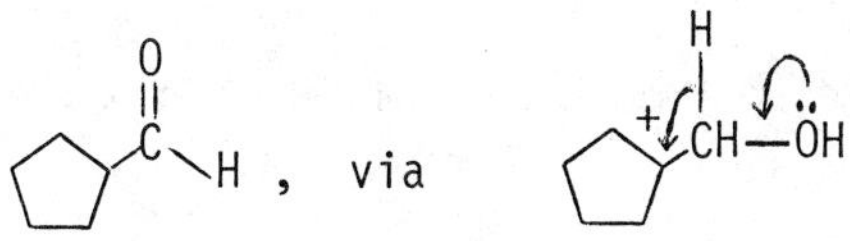

8. 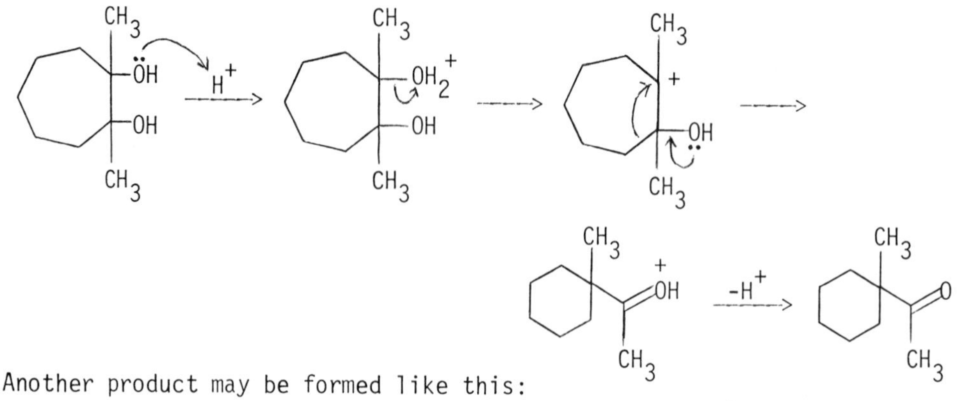

Another product may be formed like this:

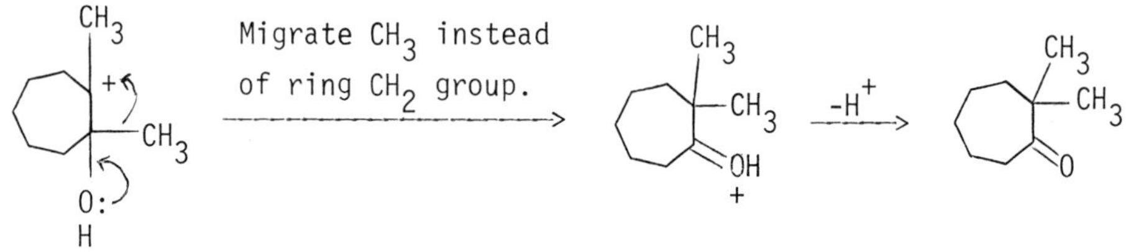

The seven-membered ring is slightly strained. The first product (with an unstrained six-membered ring) will be favored.

****

9. (a) 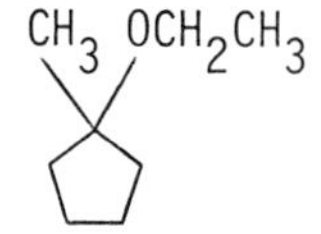 would be a likely choice, after 2° (secondary) → 3° (tertiary) carbocation rearrangement.

(b) Both $(CH_3)_3CCH_2Cl$ and $(CH_3)_2CClCH_2CH_3$. The strong Lewis acid and the relatively weak Cl^- nucleophile combine to make 1° (primary) → 3° rearrangement more likely than usual.

(c) 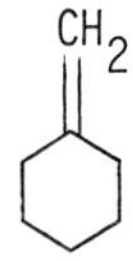 and 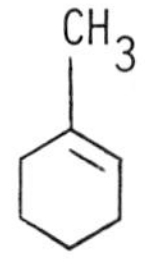 (major)

(d)
```
         OH
         |
(CH3)2C-CH(CH3)2
```
$(CH_3)_2C(OH)\text{-}CH(CH_3)_2$

(e) 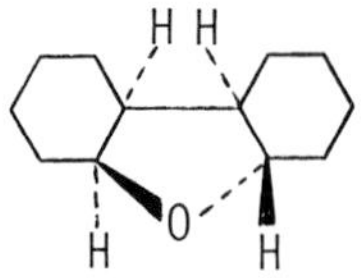 (Note stereochemical result of displacement reaction in 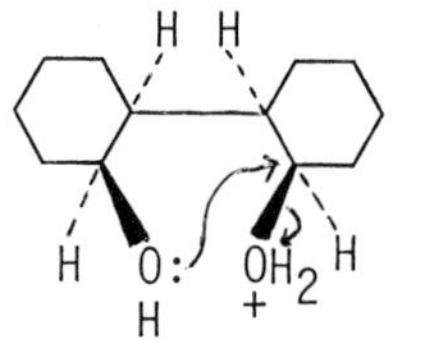)

(f) 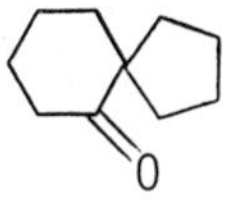 , via 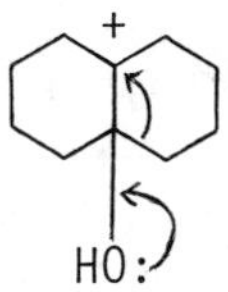

****

10. (a) through (e) are the same, via the S_N2 displacement of a phosphite leaving group by bromide ion.

(f) 

(g) 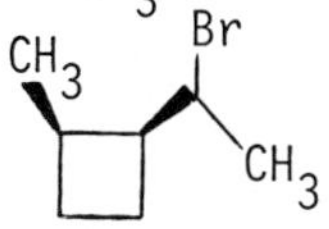 ; both (f) and (g) are S_N2 reactions, with inversion at the reacting carbon, typical for PBr_3 reacting with 2° alcohols.

(h) through (j) are 3° or highly hindered 2° alcohols, making S_N2 reactions difficult or impossible, these will give mixtures of products due to rearranging carbocations, just as aq. HBr (problem 4).

****

11. In each answer below R- = $CH_3CH_2CH_2CH_2CH_2$-.

(a) $RO^- \ K^+$ (+ $(CH_3)_3COH$)

(b) $RO^- \ Na^+$ (+ H_2)

(c) $RO^- \ Li^+$ (+ CH_4)

(d) RI

(e) RCl

(f) $R\overset{+}{O}H_2$ (+ FSO_3^-)

(g) ROR

(h) $CH_3CH_2CH{=}CHCH_3$ (mainly *trans*)

(i) $(CH_3)_2CH\overset{O}{\overset{\|}{C}}OR$

(j) RBr

(k) RCl

(l) $CH_3CH_2CH_2CH_2\overset{O}{\overset{\|}{C}}OH$

(m) $CH_3CH_2CH_2CH_2\overset{O}{\overset{\|}{C}}H$

(n) $ROC(CH_3)_3$

****

12. (a), (b), (c) 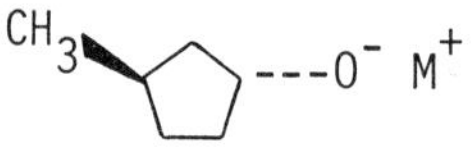 ($M^+ = K^+$, Na^+, or Li^+)

(d) 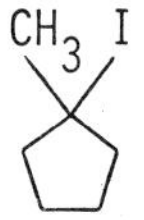

(e) 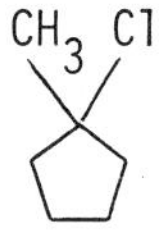

(f) 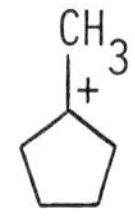

(g) and (h) 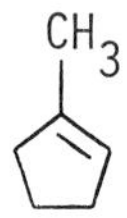

(i) 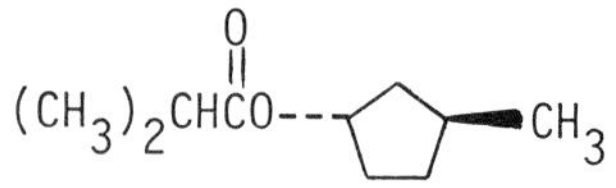

(j) 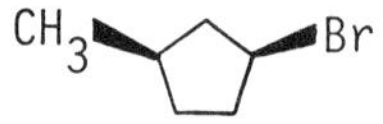

(k) 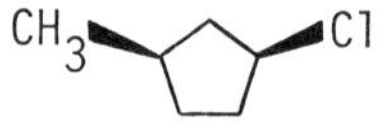

(l) and (m) 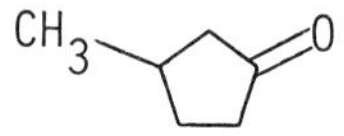

(n) 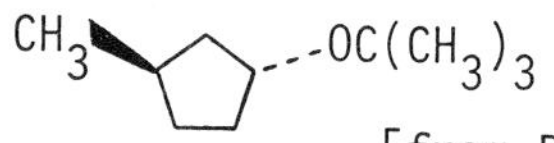

[from ROH + $^+C(CH_3)_3$]

Notice how the type of reaction determines the stereochemistry of the product as well as the presence or absence of rearrangement. In (a), (b), (c), (i), and (n), only the O-H bond is broken, so the *trans* stereochemistry around the ring is maintained. In (j) and (k) S_N2 reactions invert the stereochemistry, giving *cis* products. In (d) through (h), 2° carbocations are generated, which rearrange to 3°, giving the observed results.

****

13. Yes: (b) gives $CH_3CH_2CH_2\overset{\overset{O}{\|}}{C}O^-$ Na^+ and CHI_3

(f) gives 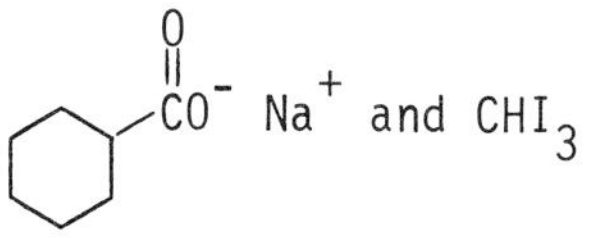

Only these two contain the $-CHOHCH_3$ group which is required for this reaction.

****

14. (a) 2-ethoxypropane

(b) 2-methoxyethanol

(c) cyclopentoxycyclopentane

(d) 1-chloro-2-(2-chloroethoxy)ethane

(e) 1-methoxy-1-methylcyclopentane

(f) *cis*-1,4-dimethoxycyclohexane

(g) chloro(methoxy)methane

****

15. Ethers lack hydrogens attached to oxygen, and therefore, unlike alcohols, ether molecules cannot hydrogen bond to one another. Ethers can hydrogen bond to the hydrogens of water, however, and therefore are about as soluble in water as alcohols of comparable molecular weight.

****

16. (a) $CH_3CH_2CH_2OCH(CH_2CH_3)_2$ (S_N2 O.K. on 1° haloalkane)

(b) $CH_3CH_2CH_2OH$ + $CH_3CH{=}CHCH_2CH_3$ (basic alkoxide gives mainly E2 with 2° haloalkane)

(c) 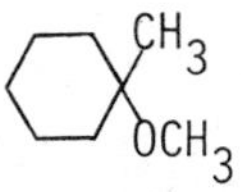

(d) $(CH_3)_2CHOCH_2CH_2CH(CH_3)_2$

(e) cyclohexanol + cyclohexene (same situation as b above)

(f) This 3° alkoxide is so bulky that even 1° haloalkanes will give mainly elimination: ethene will form in addition to some 1,1-dicyclopentylethoxyethane.

****

17. (b) Reaction is given in part (a).

(e) Use S_N1 conditions: chlorocyclohexane in neutral cyclohexanol (solvolysis, without a basic nucleophile).

(f) Use another solvolysis, this time with the 3° haloalkane:

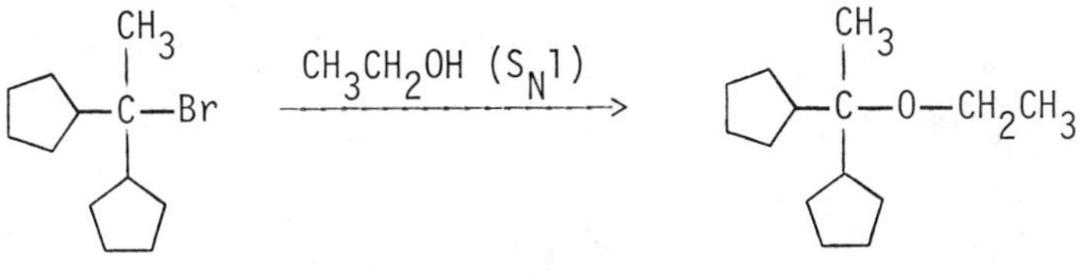

****

18. Rule of thumb: acid-base reactions are usually faster than displacement reactions. Therefore $HO^- + ROH \rightleftharpoons H_2O + RO^-$ is fast relative to $HO^- + RX \rightarrow ROH + X^-$. Apply this for each of the systems shown. Notice that each contains both alcohol and haloalkane functionality, and in each case an intramolecular displacement can lead to a reasonable product. Intramolecular displacement is further favored by maintaining a low concentration of the starting compound in solution, which minimizes competing intermolecular

processes.

(a) 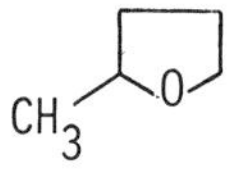 (b) 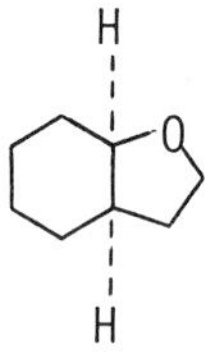 (c) 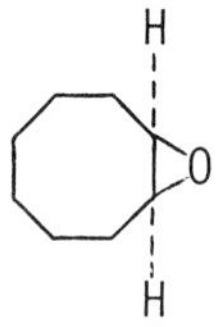

(d) 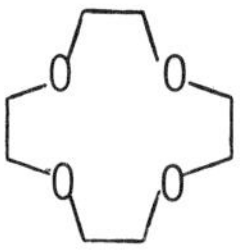 , via ring-closure of 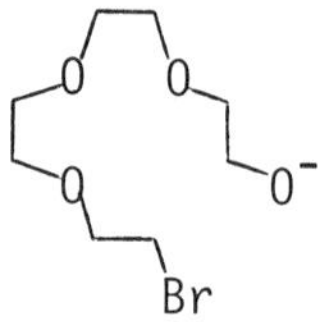

(e) 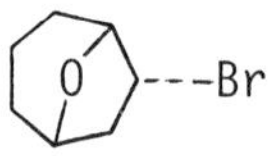 (5-membered ring forms faster than 4-membered ring)

****

19. Product is 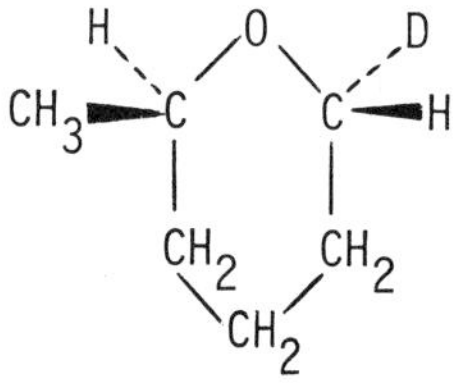 (note inversion at carbon that formerly contained the bromine; make a model if necessary).

The reaction is first order since the nucleophile and the haloalkane functional groups are in the same molecule. The mechanism is identical to that of the familiar S_N2 reaction, but the "2" here is not applicable since both reacting components are in the same molecule.

****

20. Take care to limit S_N2 syntheses to 1° haloalkanes. S_N1 reactions are most useful for 3° systems.

(a) $CH_3CH_2CHOHCH_3 \xrightarrow[]{1.\ NaH;\ 2.\ CH_3CH_2Br}$ (S_N2)

(b) 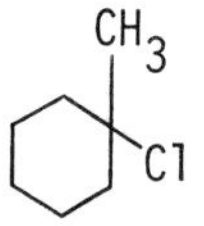 + $CH_3CH_2CH_2CH_2OH$ (solvent) ⟶ (solvolysis)

(c) $HOCH_2CH_2CH_2C(CH_3)_2Br$ ⟶ (intramolecular S_N1) or

$HOCH_2CH_2CH_2C(CH_3)_2OH \xrightarrow{H^+}$ (same)

(d) 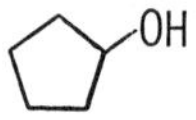 $\xrightarrow{H_2SO_4,\ 130°}$ (S_N1)

****

21. (a) CH_3CH_2I + $CH_3CH_2CH_2I$

(b) CH_3Br + $(CH_3)_2CHBr$

(c) CH_3I + ICH_2CH_2I

(d) 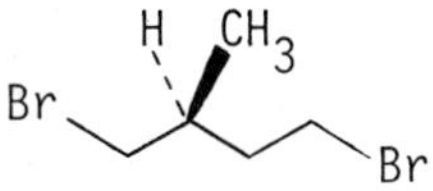

(e) 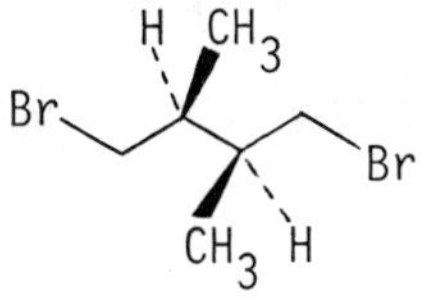

(f) 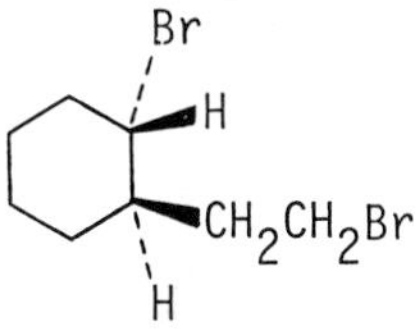

****

22. (a) $HOCH_2CH_2NH_2$ (S_N2 ring opening)

(b) 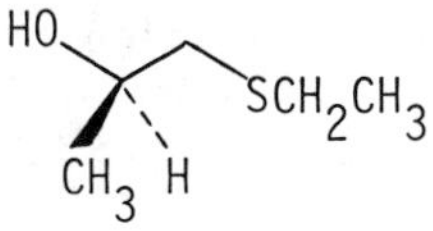 (same, reaction occurring at least substituted carbon of ring)

(c) $BrCH_2CH_2CH_2Br$

(d) $HOCH_2CH_2C(CH_3)_2OCH_3$ (S_N1 ring opening)

(e) $CH_3OCH_2CH_2C(CH_3)_2OH$ (S_N2 at least substituted ring carbon)

(f) 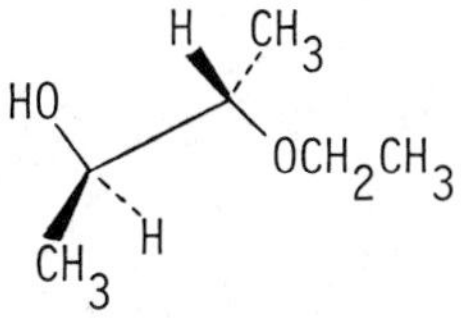 (S_N2 by ethanol on protonated oxacyclopropane - attack at either ring carbon gives same product)

(g) 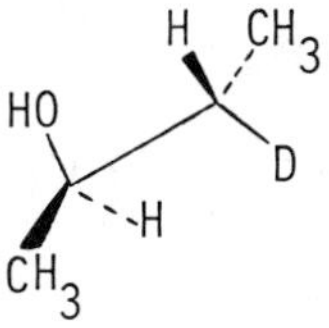 (S_N2 at either ring carbon)

(h) 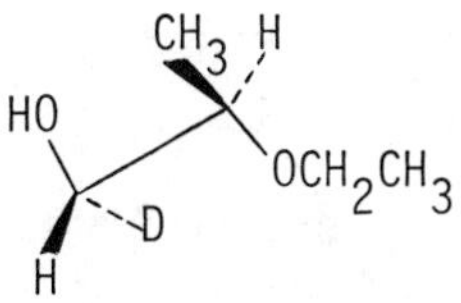 major product (greater cationic character at secondary ring carbon)

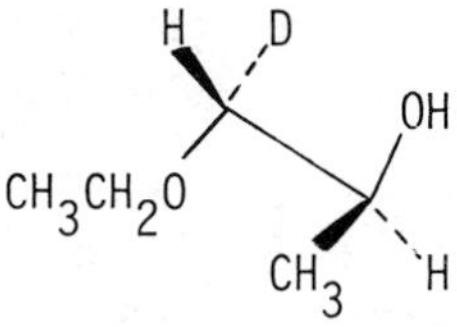 minor product (S_N2 on protonated oxacyclopropane)

****

23. (a) $HCl + ZnCl_2$ (rearrangement is unlikely in a simple primary substrate)

(b) PBr_3 (branching raises risk of rearrangement)

(c) HCl

(d) $P + I_2$ (to avoid rearrangement)

****

24. (a) 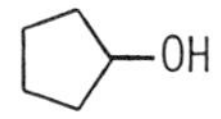 $\xrightarrow{Na_2Cr_2O_7,\ H_2SO_4,\ H_2O,\ \text{or Jones reagent}\ (CrO_3,\ H_2SO_4)}$

(b) $CH_3CH_2CH_2CH_2CH_2OH \xrightarrow{Na_2Cr_2O_7,\ H_2SO_4,\ H_2O}$

(c) 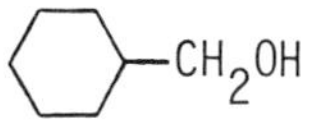 $\xrightarrow{CrO_3(\text{pyridine})_2}$ (to avoid overoxidation to 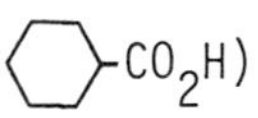)

(d) $(CH_3)_2CHCHOHCH_3 \xrightarrow{Na_2Cr_2O_7,\ H_2SO_4,\ H_2O}$

(e) $CH_3CH_2OH \xrightarrow{CrO_3(\text{pyridine})_2}$ (see above)

****

25. Good retrosynthetic disconnections are used in the solutions below.

(a) $CH_3CH_2CH_3 \xrightarrow{Br_2,\ h\nu} CH_3CHBrCH_3 \xrightarrow{Mg} CH_3CH(MgBr)CH_3$

$CH_3CH_3 \xrightarrow{Cl_2,\ h\nu} CH_3CH_2Cl \xrightarrow{Mg} CH_3CH_2MgCl$

} both to be used below

$CH_3CH_2Cl \xrightarrow{K^+\ ^-OH} CH_3CH_2OH$

$CH_3CH_2OH \xrightarrow{CrO_3(\text{pyridine})_2} CH_3CH{=}O \xrightarrow{1.\ CH_3CH_2MgCl;\ 2.\ H^+,\ H_2O} CH_3CHOHCH_2CH_3$

$\xrightarrow{Na_2Cr_2O_7,\ H^+} CH_3C({=}O)CH_2CH_3 \xrightarrow{1.\ CH_3CH(MgBr)CH_3;\ 2.\ H^+,\ H_2O}$ product

(b) $CH_3CH_2CH_2CH_3 \xrightarrow{1.\ Br_2,\ h\nu;\ 2.\ Mg} CH_3CH(MgBr)CH_2CH_3 \xrightarrow{1.\ HCH{=}O;\ 2.\ H^+,\ H_2O} CH_3CH_2CH(CH_3)CH_2OH$

$\xrightarrow{1.\ CrO_3(\text{pyridine})_2;\ 2.\ CH_3CH_2MgCl^*;\ 3.\ H^+,\ H_2O} CH_3CH_2CH(CH_3)CHOHCH_2CH_3 \xrightarrow{Na_2Cr_2O_7,\ H^+}$ product

(c) $2CH_3CH_2MgCl^*$ + $H\overset{O}{\overset{\|}{C}}OCH_3$ $\xrightarrow{\text{Then } H^+, H_2O}$ $(CH_3CH_2)_2CHOH$ $\xrightarrow[\text{2. Mg}]{\text{1. } PBr_3}$

$(CH_3CH_2)_2CHMgBr$ $\xrightarrow[\text{2. } H^+, H_2O]{\text{1. } CH_2\!-\!CH_2 \text{ (epoxide)}}$ $(CH_3CH_2)_2CHCH_2CH_2OH$ $\xrightarrow{Na_2Cr_2O_7, H^+}$ product

(d) $2CH_3\overset{MgBr}{\overset{|}{C}}HCH_3$ + $H\overset{O}{\overset{\|}{C}}OCH_3$ $\xrightarrow{\text{Then } H^+, H_2O}$ $(CH_3)_2CH\overset{OH}{\overset{|}{C}}HCH(CH_3)_2$

$\xrightarrow{H_2SO_4, \Delta}$ product

*As in part (a).

****

26. (a) Starting materials: $CH_3CH_2\overset{O}{\overset{\|}{C}}H$, cyclopentyl–Br, $CH_2\!-\!CH_2$ (epoxide).

cyclopentyl–Br $\xrightarrow[\text{3. } H^+, H_2O]{\text{1. Mg} \quad \text{2. } CH_3CH_2CHO}$ $CH_3CH_2\overset{OH}{\overset{|}{C}}H\text{–cyclopentyl}$ $\xrightarrow[\text{3. } CH_2\!-\!CH_2 \text{ (epoxide)}]{\text{1. } PBr_3 \quad \text{2. Mg}}$ $CH_3CH_2CHCH_2CH_2OH$ (on cyclopentyl)

$\xrightarrow[\text{3. } KMnO_4]{\text{1. } PBr_3 \quad \text{2. NaSH}}$ product

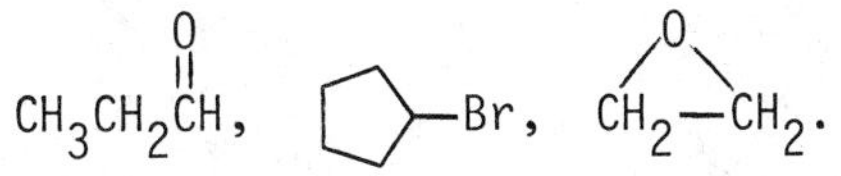

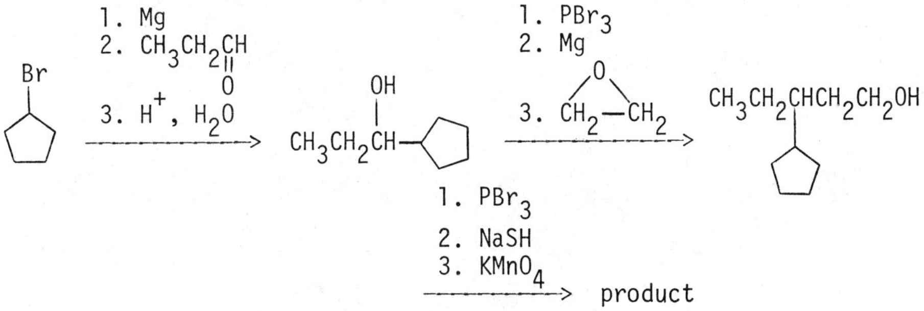

(b) Start with: $CH_3CH_2CH_2Cl$, $CH_3CH_2\overset{O}{\overset{\|}{C}}CH_3$, $H\overset{O}{\overset{\|}{C}}H$

$CH_3CH_2CH_2Cl$ $\xrightarrow[\text{3. } H^+, H_2O]{\text{1. Mg} \quad \text{2. } CH_3CH_2\overset{O}{\overset{\|}{C}}CH_3}$ $CH_3CH_2CH_2\!-\!\overset{CH_3}{\underset{CH_3CH_2}{\overset{|}{\underset{|}{C}}}}\!-\!OH$ $\xrightarrow[\text{2. Mg}]{\text{1. HBr}}$

$CH_3CH_2CH_2\!-\!\overset{CH_3}{\underset{CH_3CH_2}{\overset{|}{\underset{|}{C}}}}\!-\!MgBr$ $\xrightarrow[\text{2. } H^+, H_2O]{\text{1. } H\overset{O}{\overset{\|}{C}}H}$ $CH_3CH_2CH_2\!-\!\overset{CH_3}{\underset{CH_3CH_2}{\overset{|}{\underset{|}{C}}}}\!-\!CH_2OH$

$\xrightarrow{CrO_3(\text{pyridine})_2}$ product

****

27. (a) cyclopropylmethanethiol

(b) 2-(methylthio)butane, or methyl (1-methyl)propyl sulfide

(c) 1-propanesulfonic acid

(d) trifluoromethylsulfonyl chloride

****

28. (a) (1) CH_3SH, (2) CH_3OH

(b) (1) HS^-, (2) HO^-

(c) (1) H_3S^+, (2) H_2S

****

29. (a) $HSCH_2CH_2CH_2CH_2SH$

(b)  (via $^-SCH_2CH_2CH_2CH_2Cl$ intermediate)

(c) 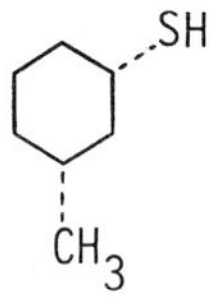 (S_N2)

(d) 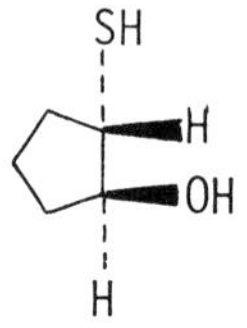 (S_N2 again)

(e) $(CH_3CH_2)_3CSCH_3$ (S_N1)

(f) $(CH_3)_2CHSSCH(CH_3)_2$

(g) 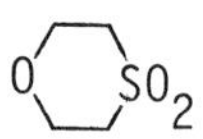

****

30. $2BrCH_2CH_2OH \xrightarrow{H_2SO_4,\ 130°} BrCH_2CH_2OCH_2CH_2Br \xrightarrow{Na_2S}$ product

****

31. $H_2SO_4/180°$: shorter route, but more prone to side reactions, e.g. rearrangements, ether formation, etc.

    PBr_3, then K^+ $^-OC(CH_3)_3$: two steps instead of one, but the only side reaction is S_N2 to give an ether in the second step, usually only a minor complication.

****

32. (a) It is a dehydration reaction (an elimination).

    (b) The Lewis acid may convert the hydroxy group into a better leaving group:

$$HOCH_2CH \big\langle \ + \ Mg^{2+} \ \rightleftharpoons \ \overset{+}{HO}-CH_2-\overset{|}{\underset{|}{C}}- \ \xrightarrow{H_2\ddot{O}} \ CH_2=C\big\langle \ + \ H_3O^+ \ + \ HOMg^+$$

with $\overset{+}{Mg}$ below.

****

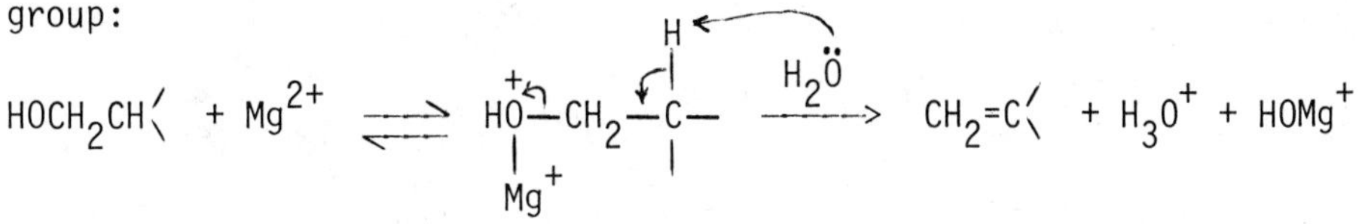

33. (a) This resembles the 1,2-diol rearrangement via a hydrogen shift:

$$\underset{H}{\overset{OH\ \ OH\ \ OH}{CH_2-CH-CH}} \ \xrightarrow[-H_2O]{H^+} \ \underset{H}{\overset{OH\ \ :OH}{CH_2-CH-CH}} \ \longrightarrow \ \overset{OH\ \ \ \overset{+}{OH}}{CH_2-CH_2-CH} \ \xrightarrow{-H^+} \ product$$

    (b) Treatment with H_2SO_4 would be a typical method.

    (c)
$$\overset{OH\ \ \ \ OH\ \ \ OH}{CD_2-CH-CD_2} \ \longrightarrow \ \overset{OH}{CD_2}-CHD-\overset{O}{\overset{||}{C}}-D \quad \text{(only one product - starting triol is symmetrical)}$$

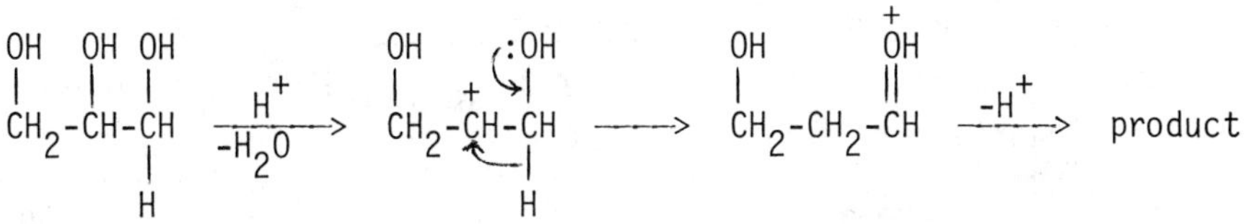

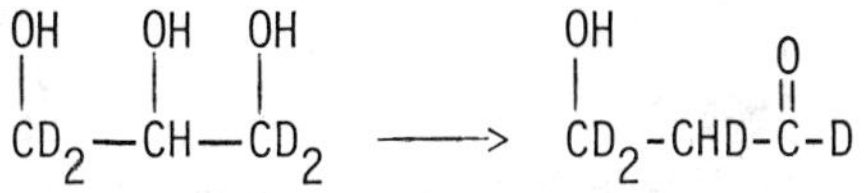

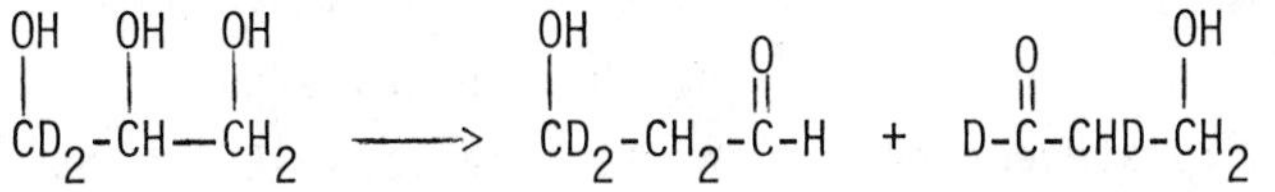

$$\overset{OH\ \ OH\ \ OH}{CD_2-CH-CH_2} \ \longrightarrow \ \overset{OH}{CD_2}-CH_2-\overset{O}{\overset{||}{C}}-H \ + \ D-\overset{O}{\overset{||}{C}}-CHD-\overset{OH}{CH_2} \quad \text{(depending on whether}$$

    D^- shifts from left carbon or H^- shifts from right carbon)

****

34. (a) The situation: $CH_3\overset{O}{\overset{||}{C}}D \ \xrightarrow[\text{NADH}]{\text{enzyme,}} \ CH_3CHDOH \ \xrightarrow[\text{NAD}^+]{\text{enzyme}} \ CH_3\overset{O}{\overset{||}{C}}D$

    The question and the hint tell you that stereochemistry is important, so let's look at how it may be involved.

Write $CH_3\overset{\overset{\displaystyle O}{\|}}{C}D$ in a plane, and try adding H^- to it, first from one side, and then from the other:

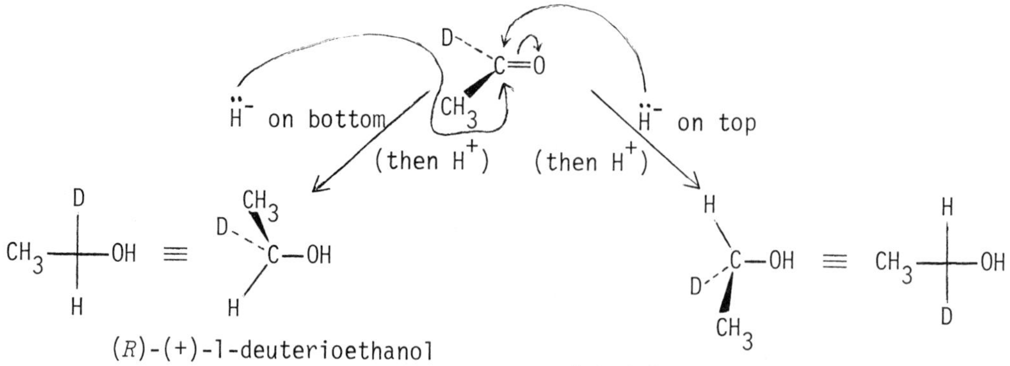

(R)-$(+)$-1-deuterioethanol

(S)-$(-)$-1-deuterioethanol

The products are *enantiomers* of each other! (For determining R and S, heavy isotopes have priority over light ones, so D>H, and the isomers are designated as shown above.)

Notice what happens now if the reaction is reversed. Removal of the atom from the <u>same side it was put on</u> *regenerates* $CH_3\overset{\overset{\displaystyle O}{\|}}{C}D$. If the opposite were to happen, you'd get $CH_3\overset{\overset{\displaystyle O}{\|}}{C}H$. See how it looks with the (S) enantiomer:

$$CH_3\overset{\overset{\displaystyle O}{\|}}{C}H \xleftarrow{\quad\text{Remove}\quad \atop \text{from bottom (D)}} CH_3\!\!-\!\!OH \text{(with H top, D bottom)} \xrightarrow{\quad\text{Remove}\quad \atop \text{from top (H)}} CH_3\overset{\overset{\displaystyle O}{\|}}{C}D$$

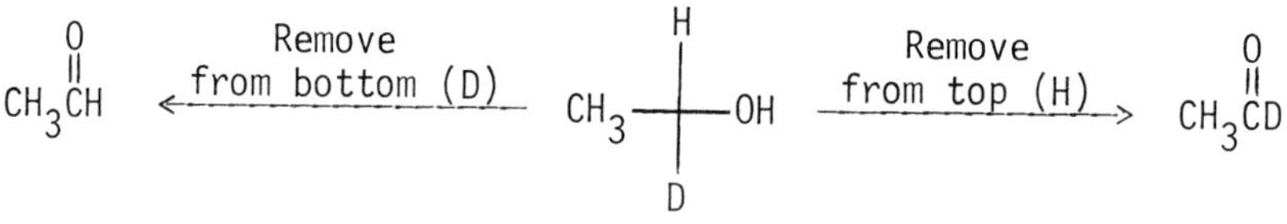

S isomer

So the answer is as follows: reduction of aldehydes by NADH + enzyme and reoxidation of the resultant alcohols by NAD^+ + enzyme must both occur on the <u>same side</u> of the substrate molecule. The enzyme system is stereospecific in its catalysis of the reaction *in both directions*. The actual situation is:

$$CH_3\overset{\overset{\displaystyle O}{\|}}{C}D \xrightarrow[\text{(H^- to top)}]{\text{NADH, enzyme}} CH_3\!\!-\!\!OH \xrightarrow[\text{(H^- from top)}]{\text{NAD^+, enzyme}} CH_3\overset{\overset{\displaystyle O}{\|}}{C}D$$

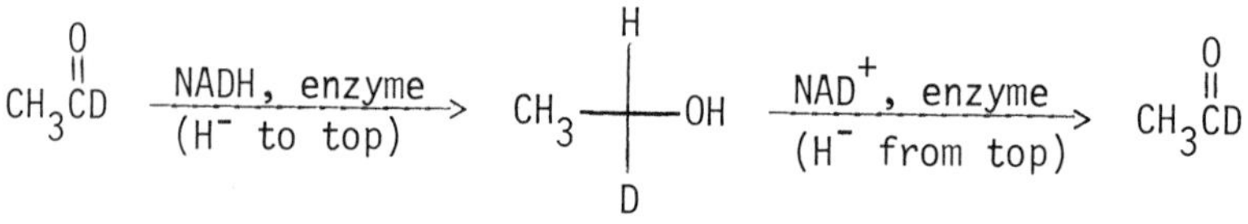

100% S

(b) As described and drawn in part a, the enzyme operates on the top side of the molecule. So,

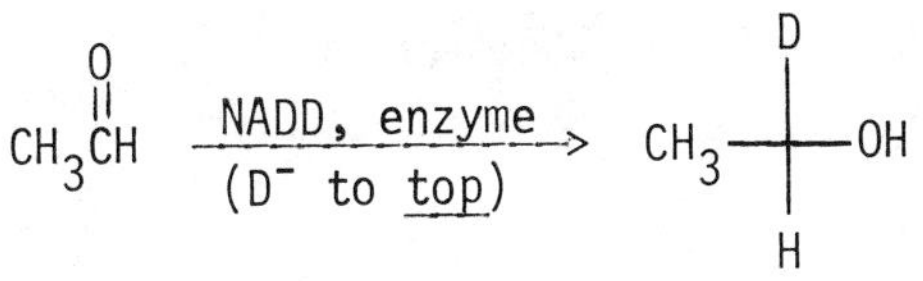
O
CH_3CH
NADD, enzyme
(D$^-$ to top)
D
CH_3
OH
H

100% *R*: the enantiomer of the ethanol involved in part a.

****

35. (a) In order to make an oxacyclopropane from 2-bromocyclohexanol the molecule must be able to adapt a geometry that allows the necessary "internal S_N2" backside displacement to occur. This requires that the alkoxide and Br be *anti* to each other, which is possible only from the *trans* isomer of the starting material:

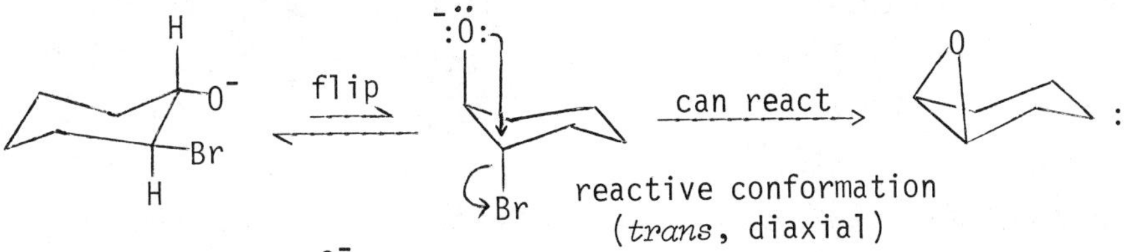

compare 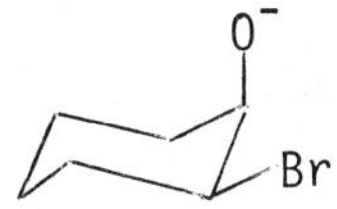

cis, no good

(b) 1. $NaBH_4$ (reduces ketone to alcohol); 2. NaOH (makes alkoxide, leading to internal displacement of Br^- and oxacyclopropane formation)

(c) The first step must form a β-OH, with the new hydroxy group *trans* to the original Br. Otherwise the second step will not give an oxacyclopropane, for the reason given in part a. Notice that the β-OH and α-Br groups are automatically *trans*, diaxial due to the natural shape of the steroid rings.

****

36. $CH_2{=}CH{-}CH_2Cl \xrightarrow{HS^-\ Na^+} CH_2{=}CH{-}CH_2SH \xrightarrow{I_2}$

$CH_2{=}CH{-}CH_2{-}S{-}S{-}CH_2{-}CH{=}CH_2 \xrightarrow{\text{one equiv. } H_2O_2}$ allicin

****

CHAPTER 10

The Use of Nuclear Magnetic Resonance Spectroscopy to Deduce Structure

General Introduction

In this chapter we address the question that faces anyone trying to identify the molecular structure of a substance, namely, "what is it?" To put it another way, this chapter will begin to answer the obvious question that you may already have been thinking after the first nine chapters of this book, namely, "how does anyone really know that all those molecules are what we say they are?" In the "olden days," tedious indirect indentification methods had to be used, and some are described in the text. Nowadays these questions are answered through the use of spectroscopy, a technique that literally serves as the "eyes" of an organic chemist with respect to the structures of molecules. The most important and widely used type of spectroscopy, nuclear magnetic resonance (NMR), will be described in this chapter.

Outline of the Chapter

10-1. What is Spectroscopy?

Or, now for something just a little bit different.

10-2. Proton Nuclear Magnetic Resonance.

An example of fairly simple physics put to very good use. A general overview of NMR spectroscopy.

10-3. The Proton Chemical Shift.

The first two pieces of information available from an NMR spectrum.

10-4. Chemical Shift Equivalence. Integration.

The third piece of information available from an NMR spectrum.

10-5. Spin-Spin Splitting.

A complication which gives rise to the fourth and, perhaps, most important kind of information present in an NMR spectrum.

10-6. Spin-Spin Splitting: Complications.

The complications get a bit more complicated.

10-7. Carbon-13 Nuclear Magnetic Resonance.

The utility of another magnetic nucleus in NMR.

Keys to the Chapter

10-1. What is Spectroscopy?

Spectroscopy is mainly physics. In spite of that, the material in this section is really very basic and quite understandable: spectroscopy detects the absorption of energy by molecules. The stake that the organic chemist has in this is also simple. Determining the structure of a molecule requires that the chemist be able to *interpret* spectroscopically observed energy absorptions in terms of structural features that an unknown molecule contains. This chapter will describe the physical phenomena associated with nuclear magnetic resonance (NMR), and will then follow with their logical implications as applied to identifying structural features in a molecule from a nuclear magnetic resonance "spectrum." Don't be frightened. The end result, the ability to interpret spectoscopic data in terms of molecular structure, is actually one of the easiest skills to acquire in this course. It's actually almost fun!

10-2. Proton Nuclear Magnetic Resonance.

In the upcoming sections the physical basis for the utility of nuclear magnetic resonance in organic chemistry will be presented. This section describes a couple of concepts that are likely to be unfamiliar to you. The first is the idea that a magnet can align with an external magnetic field in more than one way. Most of us are familiar with bar magnet compasses, which orient themselves along the earth's magnetic field in one direction only. Nuclear magnets are actually similar, except for the fact that the reorientation energies are so small that energy quantization becomes significant. Like the compass, the nuclear magnet does have one energetically preferred alignment (the α spin for a proton). Less favored alignments ("spin states") are very close in energy to the preferred one on a nuclear scale, however. So, unlike the macroscopic compass, the microscopic nuclei can commonly be observed in less favorable, higher energy orientations in a magnetic field.

The second new idea is that of resonance. This is the term that describes the absorption of exactly the correct amount of quantized energy to cause a species in a lower energy state to move to a higher energy state. For nuclear magnets this is commonly described as a "spin flip" (α spin state to β spin state for a proton). The amount of energy involved depends on the identity of the nucleus and the size of the external magnet. The chapter section describes these relationships in detail. It is the observation of resonance energy absorptions by magnetic nuclei at certain values of magnetic field strength and energy input (in the form of radio waves) that constitutes the physical basis for nuclear magnetic resonance spectroscopy.

10-3. The Proton Chemical Shift.

The normal NMR spectrum can provide four important pieces of structural information about an unknown molecule. The first two pieces of information are derived from the fact that protons in different chemical environments display separate resonance lines in a high resolution ^{1}H NMR spectrum. Thus, first, by counting the number of resonance signals in the spectrum, one knows the number of sets of protons in different chemical environments contained in the molecule. Second, the actual position of each resonance signal is characteristic of certain kinds of chemical environments, e.g., it can imply proximity to a specific type of functional group, or attachment to a certain type of atom. The phenomenon responsible for this is the magnetic shielding of a magnetic nucleus under observation, by the nearby electrons in the molecule. How this comes about physically is described in detail in the text. For our ultimate purpose, namely the *use* of NMR spectroscopy in determining molecular structure, what you really need to know are certain practical considerations. For example on a typical NMR spectrum, resonance signals to the left of the chart result from less strongly shielded ("deshielded") protons, while signals to the right are representative of more strongly shielded protons. "Deshielded" protons require lower external magnetic fields for resonance, while shielded protons require higher fields. So we have NMR spectra that have the following qualitative relationships:

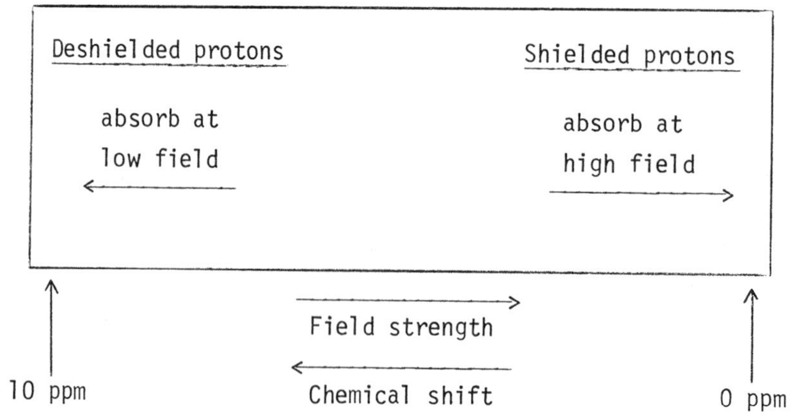

As described in the text, a resonance signal's position is measured as a *field independent* chemical shift, which has "units" of parts per million (ppm) of the total applied field, often called "δ" units. These read from right to left, with the usual proton spectrum covering a range from 0 to 10 ppm. Table 10-2 shows typical chemical shifts for common types of protons. There is a lot here, but for most purposes all you really need to know are the types of protons that resonate in several general ranges of the NMR spectrum:

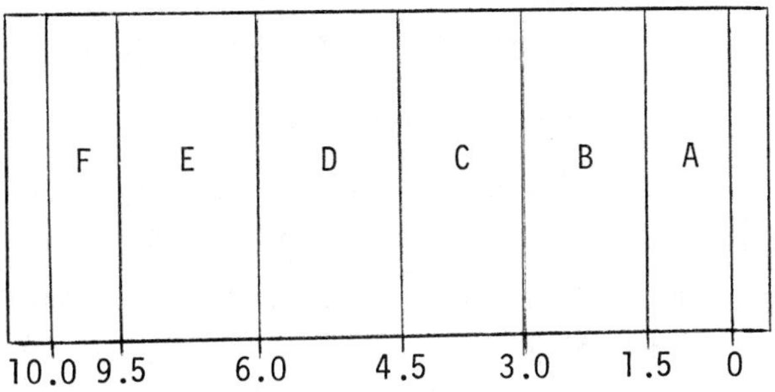

Chemical Shift

A, 0-1.5 ppm, alkane type hydrogens
B, 1.5-3 ppm, hydrogens on carbons next to carbon-containing functional groups
C, 3-4.5 ppm, hydrogens on carbons attached to electronegative atoms
D, 4.5-6.0 ppm, alkene type hydrogens
E, 6.0-9.5 ppm, benzene type hydrogens
F, 9.5-10.0 ppm, hydrogen of aldehyde group

With this as a basis you are ready to start interpreting NMR spectra. For the initial problems of this type, simply count the number of signals in the spectrum, and note the position of each one. Then see if you can come up with a structure that should display the correct number of signals in approximately the observed places, based on the material in this chapter section. If you can, you have probably picked a sensible structure for the molecule.

10-4. Chemical Shift Equivalence. Integration.

The first part of this section presents detailed procedures for determining which hydrogens in a molecule will have identical chemical shifts due to "chemical equivalence." The simplest examples of this would include the four hydrogens of methane, or the six hydrogens of ethane. There are some minor complications which might require your reviewing some of the material towards the end of Chapter 5 (Stereoisomerism), but on the whole these procedures are not difficult.

"Integration" provides the third major piece of information available from NMR: the relative number of hydrogens responsible for each separate NMR signal. The "integration" is measured electronically by the NMR spectrometer and plotted directly on the spectrum. The integration therefore tells you whether a given NMR signal is due to a single hydrogen or some number of chemical shift equivalent hydrogens in the molecule. The integration is a critical piece of information for the interpretation of NMR spectra.

10-5. Spin-Spin Splitting.

Since many atomic nuclei are magnets, the NMR signal of a nucleus under observation can, in principle, be affected by the presence of other nearby magnetic nuclei. These neighboring nuclear magnets can align with or against the magnetic field generated by the NMR machine, and so their fields can add or subtract from the field generated by the NMR machine. The result is a slight change in the resonance line position for the nucleus under observation, and is called spin-spin coupling or spin-spin splitting. Again, for spectral interpretation purposes, the theory, presented in the text (although it is not really complicated at all) is secondary to understanding the meaning of the phenomenon in terms of molecular structure. Thus it is often sufficient to rely on two simple rules:

1. Spin-spin splitting is not observed between chemical shift equivalent protons.
2. The signal of a proton with 'N' neighboring protons will be split into N+1 lines ("N+1 rule").

There are two important qualifications to rule number 2:

a. N+1 lines is a minimum. There may be more (section 10-6).
b. In determining 'N', you only count neighbors whose chemical shifts are different from that of the proton whose signal is being considered. (This is due to rule number 1.)

A little careful observation of the text examples will help you get used to the consequences of spin-spin splitting in its most common forms. Table 10-5 and Figures 10-25, 26, and 27 nicely illustrate these situations.

10-6. Spin-Spin Splitting: Complications.

The splitting rules outlined in the previous section are idealized for two conditions that are only rarely completely met in any NMR spectrum. For these rules to hold exactly, first, all the signals must be much farther apart from each other than the coupling constants in their patterns (i.e., $\Delta\nu >> J$). Second, all the coupling constants (J values) associated with any proton must be identical in size, even if that proton is coupled to more than one group of neighboring protons. If either of these conditions is not fulfilled, the spectrum won't look exactly like you might expect. Fortunately, a lot of the time these conditions are *approached*, especially for proton groups near electronegative atoms or functional groups. You will therefore have to be aware of the possible effects of "non-first-order" situations, but for the most part you won't have to worry a whole lot about them.

10-7. Carbon-13 Nuclear Magnetic Resonance.

This is an extension of NMR spectroscopy that is rapidly growing in use and importance. There are two reasons. First, new types of NMR instruments make these spectra much easier to obtain than was the case only a few years ago. Second, the spectra contain useful information that is very easy to interpret, especially under conditions of broad band proton decoupling, which "wipes out" the spin-spin splitting by neighboring hydrogens. The results are spectra that contain only "singlets," that is, a single line for each carbon or group of chemically equivalent carbons. Given such a spectrum, you can quickly determine whether or not it corresponds to a proposed structure simply by counting the lines in the spectrum. Of course, more extensive information is also available from the C-13 spectrum if desired, in the form of the carbon chemical shifts (Table 10-6), and the proton splittings of the "un-decoupled" spectrum (e.g., Fig. 10-37).

Solutions to Chapter 10 Problems

1. To do this you need to tell the difference between *frequencies*, ν, in units of sec^{-1}, and *wavenumbers*, $\tilde{\nu}$, in units of cm^{-1}. The caption to Figure 10-2 shows how they are related: $\nu = c/\lambda$ and $\tilde{\nu} = 1/\lambda$, so $\nu = c\tilde{\nu}$, or $\tilde{\nu} = \nu/c$. So for sound waves ($\nu = 10^3\ sec^{-1}$), $\tilde{\nu} = 10^3/(3 \times 10^{10}) \simeq 3 \times 10^{-8}\ cm^{-1}$; for AM radio ($\nu = 10^6\ sec^{-1}$), $\tilde{\nu} = 10^6/(3 \times 10^{10}) \simeq 3 \times 10^{-5}\ cm^{-1}$; and for FM and TV ($\nu = 10^8\ sec^{-1}$), $\tilde{\nu} = 10^8/(3 \times 10^{10}) \simeq 3 \times 10^{-3}\ cm^{-1}$. All of these are well to the right end of the chart, very low in energy relative to most of the forms of electromagnetic radiation on the chart.

****

2. The conversion formulas are $\lambda = 1/\tilde{\nu}$ and $\nu = c/\lambda$ (see caption to Figure 10-2).

(a) $\lambda = 1/(1050\ cm^{-1}) = 9.5 \times 10^{-4} cm = 9.5\ \mu m$

(b) $510\ nm = 5.1 \times 10^{-5} cm$; $\nu = (3 \times 10^{10} cm\ sec^{-1})/(5.1 \times 10^{-5} cm) = 5.9 \times 10^{14}\ sec^{-1}$

(c) $6.15\ \mu m = 6.15 \times 10^{-4} cm$; $\tilde{\nu} = 1/(6.15 \times 10^{-4} cm) = 1.63 \times 10^{3}\ cm^{-1}$

(d) $\nu = c\tilde{\nu} = (3 \times 10^{10} cm\ sec^{-1})(2.25 \times 10^{3}\ cm^{-1}) = 6.75 \times 10^{13}\ sec^{-1}$

****

3. Use $\Delta E = 28{,}600/\lambda$ from the caption to Figure 10-2, and use the equations $\lambda = 1/\tilde{\nu}$ and $\lambda = c/\nu$. Be sure to convert the units of λ to nm before calculating ΔE, though!

(a) $\lambda = 1/750 = 1.33 \times 10^{-3} cm = 1.33 \times 10^{4} nm$ ($1\ cm = 10^{-2} m$, and $1\ nm = 10^{-9} m$, so $1\ cm = 10^{7} nm$). So $\Delta E = (2.86 \times 10^{4})/(1.33 \times 10^{4}) = 2.15$ kcal/mole

(b) $\lambda = 1/2900 = 3.45 \times 10^{-4} cm = 3.45 \times 10^{3} nm$.

So, $\Delta E = (2.86 \times 10^{4})/(3.45 \times 10^{3}) = 8.29$ kcal/mole.

(c) $\lambda = 350$ nm (given) so $\Delta E = (2.86 \times 10^{4})/350 = 82$ kcal/mole.

(d) $\lambda = 3 \times 10^{10}/20 = 1.5 \times 10^{9} cm = 1.5 \times 10^{16} nm$
So $\Delta E = (2.86 \times 10^{4})/(1.5 \times 10^{16}) = 1.9 \times 10^{-12}$ kcal/mole (!).

(e) $\lambda = 3 \times 10^{10}/(4 \times 10^{4}) = 7.5 \times 10^{5} cm = 7.5 \times 10^{12} nm$
So $\Delta E = (2.86 \times 10^{4})/(7.5 \times 10^{12}) = 3.8 \times 10^{-9}$ kcal/mole.

(f) $\lambda = 3 \times 10^{10}/(8.8 \times 10^{7}) = 3.4 \times 10^{2} cm = 3.4 \times 10^{9}$ nm.
So $\Delta E = (2.86 \times 10^{4})/(3.4 \times 10^{9}) = 8.4 \times 10^{-6}$ kcal/mole

(g) $\lambda = 7 \times 10^{-2} nm$, so $\Delta E = (2.86 \times 10^{4})/(7 \times 10^{-2}) = 4.1 \times 10^{5}$ kcal/mole

****

4. Only the value of ν is needed to calculate ΔE. Use $\Delta E = 28{,}600/\lambda$, together with $\lambda = c/\nu$.

(a) $\lambda = (3 \times 10^{10} cm\ sec^{-1})/(9 \times 10^{7}\ sec^{-1}) = 333\ cm = 3.33 \times 10^{9}$ nm;
$\Delta E = (2.86 \times 10^{4})/(3.33 \times 10^{9}) = 8.59 \times 10^{-6}$ kcal/mole

(b) $\Delta E = 4.76 \times 10^{-5}$ kcal/mole

****

5. $\lambda = (3 \times 10^{10} cm\ sec^{-1})/(1.5 \times 10^{-1}\ sec^{-1}) = 2 \times 10^{11} cm = 2 \times 10^{18}$ nm.
    $\Delta E = (2.86 \times 10^{4})/(2 \times 10^{18}) = 1.43 \times 10^{-14}$ kcal/mole

****

6. (a)

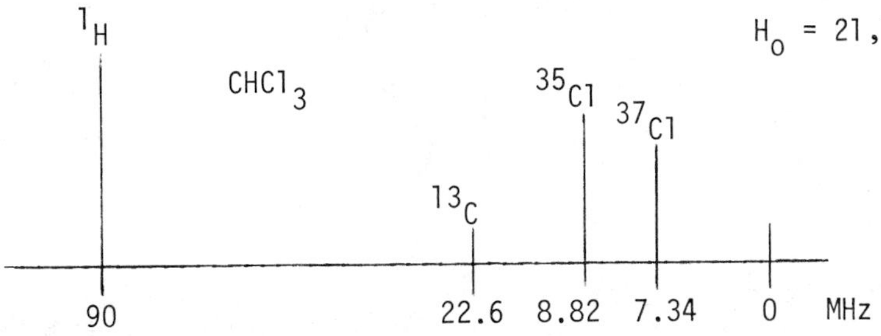

(b) Like (a), but a signal at 84.6 MHz (^{19}F) instead of 90 MHz (^1H).

(c) This will show all the signals present in both (a) and (b).

At 84,600 Gauss the positions of all lines will be at frequencies 4X greater than at 21,150 Gauss. For example, a ^1H signal will be at 360 MHz.

****

7. In (c) the high resolution spectrum around 22.6 MHz will show *two* ^{13}C resonance signals, since this molecule contains two non-identical carbon atoms.

****

8. (a) Divide by 90: $\frac{92}{90} = 1.02$; $\frac{185}{90} = 2.06$; $\frac{205}{90} = 2.28$ ppm.

(b) At 60 MHz: $92 \times \frac{60}{90} = 61$ Hz; $185 \times \frac{60}{90} = 123$ Hz; $205 \times \frac{60}{90} = 137$ Hz.

At 360 MHz: $92 \times \frac{360}{90} = 368$ Hz; $185 \times \frac{360}{90} = 740$ Hz; $205 \times \frac{360}{90} =$ 820 Hz.

(c)
$$CH_3-\overset{\overset{\displaystyle O}{\|}}{C}-CH_2-C(CH_3)_3$$
$$\uparrow \qquad\quad \uparrow \qquad\quad \uparrow$$
$$\delta2.06 \quad\ \delta2.28 \quad \delta1.02$$

****

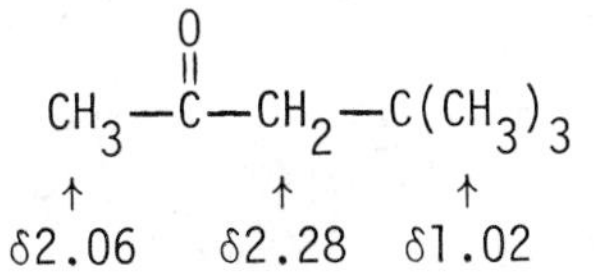

9. Chemical shifts have been estimated from the values in Table 10-2, with adjustments for nearby functional groups, and are approximate.

(a) 2 signals: CH_3-CH_2-CH_2-CH_3
↑ 0.9 (CH₃), ↑ 1.3 (CH₂)

(b) 2 signals: CH_3-CHBr-CH_3
↑ 1.5 ↑ 3.8

(c) 3 signals: H—O—CH_2-CCl$(CH_3)_2$
↑ variable ↑ 4.0 ↑ 1.4

(d) 4 signals: $(CH_3)_2$CH—CH_2-CH_3
↑ 0.9 ↑ 1.5 ↑ 1.3 ↑ 0.9

(e) 2 signals: $(CH_3)_3$C—NH_2
↑ 1.3 ↑ variable

(f) 3 signals: $(CH_3CH_2)_3$CH
↑ 0.9 ↑ 1.3 ↑ 1.5

(g) 4 signals: CH_3-O-CH_2-CH_2-CH_3
↑ 3.4 ↑ 3.8 ↑ 1.7 ↑ 1.0

(h) 2 signals:

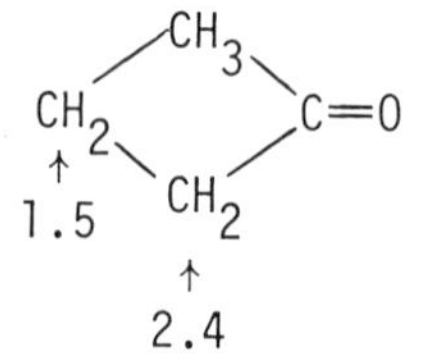

(i) 6 signals: CH_3-CH_2-CH(CH_3)(OH)
↑ 1.0 ↑ 1.4* ↑ 3.8; CH_3 ← 1.2; OH ↑ variable

(j) 8 signals:

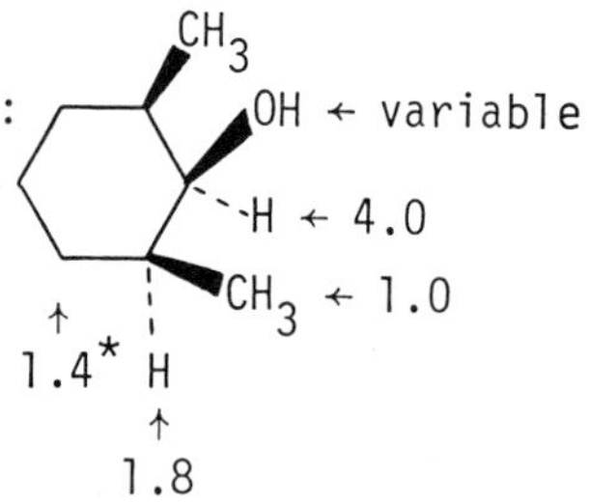

*Methylene hydrogens are diastereotopic and therefore non-equivalent.

****

10. As in the previous problem, the chemical shifts are approximations. Chemical shifts in [boxes] are most useful for distinguishing structures. Integrations are given in parentheses. Signals marked with stars (*) will be complicated by diastereotopism due to the presence of a chiral carbon in the molecule.

(a) $(CH_3)_2$CBr-CH_2-CH_3
↑ 1.5 (6) ↑ 1.8 (2) ↑ 1.1 (3)

$BrCH_2$-CH(CH_3)-CH_2-CH_3
CH_3 ← [1.1] (3)
↑ [3.5] (2)* ↑ 2.0 (1) ↑ 1.5 (2)* ↑ [0.9] (3)

$(CH_3)_2$CH-CH_2-CH_2Br
↑ [0.9] (6) ↑ 1.6 (1) ↑ 1.8 (2) ↑ [3.5] (2)

Compounds are readily distinguished by their NMR spectra: the first one has no signals downfield of δ2, while the others do. The latter will also show different numbers of signals. The middle compound has two nonequivalent methyl groups while the last has two identical methyls.

$$ClCH_2 \leftarrow \boxed{3.7}\ (2)$$

(b) $Cl-CH_2-CH_2-CH_2-CH_2-OH$ $CH_3-CH-CH_2-OH$ $(CH_3)_2CCl-CH_2-OH$

    ↑ ↑ ↑ ↑ ↑   ↑ ↑ ↑ ↑   ↑   ↑ ↑

  $\boxed{3.7}$ 1.7 1.6 $\boxed{3.6}$ var $\boxed{1.1}$ 2.0 $\boxed{3.6}$ var $\boxed{1.5}$ $\boxed{4.0}$ var

  (2) (2) (2) (2) (1)   (3) (1) (2)* (1)   (6)   (2) (1)

Compounds are again distinguishable. The number and integration of signals downfield of δ3 distinguishes the last compound. The other two are distinguished by the presence of an upfield methyl signal in one but not in the other.

     $CH_3 \leftarrow 1.5\ (3)$ $CH_3 \leftarrow 1.2\ (3)$

      | |

(c) $ClCH_2CBrCH-(CH_3)_2$ $ClCH_2-CHCBr(CH_3)_2$ $ClCH_2C(CH_3)_2CHBrCH_3$

   ↑   ↑ ↑   ↑ ↑   ↑   ↑   ↑   ↑ ↑

   4.0   2.0 1.1   3.7 2.0   1.5 $\boxed{3.7}$ 1.3 $\boxed{4.0}$ 1.5

   (2)* (1) (6)*   (2)* (1) (6)*   (2)* (6)* (1) (3)

$ClCH_2-CHBrC(CH_3)_3$

  ↑ ↑   ↑

 4.0 4.2 $\boxed{1.1}$

 (2)* (1)   (9)

The last two compounds are readily identified. The last one contains three equivalent methyl groups, giving a single signal of intensity 9. Although the remaining three compounds all have four signals, only the last of them has two signals downfield of δ3 (with a total integration of 3). The first two compounds will be difficult to distinguish by NMR - they each have the same number of signals with the same integration ratios. Only minor differences in chemical shifts will be present, and both of the spectra will be complicated by diastereotopic methyl and methylene groups (starred).

****

11. (a)   The spectrum shows two signals, at δ1.1 and δ3.3, with an integration ratio of 9:2. Since the whole formula ($C_5H_{11}Cl$) has 11 hydrogens, the δ1.1 signal must be for 9 equivalent hydrogens, and the δ3.3 signal must be for 2 equivalent hydrogens. A good way to get 9 equivalent hydrogens is with a $(CH_3)_3C$ group. The other 2 hydrogens must be on a separate, single carbon since the $(CH_3)_3C$ group contains all but one of the five carbons in the whole formula. The downfield location of these

two hydrogens suggests their carbon is attached to the Cl. So:

$(CH_3)_3C-$, $-CH_2-$, $-Cl$ $\Longrightarrow$ $(CH_3)_3C-CH_2-Cl$ as a plausible
$\uparrow$ $\uparrow$ structure.
$\delta 1.1$ $\delta 3.3$

(b)   Somewhat similar: two signals, $\delta 1.9$ and 3.8, with an integration
ratio of about 6 or 7 to 2. Since the molecule has 8 hydrogens, the
ratio of 6:2 is probably right. The signal for 6 equivalent hydrogens
is probably due to two methyl groups on the same carbon (CH_3-C-CH_3).
The 2 hydrogen signal can only be a $-CH_2-$, since there are only 4
carbons in the molecule. So:

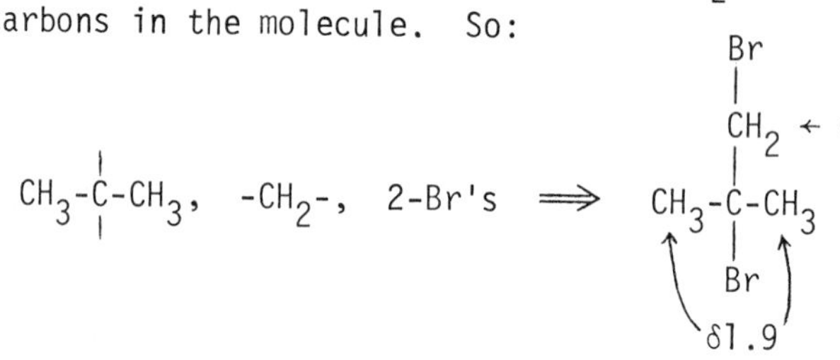

$CH_3-\overset{\mid}{\underset{\mid}{C}}-CH_3$, $-CH_2-$,   2-Br's $\Longrightarrow$ $CH_3-\overset{\mid}{\underset{\mid}{C}}-CH_3$ is the answer.

with the structure:

Br
|
CH_2 $\leftarrow$ $\delta 3.8$
|
$CH_3-\overset{\mid}{\underset{\mid}{C}}-CH_3$
|
Br
$\delta 1.9$

****

12. (a)   The spectrum has two signals in a 3:1 intensity ratio. Since the
molecule has 8 hydrogens, this means that there is one group of 6
equivalent H's, and another of 2 equivalent H's (6:2 = 3:1). Two
equivalent CH_3's and a CH_2 account for all but the 2 oxygen atoms in
the formula. The larger signal at $\delta 3.3$ is just right for hydrogens
on carbons attached to an oxygen. The downfield location for the
small signal ($\delta 4.4$) is consistent with attachment of carbon to more
than one oxygen. Putting it all together we get $CH_3-O-CH_2-O-CH_3$.
with $\delta 4.4$ for the CH_2 and equivalent, at $\delta 3.3$ for the CH_3 groups.

(b)   Again two signals, but now in a 9:1 intensity ratio. Reasoning as in
(a), there are 3 equivalent CH_3's, each attached to an oxygen, and a
CH attached to more than one oxygen due to its downfield chemical
shift ($\delta 4.9$). The only consistent structure is then $(CH_3O)_3CH$.
with $\delta 3.3$ and $\delta 4.9$.

(c)   Two signals equal in intensity imply two different groups, each with
6 equivalent H's. The signal at $\delta 3.1$ could imply two equivalent CH_3-O
groups while the signal at $\delta 1.2$ suggests two equivalent CH_3 groups not

attached to oxygen. These all add up to $C_4H_{12}O_2$, leaving one carbon unaccounted for in the formula of the molecule ($C_{\underline{5}}H_{12}O_2$). The fifth carbon can be used to connect the other four groups: $(CH_3O)_2C(CH_3)_2$, which is the answer.

By comparison, glyme has two signals in a 3:2 (= 6:4) ratio, and they are both in a region consistent with H's on a carbon attached to a <u>single</u> oxygen, as the structure $CH_3OCH_2CH_2OCH_3$ requires.

****

13. (a) There are two signals in a 3:1 intensity ratio. Since there are 12 H's in the formula, there are 9 H's in one location (not adjacent to a functional group according to the δ1.2, high-field shift) and 3 H's in another (close to a functional group based on the δ2.1 chemical shift). It is simplest to start with CH_3 groups as pieces of a possible structure. There is also a CO group since the molecule is a ketone. So we have so far:

CH_3	3 CH_3's	CO
δ2.1	δ1.2	

which adds up to $C_5H_{12}O$. One additional C is needed, but nothing else. If we draw all these pieces with the possible bonds they can form we have

$$\underset{\delta 2.1}{-CH_3} \qquad \underbrace{-CH_3 \quad -CH_3 \quad -CH_3}_{\delta 1.2} \qquad -\overset{\overset{\displaystyle O}{\|}}{C}- \qquad -\overset{|}{\underset{|}{C}}-$$

Attaching the first CH_3 to the CO will explain its chemical shift:

$CH_3-\overset{\overset{\displaystyle O}{\|}}{C}-$. None of the other 3 CH_3's can be directly on the CO because (1) the chemical shifts are wrong and (2) there would be no place left to attach the rest of the pieces. So, attach the unbonded C atom instead:

$$CH_3-\overset{\overset{\displaystyle O}{\|}}{C}-\overset{|}{\underset{|}{C}}-.$$

Now the only possible final step is to attach the 3 CH_3's:

$$CH_3-\overset{\overset{\displaystyle O}{\|}}{C}-C(CH_3)_3.$$ This is the answer.

(b) Both show two signals in a 3:1 ratio, corresponding to 9 H's and 3 H's again. Let's assume again that the same pieces are present as in part (a), plus the extra O atom. Let's also assume that three of the CH_3's are again on the extra C atom; that is, we have

$-CH_3$ $\quad -C(CH_3)_3 \quad$ $-\overset{O}{\overset{\|}{C}}-$ $\quad -O-$ as our pieces.

For Isomer 1, $-CH_3$ is at δ2.0 and $-C(CH_3)_3$ is at δ1.5. The $-C(CH_3)_2-CH_3$ is downfield relative to the ketone in part (a).

For Isomer 2, $-CH_3$ is at δ3.6, far downfield relative to the ketone in (a), but the $-C(CH_3)_3$ is at δ1.2, almost identical to the ketone in (a).

The CH_3 in Isomer 2 must be attached to the extra O, with the rest of the molecule similar to the ketone in part (a): This is an ester.

$$CH_3-O-\overset{O}{\overset{\|}{C}}-C(CH_3)_3$$

Isomer 1 has the extra O on the other side of the CO, accounting for the slight downfield shift of the $-C(CH_3)_3$: This is also an ester.

$$CH_3-\overset{O}{\overset{\|}{C}}-O-C(CH_3)_3.$$

****

14. (a) In the answers that follow, signals will be described in an abbreviated way, and possible groups to which they correspond will be given. Remember the n + 1 rule: n neighbors splits into n + 1 lines!

C - δ0.9 (triplet, 3H) - $\underline{CH_3}$, split by a neighboring CH_2 (2 + 1 = 3 = triplet)

δ1.3 (singlet, 6H) - two identical $\underline{CH_3}$'s, with no neighbor H's to split

δ1.5 (quartet, 2H) - $\underline{CH_2}$, split by a neighboring CH_3 (3 + 1 = 4 = quartet)

δ2.3 (singlet, 1H) - unsplit $\underline{CH}$ or $\underline{OH}$. OH more likely since molecule is an alcohol.

These add up to $C_4H_{12}O$. One more C is needed to give $C_5H_{12}O$, and we have the pieces $\underset{\delta 0.9\ \ \delta 1.5}{CH_3-CH_2-}$ $\quad \underbrace{CH_3- \quad CH_3-}_{\delta 1.3}$ $\quad \underset{\delta 2.3}{-OH}$ $\quad -\overset{|}{\underset{|}{C}}-$.

Putting the first four groups on to the last, unattached C gives the correct answer:

$$CH_3CH_2-\overset{CH_3}{\overset{|}{\underset{\underset{CH_3}{|}}{C}}}-OH$$

(2-methyl-2-butanol)

D - $\delta 0.9$ (doublet, 6H) - <u>two</u> <u>identical</u> CH_3's, both split by a neighbor
CH ($1 + 1 = 2 = \overline{\text{doublet}}$)

$\delta 1.3-1.9$ (multiplet, 3H) - probably more than one, overlapping
split signal

$\delta 2.0$ (singlet, 1H) - most likely the <u>OH</u>

$\delta 3.6$ (triplet, 2H) - CH_2, split by a neighboring CH_2 ($2 + 1 = 3 =$
triplet), and connected directly to O, according to the
chemical shift.

Although the $\delta 1.3-1.9$ signal is not readily interpretable, we can
make a guess that it contains the <u>CH</u> group responsible for splitting
the $\delta 0.9$ signal into a doublet, and the CH_2 group responsible for
splitting the $\delta 3.6$ signal into a triplet. This is a pretty good
guess since there are no other signals left unassigned in the spectrum.
These groups add up to $C_5H_{12}O$, so we've found everything, with the
pieces

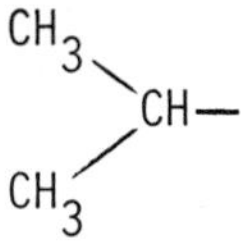

$$\begin{array}{c} CH_3 \\ \diagdown \\ CH- \\ \diagup \\ CH_3 \end{array} \quad \text{and} \quad -CH_2-CH_2-OH, \quad \text{which can be put together}$$

directly to give

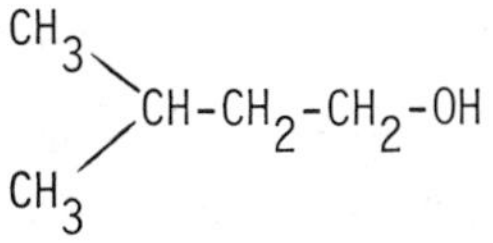

$$\begin{array}{c} CH_3 \\ \diagdown \\ CH-CH_2-CH_2-OH \quad \text{(3-methyl-1-butanol)}. \\ \diagup \\ CH_3 \end{array}$$

E - $\delta 0.9$ (triplet, sort of, 3H) - CH_3, split by a neighboring CH_2

$\delta 1.2-1.8$ (a mess, 6H) - ???

$\delta 2.1$ (broad singlet, 1H) - <u>OH</u> again

$\delta 3.6$ (triplet, 2H) - CH_2, split by a neighboring CH_2, and on the O

Again, some inferring is needed: assume that both the $\underline{CH_2}$ splitting the $\delta 0.9$ signal and the $\underline{CH_2}$ splitting the $\delta 3.6$ signal are buried
between $\delta 1.2-1.8$. We then have groups totalling $C_4H_{10}O$. There must
even be a third $\underline{CH_2}$ hiding in there, which accounts for the 6H integrated intensity. So what do we have?

$$\begin{array}{ccc} CH_3-CH_3-, & -CH_2-CH_2-OH, & \text{and} & -CH_2-. \\ \delta 0.9 \quad \delta 1.2-1.8 & \delta 1.2-1.8 \quad \delta 3.6 \quad \delta 2.1 & & \delta 1.2-1.8 \end{array}$$

There's only one way to put the pieces together to include everything: $CH_3-CH_2-CH_2-CH_2-CH_2-OH$ (1-pentanol).

F - δ0.9 (triplet, although a poor excuse for one, 3H) - C̲H̲₃, next
    to a CH₂

δ1.2 (doublet, 3H) - C̲H̲₃, next to a C̲H

δ1.4 (broad signal, 4H̲) - ???

δ2.3 (singlet, 1H) - O̲H̲

δ3.8 (four, maybe five lines, 1H) - C̲H̲, next to O, split by at
    least 3 and maybe 4 neighboring H's

Let's look at these pieces. The CH₃ at δ1.2 could be attached to
the CH at δ3.8. The CH₃ at δ0.9 could be attached to a CH₂ that is
part of the δ1.4 signal. That gives a total of $C_4H_{10}O$, requiring
another CH₂ to add up, presumably also at δ1.4. So the pieces are

$$CH_3-\underset{|}{CH}-OH, \qquad CH_3-CH_2-, \qquad and \qquad -CH_2-$$
δ1.2 δ3.8 δ2.3   δ0.9 δ1.4   δ1.4

Put them together to give $CH_3-CH_2-CH_2-\underset{\underset{CH_3}{|}}{\overset{\overset{OH}{|}}{CH}}$ (2-pentanol).

Notice how both spectra E and F have had very distorted triplets
around δ0.9 for CH₃ groups next to CH₂'s. This distorted appearance
is very common, and is due to the closeness of the chemical shifts of
the methyls (δ0.9) and the groups splitting them (δ1.2-1.8 in E and
δ1.4 in F).

(b) $CH_3-CH_2-\underset{\overset{|}{CH_3}}{CH}-CH_2-OH$ is the molecule. The doublet due to the methyl on
      4   3   2   1
C-2 is obvious at δ0.9; the (distorted) triplet due to the C-4 methyl
is presumably buried beneath it as the integrated intensity around
δ0.9 is 6H. The C-2 CH and C-3 CH₂ presumably give rise to the mess
between δ1.1-1.8 while the OH is at δ2.0. What is surprising is the
splitting of the C-1 CH₂ at δ3.5. It only has a CH as a neighbor, so
why isn't it a simple doublet?

The answer is that C-2 is a c̲h̲i̲r̲a̲l̲ c̲a̲r̲b̲o̲n̲ (a stereocenter). As
a result, the two hydrogens on C-1 are d̲i̲a̲s̲t̲e̲r̲e̲o̲t̲o̲p̲i̲c̲; i.e., they are
not in identical environments. Therefore, they have slightly different
chemical shifts, and *split each other* in addition to being split by
the neighboring CH. The complex signal around δ3.5 is the result.

****

15. Two signals, δ0.9 (doublet) and δ1.2-1.8 (multiplet) in an intensity ratio of about 5 or 6 to 1. With 14 H's in the formula the most reasonable situation is 12H for the large signal and 2H for the small one. Twelve equivalent hydrogens probably mean four equivalent CH_3 groups, which equals C_4H_{12}. That leaves C_2H_2 left to make up the molecule. The only way to do it that makes all the CH_3's identical, and split into a doublet is $(CH_3)_2CH$-$CH(CH_3)_2$, 2,3-dimethylbutane.

Figure 10-27 shows the NMR of 2-iodopropane, another molecule containing the $(CH_3)_2CH$- group. Again, the methyl signal is a doublet, but the CH signal is now resolved as a clean septet. The larger chemical shift difference betweeen the two sets of signals in 2-iodopropane gives rise to a more nearly "first-order" appearance to its spectrum, compared with the spectrum of 2,3-dimethylbutane.

****

16. At 500 MHz the triplet for the terminal methyl group is now of nearly ideal first-order appearance. This is due to the large separation between this signal and the others in the spectrum brought about by the much larger magnetic field strength of the 500 MHz instrument. The methylenes are still unresolved as a broad multiplet: they must have very similar chemical shifts indeed, for an instrument of this power to fail to resolve them.

****

17. At 60 MHz only the CH_2 next to Cl (δ3.5) is clearly resolved. The very distorted CH_3 triplet is barely separated (δ0.9) from the other three CH_2's, which overlap from δ1.0-2.0. At 500 MHz the separation of signals in Hz is so much greater that the entire spectrum is clearly resolved as nearly first-order signals: δ0.92 (triplet, CH_3), 1.36 (sextet, C-4 CH_2), 1.42 (quintet, C-3 CH_2), 1.79 (quintet, C-2 CH_2), 3.53 (triplet, C-1 CH_2). Notice how the multiplets appear so much narrower at 500 MHz. In reality, the coupling constants are unchanged. However, recall that at 60 MHz, the distance between δ0 and δ4 is only 240 Hz, while at 500 MHz the same 4 ppm spectrum width corresponds to 2000 Hz! So the 6-8 Hz splittings appear to spread out over a much larger chemical-shift range at 60 MHz than they do at 500 MHz.

****

18. Determine how many different signals would be displayed by each isomer.

Pentanes: C-C-C-C-C   3 signals

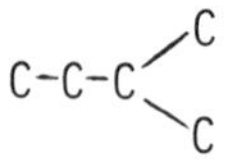

C-C-C$\diagup^C_{\diagdown C}$ 4 signals

$\begin{array}{c} C \\ | \\ C-C-C \\ | \\ C \end{array}$ 2 signals

All three can be readily identified by C-13 NMR.

Hexanes: C-C-C-C-C-C   3 signals

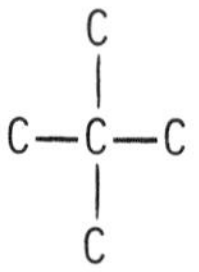

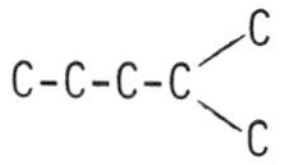

C-C-C-C$\diagup^C_{\diagdown C}$ 5 signals

$\begin{array}{c} C-C-C-C-C \\ | \\ C \end{array}$ 4 signals ←

$\begin{array}{c} C \diagdown \quad \diagup C \\ \quad C-C \\ C \diagup \quad \diagdown C \end{array}$ 2 signals

$\begin{array}{c} C \\ | \\ C-C-C-C \\ | \\ C \end{array}$ 4 signals ←

The C-13 NMR spectra of 3-methylpentane and 2,2-dimethylbutane will be similar, each having four different carbon environments. The two spectra would have to be distinguished by signal <u>intensities</u>: 2,2-dimethylbutane has three equivalent methyl carbons which will give rise to an exceptionally intense signal.

****

19. Answers include number of signals and (for the spectrum without proton decoupling) splitting by directly attached hydrogens (n+1 rule). Chemical shifts are <u>very</u> approximate, based on Table 10-6.

(a) 2 signals: δ10 (CH_3, quartet) and 20 (CH_2, triplet).

(b) 2 signals: δ25 (CH_3, q) and 45 (CHBr, doublet).

(c) 3 signals: δ25 (CH_3, q), 60 (CCl, singlet), and 65 (CH_2OH, t)

(d) 4 signals: δ10 (C-4 CH_3, q), 15 (other CH_3's, q), 25 (CH_2, t), and 30 (CH, d)

(e) 2 signals: δ30 (CH_3, q) and 50 (CNH_2, s)

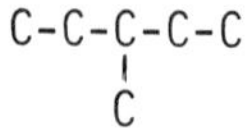

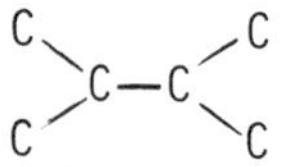

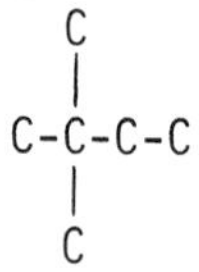

(f) 3 signals: δ10 (CH_3, q), 25 (CH_2, t), and 30 (CH, d)

(g) 4 signals: δ10 (CH_3, q), 30 (CH_2, t), 60 (CH_3O, q), and 65 (CH_2O, t)

(h) 3 signals: δ15 (CH_2, t), 45 (CH_2 next to $\overset{O}{\overset{\|}{C}}$, t), and 200 ($\overset{O}{\overset{\|}{C}}$, s)

(i) 4 signals: δ10 (CH_3, q), 20 (CH_3 near OH, q), 30 (CH_2, t), and 70 (CHOH, d)

(j) 5 signals: δ15 (CH_3, q), 20 (C-4 CH_2, t), 25 (other CH_2's, t), 40 (CH, d), and 70 (COH, d).

****

20. In each group consider the compounds from left to right. Again, chemical shifts are very rough estimates based on data in Table 10-6 and closeness of carbons to electronegative atoms.

(a) Left: 4 signals, δ15 (CH_3), 25 (2 CH_3), 35 (CH_2), 50 (CBr).

Middle: 5 signals, δ10 (CH_3), 15 (CH_3), 25 (CH_2), 40 (CH_2Br), 45 (CH).

Right: 4 signals, δ10 (2 CH_3), 30 (CH_2), 35 (CH_2Br), 40 (CH).

The first and third compounds would be difficult to distinguish based on this spectroscopic information alone.

(b) Left: 4 signals, δ25 (CH_2), 30 (CH_2), 40 (CH_2Cl), 60 (CH_2OH).

Middle: 4 signals, δ20 (CH_3), 35 (CH), 45 (CH_2Cl), 60 (CH_2OH).

Right: 3 signals, δ25 (2 CH_3), 55 (CCl), 65 (CH_2OH).

The first and second are not readily distinguished.

(c) First: 5 signals, δ15 (2 CH_3), 25 (CH_3), 45 (CH), 50 (CBr), 55 (CH_2Cl).

Second: 5 signals, δ15 (CH_3), 25 (2 CH_3), 45 (CBr), 50 (CH_2Cl), 55 (CH).

Third: 5 signals, δ15 (2 CH_3), 25 (CH_3), 40 (CHBr), 45 (C), 50 (CH_2Cl).

Fourth: 4 signals, δ10 (3 CH_3), 45 (CHBr), 50 (C), 55 (CH_2Cl).

The first three are virtually impossible to tell apart.

****

21. (a) $(CH_3)_2CHCH(CH_3)_2$: the only one that should show only two signals.

(b) 1-chlorobutane: the only one that should show exactly four signals.

(c) cycloheptanone: same reason as b (note symmetry in molecule).

(d) CH_2=$CHCH_2Cl$: the only example with alkene carbons (δ100-150 ppm).

****

22. (a) C-13, seven different carbon signals show. H-1, four signals as follows: δ0.9 (distorted t, rel area = 3), 1.3 (broad, rel area = 10), 2.7 (s, rel area = 1), 3.5 (t, rel area = 2). The first and last signals are keys: $-CH_2-(CH_3)$ (δ0.9) and $-O-(CH_2)-CH_2-$ (δ3.5). The singlet at δ2.7 is most easily interpreted as -O<u>H</u>. So we have (so far): $HO-CH_2-CH_2-$, $-CH_2-CH_3$, and C_3H_6 unaccounted for.

Since there is no sign of any other signal for a CH_3 group in the H-1 NMR, the best answer is $HO-CH_2-CH_2-CH_2-CH_2-CH_2-CH_2-CH_3$, 1-heptanol, which fits the C-13 as well. (Alternative possibilities like 3 or 4-methyl-1-hexanol should show a methyl doublet in the δ0.9 region in addition to the methyl triplet already present.)

(b) C-13, four signals, so molecule must have <u>two-fold symmetry</u> since the formula has 8 carbons. H-1: δ0.9 (d, rel area ≃ 3), 1.0-1.8 (multiplet, rel area ≃ 3), 2.3 (br s, rel area = 1), 3.4 (d, rel area = 2). The total integral areas add up to just 9, so these will all have to be <u>doubled</u> to correspond to the 18 hydrogens in the formula.

Obvious keys: 2 $-\overset{|}{C}H-(CH_3)$ (δ0.9), 2 $-\overset{|}{C}H-(CH_2)-O\underline{H}$ (δ3.4 and 2.3). These add up to $C_8H_{16}O_2$, which causes a problem - the remaining 2 hydrogens, if attached to either CH, will change the splitting. So, rethink the "obvious." Try putting the δ0.9 CH_3 and δ3.4 CH_2 groups on the <u>same</u> CH, and see what happens. That gives 2 $CH_3-\underset{|}{C}H-CH_2-OH$ pieces, adding up to $C_6H_{14}O_2$, and leaving C_2H_4 unaccounted for. Those could be two equivalent CH_2 groups easily enough, giving

$$HO-CH_2-\underset{CH_3}{\underset{|}{C}H}-CH_2-CH_2-\underset{CH_3}{\underset{|}{C}H}-CH_2-OH$$

as the answer.

****

23. An assortment of overlapping sharp singlets and doublets for the CH_3 groups are evident between δ0.6 and 1.1. Signals for the benzene H's are obvious between δ7.2 and 8.2. Three other signals may be interpreted as follows:

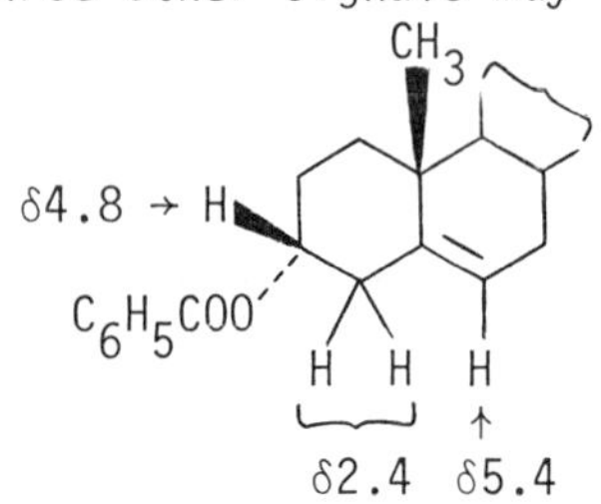

The CH_2 at $\delta2.4$ is split into a doublet by the neighboring CH. This CH is the cause of the $\delta4.8$ signal, and its complex splitting is due to its CH_2 neighbors on both sides. The alkene H ($\delta5.4$) is a doublet although it has a CH_2 for a neighbor. This must be a case where the J values between the alkene H and each H of the CH_2 are different, one being big, but the other being very small, resulting in an apparent doublet in the spectrum.

****

24. The spectrum indicates the presence of two equivalent CH_3's, not split by any neighboring H's ($\delta1.1$), a third unsplit CH_3, probably attached to a functional group due to its chemical shift ($\delta1.6$), and an alkene H showing some fine splitting ($\delta5.3$). The lack of any signal in the $\delta3-5$ range means that the alcohol carbon must not have any H's on it. Let's compare the pieces we have with the molecule framework that's supposed to be present.

2 equal CH_3's, unsplit

HO on C lacking hydrogens

finely split alkene H

unsplit CH_3 on functional group

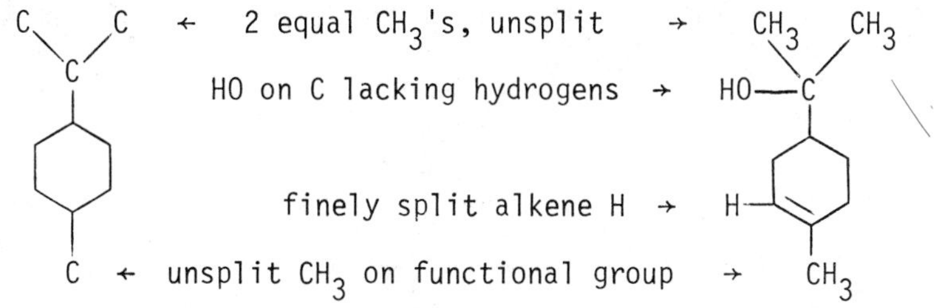

That's the answer!

****

25. (a) H ← $\delta5$

    CH_3—⬡—$CH(CH_3)_2$

(b) CH_3—⬡=$C(CH_3)_2$, via H shift:

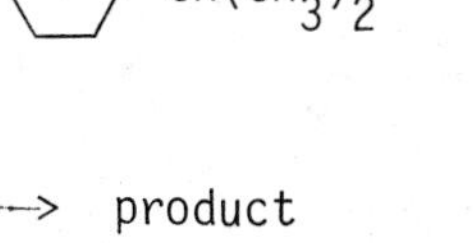

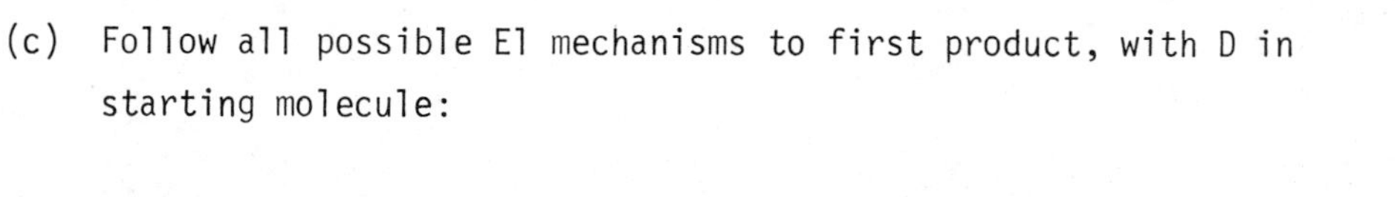

————→ product

(c) Follow all possible E1 mechanisms to first product, with D in starting molecule:

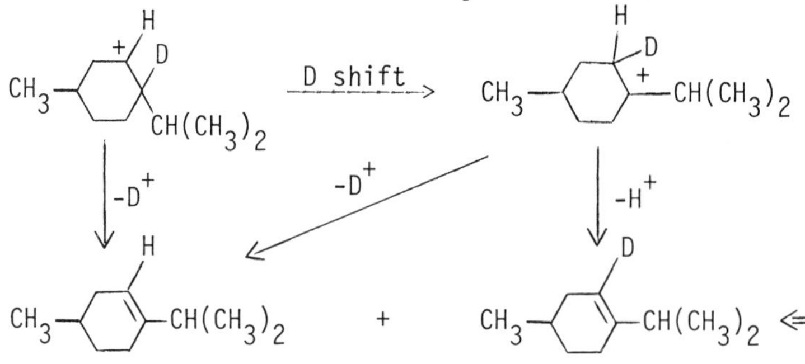

"Major product" is now a <u>mixture</u> of these two species.

According to these three pathways, some of the major product formed will have an alkene D instead of an alkene H. The molecules with alkene D will <u>not</u> show an H-1 NMR signal near $\delta 5$. So, the $\delta 5$ signal for the major product as a whole will be reduced in intensity compared with the major product from non-deuterated starting material.

This result was good evidence for the involvement of H shifts in what were previously thought to be simple E1 reactions.

****

CHAPTER 11

Alkenes: Hydrocarbons Containing Double Bonds

General Introduction

With chapters 11 and 12 we return to the presentation of a new functional group: the carbon-carbon double bond. This functional group differs from those seen so far in that it lacks strongly polarized covalent bonds. Instead, its reactivity arises from special characteristics of electrons in so-called π bonds. The properties of these electrons and their consequences will be discussed in the next chapter. Chapter 11 will be restricted to a general description of alkenes as a compound class, and a presentation of methods of preparation of double bonds. Most of the reactions will be ones you have already seen before, since the major methods of alkene syntheses are the same elimination reactions of alcohols and haloalkanes that have already been presented in chapters 7 and 9. Only some finer points of detail will be added.

Outline of the Chapter

11-1. Nomenclature.

11-2. Structure and Bonding in the Alkenes.

11-3. Nuclear Magnetic Resonance of Alkenes.

11-4. Relative Stability of Alkenes: Heats of Hydrogenation.

Comparing alkenes and alkanes.

11-5. The Preparation of Alkenes: Elimination Revisited.

11-6. Alkenes by Dehydration of Alcohols.

Mostly review material in these two sections.

Keys to the Chapter

11-1, 11-2, and 11-3. Nomenclature and Physical Properties.

Little needs to be added to the text descriptions for these two topics. The nomenclature rules are straightforward. Again, a small number of "common" names are still in use and must be learned. However, the systematic nomenclature is logical and easy to learn. Note that alkenes, like cyclic alkanes, have two distinct "sides", and therefore substituents may be either "cis" or "trans" to each other. For alkenes, however, the "cis" and "trans" designations should be restricted to molecules with exactly two substituents, one on each of the two doubly bonded carbons. If more substituents are present, the E,Z nomenclature system should always be applied.

The two "sides" of alkenes are due to the nature of the π-bond, one of the two bonds holding the alkene carbons together. The simplest picture of the double bond, which contains four electrons between the atoms involved, assigns two of these electrons to a basic, garden variety σ-bond bond between the atoms. The other two electrons are then placed in two p orbitals, overlapping *sideways*, to form the π-bond. This sideways overlap prevents the carbons at each end of the double bond from rotating with respect to one another. Ethene, as a result, is a perfectly flat molecule, and, in general, in any alkene both doubly bonded carbons and all the atoms attached to them will lie in a plane, with the π-bond electrons lying above and below.

One other significant consequence of the enforced planarity of double bonds and the cis/trans relationships of attached groups is seen in the NMR spectra of alkenes. Depending on circumstances, a molecule's alkene hydrogens do not all have to be chemical shift equivalent. When they aren't, coupling will be observable, sometimes leading to very complicated patterns due to J values that vary widely as a function of the structural relationships between the hydrogens involved (see Table 11-1). Figure 11-11 illustrates this feature. Even in complex spectra, however, you will still be able to derive the information you need for structure determination as long as you remember to look separately for the four basic pieces of information the spectrum contains: number of signals, chemical shift of each signal, integration of each signal, and splitting of each signal. If the splitting is too complicated to interpret, you can still make use of the other three pieces of data to come up with an answer.

11-4. Relative Stability of Alkenes: Heats of Hydrogenation.

The stability order of different kinds of alkenes is a well-established feature of this compound class: more substituted alkenes are more stable than less substituted, and trans are more stable than cis. This topic does not exist in isolation, however. In fact, it has important consequences for both reactions that form alkenes as well as reactions that alkenes undergo. Learn this stability order. You will need to use it later.

11-5. The Preparation of Alkenes: Elimination Revisited.

This is a review of the material from sections 7-4 and 7-5. There are two new considerations. First, many haloalkanes can give rise to several alkenes upon elimination, each with the double bond in a different position in the carbon chain. This requires only that there be several different "β-hydrogens" that can be lost in the elimination process together with the leaving group. The rule to remember is as follows: all E1 and, with one main exception, all E2 processes tend to produce the most highly substituted, most stable alkene, of those that are capable of being formed from the starting material (Saytzev elimination). The major exception is that *very bulky bases* will favor production of the least substituted, least stable alkene in E2 processes (Hofmann elimination).

The second new consideration relates to stereochemistry. As was briefly mentioned in chapter 7, the E2 elimination mechanism strongly prefers an *anti*-conformation between the leaving group and the β-hydrogen being removed. The result is that E2 eliminations will tend to give alkenes arising from the best available *anti*-conformation. E1 eliminations are not as restricted, and will simply tend to give the most stable alkene (i.e. *trans* in preference to *cis*) as the major product. This is important in the use of elimination reactions for alkene synthesis. Certain kinds of haloalkanes possess only one reactive conformation for E2 elimination (see problem 11), and will therefore give only a single stereoisomer upon reaction. This can be very useful. E1 eliminations, however, are more prone to result in mixtures of stereoisomeric products.

11-6. Alkenes by Dehydration of Alcohols.

Again, this is mainly a review of earlier material (chapters 7 and 9). Note that, unlike the situation with base-promoted E2 eliminations, under the reaction conditions for alcohol dehydration *all the mechanism steps are reversible*. The usual result therefore is formation of the most stable alkene (the thermodynamic product). Also, unlike base-promoted E2 reactions, alcohol dehydrations are susceptible to rearrangement processes leading to more stable carbocations, which, in turn, can result in even more alkene isomers forming as products. A classic example is encountered in attempted syntheses of terminal alkenes such as 1-butene. The *only* 100% reliable method is base-promoted E2 elimination of a suitable 1-butyl compound (e.g. 1-bromobutane, 1-butyl tosylate, etc.). Any other method will give mixtures at best:

$$CH_3CH_2CH_2CH_2Br \xrightarrow{K^+\ ^-OC(CH_3)_3,\ (CH_3)_3COH} CH_3CH_2CH{=}CH_2, \text{ the only elimination product}$$

$$CH_3CH_2CHBrCH_3 \xrightarrow{K^+\ ^-OC(CH_3)_3,\ (CH_3)_3COH} \underset{\text{major}}{CH_3CH_2CH{=}CH_2} + \underset{\text{minor, cis \& trans}}{CH_3CH{=}CHCH_3}$$

$$CH_3CH_2CHBrCH_3 \xrightarrow{Na^+\ ^-OCH_2CH_3,\ CH_3CH_2OH} \underset{\text{minor}}{CH_3CH_2CH{=}CH_2} + \underset{\text{major, cis \& trans}}{CH_3CH{=}CHCH_3}$$

$$\underline{\text{either}}\text{ 1- or 2-butanol} \xrightarrow{\text{conc. } H_2SO_4,\ \Delta} \underset{\text{minor}}{CH_3CH_2CH{=}CH_2} + \underset{\text{major, cis \& trans}}{CH_3CH{=}CHCH_3}$$

Solutions to Chapter 11 Problems

A Helpful Hint for solving spectroscopy/structure determination problems: Calculation of "Degrees of Unsaturation."

Concealed in the molecular formula of all organic compounds is a piece of information that can be very useful in solving spectroscopy problems: the sum of the number of π bonds and rings (called the number of "Degrees of Unsaturation") in the molecule. Compare the following formulas:

C_6H_{14}	hexane (a saturated compound)	
C_6H_{12}	any hexene (one π bond) cyclohexane (one ring)	one "degree of unsaturation"
C_6H_{10}	any hexadiene (two π bonds) cyclohexene (one π bond and one ring) any bicyclohexane (two rings)	two "degrees of unsaturation"
C_6H_6	benzene (three π bonds and one ring) - four "degrees of unsaturation"	

The formula of the acyclic alkane hexane fits the general relationship "C_nH_{2n+2}." Notice that the number of H's in a formula <u>decreases by two</u> for <u>each</u> π bond or ring present in the molecule. It is possible to work backwards from a molecular formula to derive the total number of π bonds and rings (degrees of unsaturation) in a molecule. Once this is done, you automatically know whether or not you need to consider those structural elements as possible constituents of an unknown molecule in a spectroscopy problem. The general method of calculation, good for molecules containing C, H, O, N, or halogens, follows:

Definitions: C = number of carbons in the molecule's formula

N = number of nitrogens in the molecule's formula

X = number of halogens in the molecule's formula

H_{actual} = number of hydrogens in the molecule's formula

$H_{sat'd}$ = number of hydrogens that would be present if the molecule were saturated

Step 1: calculate $H_{sat'd}$

$H_{sat'd} = 2C + 2 - X + N$ (Note that the number of oxygens is irrelevant.)

Step 2: calculate degrees of unsaturation

$$\text{Degrees of unsaturation} = \frac{H_{sat'd} - H_{actual}}{2}$$

Try it yourself! Beginning with Problem 2 of this chapter the degrees of unsaturation will be calculated for all unknown molecules in answers to such problems.

****

1. (a) cis- or Z-2-pentene

   (b) 3-ethyl-1-pentene

   (c) trans- or E-6-chloro-5-hexen-2-ol

   (d) Z-1-bromo-2-chloro-2-fluoro-1-iodoethene (Priorities are I > Br on C-1 and Cl > F on C-2.)

   (e) Z-2-ethyl-5,5,5-trifluoro-4-methyl-2-penten-1-ol

   (f) 1,1-dichloro-1-butene

   (g) Z-1,2-dimethoxypropene

   (h) Z-2,3-dimethyl-3-heptene

   (i) 1-ethyl-6-methylcyclohexene (better than 2-ethyl-3-methylcyclohexene: first number is smaller)

   (j) (2-propenyloxy)cyclohexane

****

2. (a) $H_{sat'd}$ = 8 + 2 - 1 = 9; degrees of unsaturation = $\frac{9-7}{2}$ = 1 π bond or
ring present. The integrated intensities reveal the pieces:
δ 1.9 (s, 3H) - $\underline{CH}_3$, attached to a functional group.
δ 4.0 (s, 2H) - $\underline{CH}_2$, most likely attached to Cl.
δ 4.9 and 5.1 (singlets, each 1H) - two alkene hydrogens.
Thus we have CH_3-, $-CH_2-Cl$, and $\rangle C{=}C\langle$ attached to 2 H's.

There are three ways to attach the four groups around the double
bond:

$$\underset{H}{\overset{CH_3}{\rangle}}C{=}C\underset{H}{\overset{CH_2Cl}{\langle}} \quad , \quad \underset{H}{\overset{CH_3}{\rangle}}C{=}C\underset{CH_2Cl}{\overset{H}{\langle}}, \quad \text{and} \quad \underset{ClCH_2}{\overset{CH_3}{\rangle}}C{=}C\underset{H}{\overset{H}{\langle}} .$$

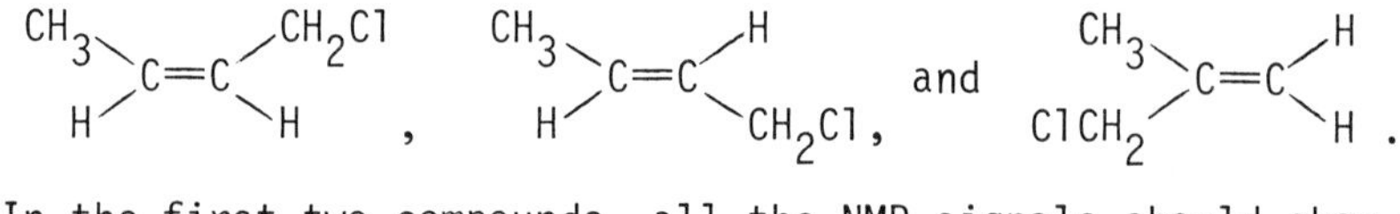

In the first two compounds, all the NMR signals should show substantial couplings. Only the third compound will show a spectrum as
simple as spectrum A (remember that $={C\underset{\backslash H}{\overset{\diagup H}{}}}$ couplings are typically
very small while cis and trans H-C=C-H couplings are large). That is
the answer.

(b) $H_{sat'd}$ = 10 + 2 = 12; degrees of unsaturation = $\frac{12-8}{2}$ = 2 π bonds
and/or rings. The NMR shows the following:
δ 2.1 (s, 3H) - $\underline{CH}_3$, next to functional group.
δ 4.5 (d, 2H) - $\underline{CH}_2$, attached to oxygen, split by one H.
δ 5.1-6.2 (m, 3H) - $-\underline{CH}{=}\underline{CH}_2$, the characteristic pattern of the ethenyl
group (see Figure 11-11(b) in the text) next to a CH_2.
The pieces are CH_3- and $CH_2{=}CH-CH_2-O-$ so far: C_4H_8O, leaving a C and
an O to add in, and one more π bond (a ring would be impossible). So
let them be $\rangle C{=}O$, giving the final solution: $CH_3-\overset{\overset{O}{\|}}{C}-O-CH_2-CH{=}CH_2$.

(c) $H_{sat'd}$ = 12 + 2 - 1 = 13; degrees of unsaturation = $\frac{13-11}{2}$ = 1 π bond
or ring.
δ 1.1 (singlet, 9H) - most likely $(\underline{CH}_3)_3C$, a t-butyl group.
δ 5.9 and 6.5 (doublets, each 1H) - two alkene H's coupling each other
by about 14 Hz, characteristic of a *trans* relationship.

The structure is unambiguous: $\underset{H}{\overset{(CH_3)_3C}{\rangle}}C{=}C\underset{I}{\overset{H}{\langle}}$.

(d) Same formula, so 1 π bond or ring present, again.
δ 0.9 (distorted triplet, 3H) - $\underline{CH}_3$, next to CH_2
δ 1.4 (multiplet, 4H) - 2 $\underline{CH}_2$'s?

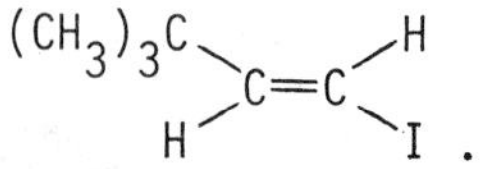

δ 2.1 (m, 2H) - $\underline{CH_2}$, next to a functional group (C=C?)

δ 5.9 (d, 1H) - alkene $\underline{CH}$, with a 14 Hz (trans) coupling

δ 6.5 (m, 1H) - the other alkene $\underline{CH}$

The pieces are:

CH_3-, two -CH_2-'s, and 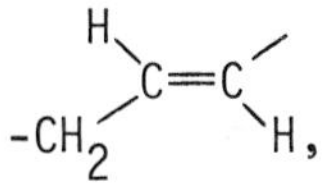 plus the -I.

δ 0.9 1.4 2.1 6.5 5.9

There are three ways to put these pieces together.

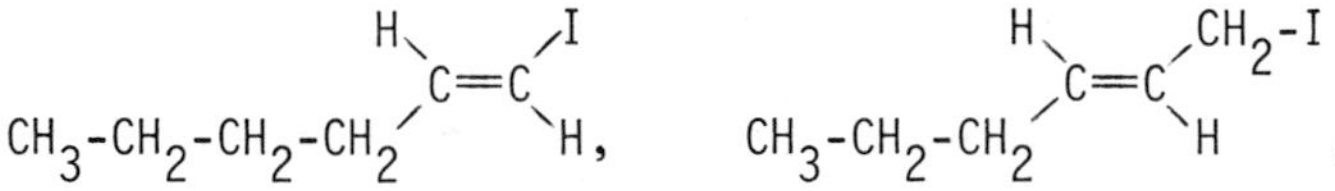

and

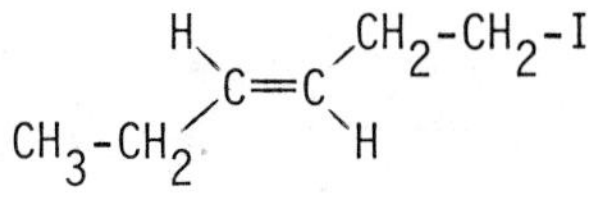

However, there is no -CH_2- group with a chemical shift reasonable for attachment to halogen, making the second and third structures unlikely. They would also show additional large splittings for <u>both</u> olefinic H's. The first structure, E-1-iodo-1-hexene, is the answer.

(e) $H_{sat'd} = 6 + 2 - 2 = 6$; degrees unsaturation $= \frac{6-4}{2} = 1$ π bond or ring.

δ 1.8 (doublet, 3H) - $\underline{CH_3}$, next to CH

δ 5.8 (quartet, 1H) - alkene $\underline{CH}$, next to CH_3

All that's left is one C and two Cl's, so the pieces, CH_3-CH=C< and two Cl's, combine to give the answer, CH_3-CH=CCl_2.

****

3. The inset shows 5 lines for the δ6.5 signal. Does this make sense? This hydrogen should be split by both the CH_2 group (into a triplet) and the other alkene H (into a doublet). In fact, this is what has happened, with the accident that two of the expected six lines overlap:

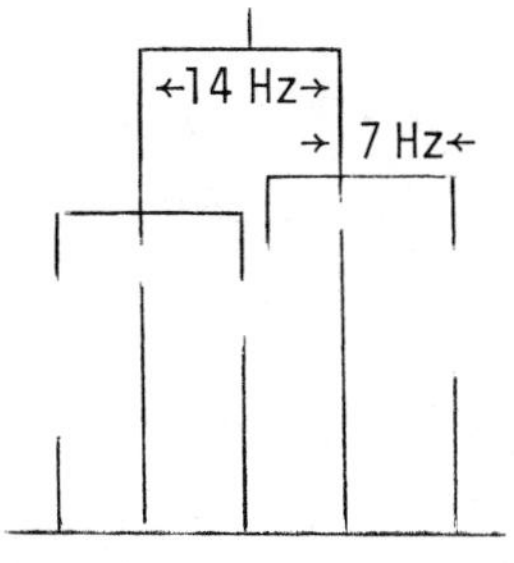

The δ5.9 signal also shows each line of the doublet further split by about 1 Hz into a triplet: this is a small "long-range" coupling for the -CH_2-C=C-H unit, only visible with such extreme expansion of the spectrum.

****

4. (a) Yes: 1-butene > *trans*-2-butene (which should be zero)

   (b) No.   (c) Yes: *cis* > *trans* (which, again, is zero)

****

5. Use the splittings together with the chemical shifts to choose between alternative possibilities. Use the $n+1$ rule to tell how many H's are on a given carbon. For example, a CH_3 carbon signal will be a quartet $(3+1)$; CH_2 will be a triplet; CH will be a doublet.

   (a) $H_{sat'd}$ = 8 + 2 = 10; degrees of unsaturation = $\frac{10-6}{2}$ = 2 π bonds and/or rings present.

   δ 30.2 (t) is a CH_2 group; δ 136.0 (d) is an alkene CH. Since those alone only add up to C_2H_3, there must be two of each. 2 -CH_2-'s, plus -CH=CH-, which can only combine to make

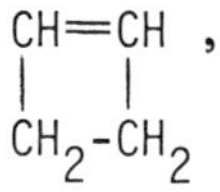

$$CH=\!\!\!=CH$$
$$|\qquad|$$
$$CH_2\!-\!CH_2$$

   cyclobutene (1 π bond and 1 ring).

   (b) $H_{sat'd}$ = 8 + 2 = 10; degrees of unsaturation = $\frac{10-6}{2}$ = 2 again. δ 18.2 (q) is a CH_3, <u>not</u> attached to the oxygen; δ 134.9 (d) and 153.7 (d) are alkene CH's; δ 193.4 (d) is in the C=O region and, therefore, must be a $-\overset{O}{\overset{\|}{C}}-H$ group since it is a doublet. The answer is therefore $CH_3-CH=CH-\overset{O}{\overset{\|}{C}}-H$ (2 π bonds). You do not have enough information about C-13 NMR to determine the stereochemistry.

   (c) $H_{sat'd}$ = 8 + 2 = 10; degrees of unsaturation = $\frac{10-8}{2}$ = 1.
   δ 13.6 (q), 25.8 (t), 139.0 (d), 112.1 (t)-answer directly available
$$CH_3\overset{\downarrow}{\rule{1cm}{0.4pt}}CH_2\overset{\downarrow}{\rule{1cm}{0.4pt}}CH\overset{\downarrow}{=\!=\!=}CH_2 \qquad \text{from the splittings.}$$

   (d) $H_{sat'd}$ = 10 + 2 = 12; degrees of unsaturation = $\frac{12-10}{2}$ = 1.
   This one has two CH_3 groups (δ 17.6, 25.4), a CH_2 downfield enough (δ 58.8) to be attached to the O, and two alkene carbons, of which only one (δ 125.7) has an H on it.

   The pieces: 2 CH_3-, -CH_2-O-, -CH=C$\underset{\diagdown}{\diagup}$. There is one H unlocated. Since it's not attached to one of the carbons, it must be on the oxygen. So the possible answers are:

$$\underset{H}{\overset{CH_3}{\diagdown}}C=C\underset{CH_2-OH,}{\overset{CH_3}{\diagup}} \qquad \underset{H}{\overset{CH_3}{\diagdown}}C=C\underset{CH_3}{\overset{CH_2-OH}{\diagup}} \quad and \quad \underset{H}{\overset{HO-CH_2}{\diagdown}}C=C\underset{CH_3.}{\overset{CH_3}{\diagup}}$$

   You do not have the information to tell which of the three is the actual compound.

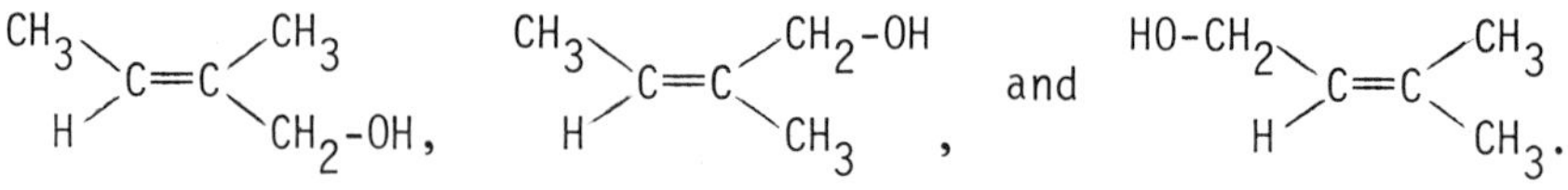

(e) Notice that there are only four signals, but there are five carbons. Be careful. $H_{sat'd}$ = 10 + 2 = 12; degrees unsat'n = $\frac{12-8}{2}$ = 2 now. δ 15.8 (t) and 31.1 (t) are CH_2 groups; δ 103.9 (t) is an alkene CH_2, while δ 149.2 (s) is an alkene C lacking hydrogens.

Where are we? The molecule has the piece $CH_2=C\overset{/}{\underset{\backslash}{}}$, leaving 3 carbons and 6 H's to make up the formula, which must still contain one more element of unsaturation (a ring?). Since the high field signals are triplets, these can only be CH_2 groups: 3 of them. Combining $CH_2=C\overset{/}{\underset{\backslash}{}}$ with 3 CH_2's can only give

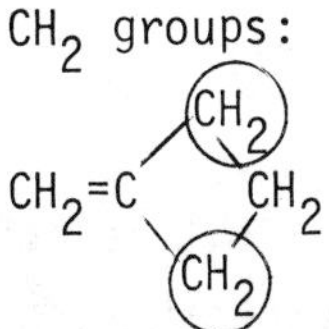

$$CH_2=C\underset{(CH_2)}{\overset{(CH_2)}{\diagdown \diagup}}CH_2$$

, where the δ 31.1 signal accounts for the two <u>equivalent</u> CH_2 groups (circled).

(f) $H_{sat'd}$ = 14 + 2 = 16; degrees unsat'n = $\frac{16-10}{2}$ = 3, or 1 π bond and <u>2</u> rings. Again be careful: now there are four signals, but <u>seven</u> carbons in the molecule. Upfield, there are two different kinds of CH_2's (δ 25.2 and 48.5) and one kind of CH (δ 41.9). There is one kind of alkene carbon (δ 135.2). Since a double bond must connect <u>two</u> alkene carbons, this signal must represent two equivalent alkene CH groups (it is a doublet): -CH=CH-. So we have at least 2 CH_2's, an alkane CH, and -CH=CH-, for a total of C_5H_7. So two carbons and three H's are still required: one more CH_2 and one more CH would do, and these each must be equivalent to groups already identified in order to keep the NMR spectrum as simple as it is. In other words, here are the pieces we have for the molecule: 2 equivalent -CH_2-'s, 2 equivalent -$\overset{|}{C}$H's, a single unique -CH_2-, and the -CH=CH- group, for a total of C_7H_{10}.

How do we put this all together? Remembering that symmetry can make groups equivalent, we can write these groups in symmetrical arrangements and connect them up in a trial-and-error manner:

$$
\begin{array}{c}
\text{-CH}_2\text{-} \quad \text{-CH}_2\text{-} \\
\text{-CH}_2\text{-} \\
\text{H}\overset{|}{\text{C}}\text{-} \qquad \text{-}\overset{|}{\text{C}}\text{H} \\
\text{-CH=CH-}
\end{array}
\implies
\begin{array}{c}
\diagup \text{CH}_2 \diagdown \\
\text{CH}_2 \qquad \text{CH}_2 \\
\diagdown \qquad \diagup \\
\text{CH} \text{——} \text{CH} \\
| \qquad | \\
\text{CH} \text{===} \text{CH}
\end{array}
\quad \text{or} \quad
\begin{array}{c}
\text{CH}_2 \text{——} \text{CH}_2 \\
\diagup \qquad \diagdown \\
\text{HC} \text{—} \text{CH}_2 \text{—} \text{CH} \\
\diagdown \qquad \diagup \\
\text{CH} \text{===} \text{CH}
\end{array}
$$

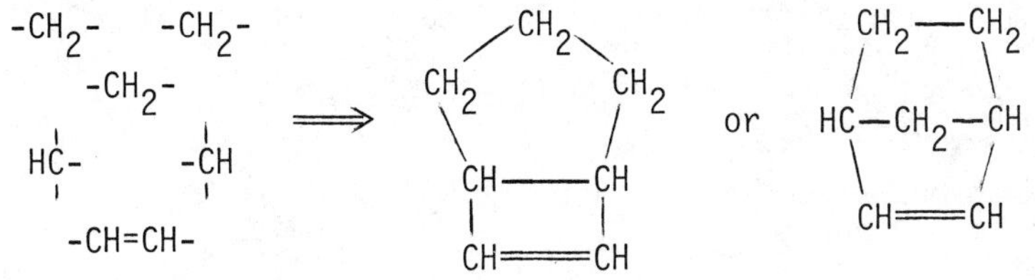

Either is a reasonable possibility (the second one, "norbornene," is actually correct).

****

6. $H_{sat'd} = 10 + 2 = 12$; degrees unsat'n $= \frac{12-10}{2} = 1$.

(a) The only way for five carbons to be equivalent is to make a ring:

 is the answer.

(b) Three CH_3's, and a $-CH=C\lt$: $CH_3-CH=C(CH_3)_2$ is the answer.

(c) Two CH_3's, one CH_2, and -CH=CH-: $CH_3-CH_2-CH=CH-CH_3$ is the answer (stereochemistry is ambiguous).

****

7. The two orders are opposite to each other, since very stable alkenes will be low in energy to start with, and will give off less heat upon hydrogenation than will less stable alkenes. The stability orders are given below.

(a) $CH_2=CH_2 < (CH_3)_2C=CH_2 < (CH_3)_2C=C(CH_3)_2$ (increasing substitution)

(b) 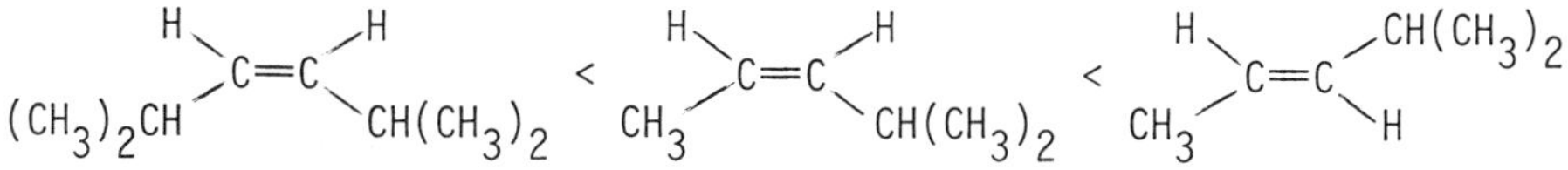

(two large groups *cis*) < (a small and a large group *cis*) < (*trans*)

(c) 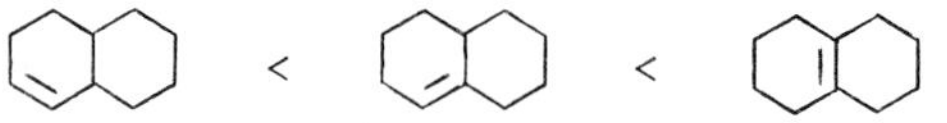 (similar to (a), above)

(d) 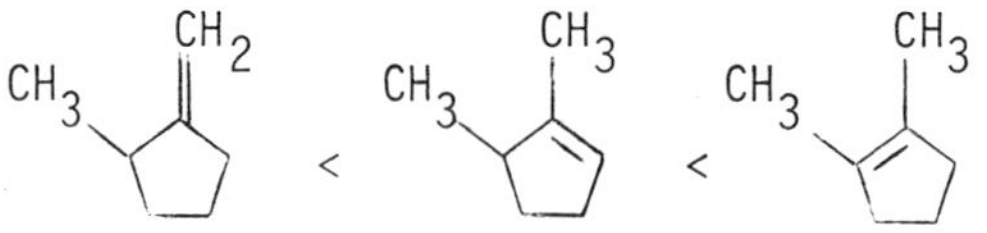 (similar to (a) and (c), above)

(e) 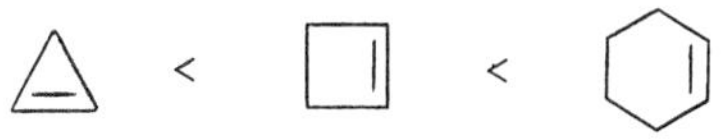 (ring strain)

****

8. Use $\Delta H° \simeq \Delta G° = -RT \ln K$, and solve for K for pairs of molecules: $K \simeq e^{-\Delta H°/RT}$, with R = 1.986 cal deg^{-1} $mole^{-1}$ and T = 298 K. Careful! Multiply energy differences by 1000 to convert to cal $mole^{-1}$.

(a) $K\left(\frac{cis\text{-2-pentene}}{\text{1-pentene}}\right) = e^{1700/(1.986)(298)} = 17.7$;

$K\left(\frac{trans\text{-2-pentene}}{\text{1-pentene}}\right) = e^{2600/(1.986)(298)} = 80.9$

At equilibrium then the ratios are *trans*-2-pentene:*cis*-2-pentene:1-pentene is 80.9:17.7:1, or approximately 81%, 18%, and 1% concentrations, respectively. This is consistent with more substituted double bonds being more stable (di- > mono-) and *trans* more stable than *cis*.

(b) $K\left(\frac{\text{2-methyl-1-butene}}{\text{3-methyl-1-butene}}\right) = e^{1700/(1.986)(298)} = 17.7;$

$K\left(\frac{\text{2-methyl-2-butene}}{\text{3-methyl-1-butene}}\right) = e^{3200/(1.986)(298)} = 223$

At equilibrium, 2-methyl-2-butene:2-methyl-1-butene:3-methyl-1-butene is 223:17.7:1, or about 92%, 7.5%, and 0.5%, respectively. Stability order is, as expected, trisubstituted > disubstituted > monosubstituted.

****

9. The six-membered ring stability order is expected on the basis of substitution (tri- > di-). However, the stability order is reversed for three-membered rings due to strain considerations. In 1-methylcyclopropene, both alkene carbons are in the ring, and their angles are compressed from 120° to near 60°. In methylene cyclopropane only one of the alkene carbons is in the ring, a less strained situation with regard to bond angle compression.

****

10.

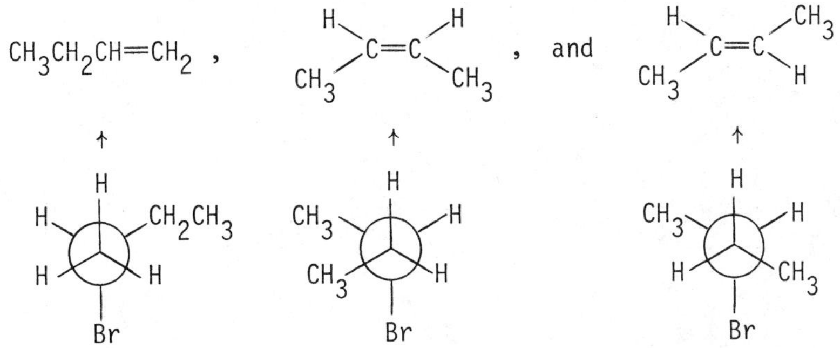

(1) (2) (3)

Conformation (2) (methyls *gauche*) is less stable than conformation (3) (methyls *anti*), which is consistent with a preference for trans over cis-2-butene. Irrespective of the C2-C3 conformation, all staggered C1-C2 conformations are equivalent (1). The choice between C1-C2 elimination and C2-C3 elimination involves other factors besides conformation, such as alkene stability based upon substitution, and choice of base.

****

11. A haloalkane of general structure R-CH_2-CHX-R' will have <u>two</u> conformations with H *anti* to X; one gives the *cis* and the other gives the *trans* alkene as product (compare conformations (2) and (3) in problem 10 above).

A haloalkane of general structure RR'CH-CHX-R" will have only one conformation with H *anti* to X. Therefore only a single alkene stereoisomer can form. Its stereochemistry will be determined by the stereochemistry of the two chiral carbons in the haloalkane.

****

12. The more hindered $(CH_3)_3CO^- K^+$ will favor removal of protons towards the less crowded "ends" of molecules, giving less stable products. Ethoxide eliminations will favor more stable products.

	(1)	structure of starting material	(2)
(a)	$CH_3OCH_2CH_3$	CH_3Cl	$CH_3OC(CH_3)_3$
(b)	$CH_3CH_2CH_2CH_2CH_2OCH_2CH_3$ + 1-pentene	$CH_3CH_2CH_2CH_2CH_2Br$	1-pentene
(c)	*trans* and *cis*-2-pentenes	$CH_3CH_2CH_2CHBrCH_3$	1-pentene

(d)

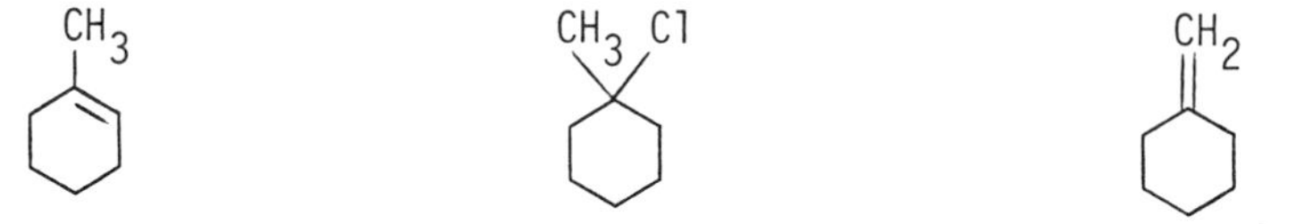

(e)

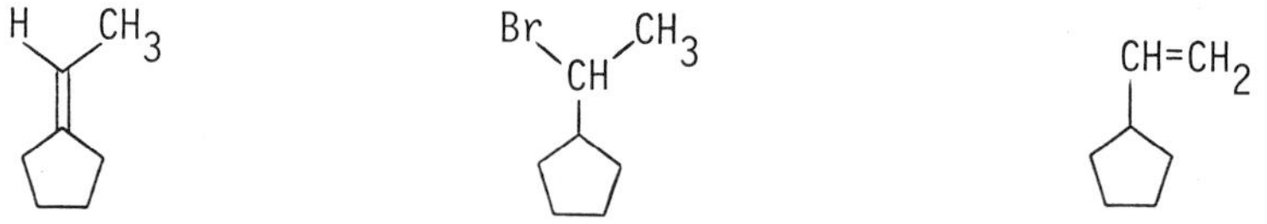

(f) 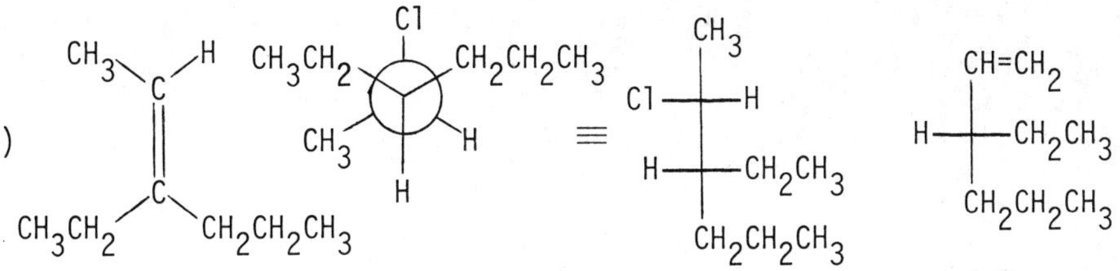

(*E*) (*R*)

(g) 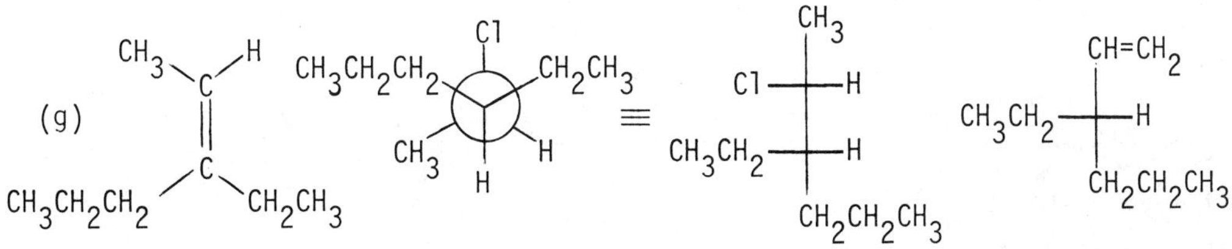

(*Z*) (*S*)

(h) 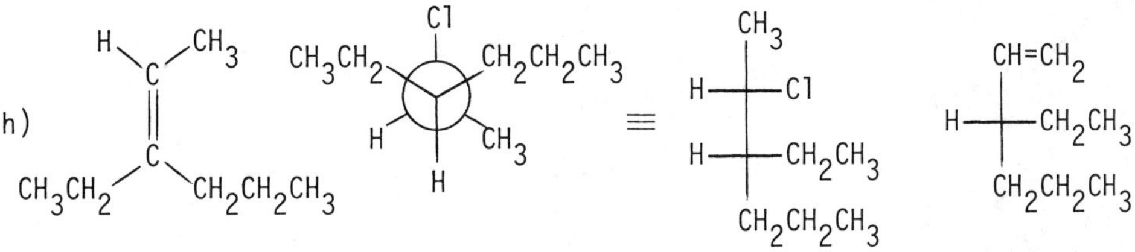

(*Z*) (*R*)

****

13. 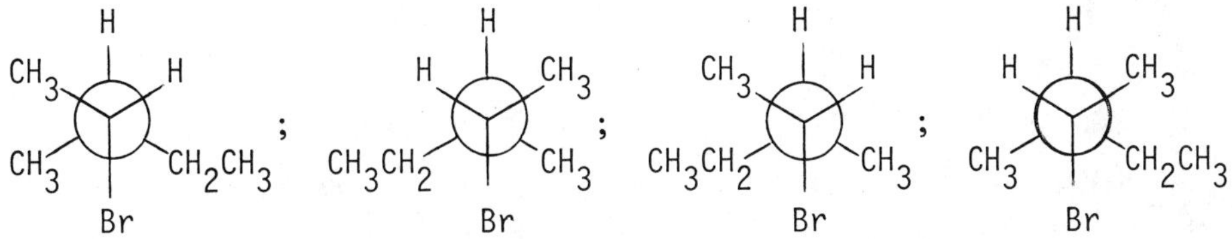

2R, 3R ; *2S, 3S* ; *2R, 3S* ; *2S, 3R*

These are probably not the most stable conformations since all contain three *gauche* interactions between alkyl groups and/or bromine. For the *R*,*R* isomer, a better conformation would probably be:

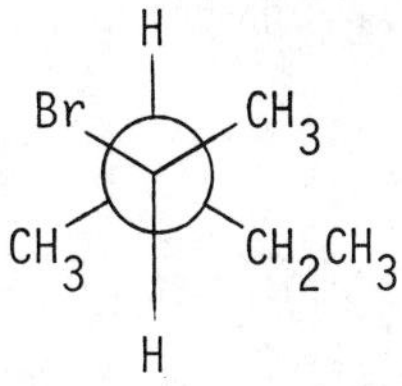

The others would be similar.

****

14. Rewrite each compound in a Newman projection with the Br and the β-H in an *anti* conformation:

(a) 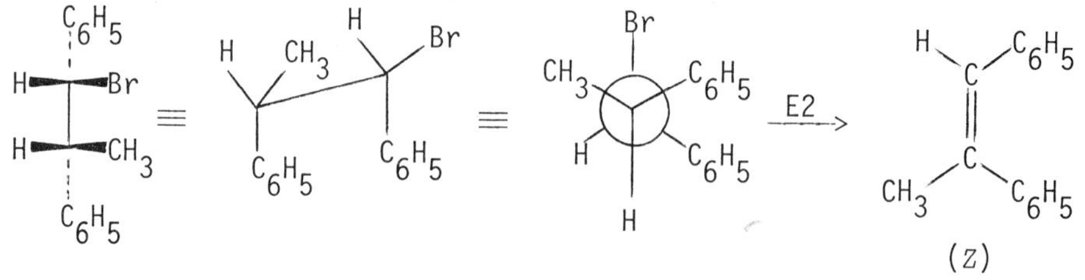

(b) 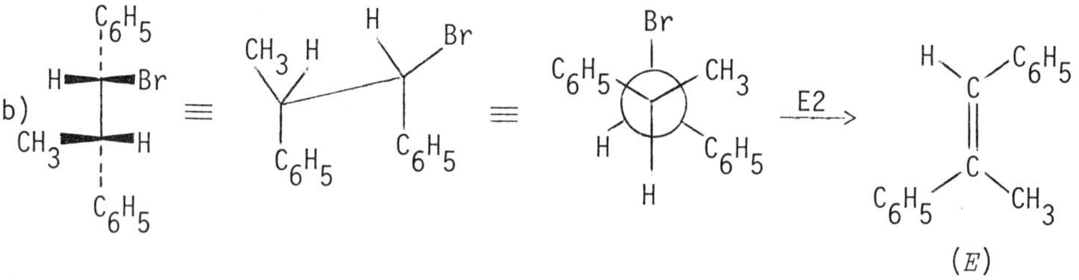

Elimination of (b) should be faster than (a) since the reactive conformation for (b) has the large C_6H_5 groups *anti* to one another, while the reactive conformation for (a) requires the C_6H_5 groups to be *gauche*.

From the Arrhenius equation, $k_{(b)}/k_{(a)} = e^{-\Delta E_a/RT}$. Use T = 298°K: $\ln 50 = -\Delta E_a/(1.986)(298)$; so the difference in E_a comes to 2.3 kcal/mole. While it is hard to be specific about all the factors that contribute to this E_a difference, it is certainly reasonable to suppose that some of it is due to the greater energy required to rotate (a) into a reactive conformation.

****

15. Notice two factors: first, dilute base favors E1 elimination while concentrated base favors E2; second, in the starting material, the Br is *cis* to both ring β-hydrogens, and E2 *anti*-elimination can *only* occur with hydrogens from the methyl group, leading exclusively to product (b).

Therefore: (1) Dilute KOH in ethanol gives mainly (a), the most stable product, via an E1 mechanism.

(2) Concentrated KOH in ethanol favors E2 elimination, which leads to product (b).

****

16. When E2 eliminations occur in cyclohexanes, the leaving group and the β-H to be removed must have a 1,2-*trans* diaxial relationship. That is the only way to reach the necessary *anti* conformation. So, first, draw the two

possible chair conformations for each starting compound, and analyze the
one in which the Cl leaving group is axial:

only possible E2
product

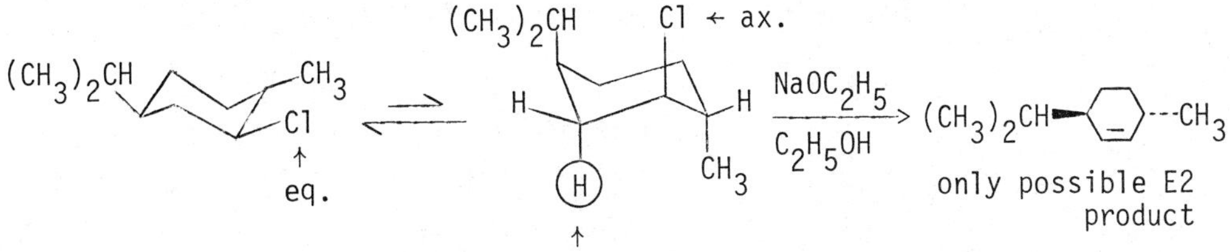

This is the only H anti to Cl - it is
therefore the only one that can be removed in an E2 process.

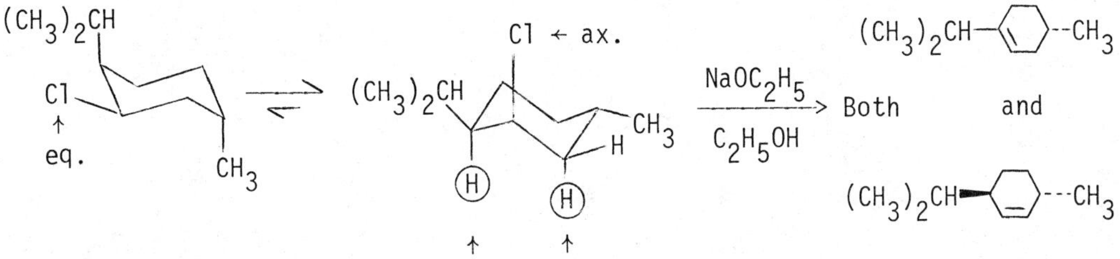

Now there are two H's anti to Cl, and available for E2 elimination.

****

17. Answer this problem by imagining precursor molecules with halogen and β-
hydrogen in an *anti* conformation. As your best answer, choose the haloalkane with only one β-H to remove leading to the regio- and stereoisomer
shown.

Below you will find the correct answer and, if appropriate, other
possible answers, and the problems they have.

(a)

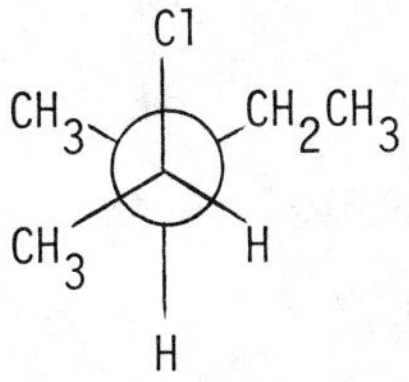

(and/or enantiomer) leads exclusively to the desired
product

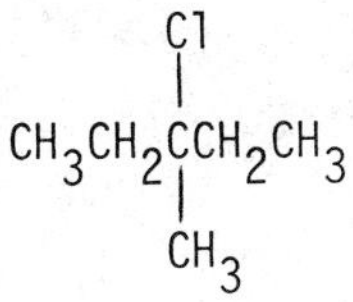

$$CH_3CH_2\underset{\underset{CH_3}{|}}{\overset{\overset{Cl}{|}}{C}}CH_2CH_3$$ will give both *E* and *Z* stereoisomers, and is not as
good a precursor.

(b) 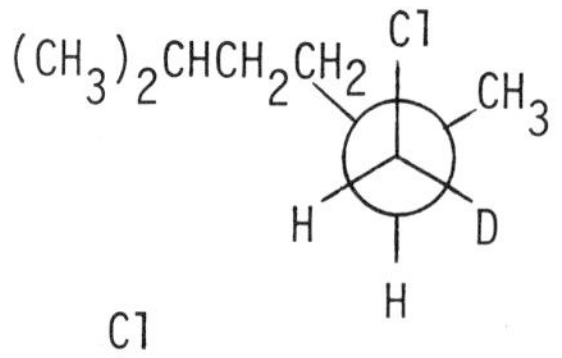 (and/or enantiomer).

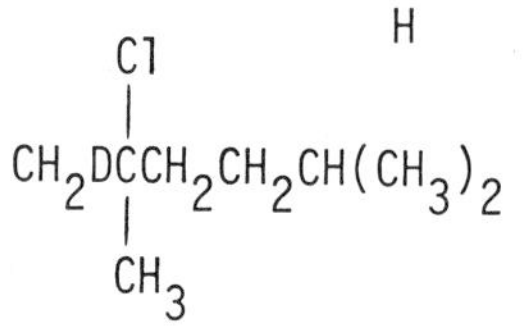

$CH_2DC(Cl)(CH_3)CH_2CH_2CH(CH_3)_2$ will give both *E* and *Z* stereoisomers of the correct regioisomer, but, worse, will give mainly internal alkene products.

(c) 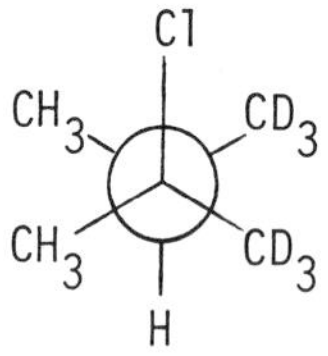

(d) 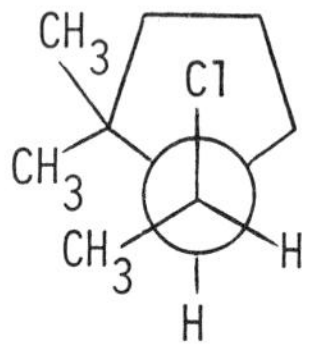 (and/or enantiomer). 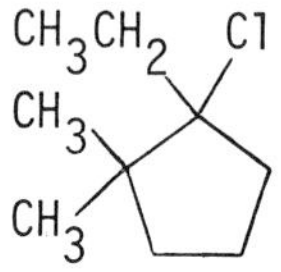 will give both *E* and *Z* stereoiosmers of the desired alkene.

****

18. Referring to problem numbers in Chapter 7:

(1b) $CH_3CH{=}C(CH_3)_2$ > $CH_2{=}C(CH_3)CH_2CH_3$

(1c) Comparable amounts

(1d) 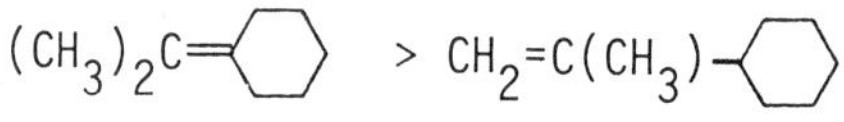

(2) 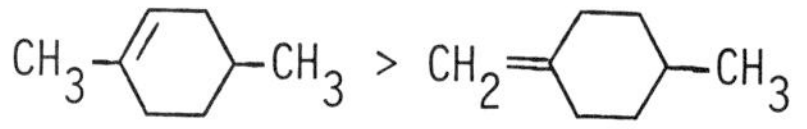

(3) $C_6H_5(CH_3)C{=}C(CH_3)C_6H_5$ > $C_6H_5(CH_3)CH{-}C(C_6H_5){=}CH_2$

These are the only elimination product mixtures in these problems.

****

19. Major products are labeled for parts (a) through (g). Generally, more highly substituted alkene isomers form in highest yields.

(h) 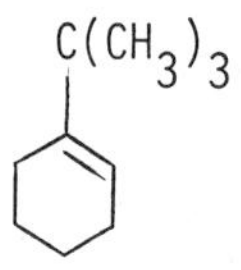 > 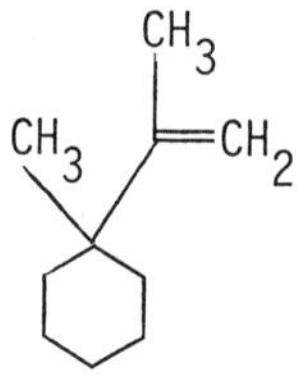

(i) 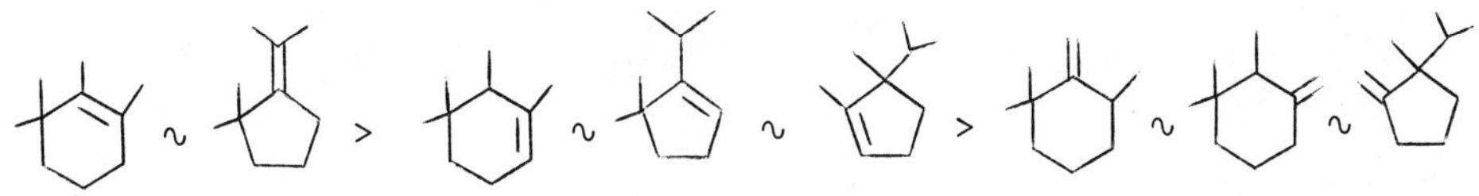

(j) 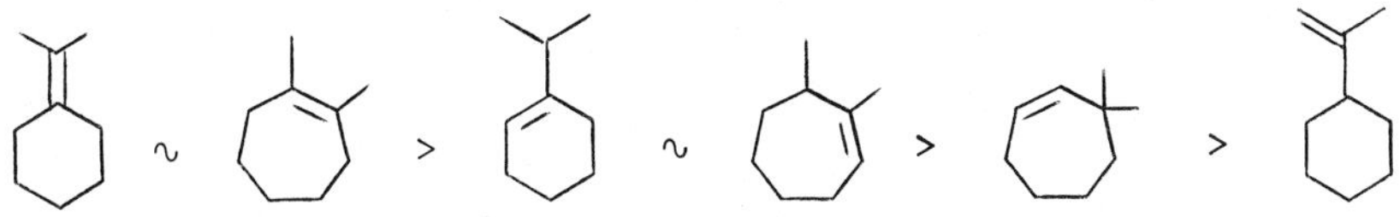

****

20. Elimination with $(CH_3)_3CO^- K^+$ is an E2 process, and gives exclusively the product shown by loss of Br and a β-hydrogen *trans* to it (circled):

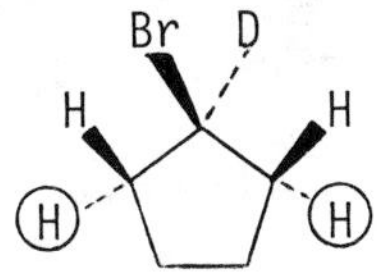

Elimination from an alcohol with acid is an E1, carbocation process. Since the cation can rearrange through hydride shifts, the result is an equilibrium mixture of alkenes:

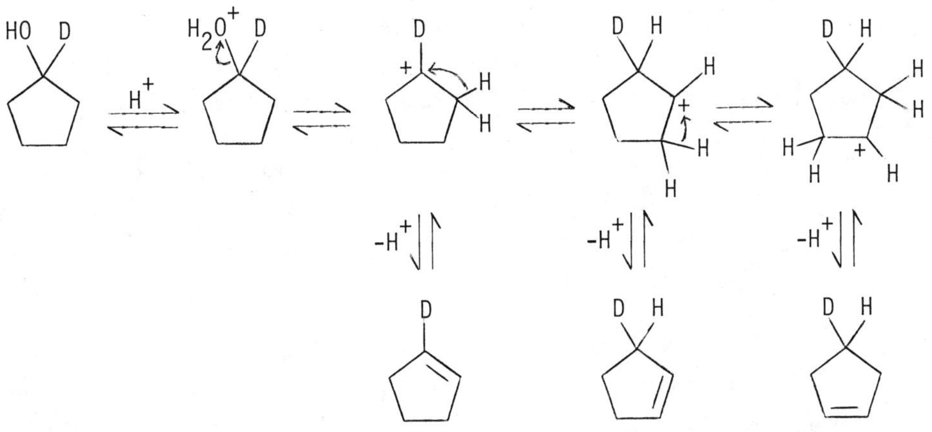

In addition, cyclopentene lacking any D is formed in this reaction. Can you see how?

****

21. (a) $(CH_3)_2CHCH_2CH\ddot{O}H \xrightleftharpoons{H^+} (CH_3)_2CHCH—CH_2—\overset{+}{O}H_2 \xrightarrow[\text{shift}]{\text{hydride}}$

$(CH_3)_2\overset{H}{C}—\overset{+}{C}HCH_3 \xrightarrow{-H^+} (CH_3)_2C=CHCH_3$ The hydride shift avoids formation of a 1° cation, and allows a more stable, internal alkene to result.

(b) $(CH_3)_2CCH{=}CH_2 \overset{H^+}{\rightleftharpoons} (CH_3)_2\overset{CH_3}{\overset{|}{C}}{-}\overset{+}{C}HCH_3 \xrightarrow[\text{shift}]{\text{methyl}} (CH_3)_2\overset{+}{C}{-}\overset{H}{\overset{|}{C}}(CH_3)_2$

$\overset{-H^+}{\rightleftharpoons} (CH_3)_2C{=}C(CH_3)_2$ The methyl shift converts a 2° cation to a 3° cation; the overall rearrangement results in a much more stable alkene.

(c) 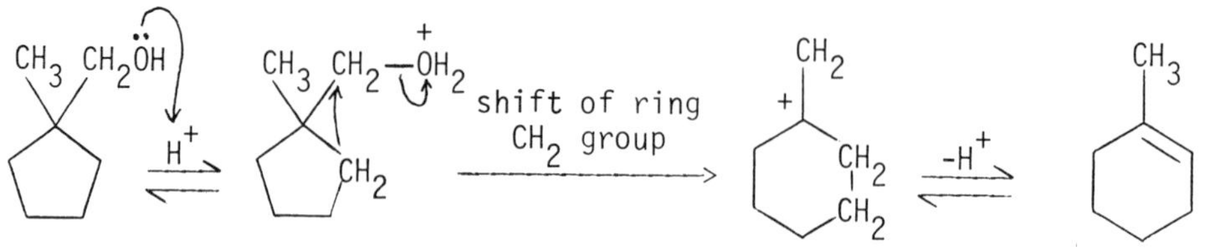

Shift of a ring carbon generates a 3° cation from the protonated 1° alcohol, and leads to a more stable six-membered ring as well.

****

22. $CH_3CH_2CH_2\ddot{O}H \overset{H^+}{\rightleftharpoons} CH_3\underset{|}{C}H{-}CH_2{-}\overset{+}{O}H_2 \longrightarrow CH_3CH_2CH_2\overset{+}{O}H_2 + CH_3CH{=}CH_2 + H_2O$

$\qquad H$

$CH_3CH_2CH_2\ddot{O}H$

****

23. *A* would be expected to give the tetrasubstituted alkene

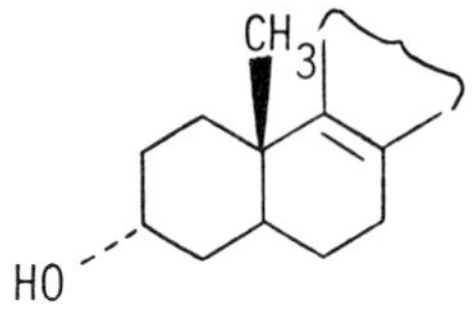

B gives the (trisubstituted) alkene shown in the problem (text, p 265). *C* is a special situation (see study guide p 136).

****

24. Similar, except that the more stable *trans*-3-decenoic acid should form in preference to the *cis* isomer.

****

25. The NMR indicates two carbonyl carbons are present (δ177.2 and 215.4), ruling out (*C*). It also indicates four alkene carbons (δ126.7, 131.0, 131.7, and 136.7), consistent only with (*B*).

****

26. $H_{sat'd} = 10 + 2 = 12$; degrees unsat'n $= \frac{12-8}{2} = 2$ π bonds and/or rings.

C-13 NMR: 3 signals requires either accidental or symmetry-equivalent carbons; therefore δ135 most likely implies two equivalent alkene carbons ($\diagup$C=C$\diagdown$). Since there are two oxygens in the formula ($C_5H_8O_2$), it is reasonable to assume that two equivalent -C-O- groups are in the molecule, corresponding to the δ80 signal. The fifth carbon is then at δ45. The alkene is one degree of unsaturation; the other is probably a ring, then.

H-1 NMR: the signals at δ1.54 and 2.70 with J = 15Hz are hydrogens on the same carbon (Section 10-6) despite the large chemical shift difference! They must be diastereotopic. The broad signal at δ3.2 could be 2 HO-groups. The signal at δ4.65 must be the hydrogens on the carbons attached to oxygen, and the alkene hydrogens are at δ6.03. So what do we have?

	J = 4Hz		J = 1Hz

		J = 7Hz		

$$H-\underset{|}{\overset{|}{C}}-H \quad , \quad 2 \quad H-\underset{|}{\overset{|}{C}}-OH \quad , \quad \text{and} \quad H-\overset{|}{C}=\overset{|}{C}-H .$$

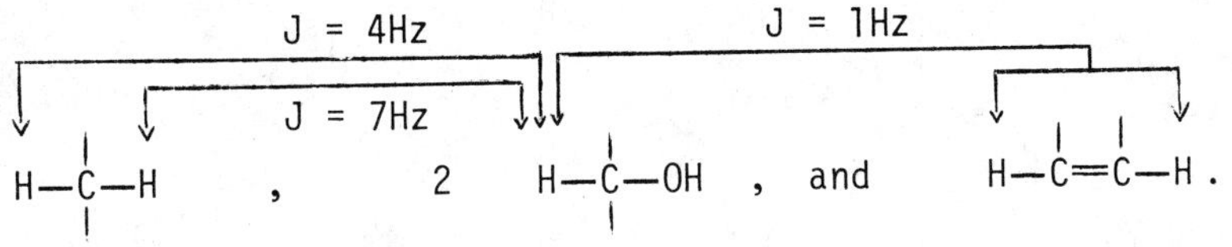

δ1.54 and 2.70   δ4.65   δ3.20   δ6.03
   J = 15Hz

Additional J values between hydrogens have been added in (arrows), suggesting ways to connect the pieces. See how much information the three splittings of the δ4.65 signal provide?

Now connect everything.

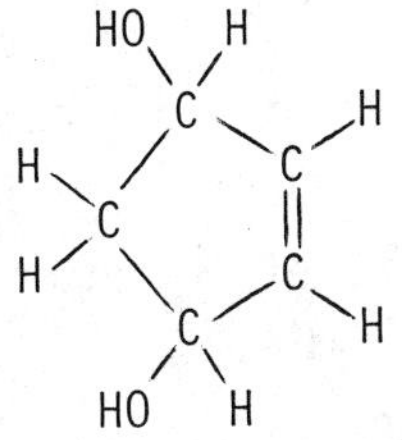

is a reasonable structure, and, more specifically, the *cis*-isomer is the answer:

The *cis* arrangement of the two alcohol groups is responsible for the big chemical shift difference between the H's on the CH_2 group: one is *cis* to both OH's, and the other is *trans* to both OH's.

****

27. (a) Newman projections help for this:

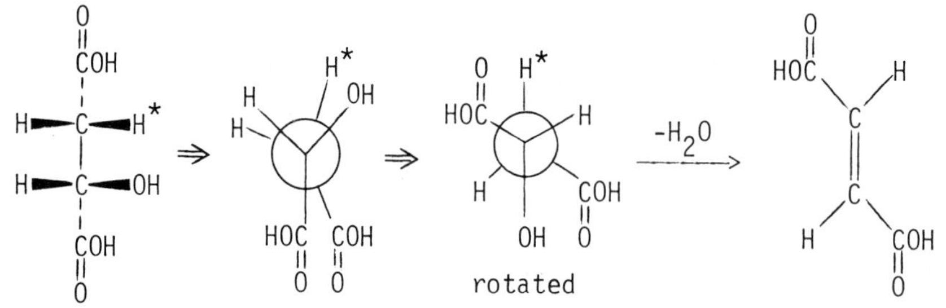

malic acid

fumaric acid

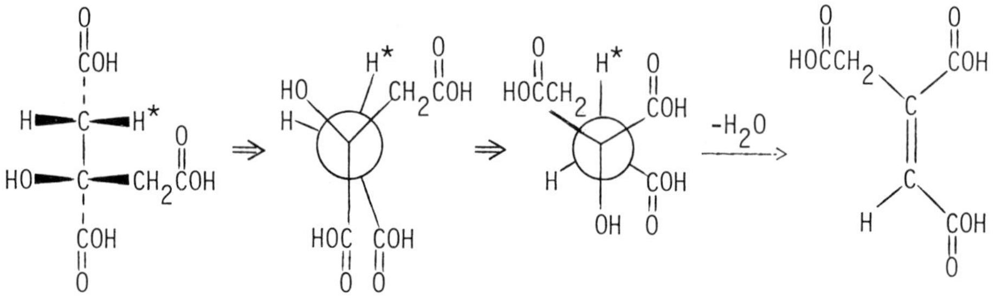

citric acid

aconitic acid

(b) Fumaric acid is *E*; aconitic acid is *Z*.

(c) Malic acid already contains a chiral carbon, so the CH_2 hydrogens are diastereotopic. Citric acid does not contain a chiral carbon (Surprise! Write it out and see for yourself!). However replacement of one of the CH_2 hydrogens makes both that carbon and the middle carbon chiral. Replacement of one of the CH_2 hydrogens in fact leads to a diastereomer of the product of replacement of the other (try it!), so these hydrogens are also diastereotopic.

(d) Four, since it contains two stereocenters which do not have identical groups attached (so there is no possibility of an achiral *meso* isomer.) Two of them will give Z-aconitic acid via *anti* elimination (circled groups are removed):

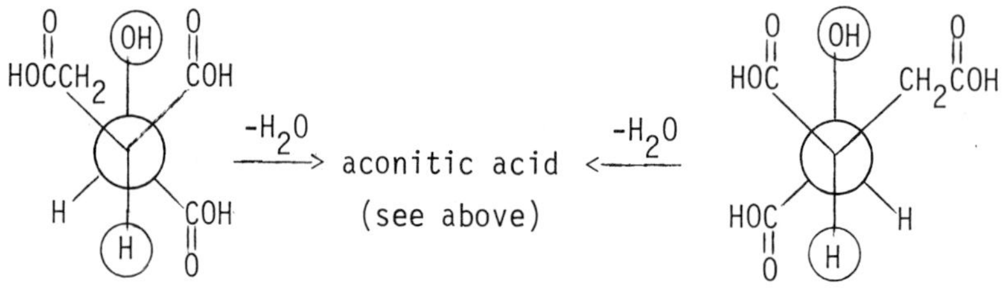

28. 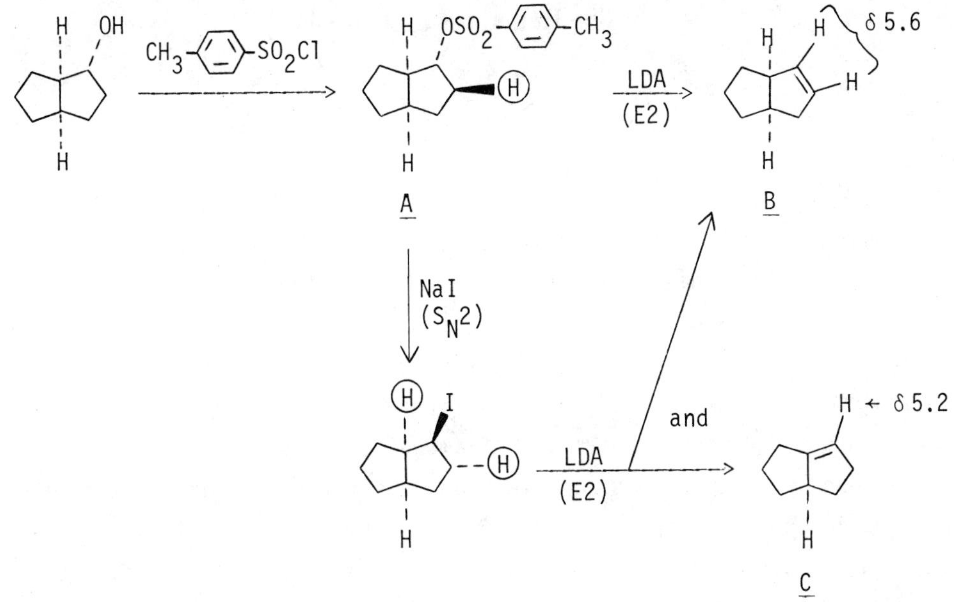

E2 *anti*-elimination on A can lead to only one alkene B via removal of the circled hydrogen. Conversion to the iodo-derivative via S_N2 inversion allows either of the two circled hydrogens to be removed in *anti*-elimination, leading to a mixture of alkenes B and C.

****

CHAPTER 12

The Reactions of Alkenes

General Introduction

Alkenes are reactive and synthetically useful molecules. Their reactivity derives from the electrons in the π-bond. These electrons are further away from, and therefore electrostatically less tightly held to the carbon nuclei, than are electrons in σ-bonds. The result is that these electrons are "available" in a "Lewis base" sense, a little like the lone-pair electrons on the oxygen of water or the nitrogen of ammonia. As you will see, attachment of an electrophile to these basic π electrons has the effect of breaking the π bond, and is the first step in many of the most common reactions of alkenes, "addition" reactions. Many of these addition reactions are known, and they allow conversion of alkenes to many other kinds of organic molecules, including ones we've seen before (haloalkanes and alcohols) as well as new ones. These reactions will expand the scope of synthetic possibilities in several ways. An updated "Functional Group Interconversions" chart will therefore be presented in this chapter of the study guide.

Outline of the Chapter

12-1. Thermodynamic Feasibility of Addition Reactions.

12-2. Hydrogenation of Alkenes.

12-3. Electrophilic Additions to Alkenes.

The largest group of reactions characteristic of alkenes.

12-4. Regio- and Stereoselective Functionalization of Alkenes by Hydroboration.

Another functional group interconversion process involving addition.

12-5. Oxidation of Alkenes.

Several more additions, and one double-bond cleavage reaction.

12-6. Free Radical Additions to Alkenes.

A new kind of "electrophile" for alkene additions: free-radicals.

12-7. Dimerization, Oligomerization, and Polymerization of Alkenes.

Reactions of, mainly, industrial use. Or, "where everything in your kitchen that you don't eat comes from."

12-8. Ethene in Industry.

12-9. Alkenes in Nature.

Keys to the Chapter

12-1. Thermodynamic Feasibility of Addition Reactions.

In general, π bonds are weaker than most σ bonds. In the addition reaction to an alkene (illustrated below), the alkene π bond is broken together with the σ bond of the molecule being added, but two new σ bonds are formed. The result is these addition reactions are generally exothermic, since one of the bonds broken is weak (the π bond), but both new bonds formed are strong:

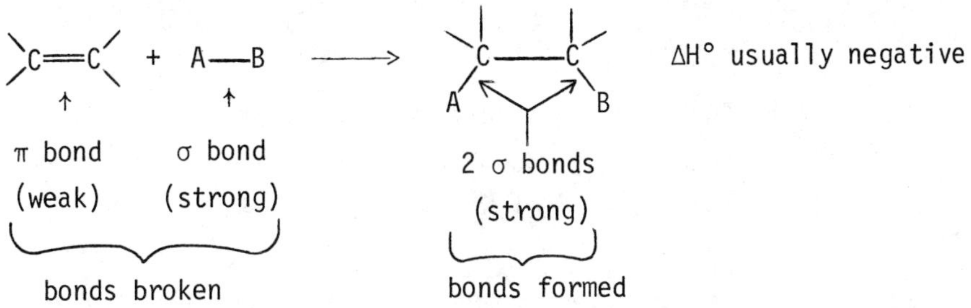

12-2. Hydrogenation of Alkenes.

The simplest addition reaction of alkenes is addition of hydrogen to form alkanes. Note, however, that as a process requiring a metal catalyst, it is not mechanistically typical of the other addition reactions of alkenes that you will see in this chapter. "Hydrogenation" is a non-polar addition process, unlike typical addition reactions which involve electrophiles attaching to the nucleophilic π-bond electrons of the alkene. Most hydrogenation reactions can be carried out equally well with any one of the heterogeneous catalysts mentioned in the chapter: platinum oxide (Adams' catalyst), palladium on carbon (Pd-C), or Raney nickel (Ra-Ni).

12-3. Electrophilic Additions to Alkenes.

In this section we turn to the largest and most typical class of addition reactions of alkenes. These are all reactions that proceed in two separate steps. The first step is attachment of an electrophilic atom to one of the alkene's double bonded carbons, forming a cationic intermediate. The reaction is completed by the combination of this intermediate with any available nucleophile to give the final, neutral addition product. Schematically,

(1) $\ce{>C=C<}$ + A—B $\left(\begin{array}{l}\text{either as}\\ \overset{+}{A} \ B^- \ \text{or}\\ A\overset{\delta+}{—}B^{\delta-}\end{array}\right)$ $\longrightarrow$ $\underset{|}{\overset{|}{-C}}\underset{|}{\overset{+}{-C}}-$ $\left(\begin{array}{l}\text{or something}\\ \text{similar}\end{array}\right)$ + $\overset{..}{\underset{..}{B}}{}^-$

(2) $\overset{\overset{\textstyle A}{|}}{\underset{|}{C}}\overset{+}{\underset{|}{C}}$ + $\overset{..}{\underset{..}{B}}{}^-$ $\longrightarrow$ $\overset{\overset{\textstyle A}{|}}{\underset{|}{C}}\overset{\overset{\textstyle B}{|}}{\underset{|}{C}}$,

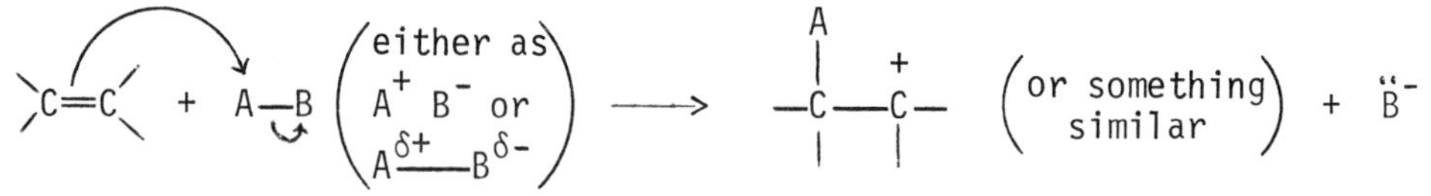

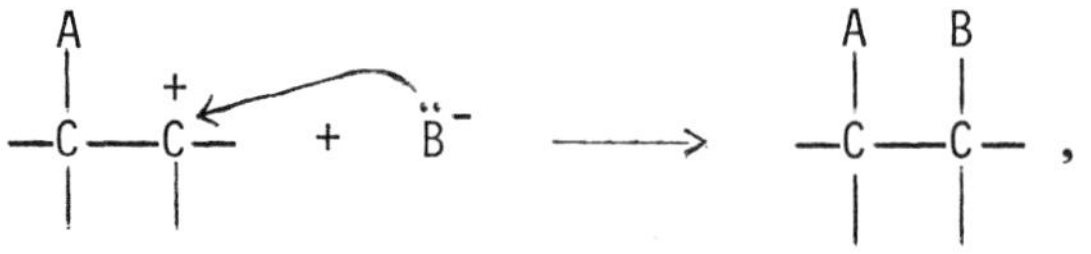

where the arrows, as usual, show movement of electron pairs. From a synthetic point of view, alkenes can be viewed as containing two carbon atoms that are potentially capable of attachment to atoms like oxygen, nitrogen, sulfur, halogens, etc. The large variety of addition reactions that exist allow either one or both double bonded carbons to be "functionalized." In other words, addition reactions allow conversion of alkenes to molecules containing new functional groups at either or both of the original alkene carbons. This section presents many examples of addition processes.

Most of the "A-B" type molecules that participate in electrophilic addition to alkenes are strongly polarized, such as $H\overset{\delta+}{—}Cl^{\delta-}$ or $H\overset{\delta+}{—}OSO_2OH$ (H_2SO_4). Others, however, are not, but can still serve as sources of electrophilic atoms. Halogens (Cl_2, Br_2) fall into this category. Although non-polar molecules like Br_2 do not have permanent dipoles, recall that electron movement can give rise to "fleeting dipoles," allowing the halogen molecule to behave as if it contained an electrophilic atom, namely "Br^+", via the fleeting dipole $X\overset{\delta+}{—}X^{\delta-}$. This can also be viewed as an S_N2-like attack of a nucleophilic π-bond on one X atom in X_2, with the other becoming the leaving group X^-.

The details of the mechanism vary somewhat with the nature of the electrophile. Simple electrophilic species like H^+, which lack lone pair electrons, add regiospecifically to give the more stable of the two possible carbocations ("Markovnikov orientation of addition"). The cation is then free to do anything carbocations normally do: attach to any available nucleophile, rearrange, etc. Electrophilic species that contain lone pairs (e.g. "$:\overset{..}{Br}{}^+$" from Br_2) add to give cationic species, too. These are not ordinary carbocations, though. They attract and attach to a lone pair on the electrophilic atom to make a three membered ring which is positively charged (bromonium ion, chloronium ion, etc.). Nucleophiles react with the carbons of these ions pretty much the same way they react with the oxonium ions of chapter 9: "S_N2-like S_N1" attachment. That means two things. First, the nucleophile attaches to the carbon that would correspond to the best carbocation ("Markovnikov" orientation). Second, it attaches from the side of the original double bond opposite to that of the electrophile ("anti" stereochemistry of addition). Additions involving molecules like halogens are therefore stereospecific in nature, giving the "anti" product only.

12-4. Regio- and Stereoselective Functionalization of Alkenes by Hydroboration.

This section describes the special characteristics and utility of the reaction between an alkene and a "borane," a molecule containing B-H bonds. Boranes are electrophilic, and their reactions with alkenes are therefore very reasonable (note carefully, though, that <u>borohydrides</u> like BH_4^- are different - they are anions, not electrophiles, and <u>don't</u> <u>react</u> <u>with</u> <u>alkenes</u>).

Borane B-H bonds add across alkenes. The reaction (a) is regioselectively anti-Markovnikov, (b) is stereospecifically a syn addition, (c) goes by a concerted, one-step mechanism, and (d) is synthetically very useful because the new carbon-boron bond can be changed into other functional groups easily. The most important is conversion to an alcohol ($-\overset{|}{\underset{|}{C}}-B\overset{\diagup}{\diagdown} \longrightarrow -\overset{|}{\underset{|}{C}}-OH$) with basic H_2O_2.

The chart on the next page summarizes sections 12-3 and 12-4, and shows several additions of different reagents to one alkene, 1-methylcyclohexene, so you can compare similarities and differences. For synthetic purposes, notice that this chart actually contains <u>three</u> methods for ultimately adding H_2O to an alkene double bond, each with its own specific characteristics:

(1) Hydroboration followed by oxidation. Anti-Markovnikov addition. E.g.,

$$CH_3-\underset{\underset{CH_3}{|}}{\overset{\overset{CH_3}{|}}{C}}-CH=CH_2 \xrightarrow[\text{THF}]{BH_3} \left(CH_3-\underset{\underset{CH_3}{|}}{\overset{\overset{CH_3}{|}}{C}}-CH_2-CH_2\right)_{3}-B \xrightarrow[H_2O_2]{NaOH} CH_3-\underset{\underset{CH_3}{|}}{\overset{\overset{CH_3}{|}}{C}}-CH_2-CH_2-OH$$

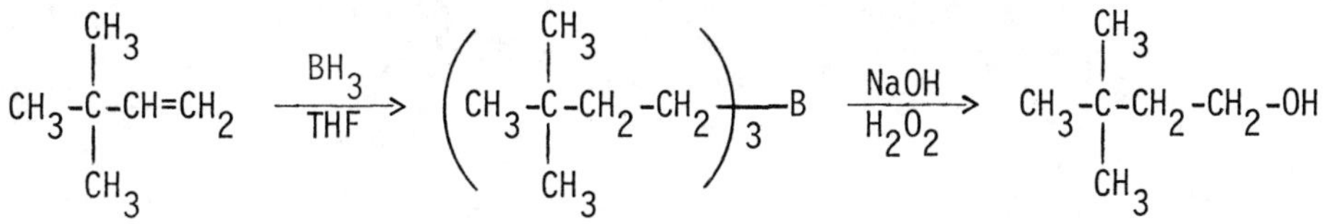

(2) Oxymercuration followed by demercuration. Markovnikov addition, without rearrangement. E.g.,

$$CH_3-\underset{\underset{CH_3}{|}}{\overset{\overset{CH_3}{|}}{C}}-CH=CH_2 \xrightarrow[\underset{THF}{H_2O}]{Hg(OAc)_2} CH_3-\underset{\underset{CH_3}{|}}{\overset{\overset{CH_3}{|}}{C}}-\underset{\underset{HgOAc}{|}}{\overset{\overset{OH}{|}}{CH}}-CH_2 \xrightarrow[NaOH]{NaBH_4} CH_3-\underset{\underset{CH_3}{|}}{\overset{\overset{CH_3}{|}}{C}}-\overset{\overset{OH}{|}}{CH}-CH_3$$

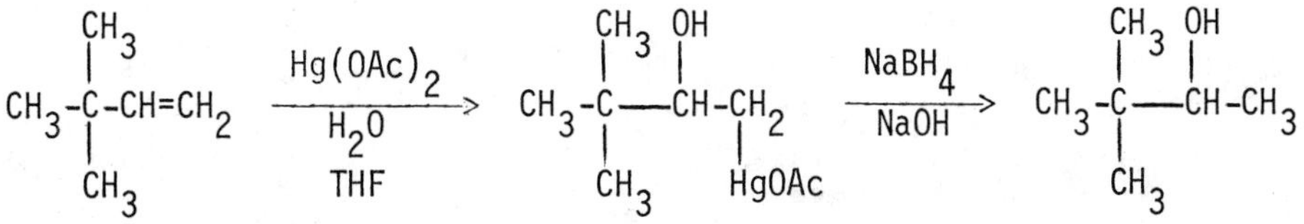

(3) Acid-catalyzed hydration. Markovnikov addition with carbocations that can rearrange. E.g.,

$$CH_3-\underset{\underset{CH_3}{|}}{\overset{\overset{CH_3}{|}}{C}}-CH=CH_2 \xrightarrow[H_2O]{H_2SO_4} \left[CH_3-\underset{\underset{CH_3}{|}}{\overset{\overset{CH_3}{|}}{C}}-\overset{+}{CH}-CH_3\right] \longrightarrow \left[CH_3-\underset{\underset{CH_3}{+|}}{\overset{\overset{CH_3}{|}}{C}}-CH-CH_3\right] \longrightarrow CH_3-\underset{\underset{OH}{|}}{\overset{\overset{CH_3}{|}}{C}}-\underset{\underset{CH_3}{|}}{CH}-CH_3$$

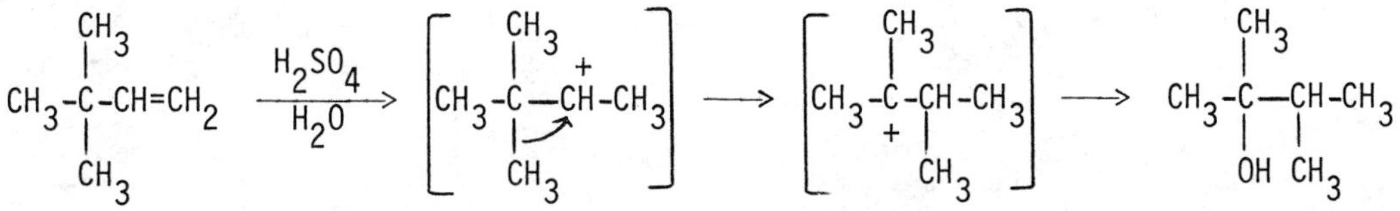

CHART OF EXAMPLES

Electrophilic additions to 1-methylcyclohexene

Example	Typical reagent	Electrophile	Nucleophile	Intermediate	Regiochem. Stereochem.	Product
Hydroboration	BH_3	$B^{\delta+}$	$H^{\delta-}$	None: 1-step rxn.[a]	anti-Markov.[d] syn addition	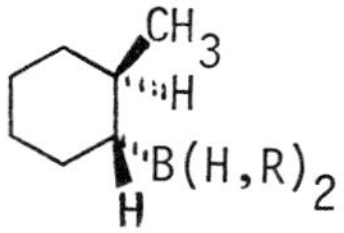
HX addition	HCl	H^+	Cl^-	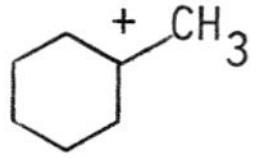	Markovnikov	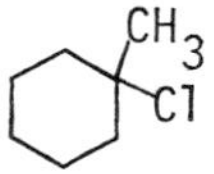
Hydration[b]	$H_2SO_4 + H_2O$	H^+	H_2O	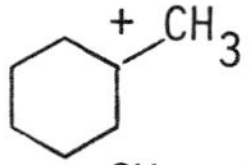	Markovnikov	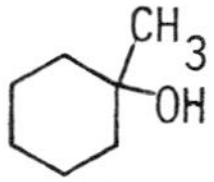
Halogenation	Br_2	$Br^{\delta+}$	Br^-	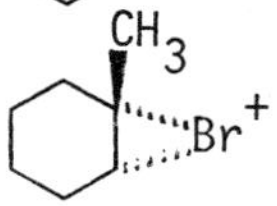	Markovnikov[e] anti addition	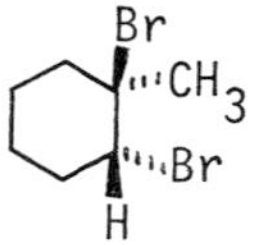
Haloalcohol[b] formation	$Cl_2 + H_2O$	$Cl^{\delta+}$	H_2O	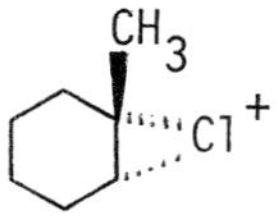	Markovnikov[d] anti addition	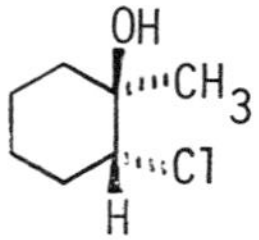
Chlorosulfenylation	CH_3SCl	$CH_3S^{\delta+}$	Cl^-	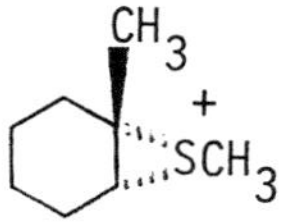	Markovnikov[d] anti addition	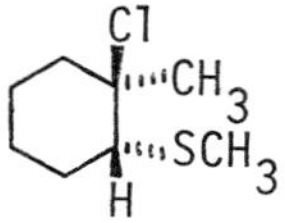
Oxymercuration[b]	$Hg(OAc)_2$[c] + H_2O	$AcOHg^{\delta+}$	H_2O	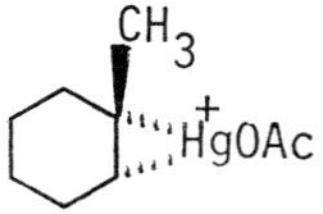	Markovnikov[d] anti addition	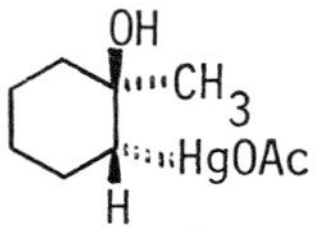

Notes: (a) Not a typical electrophilic addition. (b) Typical examples where the electrophile and the nucleophile come from separate molecules. (c) "OAc" means acetate ($O\overset{O}{\parallel}CCH_3$). (d) Mainly, but not 100%. (e) When observable, such as with A-B reagents from Table 12-2.

12-5. Oxidation of Alkenes.

This section presents several reactions where both alkene carbons wind up converted to oxygen-containing functional groups. They all involve reagents that have electrophilic characteristics, although these may not always be obvious at first glance from the mechanisms. Peroxycarboxylic acids such as peroxyethanoic acid or "MCPBA" serve as formal sources of electrophilic "HO^+." Permanganate ion, due to the extreme electron deficiency of the Mn^{VII} oxidation state, actually reacts as though one of its oxygens were electrophilic (in spite of its negative charge!). OsO_4 is similar. Finally, looking at the Lewis structure of ozone, it can also be viewed as having a very electron deficient central atom, which will allow it to react as if one of the end oxygens were electrophilic:

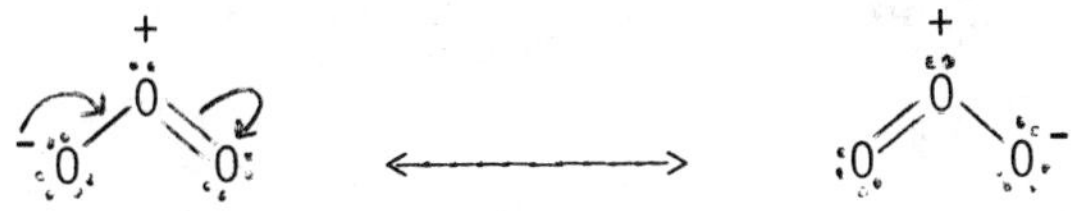

Just like the case with halogen molecules, the ends of O_3 *on the average* must be identical. At any instant, however, one end can act like an electrophile and the other like a nucleophile. The mechanism of addition of these last three reagents (MnO_4^-, OsO_4, and O_3) are similar. In each case three pairs of electrons move in a circle to simultaneously form new C-O bonds at both alkene carbons. These are all examples of *concerted cycloaddition* reactions, and the products are ring compounds:

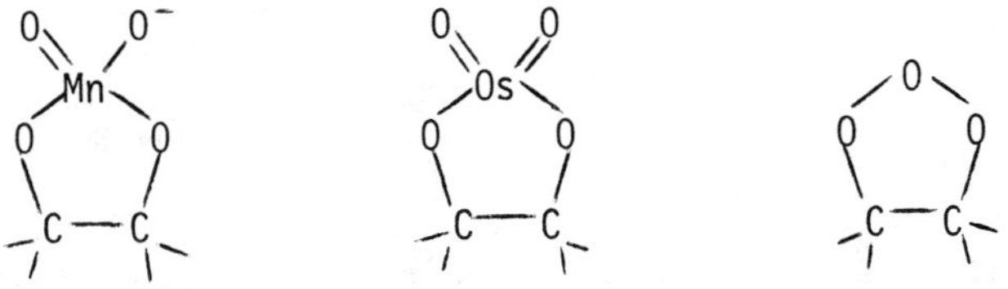

For synthetic purposes, note that ozone is the first reagent you've seen that can completely break carbon-carbon bonds. It selectively cleaves double bonds, most typically to carbonyl compounds in a two-stage process:

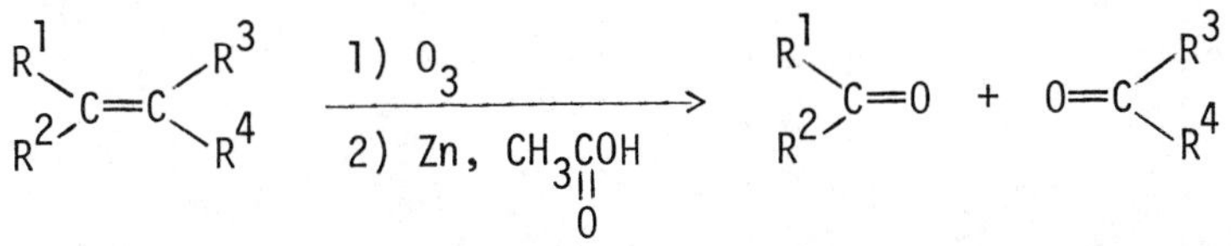

Free Radical Additions to Alkenes.

Although typical free radicals are neutral, they are electron deficient in the sense that they lack one electron from having a full octet. To a certain extent, therefore, they can be electrophilic. How electrophilic a free radical will be will depend on the kind of atom involved. Halogen atoms are quite electrophilic (they would like to have their eighth electron to make stable halide ions); so are carbon radicals with halogens attached (e.g. $\cdot CBr_3$ and $\cdot CCl_3$). Free radical electrophiles can attach to double bond electrons just like other kinds of electrophiles. The product of the attachment is just another free radical though (instead of a cation). This makes the mechanism a free radical chain process (recall chapter 3, especially sections 5, 6, and 7). Free radical chain processes occur only when all the propagation steps are energetically reasonable enough to proceed at rates competitive with other processes (terminations, or completely different mechanisms).

The text describes a brief history of the story entitled "What's the Matter with HBr?" In the free-radical addition of HBr to an alkene, the electrophile is $:\overset{..}{\underset{..}{Br}}\cdot$ instead of H^+, as in ionic additions. So the free-radical addition appears to "turn around" the direction of HBr addition to unequally substituted alkenes. Notice that *both* the free radical *and* the ionic additions regiospecifically give the most stable intermediate; it's the difference in the electrophile that makes the reaction appear to "turn around".

Ionic addition of HBr

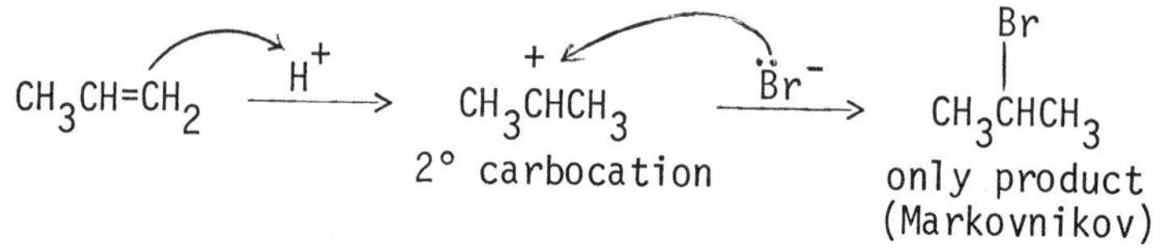

$$CH_3CH{=}CH_2 \xrightarrow{\ H^+\ } CH_3\overset{+}{C}HCH_3 \xrightarrow{\ \overset{..}{Br}{}^-\ } CH_3\overset{\underset{|}{Br}}{C}HCH_3$$

2° carbocation   only product (Markovnikov)

Free-radical addition of HBr (requires presence of initiatiors like peroxides, UV light, etc.)

$$CH_3CH{\cdot}{\odot}CH_2 \xrightarrow{\ Br{\odot}\ } CH_3\overset{\odot}{C}HCH_2Br \xrightarrow{\ H{\odot}\cdot Br\ } CH_3CH_2CH_2Br$$

2° radical   only product (anti-Markovnikov)

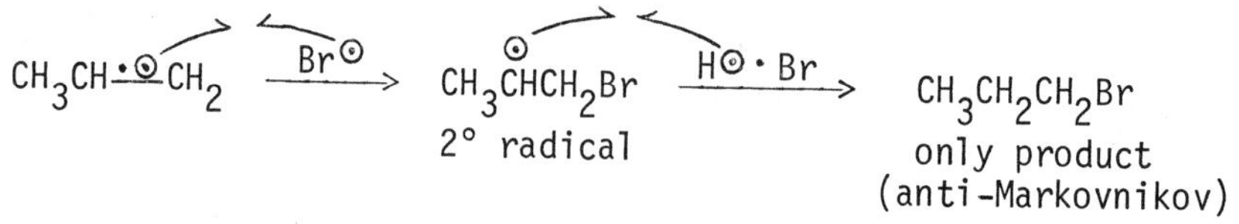

The energetic constraint mentioned earlier means that only HBr addition "turns around" in the presence of peroxides. *HCl and HI additions remain ionic, with Markovnikov orientation, whether peroxides are present or not!*

Note some of the other free-radical additions to alkenes in the chapter; some are synthetically useful.

As promised earlier, an updated chart of synthetic transformations follows, which includes the reactions of alkenes you have just seen.

Functional Group Interconversions

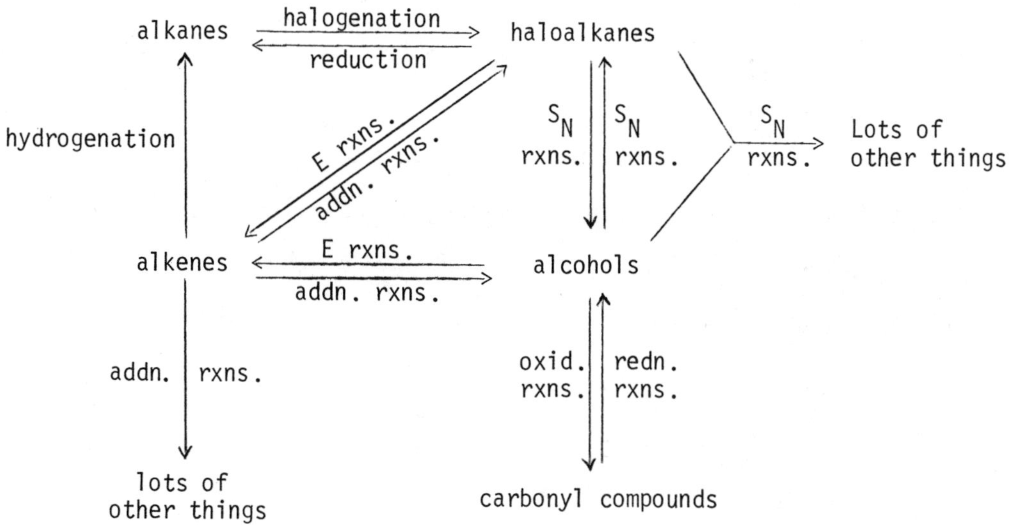

You will no doubt be relieved to know that, believe it or not, this chart is almost in its final form! There's really very little left to add.

12-7. Dimerization, Oligomerization, and Polymerization of Alkenes.

These are all addition reactions of carbon electrophiles (either carbocations or free-radicals) with alkenes. In either case the addition gives a new carbocation or free-radical (as the case may be), which can add to another alkene molecule. This can go on and on, making the molecule bigger and bigger: a "polymer." Polymers can contain units that are all identical (like teflon, which is a polymer of CF_2=CF_2) or can contain two or more different "monomer" units (Saran wrap is a "copolymer" of CH_2=CHCl and CH_2=CCl_2).

Solutions to Chapter 12 Problems

1. Careful! Use DH° for CH_3CH_2-X, not CH_3-X, from Table 3-1.

   (a) $C_2H_4 + Cl_2 \longrightarrow$ Cl-CH_2CH_2-Cl

   Heat in: 65 + 58 Heat out: 2 x 81 ∴ ΔH° = 65 + 58 - (2 x 81) = -39 kcal/mole

   (b) C_2H_4 + IF —> I—CH_2CH_2—F; ΔH° = 65 + 67 - (53 + 107) = -28 kcal/mole

   (c) C_2H_4 + IBr —> I—CH_2CH_2—Br; ΔH° = 65 + 43 - (53 + 68) = -13 kcal/mole

   (d) C_2H_4 + HF —> H—CH_2CH_2—F; ΔH° = 65 + 135 - (98 + 107) = -5 kcal/mole

   (e) C_2H_4 + HI —> H—CH_2CH_2—I; ΔH° = 65 + 71 - (98 + 53) = -15 kcal/mole

   (f) C_2H_4 + BrCN —> Br-CH_2CH_2-CN; ΔH° = 65 + 83 - (68 + 124) = -44 kcal/mole

   (g) C_2H_4 + HOCl —> HO-CH_2CH_2-Cl; ΔH° = 65 + 60 - (91 + 81) = -47 kcal/mole

   (h) C_2H_4 + CH_3SH —> CH_3S-CH_2CH_2-H; ΔH° = 65 + 88 - (60 + 98) = -5 kcal/mole

****

2. Catalytic hydrogenation is a *syn* addition.

   (a) 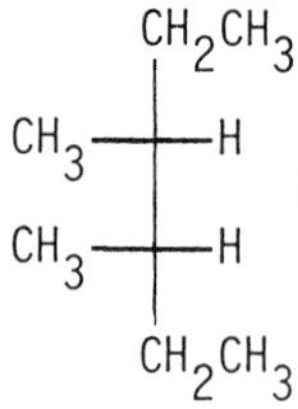

   (meso)

   (b) 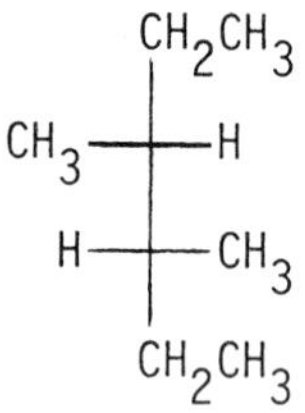

   and its enantiomer (as a racemic mixture)

   (c) 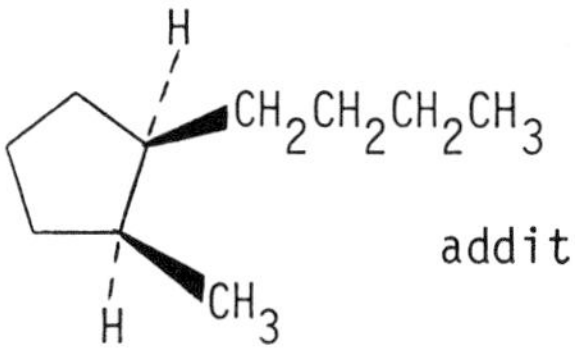

   and enantiomer (racemic mixture). Both double bonds are hydrogenated; *syn* addition to the ring gives the cis stereochemistry.

   (d) 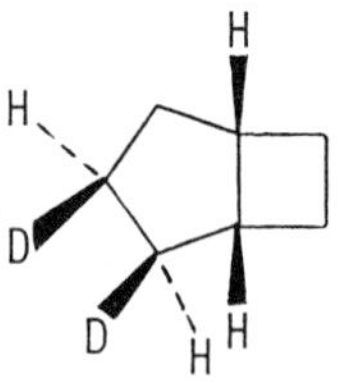

   D_2 adds on the less hindered "top" face of the "folded" bicyclic starting material:

   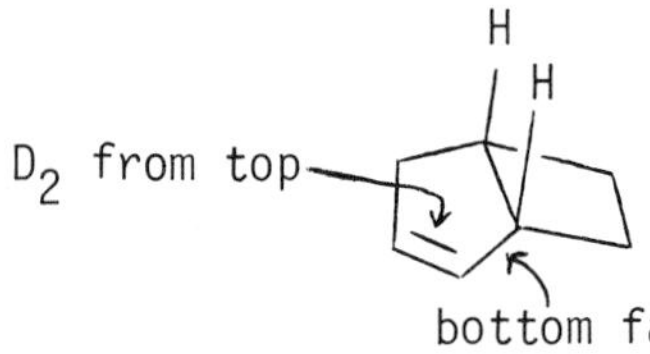

   bottom face of alkene is hard for catalyst and D_2 to reach

****

3. In all cases, identify the face of the double bond that can complex to the catalyst surface with the least steric interference. Add H_2 to that face of the π bond.

   (a) H_2 adds on the side opposite to the bulky $(CH_3)_2CH$ group:

   Circled H's are those added to the double bond.

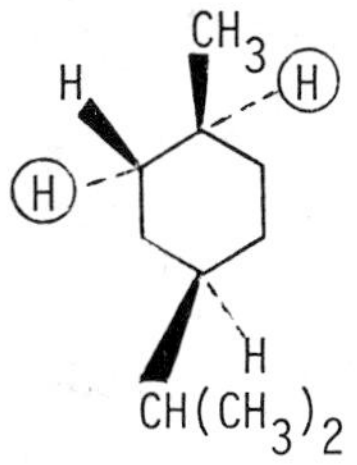

   (b) Hydrogenation occurs opposite to the methyl group:

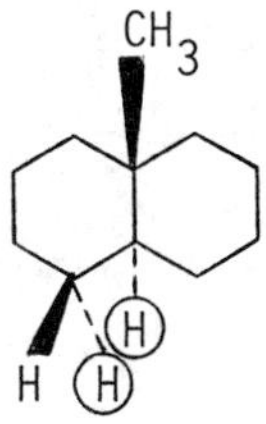

   (c) Hydrogenation occurs on the more exposed (bottom) side of the folded molecule (compare problem 2(d), above):

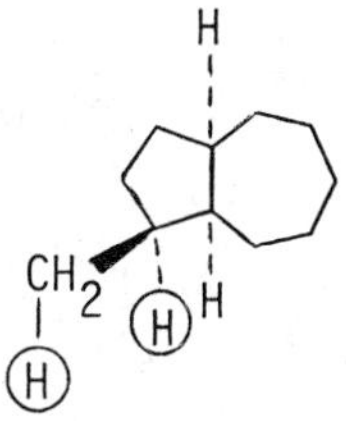

****

4. More exothermic. Alkene carbons (sp^2 hybridization) suffer more bond angle compression strain (120° → 90° for cyclobutene) in small rings than do alkane carbons (sp^3, 109° → 90° for cyclobutane). So cyclobutene is more strained than cyclobutane. Consequently, cyclobutene's heat of hydrogenation will be increased by the release of this extra strain energy when H_2 is added.

****

5. Look for good electrophiles, including Lewis acidic, or otherwise electron-deficient species. The answers: (a) strong Lewis acid; (d) very polar $\overset{\delta+}{Se}-\overset{\delta-}{Cl}$ bond; (e) electrophilic carbon ($CH_2{=}\overset{+}{\ddot{O}}H \leftrightarrow \overset{+}{C}H_2{-}\ddot{O}H$); (h) very electron-deficient for a species with electronegative atoms; (i) also electron deficient.

   Notice that NH_4^+ and Li^+ are <u>not</u> included: these are closed-shell, well-stabilized, essentially non-electrophilic cations.

****

6. Both reactions are thermodynamically favored in the forward (addition) direction.

(a) $H_2O + CH_2{=}CH_2 \xrightarrow{\text{cat. } H^+} CH_3CH_2OH$ acid-catalyzed hydration

$CH_3CH_2OH \xrightarrow{H_2SO_4,\ 180°} CH_2{=}CH_2$ use of strongly dehydrating conditions to drive equilibrium

(b) $HBr + CH_2{=}CH_2 \xrightarrow[\text{solvent}]{\text{inert}} CH_3CH_2Br$ spontaneous exothermic addition

$CH_3CH_2Br \xrightarrow{(CH_3)_3CO^- K^+} CH_2{=}CH_2$ E2 elimination driven by strong base

****

7. All chiral products are formed as racemic mixtures.

(a)

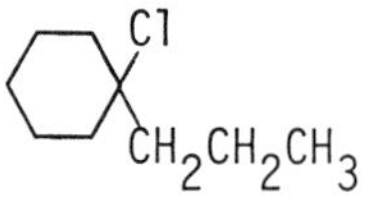

(b)

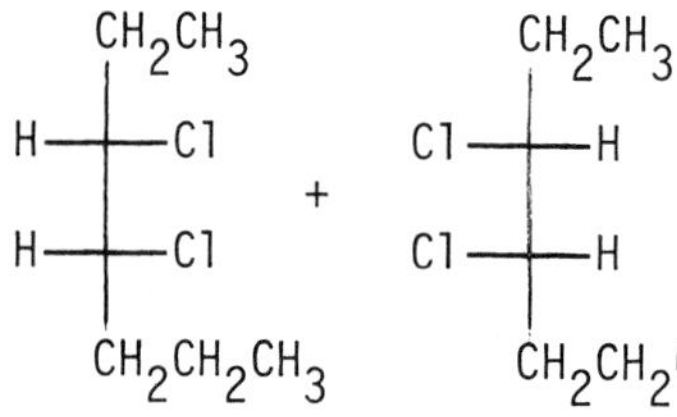

(racemic mixture)

(c)

← trans, from *anti* addition

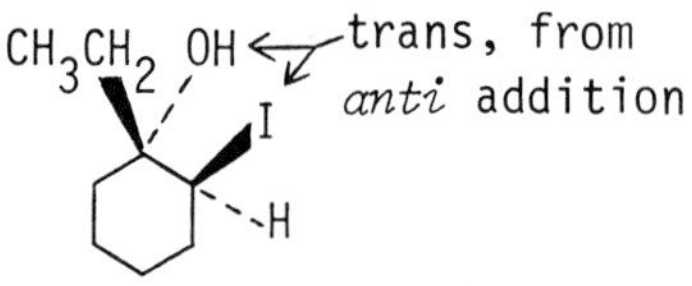

(d)

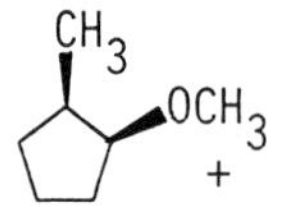

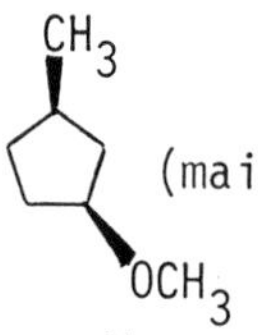

(mainly), via

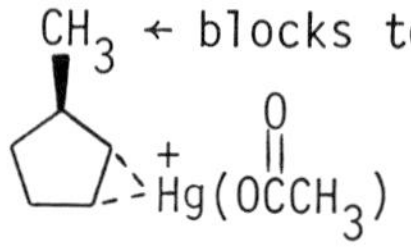

CH_3 ← blocks top, so Hg attacks bottom; all products are formed as racemic mixtures.

(e)

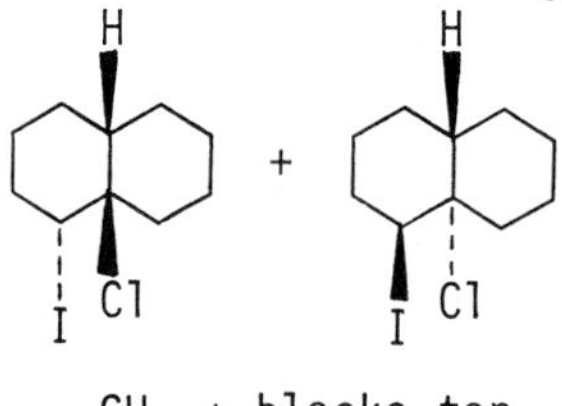

(f) See detailed discussion, below.

(g)

CH_3 ← blocks top

H ← *syn* addition to bottom

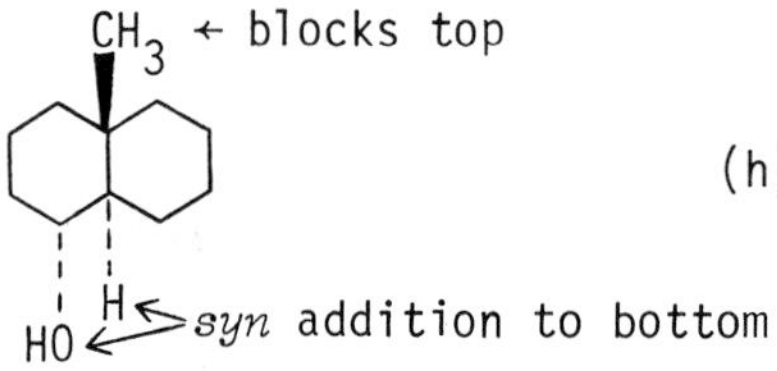

(h)

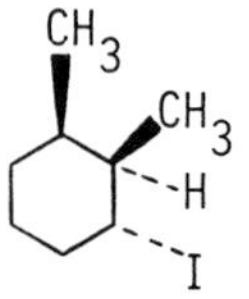

(racemic) similar stereochemical situation as in part (g)

Note the anti-Markovnikov regiochemistry for hydroboration in g and h.

(f) Compare the cations obtained from proton attachment at each end:

$CH_2=CH-\overset{+}{N}(CH_3)_3$ $\xrightarrow{H^+}$

$\overset{H}{\underset{|}{C}}H_2-\overset{+}{C}H-\overset{+}{N}(CH_3)_3$ terrible: two adjacent positively charged atoms

$\overset{+}{C}H_2-\overset{H}{\underset{|}{C}}H-\overset{+}{N}(CH_3)_3$ $\xrightarrow{Cl^-}$ $ClCH_2CH_2\overset{+}{N}(CH_3)_3$

poor, but certainly better   anti-Markovnikov addition expected

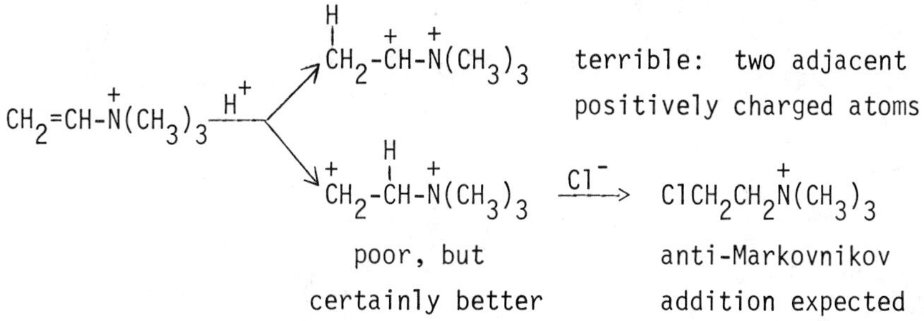

Such an addition would in fact be very difficult to achieve. It would be very slow due to the effect of the positive substituent greatly reducing the tendency for external electrophiles to approach and attack the π-bond.

****

8. A brief analysis of possible choices is provided for each problem.

(a) Need Markovnikov hydration of $(CH_3)_2\overset{\text{OH}}{\underset{\downarrow}{C}}H\overset{\text{H}}{\underset{\downarrow}{C}}H=CH_2$, or anti-Markovnikov hydration of $(CH_3)_2C=\overset{\text{H}}{\underset{\downarrow}{C}}\overset{\text{OH}}{\underset{\downarrow}{C}}HCH_3$. Either can be done:

$(CH_3)_2CHCH=CH_2$ $\xrightarrow{\text{1. Hg(OAc)}_2,\ H_2O;\ 2.\ NaBH_4}$ $(CH_3)_2CHCHOHCH_3$

$(CH_3)_2C=CHCH_3$ $\xrightarrow{\text{1. BH}_3;\ 2.\ NaOH,\ H_2O_2,\ H_2O}$ $(CH_3)_2CHCHOHCH_3$

(b) Need addition to propene of "Cl^+" and "$(CH_3)_2CHO^-$." Cl_2 is the source of "Cl^+", and $(CH_3)_2CHOH$ provides the nucleophile:

$CH_2=CHCH_3$ $\xrightarrow{Cl_2,\ (CH_3)_2CHOH\ \text{solvent}}$ $ClCH_2CH(CH_3)OCH(CH_3)_2$

(c) and (d) These involve addition of Br_2 to *cis* or *trans*-4-octene isomers. Addition is *anti*, so *trans*-octene gives *meso* and *cis* gives *dl*.

$\underset{H}{\overset{CH_3CH_2CH_2}{\diagdown}}C=C\underset{CH_2CH_2CH_3}{\overset{H}{\diagup}}$ $\xrightarrow{Br_2}$ *meso*-$CH_3CH_2CH_2CHBrCHBrCH_2CH_2CH_3$

$\underset{H}{\overset{CH_3CH_2CH_2}{\diagdown}}C=C\underset{H}{\overset{CH_2CH_2CH_3}{\diagup}}$ $\xrightarrow{Br_2}$ *dl*-$CH_3CH_2CH_2CHBrCHBrCH_2CH_2CH_3$

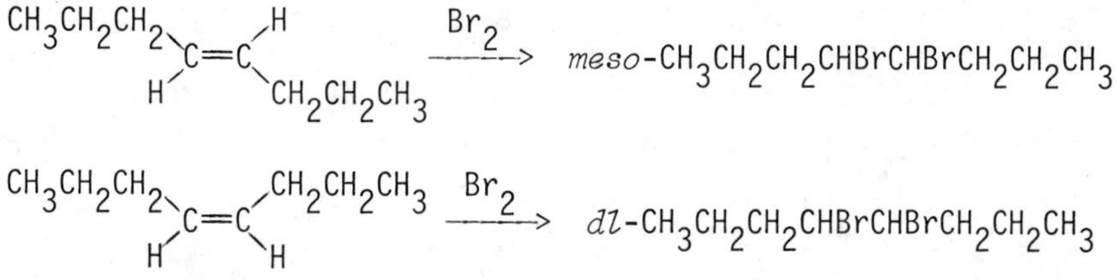

(e) This is easier - the methyl of 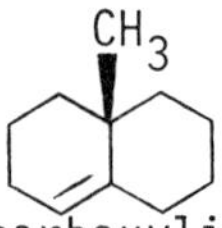 blocks the top face, allowing reaction with a peroxycarboxylic acid to occur from below:

(f) This is harder. How do you get the oxygen attached on the more crowded side? It has to be done stepwise, with an inversion step following initial attack of an electrophile on the less crowded bottom face. Apply the general oxacyclopropane synthesis sequence alkene $\xrightarrow{X_2,\ H_2O}$ haloalcohol (*anti*-addition) $\xrightarrow{\text{base}}$ oxacyclopropane (internal S_N2):

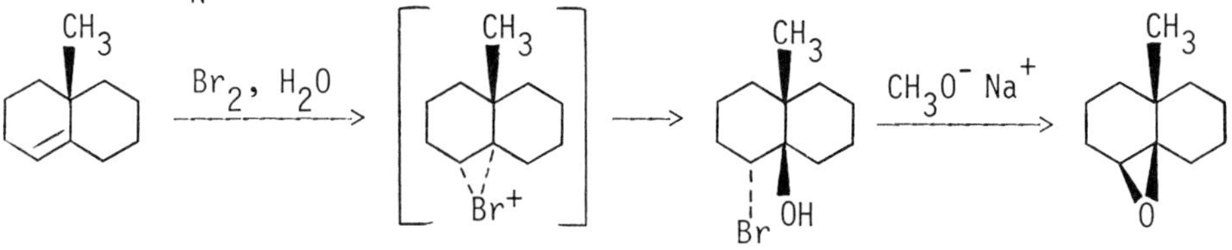

Br on bottom face

Br and OH *trans*

****

9. (a) Need to proceed via anti-Markovnikov addition to 1-butene. A bulky base is necessary to make 1-butene by elimination:

$$CH_3CH_2CHBrCH_3 \xrightarrow{(CH_3)_3CO^-\ K^+,\ (CH_3)_3COH} CH_3CH_2CH=CH_2$$

There is no way to add HI directly with anti-Markovnikov orientation. Two indirect possibilities are shown:

$$CH_3CH_2CH=CH_2 \xrightarrow{\text{HBr, peroxides}} CH_3CH_2CH_2CH_2Br \xrightarrow{\text{KI, DMSO } (S_N2)} CH_3CH_2CH_2CH_2I$$

or

$$CH_3CH_2CH=CH_2 \xrightarrow{BH_3,\ \text{THF}} (CH_3CH_2CH_2CH_2)_3B \xrightarrow[\text{THF}]{\text{ICl}} CH_3CH_2CH_2CH_2I$$

(b) and (c) Since dehydration gives mainly *trans* alkenes, these problems involve finding ways to add two OH's either *anti* (→ *meso*) or *syn* (→ *dl*). *Syn* is easy:

$$CH_3CHOHCH_2CH_3 \xrightarrow{H_2SO_4, \Delta} \begin{array}{c} CH_3 \\ \diagdown \\ H \end{array} C=C \begin{array}{c} H \\ \diagup \\ CH_3 \end{array} \xrightarrow[\text{(syn)}]{KMnO_4, H_2O, 0°} dl\text{-}CH_3CHOHCHOHCH_3$$

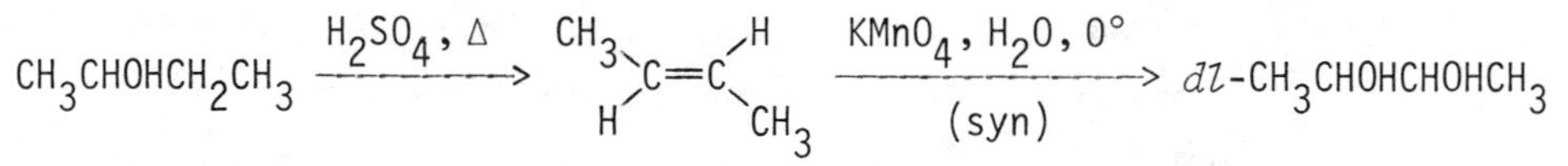

Anti is also readily achieved:

$$\begin{array}{c} CH_3 \\ \diagdown \\ H \end{array} C=C \begin{array}{c} H \\ \diagup \\ CH_3 \end{array} \xrightarrow{CH_3CO_3H} \underset{\substack{| \quad | \\ H \quad CH_3}}{CH_3\text{-}\overset{O}{\overset{\triangle}{C}\text{-}C}\text{-}H} \xrightarrow[\text{(with inversion)}]{H^+, H_2O} meso\text{-}CH_3CHOHCHOHCH_3$$

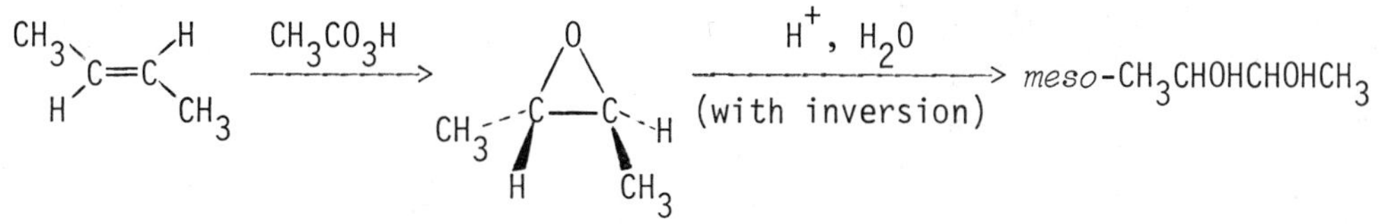

(d) Need different reactions on each double bond. Hydroboration is very selective for unhindered double bonds, so a primary alcohol is easy to make. Then MCPBA can form an oxacyclopropane at the trisubstituted double bond. Finally oxidation to an aldehyde fnishes the synthesis:

$$(CH_3)_2C=CHCH_2CH_2CH=CH_2 \xrightarrow{1.\ BH_3;\ 2.\ H_2O_2,\ HO^-} (CH_3)_2C=CHCH_2CH_2CH_2CH_2OH \xrightarrow{MCPBA}$$

$$(CH_3)_2\overset{O}{\overset{\triangle}{C}\text{-}CH}CH_2CH_2CH_2CH_2OH \xrightarrow{CrO_3(pyridine)_2} (CH_3)_2\overset{O}{\overset{\triangle}{C}\text{-}CH}CH_2CH_2CH_2\overset{O}{\overset{\|}{C}}H$$

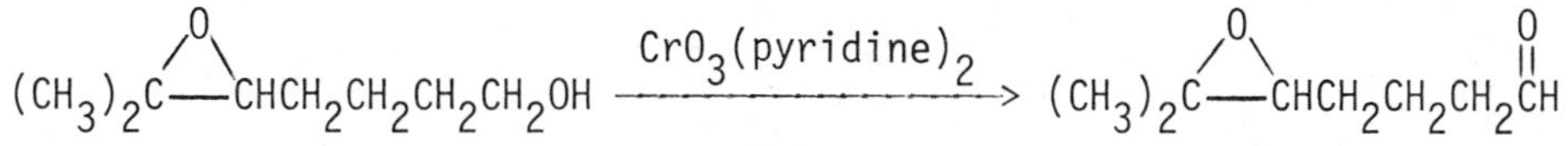

(e) Analyze this carefully: notice that no carbons are added or lost. What is required is to take away the double bond since there is no way to use it constructively, and then manufacture an aldehyde functional group at the <u>other end</u>, using only the carbons already present in the molecule. So, first:

$$(CH_3)_2CHCH_2CH=CHCH_3 \xrightarrow{Pd,\ H_2} (CH_3)_2CHCH_2CH_2CH_2CH_3$$

Next, functionality has to be introduced into the alkane. The only way is free-radical bromination. Then, a combination of reactions used in parts (a) and (d), above, allows completion of the synthesis:

$$(CH_3)_2CHCH_2CH_2CH_2CH_3 \xrightarrow{Br_2,\ h\nu} (CH_3)_2\overset{Br}{\overset{|}{C}}CH_2CH_2CH_2CH_3 \xrightarrow{(CH_3)_3CO^-K^+}$$

$$\overset{CH_3}{\underset{|}{CH_2}}=CCH_2CH_2CH_2CH_3 \xrightarrow{1.\ BH_3;\ 2.\ H_2O_2,\ HO^-} HOCH_2\overset{CH_3}{\underset{|}{C}H}CH_2CH_2CH_3$$

$$\xrightarrow{CrO_3(pyridine)_2} H\overset{O}{\overset{\|}{C}}\text{-}\overset{CH_3}{\underset{|}{C}H}CH_2CH_2CH_2CH_3$$

****

10. (a) Degress of unsaturation (see Study Guide for Chapter 11):
$H_{sat'd} = 6 + 2 - 1 = 7$; deg. unsat'n. $= \frac{7-5}{2} = 1$ π bond or ring.
Review problem 3(b) of Chapter 11 for help, if necessary. The answer is $CH_2{=}CH{-}CH_2{-}Cl$.

(b) CH_2: δ5.1-5.5; CH: 5.7-6.3; CH_2: 4.0

(c) Yes. This is an expected size of coupling for the 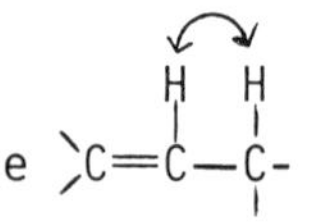 structure.

(d) This is a "long range" coupling between the "far" alkene hydrogens and the saturated CH_2 hydrogens: $H_2C{=}\overset{|}{C}{-}CH_2{-}$. Because of the distance between the hydrogens (that's what we mean by "long range") the size of the splitting is small. Since there are two such alkene hydrogens splitting the CH_2 with very similar J values, the splitting gives rise to small triplets.

****

11. $C_3H_6OCl_2$: $H_{sat'd} = 6 + 2 - 2 = 6$; these are saturated compounds.
C_3H_5OCl: $H_{sat'd} = 6 + 2 - 1 = 7$; deg. unsat'n. $= \frac{7-5}{2} = 1$ π bond or ring for compound "NMR-D".

(a) B - δ2.7 (s, 1H) - O<u>H</u> ?
δ3.8 (d, 4H) - two equivalent <u>CH$_2$</u> groups, attached to O or Cl and split by a CH
δ4.1 (quintet, 1H) - C<u>H</u>, attached to O or Cl and split by 4 neighboring H's

Since there are 2 Cl's but only 1 oxygen, the two identical CH_2's must be attached to Cl's. So the pieces are:

2 $-CH_2Cl$, $-\overset{|}{\underset{|}{C}}H$, and -OH, which equals $C_3H_6OCl_2$.

The molecule therefore must be $Cl{-}CH_2{-}\overset{OH}{\overset{|}{C}}H{-}CH_2{-}Cl$.

C - δ2.0 (broad s, 1H) - O<u>H</u>
δ3.8 (d, 2H) - C<u>H$_2$</u>, attached to O or Cl and split by a CH
δ3.9 (d, 2H) - C<u>H$_2$</u>, like the one above, but not equivalent to it
δ4.1 (m, 1H) - C<u>H</u>, attached to O or Cl, with lots of splitting

The molecule again has the framework $-CH_2{-}\overset{|}{C}H{-}CH_2{-}$, but is different from B, above, so it must be $Cl{-}CH_2{-}\overset{Cl}{\overset{|}{C}}H{-}CH_2{-}OH$.

D - All the signals are upfield. The reaction with base must have led
to an oxacyclopropane, not an alkene:

δ2.7, 2.9, and 3.2 (multiplets, each 1 H) - three CH's?

δ3.6 (doublet, 2H) - CH$_2$, split by a CH

Wait a minute! That all adds up to 4 carbons, but there are only
3 carbons in the molecule. Two of the three upfield H's must therefore be on the same carbon. So, again, the structure looks to have
the framework   -CH$_2$-CH-CH$_2$- (C$_3$H$_5$), with one Cl and one O to be
attached:

$$CH_2 \overset{\displaystyle\diagdown O \diagup}{\underset{}{—}} CH—CH_2—Cl.$$

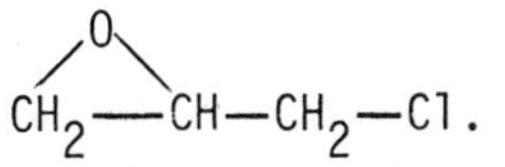

(b) Electrophilic addition of Cl$_2$ to the double bond in CH$_2$=CH-CH$_2$-Cl
gives CH$_2$—CH-CH$_2$-Cl. Attack of H$_2$O would ordinarily be favored at
the middle (2°) carbon, which should be more
cationic. However, the other Cl inductively
reduces the preference of 2° cation over 1°, so some chloronium ions
react with H$_2$O at the primary carbon instead:

****

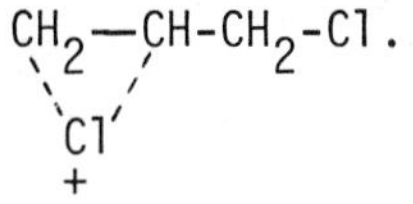

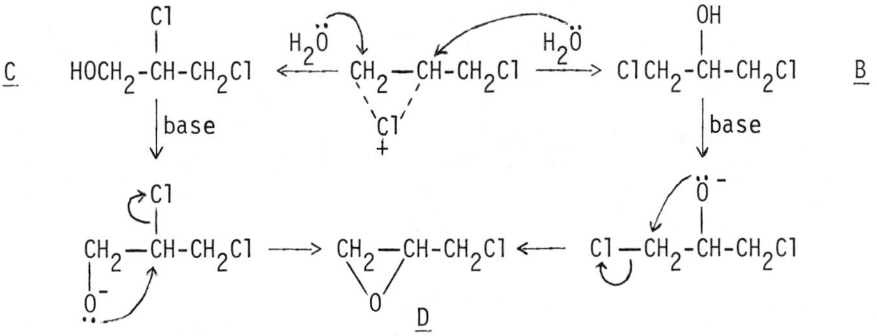

12. (a) H$_{sat'd}$ = 8 + 2 = 10; deg. unsat'n. = $\frac{10-8}{2}$ = 1 π bond or ring.

δ1.2 (d, 3H) - CH$_3$, split by a CH

δ3.4 (broad singlet, 1H) - OH

δ4.2 (quintet, 1H) - CH, split by 4 hydrogens, attached to O

δ4.8-6.0 - terminal alkene, -CH=CH$_2$

The molecule is CH$_2$=CH-$\overset{\displaystyle HO}{\underset{}{C}}$H-CH$_3$ (the only way to put the pieces together).

(b) Upfield signals are assigned above. The alkene assignments are:

$$\delta4.9 \rightarrow \overset{H}{\underset{\delta5.1 \rightarrow H}{}} C=C \overset{H \leftarrow \delta5.8}{\underset{}{}}$$

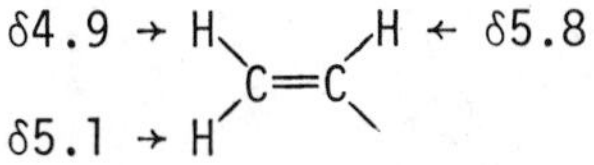

(c) Upfield splittings are assigned in part (a) on the preceding page. The δ5.8 hydrogen shows an 8 line pattern due to coupling to <u>three different hydrogens</u>, each with a <u>different</u> coupling constant:

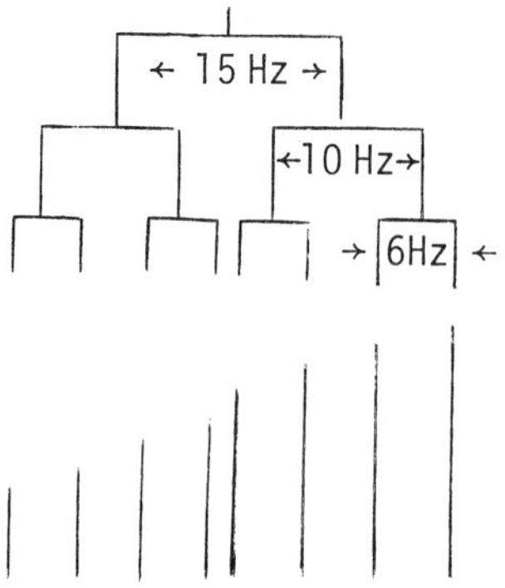

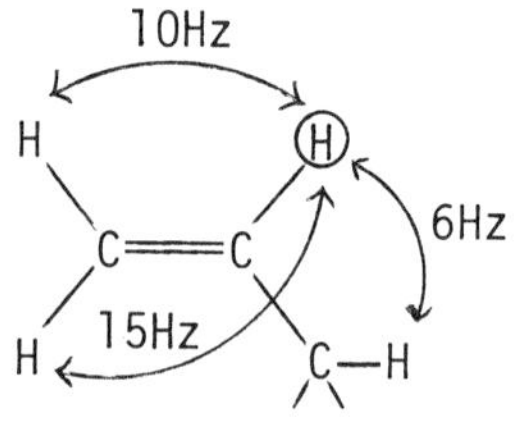

J values
for circled hydrogen

****

13. Replacement of OH by Cl has occurred: CH_2=CH-CH(Cl)-CH_3

(Reaction is ROH + $SOCl_2$ → RCl + HCl + SO_2.)

F - Reaction is just hydrogenation, forming 2-chlorobutane:

CH_3——CHCl——CH_2——CH_3

δ 1.5(d) 3.9 (sextet) 1.7 (quintet) 1.0(t)

****

14. Starting compound is CH_2=C(CH_3)$CH_2CH_2CH_3$.

(a) $(CH_3)_2CHCH_2CH_2CH_3$

(b) $CH_2DCD(CH_3)CH_2CH_2CH_3$

(c) $HOCH_2CH(CH_3)CH_2CH_2CH_3$

(d) $(CH_3)_2CClCH_2CH_2CH_3$

(e) $(CH_3)_2CBrCH_2CH_2CH_3$

(f) $BrCH_2CH(CH_3)CH_2CH_2CH_3$

(g) $(CH_3)_2CICH_2CH_2CH_3$ (peroxides don't affect HI addition)

(h) and (l) $(CH_3)_2C(OH)CH_2CH_2CH_3$

(i) $ClCH_2CCl(CH_3)CH_2CH_2CH_3$

(j) $ICH_2CCl(CH_3)CH_2CH_2CH_3$

(k) $BrCH_2C(OCH_2CH_3)(CH_3)CH_2CH_2CH_3$

(m) CH_2—C(CH_3)$CH_2CH_2CH_3$ (with O bridging CH_2 and C, epoxide)

(n) $HOCH_2C(OH)(CH_3)CH_2CH_2CH_3$

(o) H_2C=O + CH_3C(=O)$CH_2CH_2CH_3$

(p) $CH_3SCH_2CH(CH_3)CH_2CH_2CH_3$

(q) $CBr_3CH_2CH(CH_3)CH_2CH_2CH_3$

(r) $(CH_3)_2C$=$CHCH_2CH_3$

****

15. Starting compound is

$$CH_3CH_2 \quad C=C \quad H \\ CH_3 \quad \quad CH_2CH_3$$

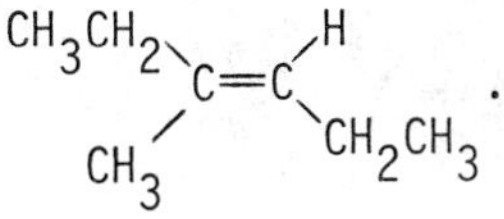

. All chiral products will be formed as racemic mixtures.

(a) $CH_3CH_2CH(CH_3)CH_2CH_2CH_3$

(b) *Syn* addition:

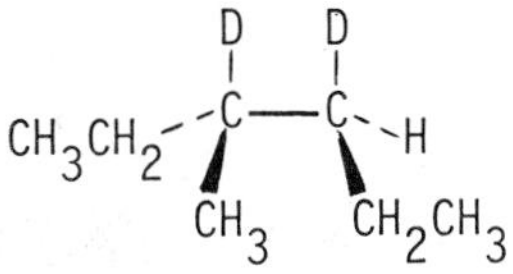

$$CH_3CH_2 - \overset{D}{\underset{CH_3}{C}} - \overset{D}{\underset{CH_2CH_3}{C}} - H$$

(c) *Syn*:

$$CH_3CH_2 - \overset{H}{\underset{CH_3}{C}} - \overset{OH}{\underset{CH_2CH_3}{C}} - H$$

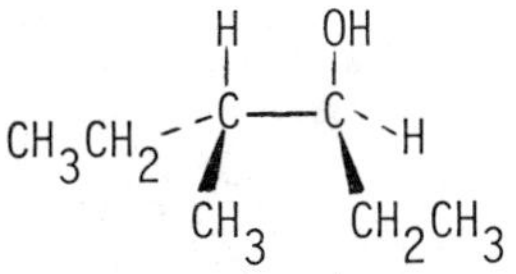

(d) $CH_3CH_2CCl(CH_3)CH_2CH_2CH_3$

(e) $CH_3CH_2CBr(CH_3)CH_2CH_2CH_3$

(f) $CH_3CH_2CH(CH_3)CHBrCH_2CH_3$ (mixture of stereoisomers)

(g) $CH_3CH_2CI(CH_3)CH_2CH_2CH_3$

(h) and (l) $CH_3CH_2C(OH)(CH_3)CH_2CH_2CH_3$

(i) *Anti* addition:

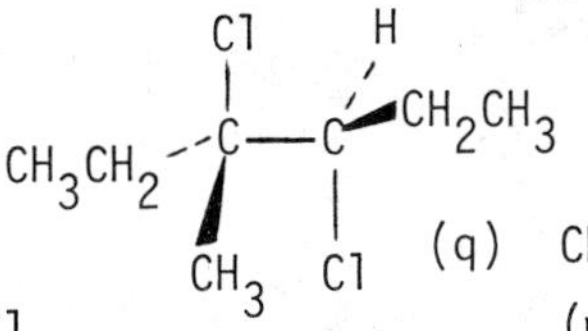

$$CH_3CH_2 - \overset{Cl}{\underset{CH_3}{C}} - \overset{H}{\underset{Cl}{C}} \overset{CH_2CH_3}{}$$

(j) *Anti*:

$$CH_3CH_2 - \overset{Cl}{\underset{CH_3}{C}} - \overset{H}{\underset{I}{C}} \overset{CH_2CH_3}{}$$

(k) *Anti*:

$$CH_3CH_2 - \overset{CH_3CH_2O}{\underset{CH_3}{C}} - \overset{H}{\underset{Br}{C}} - CH_2CH_3$$

(m)

$$CH_3CH_2 - \overset{O}{\underset{CH_3}{C}} - \overset{}{\underset{CH_2CH_3}{C}} - H$$

(n) *Syn*:

$$CH_3CH_2 - \overset{OH}{\underset{CH_3}{C}} - \overset{OH}{\underset{CH_2CH_3}{C}} - H$$

(o) $CH_3CH_2\overset{O}{\overset{\|}{C}}CH_3 + CH_3CH_2\overset{O}{\overset{\|}{C}}H$

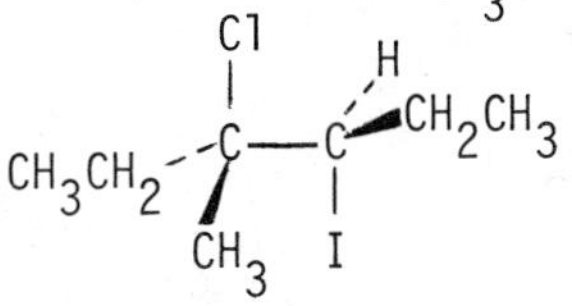

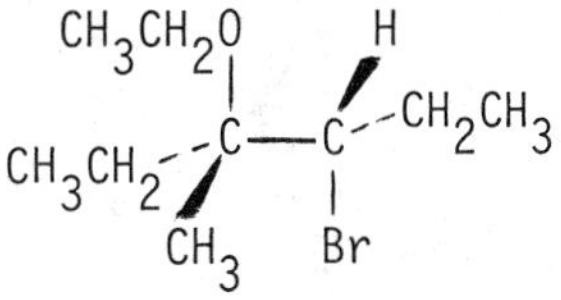

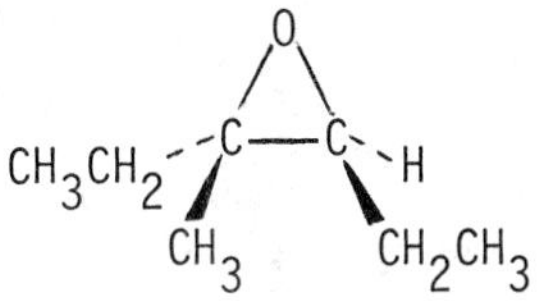

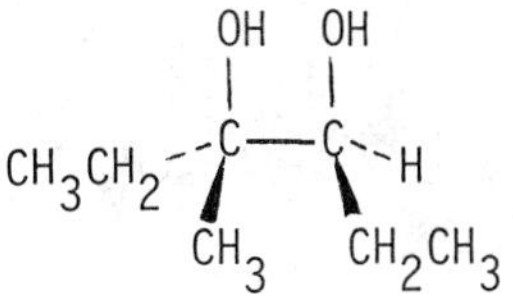

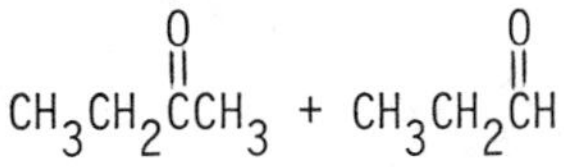

(p) $CH_3CH_2CH(CH_3)CH(SCH_3)CH_2CH_3$ (mixture of isomers)

(q) $CH_3CH_2CH(CH_3)CH(CBr_3)CH_2CH_3$ (mixture of isomers)

(r) Mixture of *E* + *Z* isomers of starting compound, and *E* + *Z* isomers of $CH_3CH=C(CH_3)CH_2CH_2CH_3$ (which is also trisubstituted)

****

16. Starting compound is

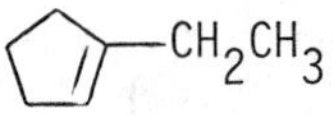

(a)

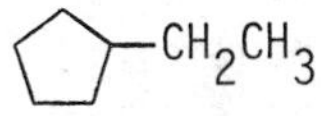

(b)

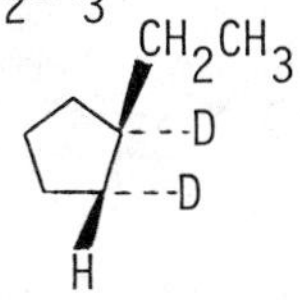

(c)

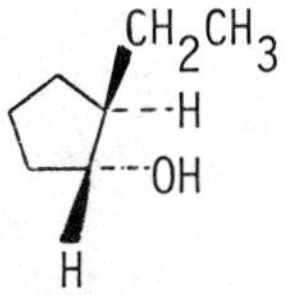

(d)

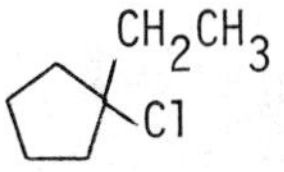

(e)

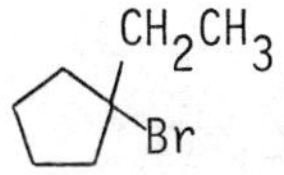

(f) (mixture of isomers)

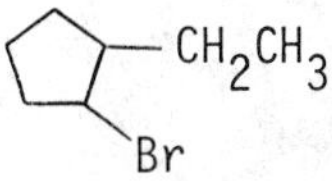

(g) 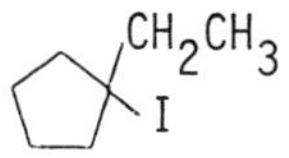 (h) and (l) 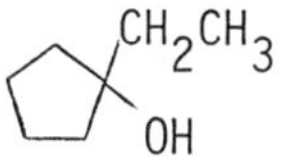 (i) 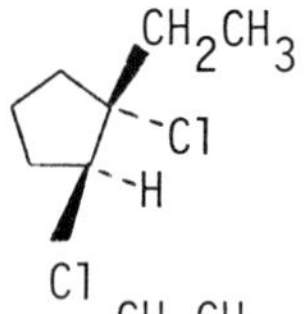

(j) 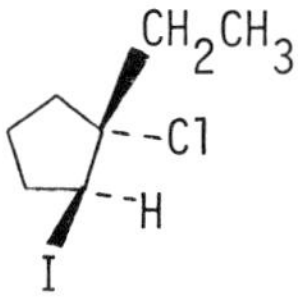 (k) 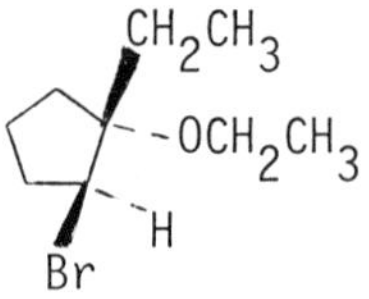 (m) 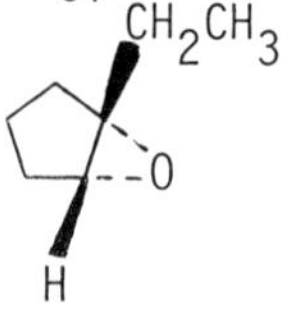

(n) 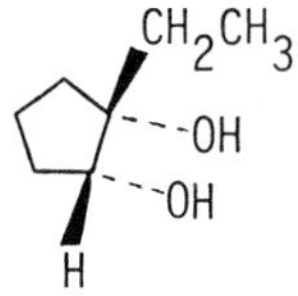 (o) 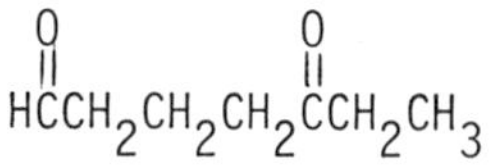 (p) 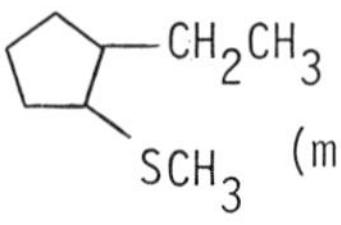 (mixture of isomers)

(q) 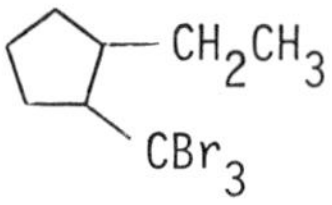 (mixture of isomers) (r) Mixture of starting compound and 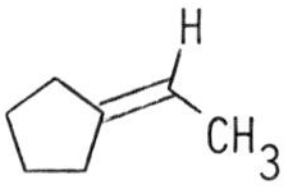 (both are trisubstituted)

****

17. (a) $H_{sat'd} = 14 + 2 = 16$; deg. unsat'n $= \frac{16-14}{2} = 1$ π bond or ring present.

First do the mechanism, to help you arrive at a reasonable structure:

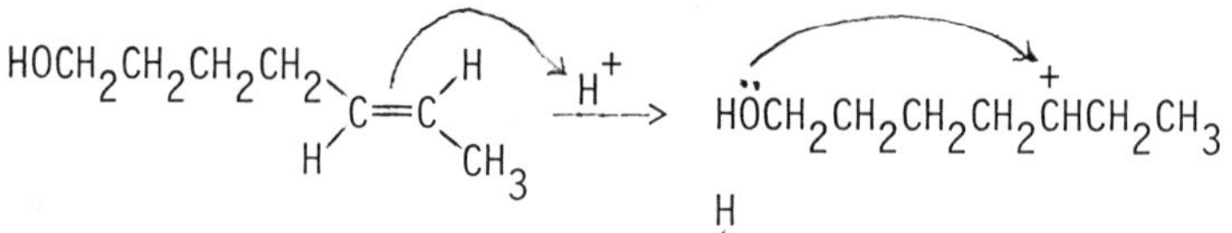

(one of two possible cations)

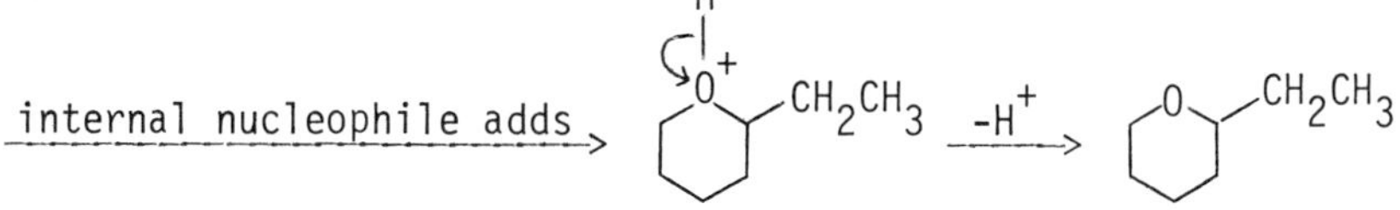

(b) $H_{sat'd} = 14 + 2 - 1 = 15$; deg. unsat'n $= \frac{15-13}{2} = 1$ π bond or ring present.

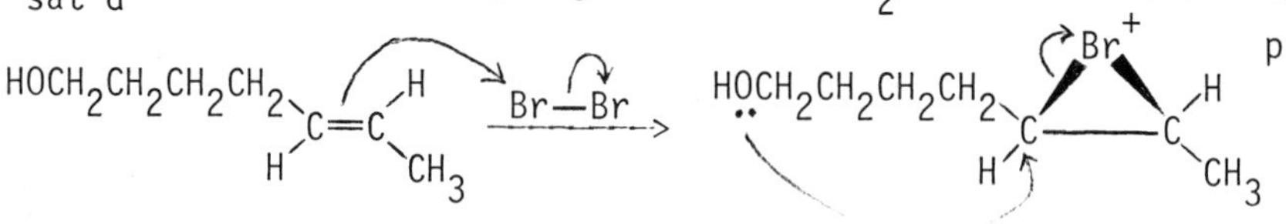

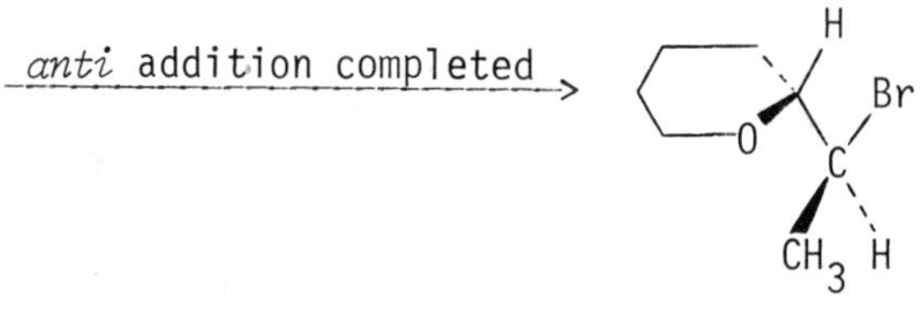 (+ enantiomer)

****

18. Both reactions have free-radical mechanisms at 600° in the gas phase (poor conditions for ions to exist). Compare the <u>first step</u> of addition (reaction i) with that of halogenation (reaction ii):

    (i) $CH_3CH=CH_2$ + Br· $\rightleftarrows$ $CH_3\overset{\bullet}{C}H-CH_2Br$ readily reversible at 600°C

    (ii) $CH_3CH=CH_2$ + Br· ⟶ HBr + $\overset{\bullet}{C}H_2CH=CH_2$ exothermic, not reversible

    Even if addition occurs very fast, it is a readily reversible process, especially at high temperature. Adding two species together to make one is entropically disfavored ($\Delta S°$ negative), and this unfavorable effect increases with temperature (remember $\Delta G° = \Delta H° - \underline{T}\underline{\Delta S°}$?). Since the competing reaction is energetically favorable and <u>not</u> readily reversible, eventually virtually all the propene will follow path (ii) to the halo-genation product, $CH_2=CH-CH_2Br$. The version of this reaction with Cl_2 is in fact the commercial method for synthesis of $CH_2=CH-CH_2Cl$.

    ****

19. Heat of light causes $I_2 \rightarrow 2\ I\cdot$; then you can have

    $$\underset{H}{\overset{R}{\diagdown}}C=C\underset{H}{\overset{R'}{\diagup}} + I\cdot \rightleftarrows R\overset{\bullet}{C}H-\overset{\overset{\textstyle I}{|}}{C}HR' \rightleftarrows I\cdot + \underset{H}{\overset{R}{\diagdown}}C=C\underset{R'}{\overset{H}{\diagup}}\ .$$

    single bond, freely rotates

    ****

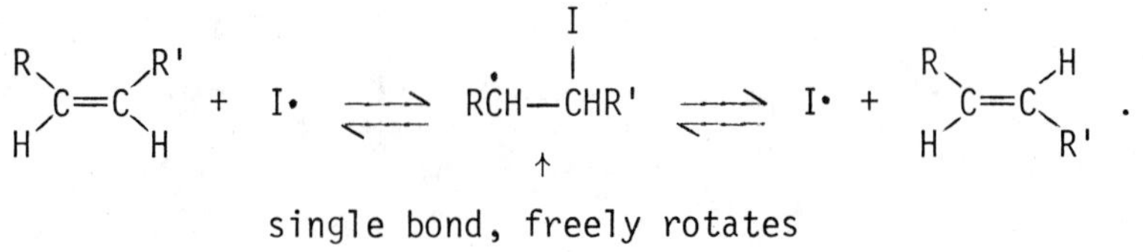

20. Assume that chiral products are actually to be made as racemic mixtures.

    (a) Best bond to make: $CH_3CH_2\overset{\overset{\textstyle O}{\|}}{C}\!\!\downarrow\!\!-CH(CH_3)_2$. Need to connect end carbon of one propene with middle carbon of other, so need to functionalize accordingly:

    $$CH_3CH=CH_2 \xrightarrow{HCl} CH_3CHClCH_3 \xrightarrow{Mg} CH_3\overset{\overset{\textstyle MgCl}{|}}{C}HCH_3$$

    $$CH_3CH=CH_2 \xrightarrow[\text{2. } H_2O_2,\ HO^-]{\text{1. } BH_3} CH_3CH_2CH_2OH \xrightarrow[\text{pyridine}]{CrO_3,} CH_3CH_2\overset{\overset{\textstyle O}{\|}}{C}H$$

    $$\text{product} \xleftarrow{CrO_3} CH_3CH_2\overset{\overset{\textstyle OH}{|}}{C}H-CH(CH_3)_2$$

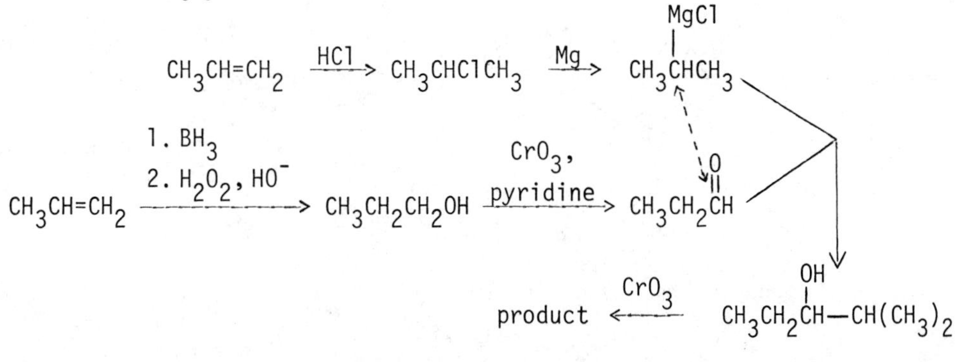

(b) Analyze: $CH_3CH_2CH_2-\overset{SCH_2CH_3}{\overset{|}{C}H}-CH_2CH_2CH_3$. The C-S bond can come from an S_N2 reaction of $CH_3CH_2S^-$ on some suitable compound, perhaps derived from 4-heptanol. This, in turn, can come from a Grignard synthesis:

$$CH_3CH{=}CH_2 \xrightarrow{\text{HBr, peroxide}} CH_3CH_2CH_2Br \xrightarrow{\text{Mg}} CH_3CH_2CH_2MgBr, \text{ first; then,}$$

$$2\ CH_3CH_2CH_2MgBr + \overset{O}{\overset{\|}{H}}COCH_3 \longrightarrow CH_3CH_2CH_2\text{-}\underset{OH}{\underset{|}{C}H}\text{-}CH_2CH_2CH_3 \xrightarrow[\text{2. } NaSCH_2CH_3]{\text{1. } PBr_3} \text{product}$$

Problems? Review Section 8-7 for help.

(c) This is not straightforward. Obviously the two bonds to the methyl groups must be made, but how? Hint: consider oxacyclopropanes derived from cyclohexenes. Here's the sequence:

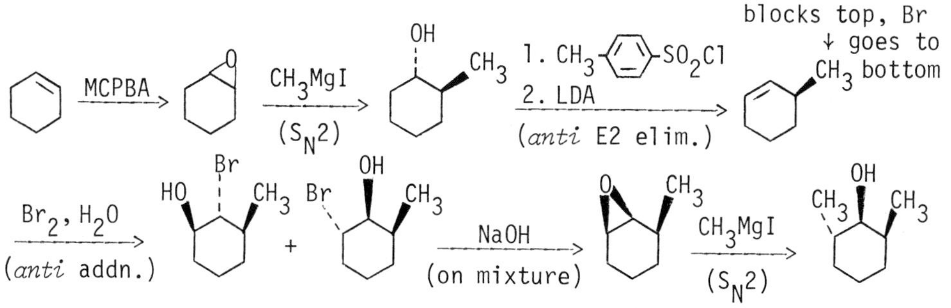

(d) Here's the toughie. Since a carbon needs to be added, make the logical deduction that becomes the carbonyl carbon: 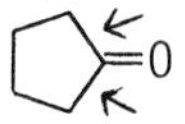

Then what? Ketones are made by oxidation of secondary alcohols. How would you make 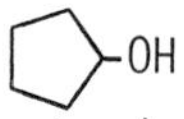 ? Review Section 8-7 again! Hint: can you think of a reagent, derivable from cyclobutene, that would react with $\overset{O}{\overset{\|}{H}}COCH_3$ to make cyclopentanol? An answer:

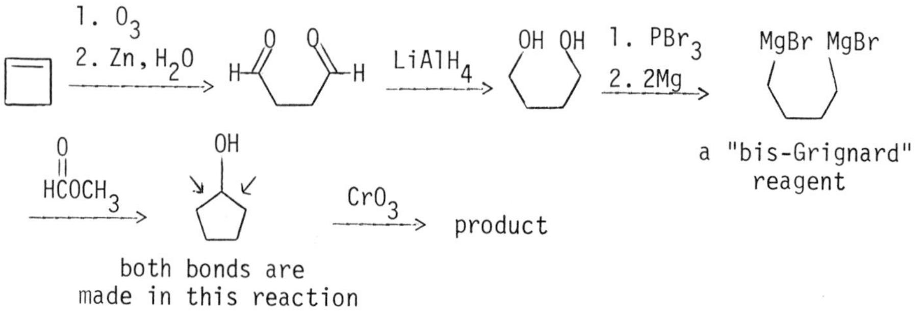

****

21. First, 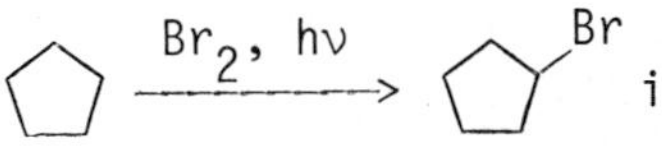 is necessary; you must functionalize the alkane before doing anything else! Note: later sections of this problem use molecules made in earlier sections.

(a) 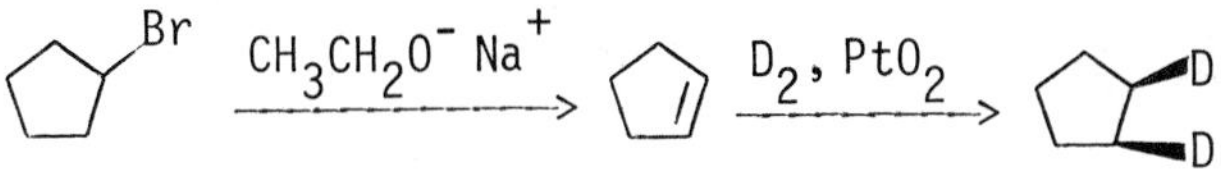

(b)  (Stop! If you didn't get this one, try to complete it yourself from here before looking at the rest of the answer!)

The rest: 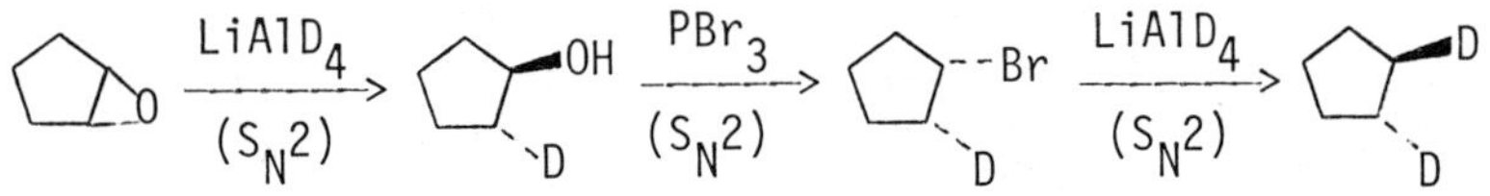

(c) 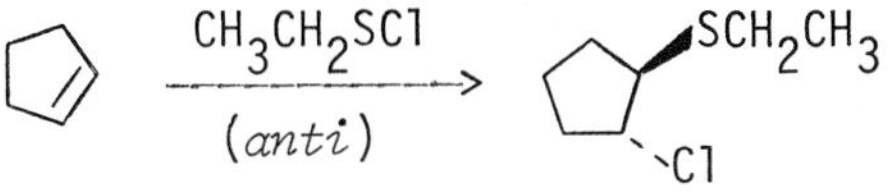

(d) 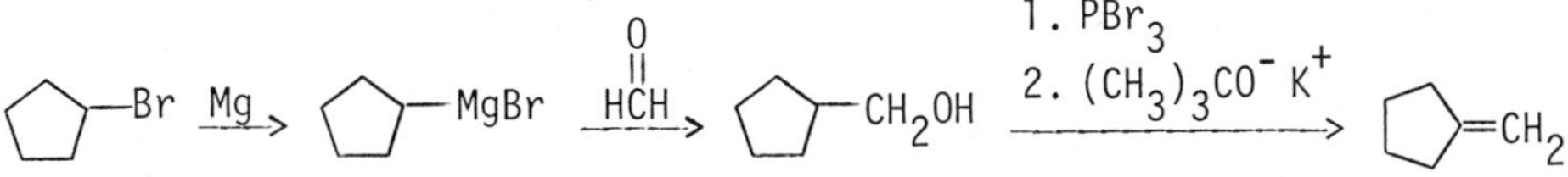

(e) 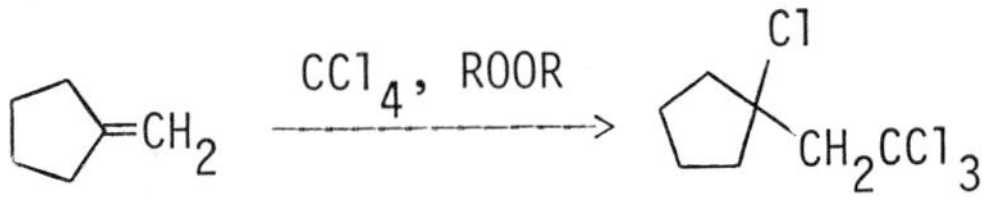

(f) 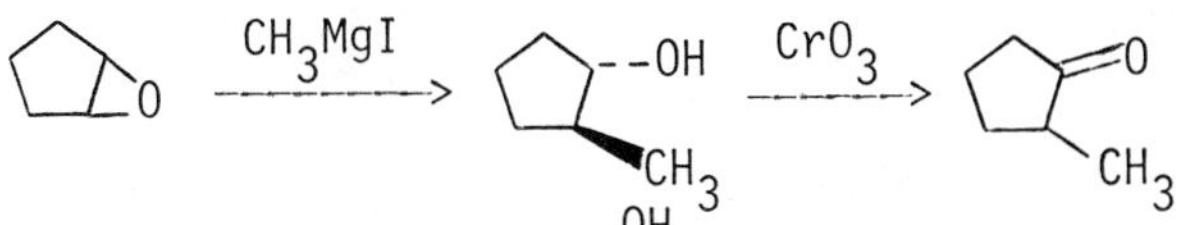

(g) 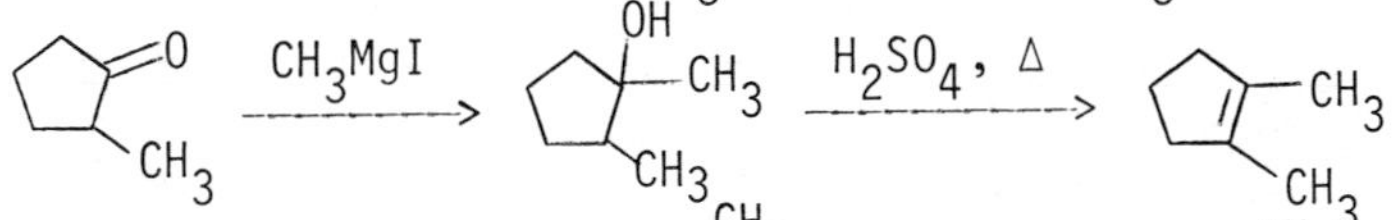

(h) 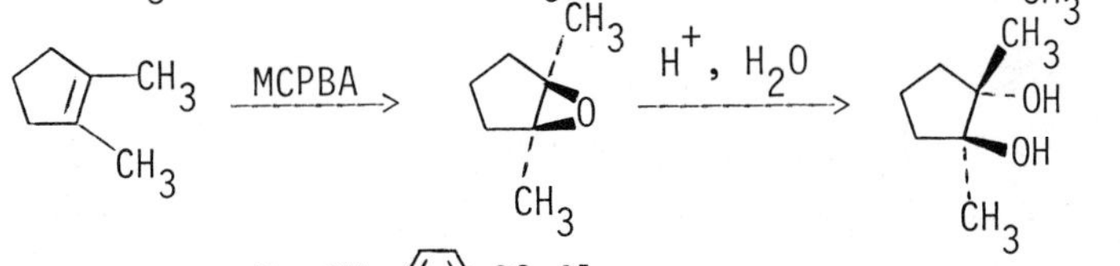

(i) 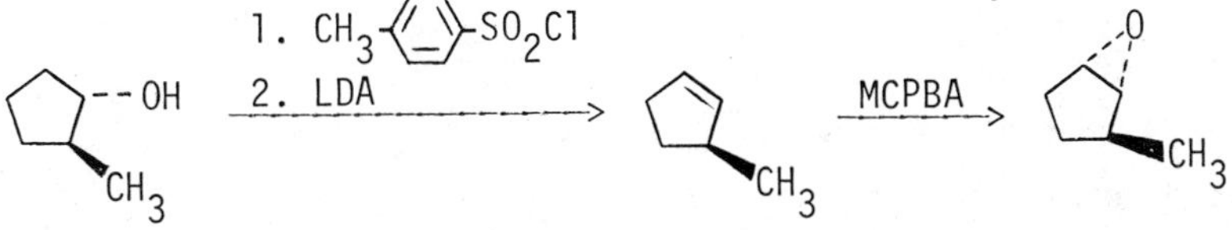

****

22. (a) $CH_3OCH_2CH_2CH(OCH_3)CH_3$ (Markovnikov ether synthesis)

(b) $HOCH_2C(OH)(CH_3)CH_2OH$ (oxacyclopropane → ring opening)

(c) Rearranges: 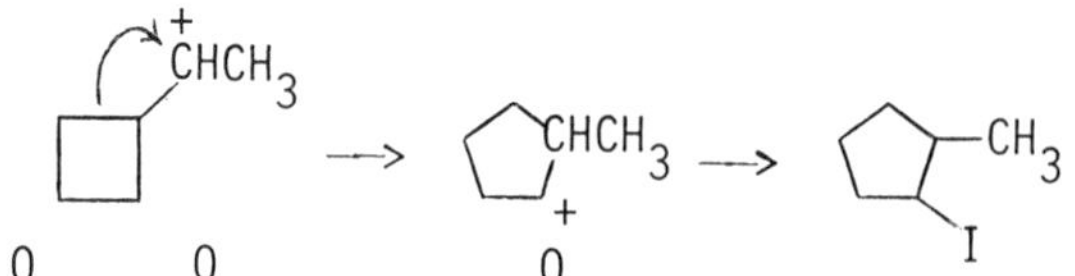 (strain relieved)

(d) $CH_3CH_2CH(=O)$ + $HC(=O)CH_2CH_2C(=O)CH_2CH_2CH_2CH_2CH(=O)$

(e) Adds as Br^+ ^-CN, *anti* stereochemistry: 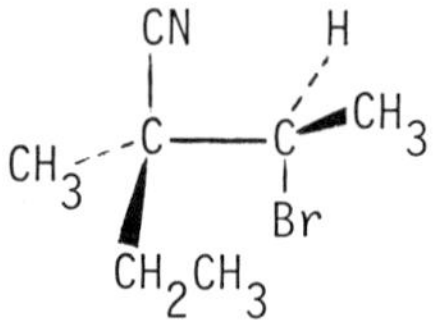

(f) 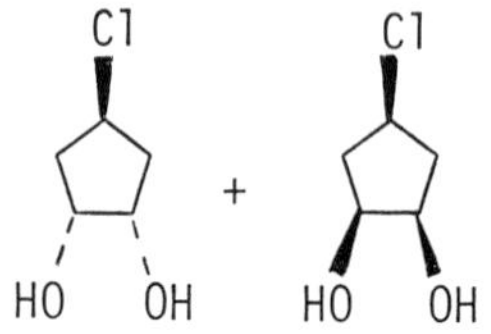

(g) $(CH_3)_2C(OH)CH_2CH_2Br$ (anti Markovnikov)

(h) *Anti* addn. to *trans* alkene ⇒ *meso* isomer: 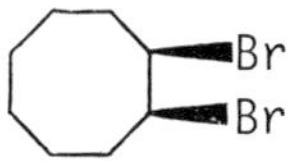

(i) $\text{-(-}CH(CH_3)\text{—}CH_2\text{-)-}_n$ ("polypropylene")

(j) Lewis structure: $CH_2\text{=}CH\text{-}N^+(\text{=}O)O^-$. Positive N implies NO_2 group is electron withdrawing. Therefore, this alkene should be readily polymerized by base, just like acrylonitrile (Section 12-7). Polymer structure will be $\text{-(-}CH_2\text{—}CH(NO_2)\text{-)-}_n$.

****

23. $H_{sat'd} = 20 + 2 = 22$; deg. unsat'n. $= \frac{22-18}{2} = 2$ π bonds and/or rings still present. Note only 7 signals in the C-13 NMR: the product must have greater symmetry than the starting material. Note, also, two signals for C attached to oxygen (δ 69.6 and 73.5), but the product's formula only contains one oxygen. The only conclusion possible is that the product contains an ether: C-O-C. How?

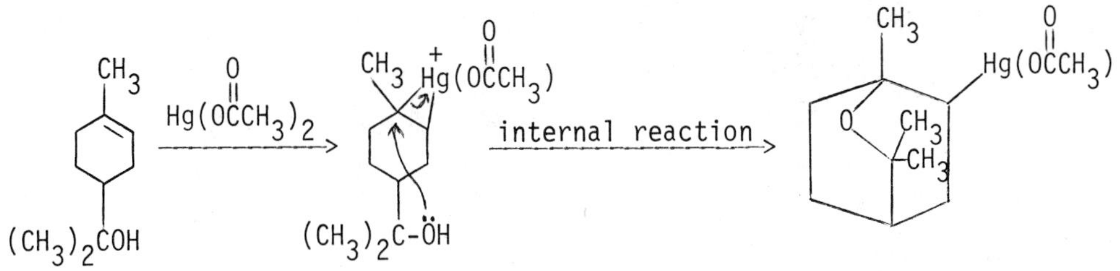

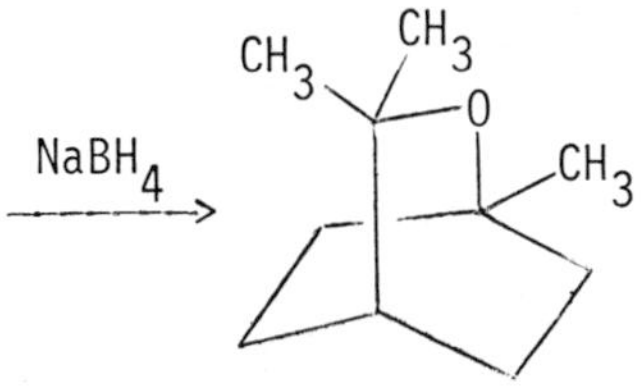

eucalyptol
(redrawn)

By the way, eucalyptol is just another name for cineole (Chapter 2, Problem 15).

****

24. Similar situation to problem 9(d):

(a)

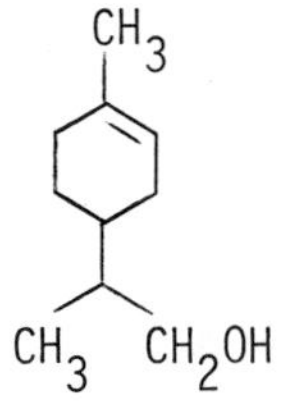

BH_3 prefers less-substituted double bonds due to their reduced steric crowding.

(b)

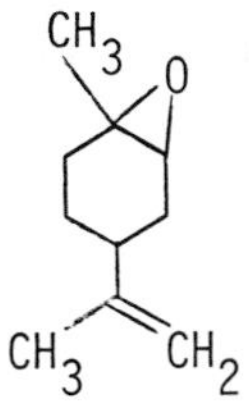

Electrophiles such as MCPBA prefer more-substituted double bonds because they are more nucleophilic (electron-rich), and their alkyl groups help stabilize both carbocations and carbocation-resembling transition states.

****

25. A "roadmap" problem. Organize your given information, and work from it, stepwise, towards the answers:

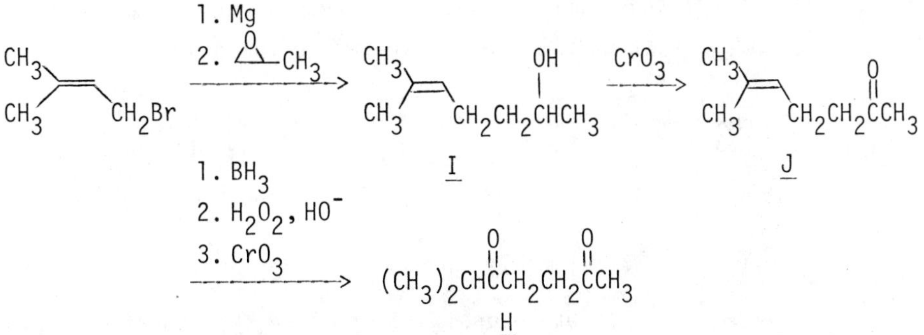

Now, how about $\underline{G}$? For $C_{10}H_{16}$, $H_{sat'd}$ = 20 + 2 = 22; deg. unsat'n. = $\frac{22-16}{2}$ = 3 π bonds and/or rings. $\underline{G}$ only contains two more carbons than $\underline{H}$, so they both must form double bonds with the two carbonyl carbons in $\underline{H}$ (note that $\underline{G}$ contains no oxygen, so the O's in $\underline{H}$ must come from the ozonolysis of double bonds in $\underline{G}$). The only way to hook everything up is as follows:

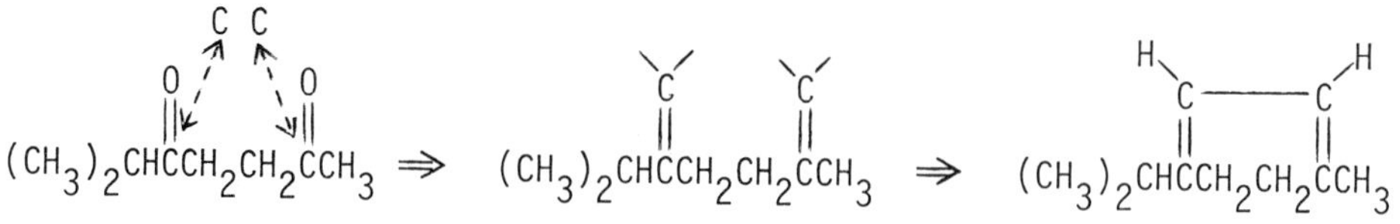

$$(CH_3)_2CHCCH_2CH_2CCH_3 \Rightarrow (CH_3)_2CHCCH_2CH_2CCH_3 \Rightarrow (CH_3)_2CHCCH_2CH_2CCH_3$$

$\underline{H}$, $C_8H_{14}O_2$ This is $C_{10}H_{14}$ - need   This must be $\underline{G}$
                          2 more hydrogens

So the answer is $\underline{G}$ =

CH_3

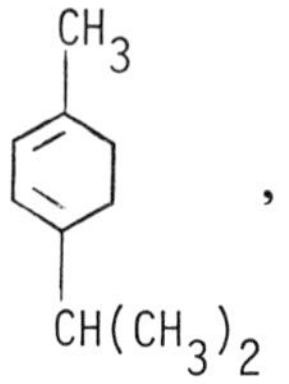

, known as α-terpinene.

CH(CH_3)_2

****

26. $H_{sat'd}$ = 30 + 2 = 32; deg. unsat'n. = $\frac{32-24}{2}$ = 4 π bonds and/or rings.

Reaction (1) tells you 2 π bonds are present (hydrogenation only adds 2 H_2), so there must be 2 rings.

Reaction (2) forms two pieces: methanal (CH_2O) and the triketone shown, which is $C_{14}H_{22}O_3$. These account for all carbons and hydrogens in caryophyllene. The oxygens came from the ozonolysis. All that's left to decide is how the four carbonyl carbons originally connected up into two alkene double bonds.

Reaction (3) gives the answer to this last question. Hydroboration converts one of the caryophyllene double bonds into an alcohol. Then, ozonolysis cleaves the other to give the diketo-alcohol shown. Working backwards from this structure, we can write the following:

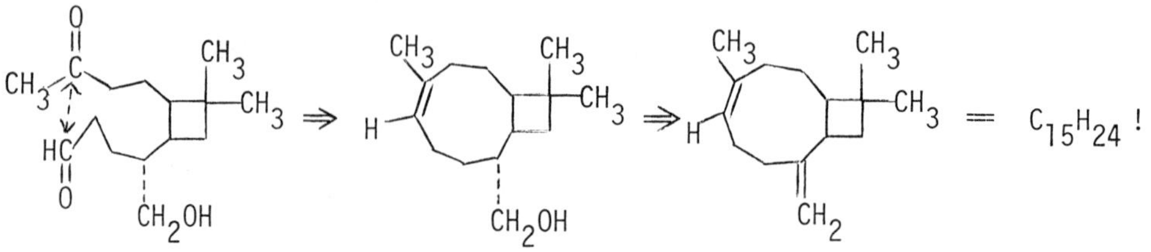

before ozonolysis   before hydroboration

The only question left is whether the double bond in the nine-membered ring is *cis* or *trans* (more properly, *Z* or *E*) - it could be either. In fact this point is the difference between caryophyllene (the *E* isomer) and isocaryophyllene (*Z*):

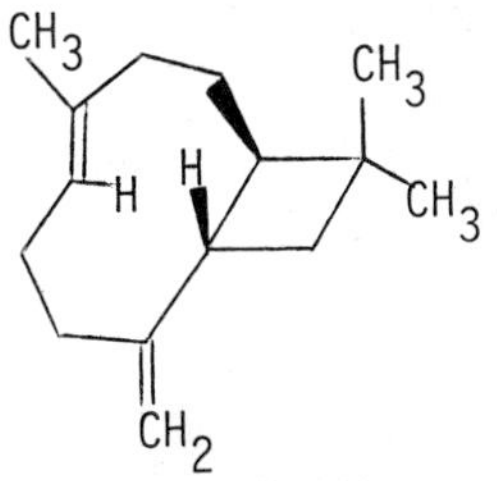

caryophyllene

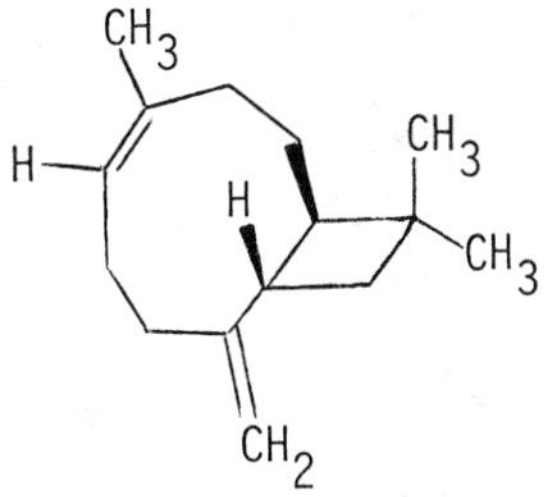

isocaryophyllene

Notice that hydroboration of the bottom double bond does not affect the *E*/*Z* relationship between these two, but once O_3 cleaves the other alkene, the products are then identical.

****

27. As usual, consider the goal to be a racemic product.

(a) This part is easy: MCPBA stereospecifically forms the necessary oxacyclopropane, with the same *Z* geometry as is present in the original alkene. A haloalcohol/base sequence would work equally well.

(b) This is tricky. How can you make an oxacyclopropane with stereochemistry reversed from that of the starting alkene? A synthetic sequence with exactly one S_N2-type inversion step is necessary. Here's one way to go about it.

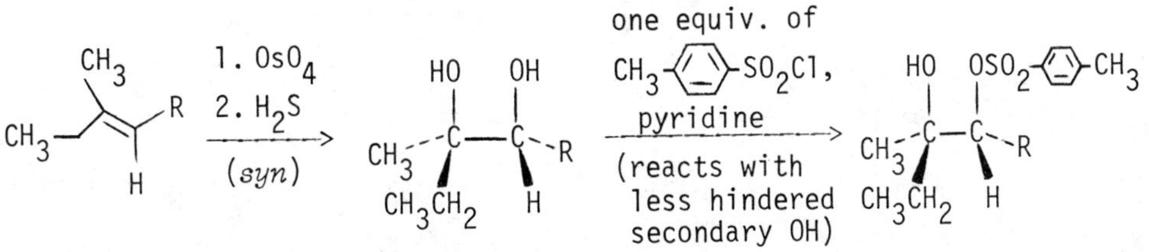

At this point one alcohol has been converted into a potential leaving group, and no inversions have yet taken place.

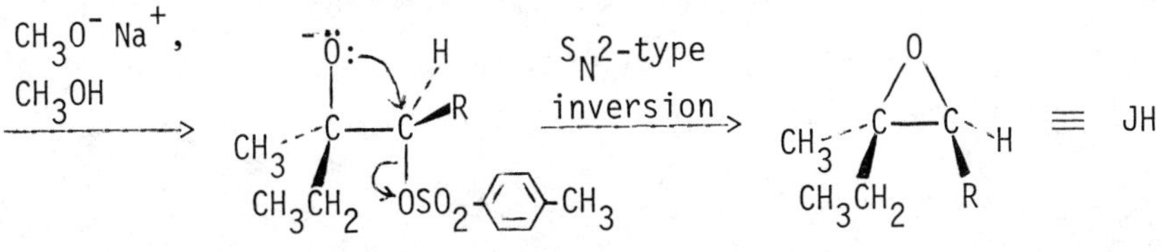

(c) Reaction with CH_3MgCl, though non-stereoselective, makes the necessary oxacyclopropane directly:

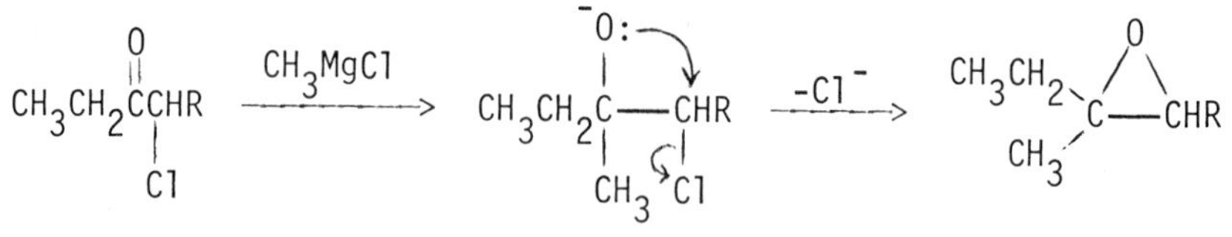

****

28. More highly substituted double bonds are more reactive towards electrophiles. So:

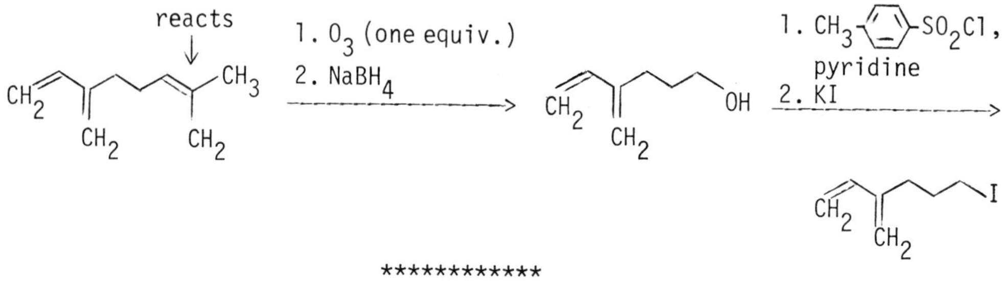

****

29. First, protonate camphene. Then, look at possible carbocation rearrangements until you find one that gives a cation that has the carbon skeleton of the product. So:

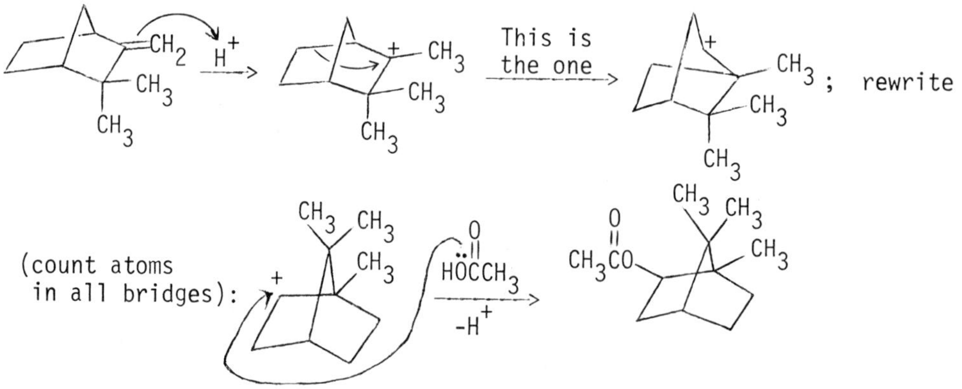

This is actually quite surprising at first glance, since it involves conversion of a tertiary carbocation into a secondary carbocation. The reason it occurs is that the last step (reaction with CH_3CO_2H) is irreversible under the reaction conditions, and drives the otherwise unfavorable equilibrium towards the product structure.

****

CHAPTER 13

Alkynes: The Carbon-Carbon Triple Bond

General Introduction

Now that the properties of carbon-carbon double bonds have been examined in detail, it's time to have a brief look at their relatives, carbon-carbon triple bonds. Not surprisingly, what you will find will be very similar to what you've just seen. Addition reactions will make up the main portion of triple bond chemistry. About the only novel features of these compounds will involve the hydrogen attached to triply-bonded carbon: it is unusually acidic, allowing ready removal by strong bases to form a new and synthetically useful class of carbanions called alkynyl anions.

Outline of the Chapter

13-1. Nomenclature.

13-2. Structure and Bonding.

13-3. Nuclear Magnetic Resonance of the Alkynes.

An unusual effect due to electron motion.

13-4. Relative Stability of the Triple Bond.

The versatile base-catalyzed alkyne isomerization reactions.

13-5. Preparation of Alkynes.

Two ways.

13-6. Reactions of Alkynes.

13-7. Ethyne as an Industrial Starting Material.

13-8. Naturally Occurring and Physiologically Active Alkynes.

Keys to the Chapter

13-1 and 13-2. Nomenclature, Structure and Bonding.

The alkyne functional group is a simpler one than the alkene functional group because the triply-bonded carbons, together with the atoms attached at each end, have a linear geometry. No "cis-trans" kind of isomerism is possible. The only consideration necessary in naming alkynes therefore is to indicate the position of the triple bond. When the triple bond is at the end of a chain it is called a "terminal" alkyne. It then possesses a -C≡C-H unit, whose hydrogen has a couple of special characteristics. These include an unusual high-field location in the proton NMR spectrum, and a very strong, but polarized carbon-hydrogen bond, making the terminal hydrogen relatively acidic. The consequences of this will be examined in sections 5 and 6 of this chapter.

13-3. Nuclear Magnetic Resonance of the Alkynes.

The high-field position of the hydrogen on the end of terminal alkynes is surprising at first, but is a logical result of the cylindrical symmetry of the triple bond that allows electrons to rotate in a tight circle about the axis of the bond. In fact, these alkyne signals are usually easy to spot due to their characteristic long-range couplings to the groups on the other side of the triple bond (see, for instance, the alkynyl hydrogen triplet in Fig. 13-5). Other NMR properties of these compounds are pretty normal.

13-4. Relative Stability of the Triple Bond.

Just as is the case for alkenes, alkynes are more stable when they are more highly substituted. For alkynes, though, there are only two choices (besides ethyne itself): terminal (monosubstituted) or internal (disubstituted). You saw earlier how alkene isomerizations could be carried out using acid catalysis, via a protonation-deprotonation mechanism involving carbocations. Alkynes, it turns out, are more readily isomerized using base since the triple bond enhances the acidity of neighboring carbon-hydrogen bonds, as in

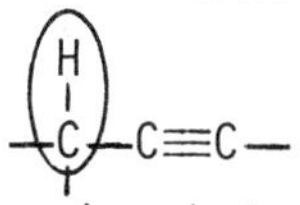

the so-called "propargyl" C-H. The isomerization involves "allenes," molecules with two adjacent double bonds (sharing a carbon between them). Pay some attention to the orbitals and their hybridization in these - they are a bit unusual.

The isomerization with bases weaker than alkynyl anion gives the thermodynamically favored internal alkyne as the product. Stronger bases than alkynyl anion go the other way, because the terminal alkyne is irreversibly deprotonated the instant it is formed in the equilibrating mixture of alkyne isomers, driving the entire equilibrium ultimately to terminal alkynyl anion:

$$\underset{\text{product}}{CH_3C{\equiv}CCH_3} \underset{\text{like NaOR}}{\overset{\text{weak base}}{\rightleftarrows}} CH_3CH_2C{\equiv}CH \rightleftarrows CH_3CH_2C{\equiv}C{:}^- \ Na^+$$

$$CH_3C{\equiv}CCH_3 \underset{\text{like KNHR}}{\overset{\text{strong base}}{\rightleftarrows}} CH_3CH_2C{\equiv}CH \xrightarrow[\text{irreversible}]{\text{essentially}} \underset{\text{product}}{CH_3CH_2C{\equiv}C{:}^- \ K^+}$$

13-5. Preparation of Alkynes.

The elimination route to alkynes involves removal of two moles of hydrogen halide by strong base, from a dihaloalkane. The most common kind of sequence involves forming the dihaloalkane by addition of halogen to an alkene double bond. Since you already know how to make alkenes, you now have access to alkynes in the following general way:

$$\underset{\text{alkane}}{-CH_2-CH_2-} \xrightarrow[\text{e.g. } Br_2,\ h\nu]{\text{halogenation,}} \underset{\text{haloalkane}}{-CH_2-CHBr-} \xrightarrow[\text{e.g. } KOC(CH_3)_3]{\text{elimination,}} \underset{\text{alkene}}{-CH{=}CH-}$$

$$\xrightarrow[\text{e.g. } Br_2]{\text{addition}} \underset{\text{1,2-dihaloalkane}}{-CHBr-CHBr-} \xrightarrow[\text{e.g. } NaNH_2]{\text{double elimination,}} \underset{\text{alkyne}}{-C{\equiv}C-}$$

The other major alkyne preparation is based on the easy accessibility of nucleophilic carbanions from terminal alkynes (section 13-2). So, a wide variety of internal alkynes may be made from any terminal alkyne, via the general scheme

$$R-C{\equiv}C-H \xrightarrow[\text{base}]{\text{strong}} \underset{\text{nucleophile}}{R-C{\equiv}C:^-} \xrightarrow[\text{"}E^+\text{"}]{\text{any electrophile}} R-C{\equiv}C-E$$

where "E" is the electrophilic carbon in a primary haloalkane, a strained cyclic ether, or a carbonyl compound.

13-6. Reactions of Alkynes.

Just as you saw with alkenes, alkynes are subject to a variety of addition reactions of various kinds. These can occur in two stages: a single addition to make an alkene, and then a second addition to result in an alkane derivative. The mechanisms, stereochemistry, and regiochemistry, are essentially analogous to those you've already seen. So, you really only have to look back to the reactions of the previous chapter as points of reference. Only an occasional detail or two will be different. When the addition reaction is chosen to stop at the alkene stage, there is often the possibility of picking reagents and conditions to allow for specific formation of either the trans or cis alkene product. This flexibility further contributes to the usefulness of alkynes in synthesis.

A special note should be made concerning hydration reactions of alkynes. Hydration of alkenes can be done several ways, and leads to alcohols. Alkynes can be hydrated, too. Markovnikov addition is done best with an aqueous acidic Hg(II) catalyst. Anti-Markovnikov addition is done via a modified hydroboration-oxidation sequence. Both initially give vinyl alcohols (or enols) as products, but these are kinetically and thermodynamically unstable, and isomerize to carbonyl compounds in a reaction called "tautomerism." The reaction is

thermodynamically favorable because of the very strong carbon-oxygen double bond that is formed. It is kinetically rapid because the enol O-H bond is acidic and easily ionized, allowing the proton to leave, eventually to find its way onto the nearby carbon. More details concerning this will be upcoming when carbonyl compounds are discussed. Note that this represents a new synthesis of aldehydes and ketones, and is therefore useful for that purpose.

Solutions to Chapter 13 Problems

1. (a) 3-chloro-3-methyl-1-butyne
   (b) 2-methyl-3-butyn-2-ol
   (c) 4-propyl-5-hexyn-1-ol
   (d) *trans*-3-penten-1-yne
   (e) *E*-5-methyl-4-(1-methylbutyl)-4-hepten-2-yne
   (f) *S*-3-butyn-2-ol
   (g) *cis*-1-ethenyl-2-ethynylcyclopentane

****

2. Bond strengths: ethyne > ethene > ethane. Ethyne C-H bond uses sp orbital from carbon. The high (50%) s character strongly attracts the bonding electrons to the carbon nucleus, contributing to the strength of the bond. Since this shifts the electrons closer to carbon, this also enhances the bond polarity, which follows same order: $^{\delta-}$C-H$^{\delta+}$ greatest in ethyne. In turn, the greater bond polarity in ethyne contributes to the acidity of the hydrogen (together with the enhanced stability of the conjugate base, the ethynyl anion, also a result of hybridization effects).

   It may seem paradoxical to you that the strongest C-H bond is the easiest one to ionize. Remember, though, that bond strength relates to homolytic cleavage (to C· and H·), while acidity refers to heterolytic cleavage (ionization, to C^- and H^+).

****

3. The bond strength should be greatest and the bond length shortest in propyne, again as a result of the sp (50% s character) orbital at C2.

****

4. Degrees of unsaturation are calculated for each compound (refer to Chapter 11 of this Study Guide).

(a) $H_{sat'd} = 12 + 2 = 14$; deg. unsat'n. $= \frac{14-10}{2} = 2$ π bonds and/or rings. NMR looks like an ethyl group: $C\underline{H}_3$ (t, δ1.1) next to $C\underline{H}_2$ (q, δ2.1). Since the molecule has 10 H's, there must be two equivalent ethyl groups, 2 CH_3CH_2-, adding up to C_4H_{10}. Two C atoms are all that are left to account for. To get two degrees of unsaturation, make a triple bond between them (2 π bonds):

$$2\,CH_3CH_2\text{-} \quad \text{and} \quad \text{-C≡C-} \quad \Rightarrow \quad CH_3CH_2\text{-C≡C-}CH_2CH_3$$

(b) $H_{sat'd} = 14 + 2 = 16$; deg. unsat'n. $= \frac{16-12}{2} = 2$ π bonds and/or rings.
NMR: δ 0.9 (distorted t, 3H) $\Rightarrow$ $C\underline{H}_3$, next to CH_2
δ 1.4 (m, 6H) $\Rightarrow$?
split by
δ 1.7 (t, 1H) $\Rightarrow$ Ah ha! How about $\underline{H}$-C≡C-CH_2- !
δ 2.2 (m, 2H) $\Rightarrow$ Perhaps the CH_2 referred to here?
So far, we have CH_3-CH_2- and -CH_2-C≡CH, or C_5H_8; need C_2H_4 more. The simplest way is $CH_3CH_2CH_2CH_2CH_2C≡CH$, 1-heptyne.

(c) Very similar, except for integrated signal intensities:
δ 0.9 (distorted t, 3H) $\Rightarrow$ $C\underline{H}_3$-CH_2- again
δ 1.4 (m, 4H) $\Rightarrow$?
δ 1.7 (t, $\underline{3}$H) $\Rightarrow$ $C\underline{H}_3$ with a *small* coupling to a CH_2 group?
δ 2.0 (m, 2H) $\Rightarrow$ Again, a -$C\underline{H}_2$-C≡C- (takes care of the 2 π bonds)?

So, CH_3-CH_2-, -CH_2-C≡C-, CH_3-, adding up to C_6H_{10}. Only need to add CH_2. Where? There are two possibilities:

(1) CH_3-CH_2-CH_2-C≡C-CH_2-CH_3, but this is wrong because both end CH_3 groups would be to high field, and be split by large J values.

(2) CH_3-CH_2-CH_2-CH_2-C≡C-(CH_3). This is the answer. The circled CH_3 is at a reasonable location (δ1.7, next to a functional group), and the small triplet splitting can be explained as <u>long-range</u>

coupling to the CH_2 on the other side of the triple bond.

****

5. (a) Four equivalent carbons: $CH_3CH_2CH_2C{\equiv}CCH_2CH_2CH_3$ (symmetrical)

   (b) Eight different carbons. Note very high field signal at $\delta 2.9$: just what you might expect for a $\underline{C}H_3$-C≡C-, since methyl carbons normally absorb at high field, and atoms attached to -C≡C- are further shielded by the triple bond electron cloud. So this is 2-octyne.

   (c) Seven different signals; two carbons must accidentally overlap. Find the answer in the chemical shifts of the two alkyne carbons: they are very different (δ 69 and 84), characteristic of a terminal alkyne: 1-octyne.

   (d) 3-Octyne, by process of elimination.

****

6. (a) Use the values for butane and 2-butyne as guides: the energy difference between them is the difference in $\Delta H°_f$ values, 34.7 - (-30.4) = 65.1 kcal/mole. This is a reasonable approximation for the energy difference between an unstrained alkane and an unstrained internal alkyne. Since cycloheptyne possesses 31.1 kcal/mole strain energy while cycloheptane possesses 7.9 kcal/mole strain energy (Table 4-2), if we add 31.1 - 7.9 = 23.2 kcal/mole extra strain to 65.1 kcal/mole, we should get the cycloheptyne-cycloheptane energy difference: 65.1 + 23.2 = 88.3 kcal/mole. So $\Delta H°_f$ (cycloheptyne) = -28.1 ($\Delta H°_f$ for cycloheptane) + 88.3 = 60.2 kcal/mole.

   (b) $\Delta H°$ (reaction) = $\Sigma\Delta H°_f$ (products) - $\Sigma\Delta H°_f$ (starting materials)
   $\Delta H°_f$ for elements in standard states = 0

(i) -36.6 kcal/mole	(iii) -62.4 kcal/mole !
(ii) -28.5 kcal/mole	(iv) -26.0 kcal/mole

****

7. The orbitals involved in the extra π bond of the triple bond in benzyne will overlap poorly, since they are greatly distorted from the ideal p orbital shape (they are actually sp^2 orbitals). Just as is the case with simpler small ring cycloalkynes (Section 13-4), this "bond" has considerable

diradical character, and is extremely reactive.

****

8. $\overset{CH_3}{\underset{CH_3}{>}}C=C=C\overset{H}{\underset{H}{<}}$ Two signals, $\underline{CH}_3$'s near $\delta 1.5$-2.0, alkene $\underline{H}$'s around $\delta 5$-6.
If long-range coupling between them is large enough to
observe, the $\underline{CH}_3$ signal will be a triplet, and the alkene signal a septet.

****

9. (a) $CH_3CH_2CH(CH_3)C\equiv CH$ (b) $CH_3OCH_2CH_2CH_2C\equiv CCH_3$

(c)

$\xrightarrow{\text{rotate}}$ $\xrightarrow[(anti)]{-\ddot{O}CH_3}$ $(R = CH_3\overset{CH_3}{\underset{|}{C}}HCH_2-)$

meso   *E*

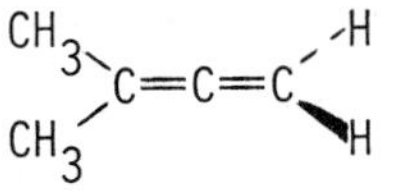

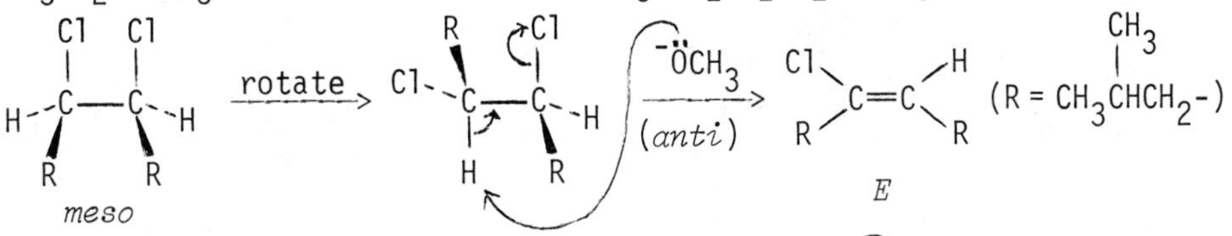

(d) Opposite to *meso* compound, this gives

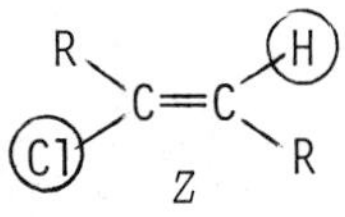

(e) *Z*, because remaining H and Cl (circled) are *trans*, good for a second
anti elimination.

****

10. Let's see:

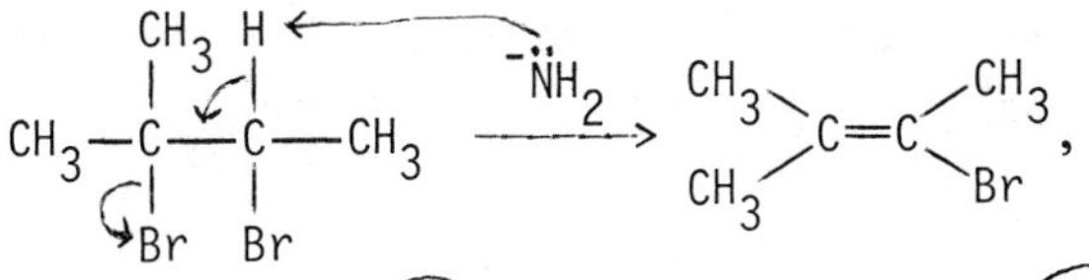

, but then what?

Perhaps

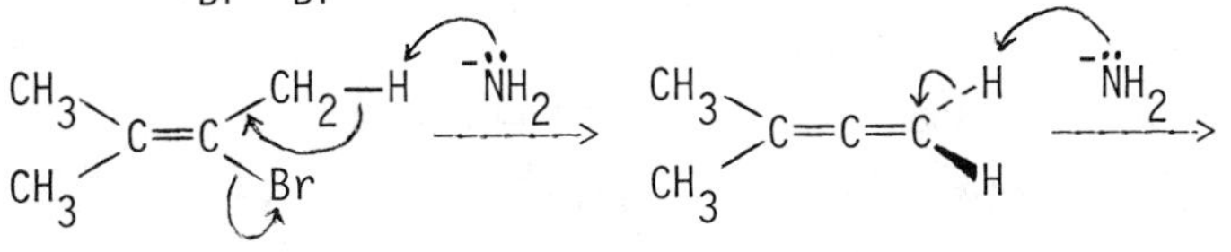

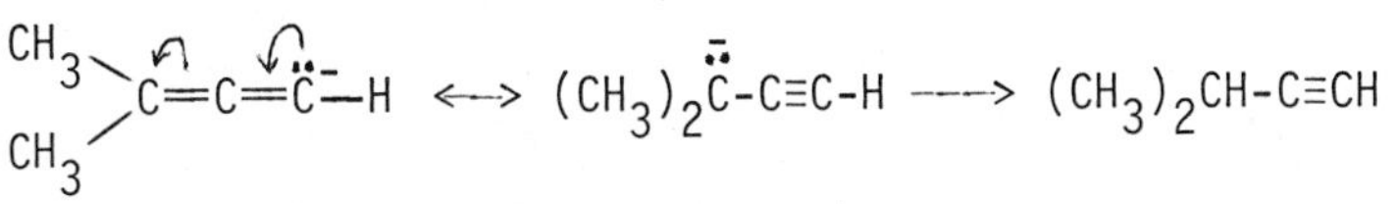

$\overset{CH_3}{\underset{CH_3}{>}}C=C=\ddot{C}-H \longleftrightarrow (CH_3)_2\ddot{C}-C\equiv C-H \longrightarrow (CH_3)_2CH-C\equiv CH$ after protonation.

****

11. Simplest answer is a version of an S_N2 reaction:

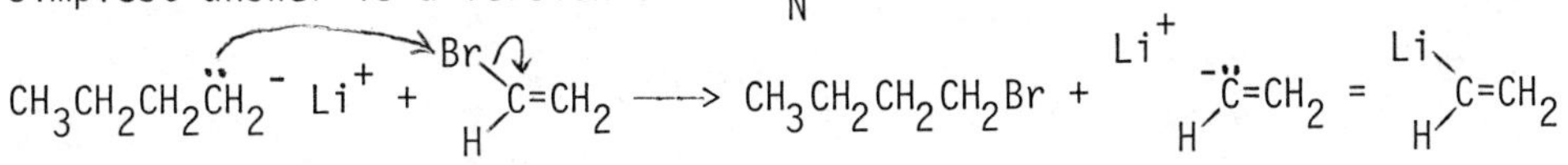

(a)

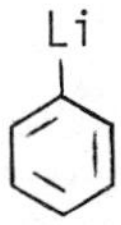

$+ \ CH_3CH_2CH_2CH_2I$ (b) $(CH_3)_3C-C\equiv C-Li \ + \ CH_3CH_2CH_2CH_2Br$

****

12. All products are those obtained after aqueous work-up.

(a) $CH_3CH_2C{\equiv}CCH_3$

(b) 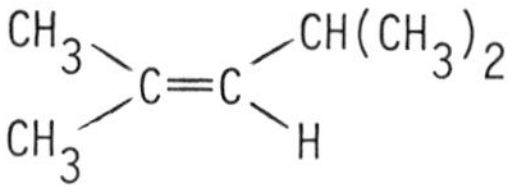 $(CH_3)_2C{=}CH{-}CH(CH_3)_2$ (via E2; haloalkane too hindered for S_N2)

(c) 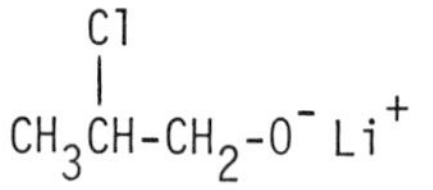 $CH_3CH(Cl){-}CH_2{-}O^- Li^+$ initially (acid/base) $\xrightarrow{-Cl^-}$ 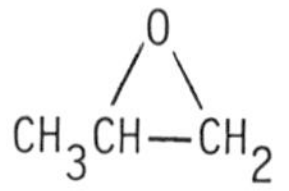 finally

(d) 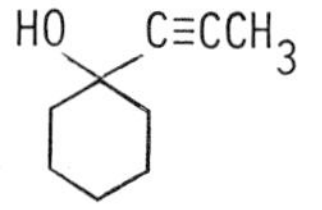

(e) 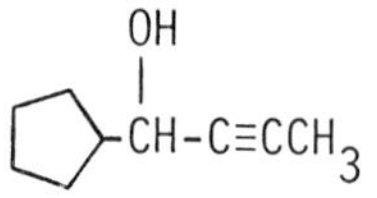

(f) 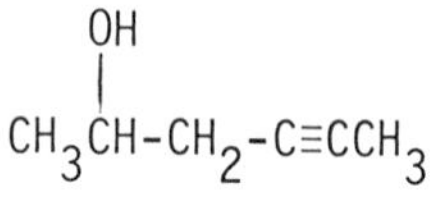 $CH_3CH(OH){-}CH_2{-}C{\equiv}CCH_3$

(g) 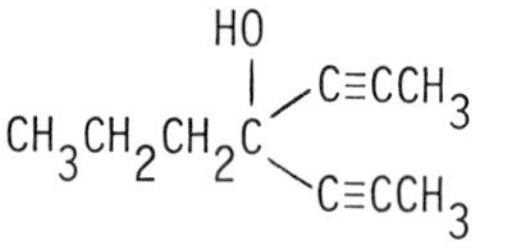 $CH_3CH_2CH_2C(OH)(C{\equiv}CCH_3)_2$

(h) 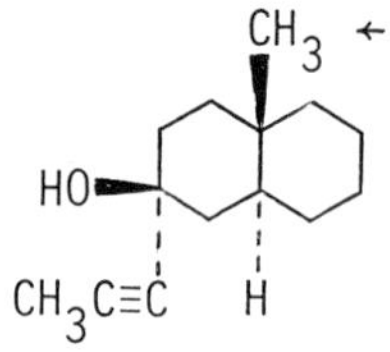

****

13. First the strongly basic Grignard reagent deprotonated the relatively acidic terminal alkyne:

$$CH_3CH_2{-}MgBr + HC{\equiv}CCH_2CH_2\overset{O}{\overset{\|}{C}}H \longrightarrow$$

$$CH_3{-}CH_3 \text{ (the gas observed)} + BrMg^+ \; ^-{:}C{\equiv}CCH_2CH_2\overset{O}{\overset{\|}{C}}H$$

The alkynyl anion that formed could then attack aldehyde groups of other similar molecules:

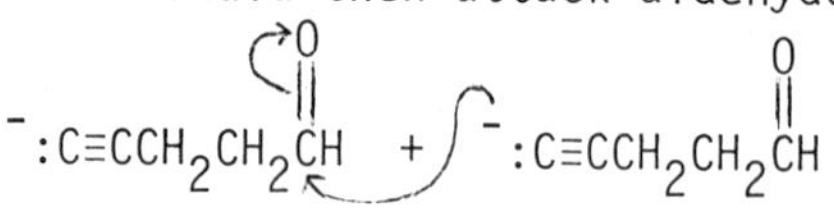

The result is a polymer: $\left(C{\equiv}CCH_2CH_2\overset{OH}{\overset{|}{C}}H\right)_n$

****

14. In most cases the answer given is just one of several correct ones.

(a) $HC{\equiv}CLi \xrightarrow{CH_3CH_2CH_2Br} HC{\equiv}CCH_2CH_2CH_3 \xrightarrow[\text{2. } CH_3CH_2Br]{\text{1. } NaNH_2,\ NH_3}$ product

(b) 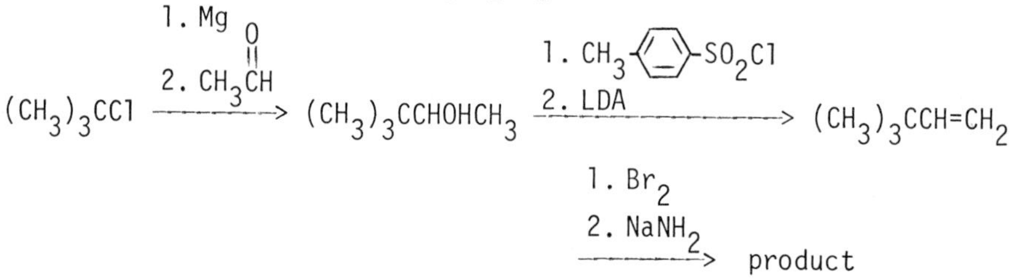 $(CH_3)_3CCl \xrightarrow[\text{2. } CH_3CHO]{\text{1. Mg}} (CH_3)_3CCHOHCH_3$  $\xrightarrow{\text{2. LDA}} (CH_3)_3CCH{=}CH_2 \xrightarrow[\text{2. } NaNH_2]{\text{1. } Br_2}$ product

(c) LiC≡CLi $\xrightarrow{\text{2 CH}_2\text{-CH}_2 \text{ (epoxide)}}$ HOCH$_2$CH$_2$C≡CCH$_2$CH$_2$OH $\xrightarrow{\text{2 H}_2, \text{ Pd-C}}$ HO(CH$_2$)$_6$OH

$\xrightarrow[\text{2. 2 (CH}_3)_3\text{CO}^-\text{K}^+]{\text{1. 2 PBr}_3}$ CH$_2$=CHCH$_2$CH$_2$CH=CH$_2$ $\xrightarrow[\text{2. 2 NaNH}_2]{\text{1. 2 Br}_2}$ product

(d) HC≡CLi + CH$_3$CH$_2$CCH$_2$ (ketone, C=O) ⟶ product

(e) 2 HC≡CLi + HCOCH$_3$ (ester, C=O) ⟶ product

(f) HC≡CLi + [cyclopentanone with Cl] ⟶ [HC≡C, O$^-$, Cl intermediate] $\xrightarrow{\text{Isomer with O}^- \text{ and Cl } trans}$ [HC≡C, O product]

Better: HC≡CLi + [cyclopentanone] ⟶ [HC≡C, OH product] $\xrightarrow{\text{H}^+, \text{ H}_2\text{O}, \Delta}$ [HC≡C, cyclopentene product]

one equiv.
$\xrightarrow{\text{MCPBA}}$ product

(g) HC≡CLi + CH$_3$CH$_2$Br ⟶ CH$_3$CH$_2$C≡CH $\xrightarrow{\text{Cu}^+, \text{ amine, O}_2}$ product

****

15. Priority of D is higher than H, but lower than anything else.

Structure is: CH$_3$C≡C—C(CH$_2$CH$_3$)(D)(H) . Best bond to make is marked (arrow).

Synthesis of the chiral product could be achieved if the chiral haloalkane could be obtained:

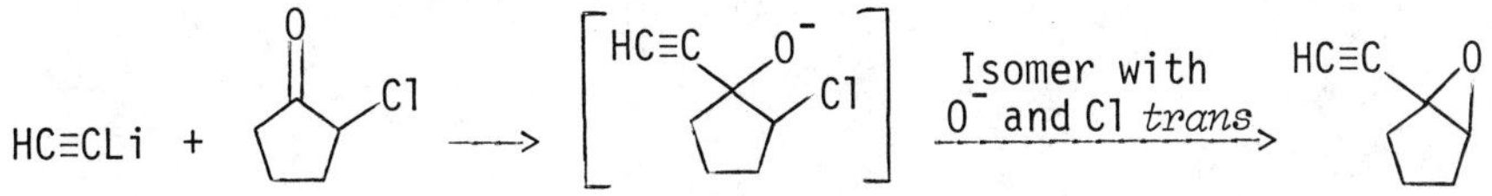

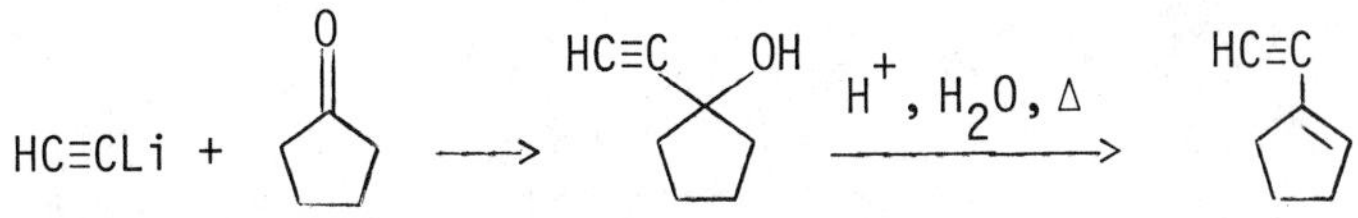

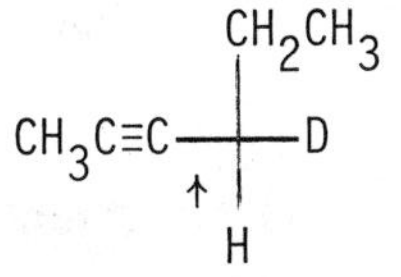

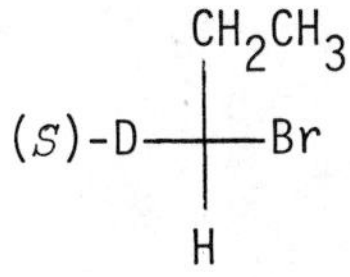

(*S*)-D—C(CH$_2$CH$_3$)(H)—Br + LiC≡CCH$_3$ $\xrightarrow{\text{S}_\text{N}2}$ product

****

16. All things being equal, sp hybridization is favored due to the very strong σ bonds it forms. In the cation this is fine since the remaining (p) orbital on carbon is empty. In the radical, though, the remaining orbital

is singly occupied, and an electron in a p orbital is not very happy at all. Thus the radical compromises with sp^2 orbitals both for σ bonds and for the extra electron.

****

17. (a) 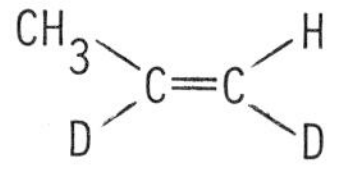 (b) 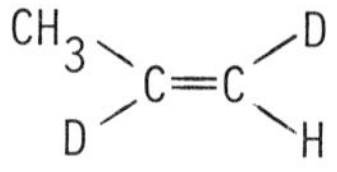 (c) 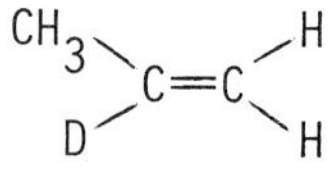

(d) 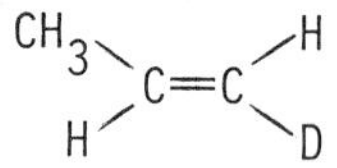 (e) $CH_3CI{=}CH_2$ (f) $CH_3CI_2CH_3$

(g) 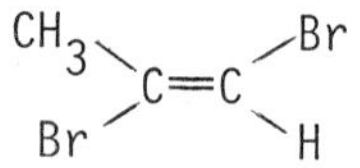 (h) 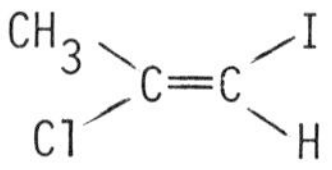 (i) $CH_3CCl_2CHI_2$

(j) $CH_3\overset{O}{\overset{\|}{C}}CH_3$ (k) $CH_3CH_2\overset{O}{\overset{\|}{C}}H$ (l) $CH_3C{\equiv}C{-}C{\equiv}CCH_3$

****

18. In the structures below R = cyclohexyl.

(a) 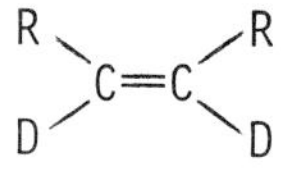 (b) 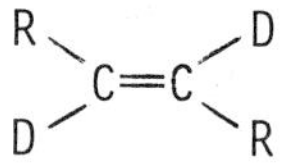 (c) and (d) 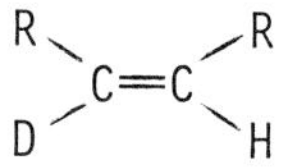

(e) RCI=CHR (*E* and *Z*) (f) RCI_2CH_2R

(g) 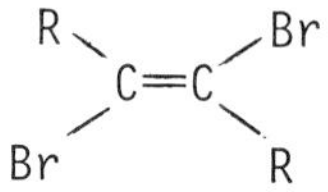 (h) 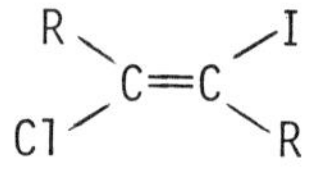 (i) $RCCl_2CI_2R$ + RCClICClIR

(j) and (k) $R\overset{O}{\overset{\|}{C}}CH_2R$ (l) no reaction with internal alkynes

****

19. In these, "*dl*" means a racemic mixture of *R*,*R* and *S*,*S* stereoisomers.

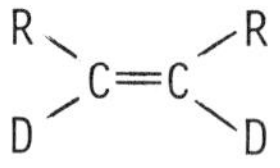

(a) *meso*-RCHDCHDR

(b) *dl*-RCDBrCDBrR

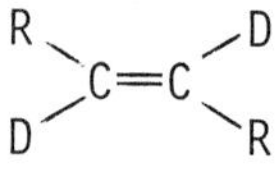

(a) *dl*-RCHDCHDR

(b) *meso*-RCDBrCDBrR

(c) 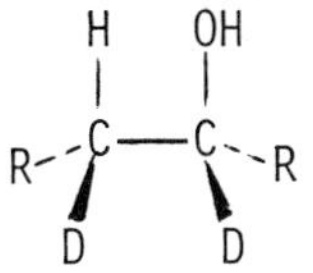 + enantiomer

(c) 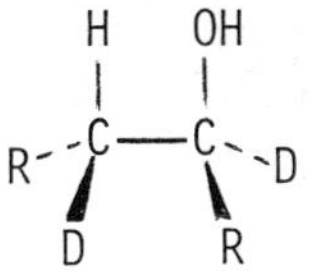 + enantiomer

(d) 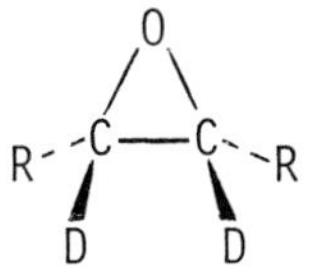

(d) 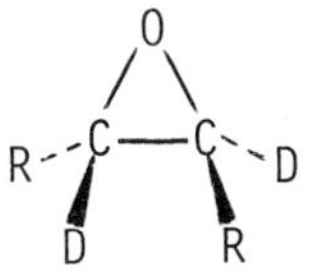 + enantiomer

(e) *meso*-RCDOHCDOHR

(e) *dl*-RCDOHCDOHR

****

20. (a) $CH_3CH_2C{\equiv}CH \xrightarrow[2.\ HBr]{1.\ HCl}$ product

(b) $CH_3CH_2CH_2CH_2C{\equiv}CH \xrightarrow{2\ HI}$ product

(c) 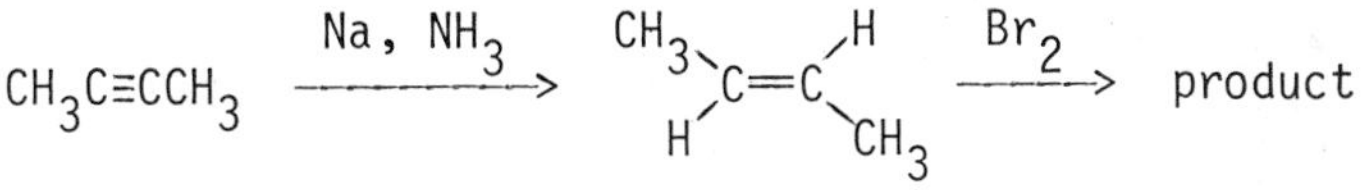 $CH_3C{\equiv}CCH_3 \xrightarrow{Na,\ NH_3}$ 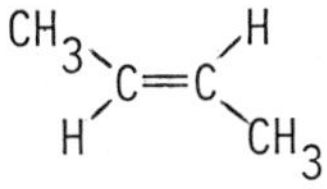 $\xrightarrow{Br_2}$ product

(d) 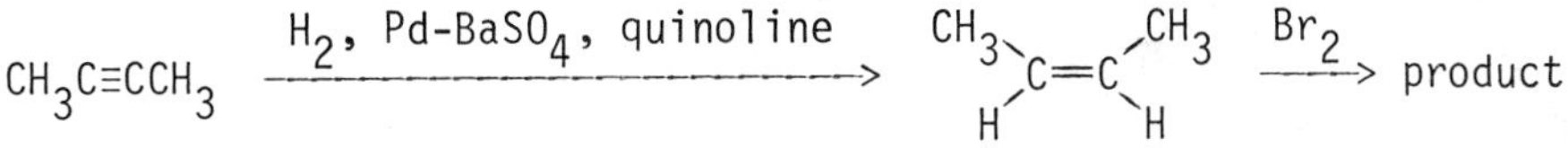 $CH_3C{\equiv}CCH_3 \xrightarrow{H_2,\ Pd\text{-}BaSO_4,\ quinoline}$ 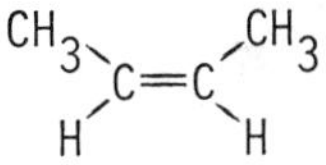 $\xrightarrow{Br_2}$ product

(e) 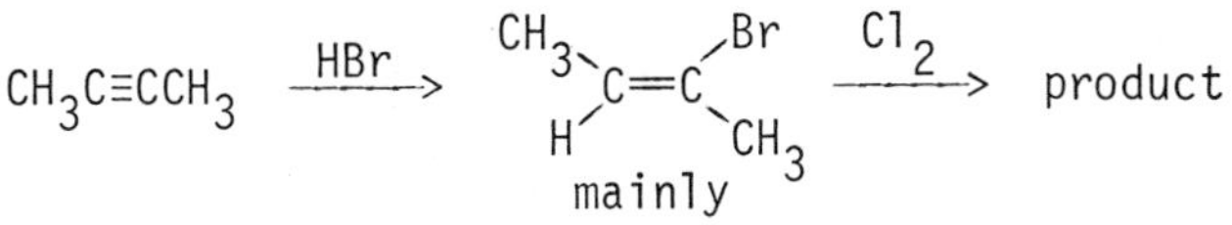 $CH_3C{\equiv}CCH_3 \xrightarrow{HBr}$ 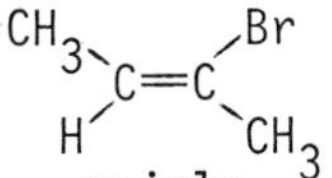 $\xrightarrow{Cl_2}$ product

mainly

(f) $CH_3CH_2CH_2C{\equiv}CCH_2CH_2CH_3 \xrightarrow{HgSO_4,\ H_2SO_4,\ H_2O}$ product

(g) $HC{\equiv}CCHOHCH_3 \xrightarrow{H_2,\ Pd\text{-}BaSO_4,\ quinoline} H_2C{=}CHCHOHCH_3 \xrightarrow[2.\ H_2O_2,\ HO^-]{1.\ BH_3}$ product

(h) $HC{\equiv}CLi \xrightarrow{CH_3CHO} HC{\equiv}CCH(OH)CH_3 \xrightarrow[\text{protect OH}]{(CH_3)_2C{=}CH_2,\ H^+} HC{\equiv}CCH(OC(CH_3)_3)CH_3 \xrightarrow[2.\ \text{ethylene oxide } (CH_2\text{-}O\text{-}CH_2)]{1.\ NaNH_2}$

$HOCH_2CH_2C{\equiv}CCH(OC(CH_3)_3)CH_3 \xrightarrow{H_2,\ Pd\text{-}C} HOCH_2CH_2CH_2CH_2CH(OC(CH_3)_3)CH_3$

1. CH_3--SO_2Cl, py
2. LDA
$\longrightarrow CH_2{=}CHCH_2CH_2CH(OC(CH_3)_3)CH_3 \xrightarrow[2.\ CrO_3]{1.\ H^+,\ H_2O}$ product

(You never can tell when one of these is going to be really complicated!)

(i)

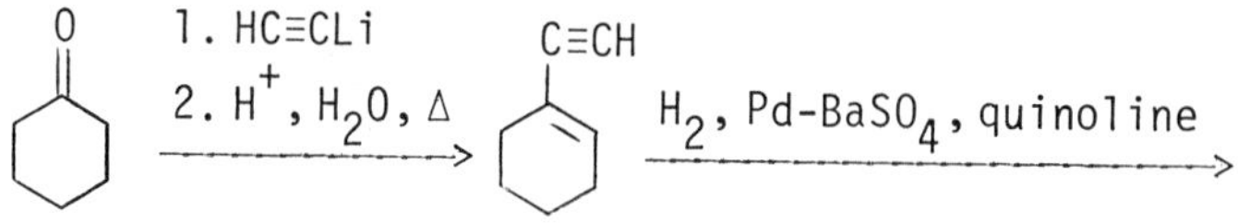

1. HC≡CLi
2. H⁺, H₂O, Δ

C≡CH

H₂, Pd-BaSO₄, quinoline ———→ product

(j) Use a cationic cyclization:

1. CH₃-⟨⟩-SO₂Cl, py
2. H⁺, H₂O, Δ ——————→

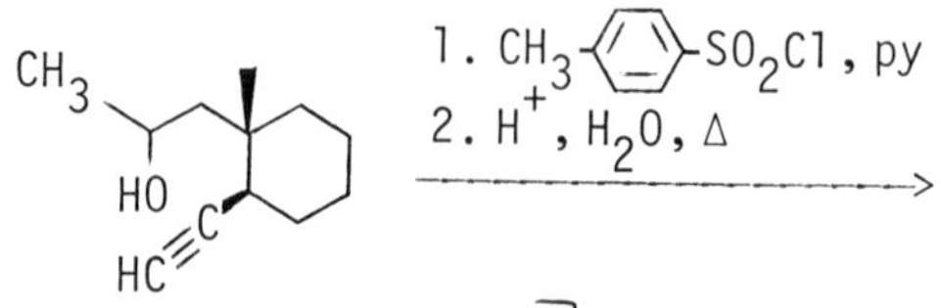

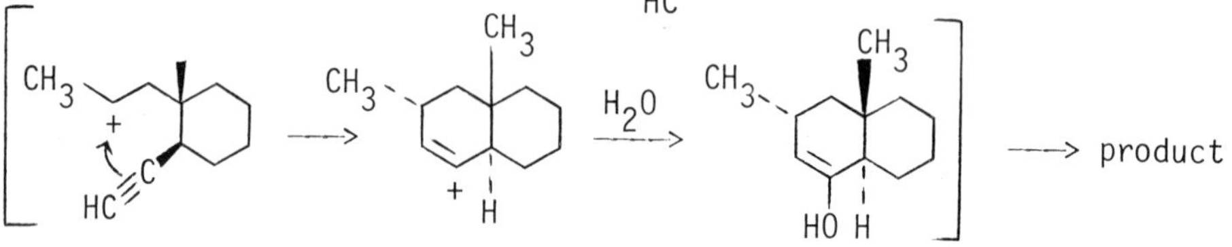

Mechanism: just for your information!

(k) Cationic cyclization can be used here as well:

OH
|
CH₃CH(CH₂)₅C≡CCH₂CH₂CH₂CH₃

1. CH₃-⟨⟩-SO₂Cl, py
2. H⁺, H₂O, Δ ——————→

H₂O ——→ product

****

21. CH₃CHCH₂CH₂CH₂C≡CCH₃ ——→

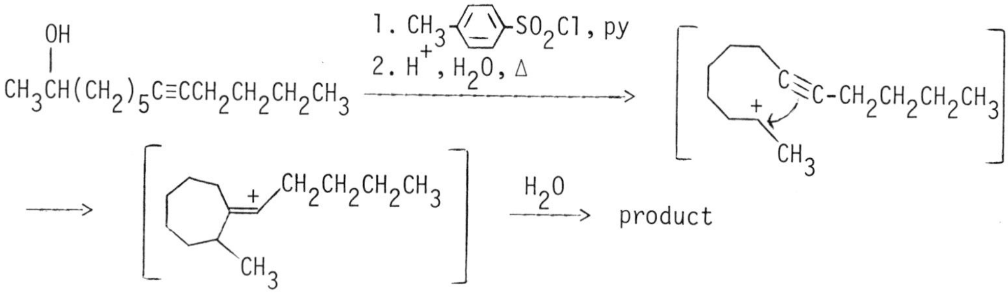

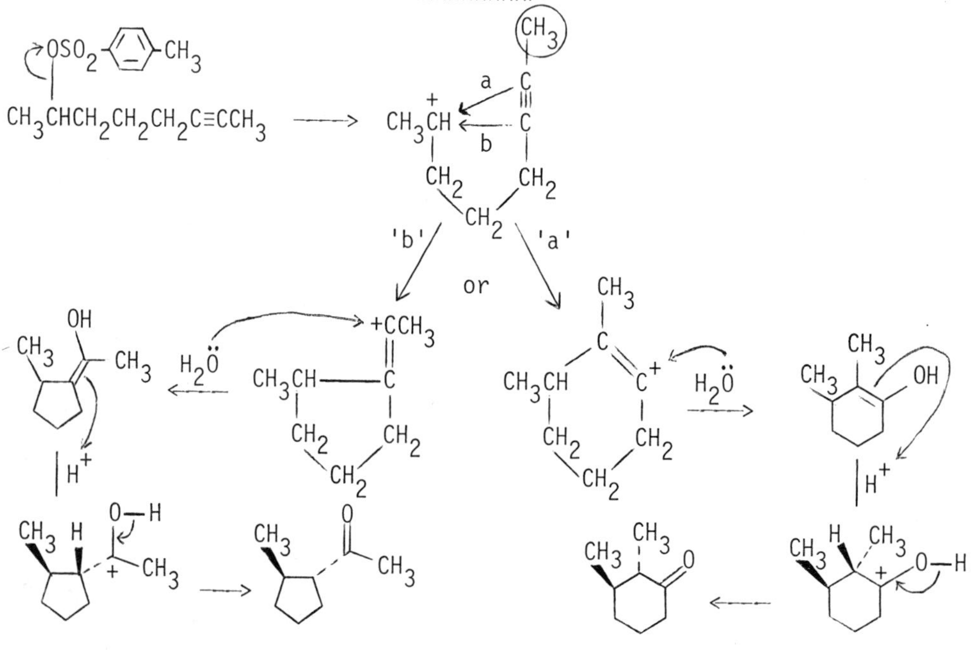

The extra methyl group (circled) makes bond formation to <u>either</u> alkyne carbon equally likely, as both lead to equally substituted alkenyl (vinyl) cations. In the 6-heptyn-2-ol system in the text the absence of a methyl group means that cyclization to form a five-membered ring gives a much poorer cation: CH_3 $\overset{+}{C}H$. In that situation, therefore, only the six-membered ring forms.

Note the preference for *trans* products, a result of steric effects.

****

22. $CH_3CH_2CHCH_2CH_2C \equiv CH$ $\xrightarrow{H^+, H_2O, \Delta}$ $CH_3CH_2\overset{+}{C}H$ ... $\longrightarrow$ CH_3CH_2CH ...

$\xrightarrow{H_2O}$ ...

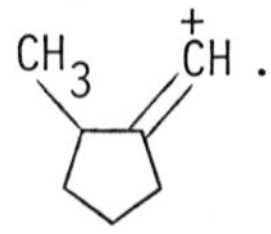

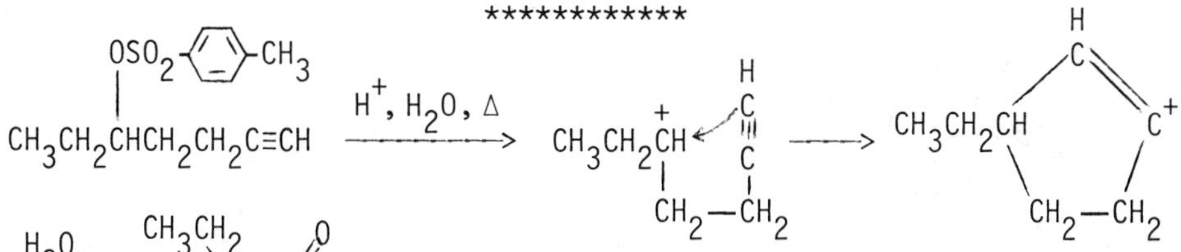

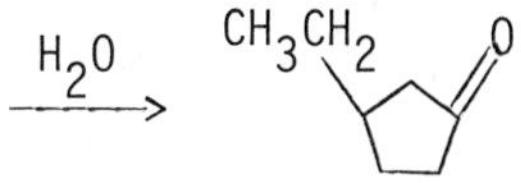

Five-membered ring formation is much preferred over four-membered ring formation (strained).

****

23. Ca^{2+} $^- :C \equiv C:^-$, a calcium salt of ethyne, is consistent with its reaction with water to form $HC \equiv CH$. One could call this material "calcium acetylide" or, perhaps "ethynediylcalcium," with the "di" referring to the doubly deprotonated ethyne.

****

24. $CrO_3(pyridine)_2$ would be the best choice as opposed to aqueous Cr^{VI} reagents like Jones reagent, which would probably give a carboxylic acid instead.

****

25. $HC \equiv CLi$ $\xleftarrow{LiNH_2}$ $HC \equiv CH$ $\xrightarrow{HBr \ (1 \ equiv.)}$ $CH_2 = CHBr$ $\xrightarrow{Mg}$ $CH_2 = CHMgBr$

1. [structure] 2. H^+, H_2O

1. [structure] 2. H^+, H_2O

$\xrightarrow{H_2, \ Lindlar's \ catalyst}$

****

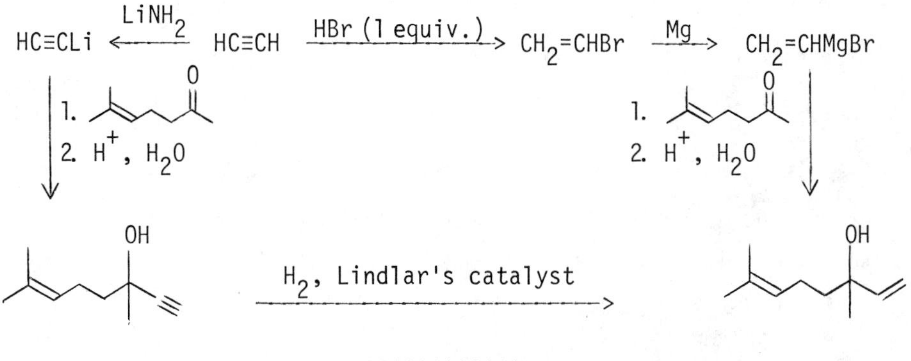

26.

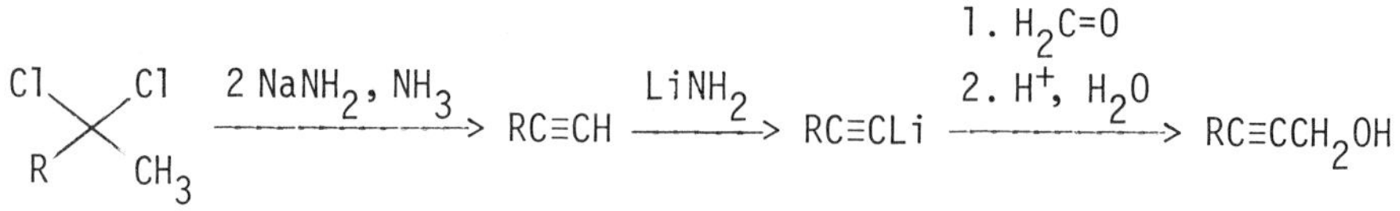

$$
\underset{\substack{R \\ CH_3}}{\overset{Cl \quad Cl}{>}}\xrightarrow{\text{2 NaNH}_2\text{, NH}_3} RC\equiv CH \xrightarrow{\text{LiNH}_2} RC\equiv CLi \xrightarrow[\substack{1.\ H_2C=O \\ 2.\ H^+,\ H_2O}]{} RC\equiv CCH_2OH
$$

****

27.

$$
\xrightarrow{(CH_3)_3CO^-\ K^+}
$$

$$
\xrightarrow[\substack{1.\ Br_2,\ CCl_4 \\ 2.\ NaNH_2,\ NH_3}]{}
$$

$$
\xrightarrow{CrO_3(\text{pyridine})_2} \text{product}
$$

****

28. $RCH_2OH \xrightarrow[\substack{1.\ CH_3-\text{⟨⟩}-SO_2Cl,\ py^* \\ 2.\ NaI}]{} RCH_2I \xrightarrow{LiC\equiv CH} RCH_2C\equiv CH \xrightarrow[\substack{1.\ (\text{⟨⟩})_2\ BH^{**} \\ 2.\ H_2O_2,\ HO^-}]{}$

$RCH_2CH_2\overset{O}{\overset{\|}{C}}H \xrightarrow[\substack{1.\ NaBH_4 \\ 2.\ PBr_3}]{} RCH_2CH_2CH_2Br \xrightarrow[\substack{1.\ Mg \\ 2.\ CH_3\overset{O}{\overset{\|}{C}}CH_3}]{} RCH_2CH_2CH_2\underset{CH_3}{\overset{OH}{\underset{|}{\overset{|}{C}}}}CH_3$

$\xrightarrow{H_2SO_4,\ \Delta} RCH_2CH_2CH=C(CH_3)_2 \equiv \text{bergamotene}$

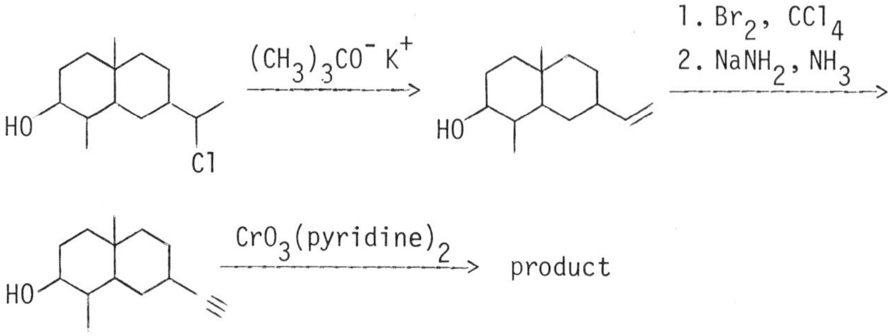

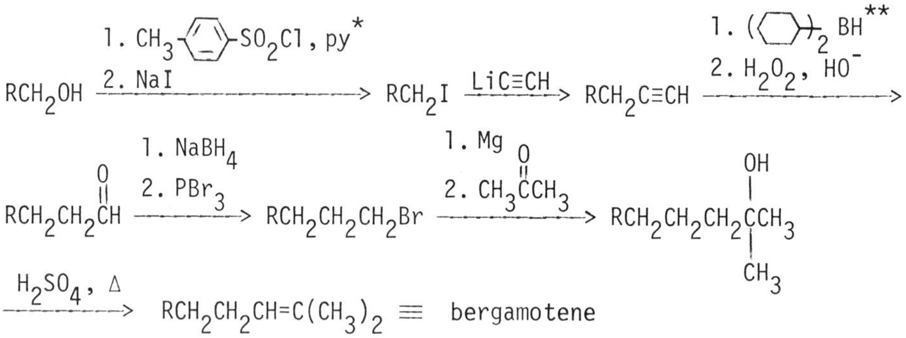

*R is so hindered that this special sequence (tosylate → iodide) is necessary to permit S_N2 reaction with alkynyl anion to be carried out.

**The unhindered triple bond is hydroborated much faster than the hindered (trisubstituted) double bond in the R group.

****

29. Work backwards from the ozonolysis result:

$$
2\ H\overset{O}{\overset{\|}{C}}H + CH_3\overset{O}{\overset{\|}{C}}-\overset{O}{\overset{\|}{C}}H \xleftarrow[\substack{1.\ O_3 \\ 2.\ Zn,\ H^+,\ H_2O}]{} \text{must have come from } CH_3-\overset{CH_2}{\overset{\|}{C}}-\overset{CH_2}{\overset{\|}{C}}-H.
$$

Continue on: ask "What compound can be hydrogenated over Lindlar's catalyst to give this diene?". Must be an alkyne, $CH_3-\overset{CH_2}{\overset{\|}{C}}-C\equiv CH$, and this fits the NMR precisely: $\delta 1.9\ (C\underline{H}_3)$, $2.7\ (C\equiv C\underline{H})$, 5.2 and $5.3\ (C=C\overset{H}{\underset{H}{<}})$.

****

CHAPTER 14

Delocalized Pi Systems and Their Investigation by Ultraviolet and Visible Spectroscopy

General Introduction

This chapter covers an assortment of topics derived from a single concept: conjugation. Conjugation refers to interaction due to π overlap of three or more p-orbitals on adjacent atoms in a molecule. The "allyl" systems are the simplest (one π-bond plus a third p orbital), and conjugated dienes (two adjacent π-bonds = 4 p orbitals) are next in line. As you will see, conjugation affects the properties of the involved orbital systems, giving rise to modified electronic characteristics, stability, chemical reactivity, and spectroscopy. Introductory aspects of all of these are presented here.

Outline of the Chapter

14-1. The Allyl System.

An introduction to the π system created by overlap of three p orbitals.

14-2. Chemistry of the Allyl System.

Consequences of conjugation on reaction types we've already seen.

14-3. Conjugated Dienes.

The π System made up of four p orbitals.

14-4. Extended Conjugation and Benzene.

14-5. Special Reactions of Conjugated π-Systems.

A new set of mechanisms for ring-forming reactions.

14-6. Polymerization of Conjugated Dienes.

14-7. Electronic Spectra: Ultraviolet and Visible Spectroscopy.

Keys to the Chapter

14-1. The Allyl System.

Conjugation generally results in stabilization. The experimental results cited in section 14-1 illustrate the relative ease of generating allyl radicals, cations, and anions, compared with ordinary 1° radicals, cations, or anions. The reasons behind the stabilization that comes from allyl conjugation are presented in two different, but equivalent ways: using resonance and using molecular orbitals. Both viewpoints offer useful insights into the allyl system. You should pay special attention to the electrostatic consequences of conjugation as implied by these resonance and M.O. pictures. First, conjugation allows π-electrons to freely "spread out" over a larger number of nuclei: this effectively increases the bonding in a molecule (remember, bonds are just electrons mutually attracted to more than one atomic nucleus). The result is net stabilization. Second, conjugation allows a center of either electron deficiency or electron excess to be "delocalized," so that the "problem" can be shared by more than one atom. Electrons can move freely through conjugated π-systems, either towards an electron deficient atom, or away from an electron rich one. This obviously is electrostatically desirable and, again, results in overall stabilization.

14-2. Chemistry of the Allyl System.

The presence of an allyl system gives rise to easily formed, stabilized intermediates. It also introduces a new regiochemical factor since the reactive character of each of these intermediates is now shared by the two carbons at the opposite ends of the allyl system. A reaction sequence involving any allyl-type radical, cation, or anion can and usually does give two isomeric products, derived from attachment of a group at either of these two "ends." A variety of examples are presented here, with some discussion of the factors affecting isomer ratios in these reactions.

Notice that *none of these reactions are fundamentally new.* All you are seeing is the modified outcome of a nucleophilic displacement, a free-radical halogenation, or a Grignard-type reaction when the substrate leads to an allyl-type intermediate as it follows the ordinary mechanistic course of any of these reactions. Learning to understand and handle situations like this requires that you "think mechanistically." That is, you need to apply what you've earlier learned about a reaction mechanism directly to a new type of molecule. You have to follow the mechanism one step at a time, see what you get, and analyze the consequences of any unusual new structural types that turn up. This is a cornerstone of organic chemistry, allowing some degree of extrapolation and predictability in new situations. You haven't been asked to do a whole lot of this up till now, but you will need to develop these skills from now on. Much of what is coming up will involve molecules with multiple functional groups that may affect each other's behaviour. Mechanistically-oriented thinking is indispensible in deciding just what these molecules are likely to do.

14-3. Conjugated Dienes.

With dienes we see the first situation where comparisons between interacting vs. non-interacting pairs of functional groups in a single molecule may be conveniently made. Conjugated dienes possess p orbitals on four adjacent atoms, and are more stable than the other two alternatives, isolated dienes, where the double bonds are separated by one or more atoms, and "cumulated" dienes (like allene), where the double bonds share a common atom:

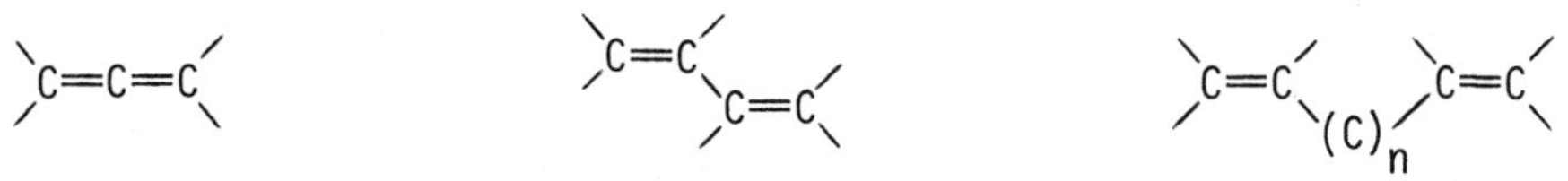

cumulated ("1,2") | conjugated ("1,3") | $n \geq 1$, isolated ("1,4", "1,5", "1,6", etc.)

As we saw with allyl systems, the presence of conjugation allows the π-type overlap of multiple p orbitals to occur, leading to stabilization. The result is greater stability for conjugated dienes relative to the others. Again, both resonance and M.O. explanations are applicable.

In their qualitative chemistry, conjugated dienes behave very much the same way alkenes do: they readily react with electrophiles in addition reactions. Just as in the case of alkenes, this addition proceeds to give the most stable intermediate. For conjugated dienes, this normally turns out to be a resonance stabilized allyl cation:

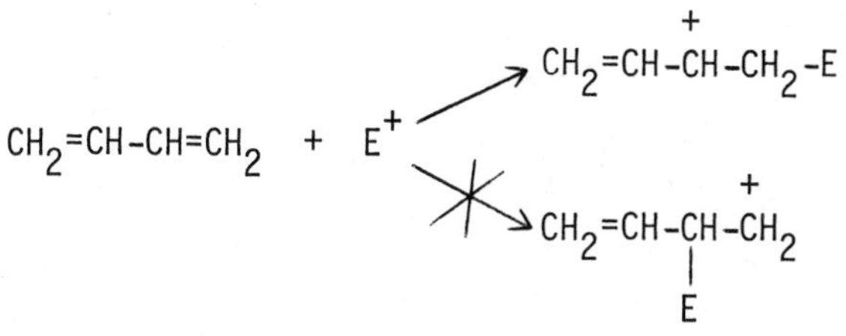

CH_2=CH-CH=CH_2 + E^+
CH_2=CH-$\overset{+}{C}$H-CH_2-E
CH_2=CH-CH(E)-$\overset{+}{C}H_2$

That represents the basic story. The rest of the section deals with details, mainly associated with the fact that the allyl cation can attach a nucleophile at either of two positions. Attachment to give "1,2-addition" is usually fastest (kinetic), although the "1,4-product", possessing a more highly substituted double bond, is usually more stable.

14-4. Extended Conjugation and Benzene.

Further extrapolation on the same themes.

14-5. Special Reactions of Conjugated π-Systems.

Up till now we haven't made any special presentations concerning reactions that form rings. This is because the ring-forming reactions you've seen so far were nothing more than intramolecular versions of ordinary reactions, such as

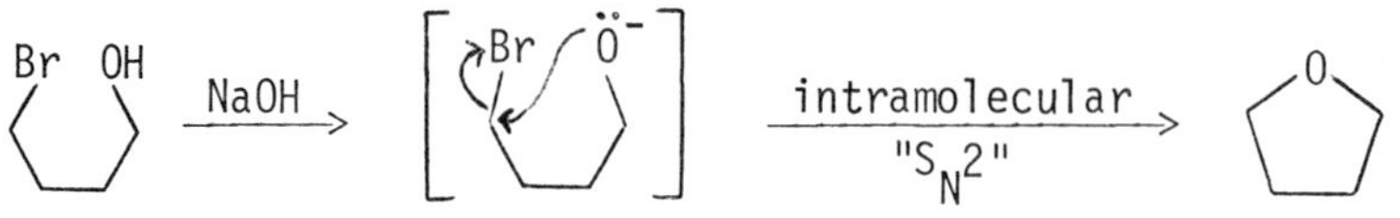

(chapter 6)

and

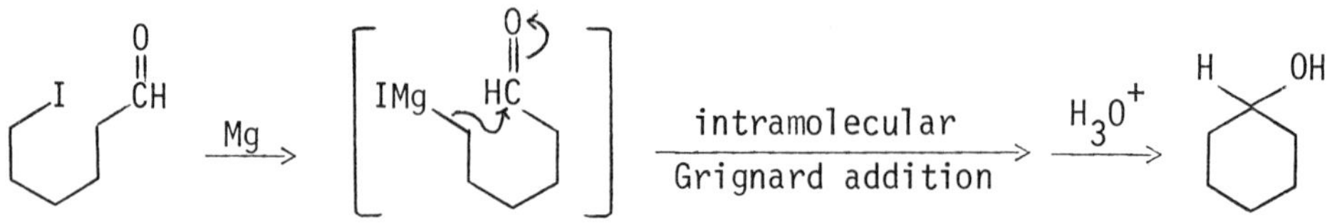

(chapter 8).

Now however, a new set of ring-forming reactions will be presented separately, because they represent a totally new mechanistic class of reactions, sometimes collectively called "pericyclic" reactions. Mechanisms for these reactions involve movement of two or more pairs of electrons *in a circle*, and the simultaneous breaking and forming of σ and π bonds. They are therefore examples of concerted reactions. These reactions generally do not involve free radicals or ions, and don't need polarized bonds to take place, although dipole-dipole attractions between reacting atoms can speed the reaction up. Since reactive species like radicals, ions, or polar bonds are not involved, you might ask why these reactions should happen at all. There are two reasons: kinetic and thermodynamic. Certain special properties of circularly moving groups of electrons give these reactions low activation barriers, and the products are more stable than the starting materials. (That was simple, wasn't it?) To convince yourself of the latter, take a look at all the examples of those reactions given in the Summary section of this chapter. In every case the products contain more σ bonds and fewer π bonds than the starting material.

Points to take particular note of have to do with the stereochemistry of these reactions. Since they are concerted, stereochemical (e.g. cis/trans) relationships in the starting materials are preserved through the reaction transition states and on into the products. You may need some practice visualizing in order to do the problems. For instance, for the Diels-Alder reaction, it may be useful to make models of two reacting molecules, and hold them in an arrangement resembling the cycloaddition transition state (Figure 14-11), to see in three dimensions where all the original groups will wind up relative to the two newly-formed σ bonds. You should be able to readily follow the positions of the atoms during the course of the reaction of a molecule like 1,3-cyclopentadiene.

The "electrocyclic" reactions towards the end of the section present a more complex stereochemical situation, where the stereochemistry of the reaction is a function both of the reaction conditions (heat or light) and the number of electrons involved. The details are beyond the scope of the course, and so only some introductory descriptive material has been presented.

14-6. Polymerization of Conjugated Dienes.

Polymers composed of diene units are significant for two reasons. Just like polymers of simple alkenes, they are industrially important (and have been for a much longer time, by the way). In addition, they are closely related to several major classes of biological molecules formally derived from isoprene (2-methyl-1,3-butadiene) as the monomeric unit. Some of the variety in this biochemistry is illustrated in this section.

14-7. Electronic Spectra: Ultraviolet and Visible Spectroscopy.

The principles behind electronic spectroscopy are very simple and, in fact, are really direct extensions of the spectroscopy of atoms, a freshman chemistry topic. Remember how absorption of light by atoms promotes electrons to higher energy levels? Here, you're seeing the same thing, but with molecules; so, the energy levels involved are best described as molecular orbitals.

The experimental techniques involved in observing these light absorptions are simple enough to do. UV/VIS spectroscopy (as it is often abbreviated) was once very important in determining the presence or absence of conjugation, etc., in an organic molecule, and therefore in structure determination. Much of its past importance has been reduced by the development of sophisticated NMR equipment and techniques. UV/VIS spectroscopy is mostly used now simply to confirm structural assignments made on the basis of NMR and IR spectroscopy (chapter 17).

Solutions to Chapter 14 Problems

1. (a) 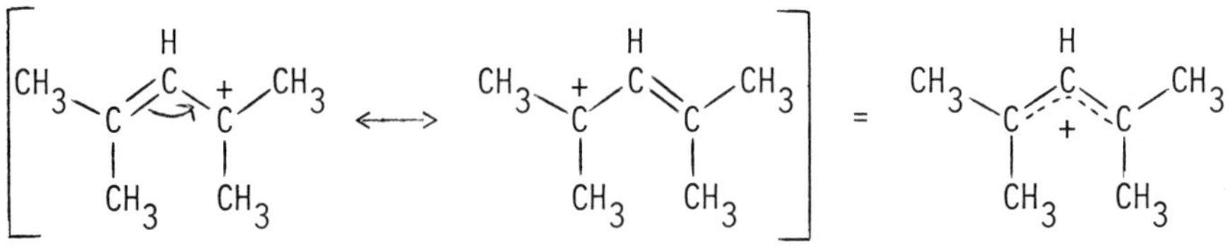

(b) 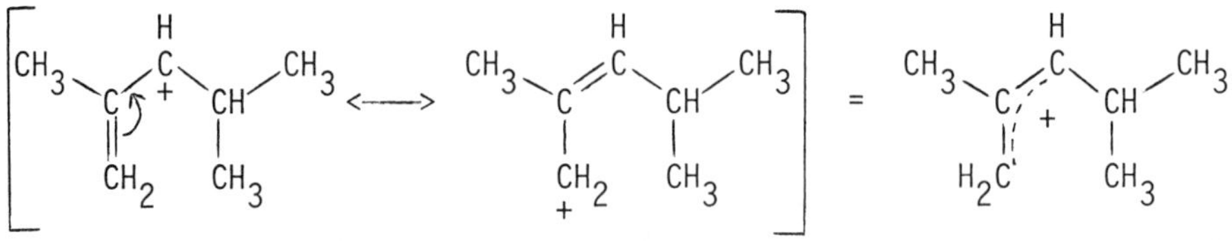

(c) 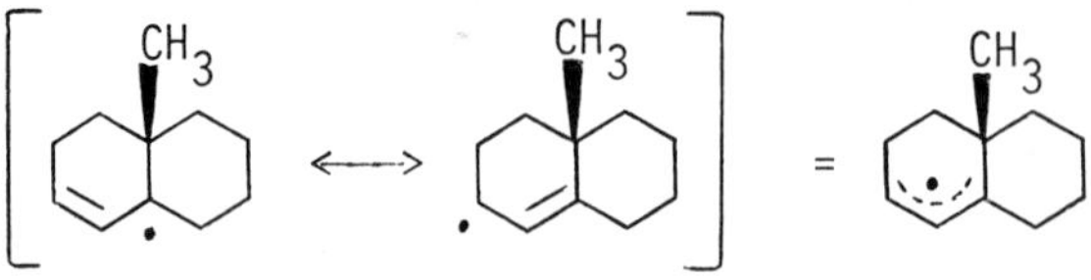

(d) 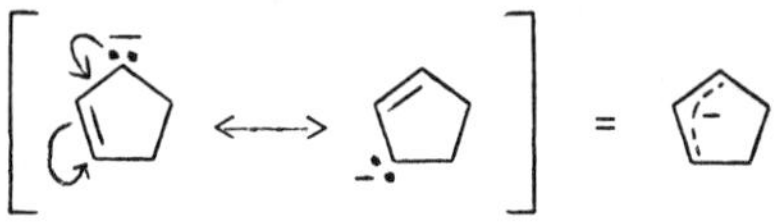

(e) 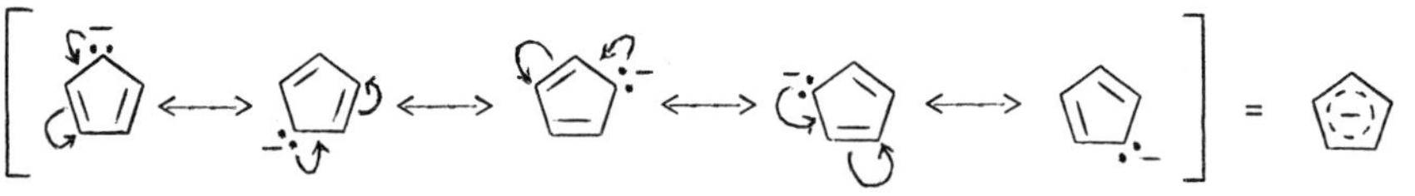

****

2. (a) $CH_3\dot{C}HCH{=}CH_2 \longleftrightarrow CH_3CH{=}CH\dot{C}H_2$

(b) 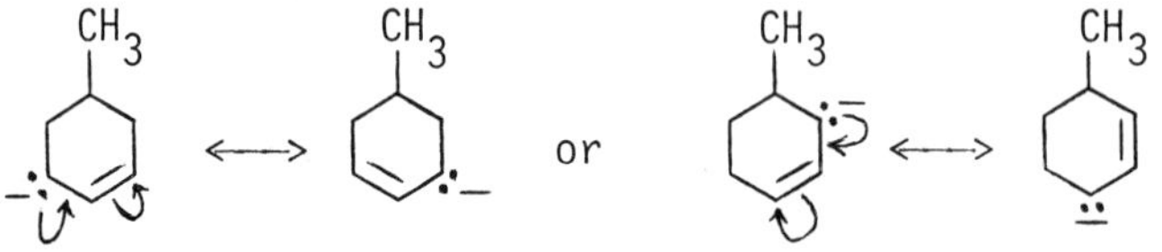

(c) 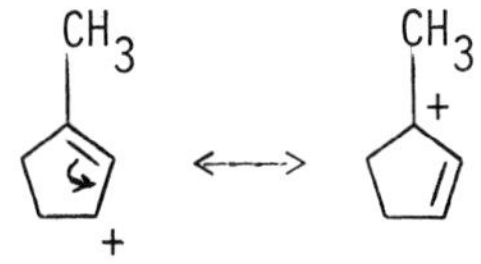

****

3. Radicals: allyl > tertiary > secondary > primary
Cations: tertiary > allyl ≃ secondary > primary

Hyperconjugation, which is responsible for the tertiary > secondary > primary stabilization order, is obviously more important for cations than for radicals. The effect is large enough for tertiary cations to exceed resonance-stabilized allyl cations in stability (the reverse of the order for radicals).

****

4. Kinetic attachment of nucleophiles is directed to the end of the allyl
    cation where the most positive charge resides: the more substituted end.
    In each, first product listed is kinetic and second is thermodynamic
    (usually with a more substituted alkene present).

(a) $(CH_3)_2CHCBr-CH=CH_2$, $(CH_3)_2CHC=CHCH_2Br$
                  | |
                 CH_3 CH_3

(b)

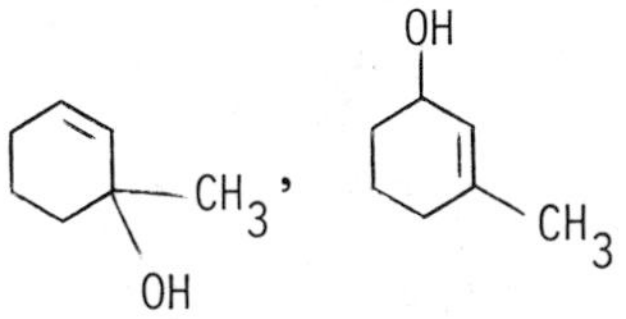

(d)

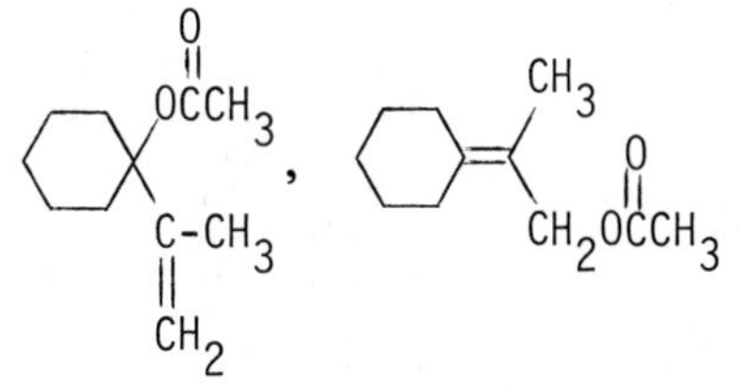

(c)

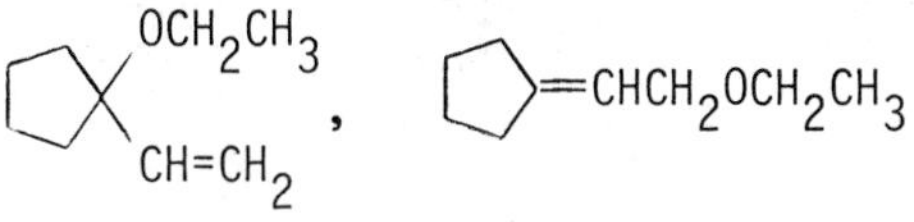

(e) Different! S_N2, not S_N1 conditions, so reaction occurs at least
     hindered carbon:

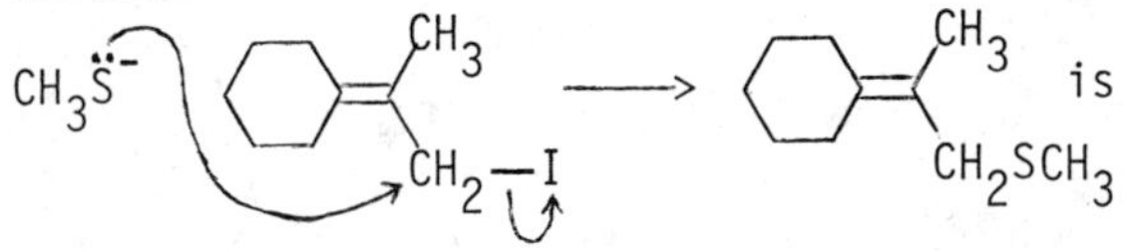

is the only product.

(f) Intramolecular version:

    Again, only one product; bond formation at other end would produce a
    somewhat strained seven-membered ring.

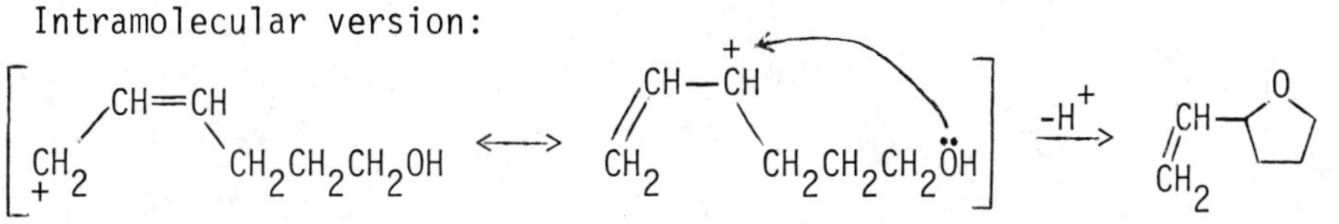

****

5. (a)

            thermo. product   kinetic product

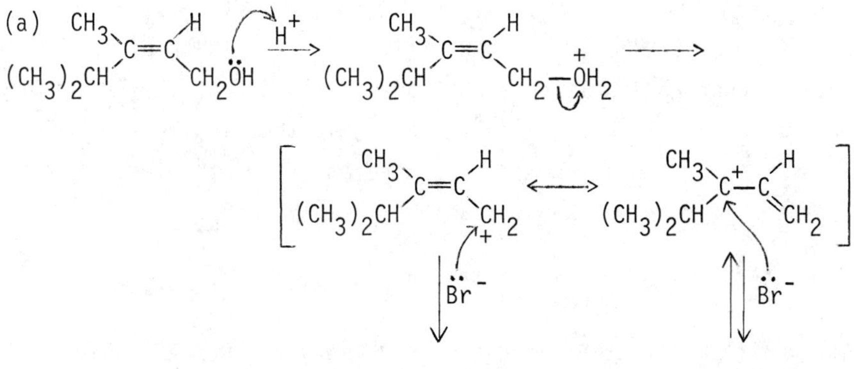

(c)

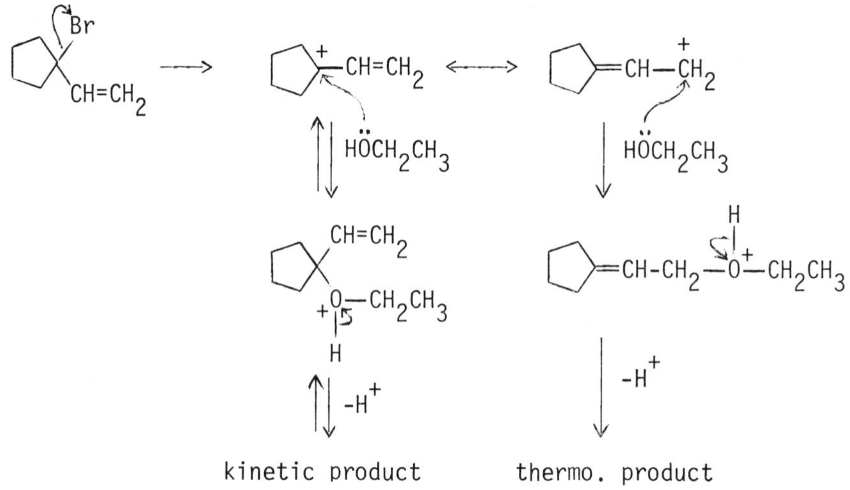

(e) (f) See answers to problem 4.

****

6. (i) tertiary > allyl ≃ secondary >> primary (order of cation stability)

   (ii) allyl > primary > secondary >> tertiary

****

7. (i) e (allyl and tertiary) > a (allyl and secondary) > d (forms same cation as 'e', but requires ionization at primary carbon, so will be slower) > c > b > f (these follow cation stability order).

   (ii) Steric hindrance predominates, so f > b > d > c > a > e (the last two will be better candidates for S_N2' mechanisms).

****

8. (i) S_N2'; (ii) S_N2'; (iii) S_N2; (iv) S_N2 Attack of good nucleophiles under non-ionizing conditions will occur at the less hindered end of the allyl system. In (i) and (ii) that is the π-bond end, leading to S_N2' displacement. In the other two the less hindered end is the primary haloalkane, leading directly to S_N2.

****

9. Write all possible allylic isomers in each case, and pay attention to stereochemistry as well.

(a) 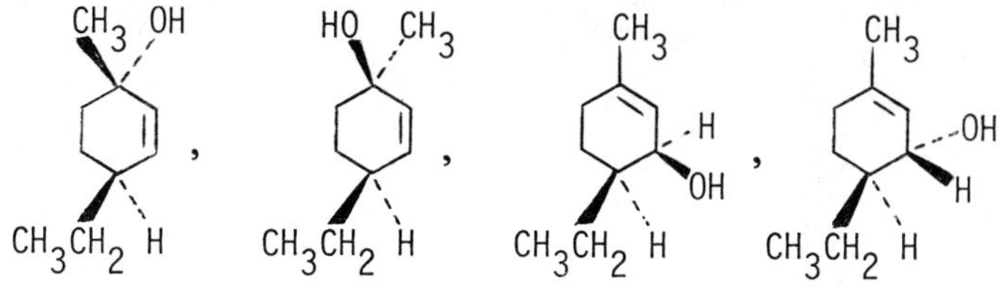

(b) 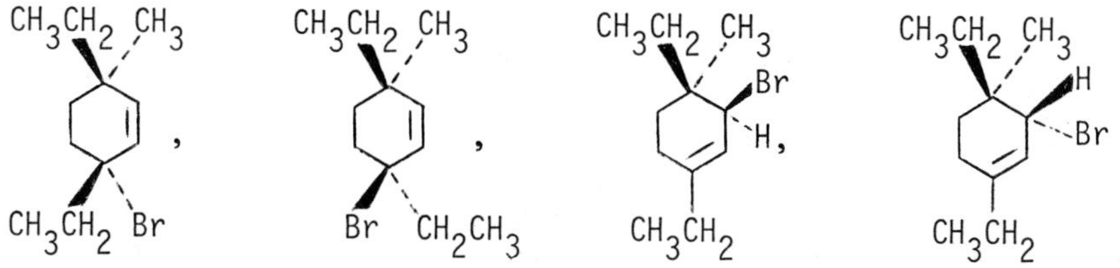

(c) $CH_3CH_2C(CH_3)(Br)—CH=CH_2$ (racemic), $CH_3CH_2C(CH_3)=CHCH_2Br$

(d) $[CH_3\bar{C}HCH=CHCH_2CH_3 \longleftrightarrow CH_3CH=CH\bar{C}HCH_2CH_3]\ Li^+$

(e) $CH_3CH(CH(OH)CH_3)CH=CHCH_2CH_3$ + $CH_3CH=CHCH(CH(OH)CH_3)CH_2CH_3$ (all possible stereoisomers for each structure)

(f) 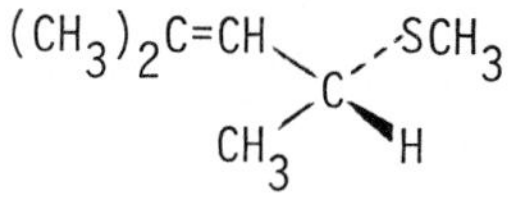 (exclusively S_N2)

****

10. 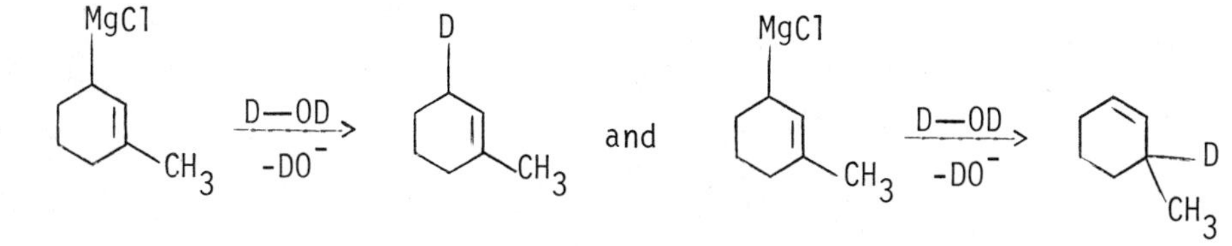

****

11. 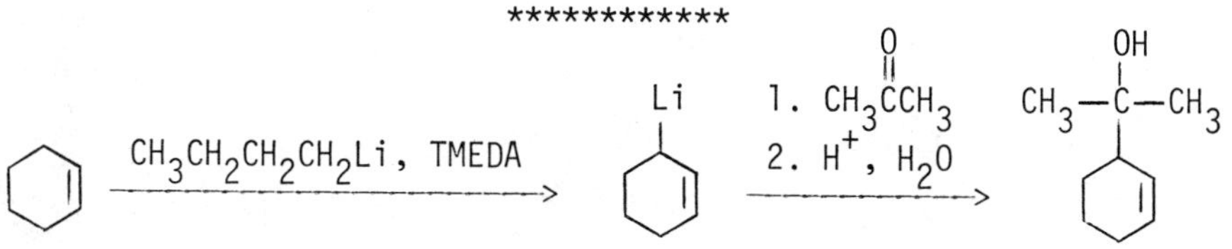

****

12. Look at another resonance form of the starting compound for a hint.

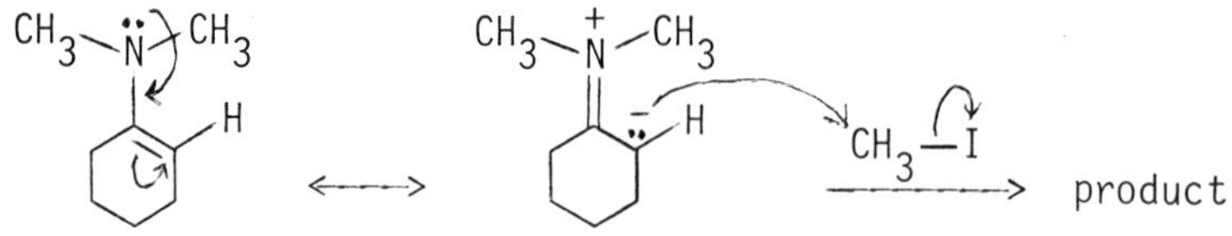

****

13. Recall the relative sizes of coupling constants between alkene hydrogens:

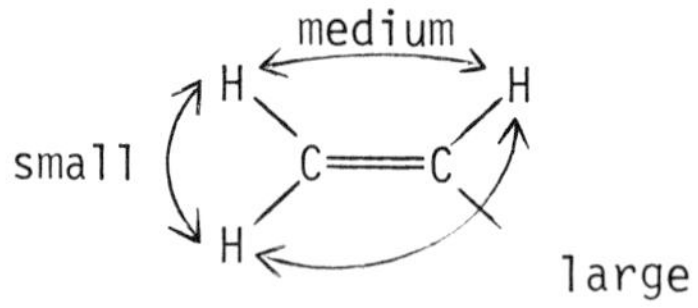

Using this as a guide the entire spectrum may be explained:

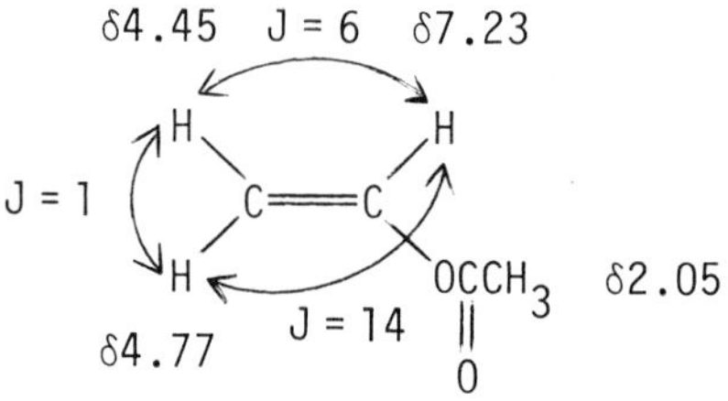

The large chemical shift difference between alkene hydrogens results from the following resonance contribution:

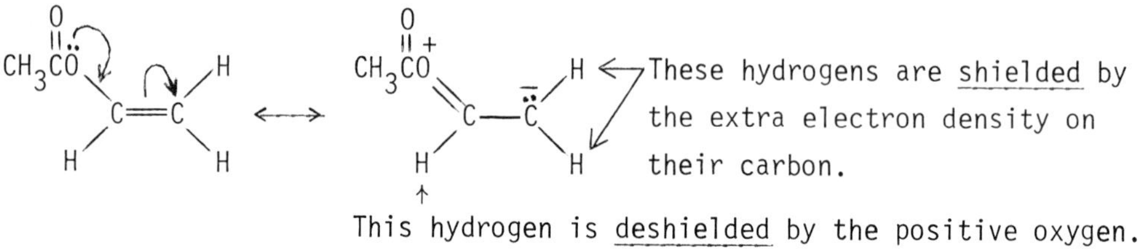

These hydrogens are shielded by the extra electron density on their carbon.
This hydrogen is deshielded by the positive oxygen.

****

14. (a) (2*E*,5*Z*)-2,5-heptadiene; (b) 2,4-pentadien-1-ol

(c) *trans*-5,6-dibromo-1,3-cyclooctadiene; (d) 4-ethenylcyclohexene

****

15. $CH_2=CH-\overset{H}{CH}-CH=CH_2$ has the weakest C-H bond (arrow), a bond that is <u>doubly</u> allylic (DH° ≃ 71 kcal/mole); it will therefore be brominated fastest. Because only a very weak C-H bond needs to be broken, bromination of this isomer is more exothermic than the other, where a stronger methyl C-H bond

needs to be broken. However, both will give identical product mixtures, since identical radicals are formed from each: $\overline{CH_2\text{-}CH\text{-}\dot{C}H\text{-}CH\text{-}CH_2} \equiv$ $[\dot{C}H_2\text{-}CH\text{=}CH\text{-}CH\text{=}CH_2 \leftrightarrow CH_2\text{=}CH\text{-}\dot{C}H\text{-}CH\text{=}CH_2 \leftrightarrow CH_2\text{=}CH\text{-}CH\text{=}CH\text{-}\dot{C}H_2]$.

****

16. $CH_2\text{=}CH\text{-}CH\text{=}CH\text{-}CH_3 \xrightarrow{H^+} CH_3\text{-}\overset{+}{C}H\text{-}CH\text{=}CH\text{-}CH_3$ allylic cation, secondary at each end

(1) conjugated diene (2)

$CH_2\text{=}CH\text{-}CH_2\text{-}CH\text{=}CH_2 \xrightarrow{H^+} CH_2\text{=}CH\text{-}CH_2\text{-}\overset{+}{C}H\text{-}CH_3$ ordinary secondary cation

(3) isolated diene (4)

(1) is more stable than (3), and (2) is more stable than (4):

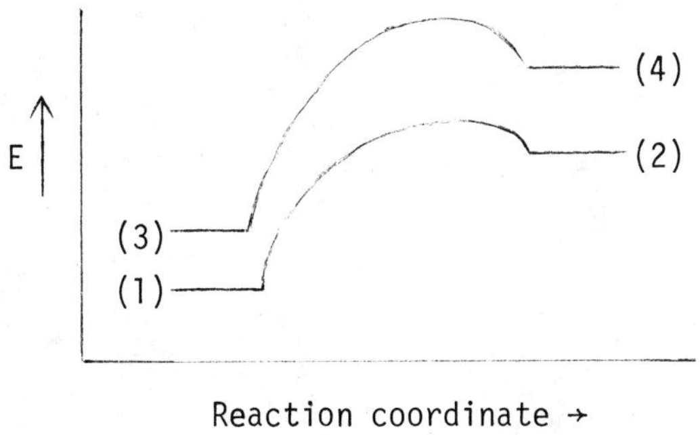

Reaction (1) + H^+ → (2) is faster and leads to the more stable cation. Note: when the text says that allyl and secondary cations are similar in energy, it is referring to the simplest allyl cation, $\overset{+}{C}H_2\text{-}CH\text{=}CH_2$, which is primary at each end. Additional alkyl groups on allyl cations increase their stability, as you might expect.

****

17. Expect 1,2- and 1,4-addition to occur in each case. Note that the 1,2-additions in (b) and (c) might be expected to show *anti* stereochemistry, similar to additions to ordinary alkenes.

(a) 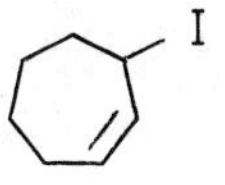

(1,2 and 1,4 products are the same molecule: 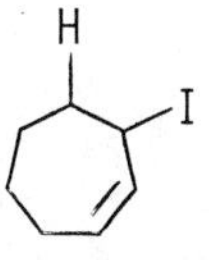

, same as 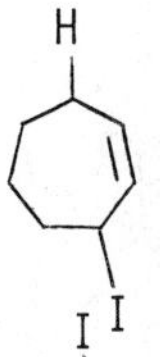

!)

(b) 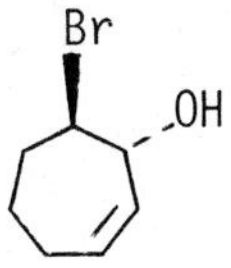

and 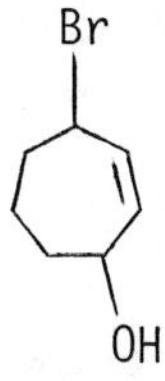

; (c) 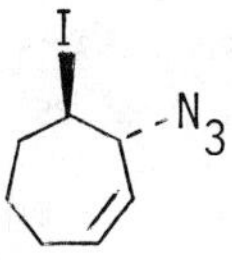

and 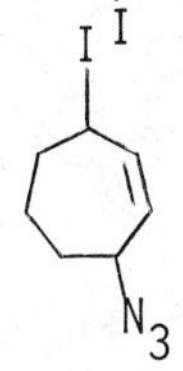

(d) 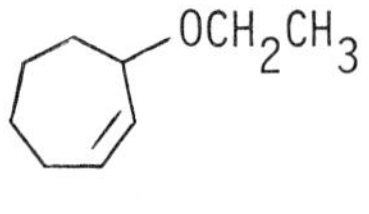

(from both 1,2- and 1,4-addn.) ; (e) 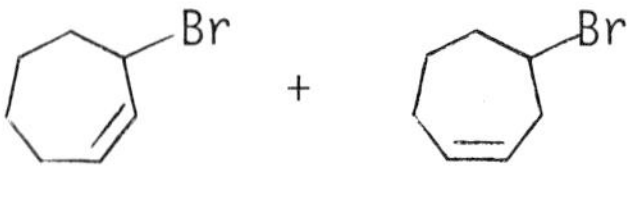

****

18. Addition of electrophile will always be at C-1, generating best allylic cation.

(a) CH_3-CHI-CH=CH-CH_3 (cis and trans)

(b) BrCH_2-CHOH-CH=CH-CH_3 and BrCH_2-CH=CH-CHOH-CH_3 (cis and trans)

(c) ICH_2-CHN_3-CH=CH-CH_3 and ICH_2-CH=CH-CHN_3-CH_3 (cis and trans)

(d) CH_3-CH(O$CH_2$$CH_3$)-CH=CH-$CH_3$ (cis and trans)

(e) BrCH_2-CH_2-CH=CH-CH_3 and BrCH_2-CH=CH-CH_2-CH_3 (cis and trans)

****

19. Same answers, but with a methyl group added to C-2 in each case.

****

20. (a) through (d): 1,2-product is kinetic and 1,4- is thermodynamic.

(e) 1,4-product is both kinetic and thermodynamic

****

21. (e) CH_2=CH-$\overset{+}{C}$H-CH=CH_2 ↔ $\overset{+}{C}H_2$-CH=CH-CH=CH_2 (doubly allylic) >

(d) CH_3-$\overset{+}{C}$H-CH=CH-CH_3 (secondary allylic at both ends) >

(a) $\overset{+}{C}H_2$-CH=CH_2 > (c) > (b)

****

22. π_5 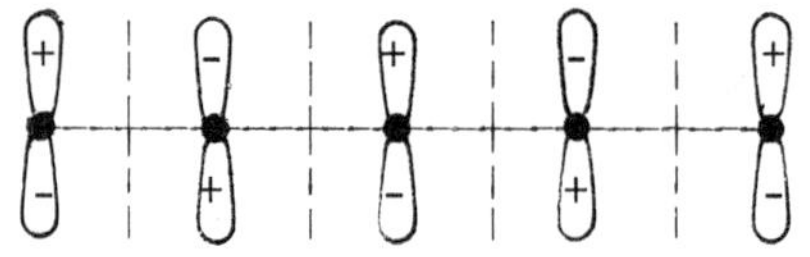

4 nodes

π_4 

3 nodes

π_3 2 nodes

π_2 1 node

π_1 no nodes

cation   radical   anion

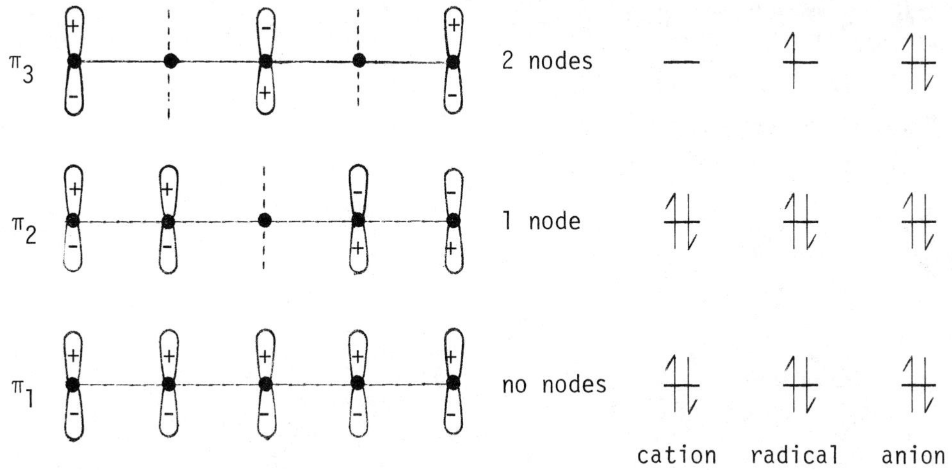

See answer to problem 21 for resonance forms of cation, and answer to problem 15 for resonance forms of radical.

****

23. $(CH_3)_2C=CH-CH_2-\overset{..}{O}H \xrightarrow{\ H^+\ } (CH_3)_2C=CH-CH_2-\overset{+}{O}H_2 \xrightarrow{-H_2O} \overset{H}{CH_2}-\overset{CH_3}{C}=CH-\overset{+}{CH_2} \xrightarrow{-H^+}$

                      product

$\overset{H}{CH_2}-\overset{CH_3}{C}=CH-CH_2-Cl \xrightarrow{\ ^-\overset{..}{N}[CH(CH_3)_2]_2\ } $ product

****

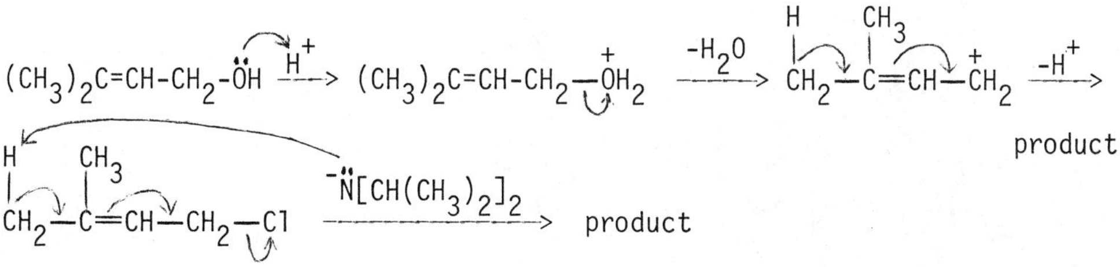

24. Any allylic hydrogen may be lost from the intermediate cation (arrows):

****

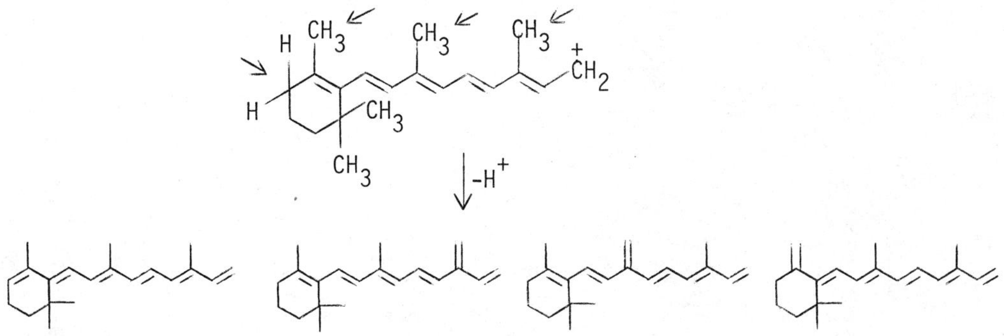

then

25. $CH_2=CH-MgBr$ + CH_3CCH_3 $\xrightarrow{\quad H^+, H_2O \quad}$ $CH_2=CH-C(CH_3)_2$ ← $\delta 1.3$

(with $\overset{O}{\overset{\|}{C}}$ carbonyl)

$\underset{OH \; ← \; \delta 2.4}{\underbrace{\qquad\qquad}}$

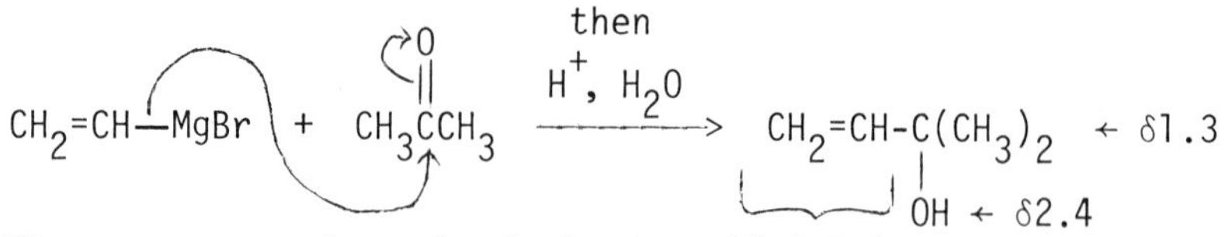

The new compound may be derived $\delta 4.8-6.2$

from ionization of the allylic alcohol upon extended contact with acid:

$CH_2=CH-\underset{\overset{|}{\overset{+}{O}H_2}}{\underset{|}{C}(CH_3)_2}$ $\rightleftharpoons$ $[CH_2=CH-\overset{+}{C}(CH_3)_2 \longleftrightarrow \overset{+}{C}H_2-CH=C(CH_3)_2 \xrightarrow[-H^+]{H_2\ddot{O}}$

$HOCH_2-CH=C(CH_3)_2$ ← $\delta 1.8$

↑   ↑ $\delta 5.5$ (triplet)

$\delta 4.1$ (doublet)

****

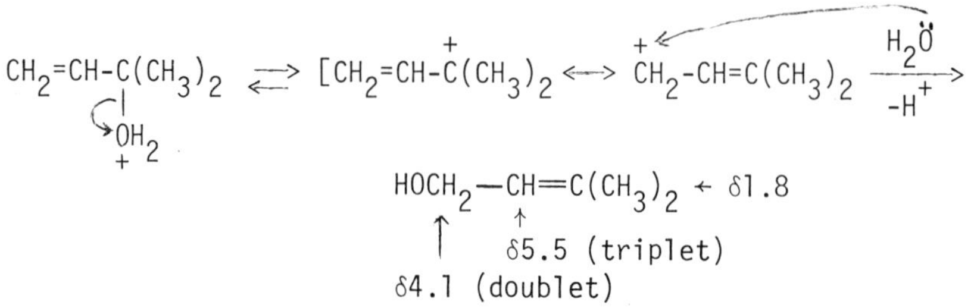

26.

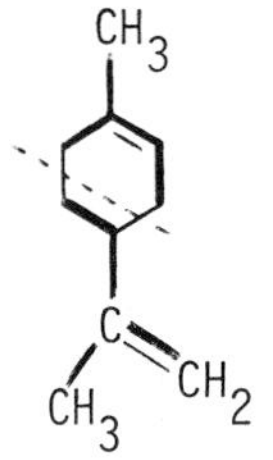

(a)

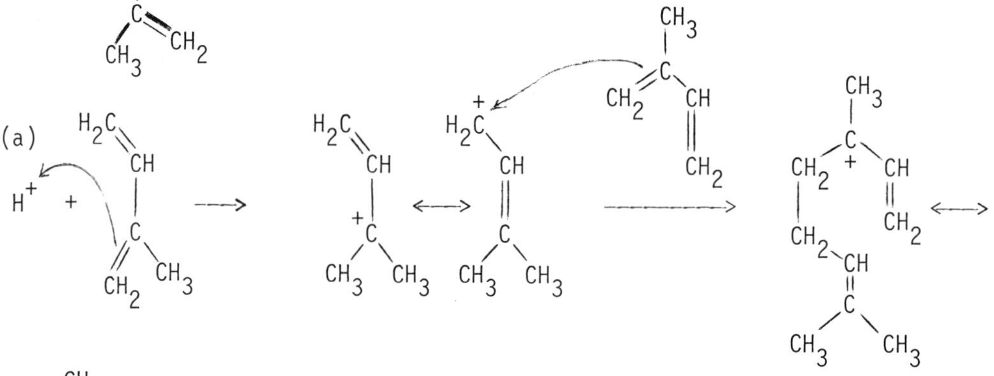

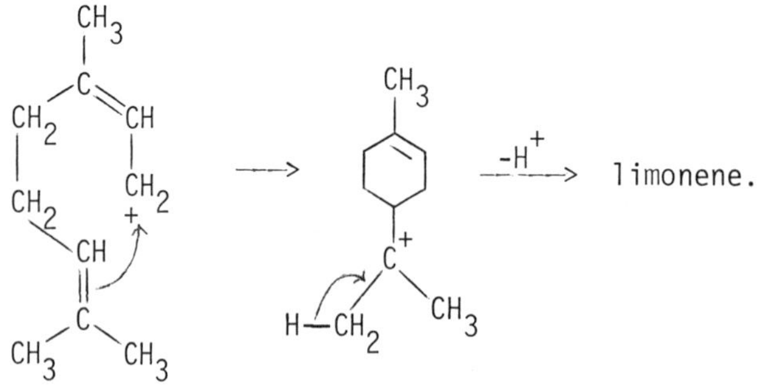

Notice that both additions
to dienes to form cations
occur to give an allylic
cation that is tertiary
at one end.

$\xrightarrow{\quad}$ $\xrightarrow{-H^+}$ limonene.

(b) 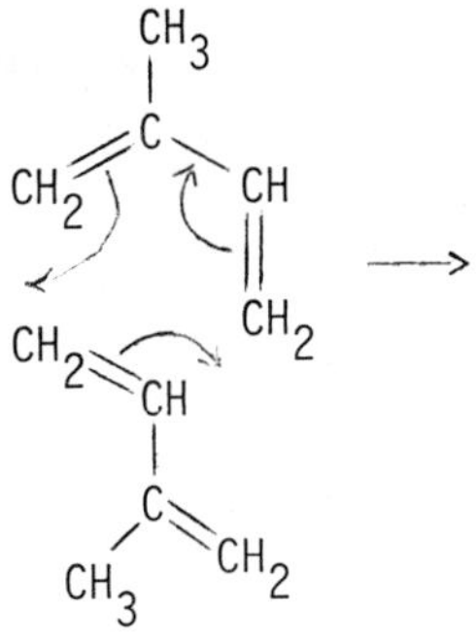 limonene, via a Diels-Alder concerted cycloaddition reaction.

****

27. 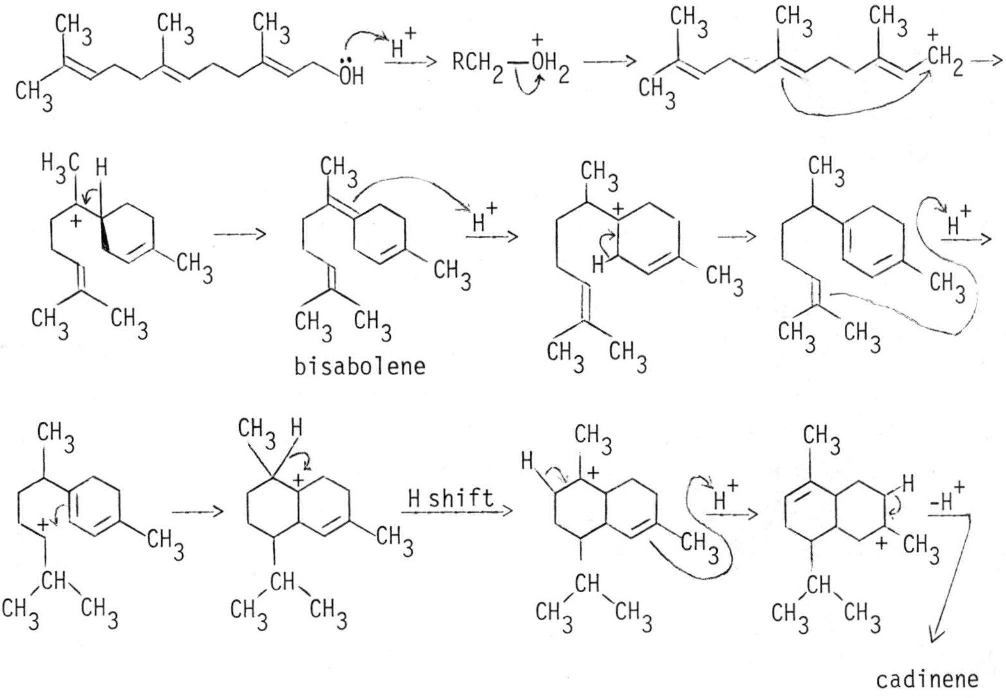

****

28. (a) 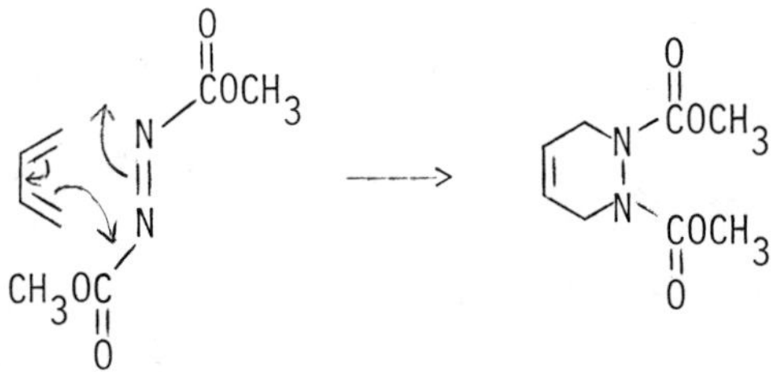

(b) 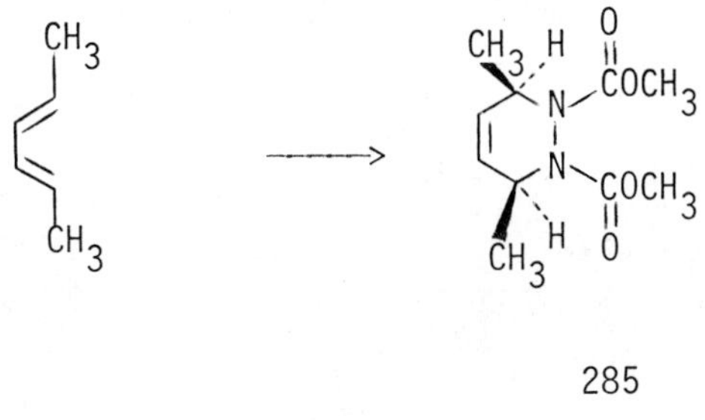

(c) 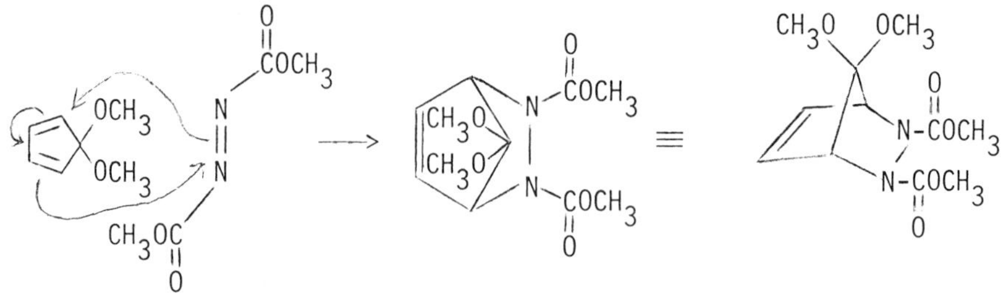

(d) 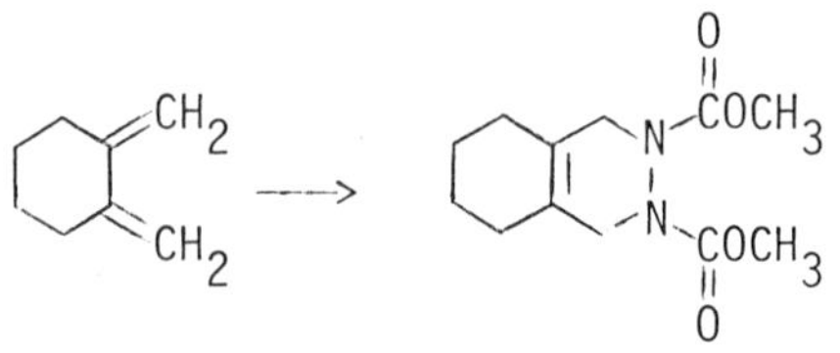

****

29. Diene 'A' is similar in structure to 1,3-cyclohexadiene, which reacts well in Diels-Alder cycloadditions (Table 14-1). In diene 'B', however, the ends of the diene are locked in a "zig-zag" conformation (called "s-trans") which puts the end carbons too far apart to bond to the two alkene carbons of a dienophile. Figure 14-11 illustrates how the Diels-Alder reaction involves a diene in a "U"-shaped conformation (called "s-cis"), which puts its end carbons close together. Dienes (like 'B') that cannot achieve this conformation will not participate with dienophiles in Diels-Alder reactions.

****

30. (a) 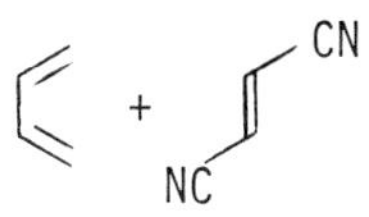 ; (b) 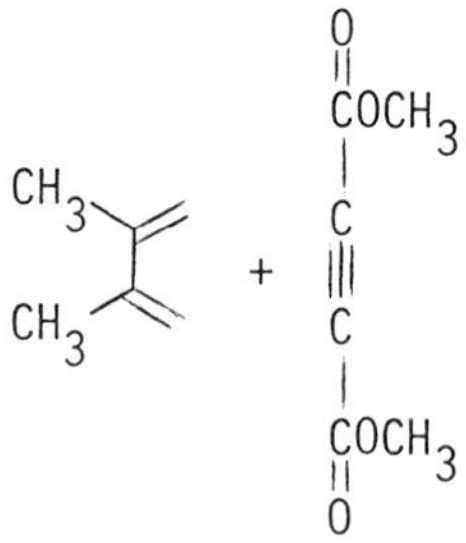 ; (c) 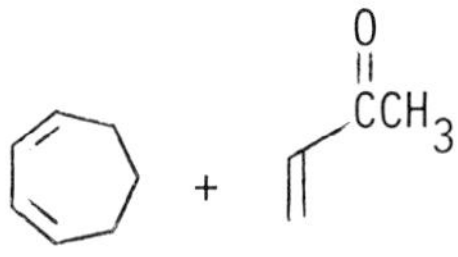 ;

(d) 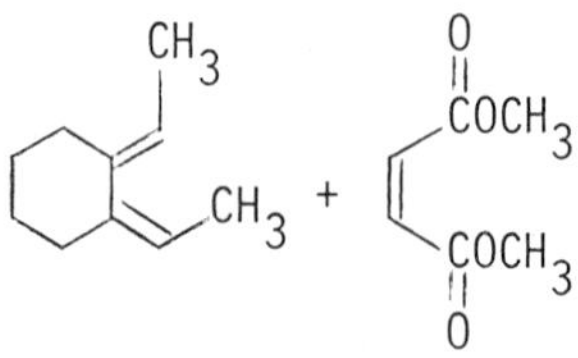 : (e) 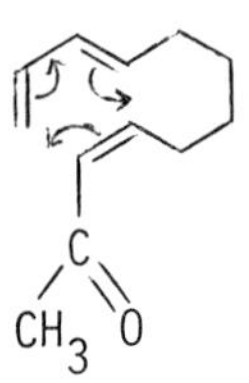 (another intramolecular example)

****

31. All are [2 + 2] cycloadditions: (a) 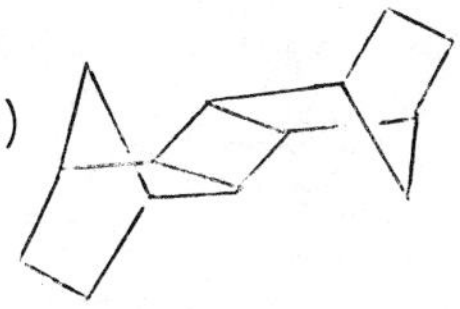 is one possible product stereoisomer

(b) 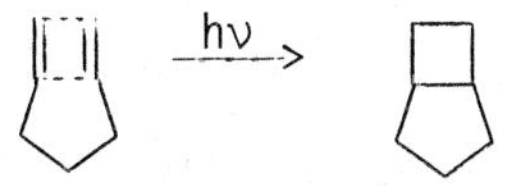

(c) 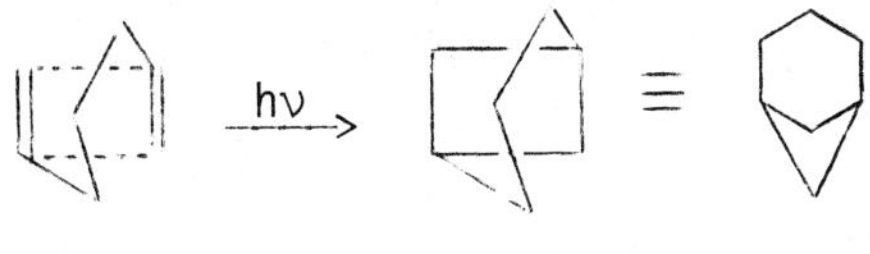

(d) 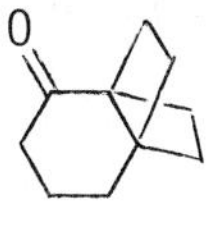

****

32. All are electrocyclic reactions. If you are a football fan and know that a TouchDown is worth 6 points, then you are eligible to learn a simple mnemonic, namely that a 6-electron Thermal electrocyclic reaction is Disrotatory. Changing either from thermal to photochemical, or the number of electrons by ±2, changes the rotation direction.

(a) A photochemical 1,3-diene ring closure (4 electrons). [Mechanism is disrotatory (Figure 14-13) although this particular diene does not contain substitution at both ends, which is necessary for the disrotatory outcome to be directly observed.]

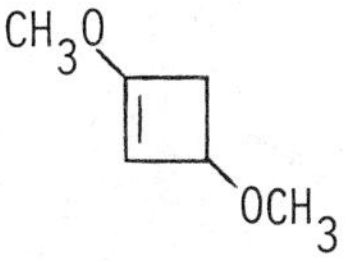

(b) Photochemical cyclohexadiene (6 electrons) ring-opening, which is conrotatory:

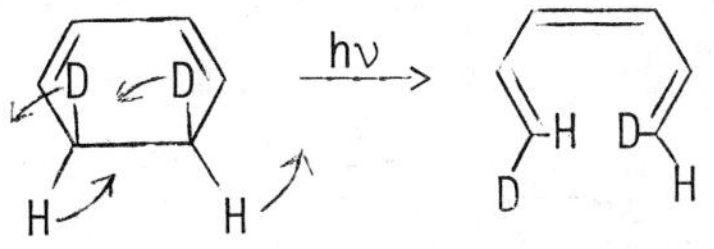

(c) Thermal cyclobutene (4 electrons) ring-opening, which is conrotatory:

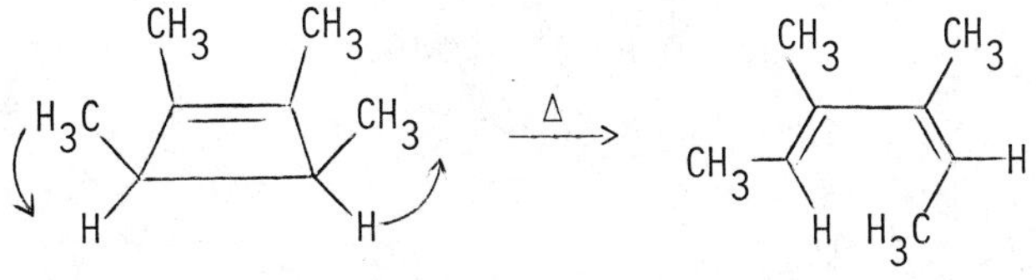

(d) Photochemical hexatriene (6 electrons) ring-closure, conrotatory:

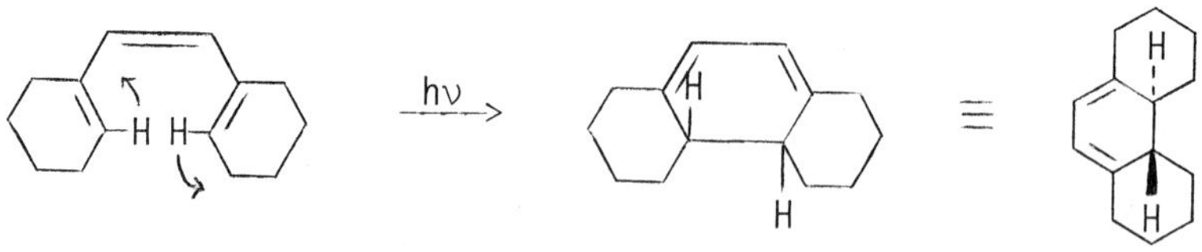

(e) Thermal version (6 electrons); disrotatory:

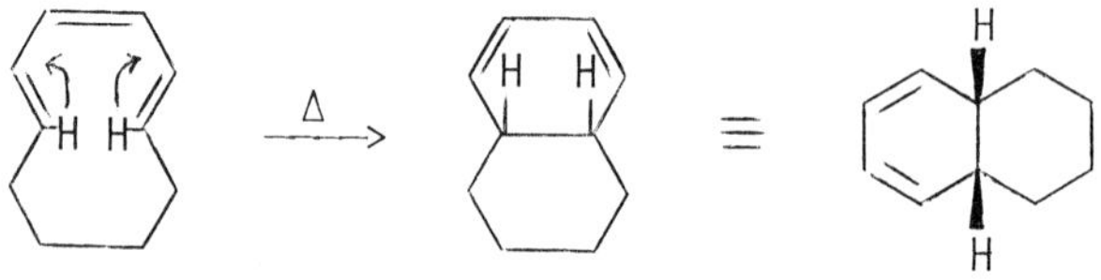

****

33. A thermal cyclobutene (4-electron) ring opening would like to be conrotatory:

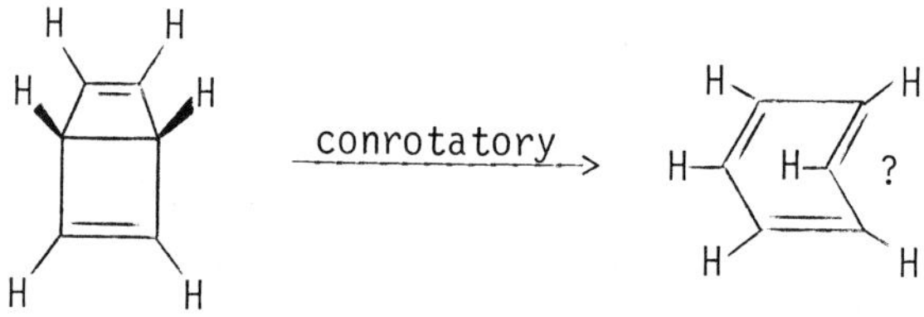

What is this?

Unfortunately, this motion is geometrically impossible, as it leads to a "benzene" with a *trans* double bond in the ring. Since that can't happen, the compound does nothing until enough energy is supplied so that it can open by rotating the "wrong," or disrotatory way, leading to the kind of benzene we're used to seeing. The high E_a is required to allow the electrocyclic reaction to follow a normally "forbidden" direction of rotation.

****

34. (a) [2 + 2] photochemical cycloaddition

(b) Photochemical cyclobutene (4-electron) ring-opening (disrotatory).

(c) Photochemical cyclohexadiene (6-electron) ring-opening (conrotatory).

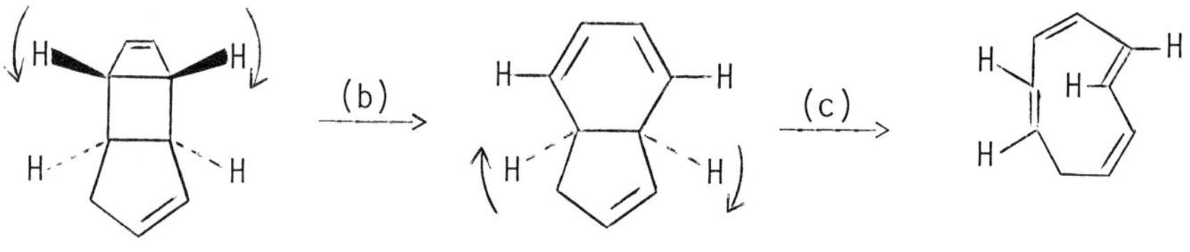

(d) Thermal hexatriene (6-electron) ring-closure (disrotatory):

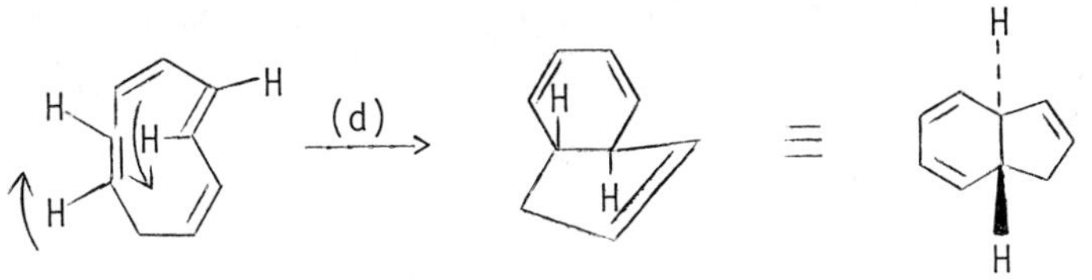

(e) Thermal hexatriene (6-electron) ring-closure (disrotatory):

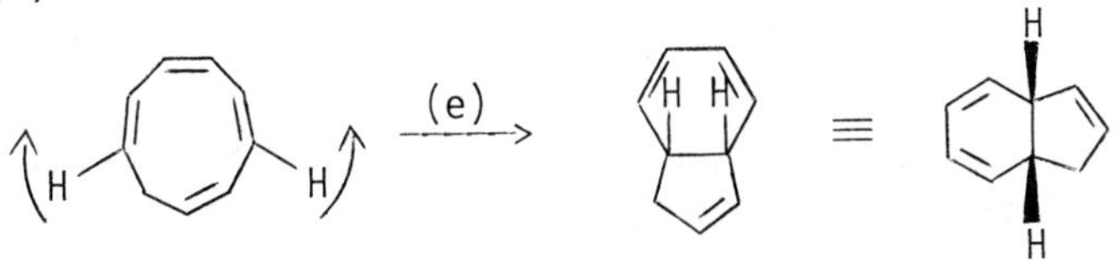

(f) Photochemical octatetraene (8-electron) ring-closure (disrotatory):

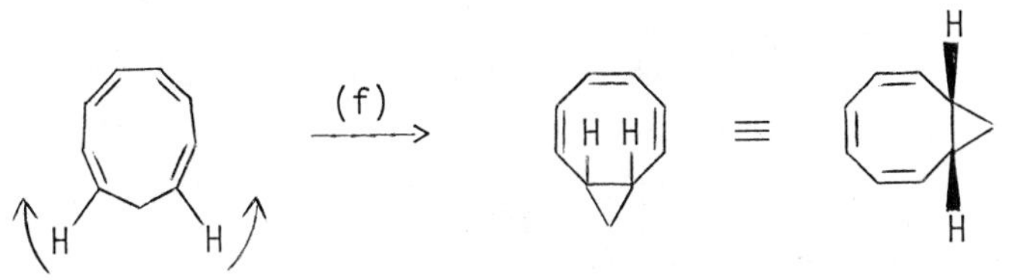

****

35.

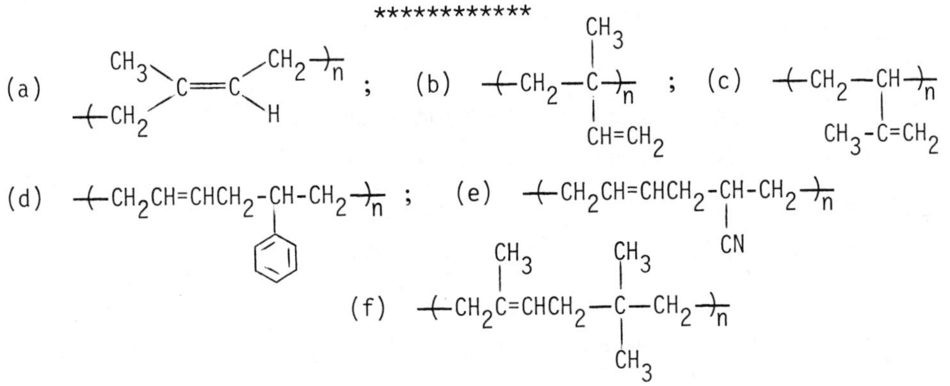

****

36.

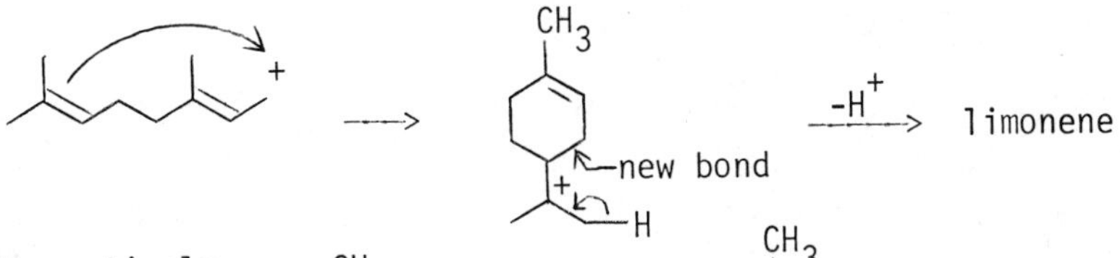

Alternatively:

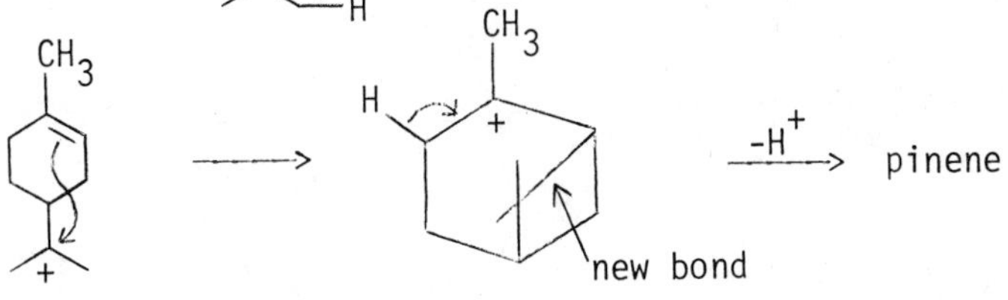

****

37. In each case the answer involves promotion of an electron in the highest occupied molecular orbital (look, in order, for n, then π, and then σ electrons) to a lowest unoccupied M. O. (π^* if present, otherwise σ^*).

    (a) $\sigma \rightarrow \sigma^*$; (b) $n \rightarrow \pi^*$; (c) $n \rightarrow \sigma^*$; (d) $\pi \rightarrow \pi^*$;

    (e) $n \rightarrow \pi^*$; (f) $\pi \rightarrow n$ (unusual, but just refer to Figure 14-3 for the necessary orbital diagram).

****

38. (a) Stereochemistry is irrelevant; look for longest conjugated system of π bonds:

1,4,7-triene
(all isolated)

1,3,8-triene
(conjugated diene)

2,4,6-triene
(conjugated triene)
ANSWER

(b) 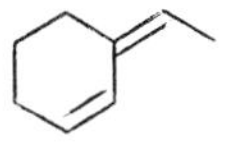 , the only conjugated system

****

39. (a) NMR: 5 alkene hydrogens; UV: isolated double bonds.
    Only possibilities are CH_2=CH-CH_2-CH=CH-CH_3, *cis* or *trans*.

    (b) NMR: 6 alkene hydrogens; UV: isolated double bonds.
    Only possibility is CH_2=CH-CH_2-CH_2-CH=CH_2.

    (c) NMR: 4 alkene hydrogens; UV: conjugated diene.
    Could be any cis/trans combination of CH_3-CH=CH-CH=CH-CH_3.

    (d) NMR: 5 alkene hydrogens; UV: conjugated diene.
    Either *cis* or *trans* CH_2=CH-CH=CH-CH_2-CH_3.

****

CHAPTER 15

Aldehydes and Ketones: The Carbonyl Group

General Introduction

Congratulations! You have finally gotten to the first of several chapters that will examine the chemistry of carbonyl compounds: the most important compounds in organic chemistry. Why are they so important? They are the most versatile class of compounds for carbon-carbon bond formation (and, therefore, synthesis). This is due to the fact that they contain an electrophilic carbonyl carbon (which you already know about) as well as a potentially *nucleophilic* carbon adjacent to it (which you will learn about shortly). This "double-barrelled" functional capability makes carbonyl compounds unique among the simple compound classes for synthetic utility. This importance spills over into biological chemistry as well, where carbonyl groups play a major role in biochemical syntheses of naturally occurring molecules in living creatures. As always, in spite of the "teasers" of carbonyl chemistry that you've seen in earlier chapters, this and later related chapters will cover the material in a complete, orderly fashion, so that you can develop a more representative overview of the topic.

Outline of the Chapter

15-1. Naming Aldehydes and Ketones.

15-2. Physical Properties of Aldehydes and Ketones.

15-3. Preparation of Aldehydes and Ketones: A Review.

15-4. The Reactivity of the Carbonyl Group: Mechanisms for Addition.

One of two major reaction patterns for carbonyl compounds.

15-5. Addition of Water and Alcohols to Aldehydes and Ketones.

15-6. Addition of Amines to Aldehydes and Ketones.

15-7. Addition of Carbon Nucleophiles to Aldehydes and Ketones.

Examples of common addition reactions, with mechanistic details and synthetic applications.

15-8. Special Oxidations and Reductions of Aldehydes and Ketones.

Including a new method for carbon-carbon bond cleavage.

Keys to the Chapter

15-1. Naming Aldehydes and Ketones.

As most of the material in these sections is of a relatively routine nature, only a few points of special interest, or with special implications, will be mentioned.

Nomenclature of carbonyl compounds presents a bit of a problem in that several alternative names may be possible for almost any compound. For example, one can give any of the following names to $(CH_3)_2CHC{\lesssim}^{O}_{CH_3}$: 3-methyl-2-butanone (IUPAC), isopropyl methyl ketone (common), α-methyl-butanone, 3-methyl-2-oxo-butane, or even 2-acetylpropane. Not all of these are ever used, but they are all unambiguous and in accord with one of the methods given in the chapter. So be prepared for some variety in general usage.

15-2. Physical Properties of Aldehydes and Ketones.

The polarized carbonyl group is the key to the physical and chemical properties of carbonyl compounds. Although they have dipole moments comparable to those found in haloalkanes, carbonyl compounds have a negatively polarized oxygen capable of hydrogen bonding to protic solvents. They are therefore much more water soluble than haloalkanes, for instance. The polarization in the carbon-oxygen double bond generates electrostatic attraction between the atoms, increasing the strength of the bond between them above that of the alkene carbon-carbon double bond as well. The strength of the carbon-oxygen double bond will become evident later on when you are introduced to reactions that generate carbonyl groups in ways that may, at first glance, seem rather surprising.

15-3. Preparation of Aldehydes and Ketones: A Review.

The number of methods that exist to synthesize carbonyl compounds is impressive to the point of being intimidating. Don't be put off, though, by the list at the beginning of this section. Each of the reactions will be presented in an appropriate, logical context. Having this listing available will help you origanize that material in terms of types of compounds that can be turned into ketones and aldehydes.

This section otherwise reiterates carbonyl syntheses that you've seen before, perhaps just with a few new examples to help reinforce those original presentations.

15-4.   The Reactivity of the Carbonyl Group: Mechanisms for Addition.

This chapter concentrates solely on one type of reaction: addition across the carbon-oxygen double bond of a carbonyl group. Except for catalytic hydrogenation, all the carbonyl additions are polar reactions that exactly follow pathways that would be expected by electrostatics:

$$\text{nucleophiles attach here} \rightarrow \underset{/}{\overset{\backslash}{C}}\!\!\!\overset{\delta^+}{=}\!\!\!\overset{\delta^-}{O} \leftarrow \text{electrophiles attach here}$$

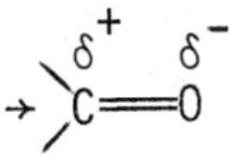

The two main mechanisms described in this section are distinguished by the order of addition: in the absence of strong electrophiles or acids, the nucleophile adds to carbon first, followed (usually) by protonation of oxygen (which may be a separate step). In the presence of protons or electrophiles, their initial attachment to oxygen activates the carbonyl group even further towards addition of a nucleophile. Whichever way the reaction proceeds in any given case, its scope is very broad, and many useful types of addition products are known. These are the subjects of the remaining sections of the chapter.

15-5 and 15-6.   Addition of Water, Alcohols, and Amines to Aldehydes and Ketones.

There are actually two fundamentally different types of reactions in these sections. The first is the reversible addition of a nucleophile to a carbonyl group, which can generally be catalyzed by either base or acid:

$$
(1)\quad
\underset{\text{aldehyde or ketone}}{R\overset{\overset{\displaystyle O}{\|}}{-}C-(H\ or\ R)}
\ +\ Nuc\text{-}H
\ \underset{\longleftarrow}{\overset{\text{base or acid}}{\rightleftharpoons}}\
\underset{\underset{\displaystyle Nuc}{|}}{R-\overset{\overset{\displaystyle OH}{|}}{C}-(H\ or\ R)}
$$

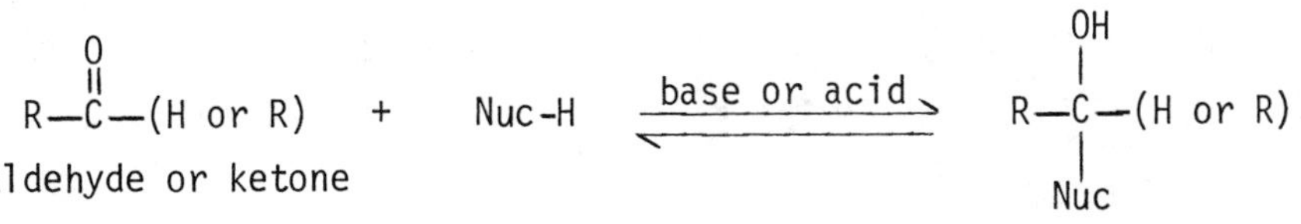

If Nuc-H is	Product is
H_2O	aldehyde or ketone hydrate
R'OH	hemiacetal or hemiketal
R'SH	hemithioacetal or hemithioketal
$R'NH_2$ or $R_2'NH$	hemiaminal

The second is really carbocation chemistry. The HO group of the product of the above reaction may be replaced by a second RO' or RS' in what is essentially an S_N1 process. Alternatively, the HO may be lost together with an

H from the nucleophile $R'NH_2$ giving an _imine_, containing a carbon-nitrogen double bond, or H from a neighboring carbon, giving an _enamine_, when the nucleophile is $R_2'NH$. These are essentially _E1 processes_. Since these reactions require conversion of HO into a leaving group and carbocation formation, they are catalyzed _only by acid_. They are reversible, but, again, they require acid to go in either direction:

$$(2) \quad R-\overset{\displaystyle OH}{\underset{\displaystyle (OR' \text{ or } SR')}{\overset{|}{\underset{|}{C}}}}-(H \text{ or } R) \; + \; \begin{pmatrix} R'OH \\ \text{or} \\ R'SH \end{pmatrix} \;\; \underset{\longleftarrow}{\overset{acid}{\longrightarrow}} \;\; R-\overset{\displaystyle (OR' \text{ or } SR')}{\underset{\displaystyle (OR' \text{ or } SR')}{\overset{|}{\underset{|}{C}}}}-(H \text{ or } R) \; + \; H_2O$$

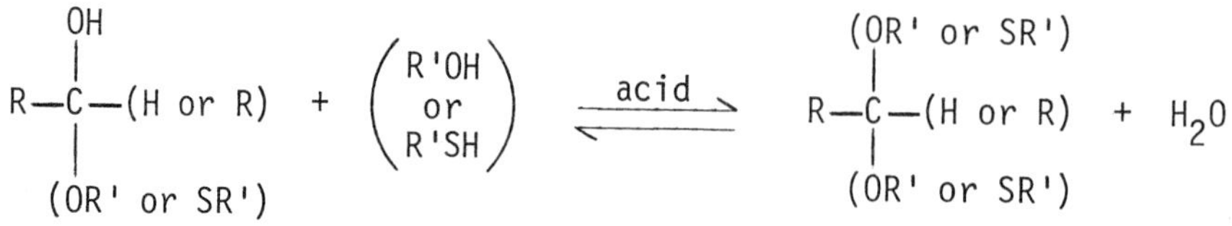

If R'OH: acetal or ketal

If R'SH: thioacetal or thioketal

$$(3) \quad R-\overset{\displaystyle OH}{\underset{\displaystyle NHR'}{\overset{|}{\underset{|}{C}}}}-(H \text{ or } R) \quad \underset{\longleftarrow}{\overset{acid}{\longrightarrow}} \quad R-\overset{}{\underset{\displaystyle NR'}{\overset{\|}{C}}}-(H \text{ or } R) \; + \; H_2O$$

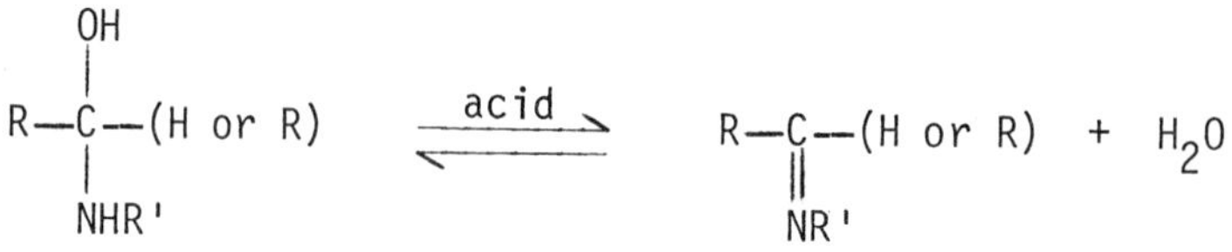

aldimine or ketimine

$$(4) \quad -\overset{\displaystyle H}{\overset{|}{C}}-\overset{\displaystyle OH}{\underset{\displaystyle NR_2'}{\overset{|}{\underset{|}{C}}}}-(H \text{ or } R) \quad \underset{\longleftarrow}{\overset{acid}{\longrightarrow}} \quad {\Large \succ}C{=}C{\Large \underset{NR_2'}{\overset{(H \text{ or } R)}{\prec}}} \; + \; H_2O$$

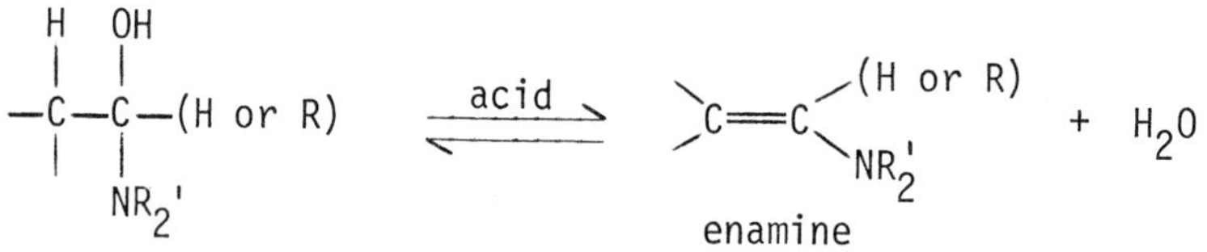

enamine

For all practical purposes, acid-catalyzed reaction of an aldehyde or a ketone with any of the nucleophiles listed in reaction 1 will continue straight through to the product of reaction 2, 3, or 4, as the case may be. Conversely, acid catalyzed hydrolysis of any of the latter products will proceed back all the way to the original aldehyde or ketone, and the free nucleophile..

15-7. <u>Addition of Carbon Nucleophiles to Aldehydes and Ketones.</u>

Grignard reagents and alkyllithiums are examples of highly reactive "carbanionic" reagents (i.e., they behave like carbanions). In this section less highly energetic carbanionic reagents are introduced. Cyanide ion is the simplest, and the products of its addition to aldehydes and ketones, cyanohydrins, have some limited synthetic utility. Ylide reagents containing phosphorus and sulfur are much more useful. The phosphorus ylide, in particular,

$$RCH{=}P(C_6H_5)_3 \qquad\qquad\qquad CH_2{=}S(CH_3)_2$$

typical phosphorus ylide   most common sulfur ylide

is of great importance in the regiospecific synthesis of alkenes, since the double bond is fixed in a single position determined entirely by the starting compounds in the reaction:

$$RCH{=}P(C_6H_5)_3 \;+\; O{=}C\!\begin{matrix} R' \\ R'' \end{matrix} \longrightarrow \underset{\substack{\text{exclusively} \\ \text{(E and Z)}}}{RCH{=}CR'R''} \;+\; (C_6H_5)_3P{=}O$$

15-8. Special Oxidations and Reductions of Aldehydes and Ketones.

Much of the material in this section is fairly routine. The ability of aldehydes to be easily oxidized to carboxylic acids forms the basis for a simple test for the presence of the aldehyde group using metal ions as oxidizing agents. Reductions of ketones and aldehydes to alcohols using hydride or hydrogen addition are also reactions that present no new mechanistic ideas. They simply give the chemist added flexibility in functional group interconversion.

Baeyer-Villiger oxidation of ketones and aldehydes to carboxylic esters or acids is more significant for two reasons. Mechanistically, it involves a nucleophilic addition to a carbonyl group, which is no big deal. The nucleophile, however, is a peroxidic species, which can lead to rearrangement, forming a new oxygen-carbon bond:

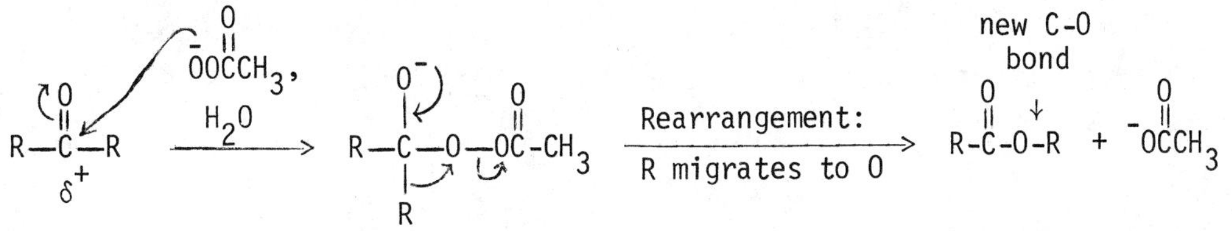

You might recall a somewhat related mechanistic rearrangement, the migration of a group from boron to oxygen during the oxidation of alkylboranes with basic hydrogen peroxide:

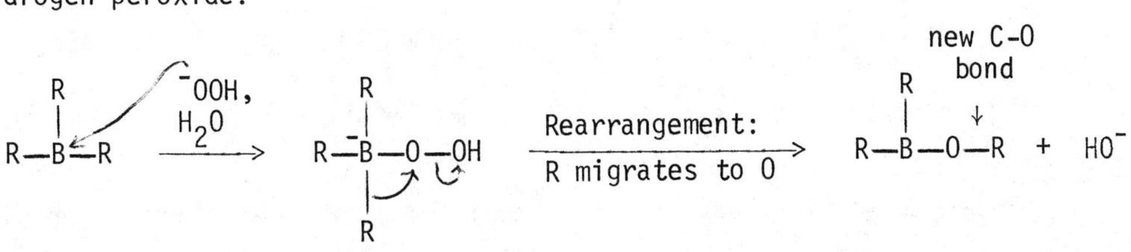

The second reason the Baeyer-Villiger reaction is significant is that it completely cleaves a carbon-carbon bond. You have seen only a very small

number of reactions capable of this (e.g. ozonolysis, Chapter 12). The power
of this method to be a synthetic tool lies both in its high selectivity when
the carbonyl compound is not symmetrical (see discussion of Migratory Aptitudes)
and in the subsequent chemistry available from the ester or acid, which will be
covered shortly.

Reductive coupling of carbonyl compounds has some use in synthesis,
mostly limited to the preparation of symmetrical diols or alkenes by coupling
two identical molecules, or ring formation by coupling two ends of a difunctional system.

Solutions to Chapter 15 Problems

1. (a) 2,4-dimethyl-3-pentanone;   (b) 4-methylpentanal;

   (c) 3-buten-2-one;   (d) *trans*-4-chloro-3-butenal;

   (e) 4-bromo-2-cyclopentenone;   (f) *cis*-1,2-dipropanoylcyclohexane

   (g)   (h)

****

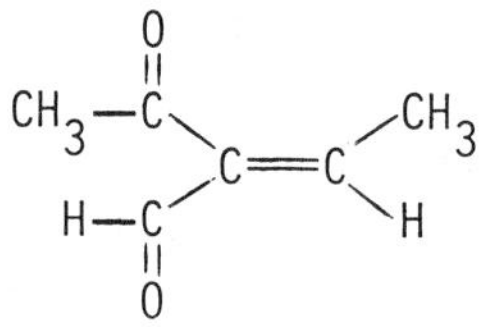

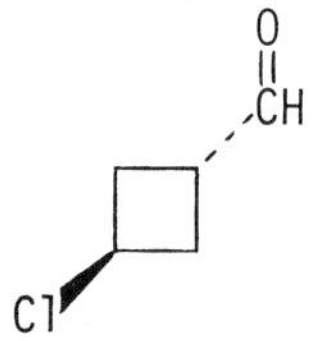

2. See Chapter 11 of the Study Guide for information concerning degrees of
    unsaturation. For $C_8H_{12}O$, $H_{sat'd}$ = 16 + 2 = 18; deg. unsat'n. = $\frac{18-12}{2}$ =
    3 π bonds and/or rings present.

    (a) C-13: molecule contains $\rangle C=O$ (δ198.6) and $\rangle C=C\langle$ (δ139.8 and 140.7).
         H-1: obvious features include δ2.15 (s, 3H), for $CH_3\overset{O}{\overset{\|}{C}}-$, and δ6.78
         (t, 1H), for $\rangle C=C\langle^{CH_2-}_{H}$. Note the absence of any other alkene
         hydrogens. So we can start with these pieces:

         $CH_3-\overset{O}{\overset{\|}{C}}-$ and $\rangle C=C\langle^{CH_2-}_{H}$, adding up to C_5H_6O.

         Still needed are three more C's, six more H's, and another degree of
         unsaturation, which will have to be a ring. A simple way to put
         together a trial structure would be to finish a six-membered ring with
         three CH_2 groups, and then attach the ethanoyl group:
         This is not the only possible answer, but it is the
         actual molecule that gives the indicated spectra.

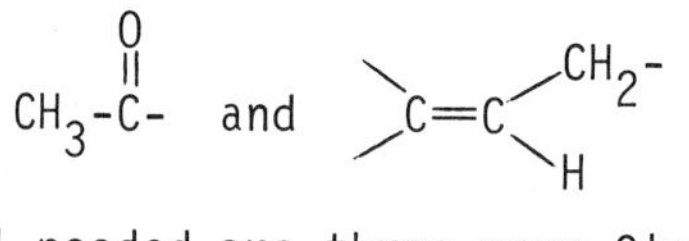

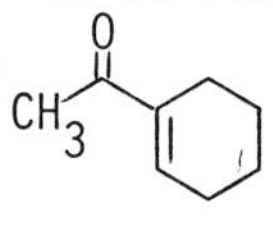

(b) C-13 NMR: one C=O (δ193.2) and <u>two</u> C=C groups (δ129.0, 135.2, 146.7, and 152.5) this time.

H-1 NMR: the carbonyl group is an <u>aldehyde</u> (δ9.56 for $-\overset{O}{\overset{\|}{C}}-H$). At the other end, we have CH_3——CH_2——CH_2—. This adds up to C_4H_8O,

↑ δ0.94 ↑ δ1.48 ↑ δ2.21

leaving C_4H_4 to account for. All four of these H's are alkene hydrogens (δ5.8-7.1), so these could most simply be two -CH=CH- groups.

The result: $CH_3CH_2CH_2CH{=}CHCH{=}CH\overset{O}{\overset{\|}{C}}H$.

****

3. Each is a conjugated carbonyl compound, giving an intense UV absorption with λ_{max} > 200 nm. The first spectrum matches

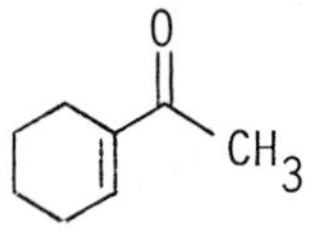

, with $\pi \rightarrow \pi^*$ absorption at 232 nm, and carbonyl $n \rightarrow \pi^*$ absorption at 308 nm. The second spectrum matches the diene-aldehyde, with the longer wavelength 272 nm band corresponding to the $\pi \rightarrow \pi^*$ absorption of the more extended conjugated system.

****

4. (a) CrO_3, H_2SO_4, propanone; (b) CrO_3, pyridine; (c) 1. O_3, 2. Zn, CH_3COOH, H_2O; (d) $HgSO_4$, H_2O, H_2SO_4; (e) same as (d).

****

5. (a) Ketone hydrates do <u>not</u> contain the $H-\overset{|}{\underset{|}{C}}-OH$ unit which is required for further oxidation to readily occur. Oxidation beyond the ketone stage would require cleavage of a carbon-carbon bond, a more difficult process.

(b) Think about it: if CrO_3 is added to an alcohol, what will be present in the mixture? There will be some aldehyde formed from oxidation, in the presence of an excess of <u>unreacted alcohol</u>. What reaction occurs between aldehydes and alcohols?

$$RCH_2OH + R\overset{O}{\overset{\|}{C}}H \rightleftharpoons RCH_2O-\underset{H}{\underset{|}{\overset{OH}{\overset{|}{C}}}}-R \quad \text{hemiacetal formation}$$

Suppose CrO_3 were to react with the hemiacetal; what would you expect to get? Does the hemiacetal have an oxidizable unit? Yes:

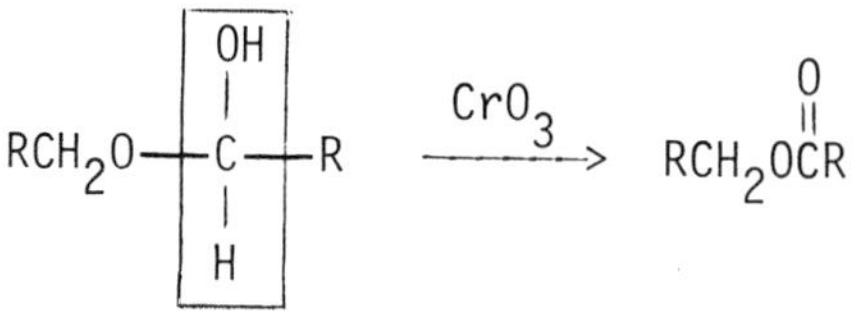

$$RCH_2O-\underset{\underset{H}{|}}{\overset{\overset{OH}{|}}{C}}-R \xrightarrow{CrO_3} RCH_2O\overset{\overset{O}{||}}{C}R \quad \text{an ester forms.}$$

****

6. (a) $CH_3CH_2CH_2\overset{\overset{O}{||}}{C}H + H\overset{\overset{O}{||}}{C}H$;   (b) $2 \langle\ \rangle{=}O$ (c) $H\overset{\overset{O}{||}}{C}CH_2CH_2CH_2CH_2\overset{\overset{O}{||}}{C}H$;

(d)

****

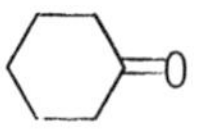

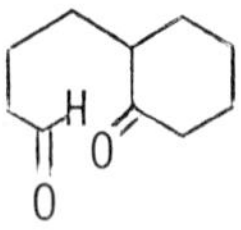

7. (a) Ask "how electrophilic is the carbon in question":

$(CH_3)_2C{=}\overset{+}{O}H > (CH_3)_2C{=}O > (CH_3)_2C{=}NH$ (order of ketone and imine
determined by electronegativity).

(b) All ketones, so what other differences are there? Strain, and steric
effects:

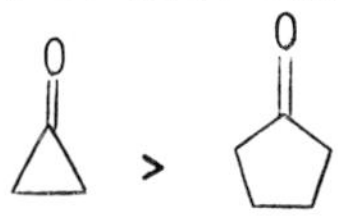

$\triangle{=}O > \langle\ \rangle{=}O > CH_3CH_2\overset{\overset{O}{||}}{C}CH_2CH_3$. Cyclopropanone wants to

reduce strain by getting rid of the sp^2 ring carbon. Otherwise,
cyclic ketones have somewhat less steric hindrance than acyclic; the
latter have more conformations that hinder approach to the carbonyl
carbon.

(c) $CH_3\overset{\overset{O}{||}}{C}\overset{\overset{O}{||}}{C}\overset{\overset{O}{||}}{C}CH_3 > CH_3\overset{\overset{O}{||}}{C}\overset{\overset{O}{||}}{C}CH_3 > CH_3\overset{\overset{O}{||}}{C}CH_3$ Adjacent carbonyl groups
enhance each other's reactivity by reinforcing the δ^+ character as
electron-withdrawing groups.

****

8. 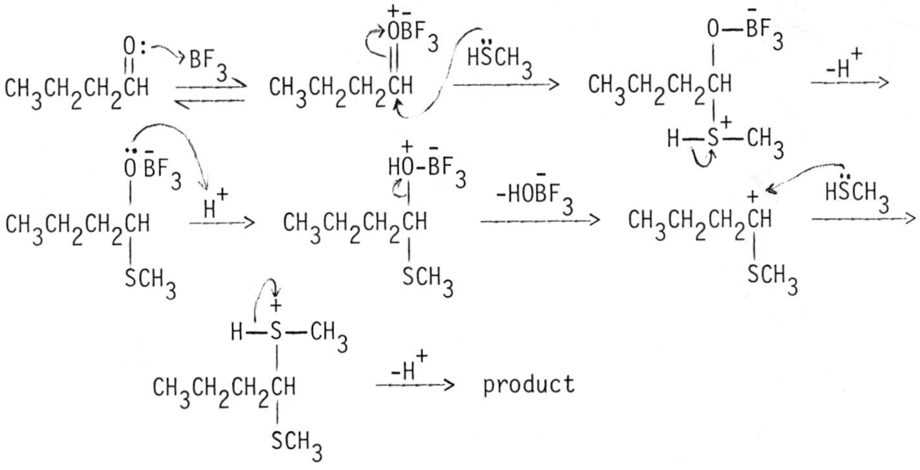

****

9. sorbose $\xrightarrow{H^+,\ 2\ CH_3\overset{O}{\overset{\|}{C}}CH_3}$ "polyether B" in Exercise 15-8 (contains only a single free hydroxy group that can be oxidized)

$\xrightarrow[\text{2. } H^+,\ H_2O]{\text{1. } KMnO_4,\ H_2O}$ product ($KMnO_4$ is useful as a non-acidic oxidizing agent for the primary alcohol → acid conversion)

****

10. (a) no reaction except for equilibration with 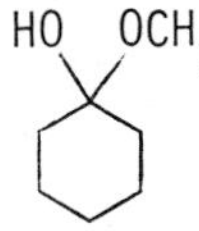 ; (b) 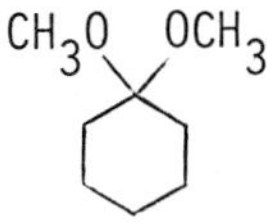 (only acid catalyzes acetal formation);

(c) 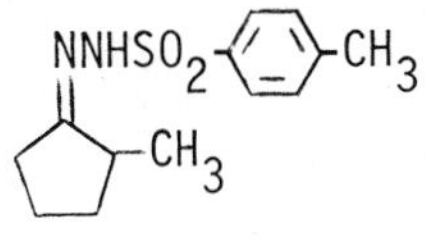 ; (d) 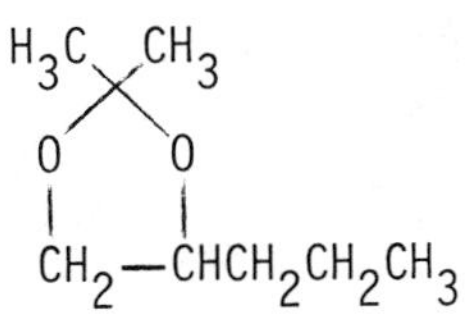 ; (e) 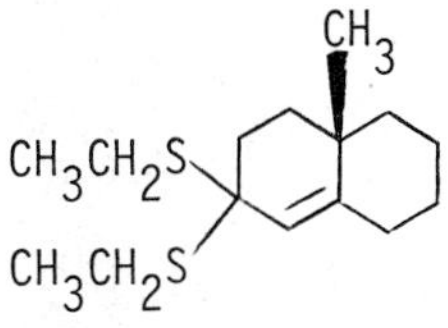 ;

(f) 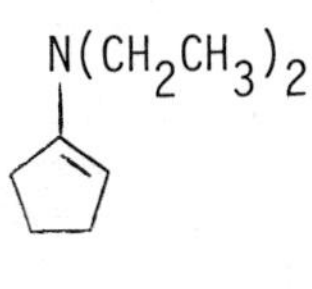 ; (g) 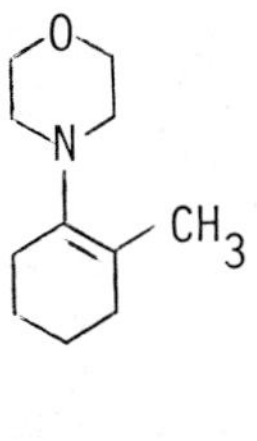

****

11. Two isomers about the CN double bond are possible in ethanal oxime:

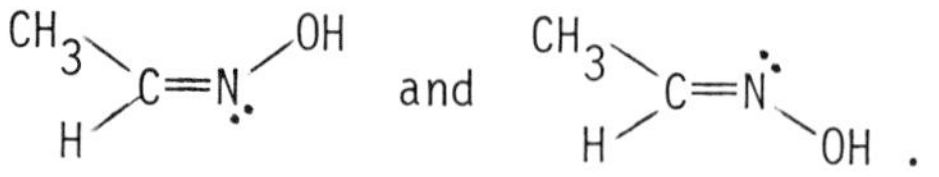

Propanone oxime has equivalent groups on carbon, so no isomerism is possible:

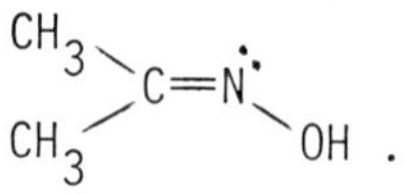

****

12. Below pH 2 the N in NH_2OH is protonated ($\overset{+}{N}H_3OH$), so the nucleophilic atom is effectively gone. At pH 4 the N is mostly free, but the solution is still acidic enough for some carbonyl groups to be made more electrophilic by protonation: $>C{=}\overset{+}{O}H$. Above pH 7, no carbonyl groups are protonated, so the rate is reduced to that of free NH_2OH attacking unactivated $>C{=}O$ groups.

****

13.

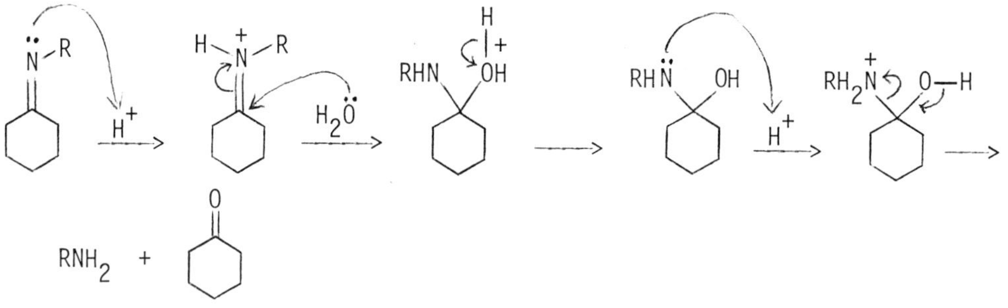

****

14. (a)

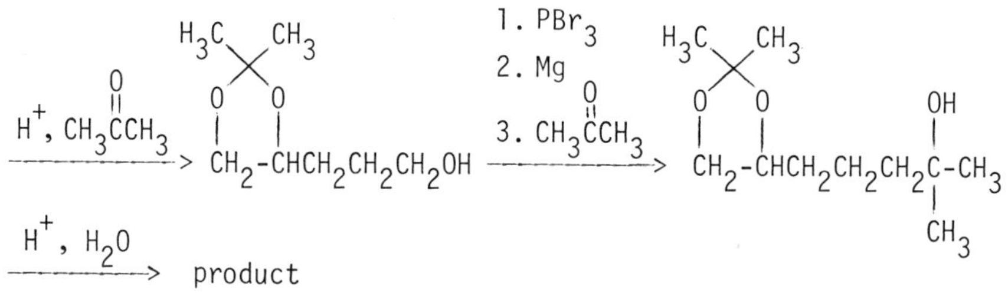

(b) $\xrightarrow{CrO_3}$ 3-pentanone $\xrightarrow{H^+,\ C_6H_5NH_2}$ product

(c) $\xrightarrow{2\ CrO_3,\ pyridine}$ 1,5-pentanedial $\xrightarrow{H_2O}$ product, via

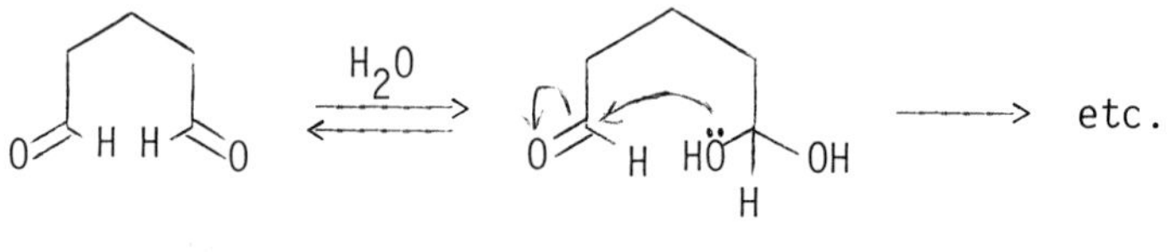

(d) $\xrightarrow[\text{OH}]{\text{H}^+, \text{HOCH}_2\text{CH}_2\text{OH}}$ [spiro acetal with vinyl cyclohexane] $\xrightarrow[\text{2. ICl}]{\text{1. BH}_3}$ [spiro acetal with CH₂CH₂I] $\xrightarrow[\text{2. CH}_3\text{CH}]{\text{1. Mg, O}}$

[spiro acetal with CH₂CH₂CH(OH)CH₃] $\xrightarrow{\text{H}^+, \text{H}_2\text{O}}$ product

(e) $\xrightarrow{\text{Br}_2, h\nu}$ [bromocyclopentane, Br] $\xrightarrow[\begin{array}{l}\text{1. K}^+\ ^-\text{OCCH}_3\\\text{2. HO}^-, \text{H}_2\text{O}\\\text{3. CrO}_3\end{array}]{}$ [cyclopentanone, O] $\xrightarrow{\text{HCN, KCN}}$ [cyanohydrin, HO CN] $\xrightarrow{\text{H}^+, \text{H}_2\text{O}, \Delta}$ product

****

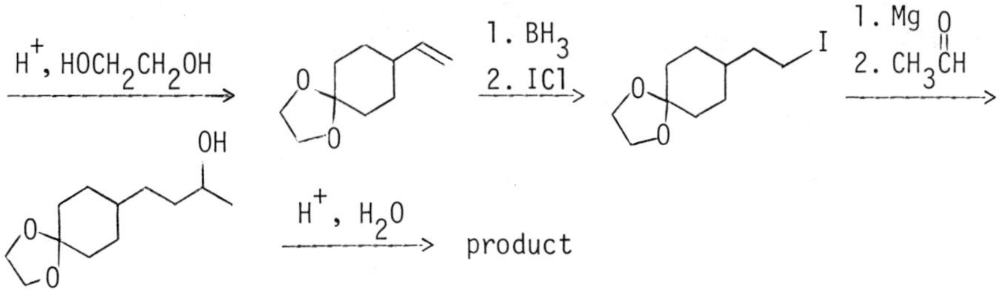

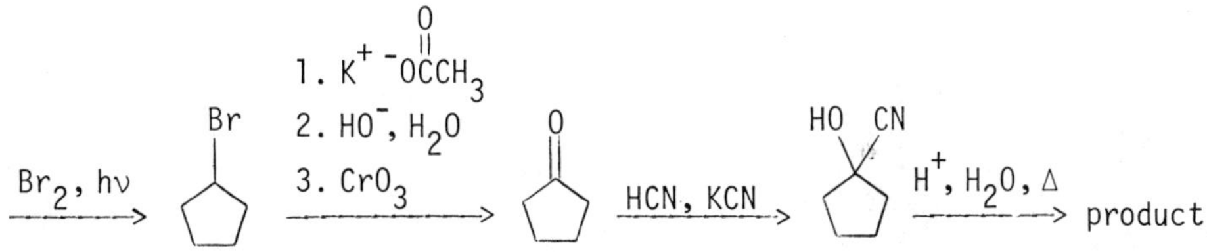

15. Extended conjugation would be expected to shift the absorptions of these hydrazones to longer wavelength, just as it does with the parent ketones. So:

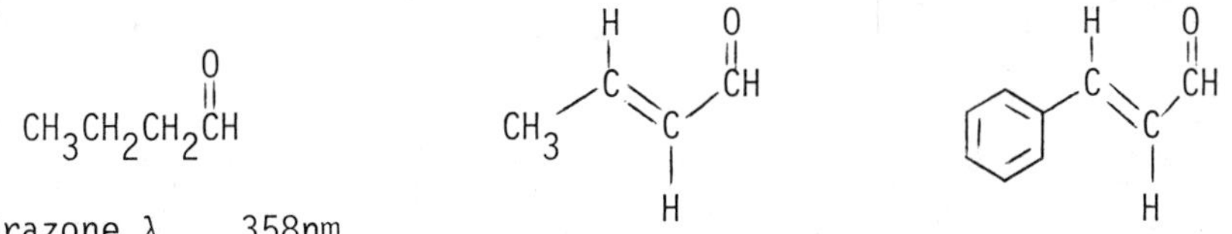

$$\text{CH}_3\text{CH}_2\text{CH}_2\overset{\overset{\text{O}}{\|}}{\text{C}}\text{H}$$

hydrazone λ_{max} 358nm

(yellow)

Bottle 2

[CH₃–C(H)=C(H)–CHO structure]

hydrazone λ_{max} 377nm

(orange)

Bottle 1

[phenyl–C(H)=C(H)–CHO structure]

hydrazone λ_{max} 394nm

(red)

Bottle 3

****

16. (a) H_2NNH_2, H_2O, HO^-, Δ (Wolff-Kishner reduction on both ketones)

(b) H_2, Pd-C (selective reduction of alkene)

(c) LiAlH_4 (selective reduction of aldehyde)

(d) H^+, cycloheptanone (formation of an unusual acetal, nothing more)

****

17. Use the hint: first make an imine, and then follow your nose.

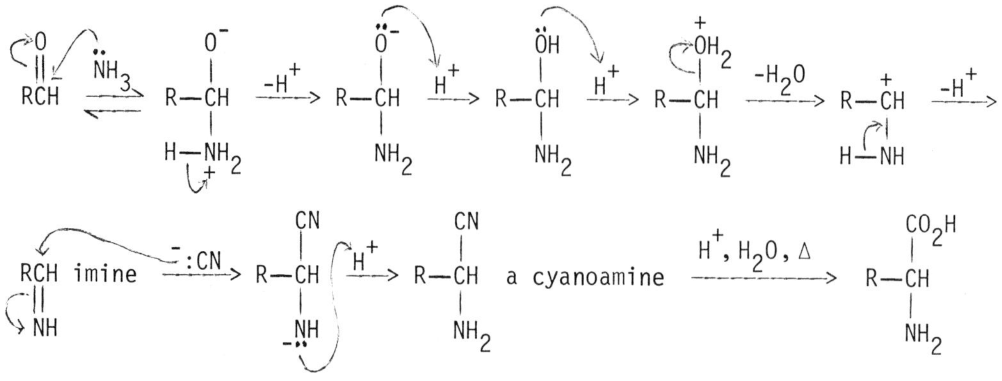

****

18. (a) $CH_3CH_2C(CH_3)=CH_2 \xrightarrow[(1)]{MCPBA}$ product $\xleftarrow[(2)]{(CH_3)_2S=CH_2} CH_3CH_2\overset{O}{\overset{\|}{C}}CH_3$

(b) $CH_3\overset{O}{\overset{\|}{C}}H + (C_6H_5)_3P{=}CHCH_2CH(CH_3)_2 \xrightarrow{(1)}$ product $\xleftarrow{(2)} CH_3CH{=}P(C_6H_5)_3 + H\overset{O}{\overset{\|}{C}}CH_2CH(CH_3)_2$

(c) 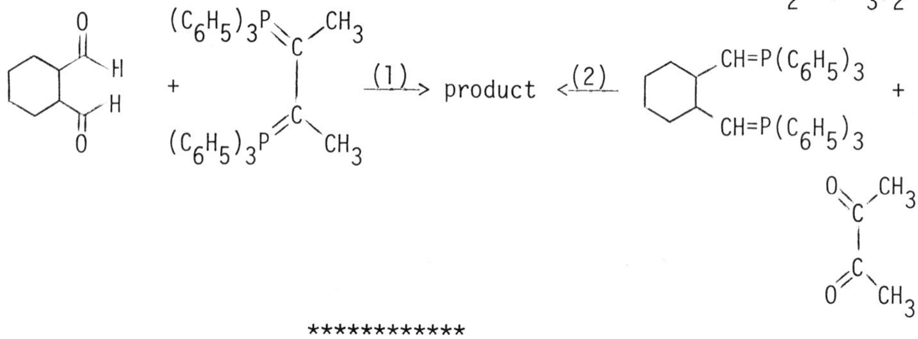

****

19. There are only three possible compounds to begin with: pentanal, 2-pentanone, and 3-pentanone. So this is really a matching problem:

$CH_3CH_2CH_2CH_2\overset{O}{\overset{\|}{C}}H \xrightarrow{\text{Baeyer-Villiger}} CH_3CH_2CH_2CH_2\overset{O}{\overset{\|}{C}}OH$ (1 product); also, aldehydes give positive Fehling's tests; pentanal must be 'C'.

$CH_3CH_2CH_2\overset{O}{\overset{\|}{C}}CH_3 \xrightarrow{\text{B.-V.}} CH_3CH_2CH_2O\overset{O}{\overset{\|}{C}}CH_3 + CH_3CH_2CH_2\overset{O}{\overset{\|}{C}}OCH_3$ (2 products); 2-pentanone must be 'B'.

$$CH_3CH_2\overset{O}{\overset{||}{C}}CH_2CH_3 \xrightarrow{\text{B.-V.}} CH_3CH_2O\overset{O}{\overset{||}{C}}CH_2CH_3 \text{ (only product due to symmetry in}$$

starting material); 3-pentanone must be 'A'.

****

20. Work backwards from given structural information.

$$CH_3\overset{O}{\overset{||}{C}}CH_2CH_2CH_2\overset{CH_3}{\overset{|}{C}H}-\overset{O}{\overset{||}{C}}OH \xleftarrow{Cr^{6+},\ H_2O} CH_3\overset{O}{\overset{||}{C}}CH_2CH_2CH_2\overset{CH_3}{\overset{|}{C}H}-\overset{O}{\overset{||}{C}}H \xleftarrow[\text{2. Zn}]{\text{1. O}_3}$$

keto-aldehyde

$$\xleftarrow{H_2SO_4,\ \Delta} \quad F \text{ and } G \xleftarrow{LiAlH_4} D \xrightarrow{CH_2P(C_6H_5)_3} E$$

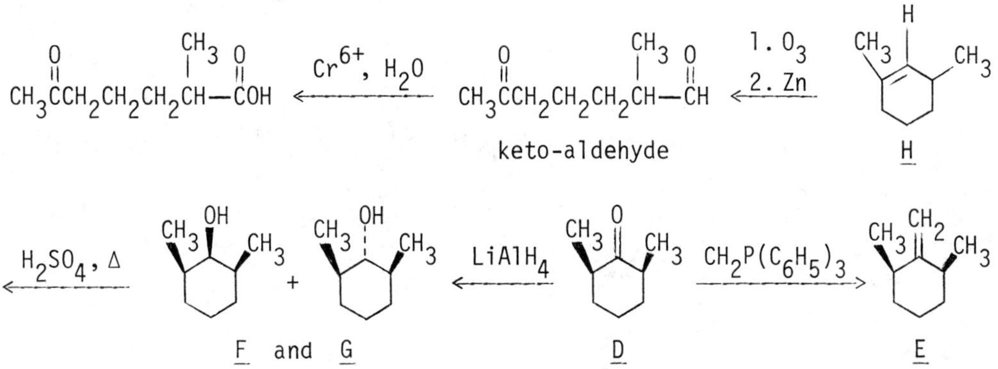

Note: F and G must be *secondary* alcohols because they have been formed by LiAlH$_4$ reduction of something (here, a ketone). The methyls in D must be *cis*. If they were *trans*, only one LiAlH$_4$ reduction product would be obtained.

****

21. (a) $CH_3CH_2CH_2CH_2CH_2\overset{}{CH}$; (b) 1-hexanol; (c) $CH_3CH_2CH_2CH_2CH_2CH=NOH$;

(d) hexane; (e) $CH_3CH_2CH_2CH_2CH_2CH=CHCH_2CH(CH_3)_2$ (*E* and *Z*); (f) hexanoic

acid; (g) $CH_3CH_2CH_2CH_2CH=CH-N$; (h) $CH_3CH_2CH_2CH_2CH_2\overset{O}{\overset{\diagup\diagdown}{CH-CH_2}}$;

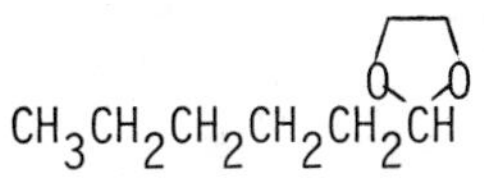

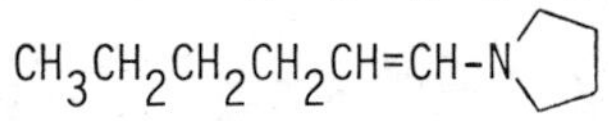

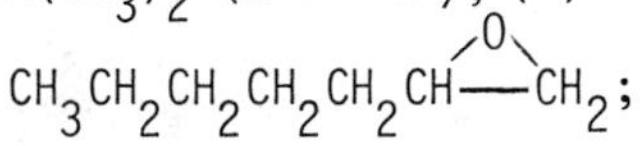

(i) hexanoic acid + Ag metal; (j) hexanoic acid; (k) 2-hydroxyheptanoic

acid (via $R\overset{O}{\overset{||}{C}}H \rightarrow R\overset{OH}{\overset{|}{C}}HCN \rightarrow R\overset{OH}{\overset{|}{C}}H-\overset{O}{\overset{||}{C}}OH$); (l) $CH_3CH_2CH_2CH_2CH_2\overset{OH}{\overset{|}{C}}H-\overset{OH}{\overset{|}{C}}HCH_2CH_2CH_2CH_2CH_3$

(pinacol reaction)

****

22. (a) ; (b) cycloheptanol; (c) ; (d) cycloheptane;

(e) $=CHCH_2CH(CH_3)_2$; (f) ; (g) ; (h)

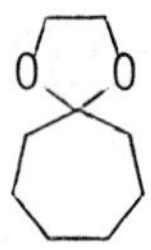

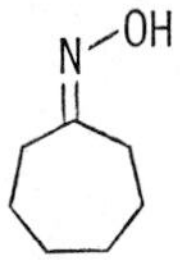

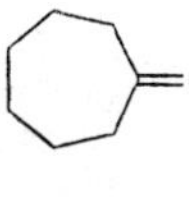

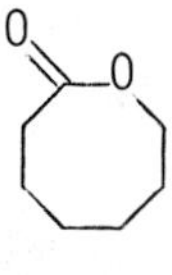

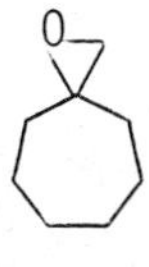

(i) and (j) no reaction (these are reactions of aldehydes only);

(k) 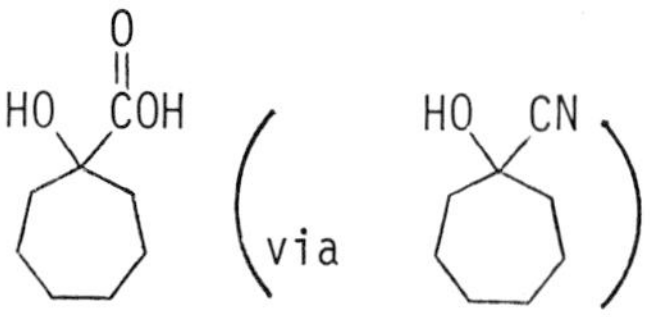

; (l) 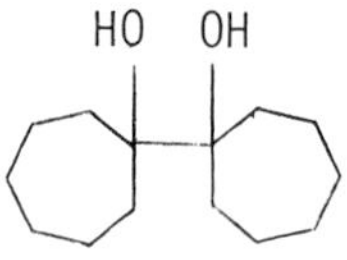

(pinacol reaction)

****

23\. (a) The starting material is $CH_3\overset{CH_3}{\overset{|}{C}}=CH-\overset{CH_3}{\overset{|}{C}H}-CH_3$. Working backwards gives an easy final step via titanium coupling:

$$
\underset{(CH_3)_2CH}{\overset{(CH_3)_2CH}{}}C{=}C\underset{CH(CH_3)_2}{\overset{CH(CH_3)_2}{}} \xleftarrow{\quad TiCl_3, \ Li \quad} 2 \quad \underset{(CH_3)_2CH}{\overset{(CH_3)_2CH}{}}C{=}O
$$

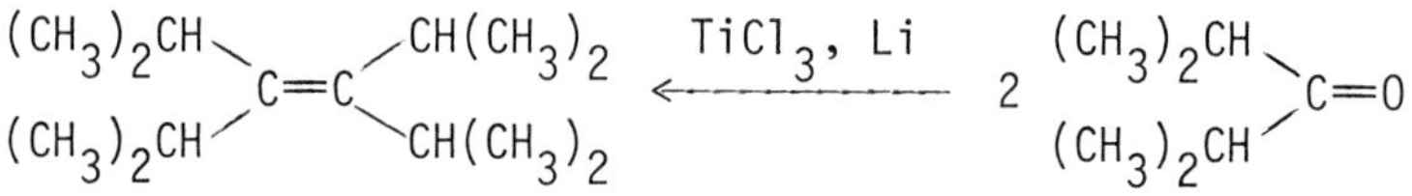

The ketone may be prepared from the alkene by anti-Markovnikov functionalization of the double bond, e.g. 1. BH_3, 2. H_2O_2, HO^-, and 3. CrO_3, H_2SO_4.

(b) Aldehydes are available from hydroboration-oxidation of terminal alkynes, so:

$CH_3CH_2CH_2Cl$ + $LiC{\equiv}CH$ (from $HC{\equiv}CH$ + $LiNH_2$) → $CH_3CH_2CH_2C{\equiv}CH$

$$\xrightarrow[\text{2. } H_2O_2,\ HO^-]{\text{1. } BH_3} CH_3CH_2CH_2CH_2\overset{O}{\overset{\|}{C}}H$$

(c) This will require some kind of coupling reaction. Think of the kinds that are available to you, and how dienes might be available from them:

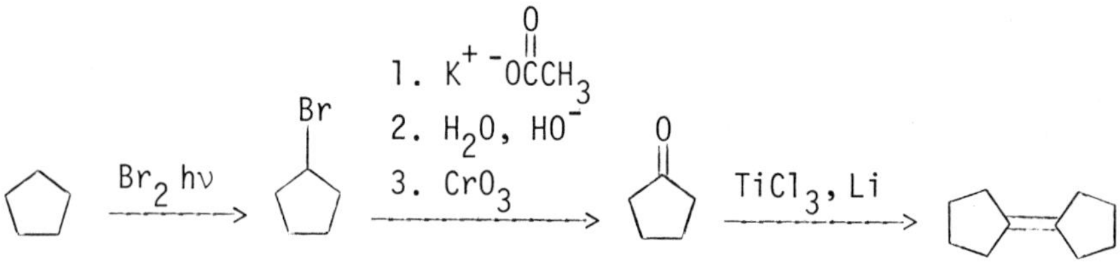

Now what?

How about adding halogen and eliminating twice? Alkyne formation is impossible, so a diene should form:

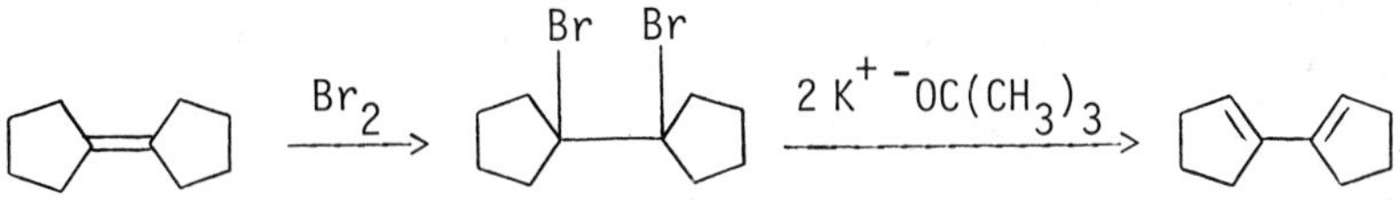

Something else to think about: would the sequence below work?

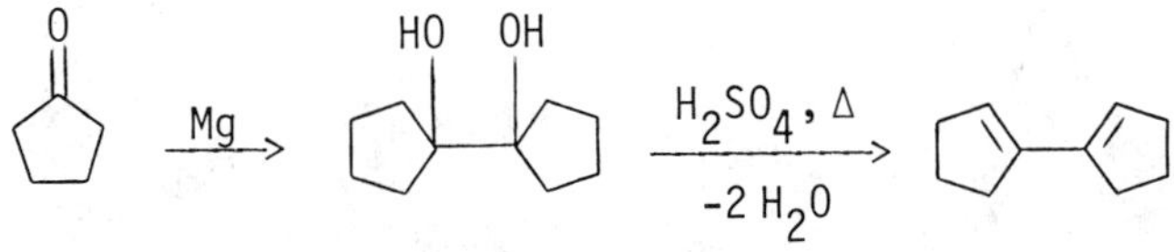

Hint: review Section 9-2.

(d) 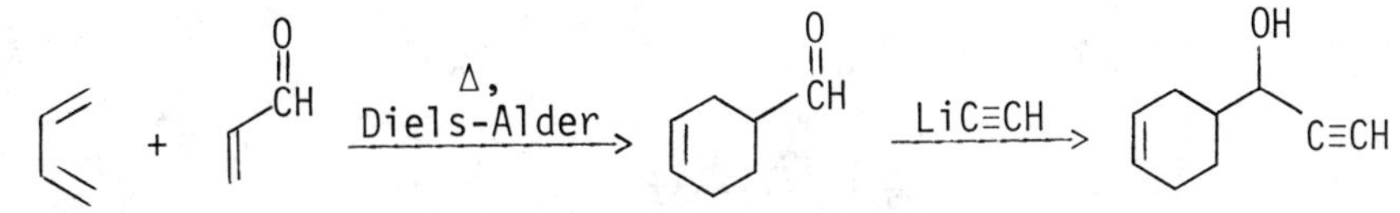

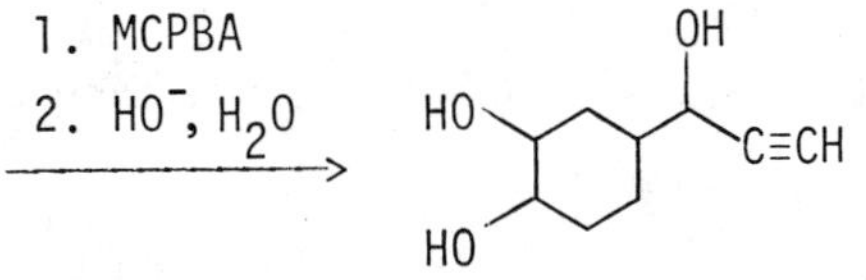

Alkenes react faster than alkynes with MCPBA.

If you chose to make the diol by reaction of the alkene with $KMnO_4$ or OsO_4, it would have to be done (1) before introducing the alkyne and (2) with the aldehyde protected as an acetal (aldehydes and alkynes both react with these reagents).

****

24. 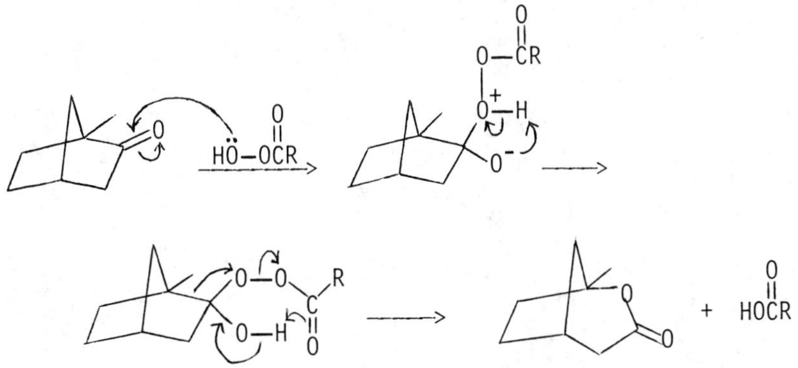

****

25. In each case insert '0' on either side of the carbonyl C. Then refer to the information on Migratory Aptitudes in Section 15-8 to help you choose the preferred product. In the answers below, the <u>first</u> structure is the preferred one.

(a) 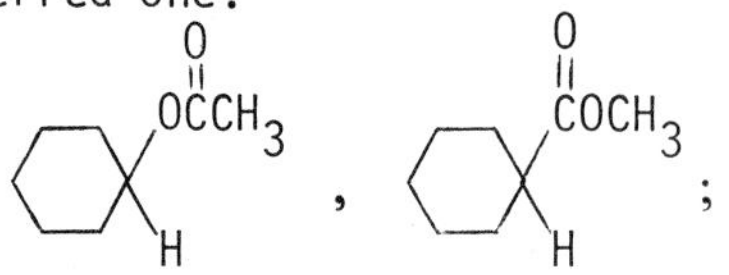 ; (b) 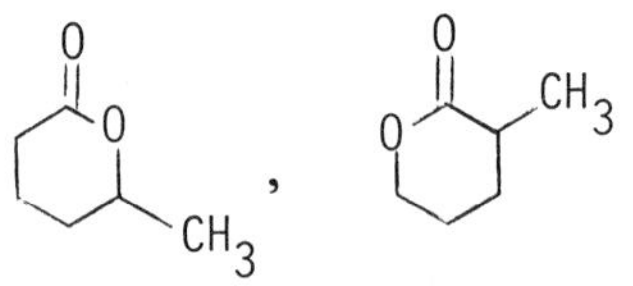

(c) $(CH_3)_2CHOCCH_2CH(CH_3)_2$, $(CH_3)_2CHCOCH_2CH(CH_3)_2$; (with C=O on the carbonyl carbon in each)

(d) 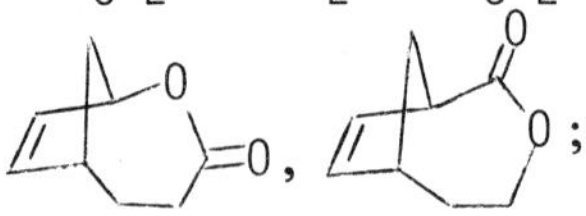 ;

(e) C_6H_5COH, C_6H_5OCH ; (with C=O on the carbonyl carbon in each)

(f) $C_6H_5OCCH_3$, $C_6H_5COCH_3$ (with C=O on the carbonyl carbon in each)

****

26. (a) Approach: will need a reaction between CH_3MgI and a ketone carbonyl, so the aldehyde will have to be protected.

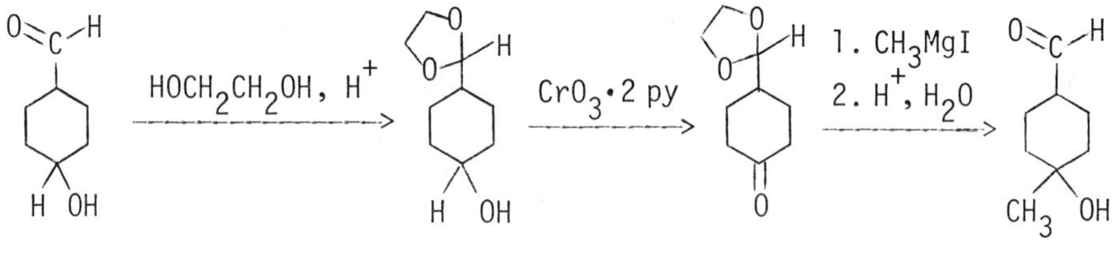

(b) Careful! Better protect the aldehyde again, or it will die when you apply any of several methods to get rid of the alcohol. Here's one:

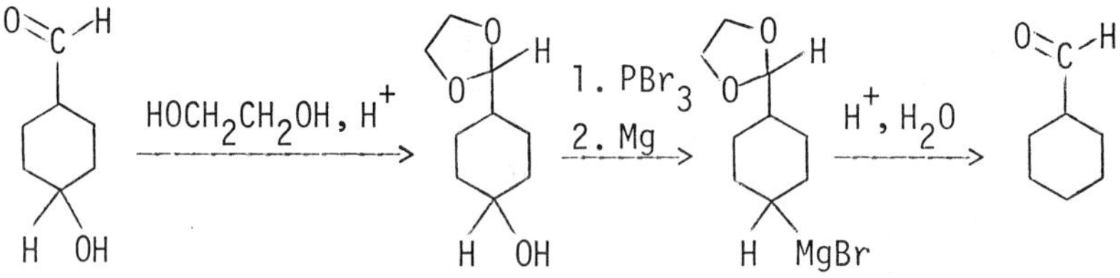

Now go to work on the rest: 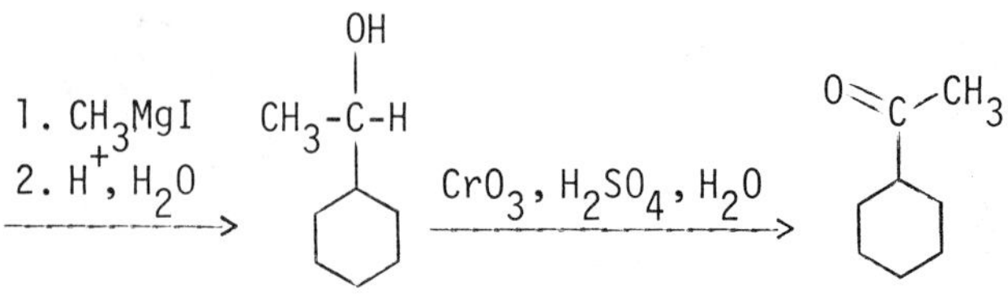

Oxidation of the alcohol to a ketone, followed by Wolff-Kishner reduction works as well.

(c) The "target" molecule is a hemiacetal. Rewrite it in "open" form (that is, its acyclic isomer):

Synthesis of the open form will automatically result in formation of the desired product. So, with care in protecting the alcohol,

$$ClCH_2CH_2CH_2OH \xrightarrow{H^+, CH_2=C(CH_3)_2} ClCH_2CH_2CH_2OC(CH_3)_3 \xrightarrow[\text{2. } CH_3CHO]{\text{1. Mg}}$$

$$\underset{\underset{CH_3CHCH_2CH_2CH_2OC(CH_3)_3}{|}}{OH} \xrightarrow{CrO_3, \text{ pyridine}} CH_3\overset{O}{\overset{||}{C}}CH_2CH_2CH_2OC(CH_3)_3$$

$$\xrightarrow{H^+, H_2O} CH_3\overset{O}{\overset{||}{C}}CH_2CH_2CH_2OH \xrightleftharpoons{} \text{product}$$

****

27. The conclusions that may be reached from each piece of information are given to you.

(i) Coprostanol is an alcohol, and J is a ketone.

(ii)

H₂, Pt
should add
from bottom
(less hindered)

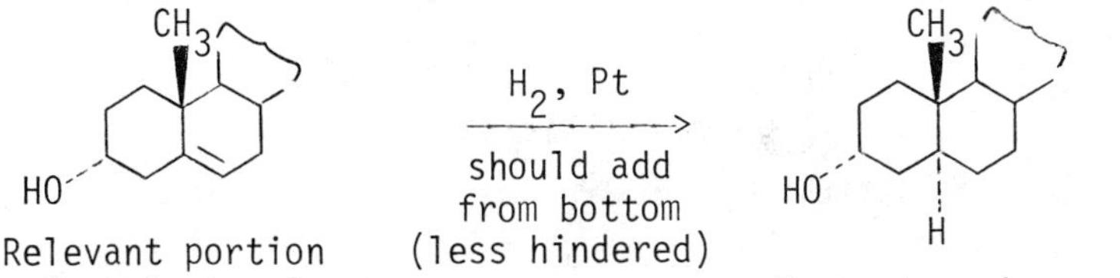

Relevant portion
of cholesterol

K, a stereoisomer
of coprostanol

Jones

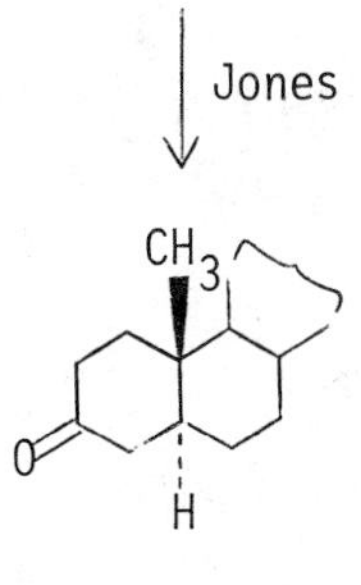

It appears likely, then,

that J is

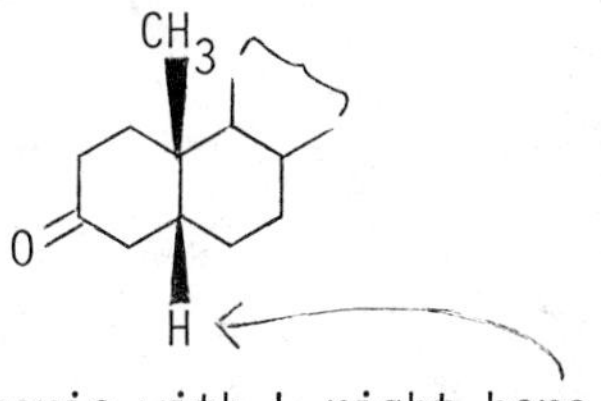

stereoisomeric with L right here.

L, a stereoisomer of J

(iii)   cholesterol $\xrightarrow{\text{Jones}}$

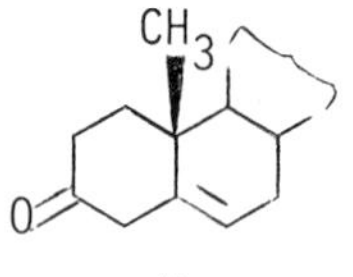

$\xrightarrow{\text{H}_2,\ \text{Pt}}$ L   again

M

This is what you would expect, based on the information in (ii). So, what's coprostanol? Since it gives J on oxidation with Jones reagent, it must be one of the two alcohols,

or   ,

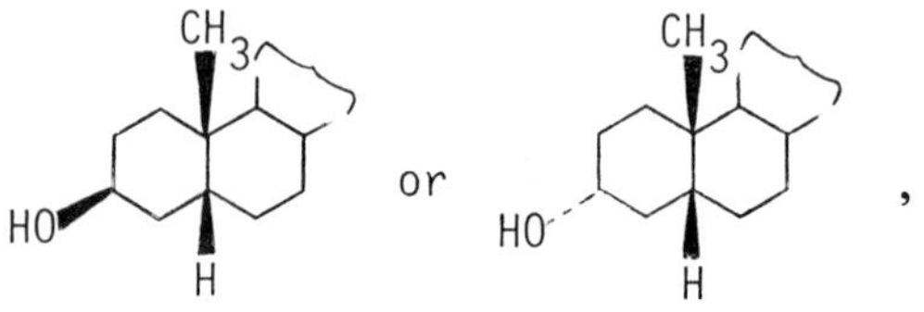

In fact, both are known, and are labeled 3β- and 3α-coprostanol, respectively.

****

28. (a)   The UV indicates a <u>conjugated</u> ketone (compare UV of 3-buten-2-one in Section 15-2, and Exercise 15-3). So N would appear to result from

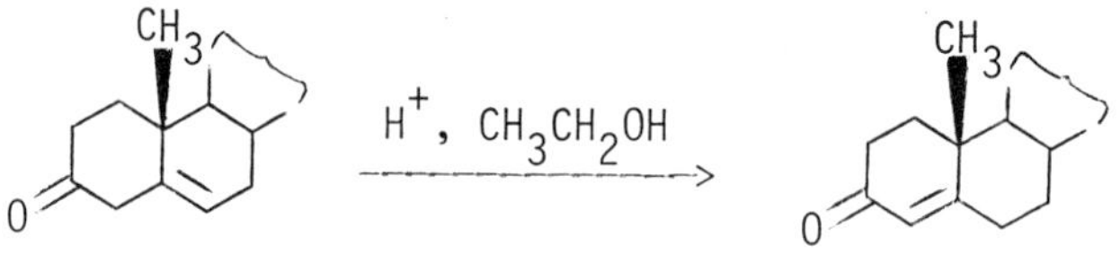

$\xrightarrow{\text{H}^+,\ \text{CH}_3\text{CH}_2\text{OH}}$

M   N

(b)   N $\xrightarrow{\text{H}_2,\ \text{Pd}}$

This is indeed odd, as the H_2 adds from the <u>more</u> hindered top face in this particular case.

J

(c)   The hydrazone forms in the usual way (Section 15-6). Then:

****

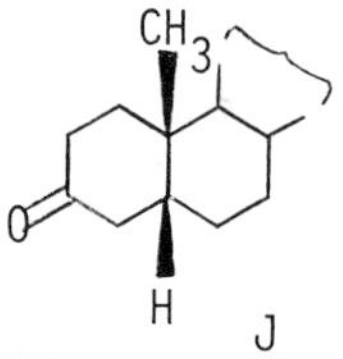

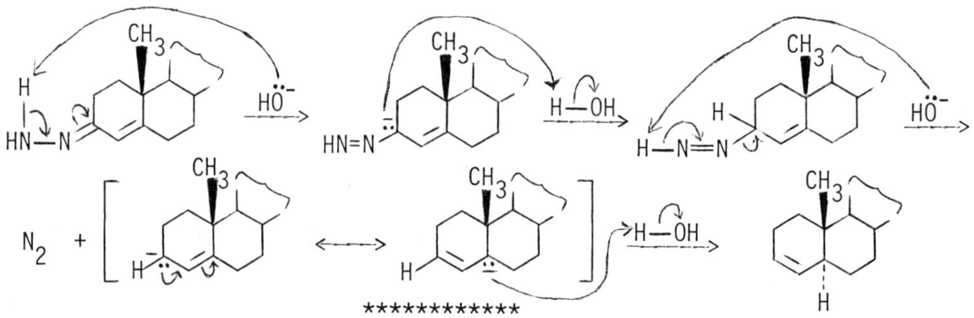

29.

2 HOCH$_2$CH$_2$OH, H$^+$
→
Protect ketones

1. LiAlH$_4$
2. CrO$_3$·2 py
→
Make aldehyde

OCH$_3$

—CH=P(C$_6$H$_5$)$_3$
→
Wittig reaction

H$_2$, Pd
→   product (ii)

OCH$_3$

****

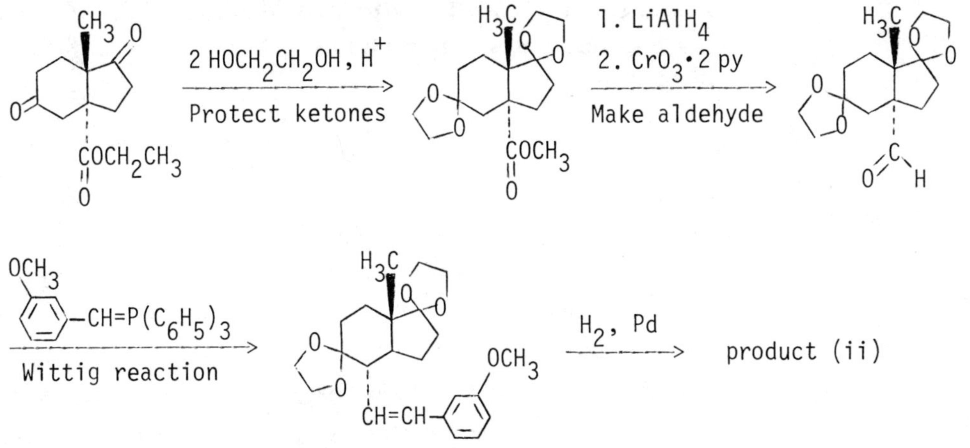

30. The necessary transformation is RCH⟨O—, O—⟩ → RCH—C(CH$_3$)$_2$.

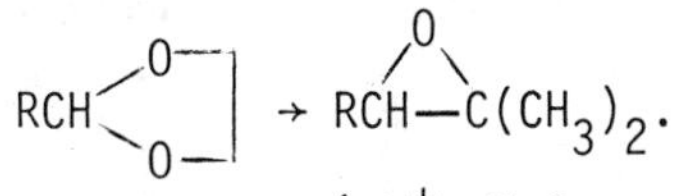

Hydrolysis to the aldehyde gets you started $\left(\xrightarrow{\text{H}^+, \text{ H}_2\text{O}} \text{RCHO} \right)$. Then there is a clever solution in one step:

$$\text{R-C-H} \xrightarrow[\text{(See Exercise 15-14)}]{(C_6H_5)_2S=C(CH_3)_2} \text{R—CH—C(CH}_3)_3$$

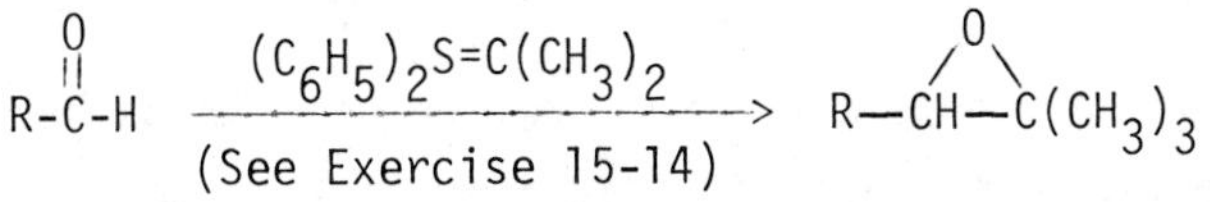

Notice that the "obvious" solution, Wittig reaction of RCHO with (C$_6$H$_5$)$_3$P=C(CH$_3$)$_2$, followed by MCPBA, would lead to disaster, since there are four other double bonds in the molecule that could be epoxidized also!

****

CHAPTER 16

Enols and Enones: α, β-Unsaturated Alcohols, Aldehydes, and Ketones

General Introduction

As we continue developing the chemistry of aldehydes and ketones, you will now see how the carbon adjacent to a carbonyl group can become nucleophilic. First, reactions of these new nucleophiles with common electrophiles like haloalkanes will be covered: alkylation reactions. More important are reactions of the nucleophilic "α-carbons" of one carbonyl compound with electrophilic carbonyl carbons of another. They are generically termed "carbonyl condensation reactions." We will see them here for aldehydes and ketones: the "aldol condensation." (In a later chapter you will be introduced to the analogous reaction of carboxylic esters: the "Claisen condensation.") The products of aldol condensations are α,β-unsaturated aldehydes and ketones, which contain additional sites of electrophilic and potential nucleophilic character.

Pay close attention to the structural relationships between starting materials and products. These are the reactions of real world organic synthesis, and they are perhaps the most important ones you will see in this book.

Outline of the Chapter

16-1. The Acidity of α-Hydrogens: Enolate Anions.

Making a nucleophile at the carbon α to a carbonyl group.

16-2. Keto-Enol Equilibria.

Revisited.

16-3. The Aldol Condensation.

A very important new reaction for synthesis.

16-4, 16-5. α,β-Unsaturated Aldehydes and Ketones.

The properties of the versatile products of aldol condensation.

16-1. The Acidity of α-Hydrogens: Enolate Anions.

Hydrogens on carbons adjacent to carbonyl or related functional groups are, as a class, the most acidic of "alkane-like" hydrogens. A short list of typical pK_a values follows. Notice how acidity is enhanced by a second carbonyl group.

Compound	pK_a	Compound	pK_a
RCH_2COR'	25	$ROCCH_2COR$	13
RCH_2CR'	20	$RCCH_2COR'$	11
RCH_2CH	17	$RCCH_2CR$	9
RCH_2CCl	16	$HCCH_2CH$	5

Any of the underlined protons in the structures above may be removed by an appropriate base, thus giving rise to the central participant in the reactions of this chapter, the enolate anion:

$$-\overset{|}{\underset{H}{C}}-\overset{O}{\overset{\|}{C}}- \quad \xrightarrow{\text{base}} \quad \left[\; -\overset{|}{\underset{-}{C}}-\overset{O}{\overset{\|}{C}}- \quad \longleftrightarrow \quad -\overset{|}{C}=\overset{O^-}{\underset{|}{C}}- \; \right].$$

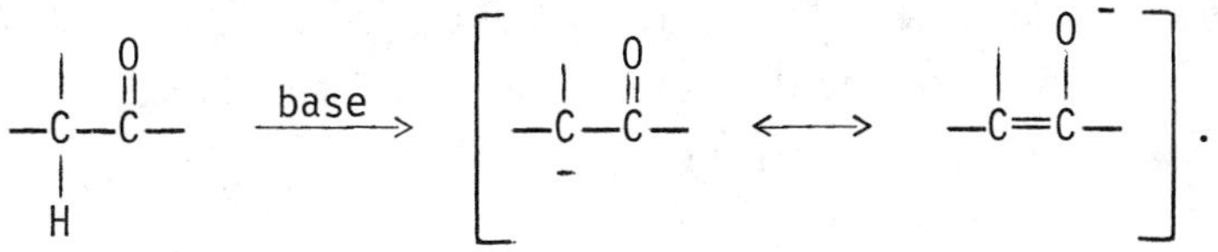

Since the enolate is basic, it is a nucleophile, capable of reaction with the typical electrophiles we've seen before. Their reaction with haloalkanes (alkylation) is the most general way to introduce alkyl substitution adjacent to carbonyl carbons.

16-2. Keto-Enol Equilibria.

In this section more mechanistic detail will be provided to a reaction first presented three chapters ago: The isomerization of vinyl alcohols (enols) to carbonyl compounds. You will see that this isomerization, although it favors the keto structure, allows small concentrations of enols to be in equilibrium with carbonyl compounds, and these enols can lead to productive chemical reactions.

16-3. The Aldol Condensation.

This section covers the first, and probably the most important carbonyl condensation reaction, the aldol condensation. Its importance comes from its ability to make relative complex structures, including rings, from much simpler starting molecules. All carbonyl condensation reactions proceed via addition of the deprotonated α-carbon of one carbonyl group to the carbonyl carbon of another. As you read this section in the text notice the location of the new carbon-carbon bond in each aldol product. Cover up the starting materials and see if you can deduce their structures solely by looking at their aldol condensation products. Although many aldol reactions between two identical molecules are useful, the most important applications fall into two categories: the so-called "mixed" aldol condensations, and intramolecular condensations of dicarbonyl compounds. Pay particular attention to the examples in this section, since they provide excellent illustrations for the various permutations of enolate and carbonyl "partners" that give successful and useful results in aldol condensations.

16-4 and 16-5. α,β-Unsaturated Aldehydes and Ketones.

Chemistry here is an extension of carbonyl and alkene chemistry. The carbon-carbon double bond in an α,β-unsaturated carbonyl compound generally shows the same addition reactions typical of simple alkenes. However, the highly polar nature of the carbonyl group strongly affects the reactivity of the alkene functional group. This is best seen by the resonance forms in these compounds: note in particular the presence of positive character at the β-carbon as well as at the carbonyl carbon:

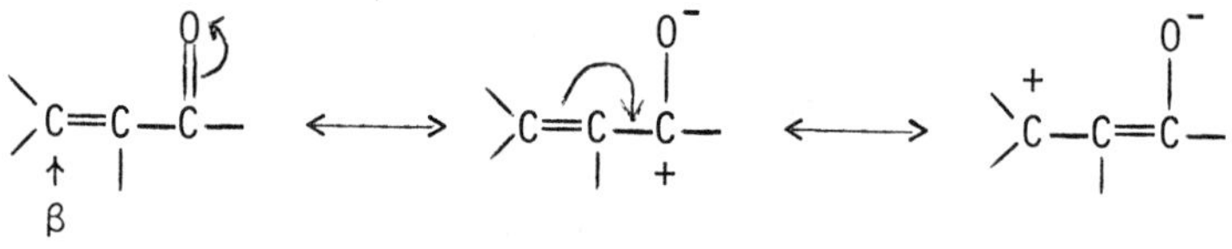

These resonance structures make most of the wide range of "enone" chemistry understandable in terms of only three fundamental mechanistic processes:

(a) Electrophilic addition at carbonyl oxygen, e.g.

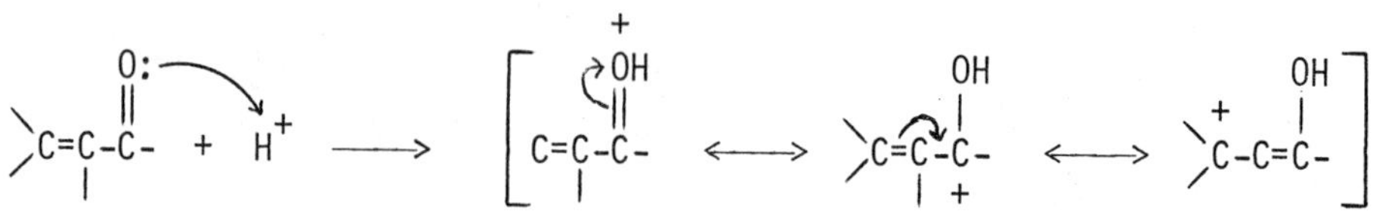

(b) Nucleophilic addition at carbonyl carbon, e.g.

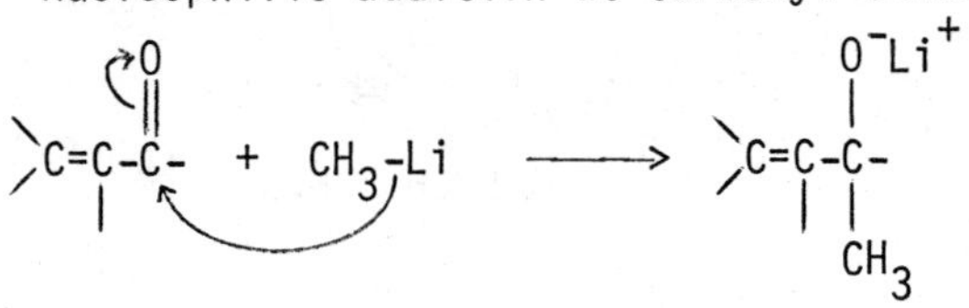

(c) Nucleophilic addition at the β-carbon, e.g.

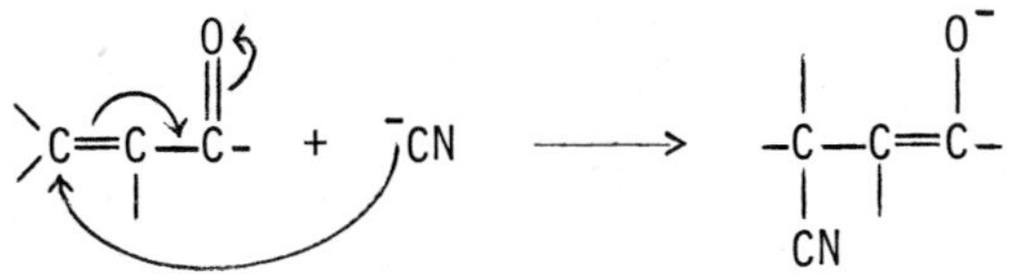

Practice by writing mechanisms for examples in the text for which specific mechanisms are not pictured. Use the appropriate mechanism above to start, and follow it with the behaviour expected for the product of that step.

Once you understand the mechanisms, concentrate on the synthetic applications of the process. Focus on the carbon-carbon bond forming examples, with particular emphasis on the Michael condensation, the 1,4-addition of enolates to enones or enals. The combination Michael addition-aldol condensation provides the most important and most general means of synthesis of six-membered rings, the Robinson Annelation. Don't worry about all these people's names; learn the retrosynthetic analysis for compounds containing six-membered rings:

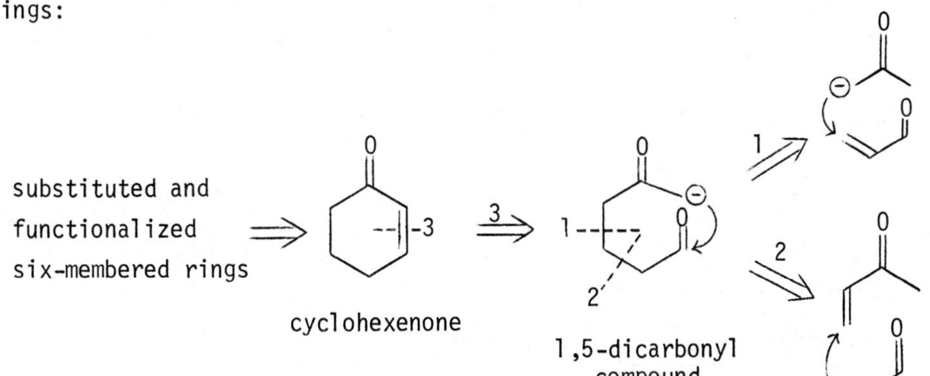

The first step is Michael addition to form a 1,5-dicarbonyl compound. This, in principle can be done in either of two ways (formation of either bond 1 or bond 2). Then intramolecular aldol condensation forms bond 3 of a cyclohexenone, which may be converted to a wide range of new compounds using the reactions of these two sections.

Solutions to Chapter 16 Problems

1. (a) (i) $CH_3CH{=}C(OH)CH_2CH_3$; (ii) $\left[CH_3\bar{\ddot{C}}HC(=O)CH_2CH_3 \leftrightarrow CH_3CH{=}C(\ddot{O}^-)CH_2CH_3\right]$

For the rest, only one of the enolate resonance forms will be written.

(b) (i) $CH_2{=}C(OH)CH(CH_3)_2$, $CH_3C(OH){=}C(CH_3)_2$; (ii) $\bar{\ddot{C}}H_2C(=O)CH(CH_3)_2$, $CH_3C(=O)\bar{\ddot{C}}(CH_3)_2$

(c) (i) 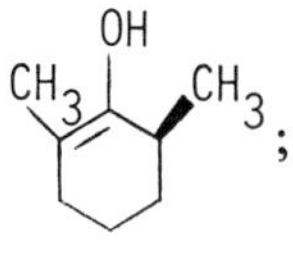; (ii) 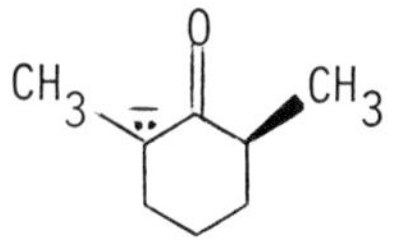. (d) Same as (c) - stereochemistry will be lost as α-carbon becomes sp^2.

(e) (i) 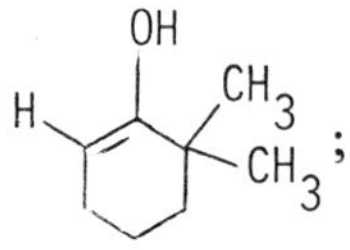; (ii) 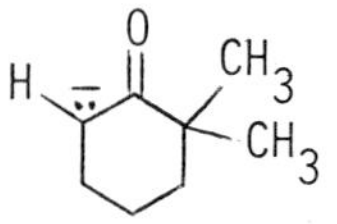. (f) (i) 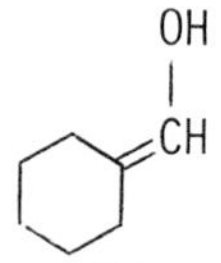; (ii) 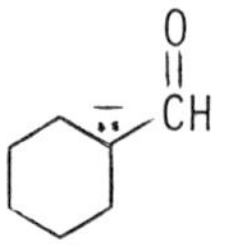

(g) none possible (no α-hydrogens!). (h)(i) $(CH_3)_3CCH{=}CH(OH)$; (ii) $(CH_3)_3C\bar{\ddot{C}}HC(=O)H$.

****

2. (a) 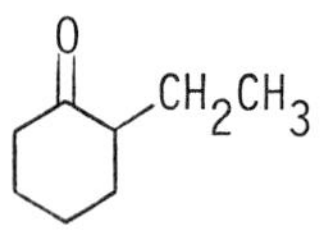; (b) 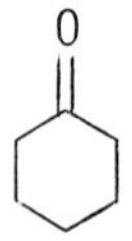 + $CH_3CH{=}CH_2$ (E2); (c) 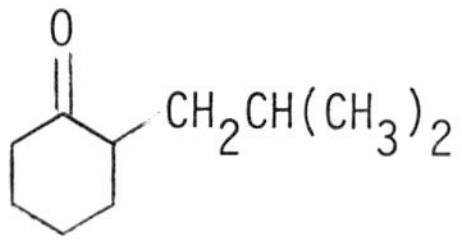;

(d) 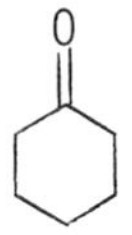 + $CH_2{=}C(CH_3)_2$ (E2 again: secondary and tertiary haloalkanes lead to elimination when treated with strongly basic enolate anions).

****

3. Both are aldehyde → enamine → alkylation sequences. The new carbon-carbon bond is marked with an arrow.

(a) $(CH_3)_2C{=}CHCH_2\overset{\downarrow}{-}CH_2CHO$ (via 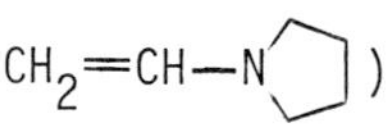).

(b) 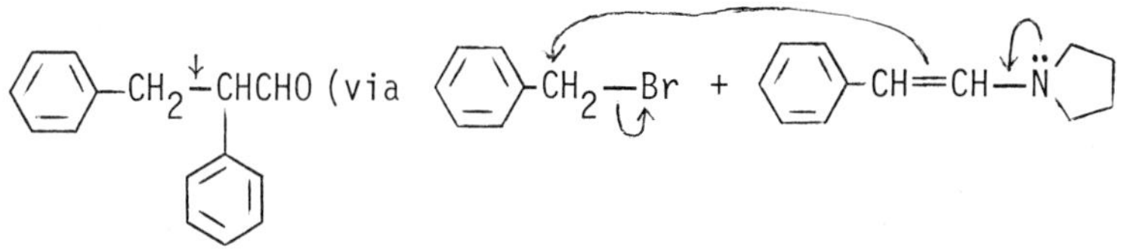 S_N2 reaction)

****

4. Illustrated with cyclohexanone: before the reaction between cyclohexanone enolate and iodomethane has gone to completion, a mixture is present containing CH_3I, 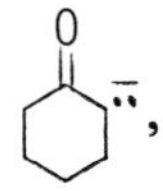, and 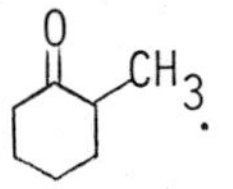. An acid-base reaction between cyclohexanone enolate and 2-methylcyclohexanone can take place under these conditions, leading to either possible enolate of the latter:

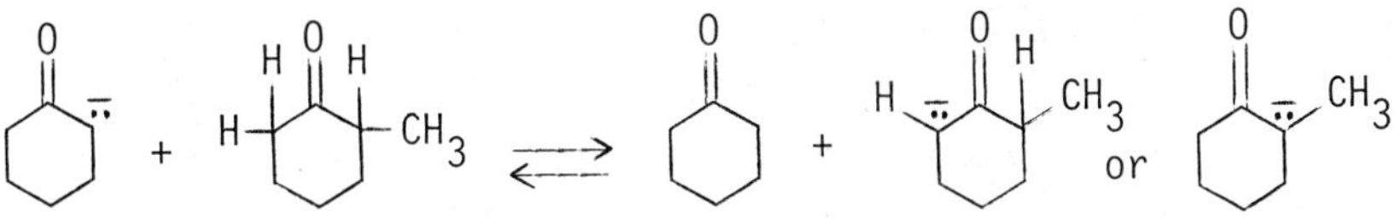

Reaction of the new enolates with CH_3I leads to double alkylation products.

Enamines eliminate this problem. The enamine alkylation product,

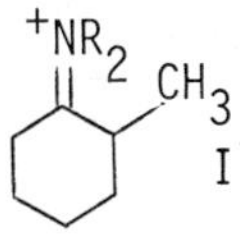

I^-, cannot be converted to another alkylatable species by either unreacted enamine or anything else in the reaction system. Specifically, unreacted enamine is not basic enough to remove a proton from the alkylation product.

****

5. Yes. Enamines (neutral) are much less basic than enolates (anionic) and show much less tendency to cause E2 elimination reactions.

****

6. Use the catalyst!! Then it's easy:

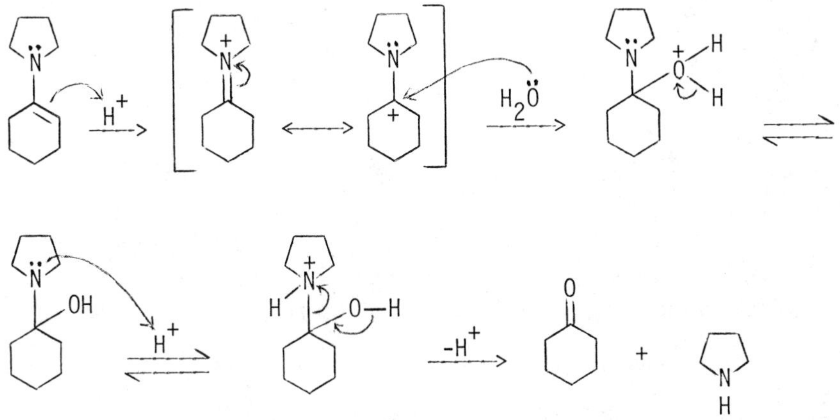

****

7. Look for the $-\overset{\text{O}}{\overset{\|}{\text{C}}}-\text{CH}_3$ fragment. $\text{CH}_3\overset{\text{O}}{\overset{\|}{\text{C}}}\text{CH}(\text{CH}_3)_2$ (b) is the only one.

****

8. (a) Replace <u>all</u> α-hydrogens with D; for instance, $\text{CH}_3\text{CH}_2\overset{\text{O}}{\overset{\|}{\text{C}}}\text{CH}_2\text{CH}_3$

gives $\text{CH}_3\text{CD}_2\overset{\text{O}}{\overset{\|}{\text{C}}}\text{CD}_2\text{CH}_3$,

gives , and

$(\text{CH}_3)_3\text{CCH}_2\overset{\text{O}}{\overset{\|}{\text{C}}}\text{H}$ gives $(\text{CH}_3)_3\text{CCD}_2\overset{\text{O}}{\overset{\|}{\text{C}}}\text{H}$ (Note how the aldehyde hydrogen is <u>not</u> replaced - it is <u>not</u> acidic).

(b) Conditions for introduction of a <u>single</u> α-halogen. In order, the products are $\text{CH}_3\text{CHBr}\overset{\text{O}}{\overset{\|}{\text{C}}}\text{CH}_2\text{CH}_3$, a mixture of $\text{CH}_3\overset{\text{O}}{\overset{\|}{\text{C}}}\text{CBr}(\text{CH}_3)_2$ and $\text{BrCH}_2\overset{\text{O}}{\overset{\|}{\text{C}}}\text{CH}(\text{CH}_3)_2$,

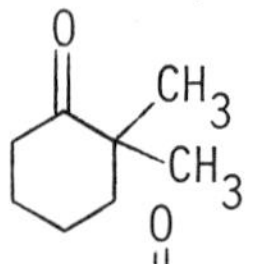

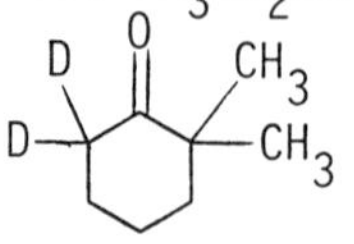

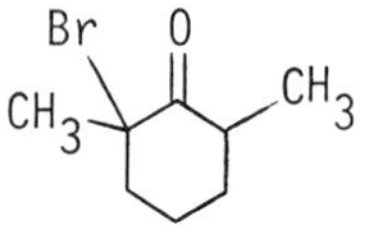

(mixture of stereoisomers from either *cis* or *trans* starting ketone),

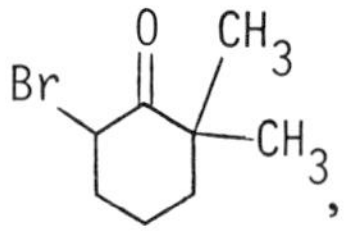

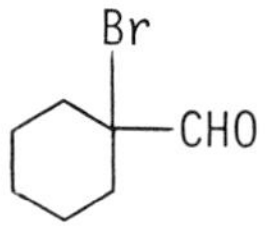

, , no reaction, and $(\text{CH}_3)_3\text{CCHBr}\overset{\text{O}}{\overset{\|}{\text{C}}}\text{H}$.

(c) All α-hydrogens are replaced by Cl under these conditions.

****

9. $\text{H}-\overset{\text{O}}{\overset{\|}{\text{C}}}-\text{CH}_2-\overset{\text{O}}{\overset{\|}{\text{C}}}-\text{H}$ ⇌ an enol, stabilized by intra-

molecular hydrogen bonding. Butanedial will not do this since it lacks α-hydrogens flanked by two carbonyl groups.

****

10. (a) An equivalent of Br_2 in ethanoic acid ($\text{CH}_3\text{CO}_2\text{H}$) solvent.

(b) Excess Cl_2 in aqueous base.

(c) One equivalent of Cl_2 in ethanoic acid.

****

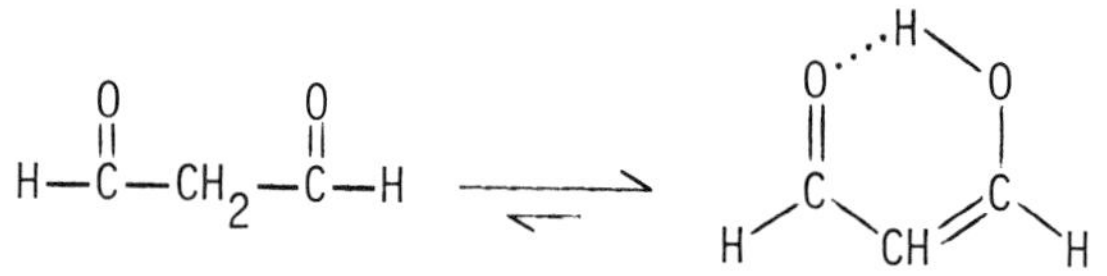

11. Aldol condensations. Abbreviated mechanisms (unnecessary for your answers) are shown, and in each case the new bond is marked in the product with an arrow.

(a) 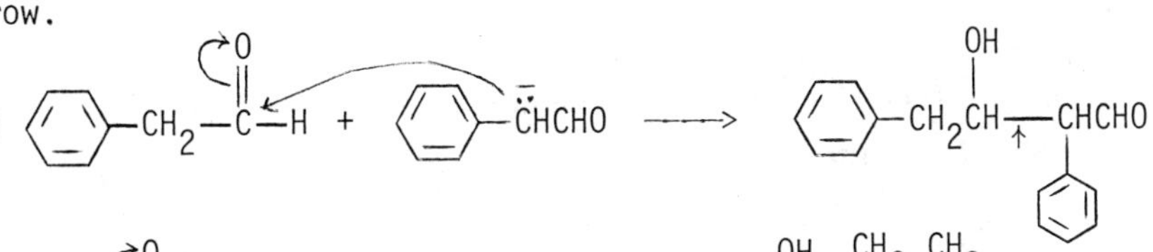

(b) 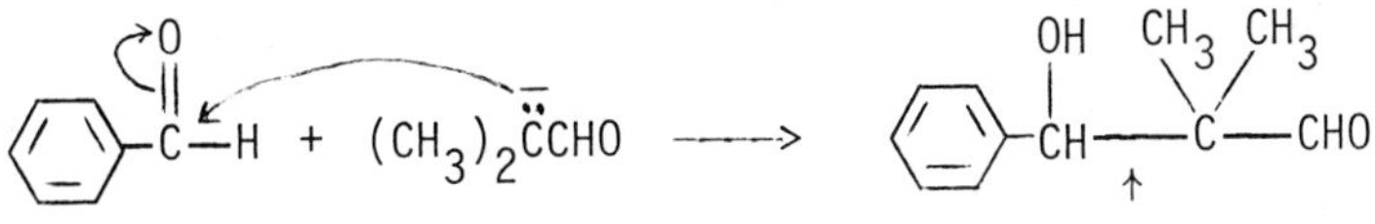

(c) 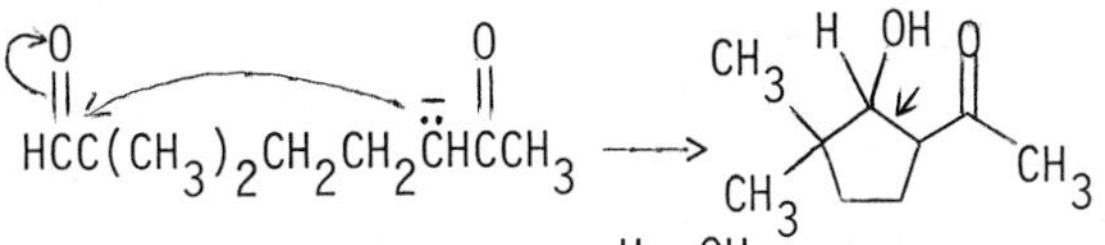

(d) 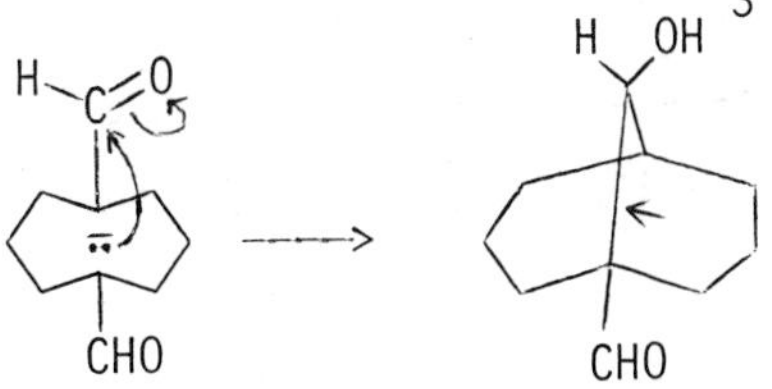

****

12. Retrosynthetic analysis is essential: You must identify the bond that the condensation reaction forms by looking for the "aldol" unit:

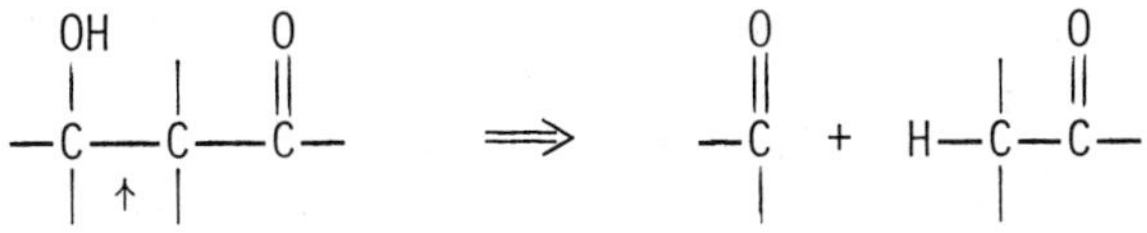

this is the new bond   these are the precursors

(a) 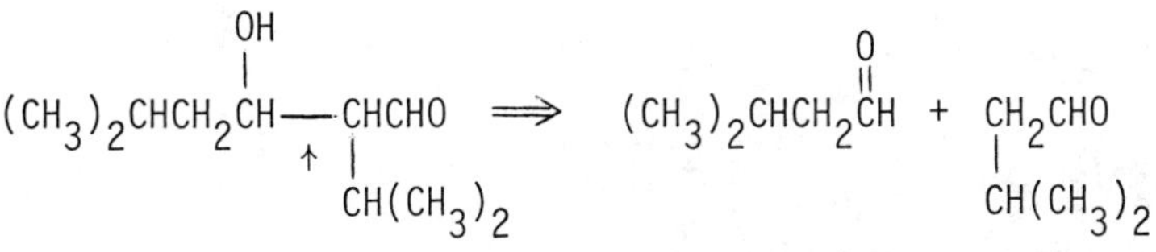

two identical aldehyde molecules

Answer is 2 $(CH_3)_2CHCH_2CHO$ $\xrightarrow{NaOH,\ H_2O}$ product

(b) 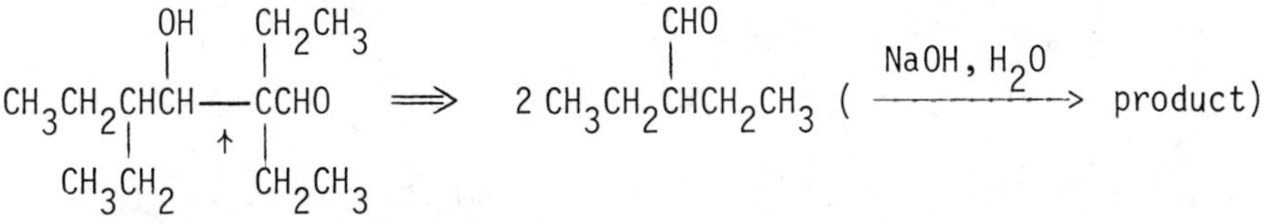

(c) 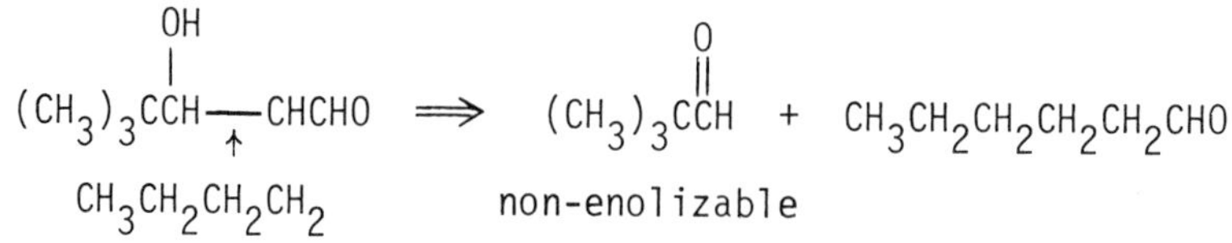

A mixed aldol condensation: will work best if $(CH_3)_3CCHO$ is in excess, to minimize self-condensations of two hexanal molecules.

(d) 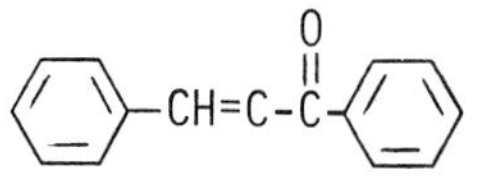 is the dehydration product derived from

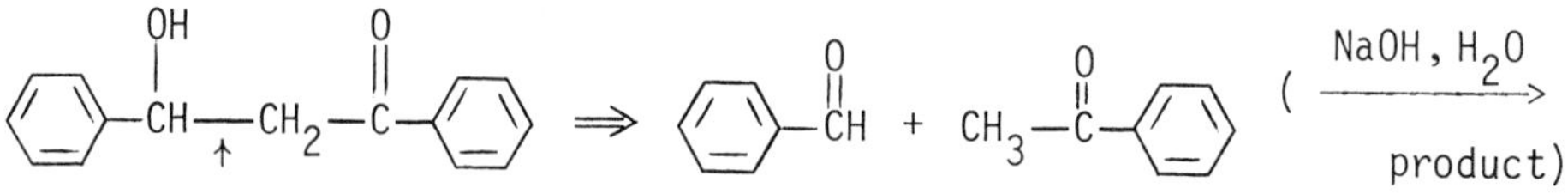

A very good mixed aldol, since the aldehyde is non-enolizable, and the ketone won't condense with itself (unfavorable equilibrium). Notice how the retrosynthetic analysis of an α,β-unsaturated ketone or aldehyde leads to aldol condensation:

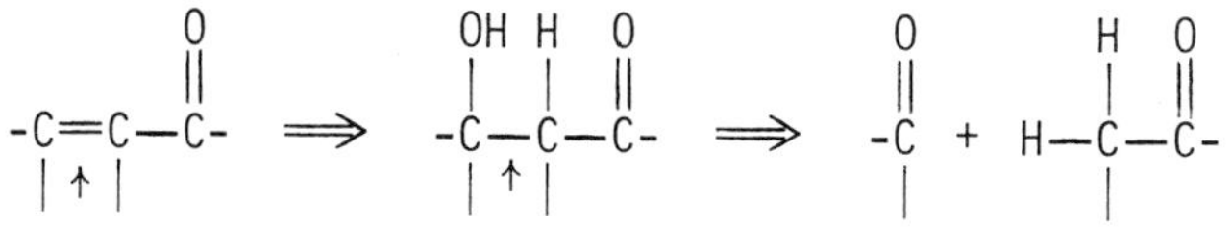

(e) Follow the pattern: 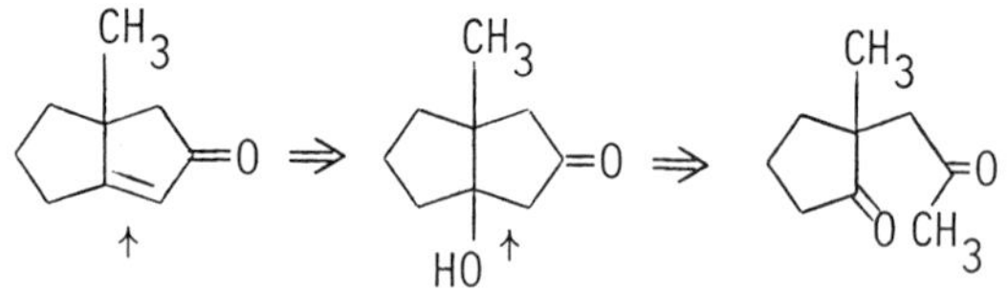

(NaOH, H_2O ——> product)

(f) 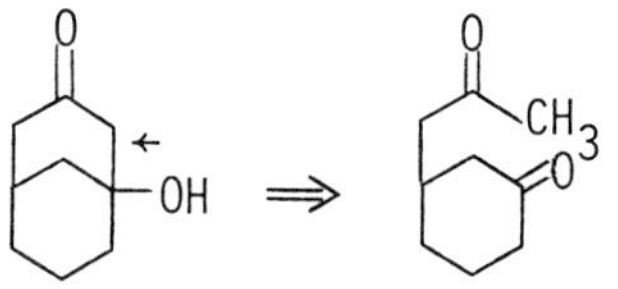 (NaOH, H_2O ——> product)

****

13. Since enolates are not feasible intermediates, consider an alternative: a neutral enol, which should be a nucleophile somewhat similar to an enamine:

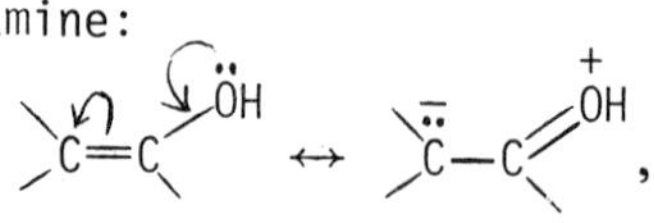, compare 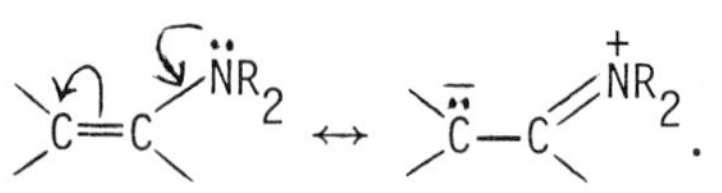.

How can acid play a role? You already know (Section 15-4) that acid can catalyze carbonyl addition reactions by attachment to oxygen, thereby generating a better electrophile. So (using ethanal for illustration):

****

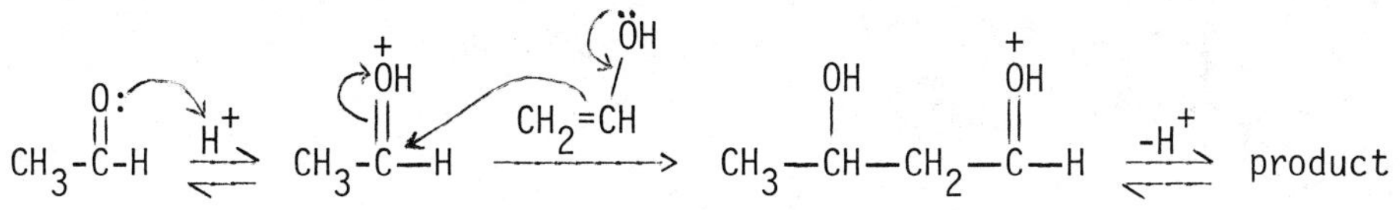

14. (a) The transformation is $RCH_2\overset{+}{N}H_3 \longrightarrow R\overset{O}{\overset{||}{C}}H$. A reasonable pathway would involve oxidation of the CH_2 group:

$$RCH_2\overset{+}{N}H_3 \xrightarrow{[O]} RCH\overset{O-H}{\underset{\overset{+}{N}H_3}{|}} \xrightarrow{-NH_3} R\overset{O}{\overset{||}{C}}H.$$

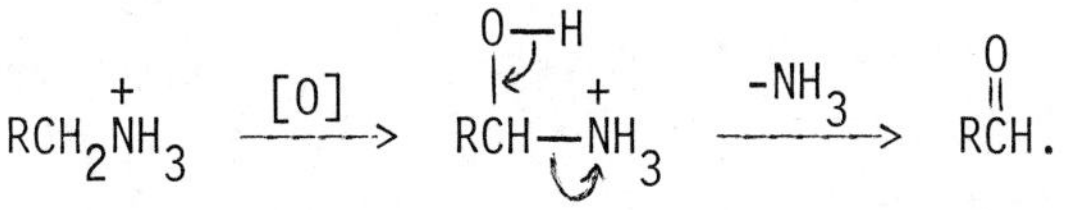

(b) Similarly,

****

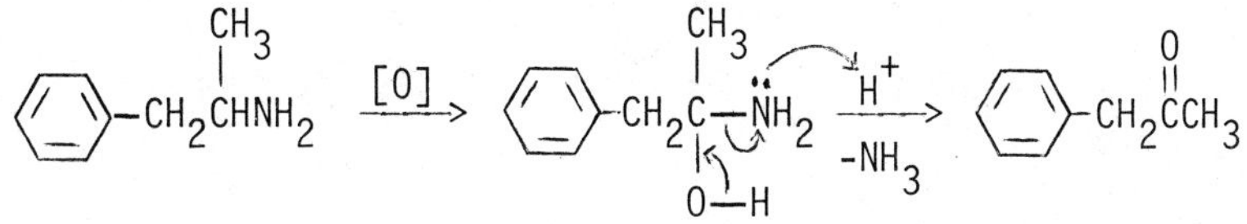

15. An exercise in <u>seeing</u>. Follow the <u>carbons</u> and see where they are going. For instance, in the product of reaction a, try to identify the carbons from the starting material, and locate bonds that were formed or broken:

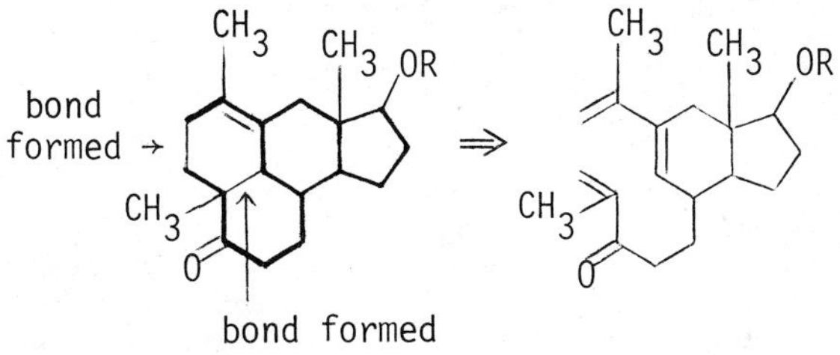

This is a Diels-Alder reaction! Answer for (a) is "Heat."

Similarly, for reaction b:

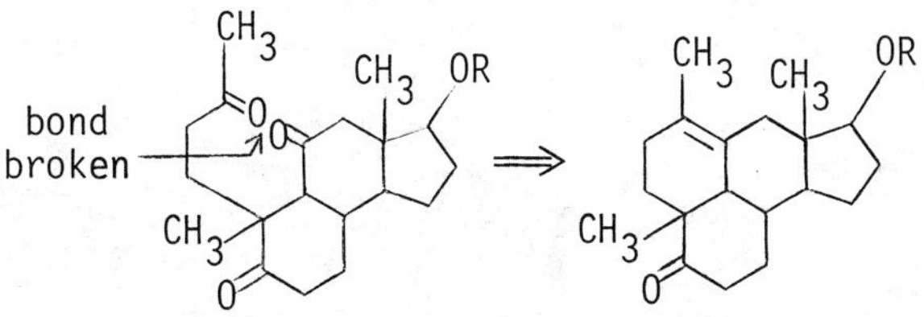

This is ozonolysis: 1. O_3, 2. Zn, H^+, H_2O.

Finally, reaction c is an aldol condensation:

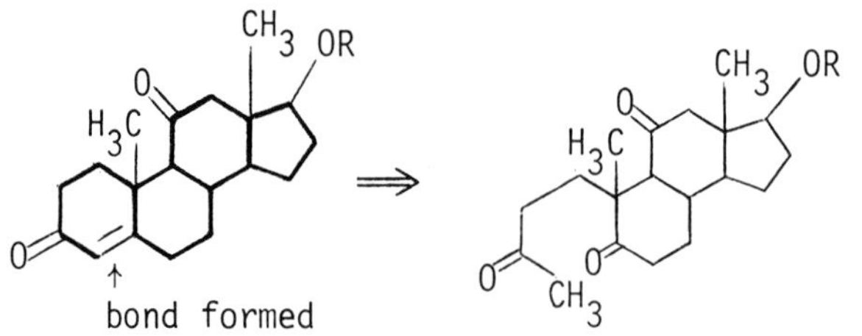

Conditions: NaOH, H_2O, Δ.

Aldol condensation the "other way," towards the ketone in the middle ring:

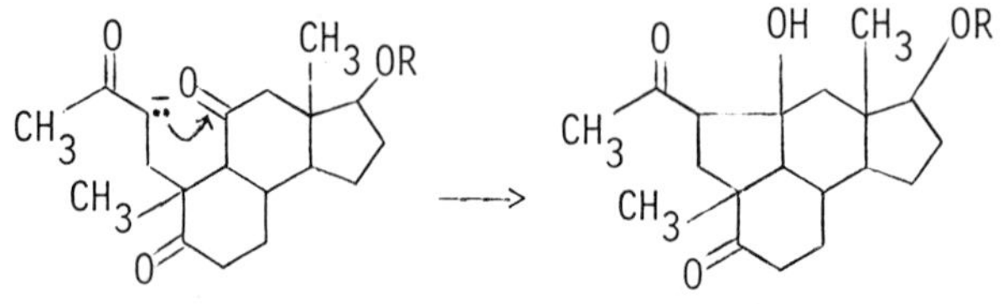

But the five-membered ring formed here is <u>more strained</u> than the six-membered ring formed above, so this alternative is not favored. When it occurs, it is readily reversible (retro-aldol process).

****

16. $CH_3CH_2CH_2CH{=}CHCHO \longleftarrow CH_3CH_2CH_2CHO + (C_6H_5)_3P{=}CHCHO$

2-hexenal

$CH_3CH_2CH_2CH_2CH{=}CH\overset{O}{\overset{\|}{C}}CH_3 \longleftarrow CH_3(CH_2)_3CHO + (C_6H_5)_3P{=}CH\overset{O}{\overset{\|}{C}}CH_3$

3-octen-2-one

$CH_3CH_2CH_2CH_2CH{=}CHCH{=}CHCHO \xleftarrow[\text{again}]{(C_6H_5)_3P=CHCHO} CH_3(CH_2)_3CH{=}CHCHO$

$\xleftarrow{(C_6H_5)_3P=CHCHO}$ pentanal

****

17. (a) 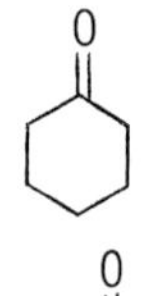 $\xrightarrow[\text{2. } Na_2CO_3]{\text{1. } Cl_2,\ CH_3CO_2H}$ product

(b) $CH_3\overset{O}{\overset{\|}{C}}CH_3 + CH_3CH_2CH_2\underset{\underset{P(C_6H_5)_3}{\|}}{\overset{O}{\overset{\|}{C}}}CH \longrightarrow$ product

(c) $CH_3(CH_2)_4\overset{O}{\overset{\|}{C}}H \xrightarrow[\text{2. } MnO_2]{\text{1. } CH_2=CHLi}$ product (using special MnO_2 oxidation of the allylic alcohol to the α,β-unsaturated ketone)

In part b the Wittig reagent would come from reaction of $(C_6H_5)_3P$ and an α-chloroaldehyde. Aldol condensation is an alternative here.

****

18. 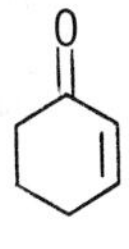 : (a) cyclohexanone; (b) 2-cyclohexenol; (c) 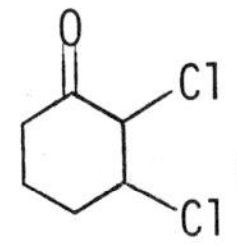 ;

(d) 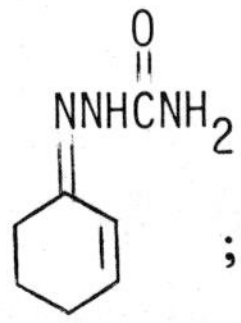 ; (e) 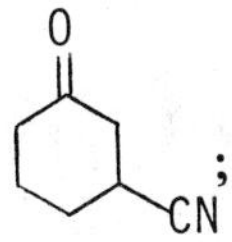 ; (f) 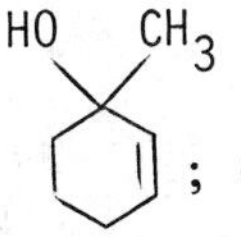 ; (g) 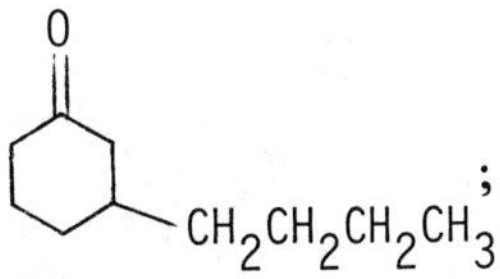 ;

(h) 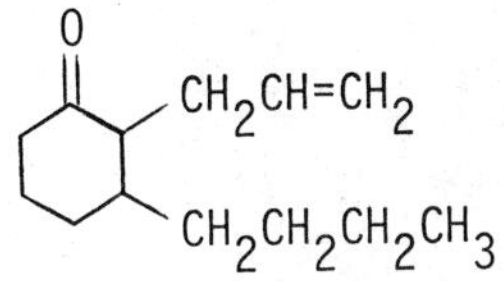 (first step forms an enolate, which is alkylated)

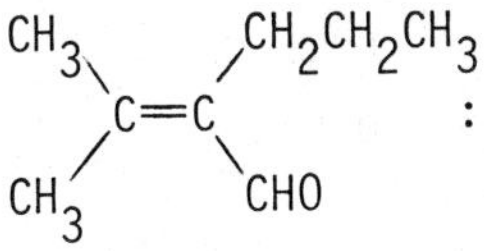 : (a) $(CH_3)_2CHCH(CHO)CH_2CH_2CH_3$; (b) $(CH_3)_2C{=}C(CH_2OH)CH_2CH_2CH_3$;

(c) $(CH_3)_2CClCCl(CHO)CH_2CH_2CH_3$; (d) $(CH_3)_2C{=}C(CH{=}NNHCONH_2)CH_2CH_2CH_3$;

(e) $(CH_3)_2C(CN)—C(CHO)HCH_2CH_2CH_3$; (f) $(CH_3)_2C{=}C(CH_3CHOH)CH_2CH_2CH_3$;

(g) $CH_3CH_2CH_2CH_2C(CH_3)_2—CH(CHO)CH_2CH_2CH_3$; (h) $CH_3CH_2CH_2CH_2C(CH_3)_2—C(CHO)(CH_2CH{=}CH_2)CH_2CH_2CH_3$

$CH_2{=}CHC(O)(CH_2)_4CH_3$: (a) 3-octanone; (b) 1-octen-3-ol;

(c) $ClCH_2CHClC(O)(CH_2)_4CH_3$; (d) $CH_2{=}CHC({=}NNHCONH_2)(CH_2)_4CH_3$;

(e) $NCCH_2CH_2C(O)(CH_2)_4CH_3$; (f) $CH_2{=}CHC(OH)(CH_3)(CH_2)_4CH_3$;

(g) $CH_3(CH_2)_5C(O)(CH_2)_4CH_3$; (h) $CH_3(CH_2)_4CH(CH_2CH{=}CH_2)C(O)(CH_2)_4CH_3$

****

19. No! The carbonyl group changes the mechanism:

$$CH_3\overset{\overset{\textstyle O:}{\|}}{C}CH{=}CH_2 \xrightarrow{\quad H{-}Cl \quad} CH_3\overset{\overset{\textstyle {+}OH}{\|}}{C}{-}CH{=}CH_2 \xrightarrow{\quad\quad} CH_3\overset{\overset{\textstyle OH}{|}}{C}{=}CHCH_2Cl \xrightarrow{\ \underline{tautomerism}\ } CH_3\overset{\overset{\textstyle O}{\|}}{C}CH_2CH_2Cl$$

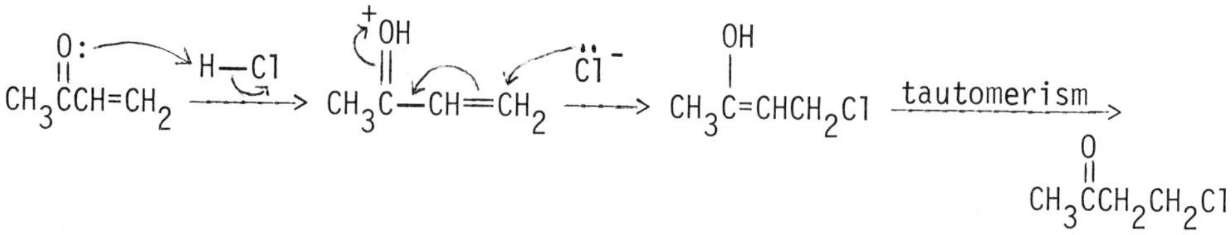

Protonation occurs on oxygen, not carbon, and the result <u>looks</u> like anti-Markovnikov orientation.

****

20. "Degrees of unsaturation" are explained in Chapter 11 of this study guide.

(a) $H_{sat'd} = 10 + 2 = 12$; deg. unsat'n. $= \dfrac{12-10}{2} = 1$ π bond or ring. UV: $n \rightarrow \pi^*$ absorption of carbonyl. NMR: $CH_3\overset{\overset{\textstyle O}{\|}}{C}{-}CH_2{-}$ and ${-}CH_2{-}CH_3$ are clear, giving as the answer 2-pentanone, $CH_3COCH_2CH_2CH_3$ (A).

(with markings: $\uparrow 3$ at δ2.1, $\uparrow 2$ at δ2.3, $\uparrow 3$ at δ0.9(t))

(b) $H_{sat'd} = 10 + 2 = 12$; deg. unsat'n. $= \dfrac{12-8}{2} = 2$ π bonds and/or rings. UV: $\pi \rightarrow \pi^*$ absorption of α,β-unsat'd carbonyl at 220 nm.

NMR: $CH_3\overset{\overset{\textstyle O}{\|}}{C}{-}$ is clear. Also 2 alkene hydrogens (δ 5.8-6.9) and another 3H at δ1.9 (CH$_3$- ?). Since UV indicates conjugation, there are three possibilities:

(markings: $\uparrow 3$ at δ2.1)

$$\underset{H}{\overset{CH_3}{}}{>}C{=}C{<}\underset{\overset{\|}{O}}{\overset{H}{C{-}CH_3}}, \quad \underset{CH_3}{\overset{H}{}}{>}C{=}C{<}\underset{\overset{\|}{O}}{\overset{H}{C{-}CH_3}}, \quad and \quad \underset{H}{\overset{H}{}}{>}C{=}C{<}\underset{\overset{\|}{O}}{\overset{CH_3}{C{-}CH_3}}.$$

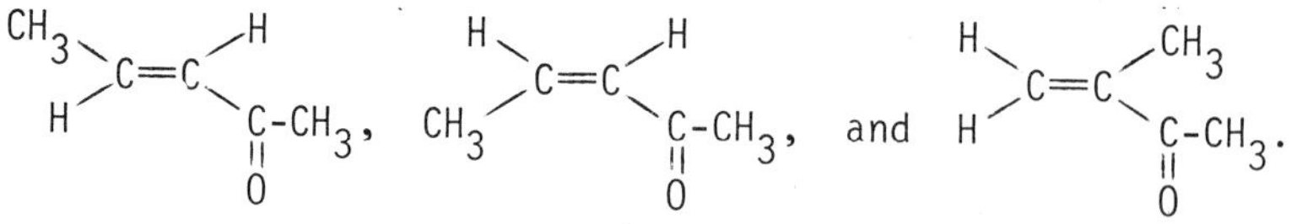

The last is ruled out because the signal at δ1.9 has a large splitting, indicating $\underset{H}{\overset{CH_3}{}}{>}C{=}$ piece is present. In the alkene region, the large splitting of the signal at δ6.0 (about 15Hz) suggests *trans* alkene H's, so the <u>first</u> of the three possibilities above is B.

(c) $H_{sat'd} = 12 + 2 = 14$; deg. unsat'n. $= \dfrac{14-12}{2} = 1$ π bond or ring. UV: $\pi \rightarrow \pi^*$ absorption of a simple alkene. NMR: $CH_3{-}CH_2{-}$ present, also

$$CH_2{=}C\underset{CH_2-CH_2-}{\overset{CH_3 \ \leftarrow\ \delta1.7(s)}{}}$$

(markings: $\uparrow 2$ at δ4.6(br s), $\uparrow 2$ at δ1.9(t))

(δ0.8(t))

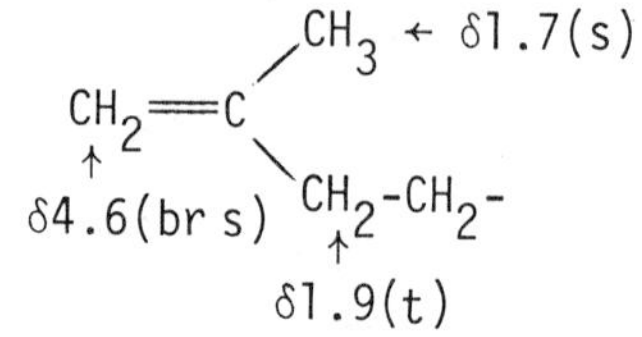

can be identified by chemical shifts and splittings. These add up to C_7H_{14}, so one CH$_2$ group has been duplicated in the two pieces. After correcting for that the answer for C becomes $CH_2{=}C(CH_3)CH_2CH_2CH_3$.

(d) Also 1 degree of unsaturation. UV: $n \rightarrow \pi^*$ absorption of a non-conjugated ketone. NMR: $(CH_3)_2CH-$ ← δ0.9 (d) and $CH_3-\overset{O}{\overset{\|}{C}}-$ (↑ δ2.0(s)) add up to $C_5H_{10}O$; just a CH_2 left to insert:

$(CH_3)_2CH-CH_2-\overset{O}{\overset{\|}{C}}-CH_3$ is D.

(e) A + $CH_2{=}P(C_6H_5)_3$ → C

(f) B + $(CH_3)_2CuLi$ → D

(g) B + H_2, Pd-C → A

****

21. (a)

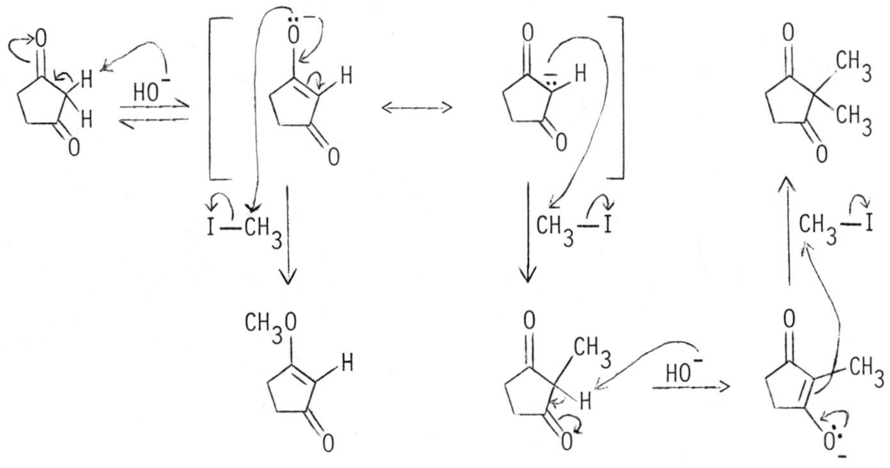

(b)

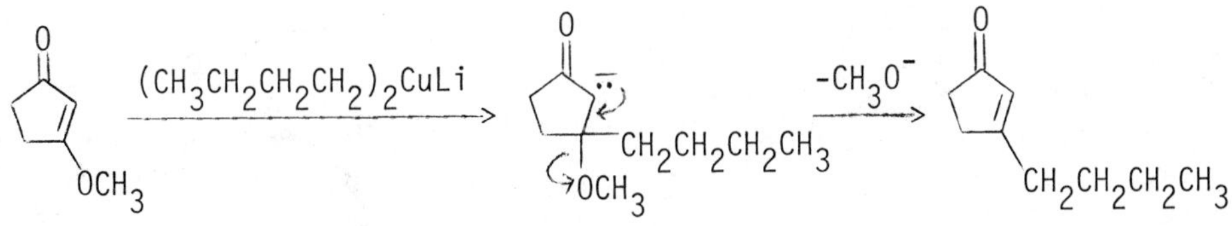

Addition-elimination mechanism is likely.

****

22. (a) A mechanism must explain the H/D exchange of all hydrogens in the molecule: the overall process occurring is

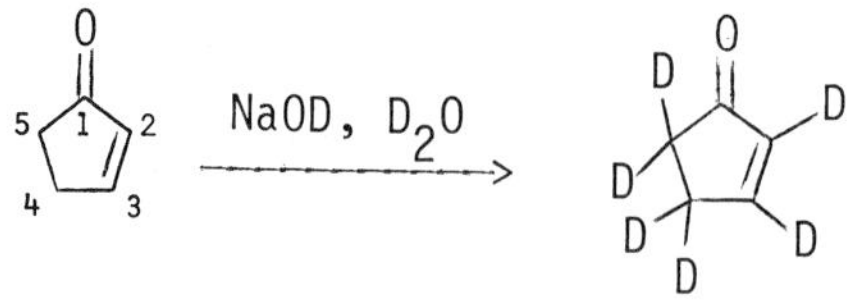

Similar C-13 NMR spectrum, but all H-1 signals gone.

H/D exchange on C-5 is the normal, expected process at α-carbons. H/D exchange on C-4 can occur via deprotonation to make a conjugated enolate-like anion:

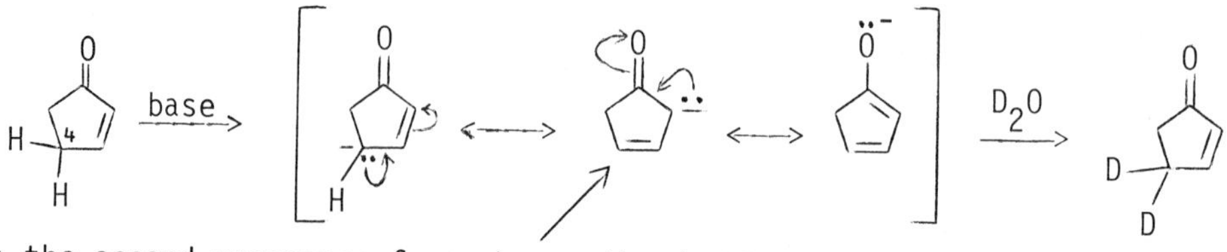

As the second resonance form shows, the double bond can migrate around the ring:

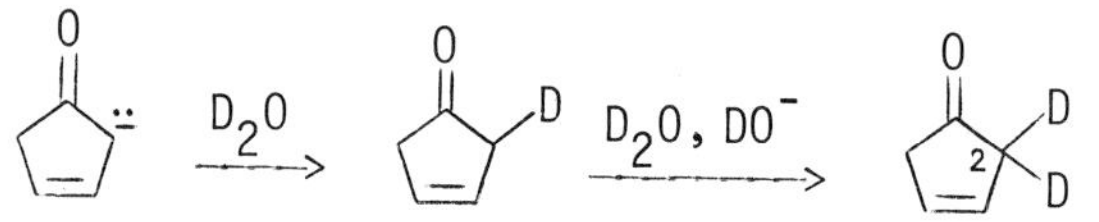

H/D exchange at C-2 is completed. Finally, deprotonation again at C-5 leads to a conjugated enolate that allows H/D exchange at C-3, the last remaining position:

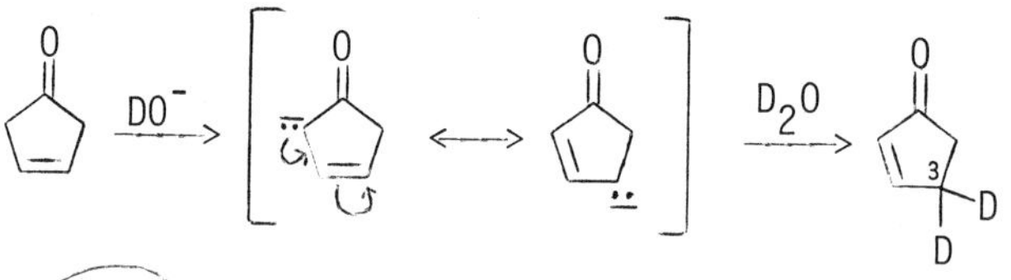

(eventually)

(b)

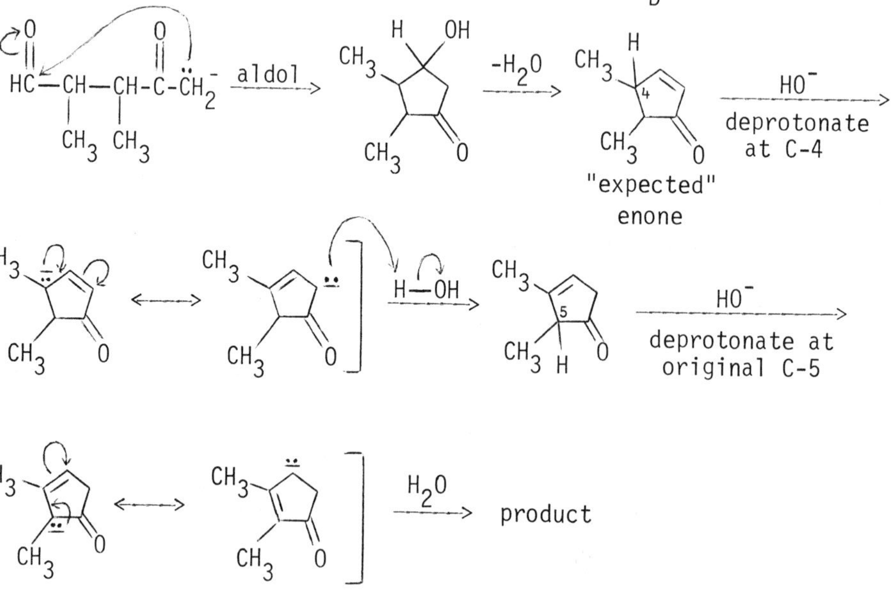

The isomerization of the double bond follows a process identical to that involved in part a, above. Since the process generates a tetrasubstituted alkene from a disubstituted one, it is energetically favorable.

****

23. (a) As in Problem 22, deprotonate "allylic" to give a conjugate enolate-like anion:

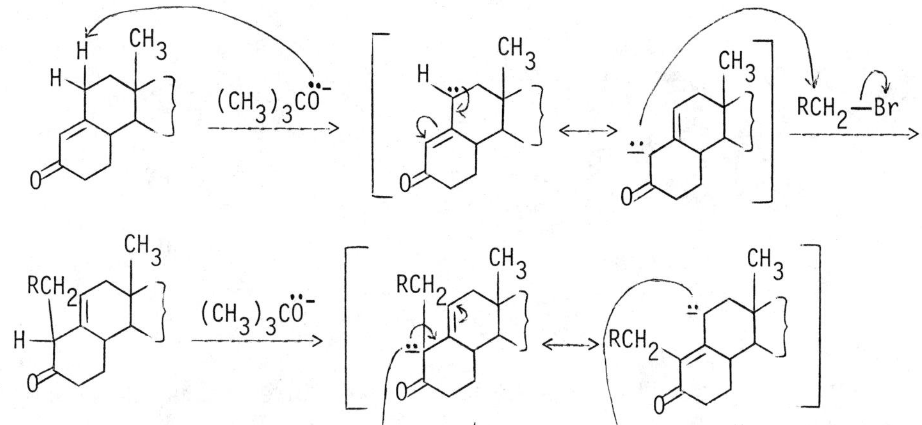

Like other allylic species, such extended, conjugated enolates can react with electrophiles at more than one carbon.

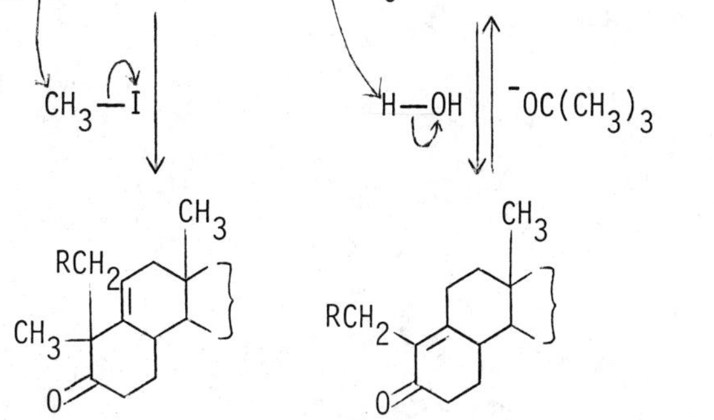

Product of second reaction

Product of first reaction

(b) H^+, H_2O followed by Jones reagent gives this: 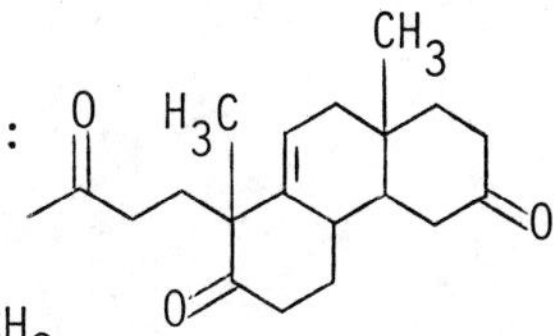

Aldol condensation is then possible:

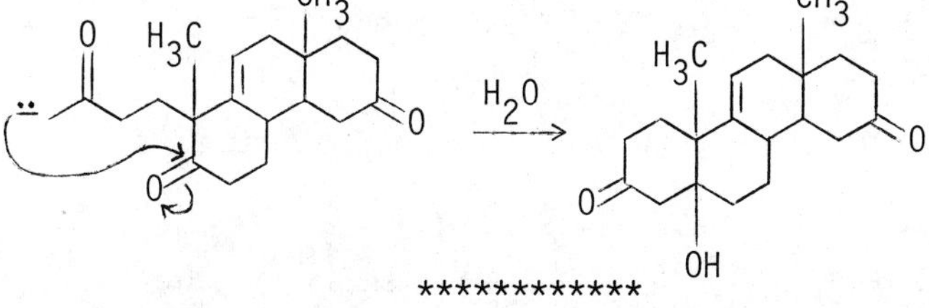

****

24. (a) $C_6H_5\overset{O}{\overset{\|}{C}}-\overset{CH_2CH_3}{\overset{|}{C}HCH_2CH_3}$;   (b) ;   (c) (via + $C_6H_5CH_2Cl$)

(d) (via + $CH_3CH_2CH_2Cl$);   (e)

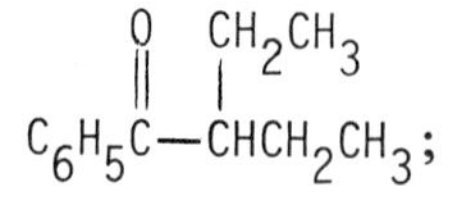

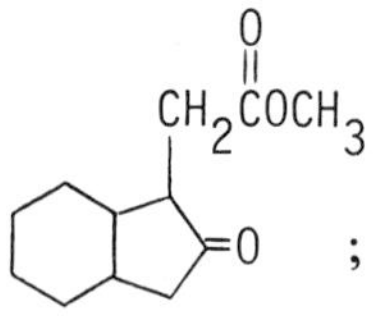

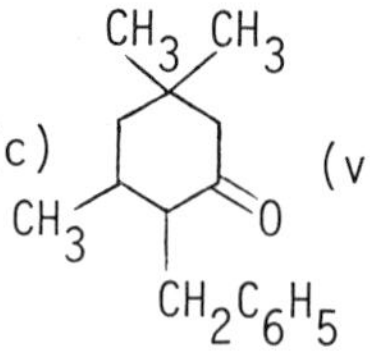

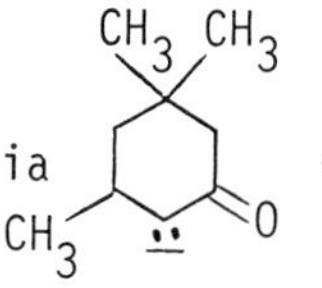

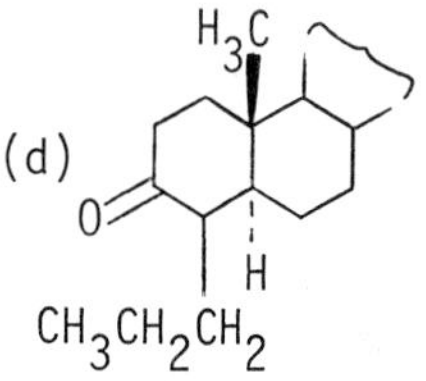

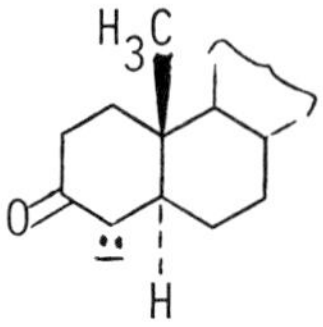

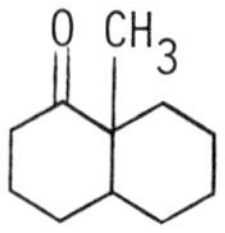

(f) $\xrightarrow{\overset{-}{\ddot{N}}[CH(CH_3)_2]_2}$ $\longrightarrow$ product

****

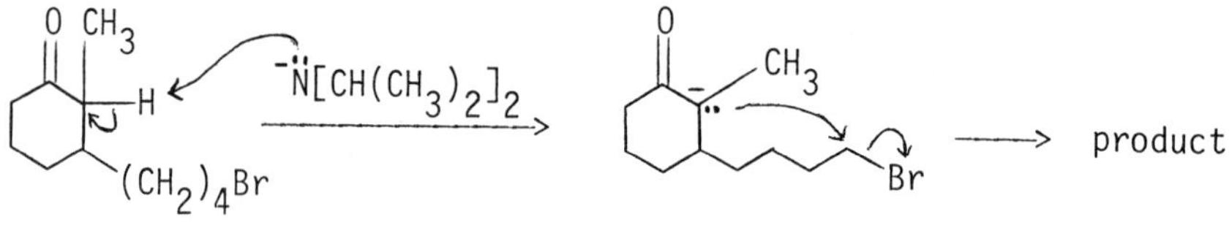

25. "Michael" additions: 1,4-additions of enolate anions to α,β-unsaturated aldehydes or ketones.

(a) $C_6H_5\overset{O}{\overset{\|}{C}}CH_2-CH_2CH_2\overset{O}{\overset{\|}{C}}C_6H_5$;   (b) ;   (c) ;

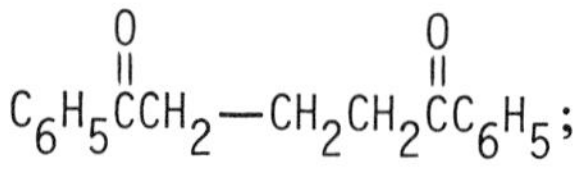

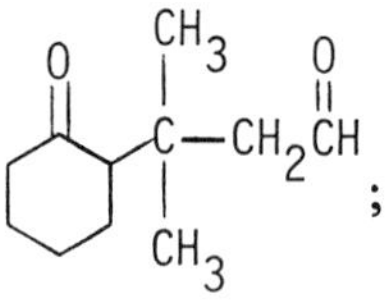

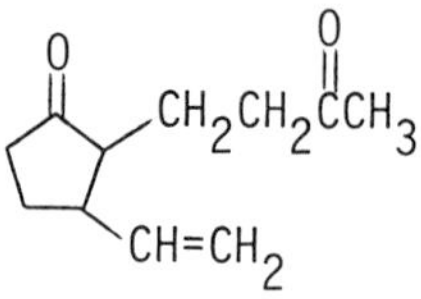

(d) ;   (e) Intramolecular aldol condensations,

leading to from (c) and

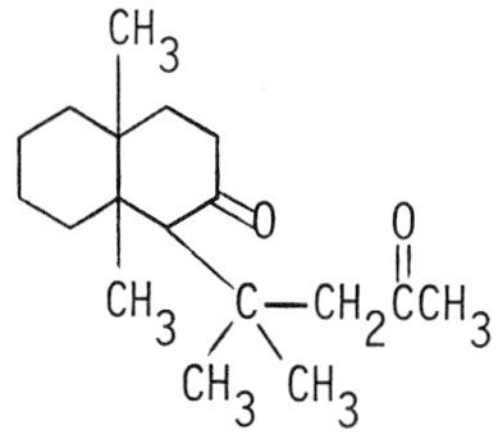

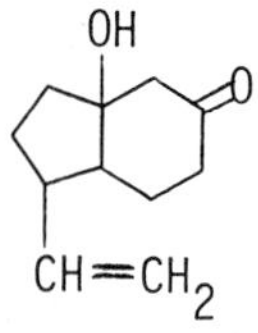

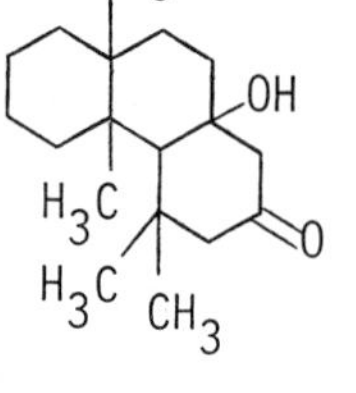

from (d).

****

26. Robinson annelation sequences (Michael addition followed by aldol).

(a) 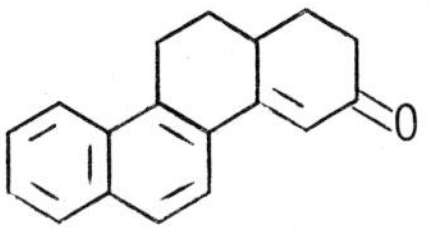 ; (b) 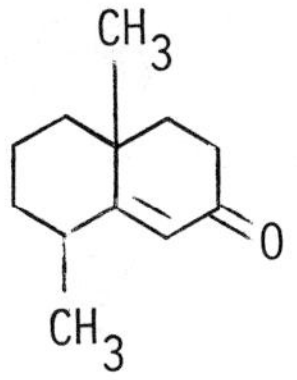 ; (c) 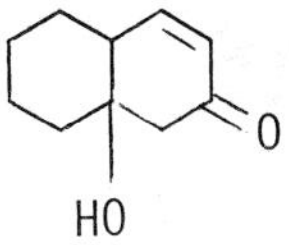

(d) 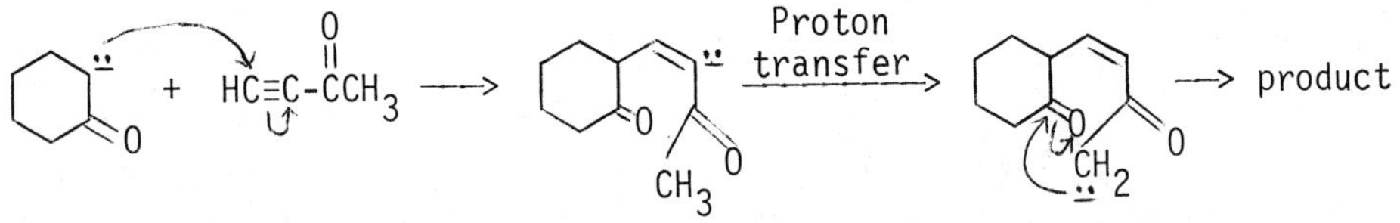

Heating in parts (a) and (b) tends to drive dehydration to give the α,β-unsaturated ketone product.

****

27. Retrosynthetically: 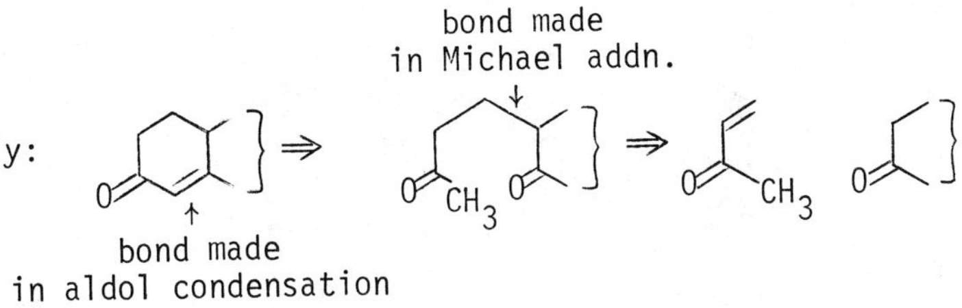

(a) 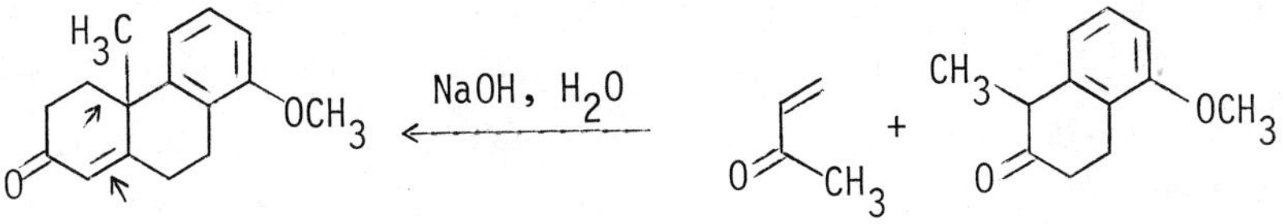

(b) 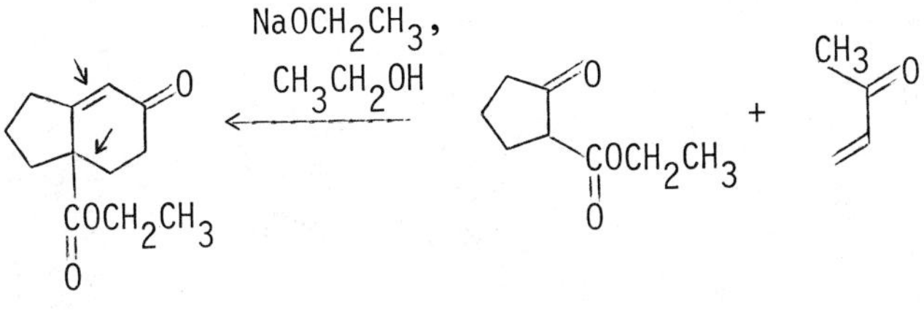

(Use alcohol/alkoxide to avoid hydrolysis of ester.)

(c) 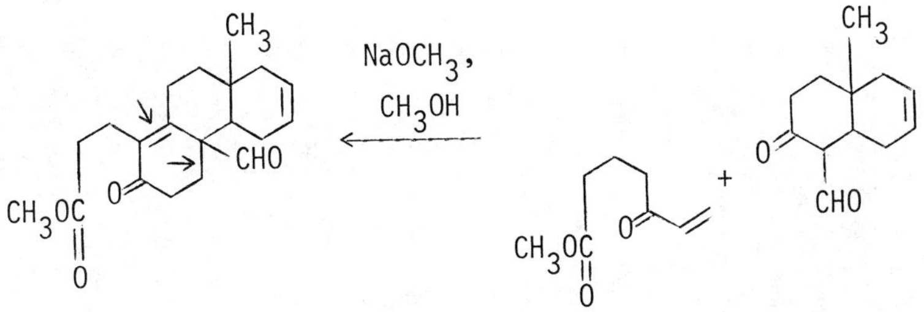

(d) 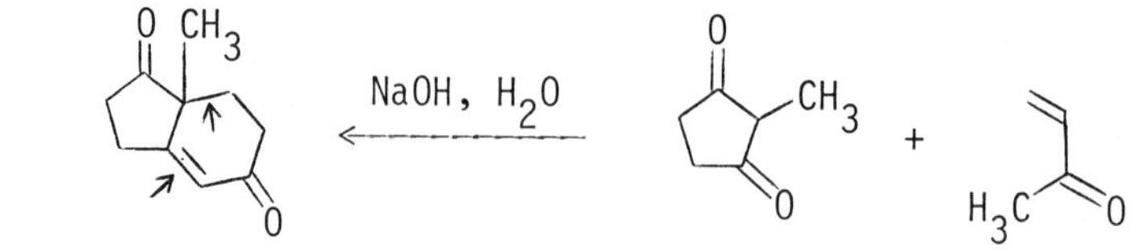

****

28. Analyze the bonds that have been formed in each step. Can you identify the nucleophilic and electrophilic carbons in each? That's the key: if you can identify one of the atoms going into a new bond as a nucleophile ('a' below), then the other *must* be electrophilic ('b'). So:

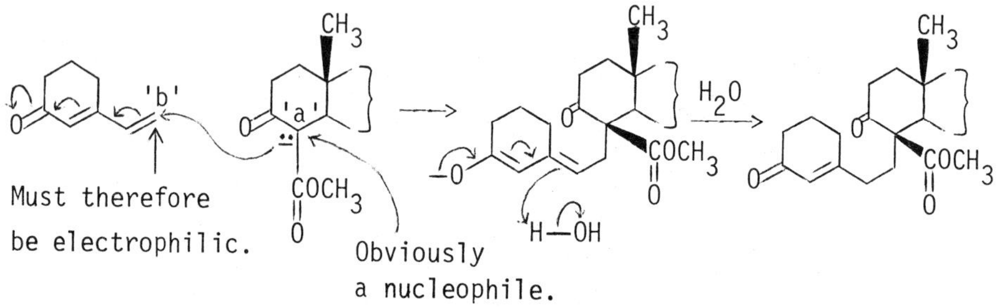

This, therefore, is a version of nucleophilic addition to an unsaturated ketone, but here the ketone is doubly ("α,β,γ,δ") unsaturated, and the process is a "1,6-addition." The product enolate protonates on the "δ" carbon, giving an α,β-unsaturated ketone as the product. In the second reaction, remove an allylic proton with base to give an "extended" enolate:

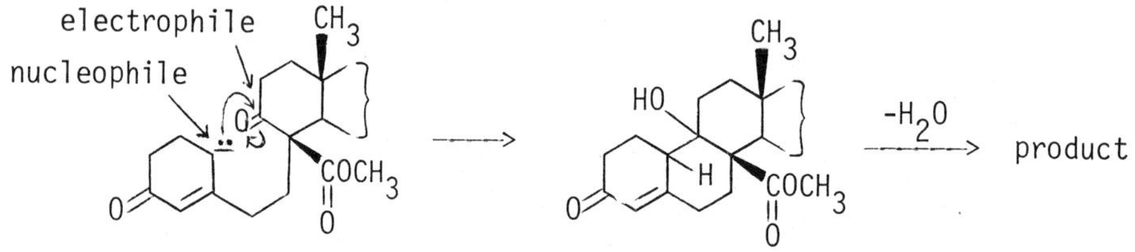

This is just a version of aldol condensation, where the nucleophile is the "extended" enolate anion at the "γ"-carbon of an α,β-unsaturated ketone, instead of the simple enolate at the α-carbon of a saturated ketone.

****

29. Work backwards.

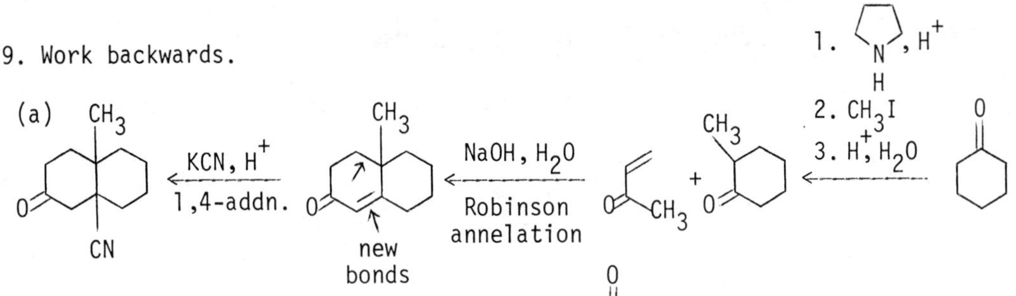

(b) Use the hint! Find the carbons of 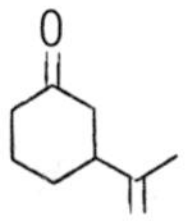 in your final target molecule:

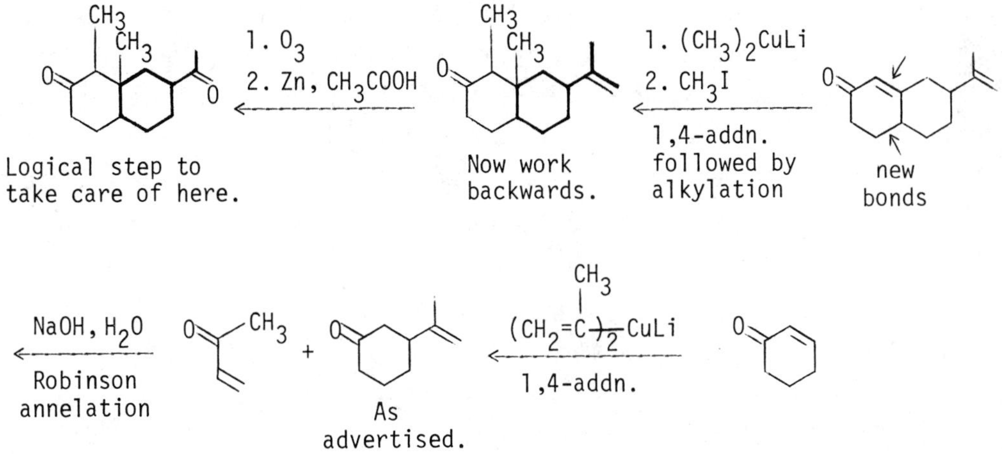

****

30. (a) $CH_3CH_2\overset{O}{\overset{\|}{C}}CH{=}CH_2$, NaOH, H_2O (Robinson annelation); (b) exactly the same reagents as 'a', but here the nucleophile is the α-carbon of the extended enolate formed by allylic deprotonation of the α,β-unsaturated ketone:

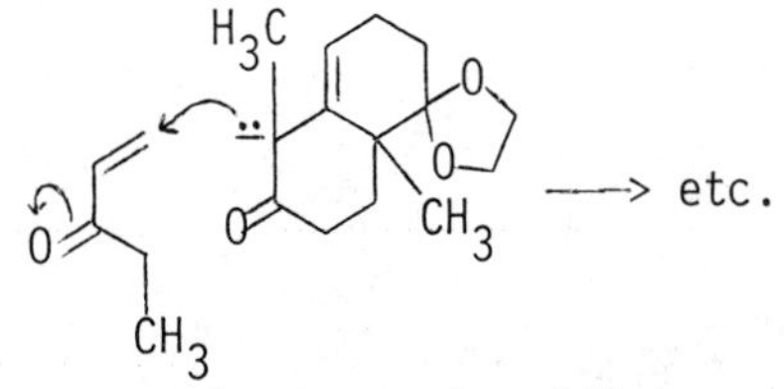

(c) 1. Li, NH_3 (reduces double bond, giving enolate), 2. CH_3I; (d) 1. excess H_2, Pt (reduces C=C and C=O bonds), 2. H^+, H_2O (hydrolyzes acetal), 3. $CH_3\overset{O}{\overset{\|}{C}}Cl$ (makes ester of newly formed alcohol); (e) 1. Cl_2, CH_3COOH (chlorinates α to ketone), 2. K_2CO_3, H_2O (eliminates HCl to make α,β-unsaturated ketone).

****

CHAPTER 17

Carboxylic Acids and Infrared Spectroscopy

General Introduction

The carboxylic acids and their derivatives contain a carbonyl group as one primary source of reactivity, and therefore will have a lot in common with aldehydes and ketones. Two major added features make carboxylic acids different. First, the HO proton is made much more acidic by the neighboring carbonyl group. Second, the HO attached to the carbonyl may behave as a leaving group under the right conditions. (Recall that aldehydes and ketones in general lack potential leaving groups on the carbonyl carbon.) This difference will be most important when you begin to study nucleophilic additions to the carboxylic acid carbonyl group.

This chapter will also present an introduction to infrared spectroscopy, a useful tool for qualitative identification of functional groups.

Outline of the Chapter

17-1. Naming Carboxylic Acids.

17-2. Physical Properties of Carboxylic Acids.

Very strongly hydrogen-bonding molecules; spectroscopy.

17-3. Infrared Spectroscopy.

A qualitatively new and useful technique.

17-4. The Acidity and Basicity of Carboxylic Acids.

An analysis of resonance and inductive effects.

17-5. The Preparation of Carboxylic Acids.

Reviewing reactions you've seen before.

17-6. The Reactivity of the Carboxy Group: Addition and Elimination.

A new, general mechanism sequence.

17-7. Alkanoyl Halides and Anhydrides.

17-8. Esters.

17-9. Amides.

Conversion of acids into their most important derivatives.

17-10. Nucleophilic Attack at a Carboxylate Group.

Reactions of acids with hydride or carbanion-like reagents.

17-11. α-Substitution and Decarboxylation.

Reactions of special value in synthesis.

17-12. Carboxylic Acids in Nature.

Keys to the Chapter

17-1 and 17-2. Nomenclature and Physical Properties of Carboxylic Acids.

Most of this material is routine in nature. The one physical characteristic that is unique to carboxylic acids is the strong tendency to form hydrogen-bonded dimers, resulting in much higher melting and boiling points relative to comparable compounds (Table 17-2). Notice also the very low field position of the COOH proton in the NMR. This is commonly associated with relatively acidic protons in molecules.

17-3. Infrared Spectroscopy.

Once the most important spectroscopic technique, infrared spectroscopy now is used with NMR in a complementary way. The IR technique helps confirm the presence or absence of common functional groups in a molecule. It is most diagnostic for the following: HO, C≡N, C≡C, C=O, and C=C. Certain special types of C-H bonds can be readily identified, although this mostly duplicates information obtained by NMR. Although occasionally the detailed data in Table 17-3 and in the text may be necessary to solve a problem, for the most part you will only need to look for bands in certain general regions of the IR spectrum, much the same way you have learned to divide up the NMR spectrum into rather general segments (e.g. aromatic C-H, alkene C-H, etc.). The following illustration, derived from the data in Table 17-3, shows these portions of the spectrum. IR data is easily converted into useful information using this chart. For instance, a molecule possessing a strong band somewhere between 1680 and 1800 cm^{-1} contains a C=O group. A molecule without an IR band in that region isn't a carbonyl compound. Combining information from a molecular formula with NMR and IR data usually permits complete determination of the structure of an unknown molecule. Several text problems will give you opportunities to practice.

this sort of exercise.

General Regions of the Infrared Spectrum

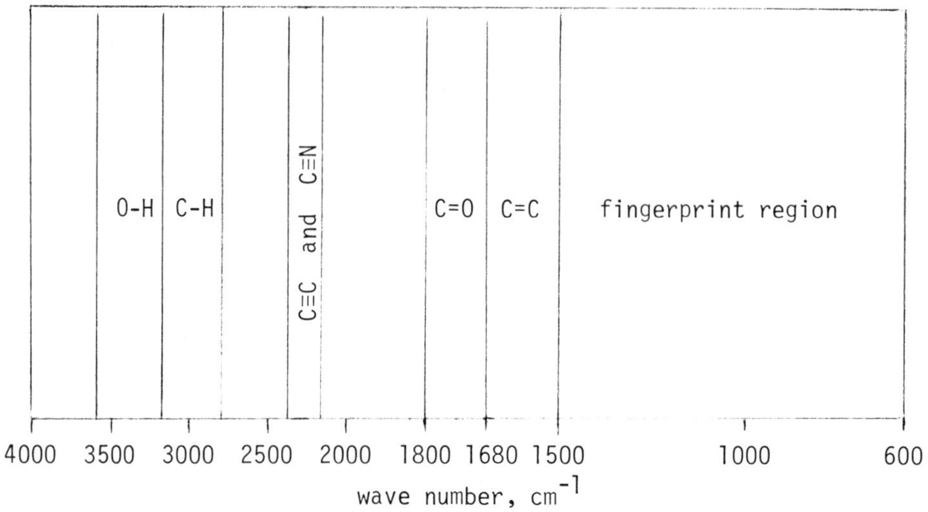

17-4. The Acidity and Basicity of Carboxylic Acids.

In order to really understand material of this sort, recall that acid and base strength is going to be determined by the charge-stabilizing ability in the structures of the acid-base conjugate pair. There will be three points to consider in evaluating the stability of a charged species: (1) the electronegativity of the charged atom(s), (2) the size of the charged atom(s), (3) stabilization of charge by either inductive effects or resonance. For carboxylic acids, the text sets up two comparisons:

Carboxylic acids vs. alcohols

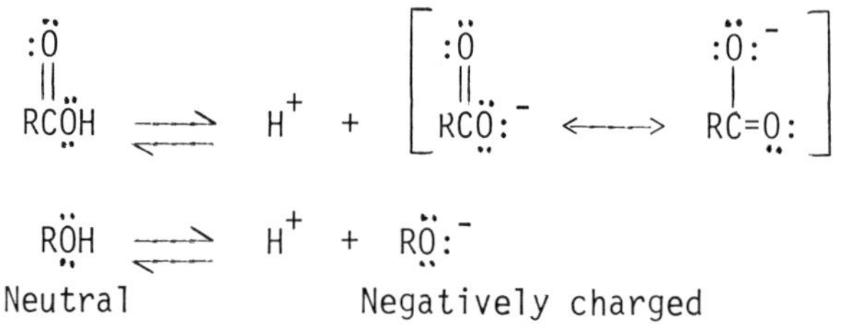

Both negatively charged conjugate bases have the same negative atom (O), but the carboxylate anion is stabilized further by inductive effects and resonance. Therefore, the carboxylate is more stable, so the carboxylic acid is a stronger acid than the alcohol.

Carboxylic acids vs. ketones or aldehydes

$$\overset{\displaystyle :\!\overset{..}{O}}{\underset{\displaystyle RCOH}{\|}} \;\; \overset{\longrightarrow}{\underset{\longleftarrow}{}} \;\; H^+ \; + \; \left[\; \overset{\displaystyle :\!\overset{..}{O}}{\underset{\displaystyle RC\overset{..}{O}:^-}{\|}} \; \longleftrightarrow \; \overset{\displaystyle :\!\overset{..}{O}:^-}{\underset{\displaystyle RC=\underset{..}{O}:}{|}} \;\right]$$

$$\overset{\displaystyle :\!\overset{..}{O}}{\underset{\displaystyle RCCH_3}{\|}} \;\; \overset{\longrightarrow}{\underset{\longleftarrow}{}} \;\; H^+ \; + \; \left[\; \overset{\displaystyle :\!\overset{..}{O}}{\underset{\displaystyle RCCH_2^-}{\|}} \; \longleftrightarrow \; \overset{\displaystyle :\!\overset{..}{O}:^-}{\underset{\displaystyle RC=CH_2}{|}} \;\right]$$

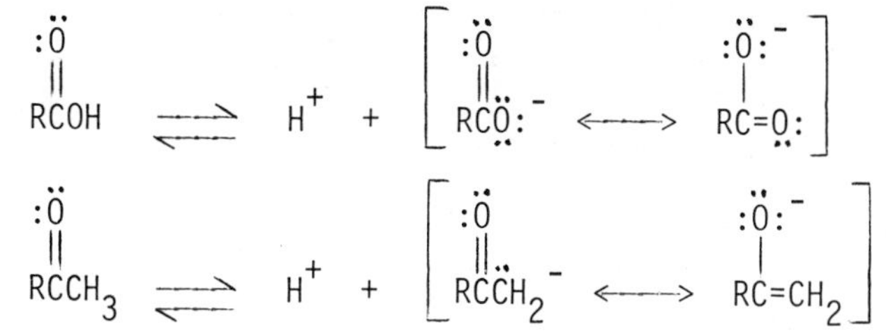

Neutral   Negatively charged

Both negatively charged conjugate bases are stabilized by inductive effects of a δ^+ carbonyl carbon. Both are also stabilized by resonance, but the carboxylate anion distributes its negative charge between two electronegative oxygens, while the enolate distributes its charge between a carbon and only one electronegative oxygen. The carboxylate anion is more stable, so the carboxylic acid is the stronger one.

Similar analyses can be applied to base strength as well. See chapter-end problems 9 and 10 and their answers for examples and explanations.

17-5. The Preparation of Carboxylic Acids.

While the most obvious synthesis of carboxylic acids are simple functional group interconversions (mainly oxidations), there are quite a few that involve breaking or forming carbon-carbon bonds. You might take the time to do a quick review, and, then begin organizing these synthetic methods into appropriate categories.

17-6. The Reactivity of the Carboxy Group: Addition and Elimination.

The mechanistic discussion at the start of this section is central to both the chemistry of carboxylic acids and the chemistry of their derivatives. Read it very carefully, and copy down some of the schemes on your own, simply to have the practice writing them down. Here are a couple of key points to keep in mind:

1. Carboxylic acids and their derivatives contain potential leaving groups attached to their carbonyl carbon. After a nucleophile adds, the leaving group may leave, giving a net substitution reaction overall. This is a two-step "addition-elimination" mechanism. It is not the same as either an S_N2 or an S_N1 reaction, mechanistically: S_N1 and S_N2 reactions do not apply to sp^2 hybridized carbons.

2. This new type of substitution process may be catalyzed by either acid or base. The text shows how these work in detail. However, for carboxylic acids, the presence of a base will lead to deprotonation much faster than

nucleophilic addition. If the base is strong and deprotonation is essentially irreversible, nucleophilic addition will be <u>very difficult</u>, and will only occur with extraordinarily powerful nucleophilic reagents (e.g. $LiAlH_4$).

In these reactions you will see some unexpected species act as leaving groups, including strong bases such as HO^- and RO^-. While these were generally far too basic to be leaving groups in ordinary S_N2 reactions (Chapter 6), they can function that way here, because the tetrahedral intermediate is relatively high in energy compared with the carbonyl product, which has a very strong, very stable carbon-oxygen double bond. So, even some poor leaving groups can leave in the elimination step, and still result in an energetically favorable process overall. You saw a similar effect in the nucleophilic ring-opening of oxacyclopropanes with bases (Chapter 9). The high energy of the strained three-membered ring ether made loss of an alkoxide leaving group possible. To summarize:

<table>
<tr><td></td><td></td><td></td><td>Energetically</td></tr>
<tr><td>(a)</td><td>$\ddot{N}u^- +\ \overset{|}{\underset{|}{C}}{-}OH\ \longrightarrow\ Nu{-}\overset{|}{\underset{|}{C}}{-}\ +\ HO^-$</td><td></td><td>unfavorable</td></tr>
<tr><td>(b)</td><td>$\ddot{N}u^- +\ \overset{O}{\triangle}\ \longrightarrow\ Nu{-}\overset{|}{\underset{|}{C}}{-}\overset{|}{\underset{|}{C}}{-}O^-$</td><td></td><td>favorable
(strain is relieved)</td></tr>
<tr><td>(c)</td><td>$Nu{-}\overset{O^-}{\underset{R}{\overset{|}{\underset{|}{C}}}}{-}OH\ \longrightarrow\ Nu{-}\overset{O}{\overset{\|}{C}}{-}R\ +\ HO^-$</td><td></td><td>favorable
(stable C=O bond is
regenerated)</td></tr>
</table>

(From $\ddot{N}u^- + R{-}\overset{O}{\overset{\|}{C}}{-}OH$)

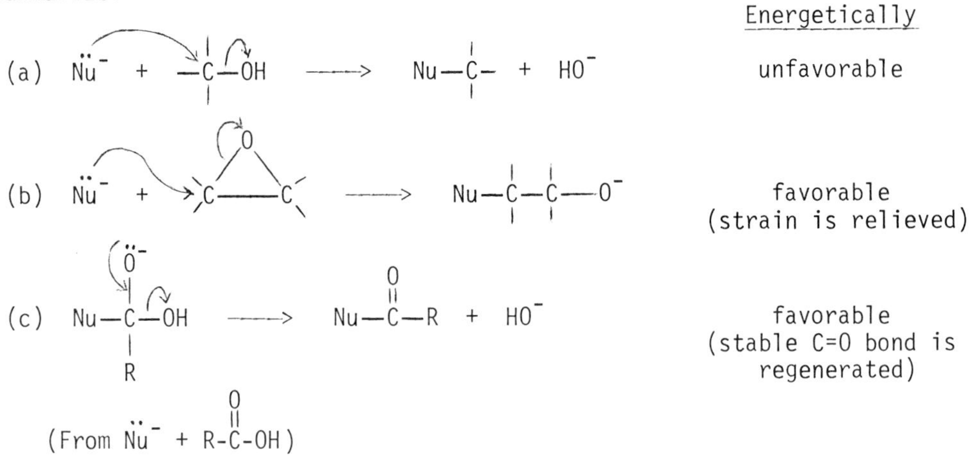

17-7, 17-8, and 17-9. <u>Alkanoyl Halides, Anhydrides, Esters, and Amides</u>.

In these sections the general mechanisms of the previous section will be applied in illustrating the transformations of carboxylic acids into their four most important derivatives. For later synthetic applications, carefully note the reagents involved in each transformation. In order to understand these reactions, pick out a few whose mechanisms are not given in detail in the text, and try to write them out, step-by-step. The practice will be worthwhile.

17-10. <u>Nucleophilic Attack at a Carboxylate Group</u>.

Strongly basic nucleophiles irreversibly deprotonate carboxylic acids, forming carboxylate anions. Addition-elimination reactions on carboxylate anions are hard to do because (1) the addition is hard to do and (2) the elimination is hard to do. More specifically, (1) it is difficult to add one anion to another due to electrostatic repulsion and (2) oxide anions are extremely bad leaving groups. Nevertheless, RLi and $LiAlH_4$ both are capable of addition to $RCOO^-$, and the product of $LiAlH_4$ addition can go on to eliminate, formally, an aluminum oxide anion leaving group. The product of an acid + RLi is a ketone, and the product of an acid + $LiAlH_4$ is a primary alcohol.

17-11. α-Substitution and Decarboxylation.

The *second* most acidic proton in a carboxylic acid molecule is an α-hydrogen. Although its actual pKa is not known, it may be removed by a second mole of very strong base, yielding a dianion. The α-carbon of this dianion is both more basic and more nucleophilic than either oxygen of the carboxylate anion; therefore S_N2 alkylations occur preferentially at the α position in the dianion. An alternative method of α-substitution in carboxylic acids is via the α-bromo derivative, synthesized using the Hell-Volhard-Zelinsky reaction.

Decarboxylation of carboxylic acids removes a carbon atom, usually as carbon dioxide. Kolbe electrolysis is of some value in generating symmetrical hydrocarbons, while the Hunsdiecker reaction is occasionally used to prepare halides that are relatively inaccessible using other synthetic routes. You will later see more generally useful decarboxylation reactions that proceed via anionic mechanisms.

Solutions to Chapter 17 Problems

1. (a) 2-chloro-4-methylpentanoic acid; (b) 2-ethyl-3-butenoic acid; (c) *E*-2-bromo-3,4-dimethyl-2-pentenoic acid; (d) cyclopentylethanoic acid; (e) *trans*-2-hydroxycyclohexanecarboxylic acid; (f) *E*-2-chlorobutenedioic acid; (g) $H_2NCH_2CH_2CH_2COOH$; (h)

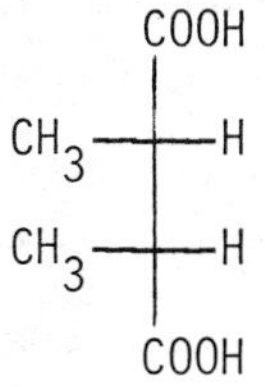

; (i)

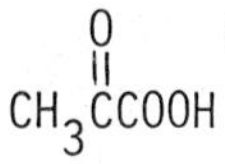

;

(j)

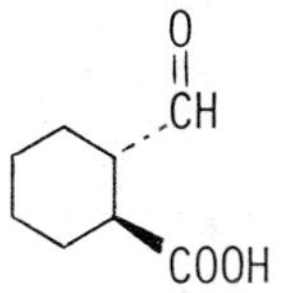

****

2. 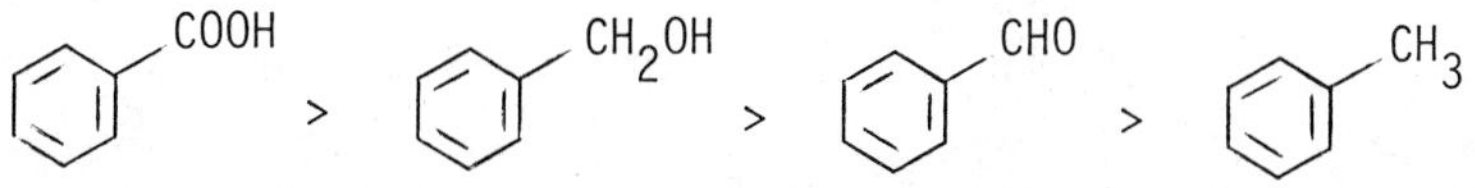

for both (1) and (2).

The acid has the most hydrogen bonding capability, and will have the highest boiling point (249°C) due to hydrogen-bonded dimer formation. The alcohol, which can also hydrogen bond, is next (205°C), the polar aldehyde third (178°C), and the nearly nonpolar hydrocarbon last (115°C). Solubilities follow similar considerations, except that the acid and alcohol are quite similar in water solubility since they can both hydrogen bond with H_2O.

****

3. Lower, because the vibrational frequency varies inversely with the square of the "reduced" mass involving the atoms about the bond. So, bonds involving heavier atoms have lower energies associated with vibrational excitation. Typically, $\tilde{\nu}_{C-Cl} \simeq 700\ cm^{-1}$, $\tilde{\nu}_{C-Br} \simeq 600\ cm^{-1}$, and $\tilde{\nu}_{C-I} \simeq 500\ cm^{-1}$.

****

4. $10{,}000/\tilde{\nu} = \mu m$

(a) 5.81 μm; (b) 6.06 μm; (c) 3.03 μm; (d) 11.24 μm; (e) 9.09 μm; (f) 4.42 μm.

****

5. C≡C-H of terminal alkyne has $\tilde{\nu}_{C-H} \simeq 3300\ cm^{-1}$.

(a) $CH_3CH_2CH_2CH_2C{\equiv}CCH_2C{\equiv}C\text{-}D$; (b) C≡C-D ($\tilde{\nu}_{C-D}$).

(c) Before reaction, m_1 is H (mass = 1) and m_2 is C_9H_{11} (mass = 119). Rewrite the Hooke's law equation as $\tilde{\nu}^2 = k^2 f \frac{(m_1 + m_2)}{m_1 m_2}$. So $(3300)^2 = k^2 f \frac{120}{119}$, or $k^2 f = 1.1 \times 10^7$. Since k and f are assumed to be constant, use this value for $k^2 f$ to predict $\tilde{\nu}^2$ for the product. Now m_1 is D (mass = 2), so $\tilde{\nu}^2 = (1.1 \times 10^7)\frac{121}{238} = 5.6 \times 10^6$ and predicted $\tilde{\nu}_{C-D} = 2366\ cm^{-1}$. The discrepancy of about 10% is typical and due to changes in k and f.

****

6. (i) Both alkene (1660) and alcohol (3350) products have formed.
(ii) Only alkene (1670) forms. (iii) Only alcohol (3350) forms.

(a) Conclusions: Isomer 'C' is probably a primary bromoalkane, which gives a primary alcohol product (S_N2). Isomer 'B' is probably a tertiary bromoalkane, which gives only alkene as product (E2). Isomer

'A' is probably a secondary bromoalkane, which gives a mixture of S_N2 and E2 products.

(b) 'A' possibilities: $CH_3CHBrCH_2CH_2CH_3$, $CH_3CHBrCH(CH_3)_2$, or $CH_3CH_2CHBrCH_2CH_3$

'B' possibilities: $(CH_3)_2CBrCH_2CH_3$ (only tertiary isomer)

'C' possibilities: $CH_3CH_2CH_2CH_2CH_2Br$, $(CH_3)_2CHCH_2CH_2Br$, or $CH_3CH_2CH(CH_3)CH_2Br$, but probably not $(CH_3)_3CCH_2Br$ (too hindered to give S_N2 reaction)

****

7. Look for the presence of bands characteristic of the major functional groups (Table 17-3) first. For example:
(1) C=C (1646); (3) C=C (1647) and C≡C or C≡N (2260); (4) also C≡C or C≡N (2260); (5) COOH (1708 and 2500-3300); (6) C=O's again (1710 and 1730), one is COOH (2500-3300); (7) C≡C-H (2120 and 3300) and either O-H or N-H (3330); (8) C=C (1666) and either O-H or N-H (3356); (9) C=O (1718); (10) C=O (1737).
Now start matching. Remember, the *absence* of a band in a characteristic region *usually* is good evidence for the absence of that functional group. (1) an alkene, no other functional groups, so choose (d). Note $R_2C{=}CH_2$ 880 cm^{-1} band. (2) Nothing much there, but 1120 cm^{-1} could be an ether C-O, so choose (a). (3) = (f). (4) = (h). (5) = (g). (6) = (j). (7) = (i). (8) = (b). (9) and (10): all that are left are the ketone (e) and the ester (c). Since esters generally have somewhat higher $\tilde{\nu}_{C=O}$ than ketones, choose (9) = (e) and (10) = (c).

****

8. See Study Guide Chapter 11 for information on degrees of unsaturation.

(a) $H_{sat'd} = 14 + 2 = 16$; deg. unsat'n. $= \frac{16-12}{2} = 2$ π bonds and/or rings are present. Compare Figures 17-4 and 17-14. This is a carboxylic acid ($\tilde{\nu}$ = 1704 and 3040 cm^{-1}).

(b) For E, $H_{sat'd} = 12 + 2 = 14$; deg. unsat'n. $= \frac{14-10}{2} = 2$ π bonds and/or rings. From the C-13 NMR (3 signals), the molecule would seem to have two-fold symmetry, with two sets of equivalent pairs of alkyl carbons, and a pair of equivalent alkene carbons. The H-1 NMR shows two equal-area upfield signals (4H each), and a 2H alkene signal. So the pieces seem to be:

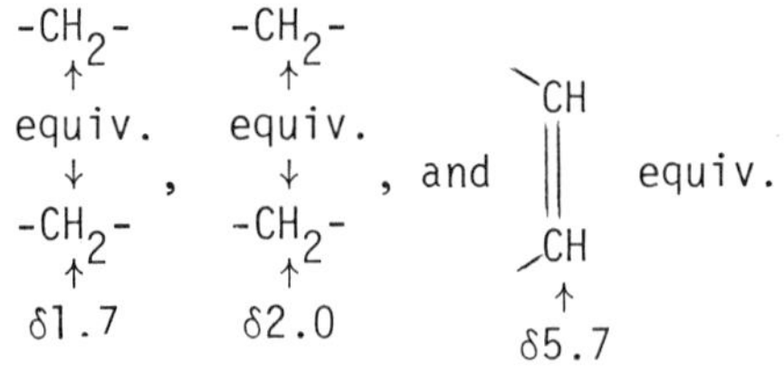

$-CH_2-$ $-CH_2-$ which can be simply put

equiv.   equiv.   together to give

$-CH_2-$ $-CH_2-$ and $\begin{array}{c}\text{CH}\\ \| \\ \text{CH}\end{array}$ equiv.   cyclohexene!

$\delta 1.7$ $\delta 2.0$ $\delta 5.7$

Then, F = [cyclohexanol with OH] $\delta 69.5$(C-13) via oxymercuration-demercuration,

G = [cyclohexanone] $\delta 208.5$(C-13), ($\tilde{\nu}_{C=O}$ = 1715 cm^{-1}), H = [methylenecyclohexane with CH_2] ($\tilde{\nu}_{C=C}$ = 1649 cm^{-1} and $\tilde{\nu}_{C=CH_2}$ = 888 cm^{-1}) via Wittig reaction, I = [cyclohexane with CH_2OH] $\delta 3.4$(d) ($\tilde{\nu}_{O-H}$ = 3328 cm^{-1}) via hydroboration-oxidation, and D = [cyclohexane with CO_2H].

(c) For J, $H_{sat'd}$ = 16 + 2 = 18; deg. unsat'n. = $\frac{18-14}{2}$ = 2 π bonds and/or rings. IR, $\tilde{\nu}$ = 1742 cm^{-1} is C=O, very possibly an ester due to the high value and the large number of oxygens in the formula. NMR, only three signals, with area ratios 2:2:3. Since there are 14H in the formula, the molecule must be symmetrical, with pieces such as 2 CH_3-O- ($\delta 3.7$), 2 $-CH_2-\overset{O}{\overset{\|}{C}}-$? ($\delta 2.4$), and 2 more equivalent $-CH_2-$'s ($\delta 1.7$). The splitting between the upfield signals suggests that the sets of CH_2's are connected, so a reasonable answer is

$$CH_3-O-\overset{O}{\overset{\|}{C}}-CH_2-CH_2$$
$$CH_3-O-\underset{\underset{O}{\|}}{C}-CH_2-CH_2$$

(d) [cyclohexene] $\xrightarrow[\text{2. Zn, H}^+, \text{H}_2\text{O}]{\text{1. O}_3}$ [hexanedial, CHO CHO] $\xrightarrow{\text{Na}_2\text{Cr}_2\text{O}_7, \text{H}_2\text{SO}_4, \text{H}_2\text{O}}$ [diacid, CO$_2$H CO$_2$H] $\xrightarrow{\text{H}^+, \text{CH}_3\text{OH}}$ J

(e) How about [cyclohexanol with OH] $\xrightarrow[\text{2. Mg}]{\text{1. PBr}_3}$ [cyclohexyl MgBr] $\xrightarrow[\text{2. H}^+, \text{H}_2\text{O}]{\text{1. CO}_2}$ [cyclohexane with CO$_2$H]

(f) [cyclohexane with CO$_2$H] $\xrightarrow{\text{LiAlH}_4}$ [cyclohexane with CH$_2$OH] $\xrightarrow[\text{2. K}^+ \text{ }^-\text{OC(CH}_3)_3]{\text{1. PBr}_3}$ [methylenecyclohexane with CH$_2$] $\xrightarrow[\text{2. Zn, H}^+, \text{H}_2\text{O}]{\text{1. O}_3}$

[cyclohexanone, C=O] $\xrightarrow{\text{LiAlH}_4}$ [cyclohexanol with OH] $\xrightarrow{\text{H}_2\text{SO}_4, \Delta}$ [cyclohexene]

****

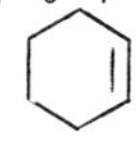

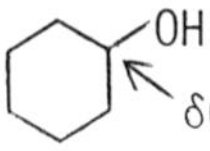

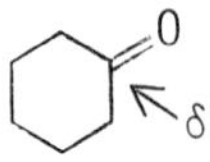

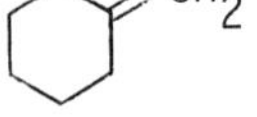

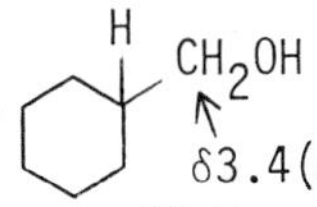

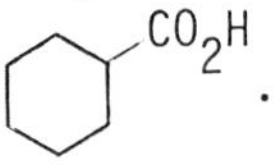

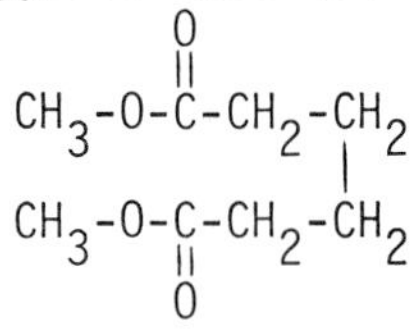

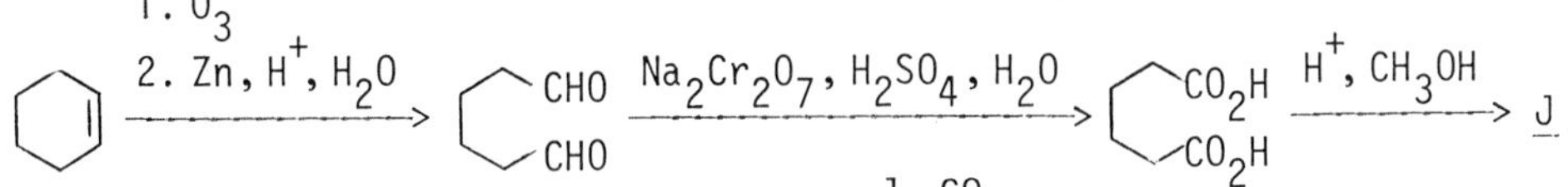

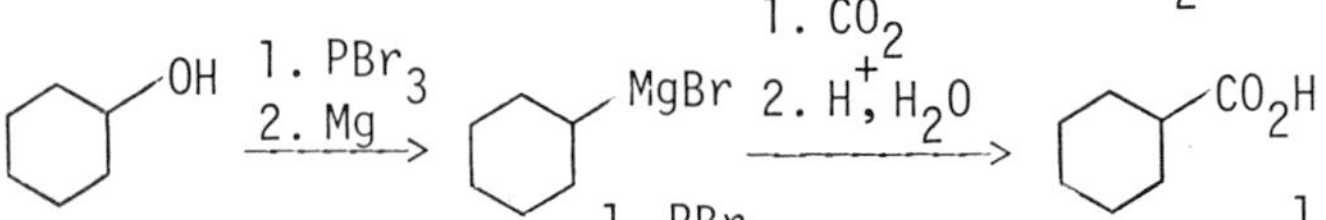

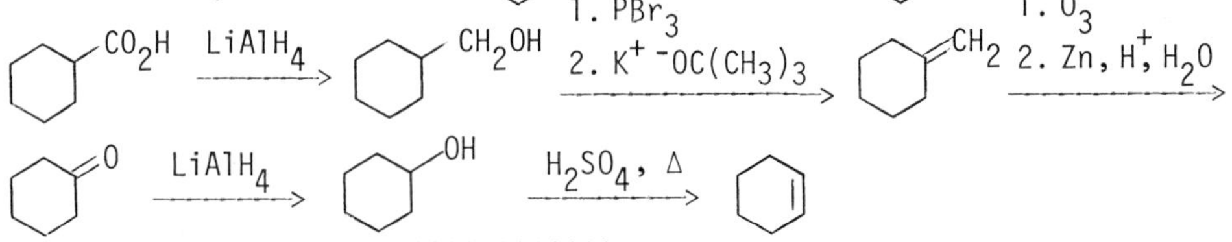

9. (a) Order is as written.   (b) Order is reverse of that given.

(c) $CH_3CH_2CHClCO_2H > CH_3CHClCH_2CO_2H > ClCH_2CH_2CH_2CO_2H$.   (d) Order is as written.

****

10. Acidity: $CH_3\overset{O}{\overset{\|}{C}}OH > CH_3\overset{O}{\overset{\|}{C}}NH_2 > CH_3\overset{O}{\overset{\|}{C}}CH_3$.   Most acidic hydrogens in $CH_3\overset{O}{\overset{\|}{C}}NH_2$ are on nitrogen.   Acidity order is determined by electronegativity.

Two possibilities: on N, giving $CH_3\overset{O}{\overset{\|+}{C}}NH_3$, and on 0, giving

$CH_3\overset{\overset{+}{O}H}{\overset{\|}{C}}-\overset{..}{N}H_2 \quad \leftrightarrow \quad CH_3\overset{OH}{\overset{|}{C}}=\overset{+}{N}H_2$.   Resonance stabilization causes protonation on 0 to be favored.

****

11. (a) $Na_2Cr_2O_7$, H_2O, H_2SO_4;   (b) $KMnO_4$, OH^-;   (c) 1. Mg, 2. CO_2, 3. H^+, H_2O;

(d) 1. NaCN, 2. KOH, H_2O, Δ, 3. H^+, H_2O, Δ;   (e) 1. $SOCl_2$ (makes alkanoyl chloride), 2. add one more mole of starting acid, Δ;   (f) $(CH_3)_3COH$, H^+;

(g) HCOOH, Δ (Did the structure fool you? $H\overset{O}{\overset{\|}{C}}NR_2$ is an amide of methanoic acid);   (h) 1. $AgNO_3$, KOH, H_2O, 2. Br_2, CCl_4.

****

12. See Problem 5 of Chapter 15.

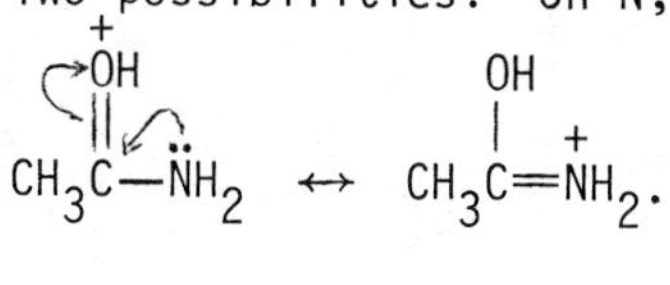

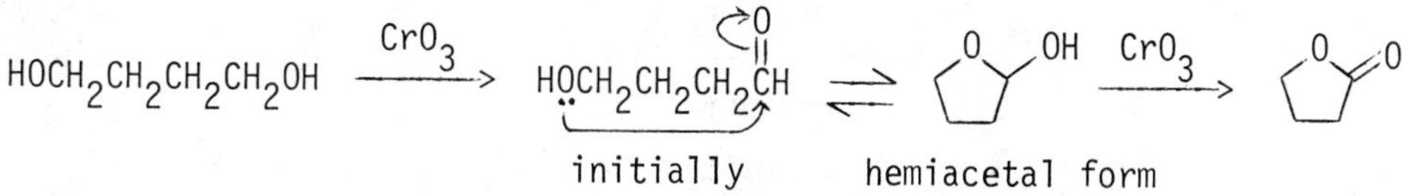

$HOCH_2CH_2CH_2CH_2OH \xrightarrow{CrO_3} HOCH_2CH_2CH_2\overset{O}{\overset{\|}{C}}H \rightleftarrows$ [cyclic structure] $\xrightarrow{CrO_3}$ [cyclic structure]

initially   hemiacetal form

****

13. (a) $CH_3(CH_2)_5Br$ Either $\begin{array}{l}1.\ Mg \\ 2.\ CO_2 \\ 3.\ H^+,\ H_2O\end{array}$ or $\begin{array}{l}1.\ NaCN \\ 2.\ KOH,\ H_2O,\ Δ \\ 3.\ H^+,\ H_2O,\ Δ\end{array}$ ⟶ product

(b) $CH_3CH=CH_2 \xrightarrow{Cl_2,\ H_2O} CH_3\overset{OH}{\overset{|}{C}}HCH_2Cl \xrightarrow{\begin{array}{l}1.\ ^-CN \\ 2.\ HO^-,\ H_2O,\ Δ \\ 3.\ H^+,\ H_2O,\ Δ\end{array}}$ product

(O.K. to start here, actually)

(c) $(CH_3)_3CCl$ $\xrightarrow{\begin{array}{l}1.\ Mg\\2.\ CO_2\\3.\ H^+,\ H_2O\end{array}}$ product

(d) $\xrightarrow{KMnO_4,\ HO^-}$ product

****

14. (a) $CH_3CH_2\ddot{O}H + Cl-\overset{O}{\underset{}{C}}-C_6H_5$ $\xrightarrow{\text{addition}}$ $CH_3CH_2-\overset{+}{\underset{H}{O}}-\overset{\bar{O}}{\underset{Cl}{C}}-C_6H_5 + \ ^-\!:OH \longrightarrow$

$CH_3CH_2-O-\overset{\bar{:O}}{\underset{Cl}{C}}-C_6H_5$ $\xrightarrow[\text{elimination}]{-Cl^-}$ $CH_3CH_2-O-\overset{O}{\underset{}{C}}-C_6H_5$

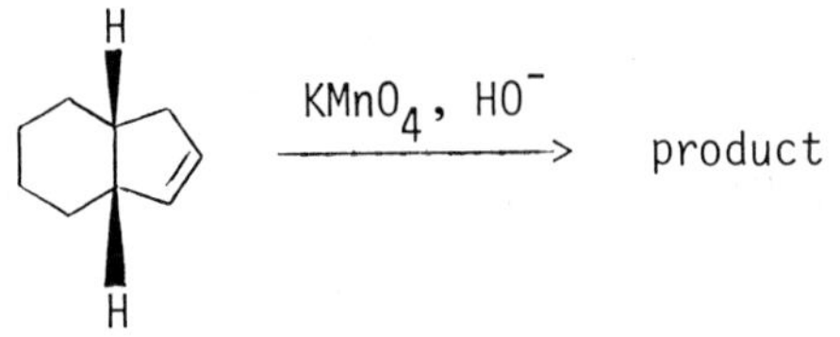

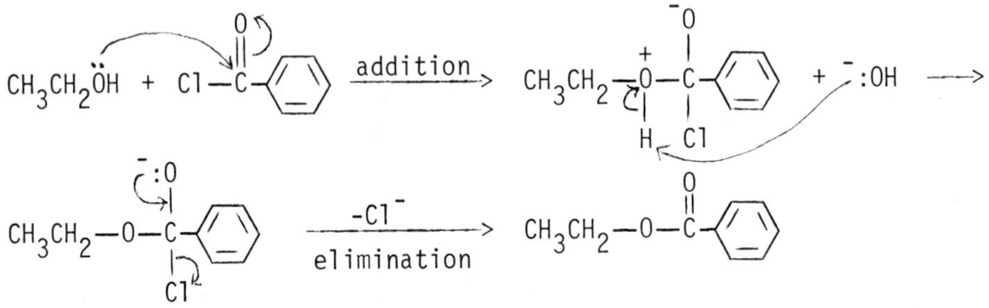

tetrahedral intermediate

(b) $CH_3-\overset{O:}{\underset{}{C}}-NH_2$ $\underset{\text{(Problem 10)}}{\overset{H^+}{\rightleftharpoons}}$ $CH_3-\overset{+OH}{\underset{}{C}}-NH_2 + H_2\ddot{O}$ $\longrightarrow$ $CH_3-\overset{OH}{\underset{NH_2}{\overset{|}{C}}}-\overset{+}{O}\overset{H}{\underset{H}{}} \longrightarrow$

$CH_3-\overset{OH}{\underset{NH_2}{\overset{|}{C}}}-OH + H^+$ $\rightleftharpoons$ $CH_3-\overset{:O-H}{\underset{+NH_3}{\overset{|}{C}}}-OH \longrightarrow NH_3 + CH_3\overset{O-H}{\underset{}{C}}-OH \xrightarrow{-H^+} CH_3\overset{O}{\underset{}{C}}OH$

****

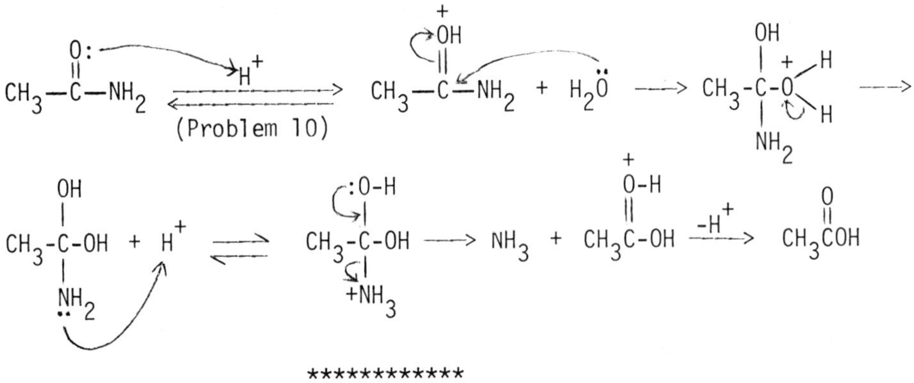

15. (a) Acid catalysis is understood for esterification. So:

$CH_3CH_2-\overset{O:}{\underset{}{C}}-OH \xrightarrow{H^+} CH_3CH_2-\overset{+OH}{\underset{}{C}}-OH \xrightarrow{CH_3CH_2{}^{18}\ddot{O}H} CH_3CH_2-\overset{OH}{\underset{{}^{18}O}{\overset{|}{C}}}-\ddot{O}H \underset{-H^+}{\overset{H^+}{\rightleftharpoons}}$

$H \overset{+}{\underset{}{}} CH_2CH_3$

$CH_3CH_2-\overset{O-H}{\underset{{}^{18}OCH_2CH_3}{\overset{|}{C}}}-\overset{+}{O}H_2 \xrightarrow{-H^+,\ H_2O} CH_3CH_2\overset{O}{\underset{}{C}}-{}^{18}O-CH_2CH_3$ is the product.

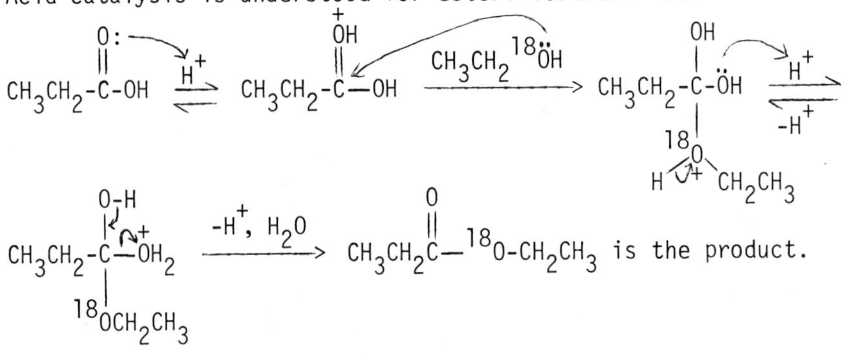

(b) 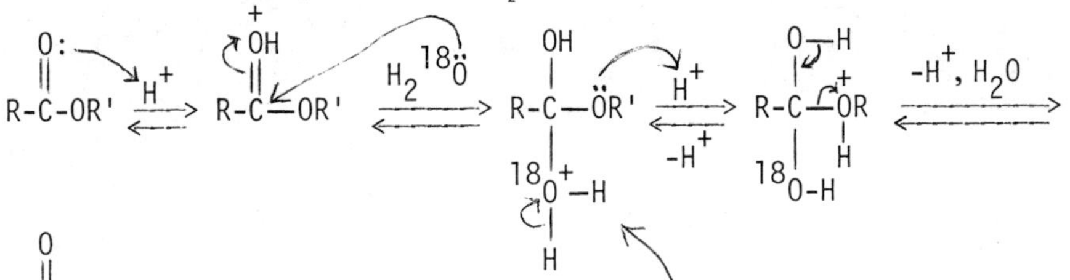

$R-C(=O)-^{18}OH$. Alternatively, though, this intermediate could protonate on the unlabeled OH group instead of the OR' group:

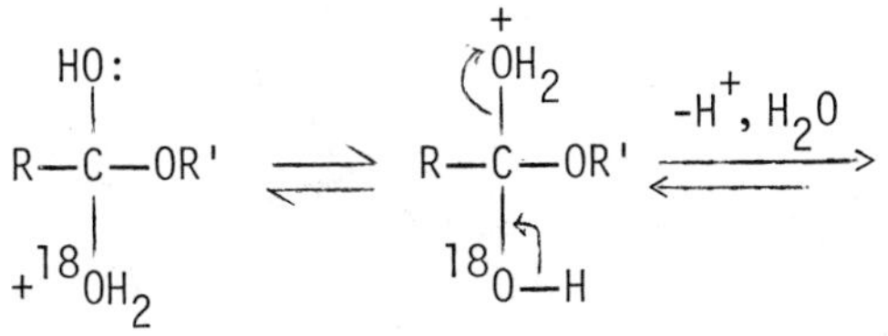

gives $R-C(=^{18}O)-OR'$! Ester containing ^{18}O in the carbonyl oxygen. Now if you follow the hydrolysis mechanism written above, the product will be $R-C(=^{18}O)-^{18}OH$!

****

16. K = 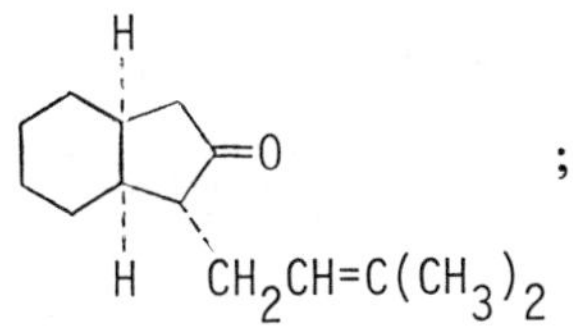 ; L = 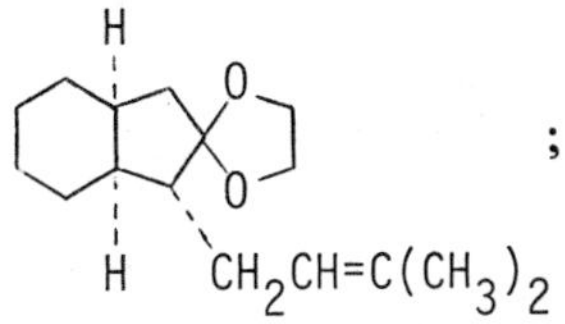 ; M = 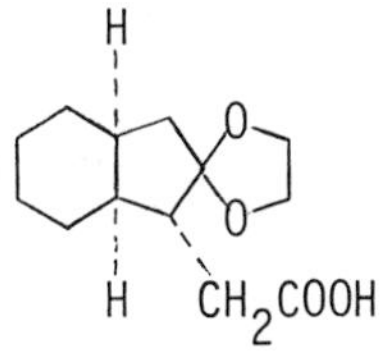 ;

(alkylation on less hindered bottom face)

N = 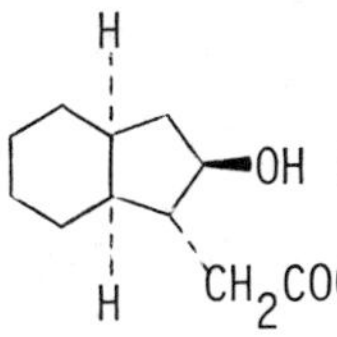 (via ketone); O = 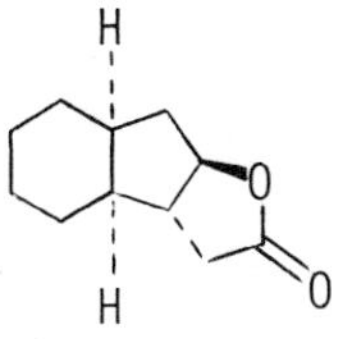 a lactone ($\tilde{\nu}_{C=O}$ = 1770 cm^{-1}).

****

17. (a) Haloalkanes are generally not very soluble in water (too much polarity difference). The reaction mixture is heterogeneous, which prevents good mixing of reactants. Water also hydrogen bonds the nucleophile, which doesn't help either.

(b) Ethanoic acid is a better solvent for the haloalkane, so the system is homogeneous, allowing for better mixing of reacting molecules.

(c) Sodium dodecanoate is a soap, and it dissolves in water to make micelles. The less-polar interior regions of the micelles form good solvents for molecules of low polarity like haloalkanes. The iodobutane dissolves *in the micelles*, and is therefore in close proximity to the nucleophilic carboxylate groups, allowing the S_N2 reaction to proceed.

****

18.  The carbon is basic.

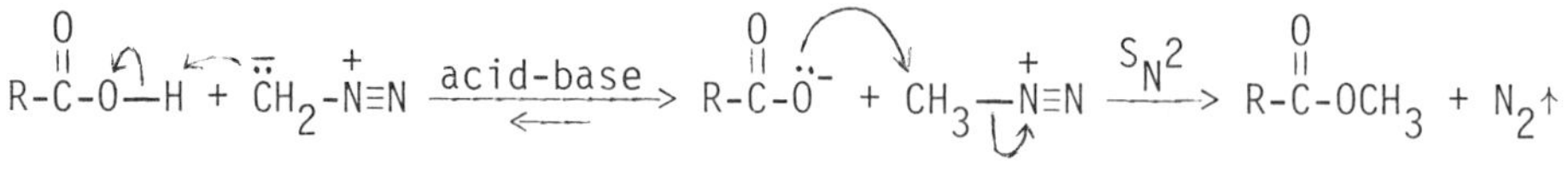

****

19.

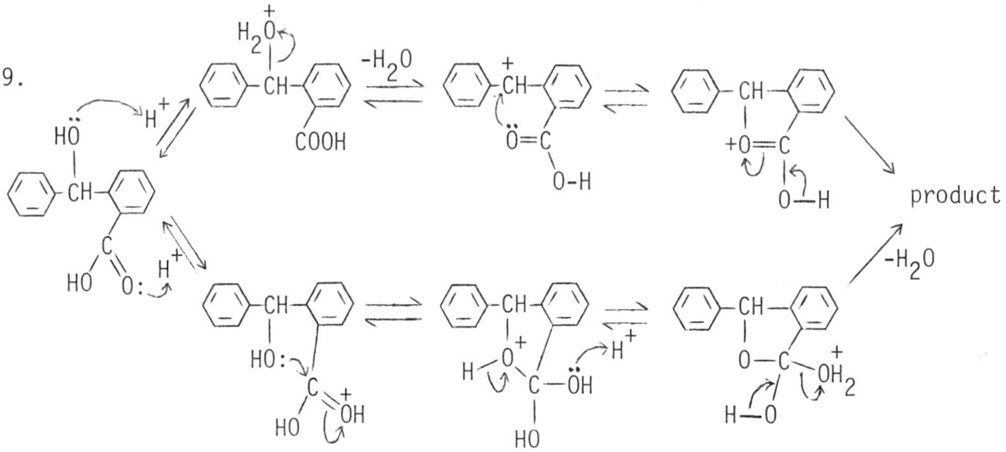

Top mechanism is an S_N1 on the alcohol, bottom mechanism is the "standard" addition-elimination on the carboxyl group. Labeling the alcohol with ^{18}O will distinguish them. The ^{18}O will be lost in the top mechanism, but it will be retained in the bottom one.

****

20. (a) $CH_3CH_2C(=O)Cl$; (b) $CH_3CH_2C(=O)Br$; (c) $CH_3CH_2C(=O)OC(=O)CH_2CH_3$; (d) $CH_3CH_2C(=O)OCH(CH_3)_2$;

(e) $CH_3CH_2C(=O)OCH_3$; (f) $CH_3CH_2C(=O)OCH_2CH_3$; (g) $CH_3CH_2C(=O)O^-$ $H_3\overset{+}{N}CH_2-C_6H_5$;

(h) $CH_3CH_2C(=O)NHCH_2-C_6H_5$; (i) $CH_3CH_2CH_2OH$; (j) $CH_3CH_2C(=O)-C_6H_5$

(k) $CH_3\bar{C}HC(=O)O^-$ $2Li^+$; (l) $CH_2=CHCH_2CH(CH_3)COOH$ after H^+, H_2O.

****

21. Analyze: convert ketone portion by adding $CH_2=\overset{\overset{\displaystyle Li}{|}}{C}-CH_3$ (makes alcohol) and

dehydrating to diene; convert acid portion by addition of $CH_2=\overset{\overset{\displaystyle Li}{|}}{C}-CH_3$ also,

since lithium reagents convert acids to ketones. How convenient -- do both

at the same time! So:

1. excess $CH_2=\overset{\overset{\displaystyle Li}{|}}{C}-CH_3$, 2. H_2SO_4, Δ.

****

22. [cyclohexyl]-OH $\xrightarrow{PBr_3}$ [cyclohexyl]-Br $\xrightarrow[\text{3. } H^+, H_2O]{\substack{\text{1. Mg}\\\text{2. HCHO}}}$ [cyclohexyl]-CH$_2$OH $\xrightarrow{CrO_3(\text{pyridine})_2}$ [cyclohexyl]-CHO

1. Li / 2. CuI   1. SOCl$_2$ / 2. Mg   for (C)

(a) $($ [cyclohexyl] $)_2$CuLi + $CH_2=CH\overset{\overset{\displaystyle O}{||}}{C}CH_3$; (b) [cyclohexyl]-CH$_2$MgCl + $CH_2\!-\!\overset{\displaystyle O}{\diagup\!\diagdown}\!CH\!-\!CH_3$, then CrO_3;

(c) [cyclohexyl]-CHO + $Ph_3P=CHCCH_3$ followed by H_2, Pd. Product: [cyclohexyl]-$CH_2CH_2\overset{\overset{\displaystyle O}{||}}{C}CH_3$

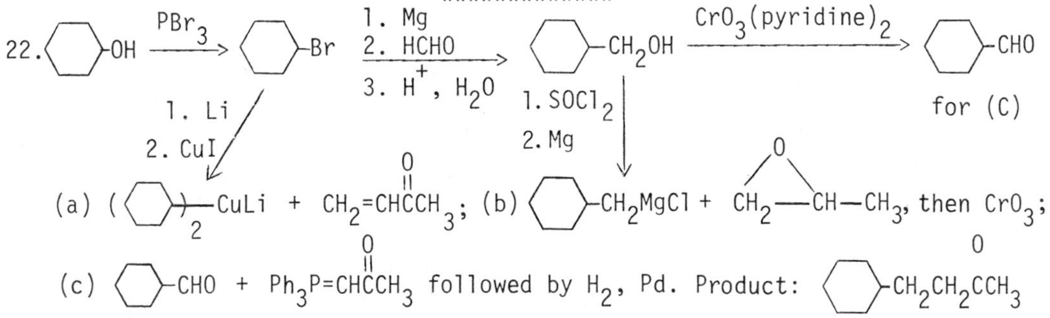

Depending on availability of starting materials either 'a' or 'b' is best.
Probably 'a', since the pieces are very simple ones.

****

23. Look for retrosynthetic disconnections. Here's one possible plan:

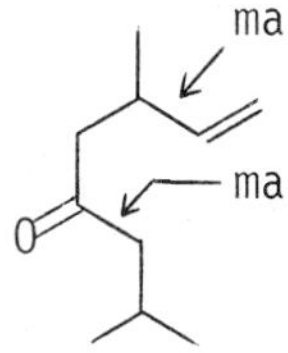

make via 1,4-addn. of cuprate to α,β-unsaturated ketone.

make via reaction of organolithium reagent with carboxylic acid.

So: $CH_3CH=CHCOOH$ + $2(CH_3)_2CHCH_2Li$ $\xrightarrow{\text{Then } H^+, H_2O}$ $CH_3CH=CH\overset{\overset{\displaystyle O}{||}}{C}CH_2CH(CH_3)_2$

$\xrightarrow[\text{1,4-addn.}]{\substack{\text{1. } (CH_2=CH)_2CuLi\\\text{2. } H^+, H_2O}}$ dihydrotagetone

****

24. 1. $LiAlH_4$ (makes 1-pentanol); 2. KBr, H_2SO_4, Δ; 3. KCN (makes 1-cyano-
pentane); 4. KOH, H_2O, Δ; 5. H^+, H_2O, Δ.

****

25. (a) $SOCl_2$ or PCl_5 or $ClC\overset{O}{\overset{\|}{C}}C\overset{O}{\overset{\|}{C}}Cl$; (b) H^+, CH_3OH; (c) H^+, 2-butanol;

(d) alkanoyl chloride (part 'a') + ethanoic acid; (e) CH_3NH_2 (via the

ammonium salt), Δ; (f) 2 CH_3Li; (g) $LiAlH_4$; (h) Br_2, cat. P; (i) 1.

2 LDA, 2. CH_3I; (j) 1. $AgNO_3$, KOH, H_2O, 2. Br_2.

****

26. (a) $CH_3CH_2CH_2COOH$ $\xrightarrow{Br_2, \text{ cat. } P}$ $CH_3CH_2\overset{Br}{\overset{|}{C}}HCOOH$ (via $CH_3CH_2CH_2\overset{O}{\overset{\|}{C}}Br$ $\rightleftharpoons$

$CH_3CH_2CH\overset{O-H}{=}\overset{}{C}-Br$ + $Br-Br$ $\longrightarrow$ $CH_3CH_2CHBr\overset{O}{\overset{\|}{C}}Br$ $\xrightarrow{\text{exchange}}$)

Then $CH_3CH_2\overset{Br}{\overset{|}{C}}HCOOH$ + $\ddot{N}H_3$ $\xrightarrow[S_N2]{-Br^-}$ $CH_3CH_2\overset{+NH_3}{\overset{|}{C}}HCOOH$ $\xrightarrow{-H^+}$ product

(b) ⬡—CH_2CO_2H $\xrightarrow[\text{2. KCN}]{\text{1. } Br_2, \text{ cat. P}}$ ⬡—$\overset{CN}{\overset{|}{C}}HCO_2H$ $\xrightarrow[\text{2. } H^+, H_2O]{\text{1. } HO^-, H_2O}$ product

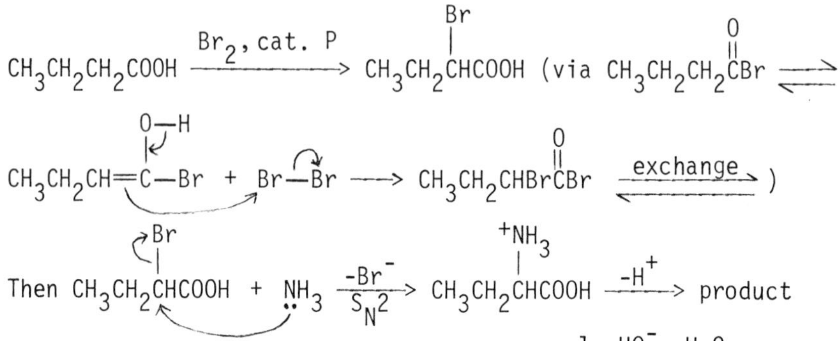

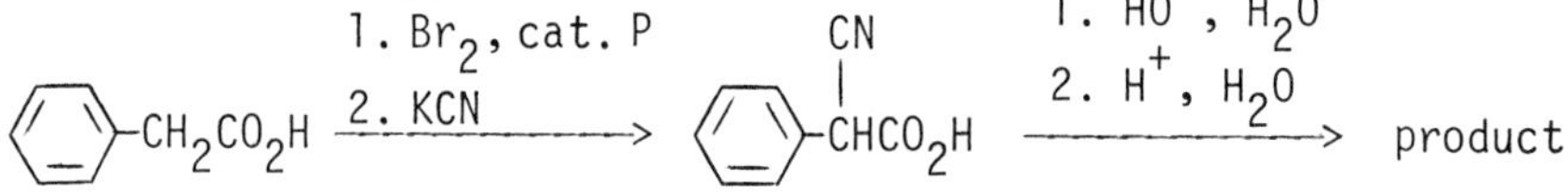

(c) $CH_3CH_2CH(CH_3)CH_2CH_2COOH$ $\xrightarrow{Br_2, \text{ cat. P}}$ $\xrightarrow[\text{2. } H^+, H_2O]{\text{Then } \text{1. } K_2CO_3, H_2O, \Delta}$ product

(d) CH_3COOH $\xrightarrow{Br_2, \text{ cat. P}}$ $BrCH_2COOH$ $\xrightarrow[\text{2. } I_2]{\text{1. excess KSH}}$ product

(e) $BrCH_2COOH$ + $(CH_3CH_2)_2NH$ $\longrightarrow$ product

(f) CH_3CH_2COOH $\xrightarrow[\text{2. } (C_6H_5)_3P]{\text{1. } Br_2, \text{ cat. P}}$ product

****

27. $^-:\ddot{O}-\overset{\overset{\ddot{O}}{\|}}{C}-\ddot{O}:^-$ and $^-\ddot{C}H_2-\overset{\overset{\ddot{O}}{\|}}{C}-\ddot{O}:^-$.

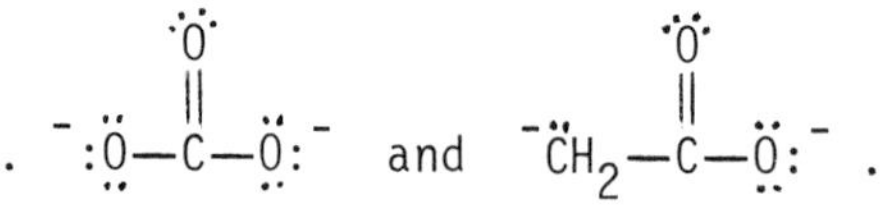

(a) The second is more basic. The two negative charges are distributed over only two electronegative oxygens and one carbon. In CO_3^{2-}, the charges are shared by three oxygens, which is better.

(b) $-\ddot{C}H_2-\overset{\overset{\textstyle O}{\|}}{C}-\ddot{C}H_2^- \leftrightarrow -\ddot{C}H_2-\overset{\overset{\textstyle :\ddot{O}:^-}{|}}{C}=CH_2$ for propanone

$-\ddot{C}H_2-\overset{\overset{\textstyle CH_2}{\|}}{C}-\ddot{C}H_2^-$ for 2-methylpropene

(c) propanone $\xrightarrow{\text{2 LDA, HMPA}}$ dianion; 2-methylpropene $\xrightarrow{\text{2 CH}_3\text{(CH}_2\text{)}_3\text{Li, HMPA}}$

dianion

(d) $-\ddot{C}H_2-\overset{\overset{\textstyle :\overset{..}{O}\cdot}{\|}}{C}-\ddot{O}:^- \leftrightarrow CH_2=\overset{\overset{\textstyle :\ddot{O}:^-}{|}}{C}-\ddot{O}:^-$ $\xrightarrow{\text{2 (CH}_3\text{)}_3\text{SiCl}}$ $CH_2=\overset{\underset{\textstyle \delta 4.0}{\uparrow}}{C}\overset{\textstyle OSi(CH_3)_3}{\underset{\textstyle OSi(CH_3)_3}{\Big\langle}}$ $\delta 0.5$

note resonance forms

****

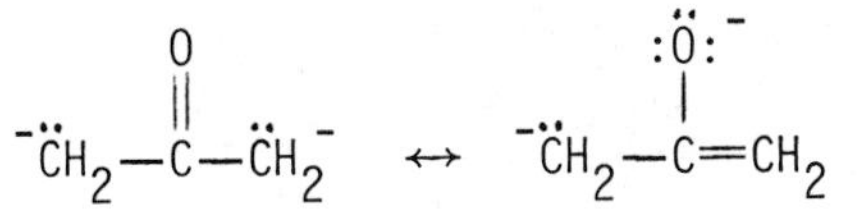

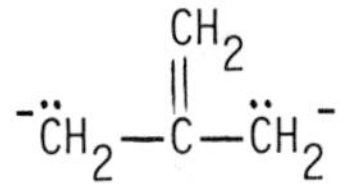

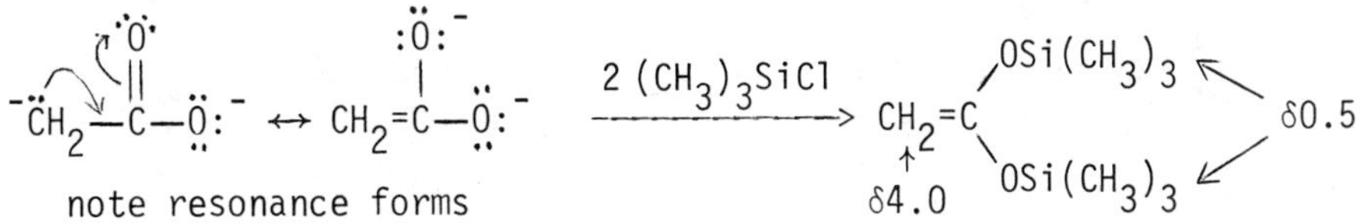

28. Only one of several possibilities is presented in each case.

(a) Make [cyclohexane ring]$-$COOH according to Problem 8. Then $\xrightarrow{\begin{array}{l}\text{1. 2LDA, HMPA}\\\text{2. } CH_2\overset{\overset{\textstyle O}{\diagdown}}{-}CH_2\\\text{3. H}^+, H_2O\end{array}}$ product

(b) $KMnO_4$, OH^- makes $HOOC(CH_2)_3COOH$. Then NH_3, Δ → product.

(c) 1. PBr_3, 2. Mg, 3. CO_2, 4. H^+, H_2O makes $(CH_3)_2CHCOOH$.

1. CrO_3, 2. $CH_2=P(C_6H_5)_3$, 3. MCPBA makes $(CH_3)_2CH\overset{\overset{\textstyle O}{\diagup\diagdown}}{-}CH_2$.

Then:

$(CH_3)_2CHCOOH \xrightarrow{\begin{array}{l}\text{1. 2LDA, HMPA}\\\text{2. } (CH_3)_2CH\overset{\overset{\textstyle O}{\diagup\diagdown}}{-}CH_2\end{array}} (CH_3)_2\overset{\overset{\textstyle OH}{|}}{C}-CH_2\overset{\overset{\textstyle CH_3 \,\, CH_3}{\diagdown\diagup}}{\underset{\textstyle C}{}}COOH \xrightarrow[-H_2O]{H_2SO_4}$ product

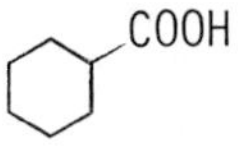

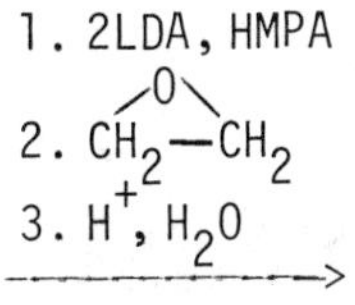

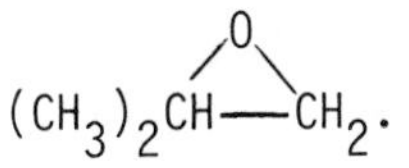

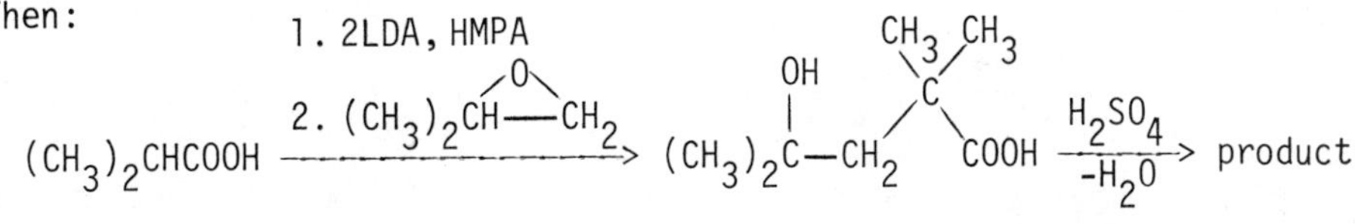

(d) $CH_3COOH \xrightarrow{\begin{array}{l}\text{1. 2LDA, HMPA}\\\text{2. } BrCH_2CH=CH_2\end{array}} CH_2=CHCH_2CH_2COOH \xrightarrow{\text{HBr, ROOR}}$

$BrCH_2CH_2CH_2CH_2COOH \xrightarrow{K_2CO_3, \, H_2O, \, \Delta}$ product (internal S_N2)

****

29. Free radical halogenation of cyclopropane itself is very difficult since the C-H bonds are so strong (recall Problem 3 of Chapter 4). Electrophilic reactions (e.g. additions to a double bond) are not useful because the ring is easily broken open. Nucleophilic substitutions are very difficult due to angle strain in the transition states of the reactions.

****

30. Work forwards and backwards from the given structure. The first reaction looks like an aldol condensation:

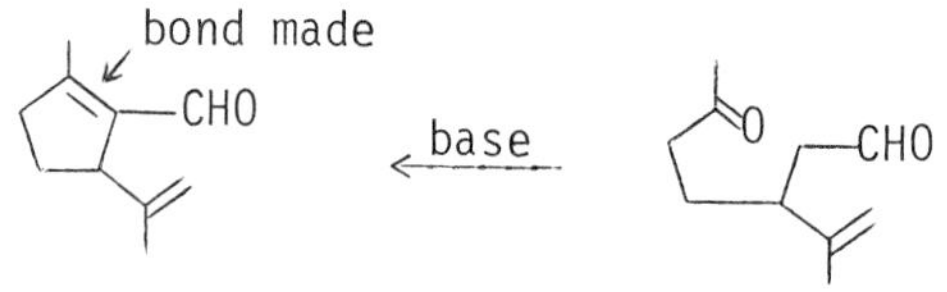

must be P

Then: Q = 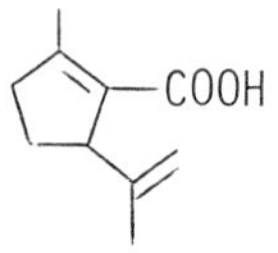

; R = 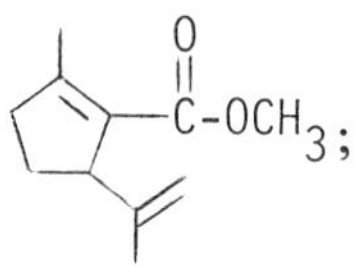

; S = 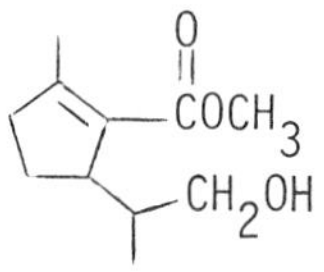

(note only the least hindered alkene is hydroborated); neonepetalactone = 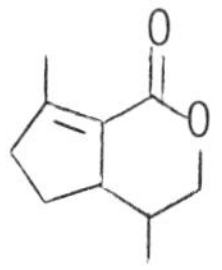

.

****

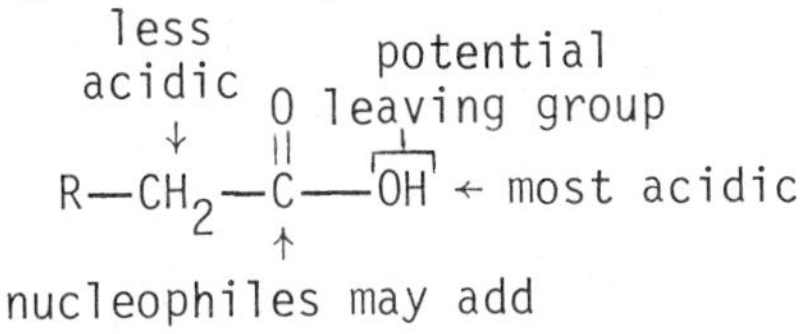

Carboxylic Acid Derivatives and Mass Spectroscopy

General Introduction

Derivatives of carboxylic acids share three properties in common with carboxylic acids themselves: (1) they have a carbonyl group which is susceptible to nucleophilic addition; (2) they have a potential leaving group attached to the carbonyl carbon; and (3) they may possess acidic hydrogens α to the carbonyl group. However, they lack an acidic -OH group on the carbonyl carbon itself. Therefore, it is the α-hydrogens in most carboxylic acid derivatives that are the most readily removed by strong bases.

$$\text{Carboxylic acid:} \quad \underset{\uparrow}{\overset{\overset{\text{less}}{\underset{\downarrow}{\text{acidic}}}}{R-CH_2}} - \overset{O}{\overset{\|}{C}} - \overset{\overset{\text{potential}}{\text{leaving group}}}{OH} \leftarrow \text{most acidic}$$

nucleophiles may add

$$\text{Carboxylic acid derivatives:} \quad \underset{\uparrow}{\overset{\overset{\text{now most}}{\underset{\downarrow}{\text{acidic}}}}{R-CH_2}} - \overset{O}{\overset{\|}{C}} - \overset{\overset{\text{potential}}{\underset{\downarrow}{\text{leaving group}}}}{L}$$

nucleophiles may add

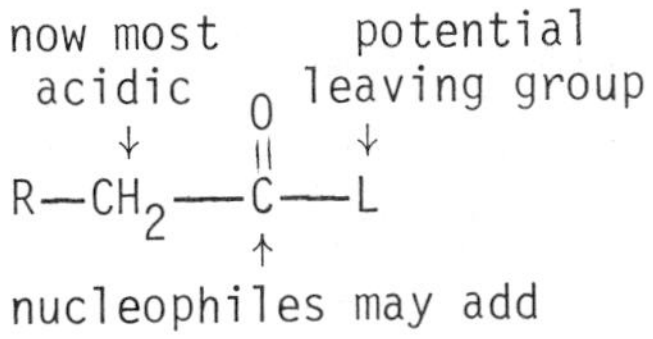

L = halide (alkanoyl halide)

$$L = O\overset{O}{\overset{\|}{C}}R' \quad \text{(anhydride)}$$

L = OR' (ester)

L = NR$_2$' (amide)

Since the mechanisms associated with reactions of these compounds have already been introduced (Section 17-6), you will find that this chapter will mainly present additional examples of reactions that follow familiar patterns. The most important new points to be made will involve (1) the relative reactivities of these derivatives and (2) how to convert each kind of derivative into any of the others, for synthetic purposes.

Finally, a brief description of mass spectroscopy will be presented. This is a technique with very specific kinds of applications in structure analysis of molecules.

Outline of the Chapter

18-1. The Relative Reactivity of Carboxylic Acid Derivatives and Their Structural and Spectral Characteristics.

Comparisons of physical properties.

18-2. Alkanoyl Halides.

18-3. Carboxylic Anhydrides.

18-4. Esters.

18-5. Amides.

18-6. Alkanenitriles.

Details of the chemistry of the four major carboxylic acid derivatives, plus nitriles, indirect relatives of amides.

18-7. Mass Spectroscopy.

A new physical technique.

Keys to the Chapter

18-1. The Relative Reactivity of Carboxylic Acid Derivatives and Their Structural and Spectral Characteristics.

In this section, differences in physical properties of the four main carboxylic acid derivatives are highlighted. The principle factor determining these differences is the electronegativity of the atom attached to the carbonyl carbon. These differences are reflected in a consistent way throughout all the reactions of these compounds: deprotonation of the α-carbon, addition to the carbonyl carbon, and protonation of the carbonyl oxygen. Make sure you see the conceptual patterns here before moving ahead to the specific sections on each derivative. Then, refer back to this text section from time to time as you go through the chapter to see how the reaction details presented in the upcoming sections reflect the general principles outlined here.

18-2. Alkanoyl Halides.

Alkanoyl (acyl) halides are very useful in synthesis because (1) they are easily made from carboxylic acids (Section 17-7) and (2) they are easily turned into every major type of carbonyl compound, including aldehydes, ketones, and all the other carboxylic acid derivatives. Of all the carboxylic acid derivatives, alkanoyl halides possess the most reactive carbonyl group towards nucleophilic addition, and the best leaving group (halide).

18-3. Carboxylic Anhydrides.

By and large, carboxylic acid anhydrides are much less commonly encountered in synthesis than are alkanoyl halides. They are generally not as easily prepared, and they are less reactive. A major drawback for anhydrides in synthesis is that only one of the two carbonyl groups of an anhydride can add a nucleophile: the other falls off as part of the carboxylate anion leaving group (see "General Nucleophilic Addition-Elimination of Anhydrides"). Cyclic anhydrides are more useful, since the two ends still stay stuck together by a carbon chain after an addition takes place (see "Nucleophilic Ring Opening of Cyclic Anhydrides").

Ketenes are interesting molecules with some synthetic utility. However, ketenes are generally not stable species and must be reacted with nucleophiles as soon as they are generated, or they rapidly decompose.

18-4. Esters.

Esters are the most prevalent carboxylic acid derivatives in nature and are, in general, the most important. They are convenient compounds for synthetic purposes because their intermediate reactivity makes them easy to prepare and store for later use. Alkanoyl halides, in contrast, are so reactive towards water that it takes some care to prevent them from hydrolyzing to some extent upon extended storage. Esters are easily prepared and readily converted into many types of compounds by reactions at both their carbonyl and α-carbons.

Pay particular attention to the Claisen condensation towards the end of the section. It is related to the aldol condensation you saw earlier (Chapter 16). Like the aldol condensation it is of special importance because (1) it makes a new carbon-carbon bond and (2) the product (a 3-ketoester) is readily utilized in further synthetic transformations, including the making of still more carbon-carbon bonds (Chapter 22).

18-5. Amides.

Amides are much less reactive than esters towards nucleophilic acyl substitution. They have greater resonance stabilization by the nitrogen lone pair, and they have a poorer leaving group (NH_3 in acid, and NH_2^- in base). Amides do show some special reactions: the possibility of deprotonation and alkylation of the nitrogen in 1° or 2° amides, reduction reactions that may form either amines or aldehydes, and a new decarboxylation method, the Hofmann rearrangement, which forms an amine with one carbon less than the original amide. Note the following two amine syntheses:

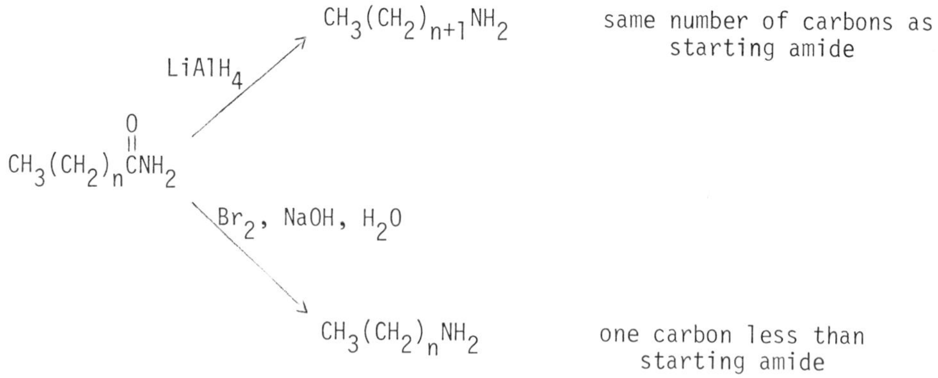

This Hofmann rearrangement has a mechanism which is related conceptually to some you've seen before, but has some very new and unusual details. It merits a careful look, especially Steps 4 and 5.

18-6.   Nitriles.

The nitrile functional group is, *formally*, a dehydrated primary amide. (In fact, a little-used nitrile synthesis involves amide dehydration:

$$R-\overset{\overset{\textstyle O}{\textstyle \|}}{C}-NH_2 \xrightarrow[(-H_2O)]{P_2O_5} R-C\equiv N.)$$

In this sense, therefore, it is related to carboxylic acids and their derivatives. The major importance of nitriles is the fact that the nitrile carbon may be introduced into a molecule as the nucleophilic cyanide ion in an S_N2 reaction. Then, using the reactions in this text section, the nitrile may be converted to carboxylic acid derivatives, ketones, or aldehydes, in which the originally nucleophilic cyanide carbon has become an electrophilic carbonyl carbon. This is the most general and most direct way to use a nucleophilic substitution to introduce a carbonyl carbon into a molecule:

$$R-CH_2-X \xrightarrow[S_N2]{^-CN} R-CH_2-CN \xrightarrow[\text{reactions}]{\text{various}} \begin{cases} R-CH_2-CONH_2 \\ R-CH_2-CO_2H \\ R-CH_2-CO_2R' \\ R-CH_2-CHO \\ R-CH_2-COR' \end{cases}$$

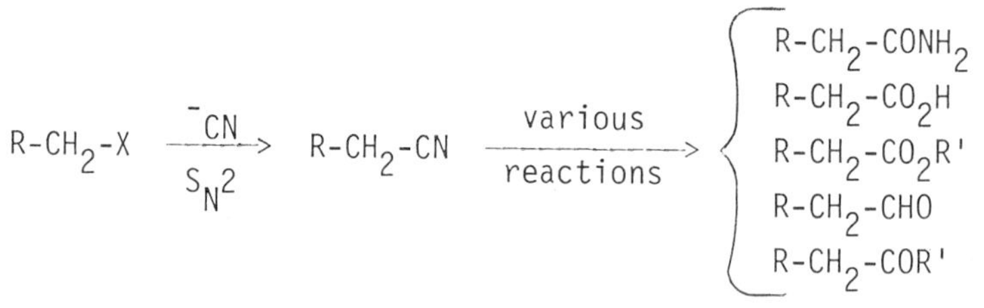

18-7.   Mass Spectroscopy.

The specific kinds of information available through the use of mass spectroscopy fall into two categories. First, the m/z value for the molecular ion provides information useful in calculating the molecular formula of the molecule. Second, the lower molecular weight fragments that appear in the mass spectrum contain clues concerning structural features of the molecule in question. As was the case for the various forms of spectroscopy that you've seen before, it is, for now, more important to understand how to extract information from mass spectral data than it is to understand the theory of the technique, or the practical considerations of actually obtaining a mass spectrum.

Solutions to Chapter 18 Problems

1. The acidity of the α-hydrogen in a carboxylic acid derivative is related to the degree the anion in the conjugate base is stabilized by both resonance and inductive effects. The relevant resonance form is $CH_2{=}\overset{O^-}{\overset{|}{C}}{-}L$, where L = Cl, OCH_3, or $N(CH_3)_2$. If that resonance form is a favored one, the anion will be well-stabilized. That is the case for L = Cl, where the electronegative Cl increases the δ^+ on the carbonyl carbon, helping it attract the electrons from the anionic α-carbon. As L changes to OCH_3, and finally to $N(CH_3)_2$, the reduced electronegativity tends to reduce the δ^+ on the carbonyl carbon, so its attraction for the electrons is reduced, and the anion is less well stabilized. In addition, as L goes from Cl to OCH_3 to $N(CH_3)_2$, the resonance form $\overset{..}{\bar{C}}H_2{-}\overset{O^-}{\overset{|}{C}}{=}L^+$, which destabilizes the anion, gains in relative importance.

****

2. (a) ethanoyl chloride (Cl is bigger than F, and bonds to it are longer)

   (b) $C\underline{H}_2(COCH_3)_2$ (H's α to ketones are more acidic than H's α to esters)

   (c) imide (The lone pair on N is shared in resonance by two carbonyl groups, and so it does not reduce their electrophilicity as much as the N in an amide. Note that the relationship between an imide and an amide is similar to that between an anhydride and an ester.)

   (d) ethenyl ethanoate ($CH_3\overset{O}{\overset{||}{C}}{-}\ddot{O}{-}CH{=}CH_2 \leftrightarrow CH_3\overset{O}{\overset{||}{C}}{-}\overset{+}{O}{=}CH{-}\bar{C}H_2$ resonance <u>reduces</u> electron donation from oxygen towards the carbonyl carbon. So the resonance form $CH_3\overset{O^-}{\overset{|}{C}}{=}\overset{+}{O}{-}CH{=}CH_2$ is reduced in importance, strengthening the C-O double bond and raising the carbonyl stretching frequency, actually to about 1760 cm^{-1}.)

****

3. In **i** and **ii** the most acidic hydrogens are α-hydrogens. Deprotonation followed by protonation provides a mechanism for isomerization:

(Similar for **ii**.)

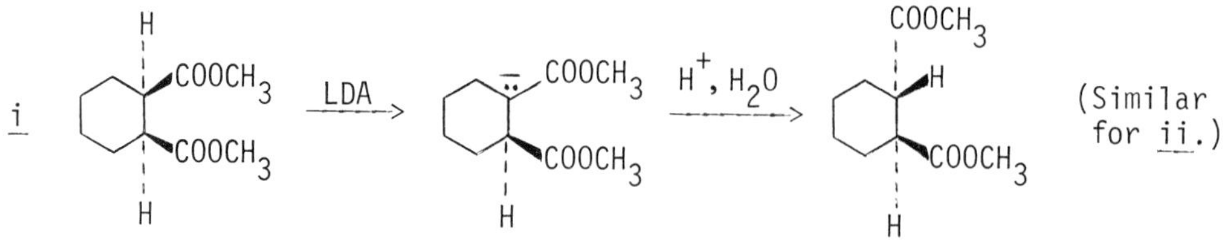

In **iii** the most acidic hydrogens are on nitrogen. The α-hydrogens are not removed, so no isomerization is observed.

****

4. (a)

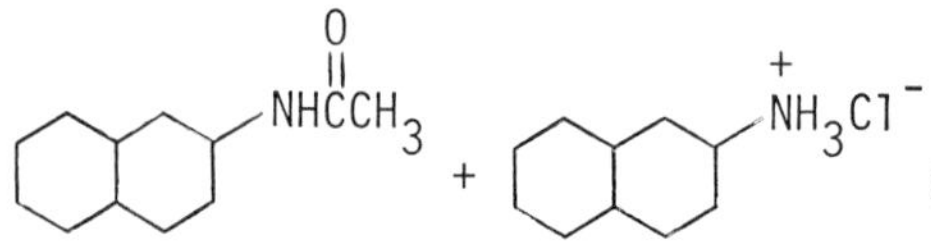

; (b) $CH_3(CH_2)_4\overset{\overset{O}{\|}}{C}-$⟨⟩ ;

(c) $(CH_3)_3C\overset{\overset{O}{\|}}{C}H$; (d) ⟨⟩$-CH_2O\overset{\overset{O}{\|}}{C}CH_2CH_2\overset{\overset{O}{\|}}{C}OCH_2-$⟨⟩ ; (e)

****

5. (a)

$$\xrightarrow{\text{Proton transfer}} CH_3CH_2COO^- .$$

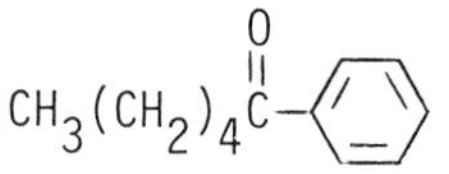

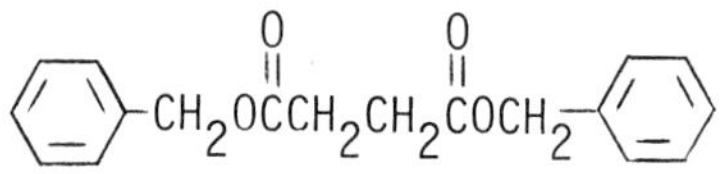

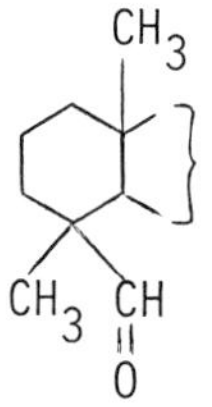

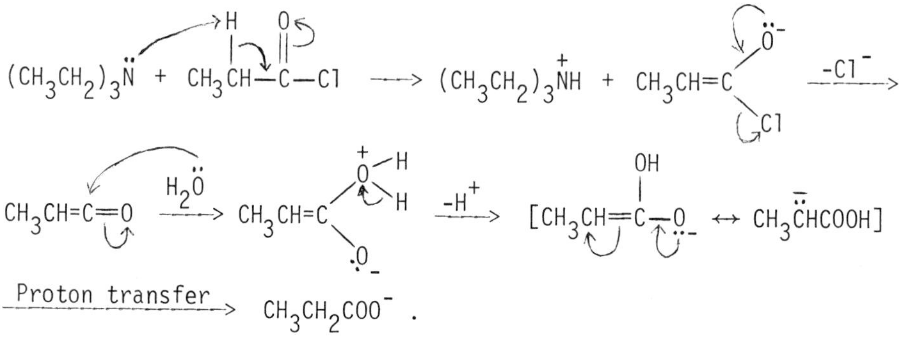

(b) Steric hindrance: less hindered amines like $(CH_3)_3N$ add more easily to make alkanoyl ammonium halides than more hindered ones, which are more likely to act as bases to make ketenes, as does $(CH_3CH_2)_3N$.

Structure: only alkanoyl halides with α-hydrogens can form ketenes.

****

6. Assume aqueous acid work-up for both this and the next problem.

(a) $CH_3C(=O)OCH(CH_3)_2$ + $CH_3C(=O)OH$; (b) $CH_3C(=O)NH_2$ + $CH_3C(=O)OH$;

(c) 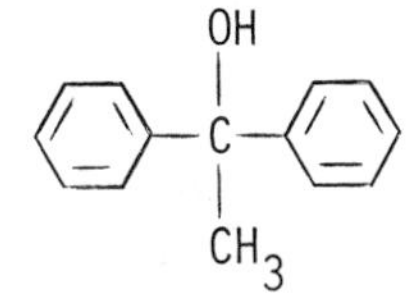 + $CH_3C(=O)OH$; (d) 2 CH_3CH_2OH

****

7. (a) $(CH_3)_2CHOC(=O)CH_2CH_2C(=O)OH$; (b) $HOC(=O)CH_2CH_2C(=O)NH_2$; (c) 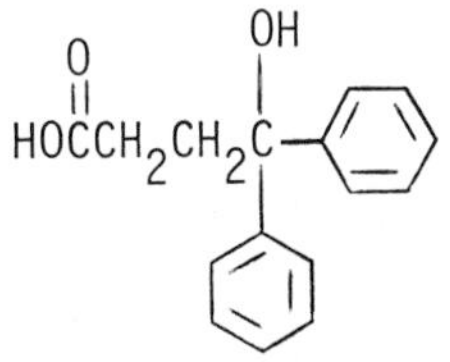 ;

(d) $HOCH_2CH_2CH_2CH_2OH$

****

8. (a) Bad idea. Residual hexanoyl chloride will be converted to hexanoic acid, which smells like an old barn on a hot day.

(b) Wash out the glassware with an alcohol like methanol. Reaction with hexanoyl chloride produces the ester methyl hexanoate, which smells like fresh fruit. Much better.

****

9. The dipolar resonance forms that weaken the carbonyl C-O bond and reduce its stretching frequency are less and less favorable in small rings because of the increased strain associated with a second sp^2 atom:

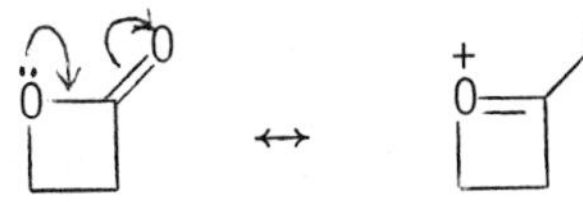

← very strained, relatively unimportant resonance form.

****

10. 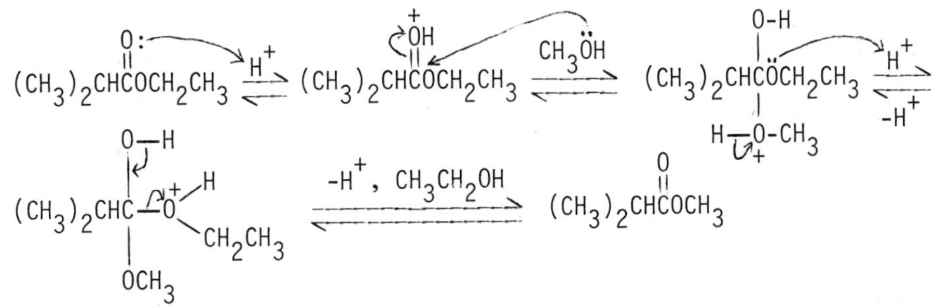

****

11. React with H^+ and CH_3OH ! The methyl ester at the upper right will stay a methyl ester since the only nucleophile around for attacking carbonyl groups is methanol. However, the ethanoate at the lower right will exchange to methyl ethanoate, and the steroid alcohol group will be displaced:

$$CH_3\overset{O}{\overset{\|}{C}}\text{-O-Steroid} \xrightarrow{H^+,\ CH_3OH} CH_3\overset{O}{\overset{\|}{C}}\text{-O-}CH_3 + \text{HO-Steroid}$$

****

12. (a) ; (b) ; (c) (after H^+, H_2O);

(d) (likewise); (e) (via);

(f)

****

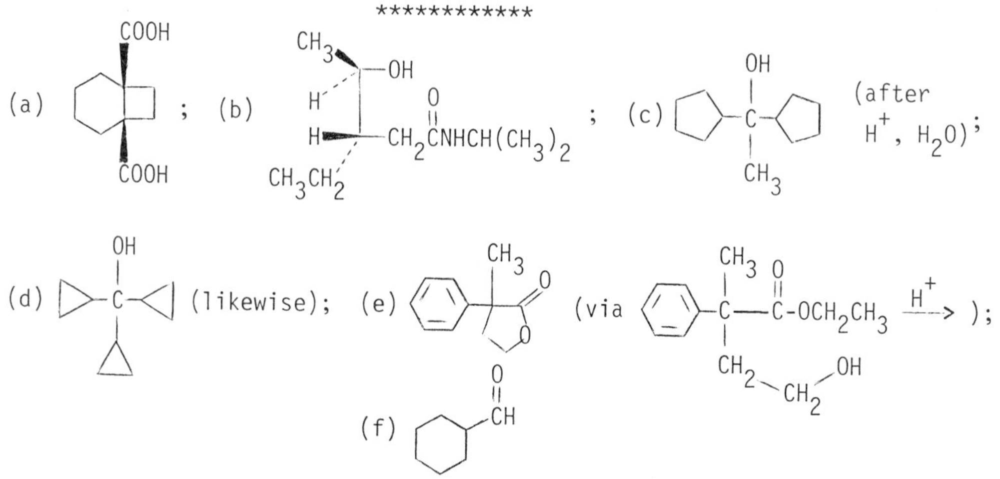

13. Baeyer-Villiger reaction, followed by ester hydrolysis:

****

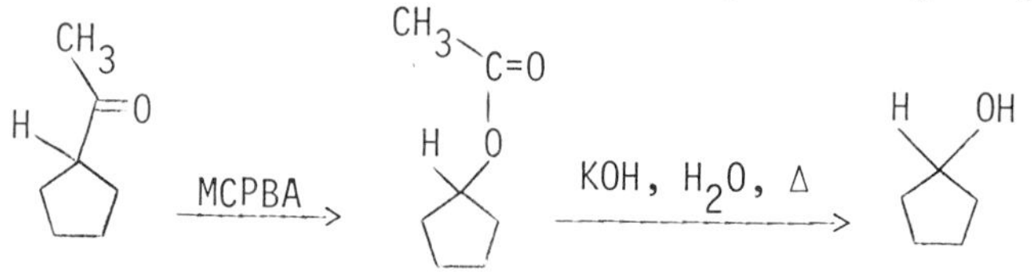

14. (a)

****

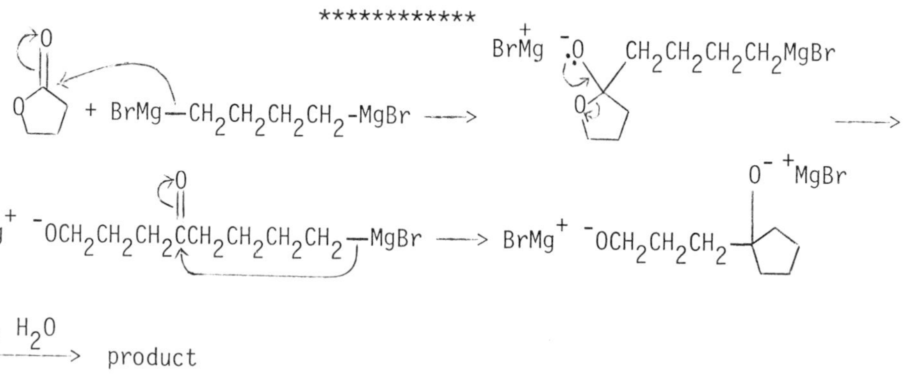

(b) + $BrMgCH_2CH_2CH_2CH_2CH_2MgBr$, then H^+, $H_2O \rightarrow$ (i)

+ $BrMg\overset{\overset{\displaystyle CH_3}{|}}{C}HCH_2CH_2\overset{\overset{\displaystyle CH_3}{|}}{C}HMgBr$, then H^+, $H_2O \rightarrow$ (ii)

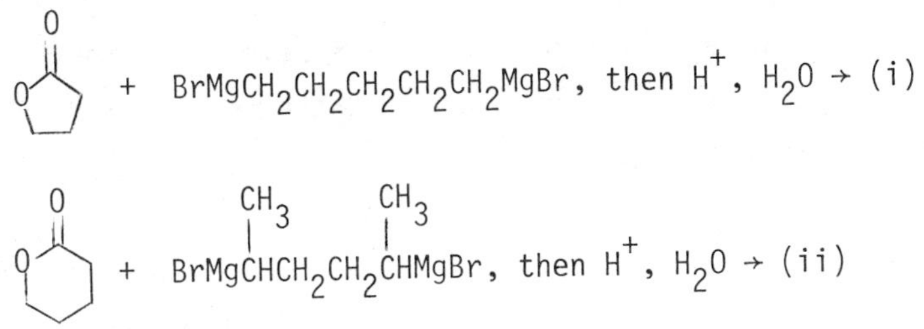

Notice how the ring is made in all of these. It comes from the carbons of the bis-Grignard + the lactone carbonyl carbon:

****

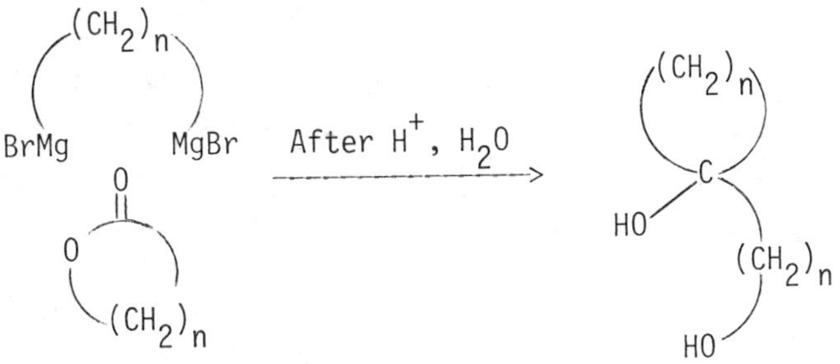

15. This will be difficult to achieve since the α-hydrogens of the aldehyde are much more acidic than those of the ester. Proton transfer from an aldehyde α-carbon to the ester enolate is likely to occur:

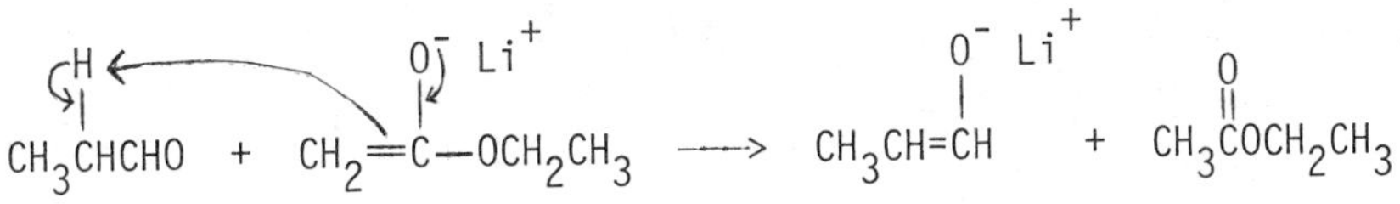

The end result is likely to be ordinary aldol condensations between propanal molecules.

****

16. Several ways will work. One that uses a reaction from this chapter (the actual route used) is shown below.

****

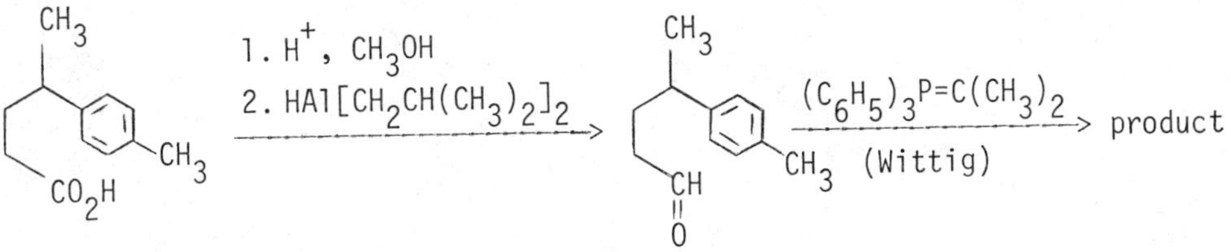

17. The acid will need to become an ester to allow synthesis of the tertiary alcohol by Grignard reagent addition. However, the ketone will need protection before that step. So:

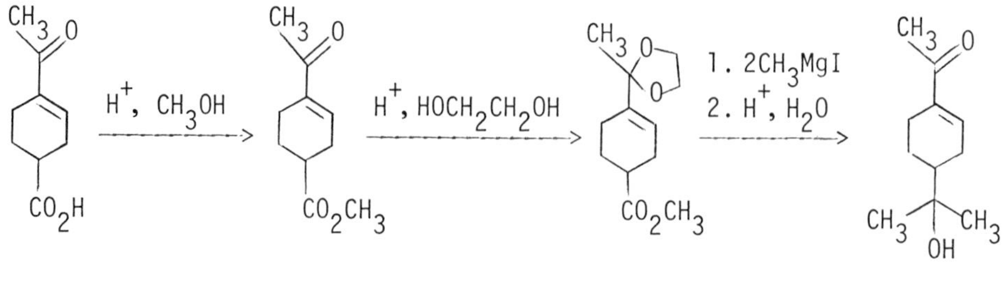

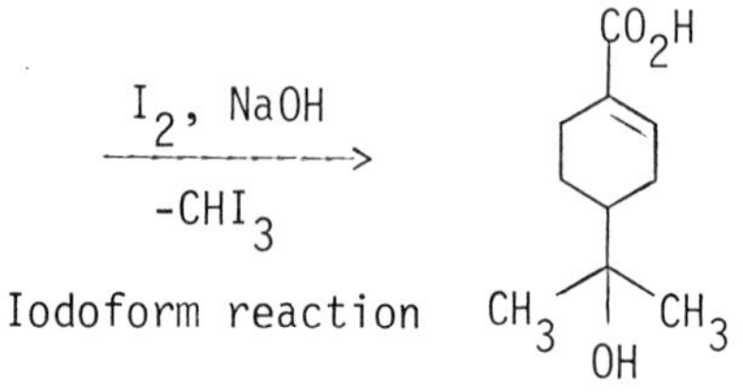

(Sections 9-4 and 16-2: an unusual use *in synthesis* for the haloform reaction)

****

18. Use ester pyrolysis for the alkene synthesis (Section 18-4) because it is a non-ionic, concerted reaction.

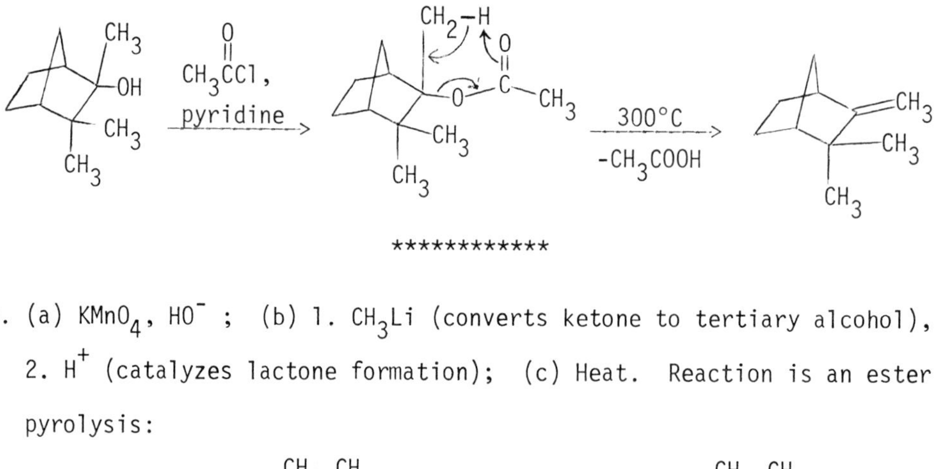

****

19. (a) $KMnO_4$, HO^- ; (b) 1. CH_3Li (converts ketone to tertiary alcohol), 2. H^+ (catalyzes lactone formation); (c) Heat. Reaction is an ester pyrolysis:

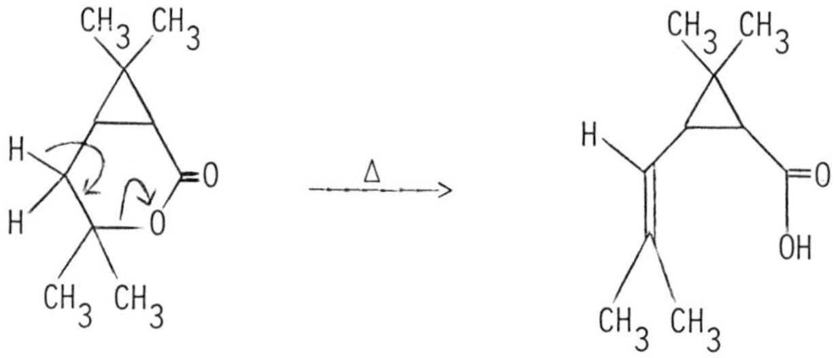

(d) 1. 2LDA (makes dianion), 2. H^+, H_2O (protonates carbon to give more stable *trans* isomer)

****

20. Analyze retrosynthetically: the bond formed is between the α-carbon of one ester and the carbonyl carbon of another.

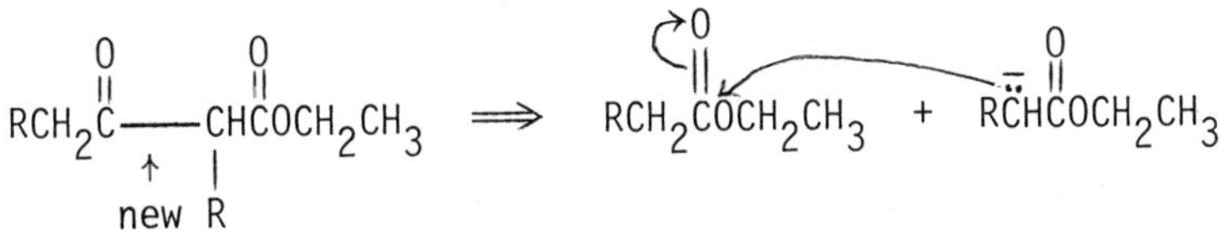

(a) $2CH_3CH_2\overset{O}{\overset{\|}{C}}OCH_2CH_3 \xrightarrow[2.\ H^+,\ H_2O]{1.\ NaOCH_2CH_3,\ CH_2CH_3OH}$ product

(b) $2(CH_3)_2CHCH_2CO_2CH_2CH_3 \xrightarrow{\text{same as 'a'}}$ product

(c) $2C_6H_5CH_2CO_2CH_2CH_3 \xrightarrow{\text{ditto}}$ product

(d) 2 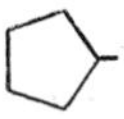 $-CH_2CO_2CH_2CH_3 \xrightarrow{\text{ditto}}$ product

****

21. Hard to do. You can't prevent condensation of 2 $CH_3CO_2CH_3$ from occurring, or 2 $CH_3CH_2CO_2CH_2CH_3$, or even the condensation of the two different esters in the opposite "sense" from that desired, namely the enolate of $CH_3CH_2CO_2CH_3$ with the carbonyl of $CH_3CO_2CH_3$. A dreadful mixture of all four possible condensation products would result:

$CH_3\overset{O}{\overset{\|}{C}}-CH_2\overset{O}{\overset{\|}{C}}OCH_3$, $CH_3CH_2\overset{O}{\overset{\|}{C}}-\underset{CH_3}{\underset{|}{C}}H\overset{O}{\overset{\|}{C}}OCH_3$, and $CH_3\overset{O}{\overset{\|}{C}}-\underset{CH_3}{\underset{|}{C}}H\overset{O}{\overset{\|}{C}}OCH_3$, in addition to the desired product.

****

22. The ester lacking α-hydrogens cannot do a Claisen condensation with itself, and it cannot act as the nucleophilic partner in a "wrong-sense" Claisen condensation with the other ester. So only two of the four possible permutations remain: the desired condensation between the nucleophile of the second ester and the carbonyl of the first, and condensation between

two moles of the other ester. The latter may be minimized by certain practical techniques like premixing the first ester molecule (in excess) with base and adding the second ester slowly to it.

(a) $C_6H_5CO_2CH_2CH_3 + CH_3CO_2CH_2CH_3 \xrightarrow[2.\ H^+,\ H_2O]{1.\ NaOCH_2CH_3,\ CH_3CH_2OH}$ product

(b) $(CH_3)_3CCO_2CH_2CH_3 + CH_3CH_2CO_2CH_2CH_3 \xrightarrow{\text{same}}$ product

(c) $\overset{O}{\overset{\|}{HC}}CO_2CH_2CH_3 + CH_3CO_2CH_2CH_3 \xrightarrow{\text{same}}$ product.

****

23. 1. $(CH_3)_2NH$, Δ (makes N,N-dimethyl carboxamide), 2. $LiAlH_4$ (makes amine), 3. H^+, H_2O (protonates alkoxide).

****

24. From 'i': 1. $SOCl_2$, 2. $(CH_3)_2NH$ (makes carboxamide), 3. $LiAlH_4$.

From 'ii': 1. $SOCl_2$, 2. NH_3, 3. Cl_2, NaOH (Hofmann rearrangement, loses CO_2 and makes simple amine), 4. 2 CH_3I, NaOH (S_N2 methylations of amine nitrogen).

****

25. (a) 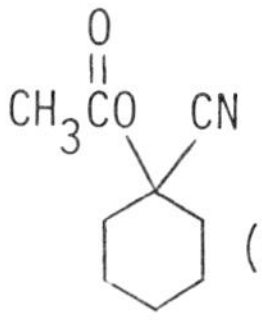

(via cyanoalcohol + anhydride); (b) 

(via ester pyrolysis)

****

26. Take care with stereochemistry:

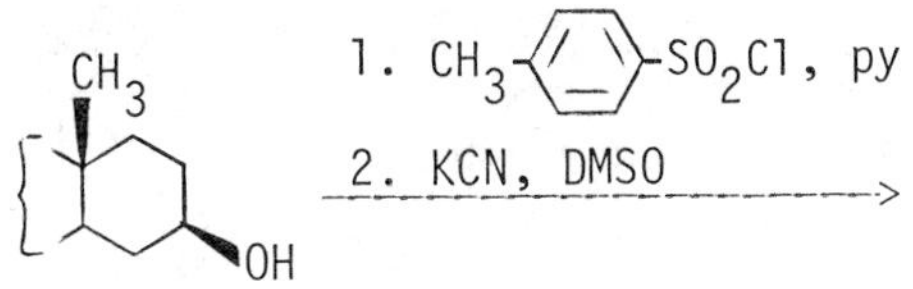

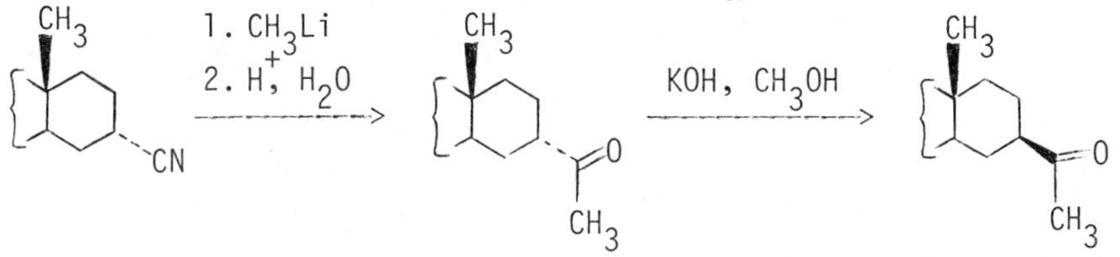

$\xrightarrow{CH_2=P(C_6H_5)_3}$ product

(deprotonation at α-carbon allows isomerization to more stable equatorial stereoisomer)

****

27. 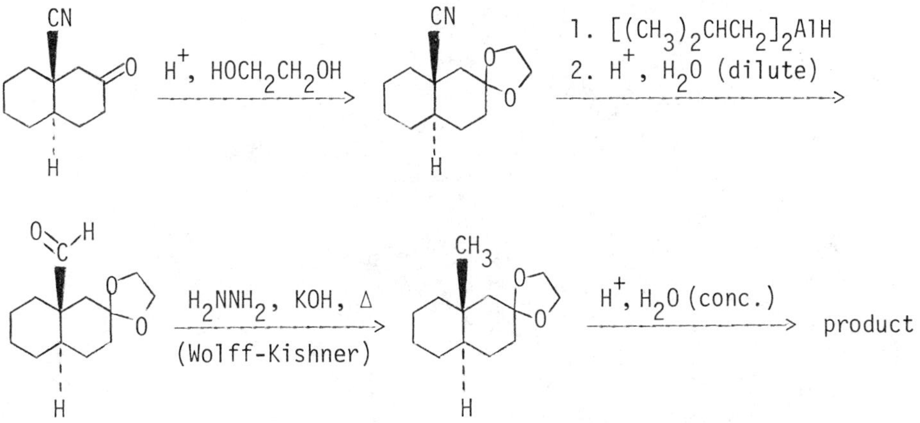

****

28. Find the bond that has been formed (refer to Problem 20):

(a) (i) 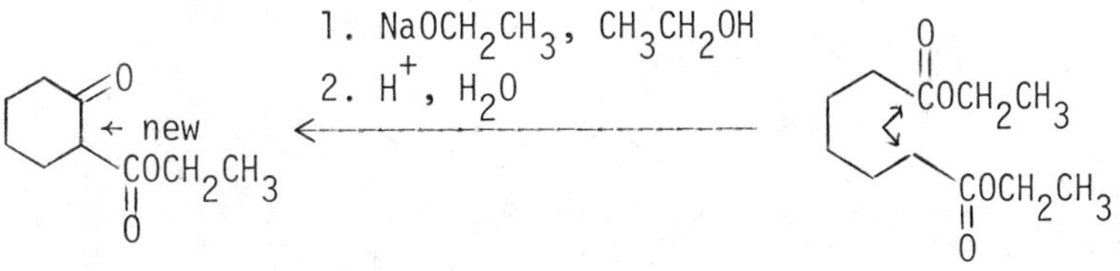

(ii) 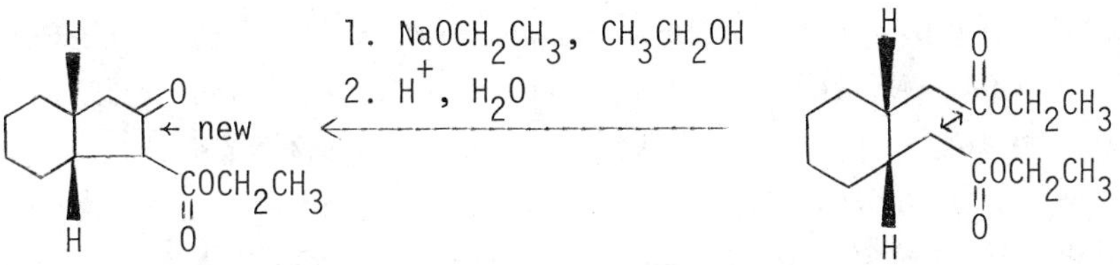

(b)

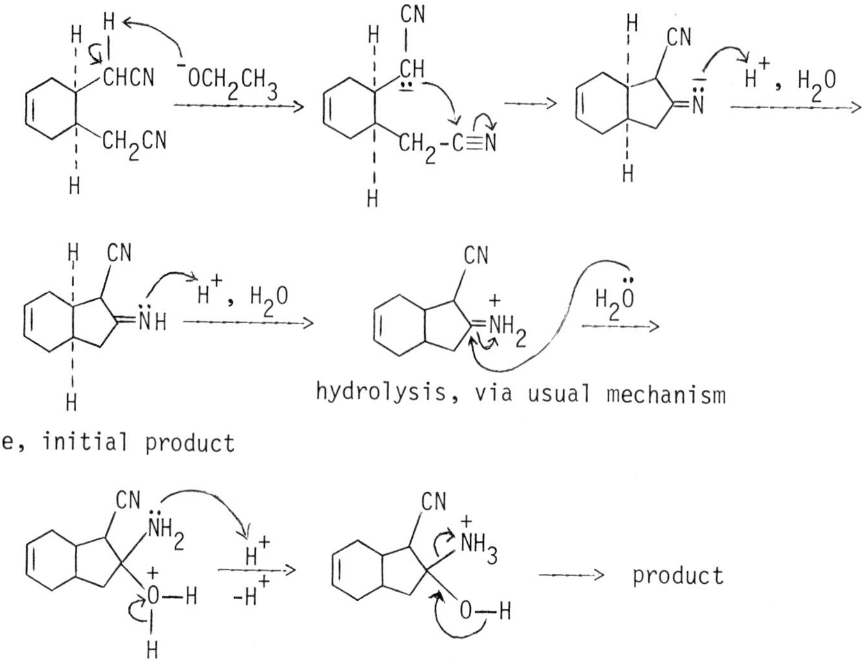

imine, initial product

hydrolysis, via usual mechanism

****

29. Major peaks: m/z 43 $(CH_3CH_2CH_2)^+$ from M-Br

m/z 41 $(CH_2CH{=}CH_2)^+$ from M-HBr-H

Minor peaks: m/z 109 $(CH_2CH_2{}^{81}Br)^+$ } from M-CH_3

m/z 107 $(CH_2CH_2{}^{79}Br)^+$ } from M-CH_3

m/z 42 $(CH_3CH{=}CH_2)^+$ from M-HBr

m/z 29 $(CH_3CH_2)^+$ from M-Br-CH_2

m/z 28 $(CH_2{=}CH_2)^+$ from M-Br-CH_3

m/z 27 $(CH_2{=}CH)^+$ from M-Br-CH_3-H

****

30. Compound is saturated (see "Degrees of Unsaturation", Study Guide Chapter 11). Try to use the general guidelines that intense fragment peaks usually result from either the loss of relatively stable neutral fragments, or lead to the formation of relatively stable cationic species.

So, looking at the high intensity m/z 73 peak for isomer C, it corresponds to $(M-15)^+$, or loss of CH_3. This is most likely if the remaining fragment is a very stable cation, for example,

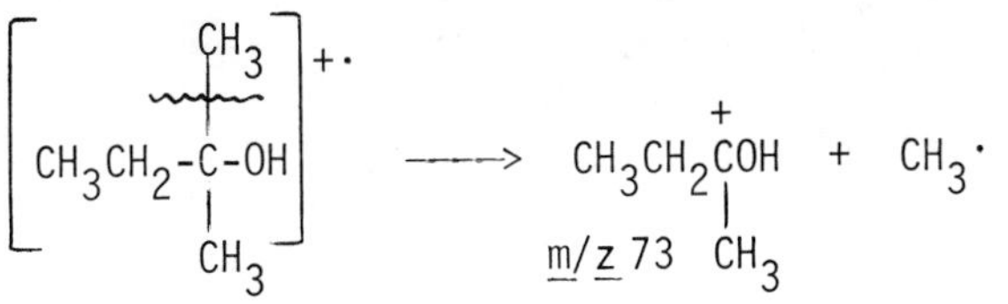

tertiary cation, stabilized by oxygen lone pair

Looking at the rest of the spectrum, the base peak is at m/z 59, or $(M-29)^+$, loss of CH_3CH_2:

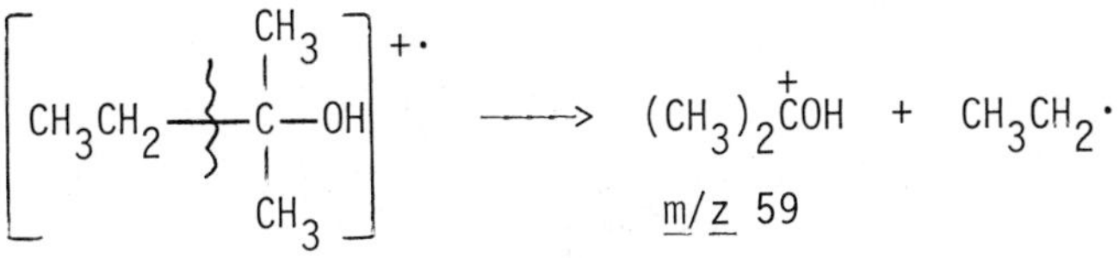

This is, all together, good evidence for isomer C being 2-methyl-2-butanol, as shown.

Isomer B also has a peak at m/z 73 for loss of CH_3. Its base peak (m/z 45) corresponds to loss of 43, or $CH_3CH_2CH_2$. These signals are what you might expect for 2-pentanol:

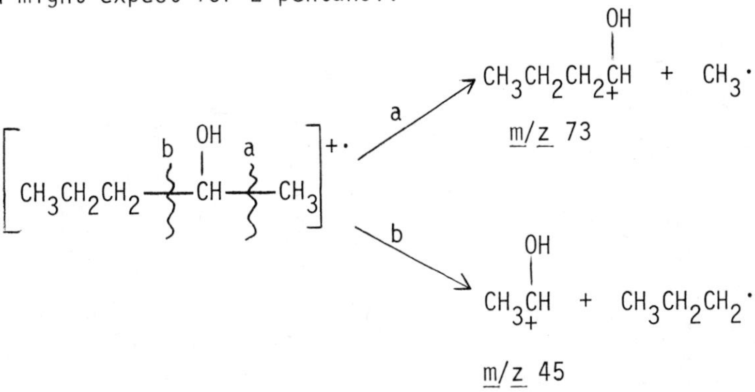

Both fragmentations give secondary cations stabilized by resonance from an oxygen lone pair. This is, in fact, the correct answer.

Isomer A does not lose CH_3 or CH_3CH_2 (no peaks at m/z 73 or 59). That pretty much rules out any tertiary or secondary alcohol structure as a possibility (any example that you can write should show those fragmentations). How about possible primary alcohol structures? Look again to intense fragment peaks for clues. The m/z 70, loss of water, doesn't really help much, except to rule out $(CH_3)_3CCH_2OH$, which has no β-hydrogens and therefore cannot dehydrate. That leaves three possibilities for A:

$$CH_3CH_2CH_2CH_2CH_2OH, \quad CH_3CH_2\overset{\overset{\displaystyle CH_3}{|}}{C}HCH_2OH, \quad \text{and} \quad CH_3\overset{\overset{\displaystyle CH_3}{|}}{C}HCH_2CH_2OH.$$

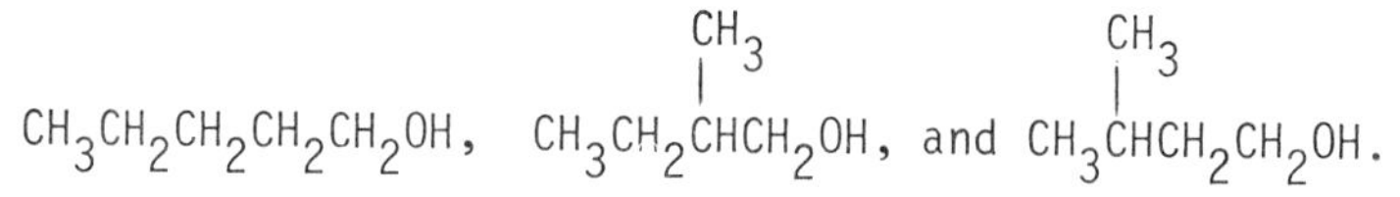

The data that you have are in fact quite consistent with either of the first two (the third is difficult to maneuver into a fragment with m/z 42). If you got this far, you are doing well! (The actual spectrum of isomer A is that of 1-pentanol, by the way.)

****

31. (a) Formula: $C_{6.25}H_{12.6}O_{0.78} \implies C_8H_{16}O$ (empirical).

MS: $M^{+\cdot}$ of 128 confirms $C_8H_{16}O$ is molecular formula as well.

$H_{sat'd} = 16 + 2 = 18$; deg. unsat'n. $= \frac{18-16}{2} = 1\ \pi$ bond or ring present.

IR, UV: a ketone C=O appears to be present.

NMR: $\underset{\underset{\delta 0.9(t)}{\uparrow}}{CH_3-CH_2-}$, $\underset{\underset{\delta 2.0(s)}{\uparrow}}{CH_3-\overset{\overset{\displaystyle O}{||}}{C}-}\underset{\underset{\delta 2.2(t)}{\uparrow}}{CH_2-CH_2-}$ are likely pieces, adding up to $C_6H_{12}O$; only C_2H_4 are left to add in. Is 2-octanone a reasonable answer?

MS: base peak (m/z 43) is $[CH_3\overset{\overset{\displaystyle O}{||}}{C}]^+$; next largest is m/z 58, consistent with McLafferty rearrangement as follows:

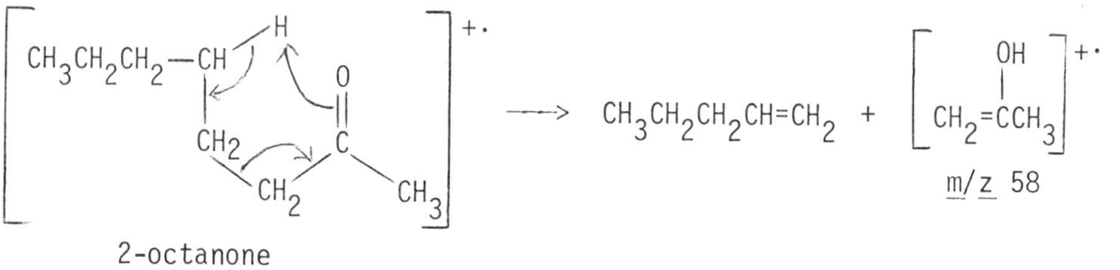

2-octanone

This answer seems quite reasonable.

(b) Formula: $C_{7.3}H_{11.8} \implies C_{10}H_{16}$ (empirical).

MS: $M^{+\cdot}$ of 136 confirms $C_{10}H_{16}$ as molecular formula.

$H_{sat'd} = 20 + 2 = 22$; deg. unsat'n. $= \frac{22-16}{2} = 3\ \pi$ bonds and/or rings.

IR, UV: one or, perhaps, two alkene double bonds ($\tilde{\nu}_{C=C}$ at 1646 and 1680), one at least of the type $\overset{R}{\underset{R}{>}}C=C\overset{H}{\underset{H}{<}}$ ($\tilde{\nu}_{bond}$ at 888 cm^{-1}).

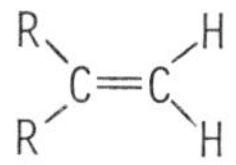

H-1 NMR: $>C{=}CH_2$ likely; also a separate $>C{=}C{<}^{H}$ present. Otherwise
$\uparrow$ δ4.6 $\qquad$ $\uparrow$ δ5.3

the only additional signals of possible use are at δ1.6-1.7, which could be two allylic CH_3's (CH_3-$\overset{|}{C}$=C$<$ fragments). Not a very helpful NMR although we can at least write down pieces:

$>C{=}CH_2$, $\quad >C{=}C{<}^{H}$, $\quad$ 2 CH_3's on double bonds

Still need to locate 4 C's and 7 H's. We could get a lot more from the C-13 data, but let's see what the mass spectrum can tell us.

MS: look for help from the fragments. Loss of 15 confirms the presence of one or more CH_3 groups. The two other main fragmentations are to m/z 95 + m/z 41, and to 2 m/z 68 pieces. Starting with the lightest first, m/z 41 = C_3H_5, which could be the combination

CH_3
|
$-C{=}CH_2$ (from the NMR pieces above). The m/z 68 fragments are each half of the original molecule, or C_5H_8. A reasonable C_5H_8 guess might come from adding C_2H_3, or $H_2C{=}CH$-, to the

CH_3 $\qquad\qquad\qquad$ CH_3
| $\qquad\qquad\qquad\qquad$ |
$-C{=}CH_2$, giving $CH_2{=}CH{-}C{=}CH_2$ (isoprene). This is beginning to look familiar. Could the molecule be a dimer of isoprene, perhaps via Diels-Alder reaction?

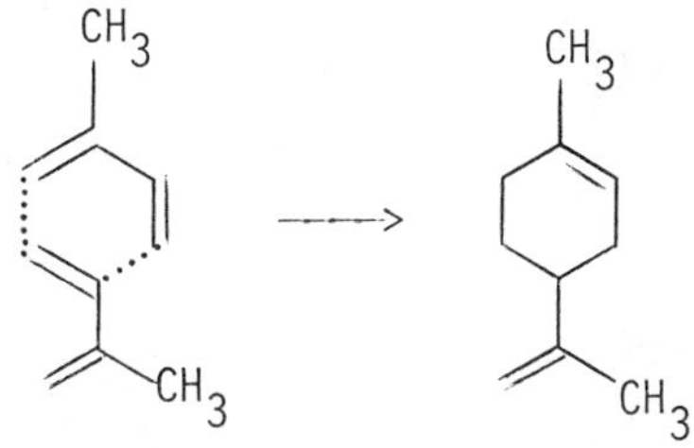

(limonene?)

This is indeed the answer (recall Problem 26 of Chapter 14). Try, on your own, to match the C-13 NMR with the structure.

****

CHAPTER 19

The Special Stability of the Cyclic Electron Sextet: Benzene and Electrophilic Aromatic Substitution

General Introduction

The most obvious feature of benzene is its superficial similarity to a molecule containing ordinary double bonds. Benzene and its derivatives are "special," however, due to the new concept of aromatic stabilization covered in the early sections of this chapter. The enhanced thermodynamic stability of benzene, relative to an ordinary triene, affects both its properties and its chemistry. So, from a conceptual point of view, each time you encounter a new property or chemical reaction of a benzene derivative, ask yourself "How would the properties or reactions of a simple alkene (or diene or triene) compare with this?" Try to apply the thermodynamic differences between benzene and alkenes to several of their reactions to see if the differences in the behavior of the two types of compounds make sense to you. After you've done that, you will be in a better position to learn the material in this and the next chapter more thoroughly, with a more balanced overview of the entire topic.

Benzene and its derivatives make up one of the most important classes of organic compounds (after carbonyl compounds and alcohols). There will, accordingly, be a lot of relatively significant material presented in these chapters concerning them.

Outline of the Chapter

19-1. Nomenclature.

A few new twists.

19-2. The Structure of Benzene: a First Look at Aromaticity.

What makes it special.

19-3. Spectral Properties.

19-4. Electrophilic Aromatic Substitution.

General introduction to the most important reaction type.

19-5. Halogenation.

19-6. Nitration and Sulfonation.

19-7. Friedel-Crafts Alkylation and Acylation.

The basic "core" reactions in benzene chemistry.

Keys to the Chapter

19-1. Nomenclature.

The systematic (IUPAC) naming system for benzenes co-exists with an assortment of names that have been in common use for over a century and show no signs of going away. So, whether anyone likes it or not, names like aniline (for benzeneamine) and styrene (for ethenylbenzene) are, and will probably always be the names people use, both in speaking as well as writing about these compounds. In addition to these common names for simple substituted benzenes, a special naming system exists exclusively for benzenes with exactly two substituents on the benzene ring: the "ortho/meta/para" system. Note, carefully, that this system is *never* to be used for benzenes with more than two ring substituents: for those a name with proper numbering is required. (It is alright, however, to use numbering instead of ortho/meta/para for a benzene with two substituents.) Finally, when numbering around the benzene ring be careful where you start: if you use one of the special names for a monosubstituted benzene as your parent name (e.g. phenol, aniline, benzaldehyde, toluene, etc.), C-1 is always the carbon containing the substituent implied by the parent name (even if starting somewhere else would result in smaller numbers). As an example:

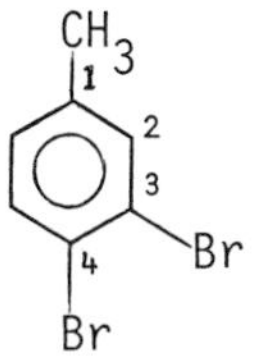

is 3,4-dibromotoluene (1,2-dibromotoluene would be nonsense, although 1,2-dibromo-4-methylbenzene is the correct IUPAC name).

19-2. The Structure of Benzene: a First Look at Aromaticity.

Aromaticity as a special property of molecules like benzene is covered only briefly in this section. Structural, thermodynamic, and electronic considerations are presented which will serve, for now, as an introduction to the more general discussion that will be presented in Chapter 25. For now, note simply that the aromaticity of benzene is reflected in (1) its symmetrical structure (as a resonance hybrid), (2) its unexpectedly enhanced thermodynamic stability, and (3) its unusual electronic structure with a completely filled set of strongly stabilized bonding molecular orbitals.

19-3. Spectral Properties.

The spectroscopy of benzene is a logical consequence of its structural and electronic properties. Special features in the spectra make the identification of benzenes relatively easy. As has been the case with other compounds, NMR is most useful, followed by IR and UV spectroscopy. A special feature in the infrared spectrum of a benzene derivative is the C-H out-of-plane bending vibration pattern, which provides information concerning the arrangement of substituents around the ring. This information is not always as easily derived from the NMR spectrum. Ultraviolet spectroscopy can be suggestive but not definite regarding the presence of a benzene derivative. If the presence of the benzene ring is already known, however, the UV spectrum can be useful in deciding whether it is conjugated with one or more π-bond containing groups.

19-4, 19-5, and 19-6. Electrophilic Aromatic Substitution: Halogenation, Nitration, and Sulfonation of Benzene.

These sections introduce the main type of chemistry displayed by benzene rings. The conceptual keys to this material are in Section 19-4. You are given a general mechanism (which will be repeated in specific form for each type of reaction that is presented later on). More important for conceptual understanding, you are given information concerning the energetics of this reaction. Pay close attention to Figure 19-16, Exercise 19-7, and the data in Section 19-4. After you understand this basic material, you will find the specific reactions a little easier to learn. Remember that benzene is stabilized by its special aromatic form of resonance. It is less reactive towards electrophiles than are ordinary alkenes, and therefore only strong electrophiles, sometimes generated in strange ways, will attack the π electrons in benzene rings. These electrophiles, and the ways they are generated, will have to be learned so that you can use these reactions later on in synthesis problems.

19-7. The Friedel-Crafts Reaction.

Since carbon-carbon bond formation is such an important part of organic synthesis, the attachment of carbon electrophiles to benzene rings is of special significance among the reactions in this chapter. Ordinary carbocations and carbocation-like species are the simplest types of carbon electrophiles, but their use in Friedel-Crafts alkylation has limitations. Rearrangements of the carbon electrophile often occur, and it is hard to prevent multiple alkylation from happening to a single benzene ring. Friedel-Crafts alkanoylation (acylation), via the acylium ion $R\text{-}\overset{+}{C}=\ddot{O}: \leftrightarrow R\text{-}C\equiv\overset{+}{O}:$, is not subject to these drawbacks and, whenever possible, is the preferred method for attachment of a carbon unit to a benzene ring.

Solutions to Chapter 19 Problems

1. (a) 1-methylethyl benzenecarboxylate, isopropyl benzoate

   (b) 1-ethenyl-4-methylbenzene, *p*-methylstyrene

   (c) 1-(2,3-dideuteriophenyl)ethanone, 2,3-dideuterioacetophenone

   (d) 2-hydroxybenzenecarbaldehyde, *o*-hydroxybenzaldehyde

   (e) 3-aminobenzenecarboxylic acid, *m*-aminobenzoic acid

   (f) 4-ethyl-2-methylbenzenamine, 4-ethyl-2-methylaniline

   (g) 1-bromo-2,4-dimethylbenzene

   (h) 4-bromo-3,5-dimethoxybenzenol, 4-bromo-3,5-dimethoxyphenol

   (i) 2-phenylethanoic acid (common name: phenylacetic acid)

   (j) 1-methoxy-4-nitrobenzene, *p*-nitroanisole

****

2. (a) 1,2,4,5-tetramethylbenzene; (b) 4-hexyl-1,3-benzenediol;

   (c) N-ethanoyl-4-hydroxybenzenamine, N-(4-hydroxyphenyl)ethanamide;

   (d) 2-[4-(2-methylpropyl)phenyl]propanoic acid

****

3. (a) 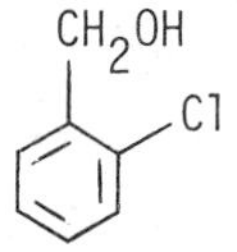

Name is acceptible. (IUPAC: (2-chlorophenyl)methanol)

   (b) 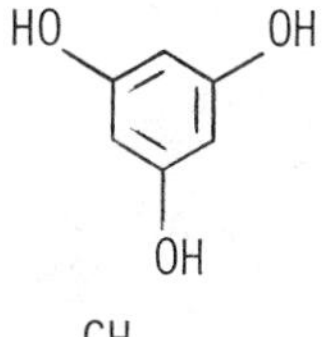

Name is numbered incorrectly: call it 1,3,5-benzenetriol.

   (c) 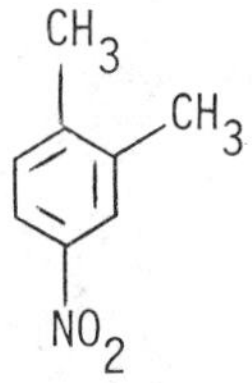

Name is incorrect - never mix *o*, *m*, *p* with numbers; call it 1,2-dimethyl-4-nitrobenzene.

(d) 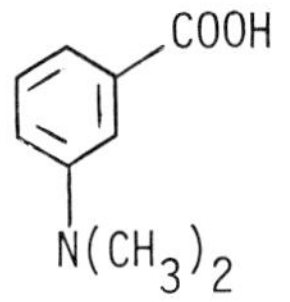 Name is acceptible. (IUPAC: 3-(N,N-dimethylamino)-benzenecarboxylic acid)

(e) 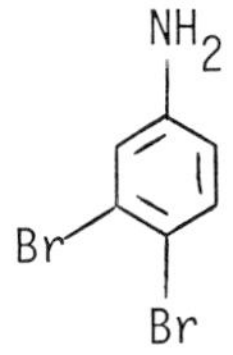 Wrong numbers. 3,4-dibromoaniline or benzenamine.

(f) 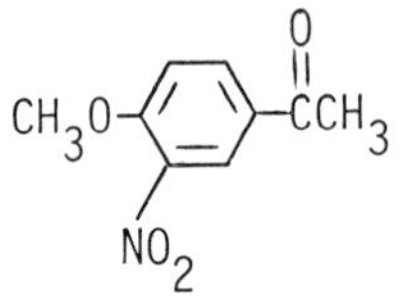 Use <u>only numbers</u>: 4-methoxy-3-nitroacetophenone or 1-(4-methoxy-3-nitrophenyl)ethanone.

****

4. Benzene would be higher in energy by about 30 kcal/mole, so ΔH_{comb} would be -819 kcal/mole.

****

5. No. If it were aromatic its hydrogenation would be <u>less</u> exothermic than the hydrogenation of four isolated π bonds. The data show the opposite: there doesn't even seem to be any resonance stabilization at all!

****

6. The data in problem 5 imply that cyclooctatetraene lacks resonance stabilization: its double bonds behave as if they were isolated, not conjugated. This is actually the case. Due to the geometry of the molecule (which is <u>not</u> planar) the double bonds do not overlap into conjugated systems. So resonance like this does NOT occur:

Does not apply to this molecule.

So, 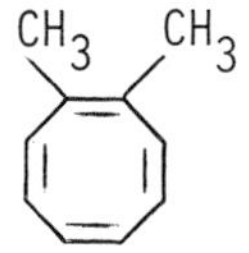 and 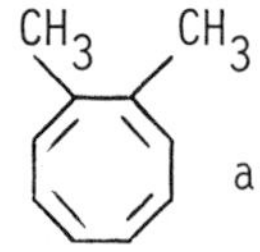 are actually <u>different</u> molecules!

Names are 1,2-dimethylcyclooctatetraene and 2,3-dimethylcyclooctatetraene.

****

7. (a) Draw the molecular orbitals by referring to the ones in Figure 19-5, and putting the nodes in your orbital illustrations the same way:

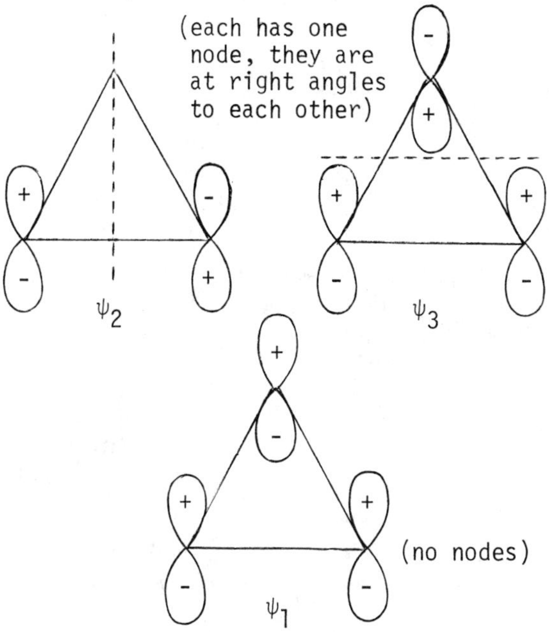

cyclopropenyl

ψ_2 and ψ_3 in cyclopropenyl are degenerate orbitals.

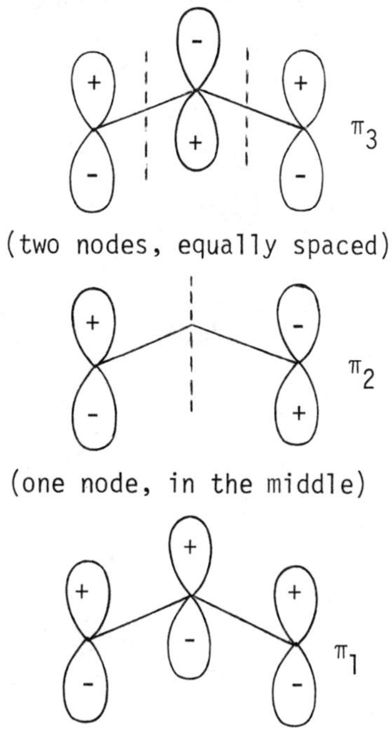

(no nodes)

allyl

(b) Two electrons are best. They would fill the cyclopropenyl ψ_1 orbital, and be stabilized relative to electrons in the π_1 allyl orbital. Electrons in ψ_2 or ψ_3 of cyclopropenyl are destabilized relative to π_2 electrons in allyl. Lewis structures for the two electron cyclopropenyl and allyl systems (both are cations):

(c) Yes! The electrons in cyclopropenyl cation can be represented as being delocalized in a cyclic manner, and the system is stabilized compared with the best acyclic analogue, allyl cation.

****

8. Reactions of alkenes with O_3, $KMnO_4$, and OsO_4 all have 6-electron cyclic transition states. So does the hexatriene-cyclohexadiene electrocyclic interconversion reaction.

****

9. (a) Formula: $C_{2.5}H_{1.7}Br_{0.85} \Rightarrow C_3H_2Br$ (empirical). The chapter is on benzene, so cheat and assume the molecule has 6 carbons: $C_6H_4Br_2$. UV supports presence of benzene ring, too.

C-13: 3 peaks, so the molecule must have symmetry

H-1 NMR: two sets of signals in equal intensity.

Looking at the 3 possible dibromobenzenes, the answer is clear:

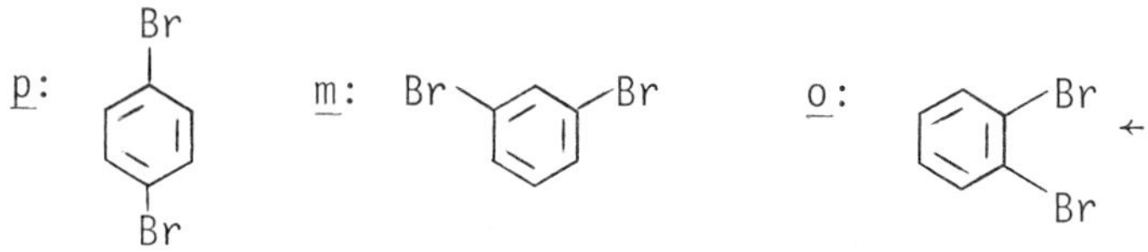

← *ortho* isomer is the answer

	p	m	o
C-13:	2 kinds of carbons	4 kinds of carbons	3 kinds of carbons
H-1:	all equivalent	3 kinds of hydrogens	2 kinds of hydrogens

The IR (single band at 745 cm^{-1}) agrees with the conclusion.

(b) Formula: $C_{6.7}H_{6.7}O_{0.83} \Rightarrow C_8H_8O$. H-1 NMR: 5 benzene hydrogens and a CH_3. C-13 NMR and IR: a C=O (δ 197.4 and $\tilde{\nu}$ 1680 cm^{-1}). This one is easy:

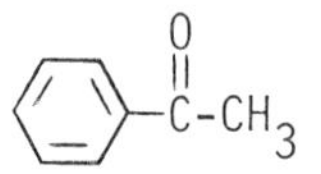

(c) Formula: $C_{5.9}H_{5.9}O_{1.5} \Rightarrow C_4H_4O$ (empirical). Make it $C_8H_8O_2$.

NMR: $-\overset{O}{\overset{\|}{C}}H$ (δ9.8) ; 4 benzene H's ; CH_3-O- (δ3.8). IR: *para*-disubstituted benzene, also aldehyde >C=O presence confirmed.

Answer: 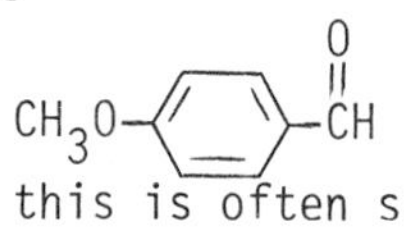

. Note the two NMR doublets in the δ6.5-8.0 region - this is often seen in *para* disubstituted benzenes.

(d) Formula: $C_{3.7}H_{3.8}Br_{0.53}O_{0.53} \Rightarrow C_7H_7BrO$. NMR: 4 benzene H's, CH_3O- (δ3.7). IR: *meta* disubstituted benzene. So:

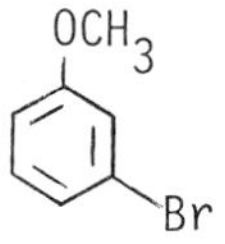

is the answer.

(e) Formula: $C_{4.5}H_{5.6}Br_{0.5} \Rightarrow C_9H_{11}Br$. H-1 NMR: 2 benzene H's, three CH_3's (two equivalent - note just two quartets in C-13 NMR). Also, just 4 benzene carbons in C-13 spectrum, so molecule has some symmetry to it.

Answer, from trial and error, is:

****

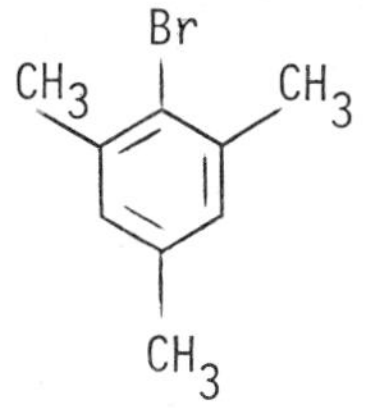

δ52.2 (because 2 H's split it into a triplet)

10.

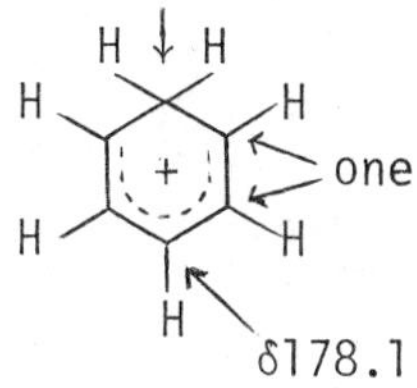

one is at δ136.9, other is at δ186.6   ← Assign these more precisely by looking at resonance forms:

δ178.1

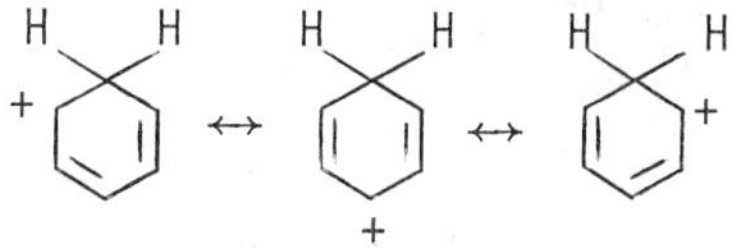

In the resonance forms, positive charges are at only three of the carbons: they should be the most deshielded. That explains the δ178.1 chemical shift of the "bottom" carbon. The δ186.6 signal must therefore correspond to the positively charged "end" carbons of the delocalized cation:

← δ186.6

← so this is δ136.9.

****

11. (a)   ; (b)   eventually; (c)   ; $\Delta H°$ = $DH°(ICl)$ +

$DH°(C_6H_5-H)$ - $DH°(C_6H_5-I-)$ - $DH°(HCl)$ = 50 + 111 - 65 - 103 = -7 kcal/mole, barely exothermic! ; (d) NO$_2$; (e) $C(CH_3)_3$ (Friedel-Crafts alkylation involving $(CH_3)_3C^+$ cation) ;

(f) Careful! $(CH_3)_3CCH-CH_2-Cl-\bar{A}lCl_3$ $\xrightarrow{\text{H shift}}$ $(CH_3)_2C-CH-CH_3$ $AlCl_4^-$ $\xrightarrow{\text{- shift}}$

$(CH_3)_2\overset{+}{C}-CH(CH_3)_2$ $\longrightarrow$ $(CH_3)_2CH-\underset{CH_3}{\overset{CH_3}{\underset{|}{\overset{|}{C}}}}$ $\xrightarrow{-H^+}$ $(CH_3)_2CH-\underset{CH_3}{\overset{CH_3}{\underset{|}{\overset{|}{C}}}}$

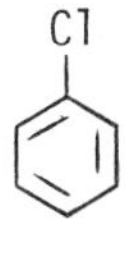

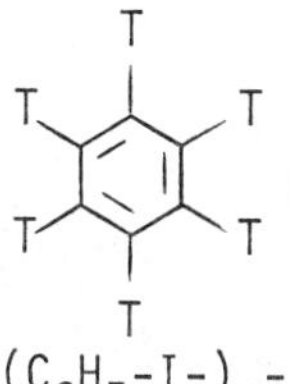

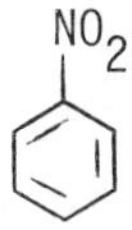

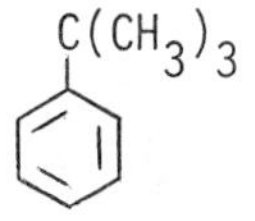

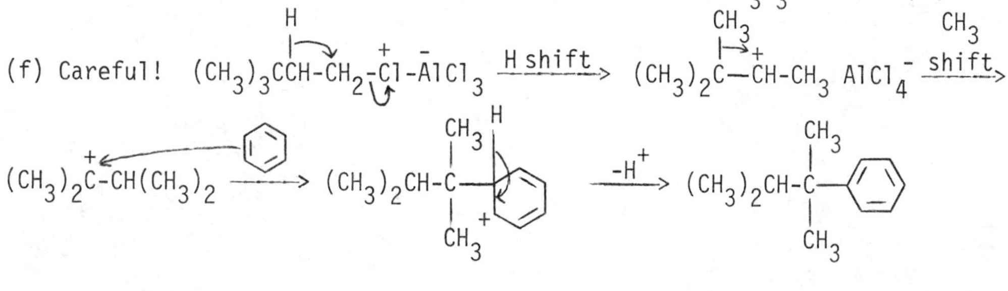

(g) ; (h)

****

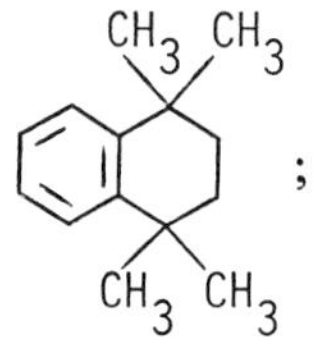

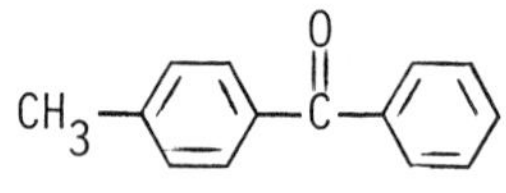

12. (c) $I-Cl: \rightarrow FeCl_3 \longrightarrow I\overset{}{\underset{}{-}}Cl-FeCl_3 \xrightarrow[-FeCl_4^-]{} $ $\xrightarrow{-H^+}$

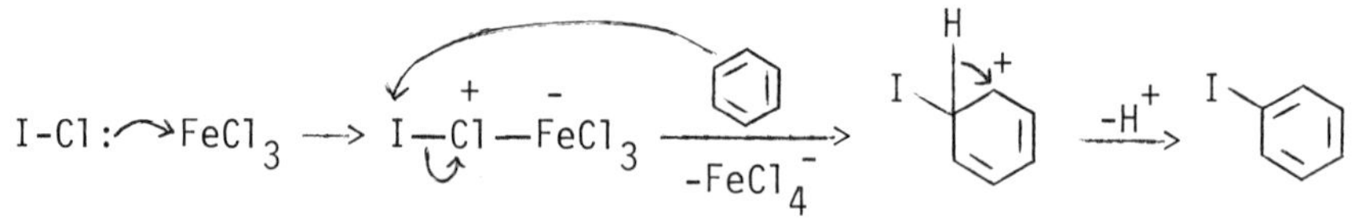

(f) is shown in answer to Problem 11.

****

13. Identify a likely electrophilic atom, and follow a reasonable mechanistic pattern:

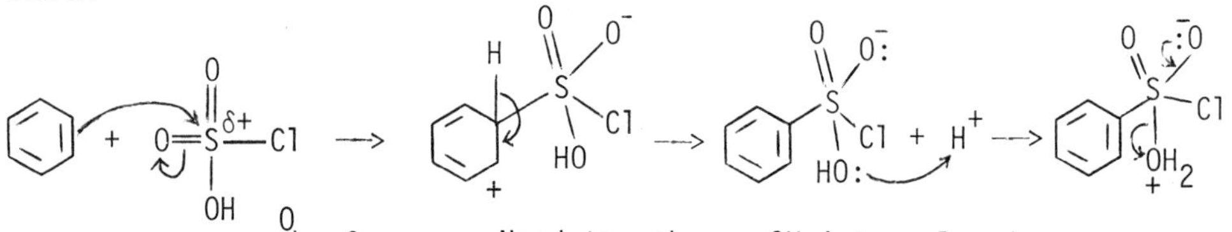

Need to make an OH into a leaving group.

$\longrightarrow H_2O + $; H_2O then reacts with excess $ClSO_3H$ to make

H_2SO_4 and HCl. (Note: this is just one of several possible parallel mechanisms.)

****

14. Electrophile?

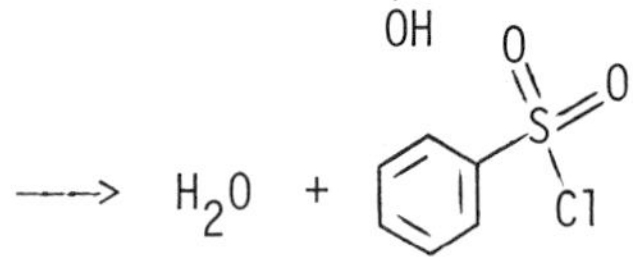

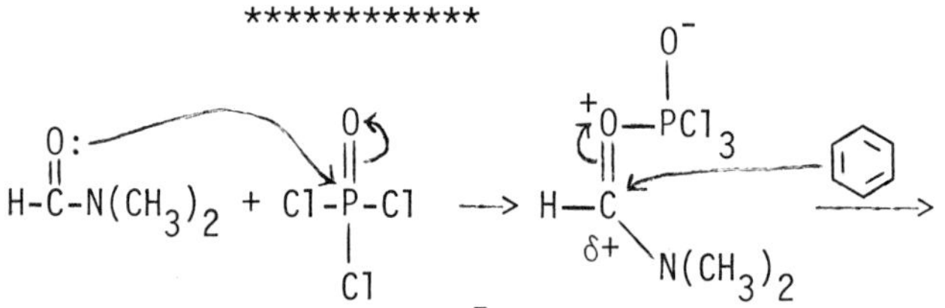

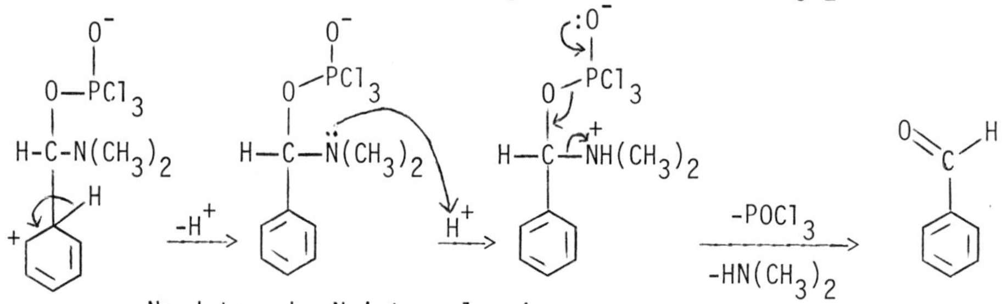

Need to make N into a leaving group.

****

15. Look at $AlCl_3$ as a Lewis acid, and benzene as a nucleophile. Recall (Section 9-6) that acid catalyzed ring openings of oxacyclopropanes give S_N1 regiochemistry (most stable carbocation) but S_N2 stereochemistry (backside nucleophilic attack). So:

$$\xrightarrow{-H^+} \quad \xrightarrow[\text{-Al}^{3+}\ \text{salts}]{\text{After } H^+,\ H_2O}$$

exclusively

****

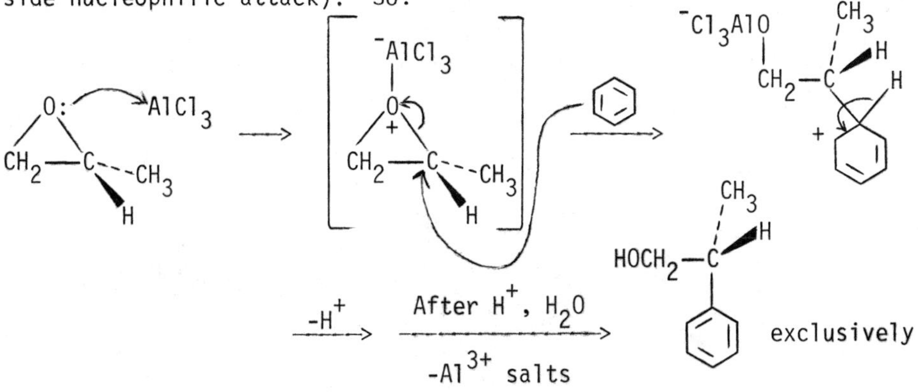

16. (a) Need an electrophile:

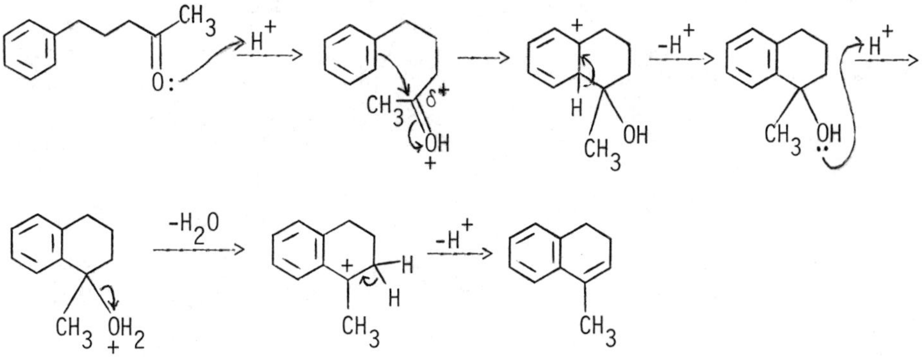

Conditions are identical to those used for dehydration of alcohols.

(b) How about 1,4-addition of a cuprate to an enone to form the marked bond:

$$\longleftarrow \quad CH_2{=}CHCCH_3 \ + \ \left(\begin{array}{c} \end{array} \right)_2 CuLi$$

Start:

$$\xrightarrow{Cl_2,\ h\nu} \qquad \xrightarrow{Li} \qquad \xrightarrow{CuI}$$

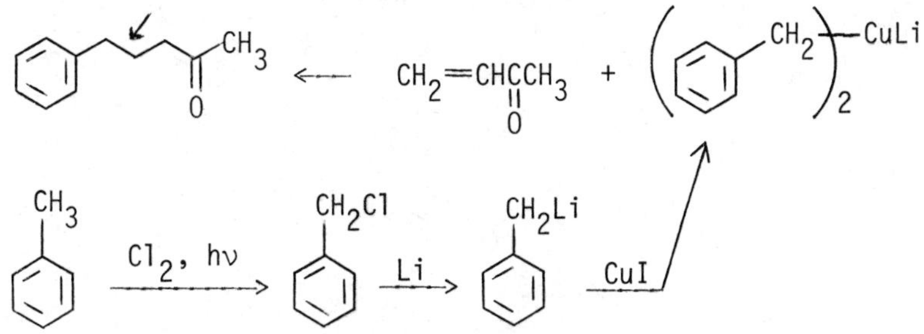

(c) Friedel-Crafts acylation: [structure: phenyl-C(=O)-CH₂-CH₂-C(=O)-OH] is the product after H^+, H_2O work-up. Then:

$\xrightarrow{NH_2NH_2, KOH, \Delta}$ [structure: phenyl-CH₂CH₂CH₂-C(=O)-OH] $\xrightarrow[\text{2. } H^+, H_2O]{\text{1. } 2CH_3Li}$ [structure: phenyl-CH₂CH₂CH₂-C(=O)-CH₃] $\xrightarrow{}$ as in part a

Or: $\downarrow SOCl_2$

[structure: phenyl-CH₂CH₂CH₂-C(=O)-Cl] $\xrightarrow{AlCl_3}$ [bicyclic tetralone structure] $\xrightarrow[\text{2. } H_2SO_4, \Delta]{\text{1. } CH_3MgI}$ product

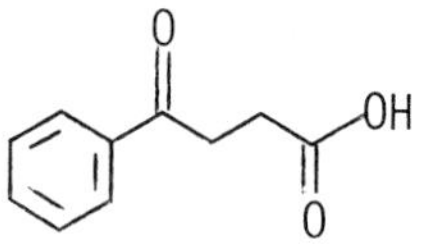

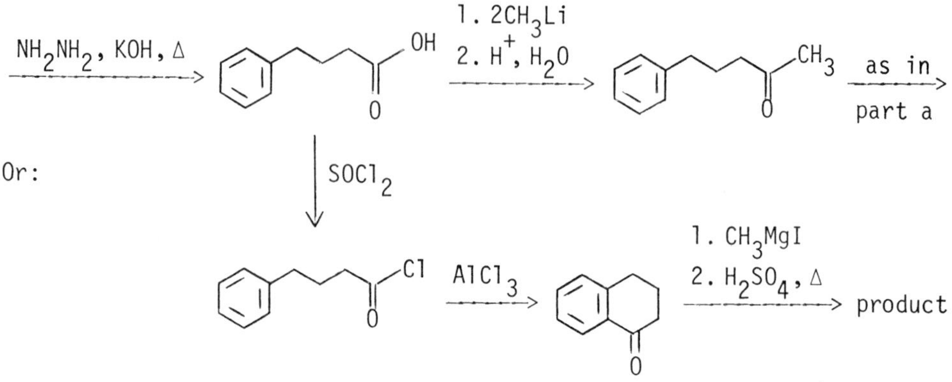

(Normal Friedel-Crafts acylation)

****

17. (a) Attempted F.-C. alkylation will give rearranged products from primary haloalkanes. Use acylation followed by reduction:

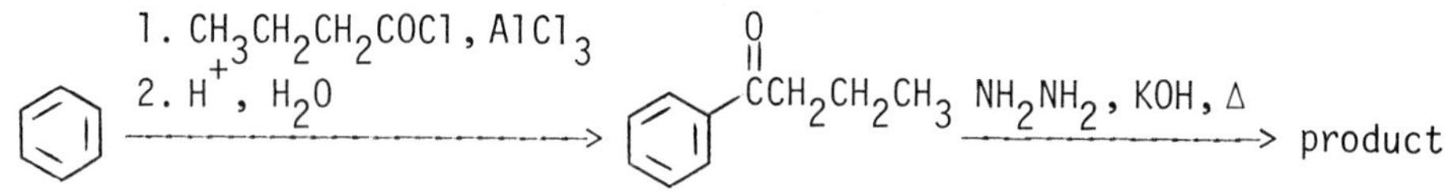

[benzene] $\xrightarrow[\text{2. } H^+, H_2O]{\text{1. } CH_3CH_2CH_2COCl, AlCl_3}$ [structure: phenyl-C(=O)CH₂CH₂CH₃] $\xrightarrow{NH_2NH_2, KOH, \Delta}$ product

(b) [benzene] $\xrightarrow[\text{2. } H^+, H_2O]{\text{1. } (CH_3CH_2)_3CCl, AlCl_3}$ product.

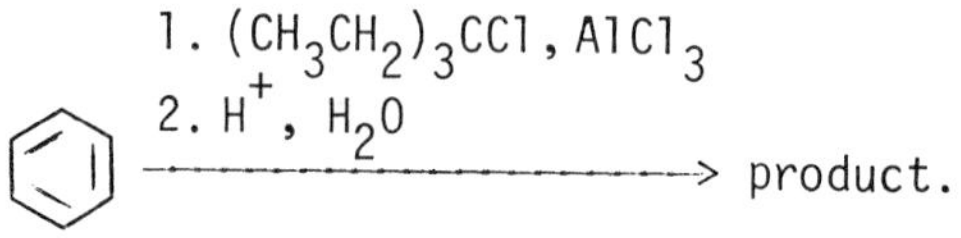

Alkylation works here since the <u>tertiary</u> cation intermediate doesn't tend to rearrange.

(c) 2[benzene] $\xrightarrow[\text{2. } H^+, H_2O]{\text{1. } Cl\overset{O}{\overset{\|}{C}}CH_2CH_2\overset{O}{\overset{\|}{C}}Cl, AlCl_3}$ product

(d) [benzene] + [structure: benzene with CH₂COCl and CH₂CO₂H substituents] $\xrightarrow[\text{2. } H^+, H_2O]{\text{1. } AlCl_3}$ [structure with C(=O)CH₂ and HOCCH₂] $\xrightarrow{NH_2NH_2, KOH, \Delta}$

[structure: phenyl-CH₂CH₂-benzene with HOCCH₂] $\xrightarrow[\text{3. } H^+, H_2O]{\substack{\text{1. } SOCl_2 \\ \text{2. } AlCl_3}}$ [bicyclic structure: CH₂CH₂ and C—CH₂ with C=O] $\xrightarrow{NH_2NH_2, KOH, \Delta}$ product

****

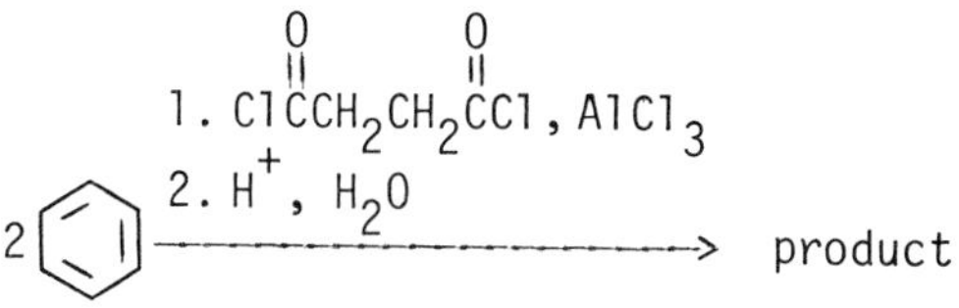

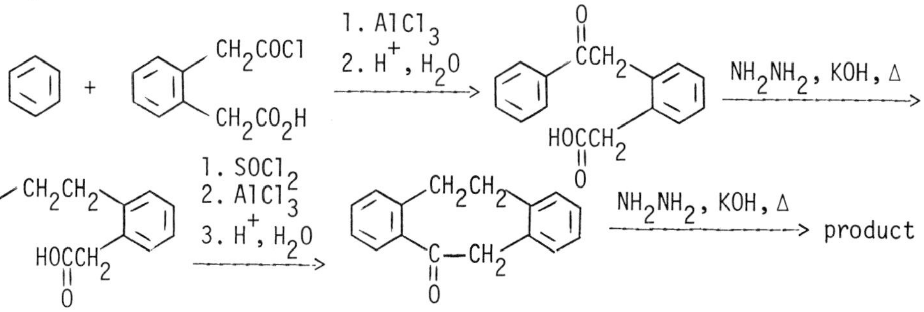

18.

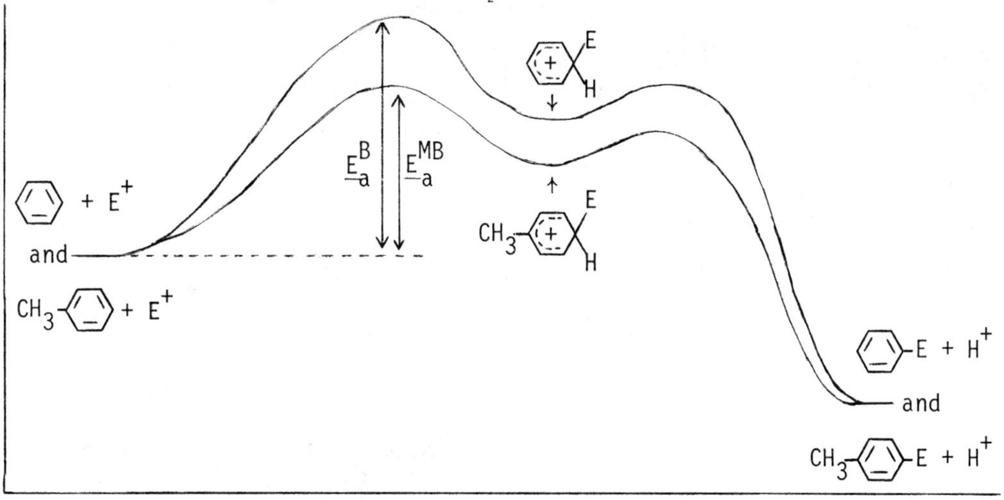

Reaction coordinate

The reaction of methylbenzene should proceed with a lower energy of activation than that of benzene ($E_a^{MB} < E_a^{B}$), and the intermediate cation should be more stable as shown.

****

19.

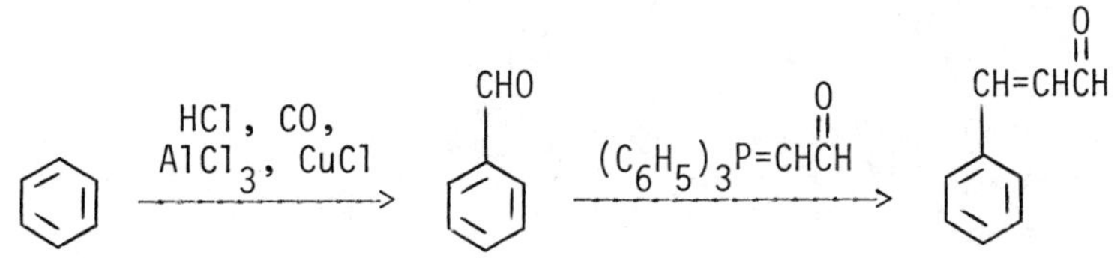

IUPAC name: 3-phenyl-2-propenal.

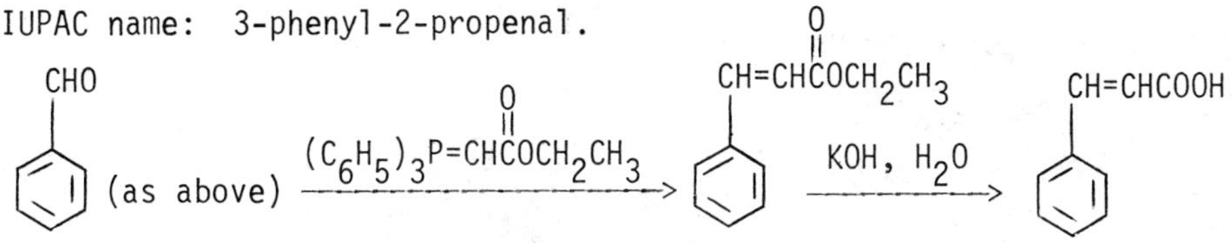

IUPAC name: 3-phenyl-2-propenoic acid.

****

20. How about a simple electrophilic substitution? Hg in $Hg(O\overset{O}{\overset{\|}{C}}CH_3)_2$ is electrophilic, so try

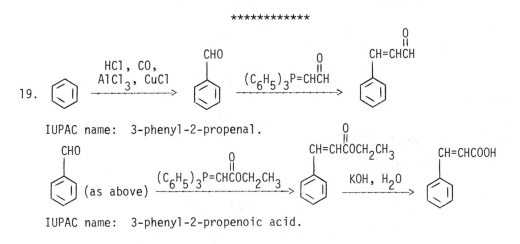

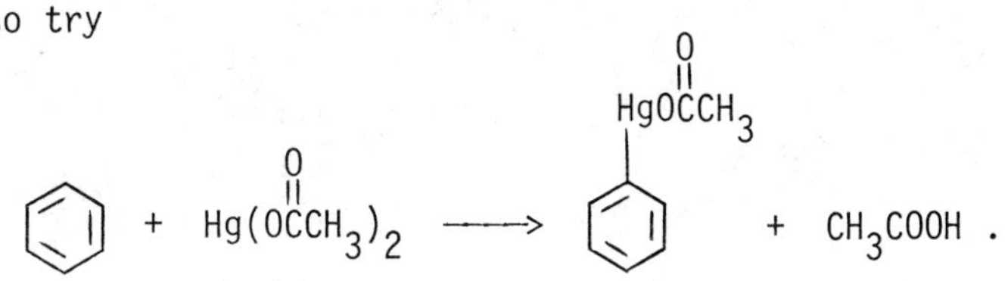

****

21. (a) $C_6H_5CHOHCH_3$; (b) $C_6H_5CH_2CH_2OH$; (c) $(C_6H_5)_2C(OH)CH_2CH_3$;

(d) 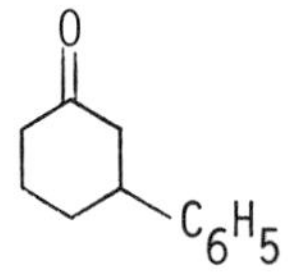

****

22. (a) $C_6H_6 \xrightarrow[\text{2. Mg}]{\text{1. } Br_2\text{, Fe}} C_6H_5MgBr \xrightarrow[\text{2. } H^+\text{, } H_2O]{\text{1. HCHO}} C_6H_5CH_2OH$ (standard approach)

(b) Hint: consider a Hofmann rearrangement approach (Section 18-5). Retrosynthetically:

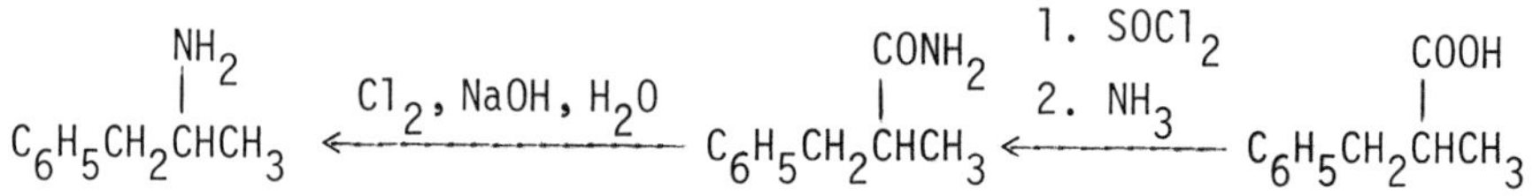

$$C_6H_5CH_2CH(NH_2)CH_3 \xleftarrow{Cl_2\text{, NaOH, } H_2O} C_6H_5CH_2CH(CONH_2)CH_3 \xleftarrow[\text{2. } NH_3]{\text{1. } SOCl_2} C_6H_5CH_2CH(COOH)CH_3$$

Now what? How about the haloform reaction as an acid synthesis (Section 16-2):

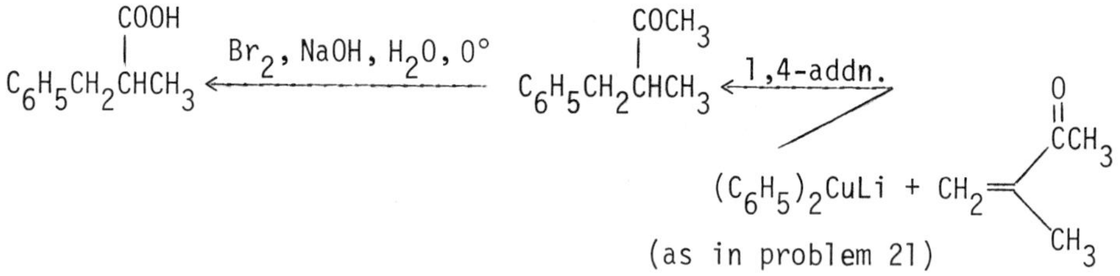

$$C_6H_5CH_2CH(COOH)CH_3 \xleftarrow{Br_2\text{, NaOH, } H_2O\text{, } 0°} C_6H_5CH_2CH(COCH_3)CH_3 \xleftarrow{\text{1,4-addn.}} (C_6H_5)_2CuLi + CH_2{=}C(CH_3)CCH_3(=O)$$

(as in problem 21)

(c) Work backwards, again, step-by-step:

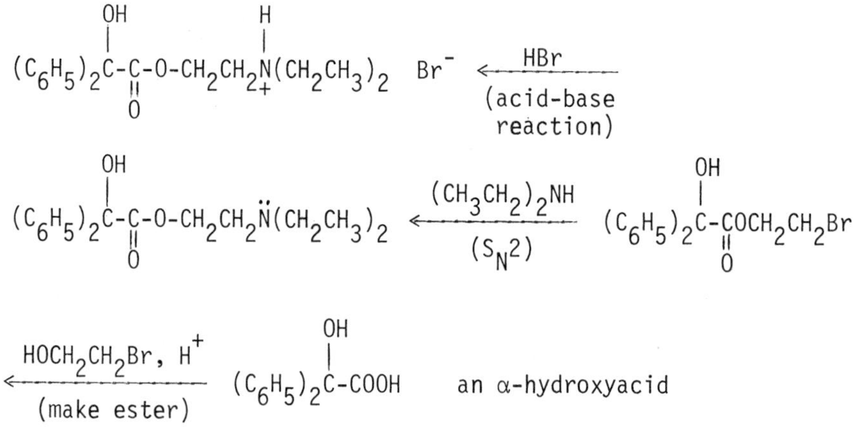

$$(C_6H_5)_2C(OH)\text{-}C(=O)\text{-}O\text{-}CH_2CH_2\overset{+}{N}H(CH_2CH_3)_2\ Br^- \xleftarrow[\text{(acid-base reaction)}]{HBr}$$

$$(C_6H_5)_2C(OH)\text{-}C(=O)\text{-}O\text{-}CH_2CH_2\ddot{N}(CH_2CH_3)_2 \xleftarrow[(S_N2)]{(CH_3CH_2)_2NH} (C_6H_5)_2C(OH)\text{-}C(=O)OCH_2CH_2Br$$

$$\xleftarrow[\text{(make ester)}]{HOCH_2CH_2Br\text{, } H^+} (C_6H_5)_2C(OH)\text{-}COOH$$ an α-hydroxyacid

We've seen α-hydroxy acids before:

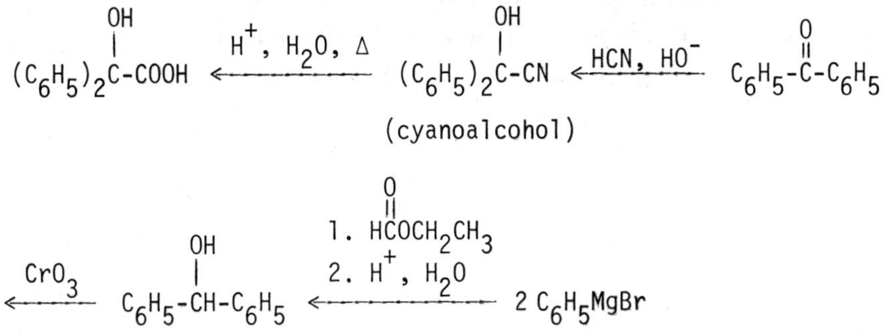

$$(C_6H_5)_2\overset{\overset{\large OH}{|}}{C}\text{-}COOH \xleftarrow{H^+,\ H_2O,\ \Delta} (C_6H_5)_2\overset{\overset{\large OH}{|}}{C}\text{-}CN \xleftarrow{HCN,\ HO^-} C_6H_5\text{-}\overset{\overset{\large O}{\|}}{C}\text{-}C_6H_5$$

(cyanoalcohol)

$$\xleftarrow{CrO_3} C_6H_5\text{-}\overset{\overset{\large OH}{|}}{CH}\text{-}C_6H_5 \xleftarrow[\text{2. } H^+,\ H_2O]{\text{1. } H\overset{\overset{\large O}{\|}}{C}OCH_2CH_3} 2\ C_6H_5MgBr$$

****

CHAPTER 20

Electrophilic and Nucleophilic Attack on Derivatives of Benzene: Substituents Control Regioselectivity

General Introduction

The previous chapter introduced you to the properties and chemistry of benzene itself. In this chapter the chemistry will be expanded to include several new reactions of not only benzene, but also derivatives of benzene containing various substituents. The text will focus on the effects of substituents on the chemistry of the benzene ring. You will see that different types of substituents can change the electron density of the benzene π orbitals, making them more or less susceptible to electrophilic attack. With certain electron-withdrawing substituents the π orbitals can become so electron deficient that attack by *nucleophiles* on the benzene can also occur. You will also see how substituents on a benzene ring can direct the attack of an electrophile or a nucleophile to specific carbons of the benzene ring. This study guide chapter will contain a general summary of this sort of information in order to help you avoid a lot of memorization and, instead, be able to look at the structural characteristics of any substituent and predict its effect on benzene chemistry.

Outline of the Chapter

20-1. Activation and Deactivation of the Benzene Ring

20-2. Where Does the Second Group Go? Directing Inductive Effects.

20-3. Directing Effects by Substituents in Resonance with the Benzene Ring.

20-4. Electrophilic Attack on Disubstituted Benzenes.

Effects of substituents on the reactivity and regioselectivity of further electrophilic substitution on a benzene ring.

20-5. Synthetic Aspects of Benzene Chemistry.

General principles, and strategic considerations.

20-6. Ipso-Substitution.

Three new processes of lesser overall significance.

20-7. A Summary of Organic Reaction Mechanisms.

Keys to the Chapter

20-1. Activation and Deactivation of the Benzene Ring.

Don't forget the *basics*: *electrophiles* seek *electrons*! So reactivity of a benzene ring towards electrophiles will be enhanced by substituents that donate electron density into the ring, and it will be reduced by substituents that withdraw electron density from the ring. Both inductive and resonance effects can be involved, to relative degrees determined by the atoms in each ring substituent. Notice (Table 20-1) that in many instances the inductive and resonance effects oppose each other.

20-2, 20-3, and 20-4. Directing Effects: Where the Next Group Goes.

When a benzene containing a substituent undergoes further electrophilic substitution, the substituent already present directs the position of the subsequent reaction. Again, both inductive and resonance effects are involved. The favored reaction proceeds through the most stabilized (or least destabilized) intermediate carbocation. Study *carefully* the resonance forms pictured for the possible cations derived from electrophilic attack on methylbenzene and trifluoromethylbenzene (Section 20-2), and benzenamine, benzenecarboxylic acid, and a halobenzene (Section 20-3). Notice the types of groups that fall into the two categories in Table 20-2. In particular, notice the following two general observations:

(1) All substituents with lone pairs on the atom attached to the benzene ring are ortho,para-directors.

(2) All substituents which have a positively polarized (δ^+) atom lacking a lone pair attached to the benzene ring are meta-directors.

These generalizations always hold, and may be used as aids to help you remember whether a group belongs in one category or the other.

20-5. Synthetic Aspects of Benzene Chemistry.

This section shows how two interconversions of benzene substituents may be profitably used in synthesis: the interconversion of NH_2 and NO_2 groups, which may be done in either direction, and reduction of alkanoyl (acyl) to alkyl. Both interconvert an *o*,*p*-director with a *m*-director. In addition, the use of SO_3H as a *para*-blocking group is illustrated.

20-6. *Ipso* Substitution.

What you have seen so far comprises by far the bulk of the most important substitution reactions for benzenes. In this section three processes involving attack at an already-substituted benzene carbon are presented. The first, electrophilic ipso-substitution, is not an overly common reaction, and is synthetically useful to only a limited extent. You have already seen the most important example: the removal of the SO_3H blocking group by strong acid. Protodealkylation is of mechanistic interest, but little practical synthetic utility.

The two *nucleophilic* aromatic (*ipso*) substitution reactions are much more useful. The addition-elimination version is a common reaction of benzenes containing a leaving group together with good electron-withdrawing (anion-stabilizing) groups like NO_2. The elimination-addition ("benzyne") mechanism occurs when benzenes containing a leaving group, but no other anion-stabilizing groups, are treated with strong bases. Although these nucleophilic substitution reactions are indeed useful, you should keep them in perspective: they are encountered only rarely relative to the electrophilic reactions described in these two chapters. You have already seen the reason for this: benzenes normally contain electron-rich π-systems, and are naturally most easily attacked by electrophiles. Only in the presence of strong electron-withdrawing groups or very strong bases will nucleophilic attack have any likelihood of occurring.

Solutions to Chapter 20 Problems

1. Order of decreasing reactivity; for brevity only the substituents are listed.

   (a) $-CH_3 > -CH_2Cl > -CHCl_2 > -CCl_3$ (electronegative Cl's make carbon δ^+, so inductive effect becomes increasingly electron withdrawing and deactivating).

   (b) $-CH_2CH_3 > -CH_2CCl_3 > -CH_2CF_3 > -CF_2CH_3$ (inductive effects again, combined with distance to ring).

   (c) $-O^-\ Na^+ > -OCH_3 > -O\overset{O}{\overset{\|}{C}}CH_3$ (resonance activators; order is determined by availability of lone pairs on O to be donated to ring: $-O\overset{O}{\overset{\|}{C}}CH_3$ is weakest activator due to this resonance form: $-\overset{+}{O}{=}\overset{O^-}{\overset{|}{C}}CH_3$).

   (d) $-\overset{O}{\overset{\|}{C}}O^-\ Na^+ > -\overset{O}{\overset{\|}{C}}NH_2 > -\overset{O}{\overset{\|}{C}}CH_3$ (order is determined by size of δ^+ on carbonyl carbon: note that it is the reverse of the reactivity of the carbonyl carbons to nucleophilic attack).

****

2. Activated: (c), (d), (f), (h)

****

3. *Ortho* attack:

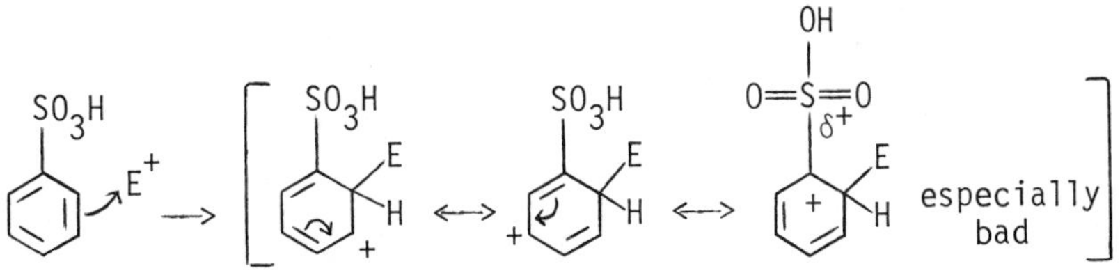

Para attack:

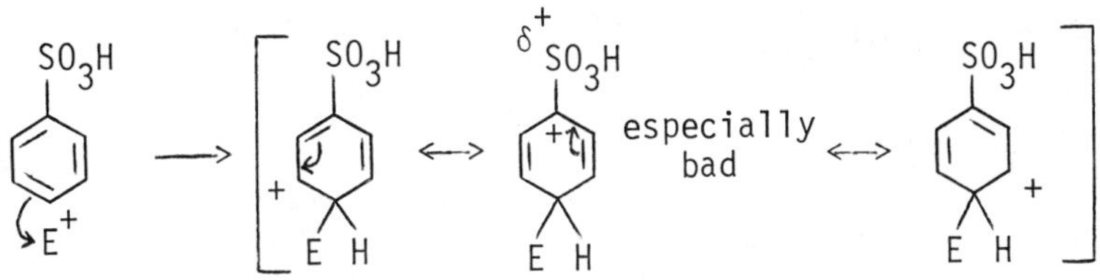

Meta attack:

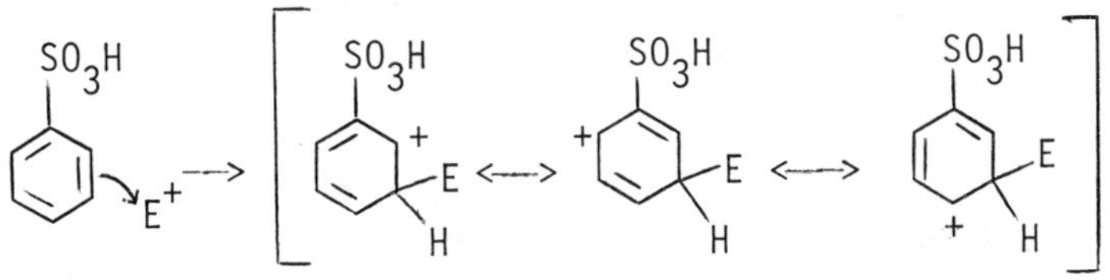

no resonance forms with + adjacent to δ^+ sulfur

****

4. Statement is correct. All *meta*-directors deactivate the entire ring by inductive electron withdrawal. Deactivation at the *ortho* and *para* positions is most intense due to resonance (see, for example, the answer to problem 3, above). *Meta* substitution occurs simply because the deactivation is felt least strongly at that position.

****

5. Where both *ortho* and *para* products are formed, the *para* is generally the major one.

(a) 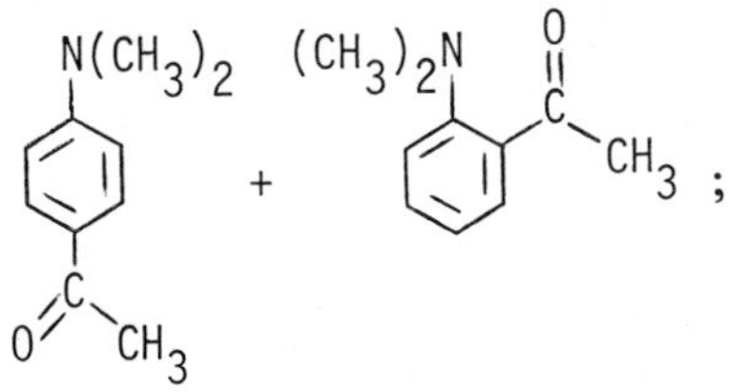

; (b) 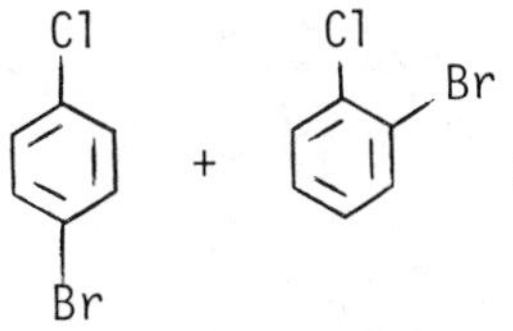

;

(c) 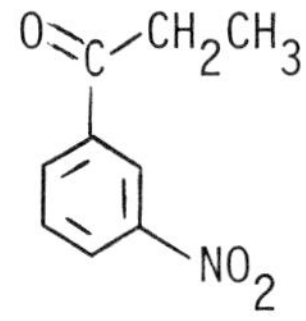 ; (d) 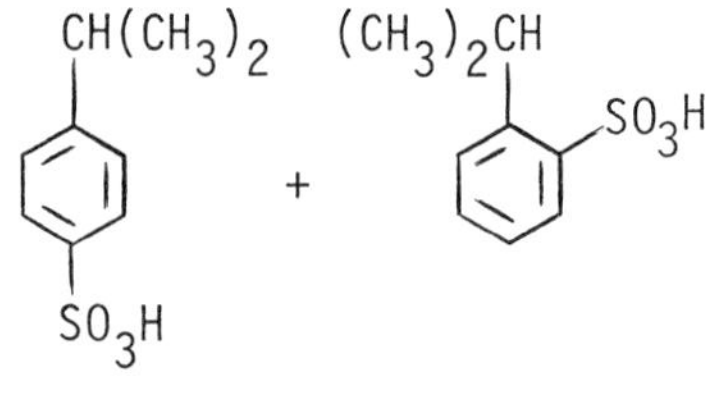 (e) 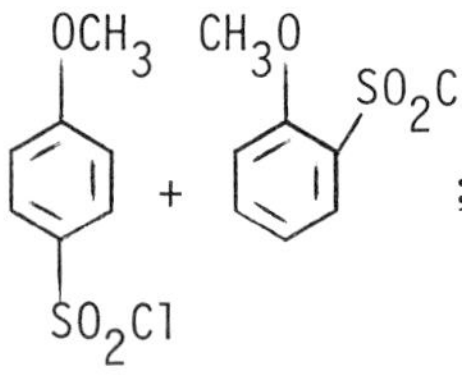 ;

(f) 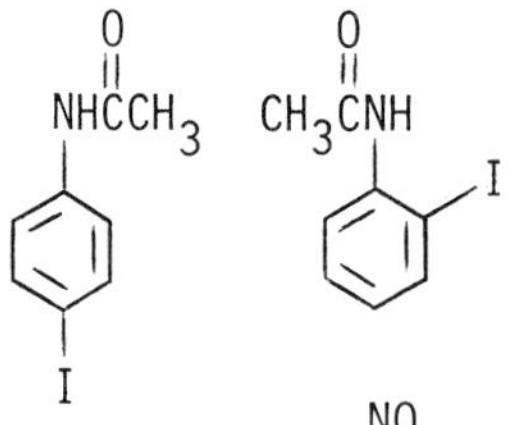 ; (g) 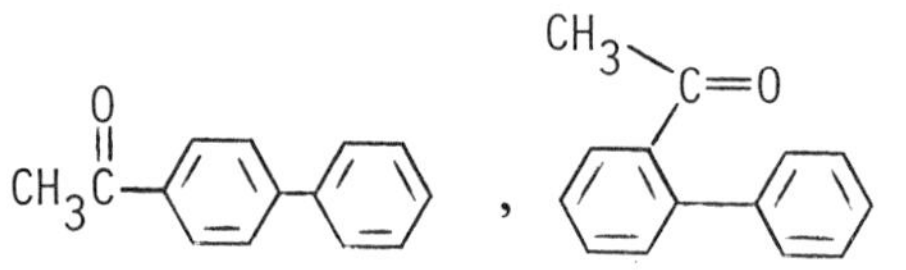 ;

(h) 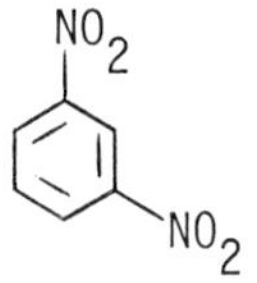

****

6. 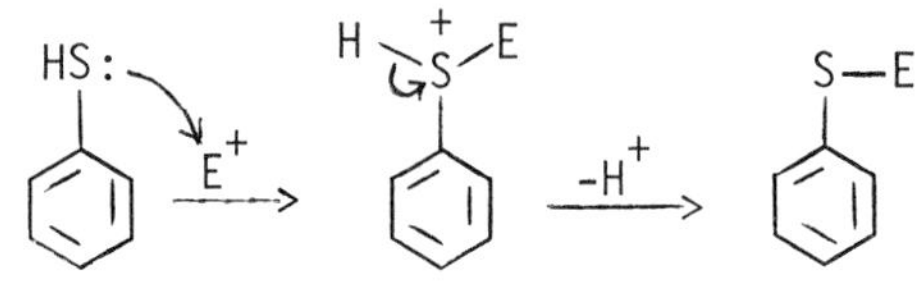 favored because of high nucleophilicity of sulfur atom.

****

7. The methoxy group is *inductively electron withdrawing* due to the electronegative oxygen atom. The overwhelming resonance effect strongly activates the *ortho* and *para* positions, but it is not directly felt at the *meta* positions (see related resonance forms for benzenamine, section 20-3). The deactivating inductive effect wins at the *meta* positions.

****

8. Orientation of reaction is determined by more activating (or less deactivating) substituent (marked in each case below). Again, *para* product may be expected to predominate where a choice of *ortho* or *para* exists.

(a) 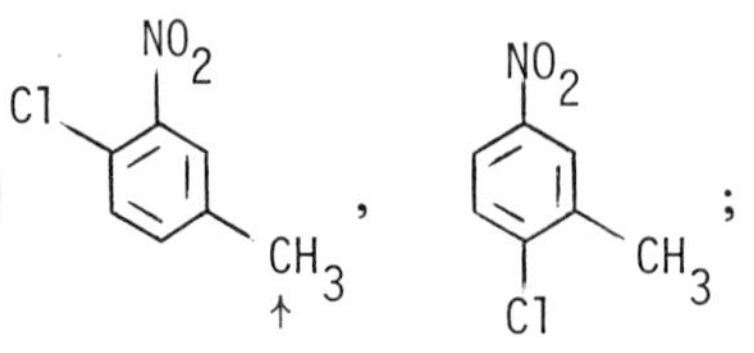 ; (b) 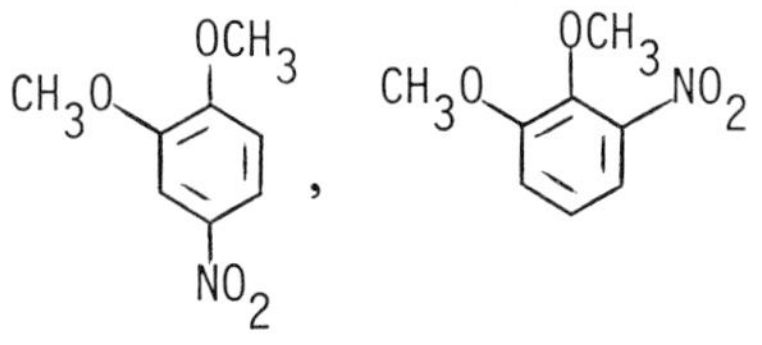 ;

(c) 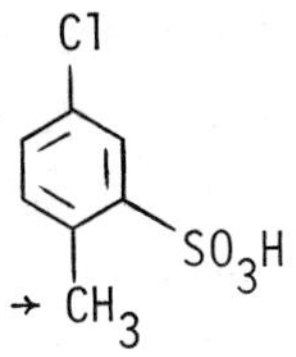 ; (d) 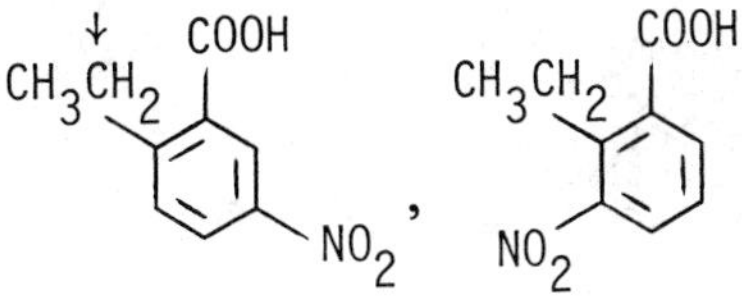 ; (e) 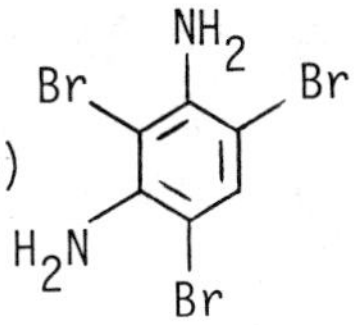 ;

(f) 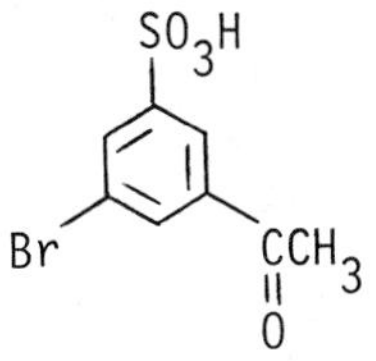 ; (g) 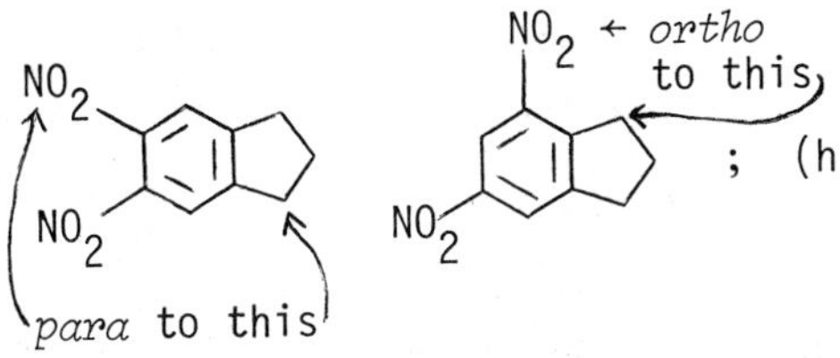

; (h) 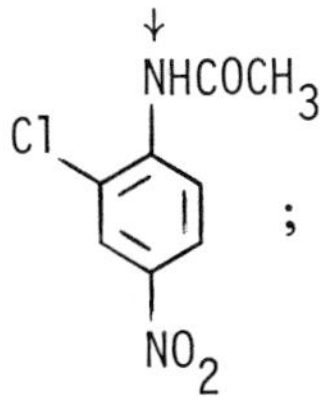 ;

(both *meta* directing)

(i) No reaction (Friedel-Crafts reaction does not occur on rings containing *meta*-directing groups: the ring is too deactivated.) ; (j) 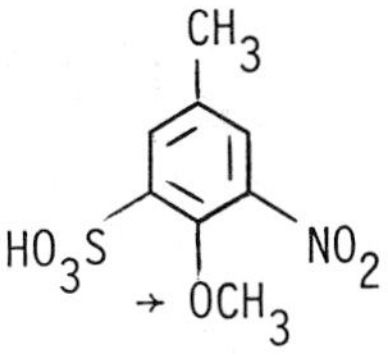

****

9. Activating effects are additive. In each structure count up the number of methyls *ortho* or *para* to each open position:

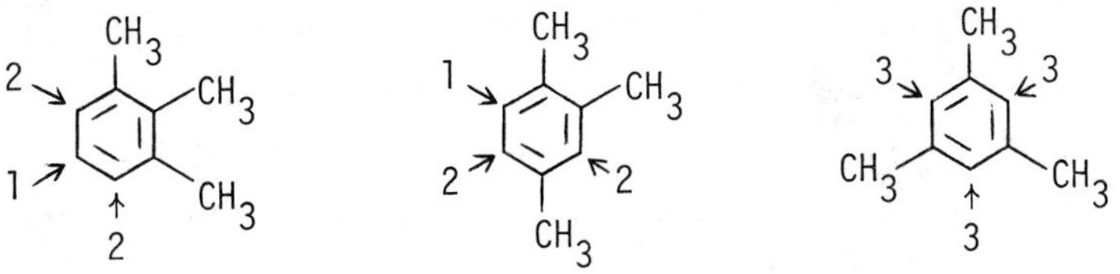

The last should be the most reactive toward electrophiles: each vacant position is activated by being *ortho* or *para* to <u>all three</u> methyl groups.

****

10. Lewis structure: —N̈=Ö: . The lone pair on N will favor *ortho* and *para* substitution through the following resonance forms:

<u>*Ortho*</u>: 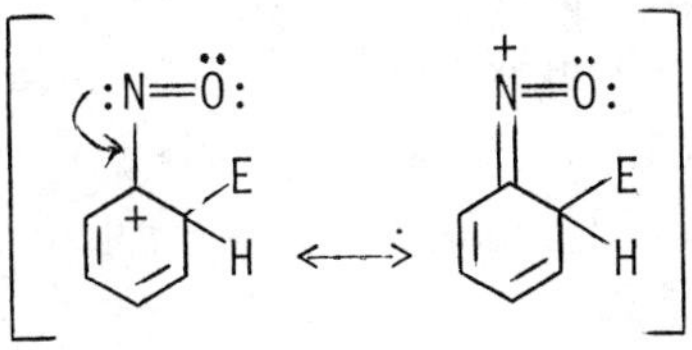 <u>*Para*</u>: 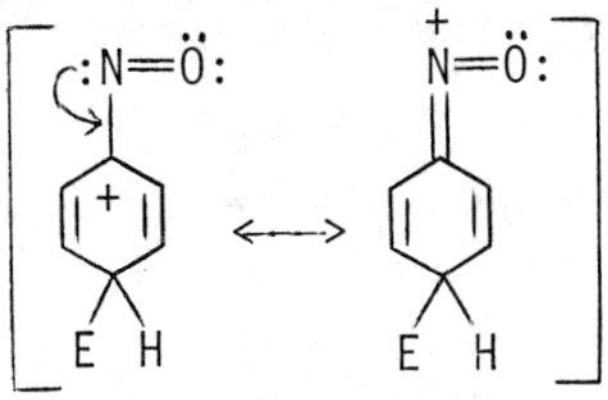

However, the -NO group is inductively electron withdrawing. As is the case with halogen substituents, this deactivating inductive effect is on the average stronger than the resonance effect, so nitrosobenzene is deactivated overall, even though substitution is preferred (by the resonance effect) at the *ortho* and *para* positions.

****

11. The electrophile: $:\ddot{O}=\ddot{N}-\ddot{O}:^- \xrightarrow{2H^+} :\ddot{O}=\ddot{N}-\overset{+}{O}H_2 \xrightarrow{-H_2O} [:\overset{..}{O}=\overset{+}{N}: \longleftrightarrow :\overset{+}{O}\equiv N:]$

nitrosonium ion

Then:

and

****

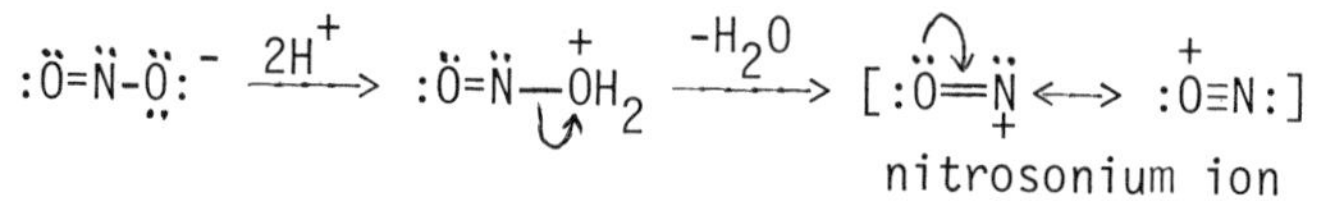

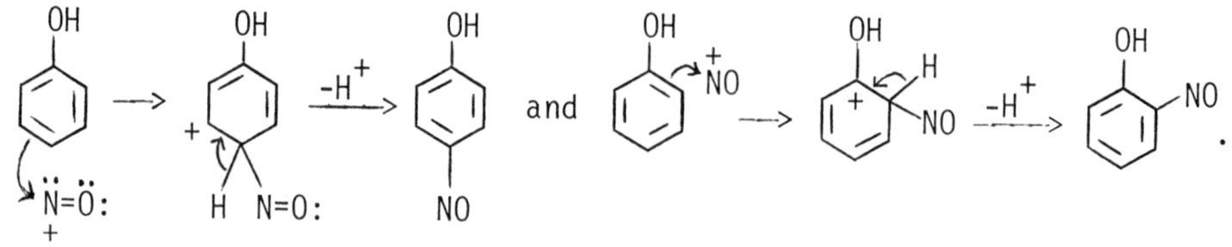

12. **A:** formula, $C_{3.8}H_{3.2}Br_{0.64} \Rightarrow C_6H_5Br$, ⟨_⟩—Br. Note IR bands at 685 and 735 cm^{-1} for monosubstituted benzene.

B: formula, $C_{3.5}H_{3.5}Br_{0.58}N_{0.58} \Rightarrow C_6H_6BrN$. IR: bands at 3378 and 3463 cm^{-1} suggestive of N-H bond(s). NMR: 4 benzene H's and 2 H's as broad peak near $\delta 3.5$, $-NH_2$ group? So pieces may be -Br, $-NH_2$, and "C_6H_4". IR band at 820 cm^{-1} and symmetrical "two doublets" appearance of benzene H signals in NMR are evidence for *para*-disubstituted isomer: Br—⟨_⟩—NH_2.

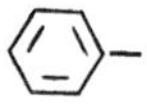

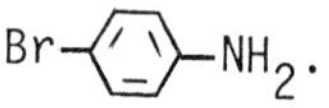

C: also C_6H_6BrN. Again $-NH_2$ is suggested by both spectra, as for **B**. IR shows a 745 cm^{-1} band, consistent with *ortho*-disubstitution:

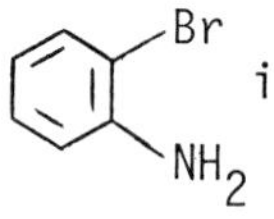

is the answer. The NMR is complicated between δ 6 and 7.5, as you might expect.

D: formula: $C_{2.4}H_{2.0}Br_{0.8}N_{0.4} \Rightarrow C_6H_5Br_2N$. Again contains an $-NH_2$ group. Now there are two Br's, and 3 benzene hydrogens which give a 1H triplet and a 2H doublet in the NMR. How can we arrange these six groups, 2 Br, 3H, NH_2, to get this pattern? We need one H split by two equivalent H's:

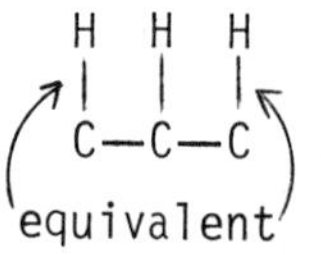

. Since we have a benzene ring, this could result from the structure on the right which is the answer.

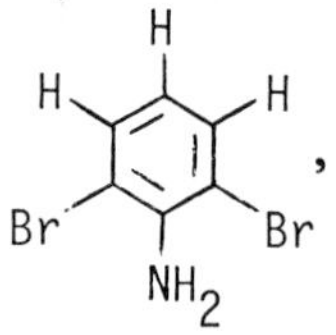

Synthesis (assume any *ortho* + *para* mixtures can be readily separated to give the *para* product in good yield):

$$\underline{A} \xrightarrow[\text{2. }H_2\text{-Ni}]{\text{1. }HNO_3,\ H_2SO_4} \underline{B};\quad \underline{A} \xrightarrow{SO_3,\ H_2SO_4}$$

Br
[benzene ring] SO$_3$H
mainly

$$\xrightarrow[\text{2. }H_2\text{-Ni}]{\text{1. }HNO_3,\ H_2SO_4}$$

Br
[benzene ring]—NH$_2$
SO$_3$H

$$\xrightarrow[\text{removes}\ SO_3H]{H_2O,\ \Delta} \underline{C};\quad \underline{A} \xrightarrow{\text{again}} \underline{C} \xrightarrow{CH_3COCl^*}$$

Br
[benzene ring]—NHCOCH$_3$

$$\xrightarrow[\substack{\text{blocks position}\\ \textit{para}\text{ to amide}}]{SO_3,\ H_2SO_4}$$

Br
[benzene ring]—NHCOCH$_3$
SO$_3$H

$$\xrightarrow{Br_2,\ Fe}$$

Br
[benzene ring]—NHCOCH$_3$ with Br and SO$_3$H substituents

$$\xrightarrow[\substack{\text{removes }SO_3H\\ \text{and hydrolyzes amide}}]{H^+,\ H_2O,\ \Delta} \underline{D}.$$

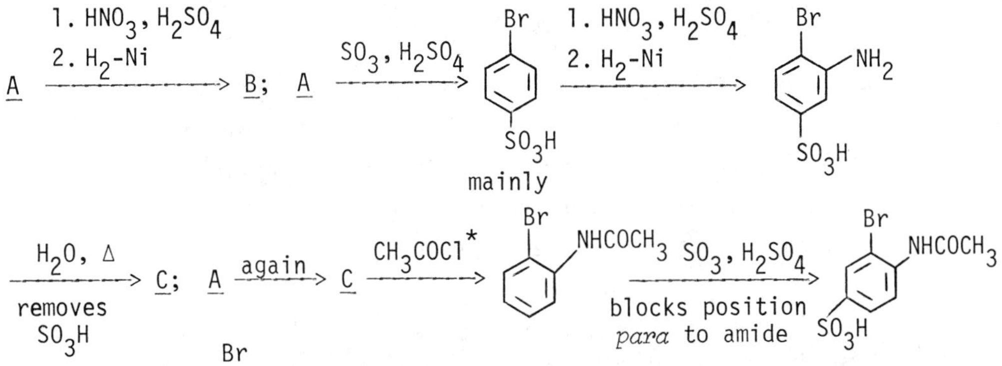

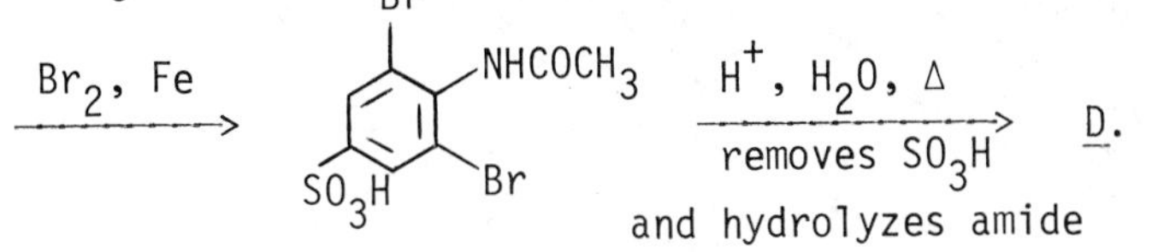

*The reason for making the amide is to reduce the basicity of the amine nitrogen. If you don't do this, the amine will be protonated by the acid upon attempted sulfonation, turning it into a *meta*-directing -NH$_3^+$ group which will mess up the sulfonation reaction. (See Section 20-5 for more on this.)

****

13. Friedel-Craft's reactions are understood to be followed by H$^+$, H$_2$O work-up.

(a) 1. CH$_3$COCl, AlCl$_3$; 2. NH$_2$NH$_2$, KOH, H$_2$O, Δ; 3. CH$_3$COCl, AlCl$_3$.

(b) 1. HNO$_3$, H$_2$SO$_4$; 2. Cl$_2$, FeCl$_3$.

(c) 1. CH$_3$COCl, AlCl$_3$; 2. SO$_3$, H$_2$SO$_4$; 3. HCl, Zn(Hg) (Section 20-5).

(d) 1. HNO$_3$, H$_2$SO$_4$; 2. HCl, Zn(Hg); 3. CH$_3$COCl (makes [benzene ring]-NHCOCH$_3$; see answer to problem 12); 4. HNO$_3$, H$_2$SO$_4$; 5. H$^+$, H$_2$O, Δ.

(e) 1. Cl$_2$, FeCl$_3$; 2. excess conc. HNO$_3$, H$_2$SO$_4$, Δ.

(f) 1. Br$_2$, FeBr$_3$; 2. HNO$_3$, H$_2$SO$_4$, separate *para* from *ortho*; 3. HCl, Zn(Hg) (makes Br-[benzene ring]-NH$_2$); 4. Cl$_2$, CHCl$_3$, 0° (chlorinates once, *ortho* to NH$_2$; see Section 20-4); 5. CF$_3$CO$_3$H.

(g) 1. Br$_2$, FeBr$_3$; 2. SO$_3$, H$_2$SO$_4$ (blocks *para*); 3. Cl$_2$, FeCl$_3$; 4. H$_2$O, Δ.

(h) 1. CH$_3$Cl, AlCl$_3$; 2. SO$_3$, H$_2$SO$_4$; 3. excess Br$_2$, FeBr$_3$; 4. H$_2$O, Δ.

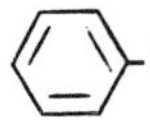

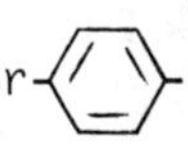

(i) 1. CH_3CH_2COCl, $AlCl_3$; 2. Cl_2, $FeCl_3$ (goes *meta*); 3. NH_2NH_2, KOH, Δ

(makes [structure: phenyl with Cl and $-CH_2CH_2CH_3$]); 3. SO_3, H_2SO_4 (to HO_3S-[phenyl with Cl]$-CH_2CH_2CH_3$);

4. HNO_3, H_2SO_4; 5. H_2O, Δ.

(j) This one is tricky! To get two *ortho/para* directing groups like these in *meta* positions requires the use of two removable groups:

First, you need a removable group 'A' which is *ortho/para* directing, and then you need a second removable group 'B' which will block the position *para* to 'A'. Here's the answer:

[Reaction scheme:]
benzene $\xrightarrow{(CH_3)_3CCl, AlCl_3}$ 'A'→$C(CH_3)_3$ [phenyl with $C(CH_3)_3$] $\xrightarrow{SO_3, H_2SO_4}$ [phenyl with $C(CH_3)_3$ and SO_3H ('B')] $\xrightarrow[2. Br_2, Fe]{1. Cl_2, Fe}$

[structure: ring with $C(CH_3)_3$, Br, Cl, SO_3H] $\xrightarrow[\text{protodealkylation of } C(CH_3)_3 \text{ group and removal of } SO_3H \text{ as well}]{H^+, H_2O, Δ}$ $CH_2=C(CH_3)_2$ + [ring with Br and Cl]

****

14. [structure: CH_3O-phenyl] $\xrightarrow{Cl_2, CHCl_3, 0°}$ [CH_3O-phenyl-Cl] $\xrightarrow{Mg, THF}$ [CH_3O-phenyl-MgCl] $\xrightarrow[2. H^+, H_2O]{1. HCHO}$ anisyl alcohol

****

15. [benzene] $\xrightarrow[2. Mg]{1. Br_2, Fe}$ [phenyl-MgBr] $\xrightarrow[2. H^+, H_2O]{1. CO_2}$ [phenyl-CO_2H] $\xrightarrow{Br_2, Fe}$ [ring with CO_2H and Br] $\xrightarrow[2. H_2, Pd-BaSO_4]{1. SOCl_2}$

[structure: CHO-phenyl-Br] $\xrightarrow{NH_2NH_2, KOH, Δ}$ [CH_3-phenyl-Br] $\xrightarrow[3. H^+, H_2O]{1. Mg \\ 2. CO_2}$ [ring with CH_3 and CO_2H] $\xrightarrow[2. (CH_3CH_2)_2NH]{1. SOCl_2}$ product

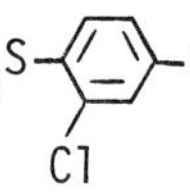

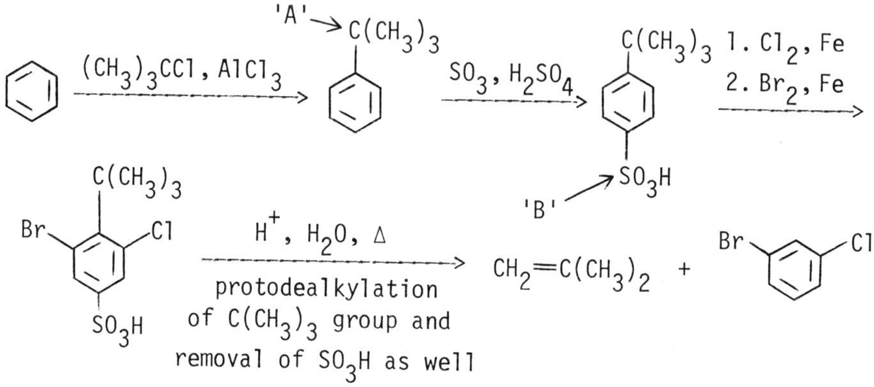

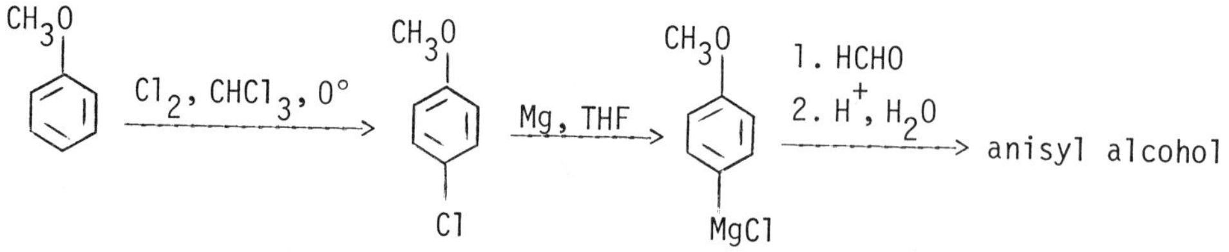

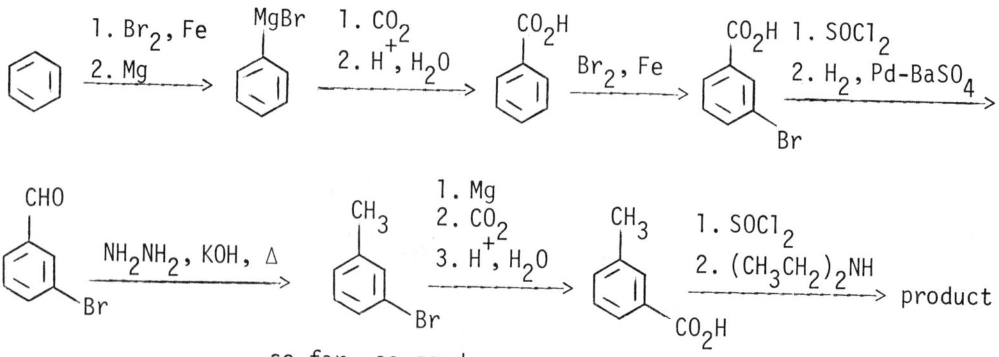

so far, so good

Note: both the Gatterman-Koch (Exercise 19-17) and Vilsmeier-Hack (Problem 14 of Chapter 19) reactions would provide shortcuts:

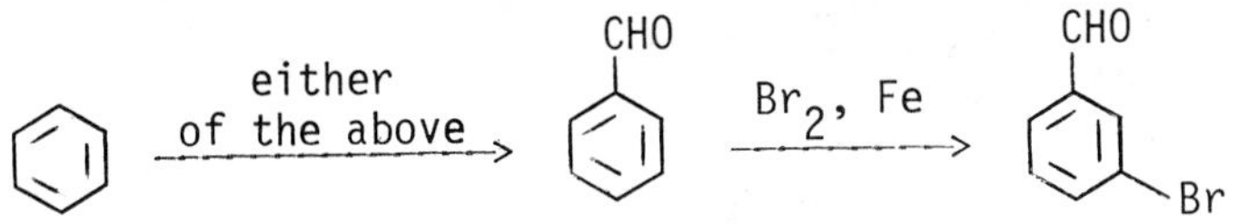

****

16. Want 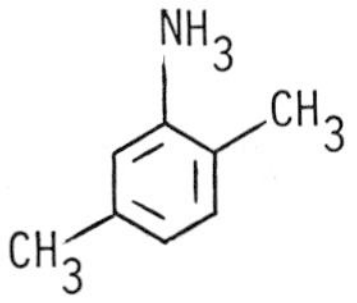

. A good problem to illustrate strategy. The methyls are *para* to each other, so they can go in first. Then nitration and reduction finish the synthesis:

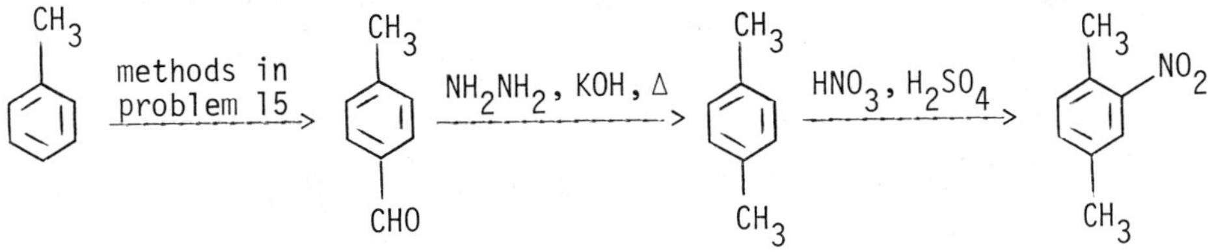

$\xrightarrow{\text{HCl, Zn(Hg)}}$ product

****

17. Most reactive ones have NO_2 groups *ortho* and/or *para* to the leaving group.

So:

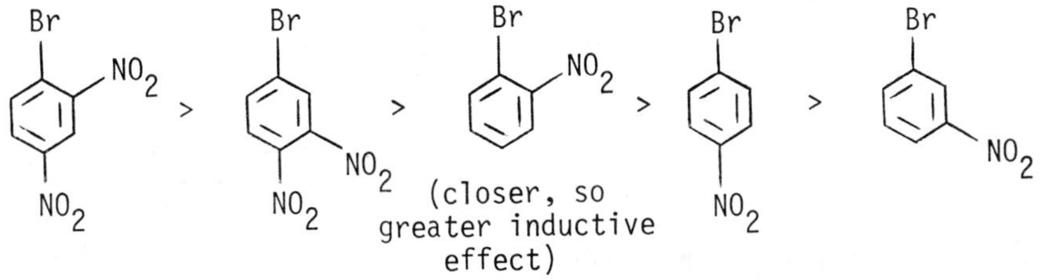

****

18. (a) 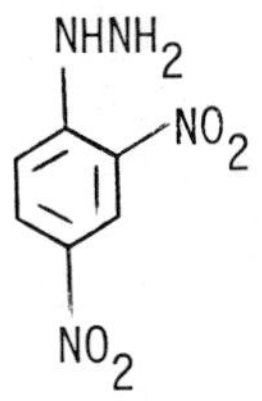

; (b) 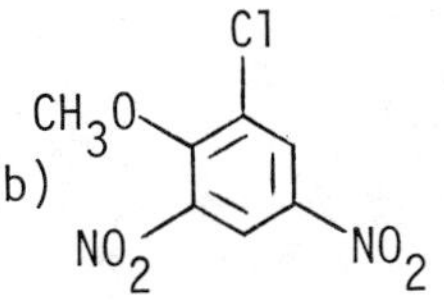

(Cl *ortho/para* to NO_2's is most easily displaced) ;

(c) 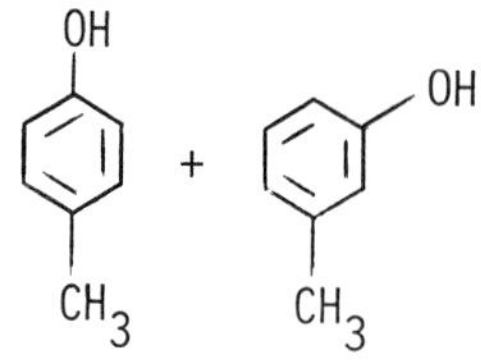 (benzyne mechanism); (d) 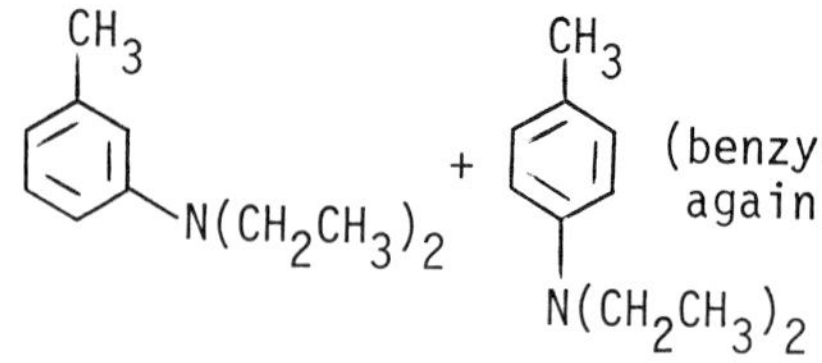 (benzyne again)

****

19. (a) 1. Cl_2, Fe; 2. Br_2, Fe. (b) 1. Mg, $(CH_3CH_2)_2O$; 2. CO_2 followed by H^+, H_2O. (c) excess HNO_3, H_2SO_4, Δ. (d) 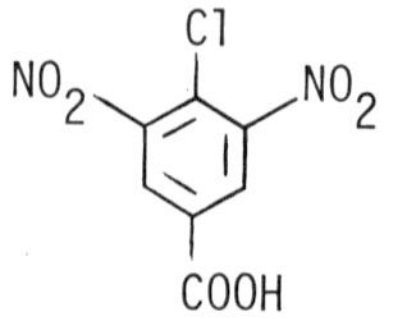 all set up for nucleophilic aromatic substitution.

(e) 1. $SOCl_2$; 2. $LiAlH[OC(CH_3)_3]_3$, THF, -78°; 3. NH_2NH_2, KOH, Δ. Name: 4-methyl-2,6-dinitro-N,N-dipropyl-benzenamine.

****

20. Nucleophilic aromatic substitution, the ring activated towards reaction by the chlorines:

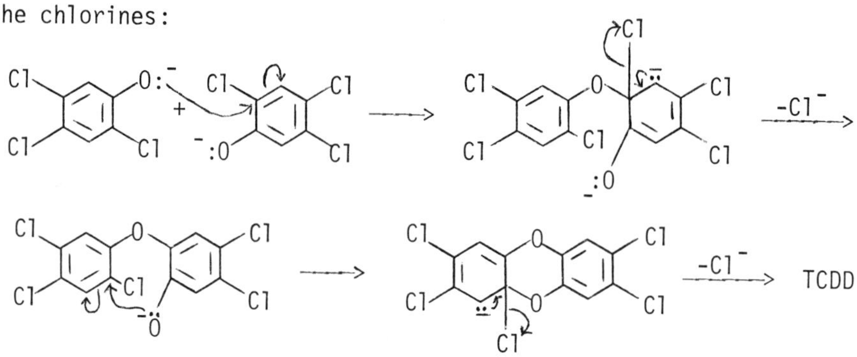

****

21. (a) 1. CH_3COCl; 2. Br_2, $CHCl_3$; 3. KOH, H_2O, Δ. (b) 1. CF_3CO_3H; 2. Cl_2, Fe. (c) KCN (nucleophilic aromatic substitution). (d) H^+, H_2O, Δ. Name: 2-chloro-4-nitrobenzenecarboxamide

****

22. 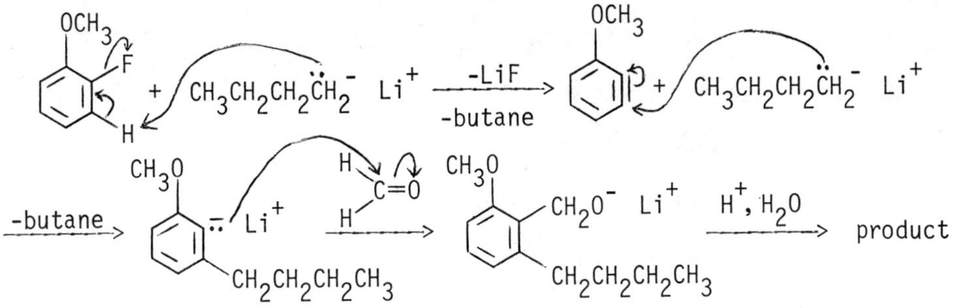

Strongly basic butyllithium removes HF in first step, generating benzyne. Second mole of butyllithium adds to benzyne as a nucleophile. The reason for the direction of addition is explained in the answer to Exercise 20-17.

****

23. 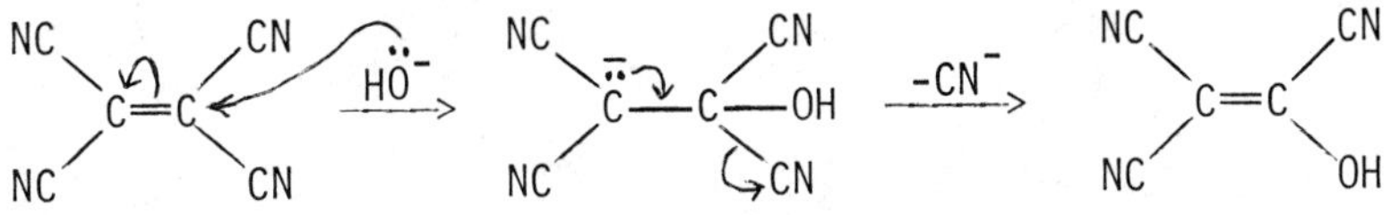

anion is stabilized by nitrile groups

****

24. (ii) 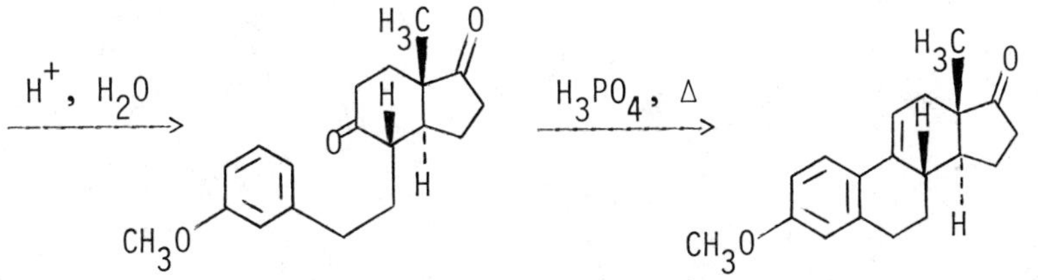

Friedel-Crafts reaction, directed *para* to methoxy group.

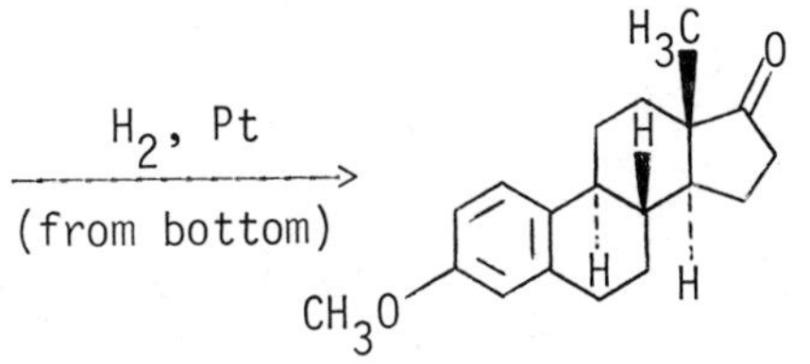

****

25. A: 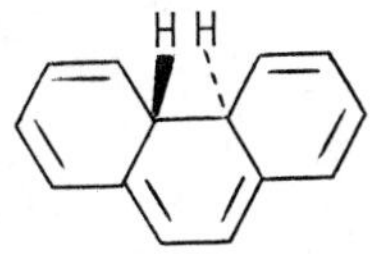, from photochemical conrotatory ring-closure.

B: 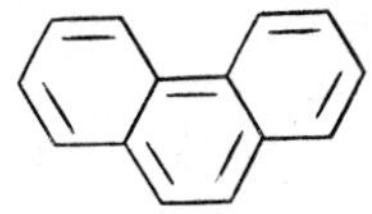, aromatization by sulfur dehydrogenation.

****

26. (a) Nucleophilic substitution, S_N2

(b) Nucleophilic addition to a carbonyl

(c) Nucleophilic substitution, S_N2

(d) Electrophilic addition to an alkene

(e) Electrophilic addition to an alkyne

(f) Nucleophilic substitution, S_N2

(g), (h), (i) Nucleophilic addition to a carbonyl

(j) Electrophilic aromatic substitution

****

CHAPTER 21

Amines and Their Derivatives: New Functional Groups Containing Nitrogen

General Introduction

Amines represent the last of the simple functional groups that you will encounter in organic chemistry. They are not entirely new to you, of course. They have popped up as early as Chapter 6, as the results of nucleophilic substitution reactions between ammonia and haloalkanes. More recently you have been introduced to amine syntheses starting from carboxamides and nitriles (Sections 20-5 and 20-6). As usual, the chapter will begin by presenting in detail the usual body of descriptive information concerning the properties of amines as a class of compounds. It will then focus in more detail on the limitations and variations associated with the various amine syntheses, finishing with a relatively short section on reactions of amines. Amines are of substantial importance biologically, as you will see. Unlike other biologically important compound classes, however, amines are not involved in a very wide range of distinctly different types of reactions. Thus you should find this aspect of amine chemistry relatively manageable.

Outline of the Chapter

21-1. Nomenclature.

21-2, 21-3. Physical and Acid-Base Properties of Amines.

Qualitative and quantitative characteristics of the functional group.

21-4. Synthesis.

Guidelines for choosing synthetic strategies.

21-5. Reactions.

Mostly extensions of earlier material; a couple of special reactions,too.

21-6. Some Uses of Amines.

Keys to the Chapter

21-1. Nomenclature.

To an even greater extent than with most other compounds, common names for amines are still almost universally used. It is therefore necessary to be able to recognize structures from both alkylamine- and aniline-based names. The systematic alkanamine method looks tricky at first, but becomes simple once you recognize that it works much the same way that the IUPAC alcohol (alkanol) naming system works.

21-2 and 21-3. Properties of Amines.

Amines are related to alcohols in the same way that ammonia is related to water. This makes the properties of amines easy to predict, since the main qualitative difference is simply that N is less electronegative than O. So, hydrogen bonding in amines is present, but is weaker than in alcohols; deshielding of nearby H-1 and C-13 NMR signals is observed, but to a lesser extent than in alcohols; IR spectra are similar; mass spectra are rather predictable. Tertiary amines (R_3N) may be viewed as nitrogen analogues of ethers (R_2O).

By the way, all these nice, tidy analogies do not extend to the *smells* possessed by most amines. While alcohols tend to have, at worst, somewhat heavy, sweetish odors, amines, at best, smell like ammonia, and, at worst, richly deserve the common names that have been bestowed upon some of their representatives. These include names like cadaverine, putrescine, and skatole. Dead fish would be an improvement.

The acid-base properties of amines are an extension of what you know about ammonia: they are weaker acids and stronger bases than are water or alcohols. It will repay you many times over, however, to go over the information involving pK_a's and pK_b's of these molecules. The qualitative ability to handle acid-base concepts is one of the more useful capabilities you can take out of a course in organic chemistry.

21-4. Synthesis.

By the time you finish reading this section of the text you will be aware of the fact that the first amine synthesis you learned, alkylation of NH_3 via S_N2 reaction, is also generally the worst amine synthesis, as well. It is much better to use any one of the special N-containing nucleophiles that give clean monoalkylation products, which can then be turned into amines. For simple systems lacking sensitive functional groups, all the methods will work comparably well. The choice becomes more critical if the molecule is more sensitive. For example, 1. N_3^-, 2. $LiAlH_4$ would be a poor choice for the conversion of $Br(CH_2)_3COCH_3$ into the corresponding amine, since the ketone will be reduced by the hydride reagent along with the azide group. The ketone could be protected before starting, but a better solution would be the Gabriel sequence which involves hydrolysis instead of reduction in the second step.

An important additional amine synthesis in this section is reductive amination of aldehydes and ketones. In particular, reductive amination of a ketone is a better way to make an amine attached to a 2° alkyl group, than is S_N2 reaction with a 2° haloalkane.

The text section presents two new methods for making an amine with one less carbon than is present in a starting haloalkane: The Curtius and Schmidt rearrangements. Their value over the Hofmann rearrangement is that they don't involve the use of bromine, which could also react with other groups in a molecule, like double bonds.

You've already seen how to make an amine with one more carbon using S_N2 reaction with CN^-, followed by reduction. What would you do, however, if you faced the particularly nasty problem of needing to make an amine attached to a 3° alkyl group (R_3CNH_2)? That's tricky, since S_N2 reactions won't work. If you could add a carbon somehow to get to R_3CCONH_2, then you would be all set to use one of the above rearrangements, right? O.K., think about that one for awhile. You will find help in Section 17-5. The solution will be given in the answer to Problem 12(b).

21-5. Reactions.

Beyond simple displacement reactions in which an amine behaves as a nucleophile, there is a small group of specialized reactions of amines, each of which has a very specific use. The Hofmann and Cope eliminations have been more important in structure determination than anything else. They are frequently combined with the Mannich reaction, however, to make an important synthetic entry to cyclic carbonyl compounds with methylene groups next to the carbonyl (see Problem 28). Such structures are present in many naturally occurring (plant-derived) anti-tumor agents.

The nitrosation reactions and the chemistry of diazoalkanes are also used in synthesizing just certain specific types of compounds, like α-chloroketones and cyclopropanes. The mechanisms here are more involved, however, and an understanding of their steps at this point is helpful since similar types of chemistry will be returning later, in Chapter 24. As you plow through this, try to focus on the relationship of each mechanistic step to processes you've seen before: almost all of this is based on relatively fundamental sorts of events, like protonation and deprotonation, combined with elimination and/or addition.

Solutions to Chapter 21 Problems

1. (a) 3-hexanamine, 3-aminohexane; (b) N-methyl-2-propanamine, 2-(methylamino)propane; (c) 2-chlorobenzenamine, o-chloroaniline; (d) N-methyl-N-propylbenzenamine; N-methyl-N-propylaniline; (e) N,N-dimethylmethanamine (common: trimethylamine); N,N-dimethylaminomethane; (f) 4-(N,N-dimethylamino)-2-butanone (only satisfactory name); (g) 6-chloro-N-cyclopentyl-N,5-dimethyl-1-hexanamine (numbers refer to substituents on parent hexane chain); 1-chloro-6-(N-cyclopentyl-N-methylamino)-2-methylhexane; (h) N,N-diethyl-2-propen-1-amine, 3-(N,N-diethylamino)-1-propene.

****

2. (a) 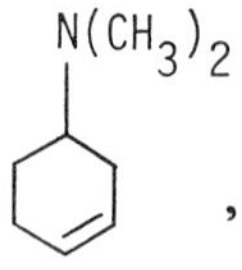

, (b) 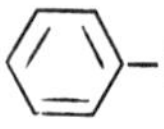 $-CH_2CH_2NHCH_2CH_3$, (c) $HOCH_2CH_2NH_2$, (d) 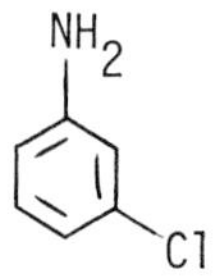

****

3. (a) 5-7 kcal/mole, the E_a for inversion.

(b) Methyl anion is isoelectronic with ammonia and, likewise is tetrahedral (sp^3 hybridized). Methyl radical and cation, with one and two fewer electrons, respectively, are more stable when trigonal planar. They gain stronger bonds by rehybridizing to use sp^2 orbitals in the σ bonds, with either a singly-occupied or vacant p orbital "left over." The sp^2 scheme is not as good for the anion or for ammonia since two electrons in an unhybridized p orbital is quite unfavorable in the absence of other stabilizing influences: such electrons are far from and attracted only poorly by the atom's nucleus.

****

4. The odd atomic weights suggest that each contains a single nitrogen. The total number of hydrogens is available from the NMR, so the number of carbons can be determined by difference: m/z 129 = 14 (one N) + 19 (19 H's) + weight of carbons. Weight of carbons = 96 ⇛ 8 carbons; $C_8H_{19}N$ is the formula for each of these unknowns. Degrees of unsaturation (see Chapter 11 of the Study Guide): $H_{sat'd}$ = 16 + 2 + 1 (for the N) = 19; compounds are saturated.

<u>A</u> NMR: CH_3-CH_2- and $-CH_2-CH_2-NH_2$; notice that signal at $\delta 2.7$ is

$\qquad$ $\underset{\delta 0.9(t)}{\uparrow}$ $\qquad\qquad$ $\underset{\delta 2.7(t)}{\uparrow}$ $\underset{\delta 2.3}{\uparrow}$ $\underline{not}$ split by the $-NH_2$ hydrogens

(as is the case for alcohols as well). The splittings nicely reveal the
number of neighboring H's. MS: $\underline{m/z}$ 30 for $[CH_2=NH_2]^+$ fragment. All that
remains is to insert C_4H_8, and the simplest way to do that is as
$CH_3(CH_2)_7NH_2$ (1-octanamine). Other isomers would show additional methyl
signals in the NMR near $\delta 0.9-1.0$.

<u>B</u> NMR: $(CH_3)_3C-$ likely, also 2 equivalent CH_3-'s, perhaps a CH_2 and an

$\qquad$ $\underset{\delta 1.0(s)}{\uparrow}$ $\qquad\qquad\qquad\qquad\qquad$ $\underset{\delta 1.2}{\uparrow}$ NH_2? (Signals at $\delta 1.3$

and 1.4). MS $\underline{m/z}$ 114 is $[M-CH_3]^+$, 72 is $[M-(CH_3)_3C]^+$, and 58 most likely
an iminium ion. Before guessing, notice that there are $\underline{no}$ NMR signals in
the $\delta 2.7$ region, where you might expect to find (H) signals. So,
most likely the N is attached to a <u>tertiary</u> $\quad -\overset{|}{\underset{|}{C}}-N\overset{\diagup}{\diagdown}$
carbon. Possible pieces:

$(CH_3)_3C-$, 2 CH_3-'s, $-CH_2-$, $-\overset{|}{\underset{|}{C}}-NH_2$.

All atoms in the formula are present, so put it together: $(CH_3)_3C-CH_2-\overset{\underset{\displaystyle |}{CH_3}}{\underset{\displaystyle |}{\underset{\displaystyle CH_3}{C}}}-NH_2$
is indeed the answer. The $\underline{m/z}$ 58 fragment therefore is
$[(CH_3)_2C=NH_2]^+$.

$$************$$

5. As you do each of these, keep the $C_6H_{15}N$ formula in mind.

(a) CMR: splittings are very useful since they tell you that the $\delta 23.7$ peak
    corresponds to one or more equivalent CH_3- groups, and the peak at
    $\delta 45.3$ is one or more equivalent $>CH-$ units (attached to N due to
    chemical shift). IR: a <u>secondary</u> amine, $-NH-$. No other signals are
    present, so attach as many of each as are necessary:

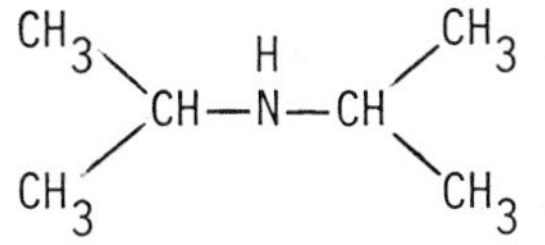

$\underset{CH_3}{\overset{CH_3}{\diagdown}}CH-\underset{}{\overset{H}{N}}-CH\underset{\diagdown CH_3}{\overset{\diagup CH_3}{}}$ is the answer.

(b) CMR: now we have only CH_3- and $-CH_2-$ groups (the latter attached to N).
    IR: a <u>tertiary</u> amine. So: $(CH_3CH_2)_3N$.

(c) CMR: CH_3- groups, $-CH_2-$ groups <u>not</u> attached to N, and $-CH_2-$ groups
    that <u>are</u> attached to N. IR: amine is <u>secondary</u>. So:

$$CH_3CH_2CH_2\overset{\overset{\displaystyle H}{|}}{-}N-CH_2CH_2CH_3.$$

(d) CMR: One CH_3- and five $-CH_2$-'s. IR: <u>primary</u> amine $(-NH_2)$. This is $CH_3(CH_2)_5NH_2$.

(e) CMR: two different CH_3- types, one $(\delta 38.7)$ attached to N; also a quaternary C attached to N $(\delta 53.2)$. IR: a <u>tertiary</u> amine. Remembering the $C_6H_{15}N$ formula, we can construct the molecule

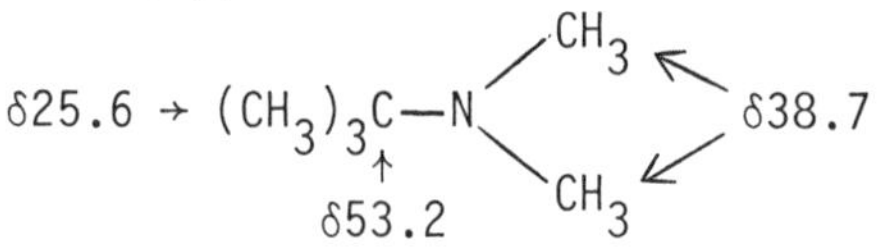

$$\delta 25.6 \rightarrow (CH_3)_3\underset{\underset{\displaystyle \delta 53.2}{\uparrow}}{C}-N\overset{\nearrow CH_3 \;\nwarrow}{\underset{\searrow CH_3 \;\swarrow}{}} \delta 38.7 \quad \text{as the answer.}$$

****

6. Figure 21-5 is $(CH_3CH_2)_3N$ and Figure 21-6 is $CH_3(CH_2)_5NH_2$, for comparison purposes (neither one matches the data in this problem). Look in each case for important fragments from $C \overset{|}{-} C-N$ cleavage to make iminium ions.

(a) $\underline{m/z}$ 72 is important, which is $[M-29]^+$ or loss of CH_3CH_2-. The only amine that should easily lose an ethyl group from those in problem 5 is $CH_3CH_2\overset{|}{-}CH_2-NH-CH_2CH_2CH_3$ (part c). This is the answer.

(b) $\underline{m/z}$ 86 is rather large, corresponding to loss of CH_3-. Three amines in problem 5 should lose CH_3- easily: a, b, and e. N,N-diethylethanamine (triethylamine, 'b') is ruled out because its MS (Figure 21-5) doesn't match. The $\underline{m/z}$ 58 peak is loss of 43, or C_3H_7. That's easy to visualize from 'a': $(CH_3)_2CH\overset{|}{-}NH-CH(CH_3)_2$ (the correct answer), but not from amine 'e'.

****

7. Weaker. $B: + H_2O \xrightleftharpoons{} BH^+ + HO^- \qquad K_b = \dfrac{[BH^+][HO^-]}{[B:][H_2O]}$

K_b is larger for stronger bases. Since $pK_b = -\log K_b$, high pK_b values correspond to low K_b values, or weaker bases.

****

8. (a) Weaker bases since lone pair on N is "tied up" by resonance:

$$\overset{\curvearrowright O}{\underset{\displaystyle RC-\ddot{N}H_2}{\overset{\displaystyle \|}{}}} \overset{\curvearrowleft}{} \leftrightarrow \underset{\displaystyle RC=NH_2^+}{\overset{\overset{\displaystyle O^-}{|}}{}} .$$

Stronger acids since conjugate base is stabilized by resonance:

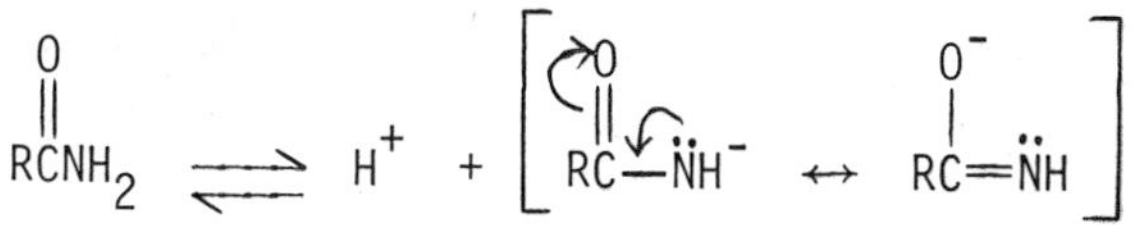

(b) Same as carboxamides, only to a greater extent for both acidity and basicity due to the two carbonyl groups.

(c) Somewhat weaker bases due to resonance: 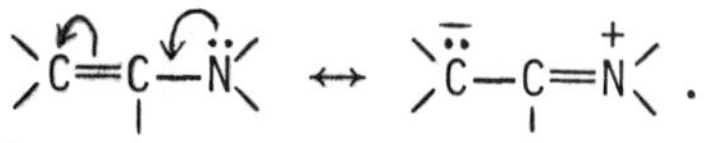 . Not acidic due to lack of H's on nitrogen.

(d) Weaker bases and stronger acids, for same reasons as carboxamides.

****

9. (a) Protonate doubly-bonded nitrogen in each case to get a resonance stabilized cation:

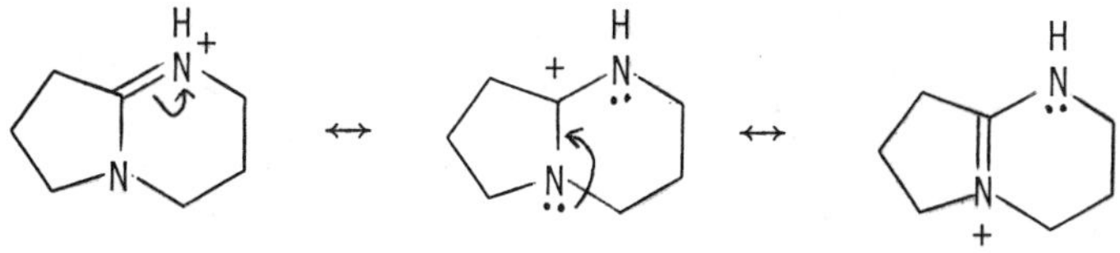

for DBN (DBU is similar)

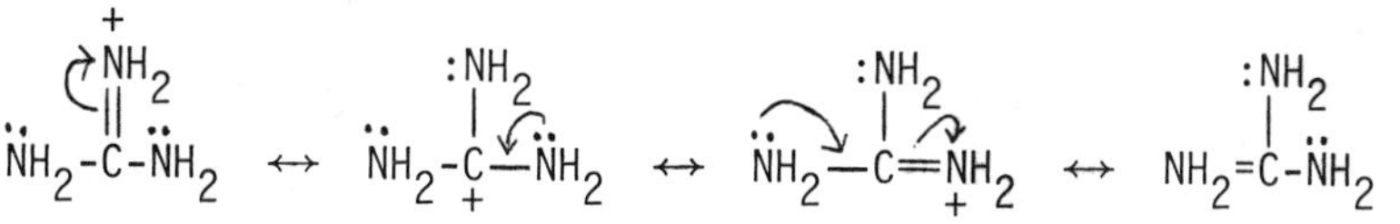

guanidine

Resonance stabilization of conjugate acids enhances base strengths.

(b) Amidines $-\overset{\overset{N^-}{\|}}{C}-N\langle$ are related to carboxamides $-\overset{\overset{O}{\|}}{C}-N\langle$ and carboxylic acid derivatives in general, $-\overset{\overset{O}{\|}}{C}-OH$, etc. Guanidine $NH_2-\overset{\overset{NH}{\|}}{C}-NH_2$ is related to urea, $NH_2-\overset{\overset{O}{\|}}{C}-NH_2$, carbamic acid, $HO-\overset{\overset{O}{\|}}{C}-NH_2$, and derivatives of carbonic acid in general, $HO-\overset{\overset{O}{\|}}{C}-OH$.

****

10. (a) 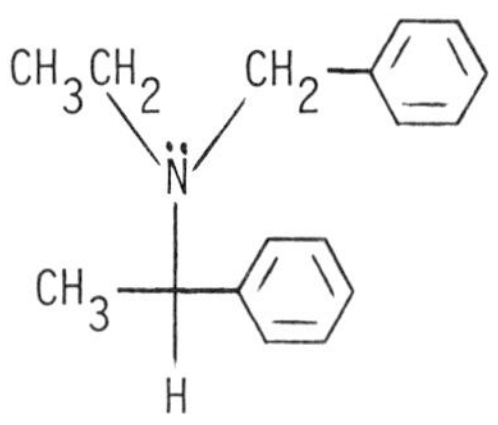

(b) 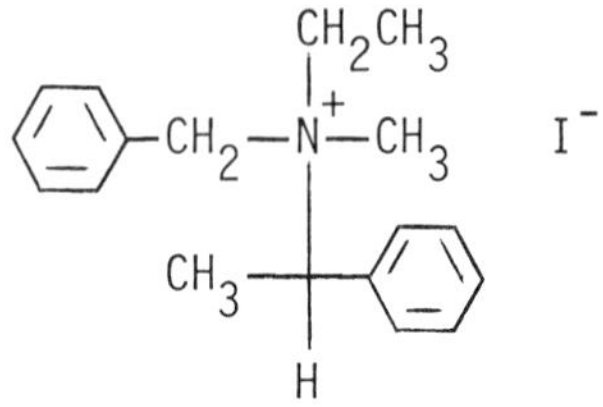 and 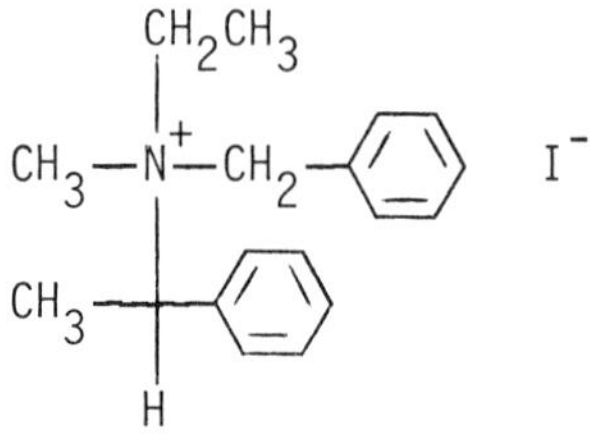

(N*S*,1*R*)-N-benzyl-N-ethyl-N-methyl-1-phenylethanammonium iodide

(N*R*,1*R*)-N-benzyl-N-ethyl-N-methyl-1-phenylethanammonium iodide

(c) Two stereocenters in each, one different, one the same: these are stereoisomers but not mirror images, diastereomers.

****

11. (a) Not at all. This process adds a carbon (the ^{-}CN group), making 1-pentanamine.

(b) Not at all. S_N2 reactions with tertiary haloalkanes are not possible.

(c) Well.

(d) Poorly. Further alkylation can occur, making 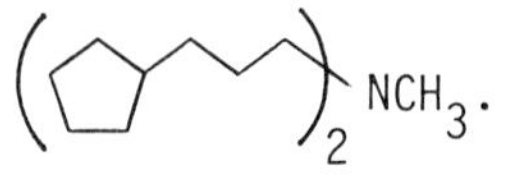

(e) Poorly. The haloalkane, although primary, is highly branched and will not react well in S_N2 reactions.

(f), (g) Well.

(h) Poorly. Four-member rings are strained and difficult to form. The method would work well for a five- or six-member ring.

(i) Not at all. Reaction shown is for a benzene, not a cyclohexane compound.

(j) Well.

****

12. H^+, H_2O work-up is understood after Grignard or hydride reactions.

(a) 1. NaN_3, 2. $LiAlH_4$. (b) Need to be devious: add a carbon and then take it out again!

$$(CH_3)_3CCl \xrightarrow[\text{2. } CO_2]{\text{1. Mg}} (CH_3)_3C\overset{O}{\overset{\|}{C}}OH \xrightarrow[\text{2. } NH_3]{\text{1. } SOCl_2} (CH_3)_3C\overset{O}{\overset{\|}{C}}NH_2 \xrightarrow[\substack{\text{(Hofmann} \\ \text{rearrangement)}}]{Br_2, \text{ NaOH}} (CH_3)_3CNH_2$$

(d) 1. NaN_3, 2. $LiAlH_4$ (makes primary amine), 3. $H_2C=O$ (makes imine), 4. $NaBH_3CN$ (completes reductive amination). Note how CH_3 group is intro- duced as <u>methanal</u>, with a subsequent reduction step. (e) Same as part 'b'. (h) No simple way to improve the situation. (i) Start with ⟨benzene⟩—Br and do reactions shown, making Br—⟨benzene⟩—NH_2. Then H_2, Pd (Section 14-4) will slowly hydrogenate the ring.

****

13. Extraction with aqueous acid protonates amine and transfers it as its ammonium salt into the aqueous layer together with water-soluble inorganics ('A'), separating them from all water-insoluble organic impurities ('B'). Addition of base converts the ammonium salt back into the neutral amine. Extraction with an organic solvent separates the pure amine ('D') from the remaining water-soluble inorganic impurities ('C').

****

14. (a) Assume alcohol solvent, and a source of protons.

$$(CH_3)_3CCH_2\overset{..}{N}H_2 + H_2C\overset{\frown}{=}\overset{..}{O} \rightleftharpoons R\overset{H}{\overset{|}{\underset{+}{N}}}HCH_2O^- \xrightarrow{-H^+} R\overset{..}{N}HCH_2\overset{..}{O}^- \xrightarrow{H^+} R\overset{+}{\underset{\overset{|}{H}}{N}}-CH_2-\overset{\frown}{OH}$$

$$\xrightarrow{-H_2O} R\overset{+}{N}=CH_2 \xrightarrow{H^-} R\overset{..}{N}-CH_3 \xrightarrow{H^+} R\overset{..}{N}HCH_3 + H_2\overset{\frown}{C}=O \rightleftharpoons R\overset{H}{\overset{|}{\underset{+}{N}}}(CH_3)CH_2O^-$$

$$\xrightarrow{-H^+} R\overset{..}{N}(CH_3)CH_2\overset{..}{O}^- \xrightleftharpoons[\text{again}]{H^+} \xrightarrow{H^+} R-\overset{..}{\underset{\overset{|}{CH_3}}{N}}-CH_2-\overset{+}{O}H_2 \xrightarrow{-H_2O} R-\overset{+}{\underset{\overset{|}{CH_3}}{N}}=CH_2 \xrightarrow{H^-} R\overset{..}{N}(CH_3)_2.$$

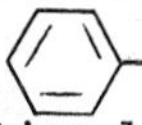

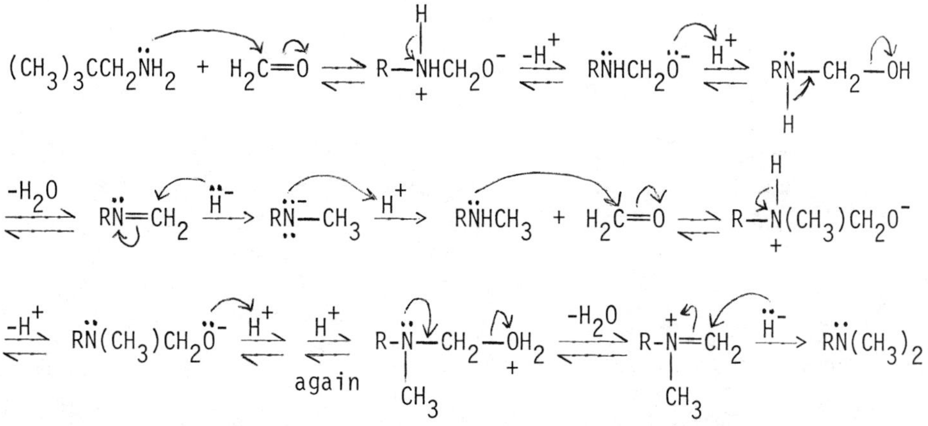

(b) $R-\overset{+}{N}=N=\overset{..}{N}:^{-}$ $\overset{..}{H}:^{-}$ → $R-\overset{..}{N}H-N=\overset{..}{N}:^{-}$ ——→

$N\equiv N\uparrow$ + $R-\overset{..}{N}H^{-}$ $\xrightarrow{\text{Then } H^{+}, H_2O}$ $R\overset{..}{N}H_2$

(c)

(as aluminum
oxide)

(d) $R\overset{O:}{\underset{\parallel}{C}OH}$ $\underset{H^{+}}{\overset{H^{+}}{\rightleftharpoons}}$ $R\overset{+OH}{\underset{\parallel}{C}OH}$ $\xrightarrow{\overset{-..}{N}=\overset{+}{N}=\overset{..}{N}^{-}}$ $R-\overset{OH}{\underset{\underset{N=N=\overset{..}{N}^{-}}{\overset{|}{C}}}{-\overset{..}{O}H}}$ $\underset{H^{+}}{\overset{}{\rightleftharpoons}}$ $R-\overset{O-H}{\underset{\underset{N=N-\overset{..}{N}^{-}}{\overset{|}{C}}}{-\overset{+}{O}H_2}}$ $\xrightarrow{-H_2O}$ $\left[R-\overset{O}{\underset{\parallel}{C}}-\overset{..}{N}=\overset{+}{N}=\overset{..}{N}^{-} \right.$

$\leftrightarrow$ $\left. R-\overset{O}{\underset{\parallel}{C}}-\overset{..}{N}-\overset{+}{N}\equiv\overset{..}{N} \right]$ ——→ $N\equiv N\uparrow$ + $R-\overset{O}{\underset{\parallel}{C}}-\overset{..}{N}:$ ——→ $R-\overset{..}{N}=C=O$ $\xrightarrow{H_2\overset{..}{O}:}$

nitrene

$R-\overset{H}{\underset{}{N}}-\overset{O}{\underset{}{C}}=O$ ——→ $R-\overset{..}{N}H-\overset{O-H}{\underset{}{C}}=O$ $\xrightarrow{H^{+}}$ $R-\overset{+}{N}H_2-\overset{O-H}{\underset{}{C}}=O$ $\xrightarrow{-H^{+}}$ $CO_2\uparrow$ + RNH_2

****

15. (a) $CH_3CH_2CH_2\overset{NO_2}{\underset{|}{C}H}-CH_2CH=CH_2$ (alkylation); (b) $C_6H_5CH=CHNO_2$ (aldol-type condensation); (c) (Michael-type 1,4-addition).

****

16. Make pseudoephedrine from phenylpropanolamine using reductive amination:

RNH_2 $\xrightarrow{H_2C=O, \ NaBH_3CN}$ $RNHCH_3$.

****

17. Secondary (general structure RR'NH)

(a) 1. $CH_3CH_2NH_2$, H^{+}; 2. $NaBH_3CN$. (b) 1. NaN_3, DMF; 2. $LiAlH_4$, THF;

3. CH_3CHO, H^{+}; 4. $NaBH_3CN$. (c) 1. $SOCl_2$; 2. NH_3; 3. Br_2, NaOH, H_2O;

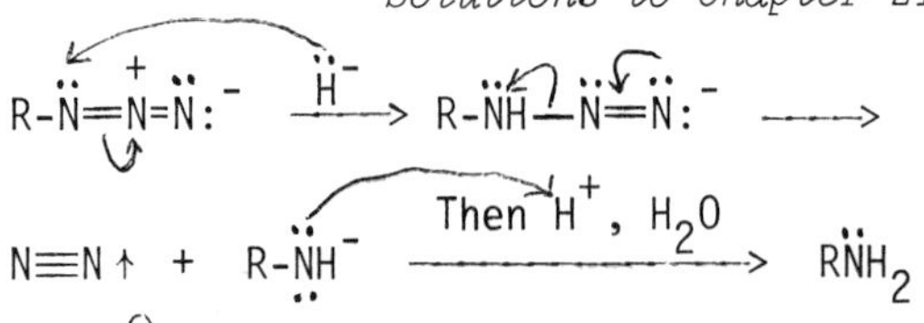

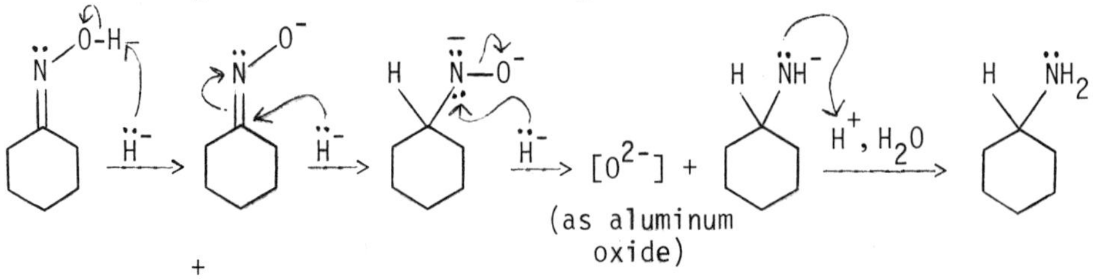

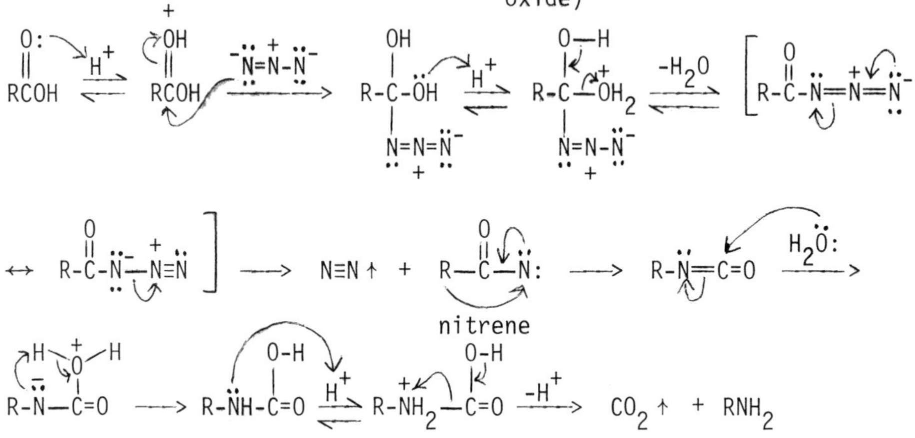

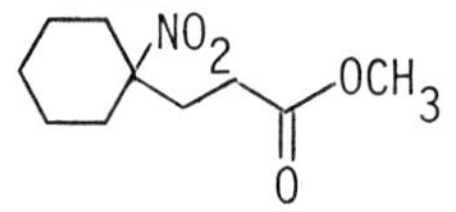

4. CH_3CHO, H^+; 5. $NaBH_3CN$.

****

18. 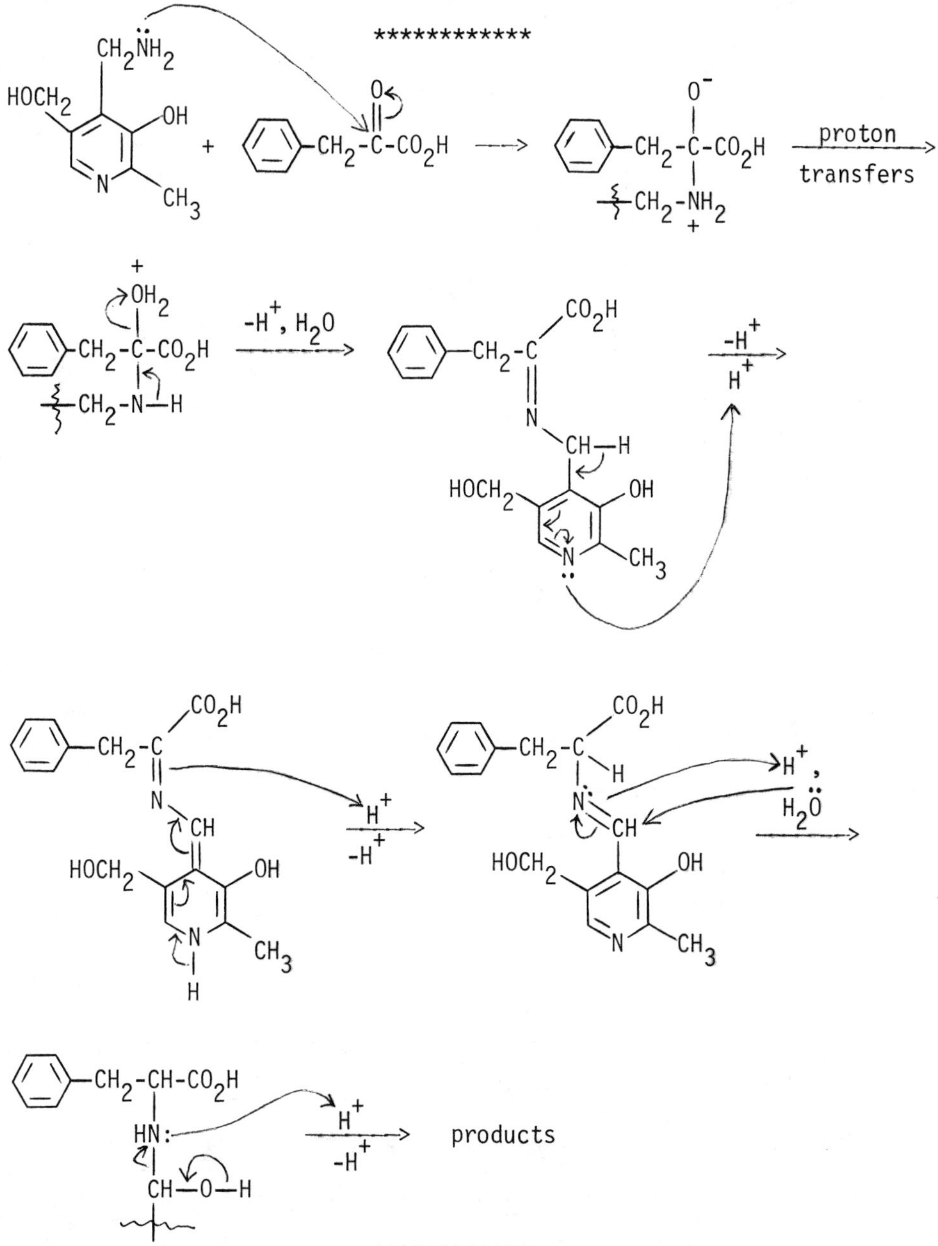

****

19. (a) 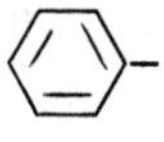$-CH{=}CHCH_3$ (*Z* and *E*); (b) 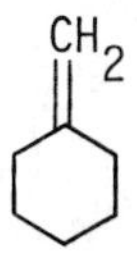 and 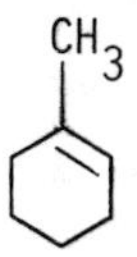 ;

(c) First cycle: $CH_2=CH(CH_2)_3NHCH_3$, $CH_3CH=CH(CH_2)_2NHCH_3$, and $CH_3CH(NHCH_3)CH_2CH=CH_2$. Second cycle: $CH_2=CHCH_2CH=CH_2$ and $CH_3CH=CHCH=CH_2$.

(d) 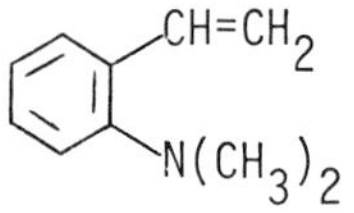

(e) First cycle: 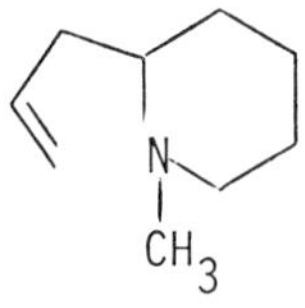, 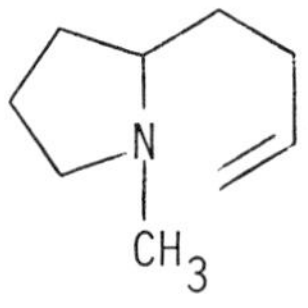, 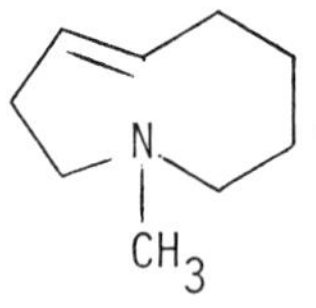, and 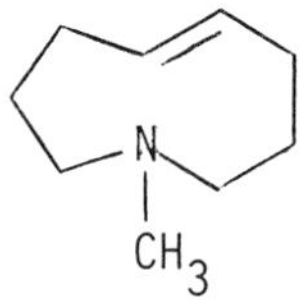.

Second cycle: 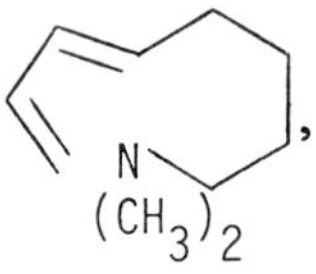, 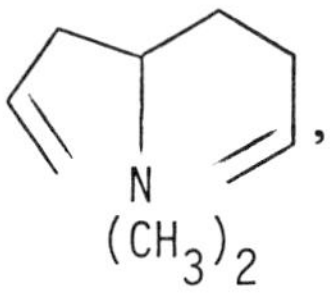, 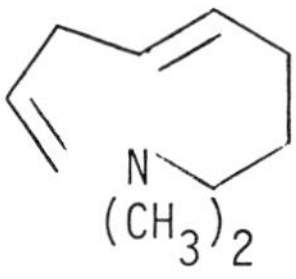, 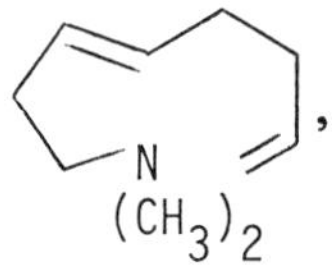, and 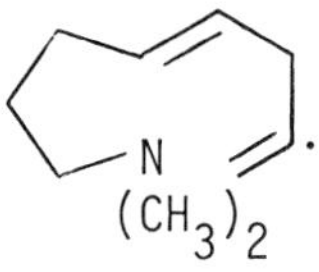.

Third cycle: 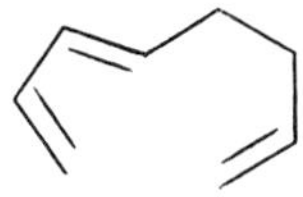 and 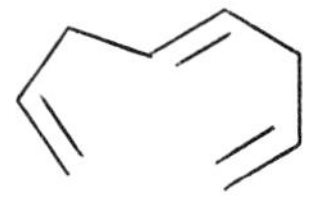.

****

20. IR: secondary amine. NMR: CH_3-CH_2- (δ0.9(t) for CH_3) and -CH_2—CH_2—N(H)—CH< (δ2.7(t) for CH_2; δ1.3(s) for NH; δ3.0(m) for CH)

identifiable. Total of 17 hydrogens in the molecule. MS: m/z 127 - 17 (H's) - 14 (N) = 96 or 8 carbons, so $C_8H_{17}N$. $H_{sat'd} = 16 + 2 + 1 = 19$; deg. unsat'n. $= \frac{19-17}{2} = 1$ π bond or ring present. MS: base peak is $[M-43]^+$, or loss of C_3H_7, perhaps CH_3-CH_2-CH_2-. (CH_3-CH_2 from NMR)

Hofmann elimination results: reattach N to alkene carbons in various ways to see what's reasonable. Only structures that can eliminate to give <u>both</u> 1,4- and 1,5-octadiene are worth further consideration:

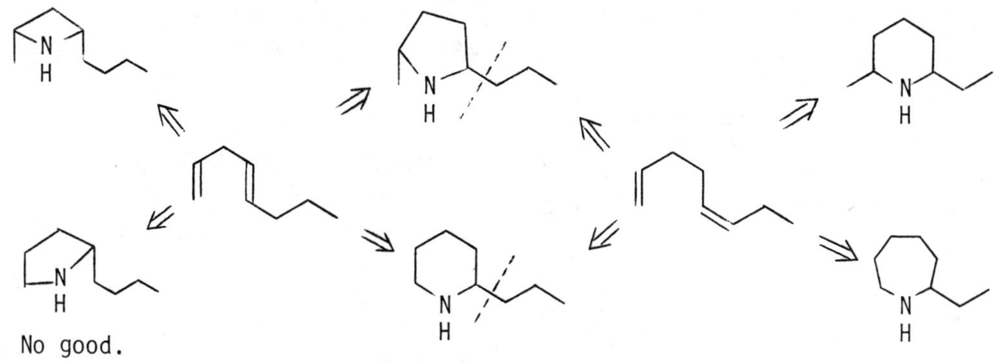

No good.
Can't give 1,5-diene.

Work with these.

No good.
Can't give 1,4-diene.

Both structures in the center should lose C_3H_7 in the MS (see dashed lines). The top one doesn't fit the NMR though: should have only 2H's on carbons attached to N. It also should show a strong $[M-15]^+$ peak in the MS (loss of CH_3), which is not seen, and it should give another Hofmann product: 2,4-octadiene. The only possible correct structure therefore is

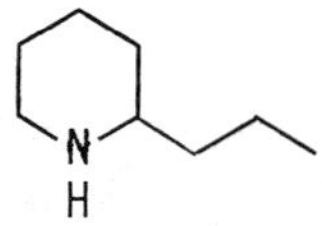

****

21. Work backwards; make sure you include all 15 carbons in your answer.

(a) 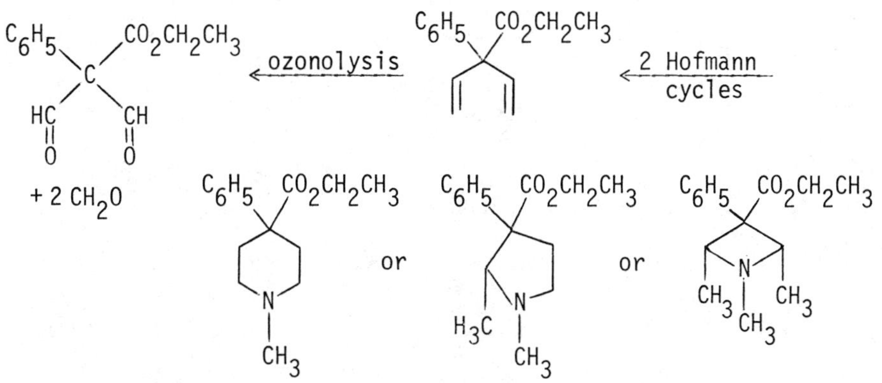

(The extra CH_3 on nitrogen is necessary to add up to the correct molecular formula.) No way yet to choose which of the three is the correct structure.

(b) Big hint: 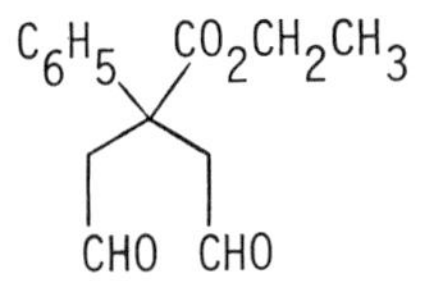 can be converted into pethidine.

This strongly suggests that pethidine is the <u>six-member ring</u> amine, since that one is readily accessible from the dialdehyde as follows:

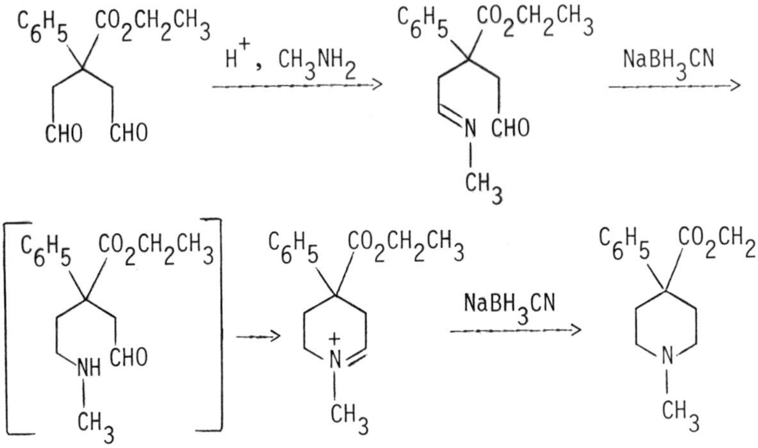

The sequence is actually carried out all at once, by mixing amine, dialdehyde, and $NaBH_3CN$ together.

The dialdehyde synthesis:

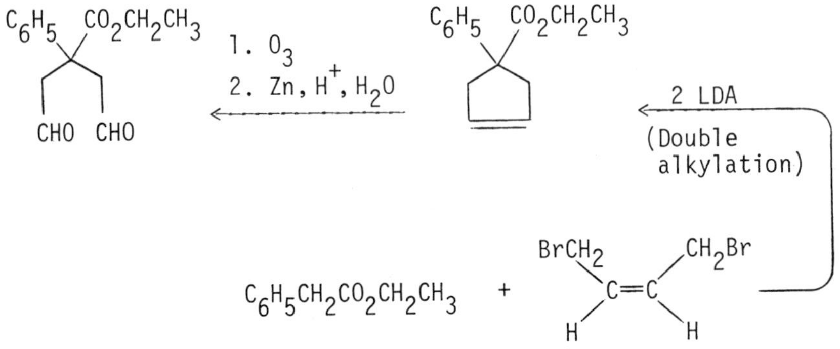

****

22. $H_{sat'd} = 22 + 2 + 1(N) = 25$; deg. unsat'n. $= \frac{25-21}{2} = 2$ π bonds and/or rings. IR: no N-H bonds, so amine is tertiary. NMR: two dissimilar CH_3-CH< units (δ1.2 and 1.3); one unsplit CH_3 (on N, perhaps?).

Now work backwards:

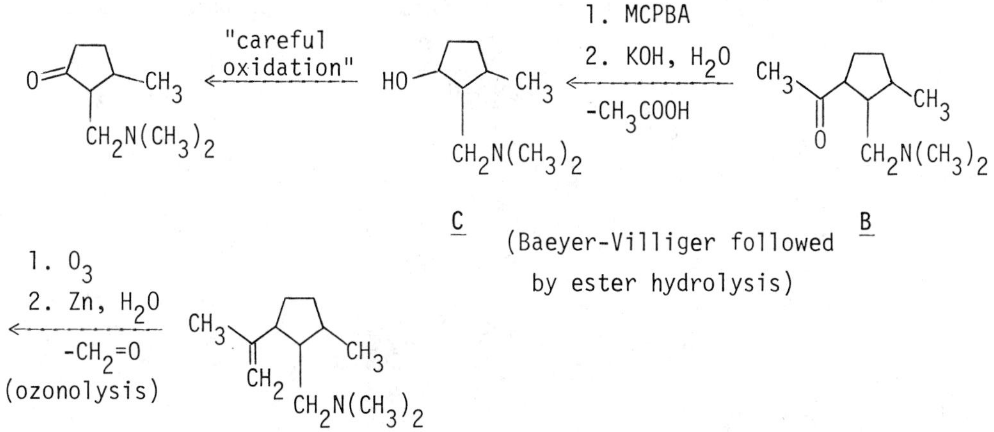

C (Baeyer-Villiger followed by ester hydrolysis) B

A

Following everything so far? Now reconnect the nitrogen in A with each of the alkene carbons to establish possible structures before Hofmann elimination:

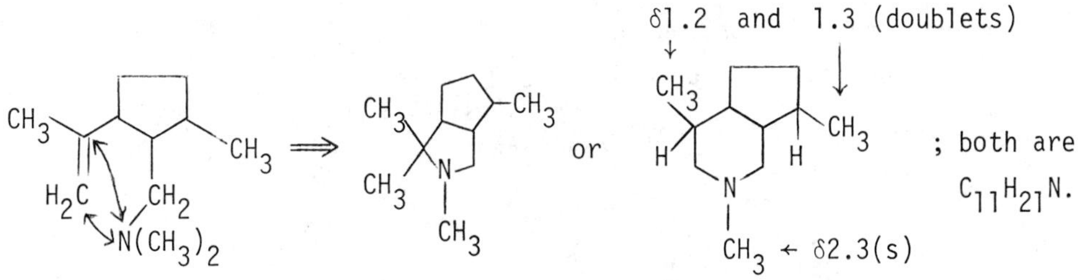

; both are $C_{11}H_{21}N$.

(either one) skytanthine

The methyl signals in the NMR match only the second structure, which is the correct one.

****

23. Tropinone is a tertiary amine. Alkylation of nitrogen can occur from either the "left" or "right" (arrows, below), giving stereoisomeric products:

(a)

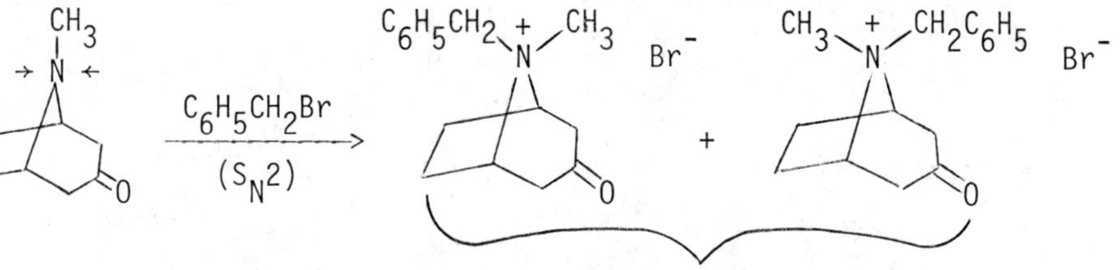

A and B

(b) Diastereomers (they are not mirror images).

(c) Where are acidic hydrogens in **A** and **B**? At the carbons "α" to the ketone carbonyl:

$$\underset{\text{C}}{}$$

$$\xleftarrow[\text{N, then add}]{\text{Invert at}}$$

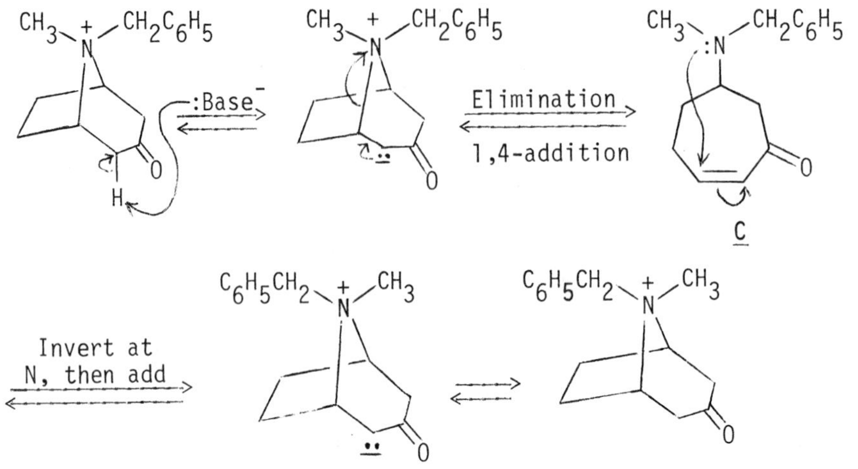

Deprotonation and elimination gives an enone, **C**. The amine is free to add back, re-forming the original ketone, or it can invert at nitrogen first and then add back, which gives the stereoisomeric product (CH_3 and $C_6H_5CH_2$ groups switched places).

****

24. (a) $HOCH_2CH_2NH_2$ $\xrightarrow[(S_N2's)]{\substack{\text{excess}\\ CH_3I}}$

$\xrightarrow[S_N2]{\text{internal}}$

+ $(CH_3)_3N:$ ⟶ + $(CH_3)_3NH^+$ I^- final products.

(b) Work backwards:

Ephedrine:

$\xleftarrow[S_N2]{\text{Internal}}$ $\xleftarrow[CH_3I]{\text{excess}}$

answer

Pseudoephedrine:

$\xleftarrow{\text{similarly}}$

answer

(diastereomers!)

****

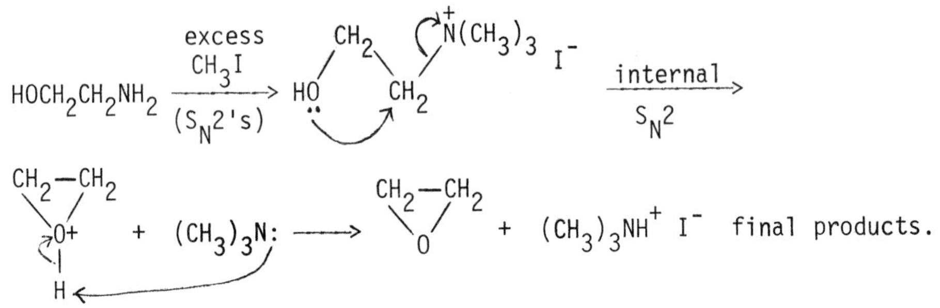

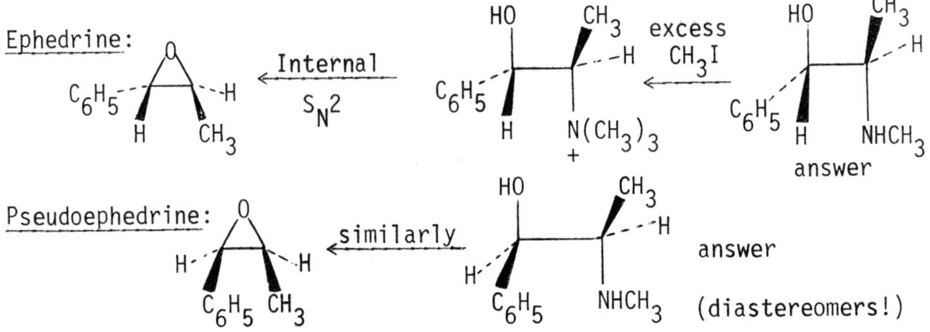

25. Analyze in terms of the functional unit the Mannich reaction constructs:

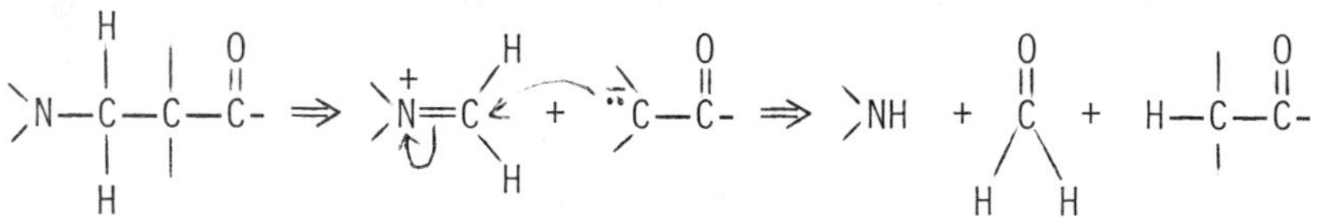

Relevant bonds are emphasized in the answers below.

(a) $CH_3\overset{O}{\overset{\|}{C}}CH_2—CH_2—N(CH_2CH_3)_2 \xleftarrow[2.\ HO^-]{1.\ HCl} CH_3\overset{O}{\overset{\|}{C}}CH_3 + CH_2{=}O + HN(CH_2CH_3)_2$

(b) 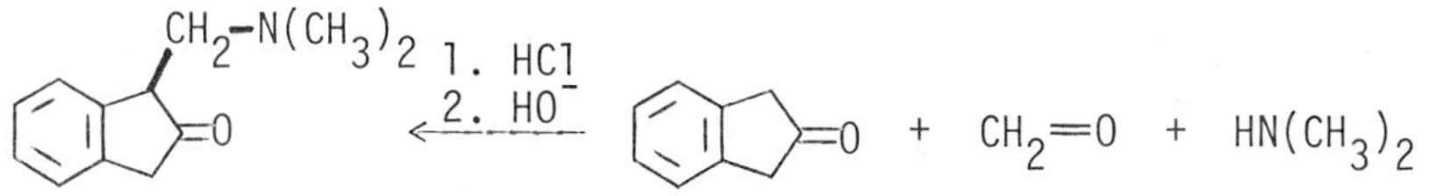

(c) $CH_3CH_2CH_2\overset{O}{\overset{\|}{C}}\underset{CH_2CH_3}{\underset{|}{CH}}—CH_2—N(CH_3)_2 \xleftarrow[2.\ HO^-]{1.\ HCl} CH_3CH_2CH_2\overset{O}{\overset{\|}{C}}CH_2CH_2CH_3 + CH_2{=}O + HN(CH_3)_2$

(d) $CH_3\overset{O}{\overset{\|}{C}}CH_2–CH_2–\underset{CH_3}{\underset{|}{N}}–CH_2–CH_2\overset{O}{\overset{\|}{C}}CH_3 \xleftarrow[2.\ HO^-]{1.\ HCl} 2\ CH_3\overset{O}{\overset{\|}{C}}CH_3 + 2\ CH_2{=}O + H_2NCH_3$

Two Mannich reactions are involved in this example. Note the primary amine and the presence of two moles each of methanal and propanone.

(e) $(CH_3CH_2)_2N–CH_2–CH_2NO_2 \xleftarrow[2.\ HO^-]{1.\ HCl} (CH_3CH_2)_2NH + CH_2{=}O + CH_3NO_2$

Instead of a carbonyl compound serving as the source of an enolate nucleophile, a nitroalkane takes its place, giving the anion $\overset{-}{\ddot{C}}H_2NO_2$ upon deprotonation by base (Exercise 21-9).

(f) $H_2N—\underset{CH_3}{\underset{|}{CH}}—CN \longleftarrow NH_3 + CH_3CHO + HCN$

Here the nucleophile is again different, being cyanide ion. (Recall problem 17 of Chapter 15.)

****

26. A double Mannich reaction, similar to part d of problem 25.
Abbreviated mechanism follows on next page:

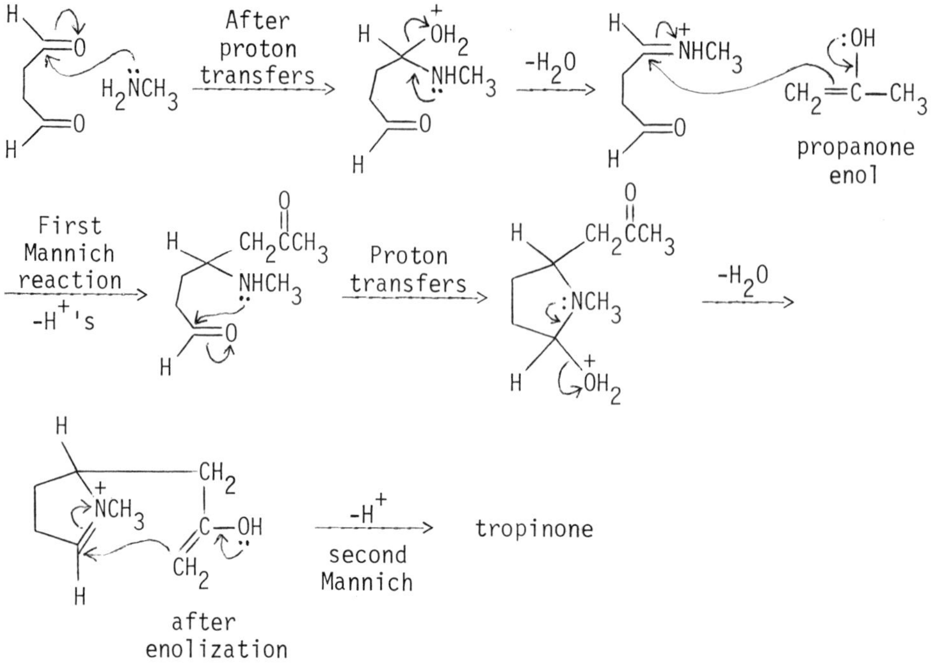

****

27. 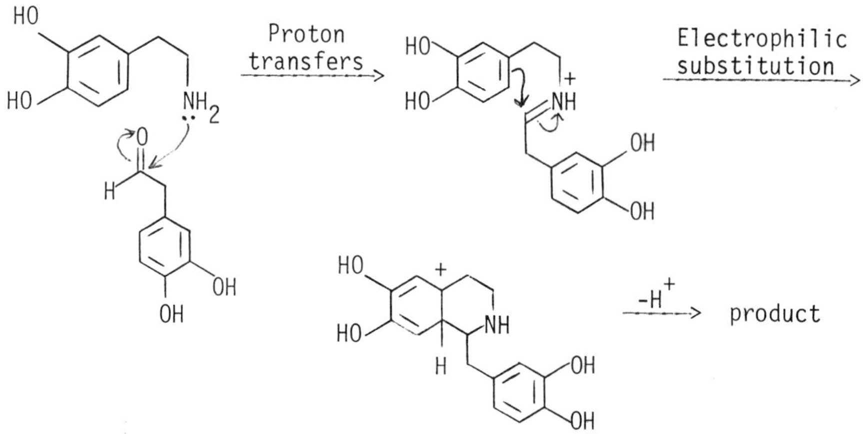

The electrophilic substitution is in fact another variation of the Mannich reaction as well, with the electron-rich benzene ring acting as the nucleophile.

****

28. 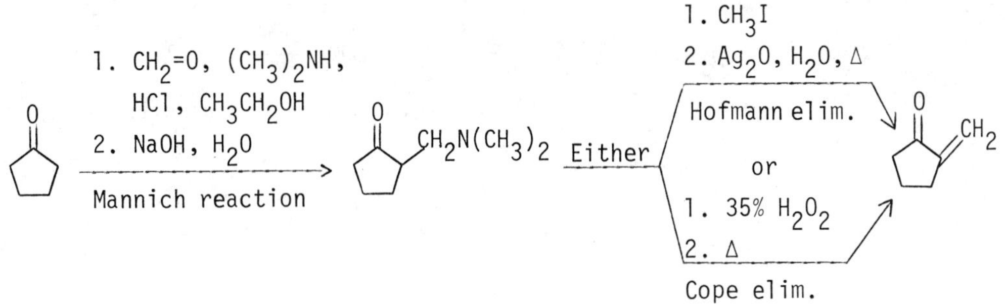

****

29. (a) All possible products of 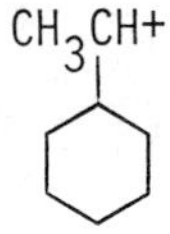

! So, 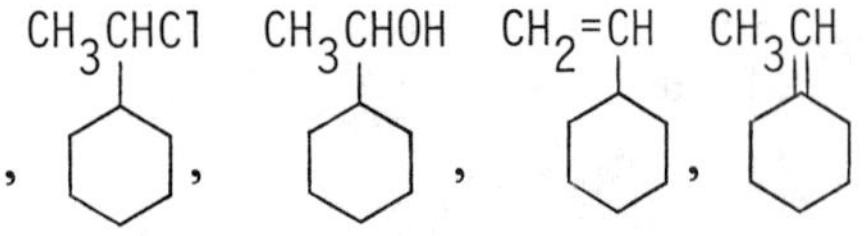

and, after hydrogen shift to 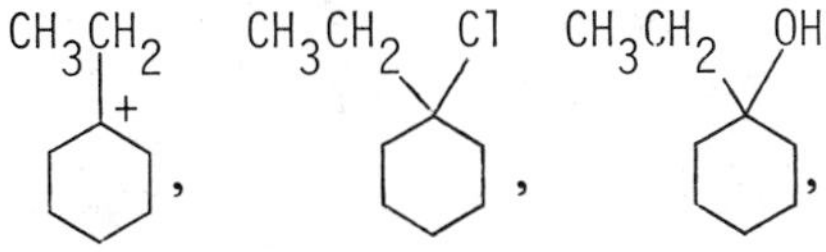

and 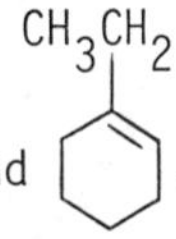

.

(b) 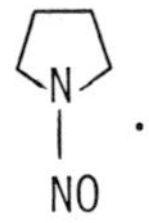

. (c) $N_2CHCOOCH_2CH_3$, an α-diazoester, which is stabilized by resonance, similar to an α-diazoketone.

(d) 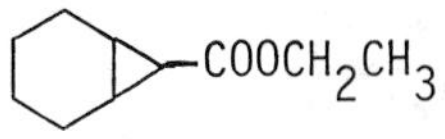

(Compare Exercise 21-19). (e) 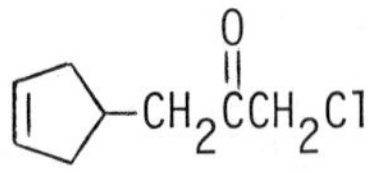

(chloromethyl ketone from 1 eq. CH_2N_2). (f) Initial product is

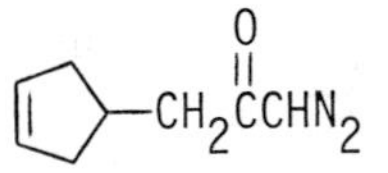

(α-diazoketone from 2 eq. CH_2N_2). Heating with $CuSO_4$ gives a carbene which can react with the double bond!

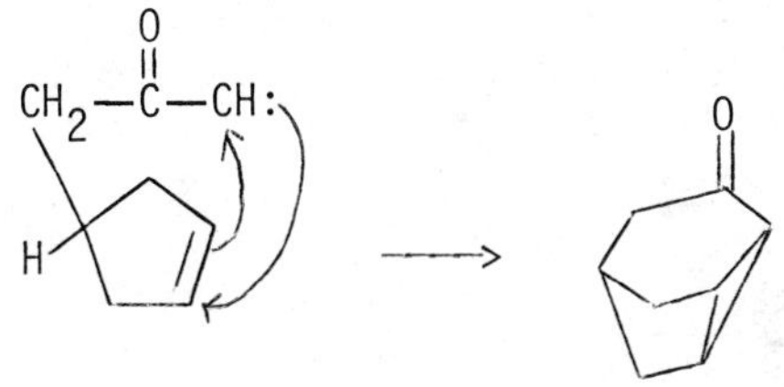

, $C_8H_{10}O$ ketone product.

****

30. Consider the mechanism: $HCCl_3 \xrightarrow{NaOH} {}^{-}{:}CCl_3 \xrightarrow{-Cl^-} {:}CCl_2$ first.

The ${}^{-}{:}CCl_3$ anion may well be a reasonable anion for transfer as follows:

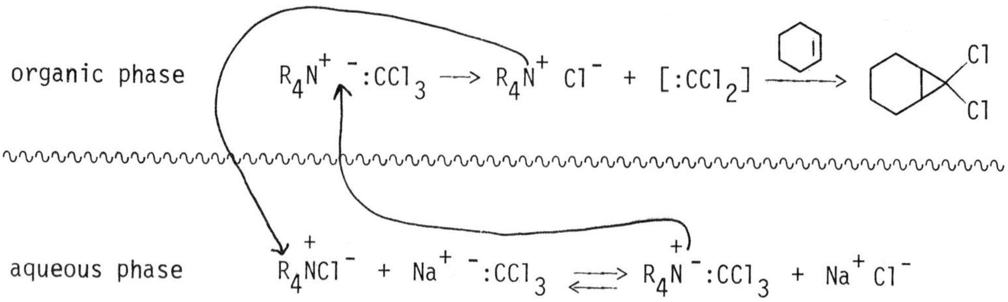

****

CHAPTER 22

Difunctional Compounds

General Introduction

A large proportion of organic compounds of biological importance and practically all organic compounds involved in synthetic work contain more than one functional group. It is obviously necessary to be able to recognize when multiple functional groups in a single molecule will affect each other's chemical reactivity. The introduction to the text chapter presents two obvious situations, one arising when two functional groups are conjugated, and the other occurring when the groups can "reach around" to each other intramolecularly. There are other situations as well, but the general lesson should be clear: be aware of complications and changes that can result from this sort of thing, and, also, note the opportunities that interactive functional groups can provide for useful types of new chemistry. The importance of carbonyl and alcohol groups is reinforced in the importance of molecules containing more than one of either, or both. These types of molecules will be the subject of the material in this chapter.

Outline of the Chapter

22-1. α-Dicarbonyl and α-Hydroxy Carbonyl Compounds.

Adjacent functional groups: a reasonable place to start.

22-2. 1,3-Dithiane Anions: Alkanoyl (Acyl) Anion Equivalents.

Reversal of the normal polarity of a functional group carbon.

22-3, 22-4, 22-5. β-Dicarbonyl Compounds: Preparation, Properties, and Synthetic Applications.

The most important combination of carbonyl functional groups.

Keys to the Chapter

22-1. α-Dicarbonyl and α-Hydroxy Carbonyl Compounds.

Syntheses of these difunctional compounds rely on reactions that probably have a rather unfamiliar look to them. After all, since virtually the beginning of this book the electrophilic nature of carbon atoms in carbonyl groups has been drilled into your brain. All of a sudden, here come an assortment of reactions where carbonyl carbons are turned into free radicals or, worse yet, anions. Such is life. It will probably help you to review section 15-8 (the pinacol reaction) and to write out, one above the other, the pinacol reaction of a typical ketone (e.g., 2-propanone) and the acyloin condensation of a typical ester (e.g., methyl ethanoate). Then do the same for their mechanisms. This will allow you to more clearly visualize the relationship between the two, which is stated but not illustrated in the text section.

The benzoin condensation and its aliphatic analogue are reactions in which one carbonyl carbon is chemically modified to allow it to become nucleophilic. [This is new, and for study purposes you should carefully separate these processes from other reactions of carbonyl compounds.] Almost from the start of this course you have been shown how functional groups are readily classified as to nucleophilic or electrophilic character of the carbons in them, and furthermore, you have been shown over and over again how to understand reactions and plan syntheses by making sure that bonds are formed between atoms of different polarities. In these reactions you are seeing the first of several methods to reverse the polarity of carbonyl carbons. Once one carbonyl carbon has been made nucleophilic, it can add to the normal, electrophilic carbonyl group of another molecule in the usual way. *The result is a new carbon-carbon bond between carbons that both started out with the same polarity (electrophilic).* This is *important*.

These methods create from carbonyl groups new functional groups that are able to support nucleophilic negative charges at what used to be a carbonyl carbon. So they aren't magical. But they can be troublesome to try to learn. You will help yourself by making a table, for study purposes, containing all such species in both this and the next text section. Your table should contain the method by which the species is generated, and a representative reaction.

22-2. 1,3-Dithiane Anions. Alkanoyl (Acyl) Anion Equivalents.

The aldehyde-derived anions in Section 22-1 can only be used in reactions with other molecules of the same aldehyde from which they are made. This is because they are not stable enough to be isolated. In this section, however, you learn about a class of anions which may be made from any ketone or aldehyde you like, and reacted with any other type of organic molecule which typically reacts with anionic nucleophiles. Thus the available range of application of this sort of chemistry is enormously expanded by these reagents, the 1,3-dithiane anions.

For purposes of designing syntheses, analyze from the structure of the desired product, as usual. The bonds to the ketone/aldehyde carbon are the ones made by reaction of a 1,3-dithiane anion with an electrophile. Problems 10, 11, and 12 are for you to practice on.

22-3. β-Dicarbonyl Compounds: Preparation and Properties.

With this section we return to more "normal" chemistry. The Claisen condensation, first introduced in Section 18-4, returns in more detail as the main method for synthesizing 1,3-dicarbonyl compounds. Analyze this reaction on the basis of its similarities to the aldol condensation (Section 16-3): it is an enolate + carbonyl process, so bond formation occurs between the α-carbon of one carbonyl compound (which may be either an ester or a ketone) and the carbonyl carbon of another (an ester). Note the limitation: under the conditions given, the reaction works only when the 1,3-dicarbonyl product still possesses a hydrogen on the carbon between the two carbonyl groups. Deprotonation of this acidic H allows the equilibrium to shift to the product.

Since there are several types of β-carbonyl compounds available from the Claisen condensation, a table is presented below, with examples, to help you keep them straight.

Reactant Partners		Product	
Carbonyl	Enolate	New Functional Groups	Structure (New bond shown)
$CH_3CH_2OC(=O)OCH_2CH_3$ carbonate	$CH_3C(=O)OCH_2CH_3$ general ester	ester + ester	$CH_3CH_2OC(=O)\text{-}CH_2C(=O)OCH_2CH_3$ 1,3-diester
$CH_3C(=O)OCH_2CH_3$ general ester	$CH_3C(=O)OCH_2CH_3$ general ester	ketone + ester	$CH_3C(=O)\text{-}CH_2C(=O)OCH_2CH_3$ 3-ketoester
$HC(=O)OCH_2CH_3$ methanoate	$CH_3C(=O)OCH_2CH_3$ general ester	aldehyde + ester	$HC(=O)\text{—}CH_2C(=O)OCH_2CH_3$ methanoyl ester
$CH_3CH_2OC(=O)OCH_2CH_3$ carbonate	$CH_3C(=O)CH_3$ ketone	ester + ketone	$CH_3CH_2OC(=O)\text{—}CH_2C(=O)CH_3$ 3-ketoester (the "hard" way)

	Carbonyl	Enolate	New Functional Groups	Structure

$$\underset{\text{general ester}}{CH_3\overset{\overset{O}{\|}}{C}OCH_2CH_3} \quad \underset{\text{ketone}}{CH_3\overset{\overset{O}{\|}}{C}CH_3} \qquad \text{ketone + ketone} \qquad \underset{\text{1,3-diketone}}{CH_3\overset{\overset{O}{\|}}{C}-CH_2\overset{\overset{O}{\|}}{C}CH_3}$$

$$\underset{\text{methanoate}}{H\overset{\overset{O}{\|}}{C}OCH_2CH_3} \quad \underset{\text{ketone}}{CH_3\overset{\overset{O}{\|}}{C}CH_3} \qquad \text{aldehyde + ketone} \qquad \underset{\text{3-ketoaldehyde}}{H\overset{\overset{O}{\|}}{C}-CH_2\overset{\overset{O}{\|}}{C}CH_3}$$

22-4. β-Dicarbonyl Compounds as Synthetic Intermediates.

In this section two reactions of β-dicarbonyl compounds are presented. The first is alkylation of the readily deprotonated "carbon in the middle." The second pertains to β-dicarbonyl compounds where at least one of the carbonyl groups is an ester. Ester hydrolysis leads to a carboxylic acid which readily loses CO_2 (decarboxylation). When this sequence is carried out on a β-ketoester, the result is a ketone. When carried out on a diester of propanedioic (malonic) acid, the result is a carboxylic acid. In each case, groups attached in the preliminary alkylation step(s) wind up in the product.

Notice that the acetoacetic ester synthesis only makes *methyl* ketones. This is because the CH_3CO- portion of the acetoacetic ester molecule is carried unchanged into the final product. To make other kinds of ketones, other 3-keto-esters must be prepared first. Problem 19 outlines the situation, and the general scheme below illustrates the process.

General 3-Ketoester Synthesis of Ketones

$$\begin{array}{c} R\overset{\overset{O}{\|}}{C}OCH_2CH_3 \\ + \\ CH_3\overset{\overset{O}{\|}}{C}OCH_2CH_3 \end{array} \Big\} \longrightarrow R\overset{\overset{O}{\|}}{C}CH_2\overset{\overset{O}{\|}}{C}OCH_2CH_3 \longrightarrow R\overset{O}{\overset{\|}{C}}-\overset{\overset{R'}{|}}{\underset{R''}{C}}-\overset{\overset{O}{\|}}{C}OCH_2CH_3 \longrightarrow R\overset{\overset{O}{\|}}{C}\overset{\nearrow R'}{\underset{\searrow R''}{CH}}$$

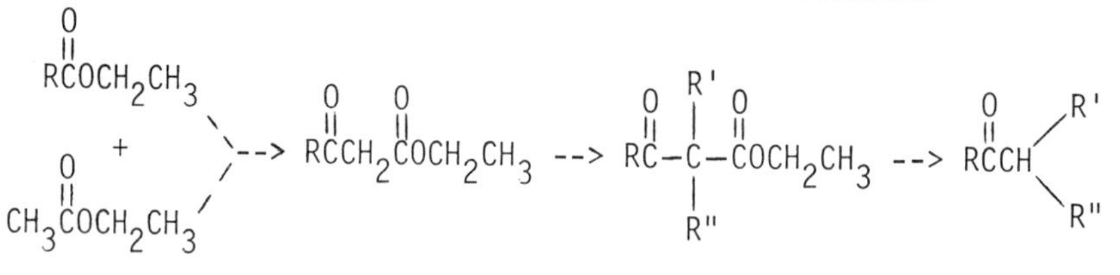

Note that the necessary 3-ketoester comes from a crossed Claisen condensation. As a result, $RCO_2CH_2CH_3$ must be an ester that does not do Claisen condensations with itself (i.e., R must not have an α-CH_2 group). Otherwise the crossed condensation will be a disaster.

22-5. Extensions of β-Dicarbonyl Chemistry.

The two additional reactions in this section serve only to reinforce the fact that anions of β-dicarbonyl compounds are still enolates. Thus you find that they do aldol-type condensations with ketones and aldehydes, just like enolates (the Knoevenagel condensation), and they do 1,4-additions to α,β-unsaturated carbonyl compounds (Michael addition).

There are loads of synthesis questions at the end of the chapter. Hopefully they will give you a feeling for the versatility of carbonyl chemistry as a practical tool for the preparation of complicated organic structures.

Solutions to Chapter 22 Problems

1. (a) O.K. as written. (Halogenation of ketone α-carbons requires acid or base).

(b) $^{-}$CN also adds '1,4' to enone.

(c) O.K. as written.

(d) Friedel-Crafts reaction may occur:

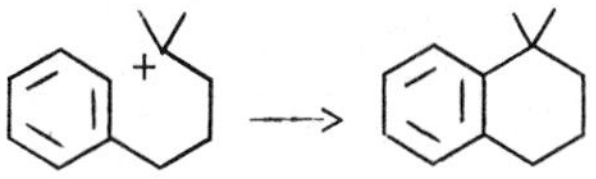

(e) Intramolecular alkylation will occur:

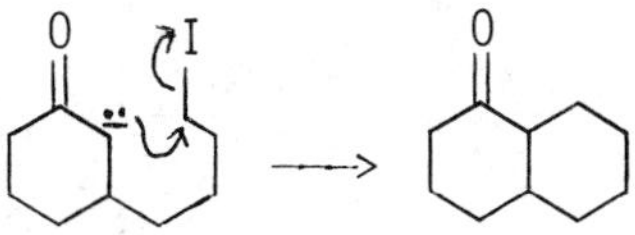

(f) Intramolecular amide formation:

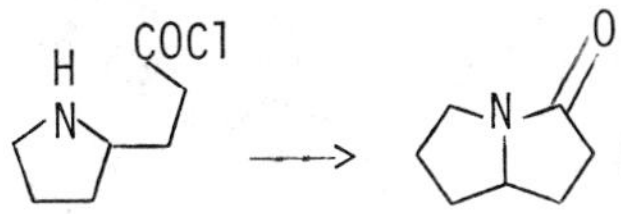

(lactam)

(g) O.K. as written.

(h) O.K. as written. If the stereochemistry were different, it might to on to form another lactone:

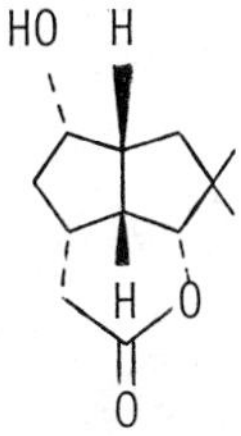

(Make a model!)

****

2. 1. OsO_4, cat. H_2O_2 (makes diol); 2. CrO_3, pyridine (oxidizes secondary alcohol to ketone, giving 'ii'); 3. NH_2NH_2, KOH, Δ (→ maaliol).

****

3\. (a) A: IR: ketone and alcohol groups (cannot be an amine because molecular weight is an even number).

NMR: CH_3—CH< (δ1.4(d)), δ4.2(q) , CH_3—C(=O)– (δ2.2(s)), –OH (δ3.7). Structure is $CH_3CH(OH)—C(=O)—CH_3$.

B: molecular weight is reduced by 2 units, so formula is probably now $C_4H_6O_2$. IR: ketone signal only. NMR: all H's equivalent. MS: molecule breaks in half readily, giving m/z 43, C_2H_3O fragments.

Simplest interpretation: CH_3-C(=O)-, so molecule is $CH_3C(=O)C(=O)CH_3$.

(b) Oxidation. Churning cream mixes it with air, allowing O_2 to react with ketoalcohol A to make diketone B.

(c) Acyloin condensation of an ethanoate ester:

$$CH_3CO_2H \xrightarrow[H^+]{CH_3CH_2OH} 2\ CH_3\overset{O}{\overset{\|}{C}}OCH_2CH_3 \xrightarrow[2.\ H^+,\ H_2O]{1.\ Na,\ (CH_3CH_2)_2O} \underset{A}{CH_3\overset{OH}{\overset{|}{C}H}—\overset{O}{\overset{\|}{C}}—CH_3}$$

$$\xrightarrow{Cu(O\overset{O}{\overset{\|}{C}}CH_3)_2,\ CH_3CO_2H} \underset{B}{CH_3\overset{O}{\overset{\|}{C}}\overset{O}{\overset{\|}{C}}CH_3}$$

(d) The diketone is conjugated.

****

4\. Acyloin condensation for ring formation:

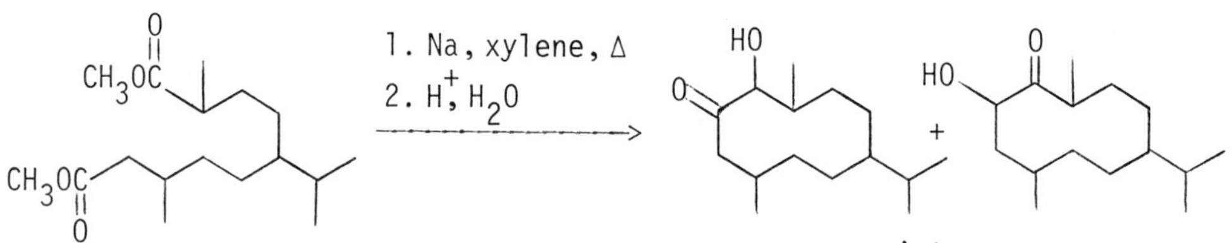

mixture

Then, as it turns out, Clemmensen reduction (HCl, Zn-Hg, Δ; section 15-8) completely reduces α-hydroxyketones to hydrocarbons.

So, above mixture $\xrightarrow{HCl,\ Zn(Hg),\ \Delta}$ germacrane.

The reduction can, of course, also be done stepwise by dehydrating the alcohol to an alkene, hydrogenation of the double bond, and then removal of the carbonyl group by any of the methods in Chapter 15.

****

5. (a) ; (b) $(CH_3)_2CHCH-\overset{O}{\overset{\|}{C}}-CH(CH_3)_2$; (c) ;

(via $R\overset{O}{\overset{\|}{C}}CN$)

(d) , via "benzilic acid" rearrangement:

****

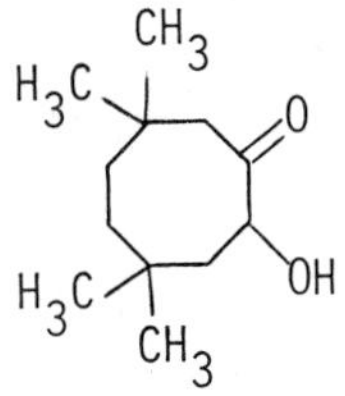

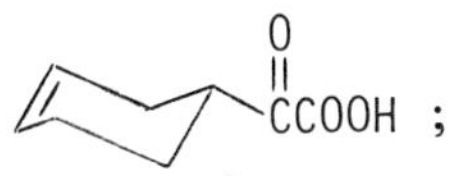

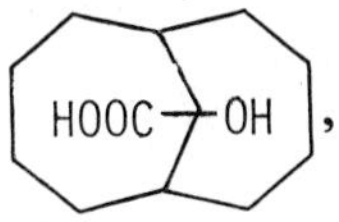

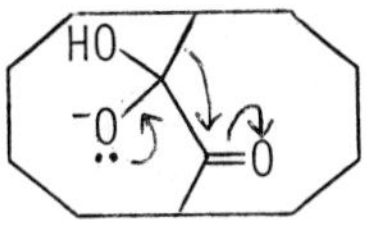

6. Write a plausible start for a mechanism, and follow it to its logical conclusion:

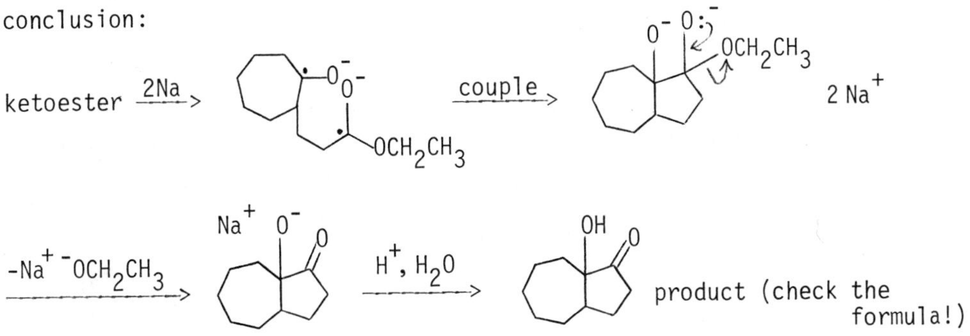

ketoester $\xrightarrow{\text{2Na}}$ $\xrightarrow{\text{couple}}$ 2 Na$^+$

$\xrightarrow{-Na^+ \; ^-OCH_2CH_3}$ $\xrightarrow{H^+, H_2O}$ product (check the formula!)

****

7.

reversible phenyl $\xrightarrow[\longleftarrow]{\text{migration}}$ $\xrightarrow{H^+, H_2O}$ product

more stable

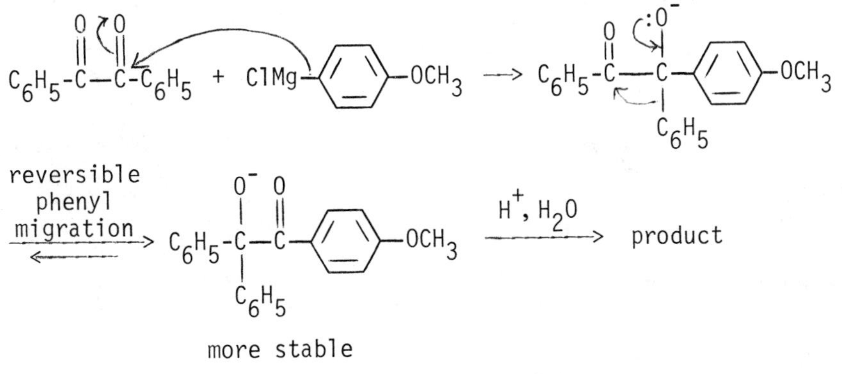

The rearrangement shown, involving migration of a phenyl group, is analogous to that in the benzilic acid rearrangement, except that the nucleophile is different. Here, though, it is an equilibrium process (reversible). The product of rearrangement is more stable due to additional conjugation of the methoxy group with the benzene ring and carbonyl function:

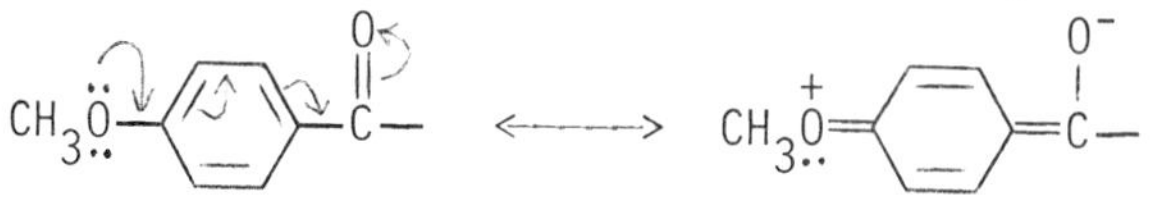

The reaction is therefore controlled thermodynamically.

****

8. (a) 1. $SOCl_2$ (makes -COCl); 2. , $AlCl_3$ (Friedel-Crafts alkanoylation); 3. Cl_2, CH_3COOH (chlorinates 'α' to ketone, makes 'ii').

(b)

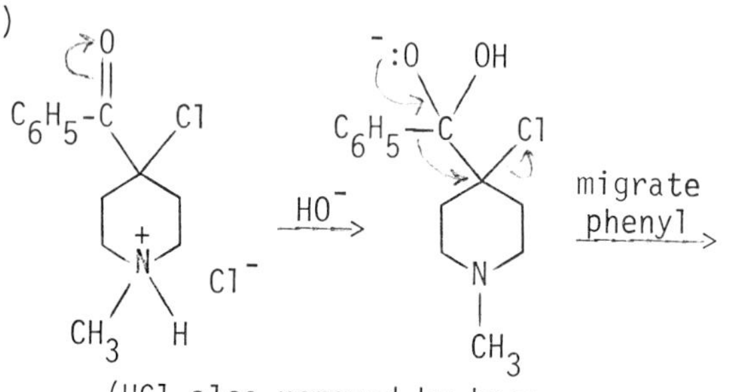

(HCl also removed by base during this step)

Phenyl migrates to displace chloride in this reaction.

****

9. Addition to carbonyl: 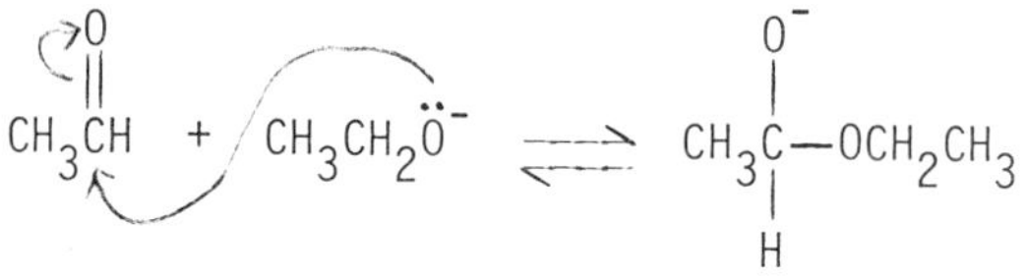

Deprotonation of α-carbon: 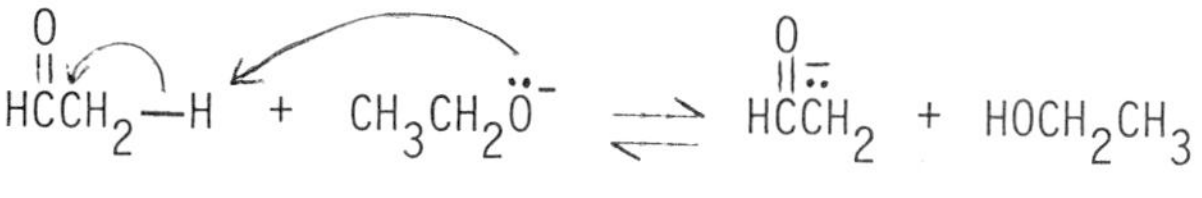

enolate

Deprotonation of the aldehyde carbon leads to a much poorer anion than the enolate: 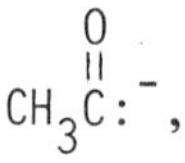, electron pair in an sp^2 orbital, unable to be stabilized by resonance. Given the two favorable processes shown above, deprotonation of the —C(=O)H group is simply not competitive.

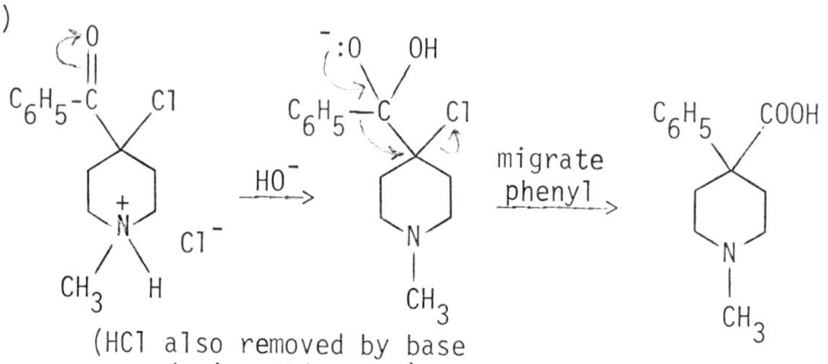

****

10. Working backwards might be easiest here:

(a)

$$CH_3 \text{—} \bigcirc \text{—} \overset{OH}{\underset{}{C}} \text{—} COOH \xleftarrow[CH_3CH_2OH, \Delta]{KOH, H_2O,} CH_3 \text{—} \bigcirc \text{—} \overset{O}{C} \text{—} \overset{O}{C} \text{—} \bigcirc \text{—} CH_3$$

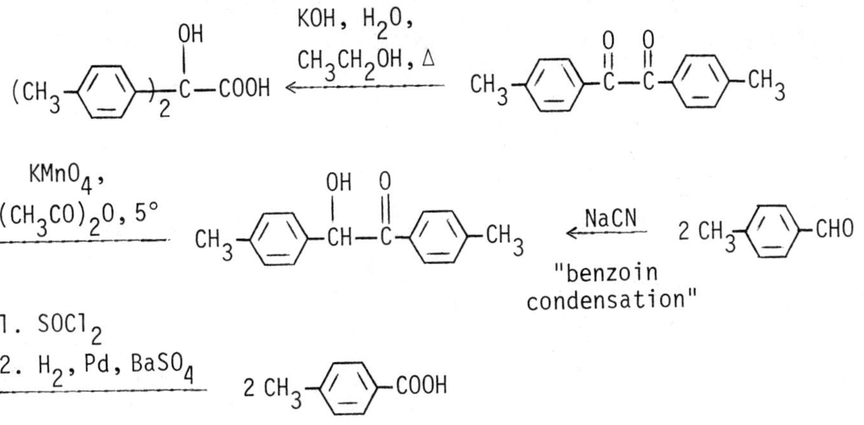

For the next two, working backwards is <u>essential</u>:

(b) $C_6H_5 \text{—} \overset{OH}{\underset{H}{C}} \text{—} COOH \xleftarrow[CH_3CH_2OH, \Delta]{KOH, H_2O,} C_6H_5 \text{—} \overset{O}{C} \text{—} \overset{O}{C} \text{—} H$ Use dithiane chemistry to prepare unsymmetrical α-dicarbonyl compounds (section 22-2):

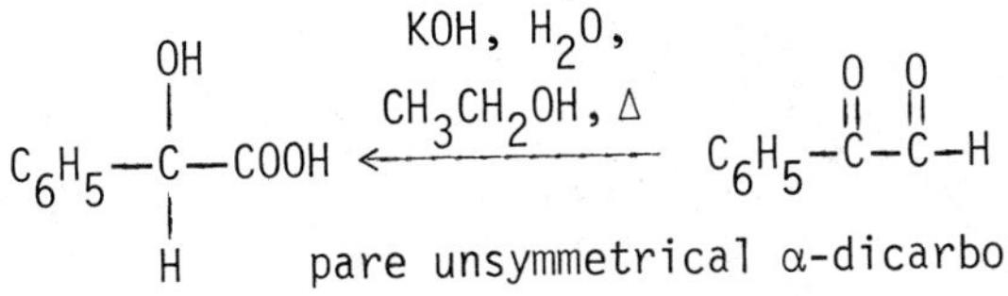

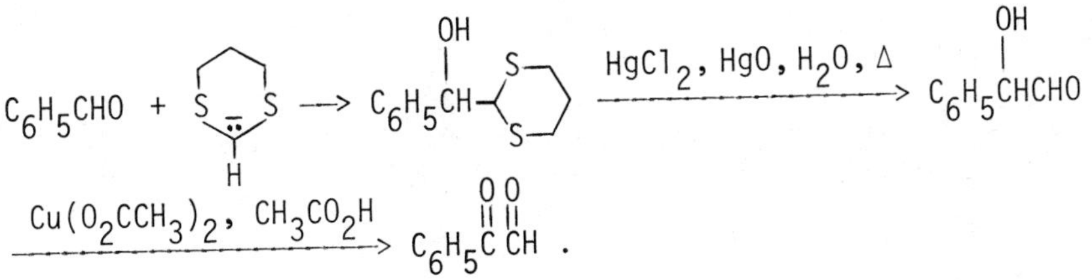

(c)

****

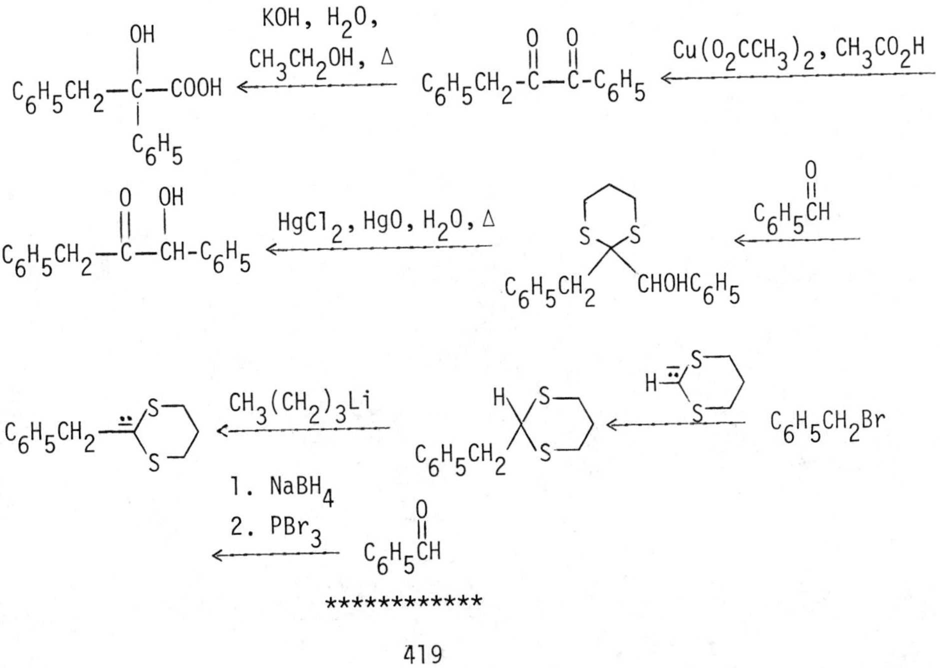

11. These are not easy. If you didn't get them, look at the answer for part 'a', and then try 'b' and 'c' again on your own. Retrosynthetic disconnections are indicated.

(a)

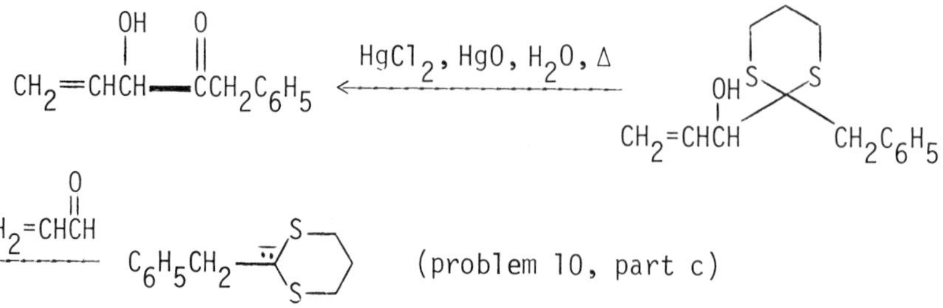

(problem 10, part c)

(b)

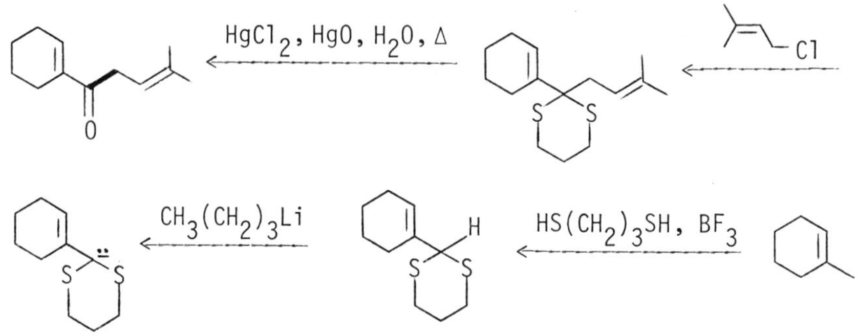

(c)

****

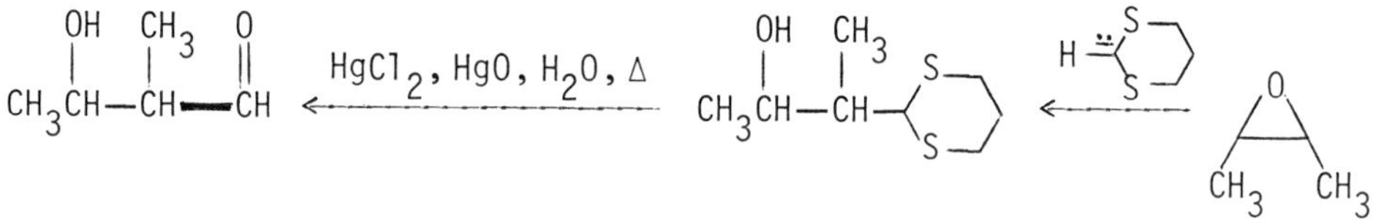

12. Identify the bond being made. It looks like the result of 1,4-addition to the α,β-unsaturated lactone by an alkanoyl anion equivalent:

1,4-addition takes place in this case

****

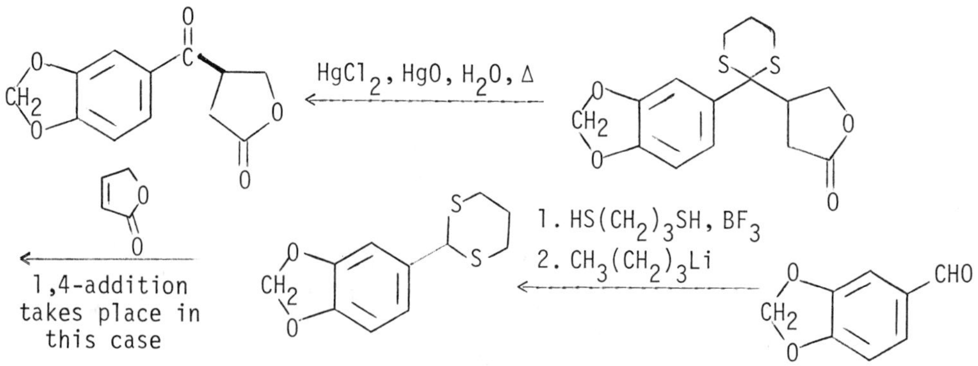

13. Claisen condensations. Parts a-c involve two identical molecules, parts d and e are intramolecular examples, and the rest are mixed condensations. Make your new carbon-carbon bond (indicated) between the carbonyl carbon of one ester and the α-carbon of another.

(a) $CH_3CH_2CH_2\overset{O}{\overset{\|}{C}}-\underset{CH_3CH_2}{\underset{|}{C}}H\overset{O}{\overset{\|}{C}}OCH_2CH_3$; (b) $C_6H_5CH(CH_3)_2CH_2\overset{O}{\overset{\|}{C}}-\underset{C_6H_5CHCH_3}{\underset{|}{C}}H\overset{O}{\overset{\|}{C}}OCH_2CH_3$;

(c) Unfavorable equilibrium: Claisen product not stable, no reaction is observed.

(d) 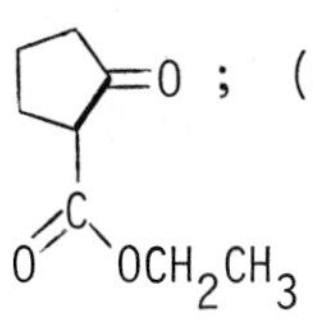 ; (e) 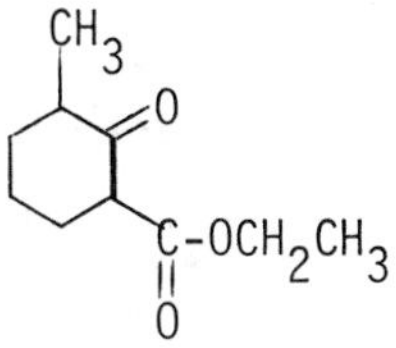 (other possible product, 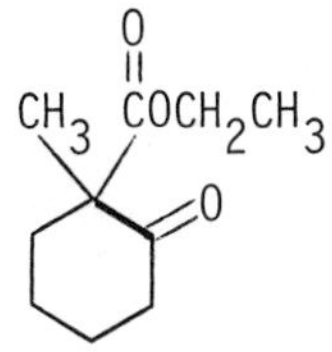 is not stable and will not be isolated);

(f) $H\overset{O}{\overset{\|}{C}}-\underset{C_6H_5}{\underset{|}{C}}H\overset{O}{\overset{\|}{C}}OCH_2CH_3$; (g) $C_6H_5\overset{O}{\overset{\|}{C}}-\underset{CH_3CH_2}{\underset{|}{C}}H\overset{O}{\overset{\|}{C}}OCH_2CH_3$; (h) 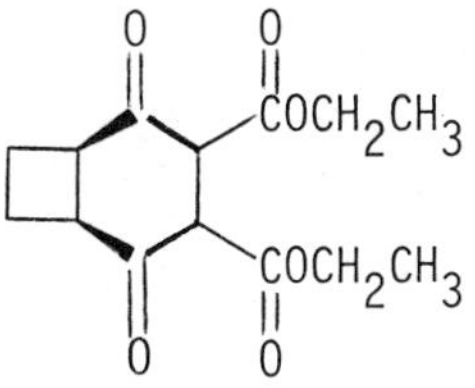 ;

(i) 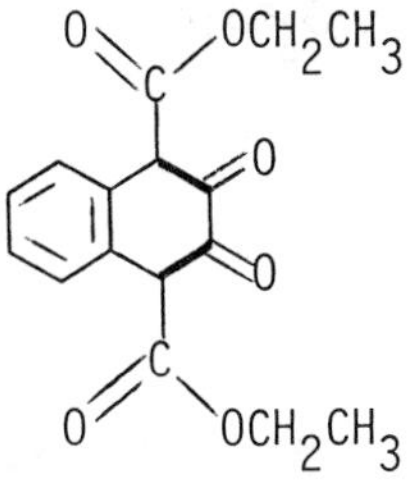

****

14. The second ester, $(CH_3)_2CH\overset{O}{\overset{\|}{C}}OCH_3$, should be present in excess because (1) it does not form a stable product from Claisen condensation with itself and (2) it will be able to preferentially react with enolate ions from the first ester.

Side reaction: $2\ CH_3CH_2CO_2CH_3 \xrightarrow{NaOCH_3,\ CH_3OH} CH_3CH_2\overset{O}{\overset{\|}{C}}\underset{CH_3}{\underset{|}{C}}HCO_2CH_3$

(condensation of first ester with itself).

****

15. Analyze similarly to problem 13. "Claisen" means 1. $NaOCH_2CH_3$, CH_3CH_2OH; 2. H^+, H_2O.

(a) 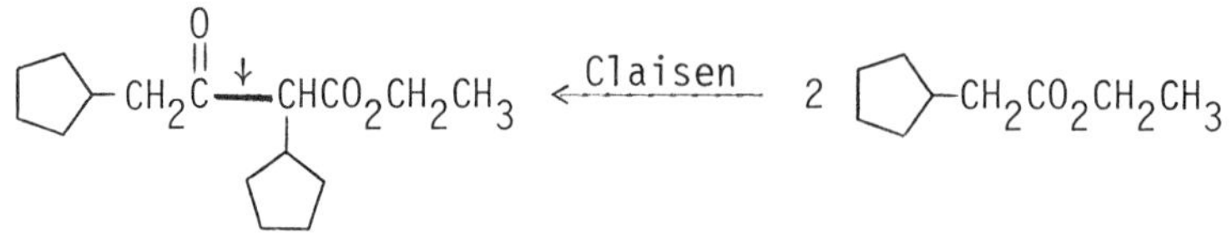

(b) $C_6H_5\overset{O}{\overset{\|}{C}}\overset{\downarrow}{—}\underset{\underset{C_6H_5}{|}}{C}HCO_2CH_2CH_3 \xleftarrow{\text{Claisen}} C_6H_5CO_2CH_2CH_3 + C_6H_5CH_2CO_2CH_2CH_3$

(c) 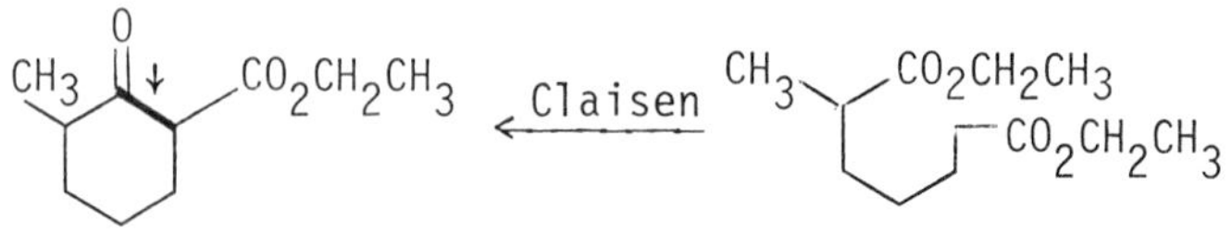 (problem 13, part c!)

(d) 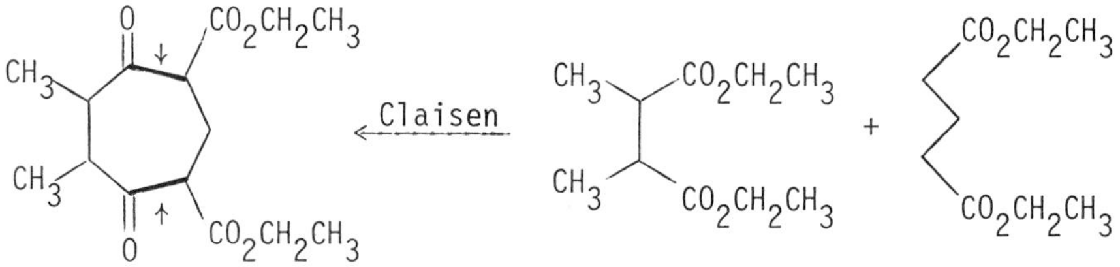

(e) $H\overset{O}{\overset{\|}{C}}\overset{O}{\overset{\|}{C}}\underset{\uparrow}{—}CH_2CO_2CH_2CH_3 \xleftarrow{\text{Claisen}} H\overset{O}{\overset{\|}{C}}CO_2CH_2CH_3 + CH_3CO_2CH_2CH_3$

(f) $C_6H_5\overset{O}{\overset{\|}{C}}\underset{\uparrow}{—}CH_2\overset{O}{\overset{\|}{C}}C_6H_5 \xleftarrow{\text{Claisen}} C_6H_5CO_2CH_2CH_3 + CH_3\overset{O}{\overset{\|}{C}}C_6H_5$ (ketone + ester version)

(g) $CH_3CH_2O\overset{O}{\overset{\|}{C}}\underset{\uparrow}{—}CH_2\overset{O}{\overset{\|}{C}}OCH_2CH_3 \xleftarrow{\text{Claisen}} CH_3CH_2O\overset{O}{\overset{\|}{C}}OCH_2CH_3 + CH_3CO_2CH_2CH_3$

(carbonate + ester version)

(h)  (ester + ketone)

(i)  (intramolecular, ester + aldehyde)

****

16. $H\overset{O}{\overset{\|}{C}}—CH_2\overset{O}{\overset{\|}{C}}H \Rightarrow HCO_2CH_2CH_3 + CH_3\overset{O}{\overset{\|}{C}}H$? Not likely to work since aldol condensation of 2 CH_3CHO would be a major competing process.

****

17. First sequence: 1. $HCO_2CH_2CH_3$, $NaOCH_2CH_3$, CH_3CH_2OH; 2. H^+, H_2O (mixed Claisen, ester + ketone). Second sequence: 1. NaOH; 2. CH_3I. Third sequence: 1. $CH_3C(=O)CH_3$, NaOH; 2. H^+, H_2O, Δ (double aldol condensation:

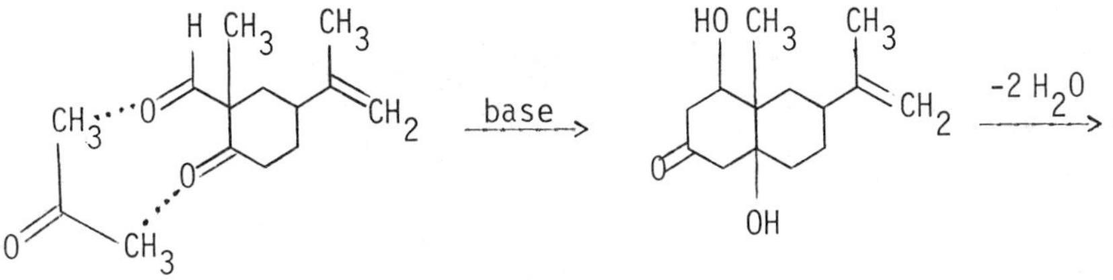

product).

Last reaction: 1. $(CH_3)_2CuLi$; 2. H^+, H_2O (1,4-addition).

****

18. Analysis: $CH_3C(=O)CH(R')—R$ ⇒ $CH_3C(=O)—C(R)(R')—CO_2CH_2CH_3$ ⇒ $CH_3C(=O)CH_2CO_2CH_2CH_3$ starting material for each synthesis

(a) R = $-CH_2CH(CH_3)_2$, R' = H: 1. $NaOCH_2CH_3$; 2. $(CH_3)_2CHCH_2Br$; 3. NaOH, H_2O; 4. H^+, H_2O, Δ.

(b) R = $-CH_2C_6H_5$, R' = $-CH_2CH{=}CH_2$: 1. $NaOCH_2CH_3$; 2. $C_6H_5CH_2Br$; 3. $NaOCH_2CH_3$; 4. $CH_2{=}CHCH_2Br$; 5. NaOH, H_2O; 6. H^+, H_2O, Δ.

(c) R = R' = $-CH_2CH_2CH_2-$: 1. 2 $NaOCH_2CH_3$; 2. $BrCH_2CH_2CH_2Br$; 3. NaOH, H_2O; 4. H^+, H_2O, Δ.

(d) R = $-CH_2CH_3$, R' = $-CH_2CO_2CH_2CH_3$: 1. $NaOCH_2CH_3$; 2. $BrCH_2CO_2CH_2CH_3$; 3. $NaOCH_2CH_3$; 4. CH_3CH_2Br; 5. NaOH, H_2O; 4. H^+, H_2O, Δ (decarboxylates only the -COOH on the α-carbon to the ketone); 5. CH_3CH_2OH, H^+ (converts other -COOH group back to ethyl ester).

****

19. The "acetoacetic ester" ketone synthesis is only good for <u>methyl</u> ketones: $CH_3C(=O)$-CHRR', from $CH_3C(=O)$-$CH_2CO_2CH_2CH_3$. For other ketones, the appropriate

3-ketoester must be prepared using a Claisen condensation.

(a) 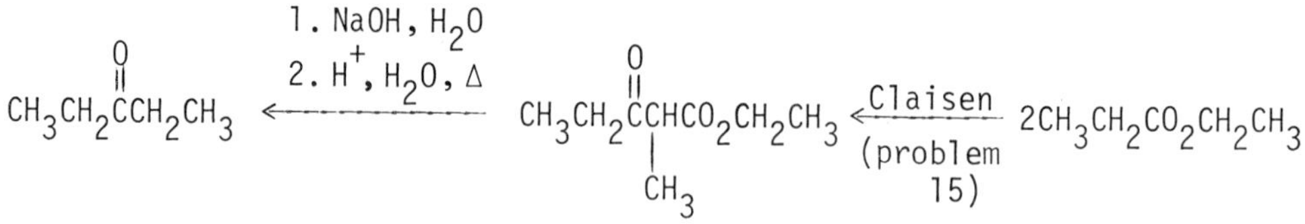

(b) 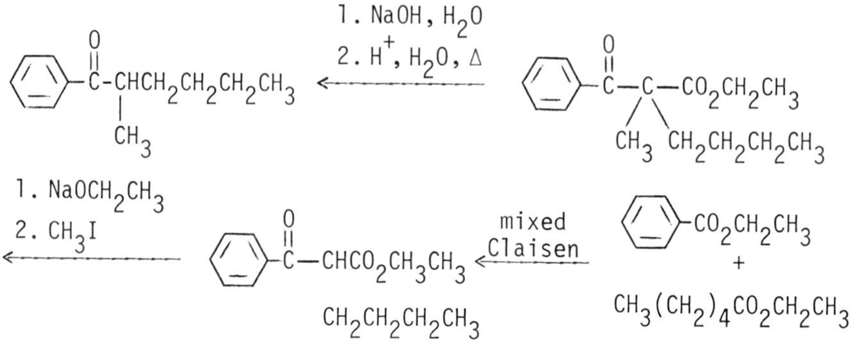

(c) 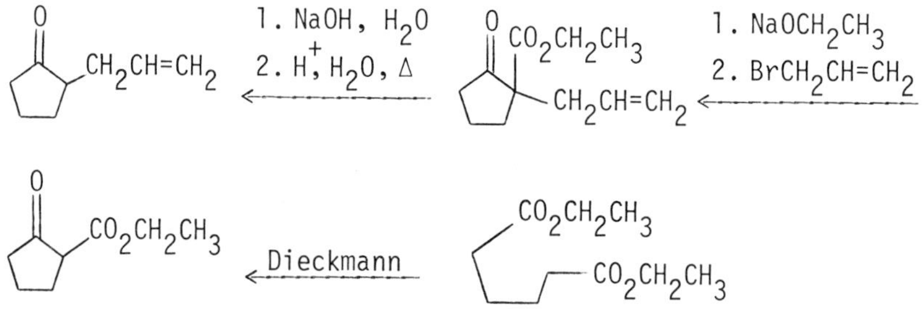

(d) 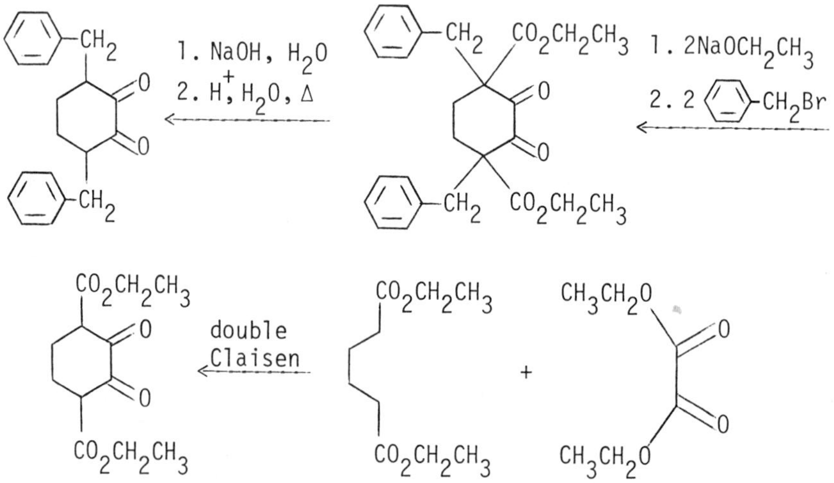

****

20. General pattern:

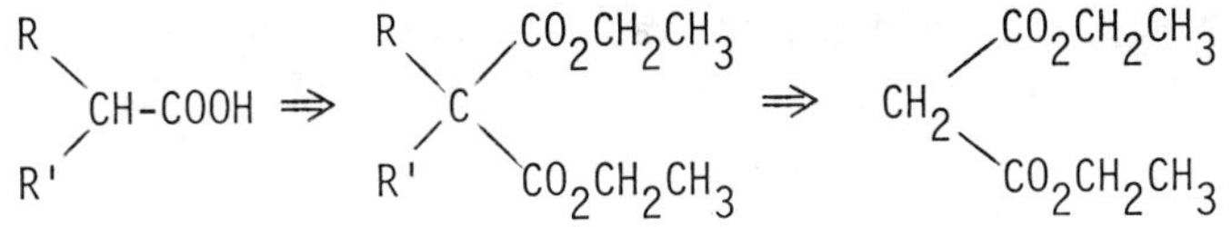

$$\underset{R'}{\overset{R}{\diagdown}}CH\text{-}COOH \Rightarrow \underset{R'}{\overset{R}{\diagup}}C\underset{CO_2CH_2CH_3}{\overset{CO_2CH_2CH_3}{\diagup}} \Rightarrow CH_2\underset{CO_2CH_2CH_3}{\overset{CO_2CH_2CH_3}{\diagup}} \qquad \text{Starting compound.}$$

(a) 1. $NaOCH_2CH_3$; 2. $CH_3CH_2CH_2CH_2I$; 3. $NaOCH_2CH_3$; 4. ⟨ ⟩-CH_2Br (completes necessary alkylations); 5. NaOH, H_2O (hydrolyzes esters); 6. H^+, H_2O, Δ (decarboxylation).

(b) 1. $NaOCH_2CH_3$; 2. $BrCH_2CO_2CH_2CH_3$ [alkylation, makes $CH_3CH_2O_2CCH_2CH$-$(CO_2CH_2CH_3)_2$]; 3. NaOH, H_2O; 4. H^+, H_2O, Δ.

(c) 1. 2 $NaOCH_2CH_3$; 2. ⟨ ⟩ with CH_2Br / CH_2Br ; 3. NaOH, H_2O; 4. H^+, H_2O, Δ.

(d) Written out:

[structure] ⟵ 1. NaOH, H_2O / 2. H^+, H_2O, Δ ⟵ [structure with $CO_2CH_2CH_3$] ⟵ 1. $NaOCH_2CH_3$ / 2. $CH_2{=}CHCH_2Br$

[structure with $CO_2CH_2CH_3$] ⟵ 1. $NaOCH_2CH_3$ / 2. $CH_2\text{—}CH_2$ (epoxide) / 3. H^+, H_2O ⟵ $CH_2(CO_2CH_2CH_3)_2$ (Write out a mechanism!!)

****

21. CH_3[structure, two C=O] ⇄ H^+, H_2O, Δ → CH_3[structure with CO_2H and OH] —Eventually→ $-CO_2$ → $CH_3CCH_2CH_2CH_2OH$ (with C=O)

****

22. ⟨ ⟩-CH_2-$CH(CO_2CH_2CH_3)_2$ →(1. NaH, C_6H_6 / 2. $(CH_3)_3CCOCl$)→ ⟨ ⟩-CH_2-$C(CO_2CH_2CH_3)_2$ with $O{=}C{-}C(CH_3)_3$ →(H^+, H_2O, Δ)→

[⟨ ⟩-CH_2-$C(COOH)_2$ with $O{=}C{-}C(CH_3)_3$] —$-2CO_2$→ ⟨ ⟩-CH_2|-CH_2-|$C{-}C(CH_3)_3$ (with O)

From: $C_6H_5CH_2Br$ malonic ester   acyl halide

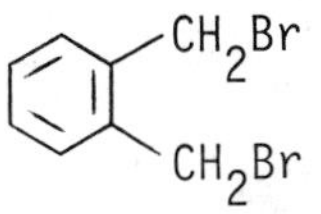

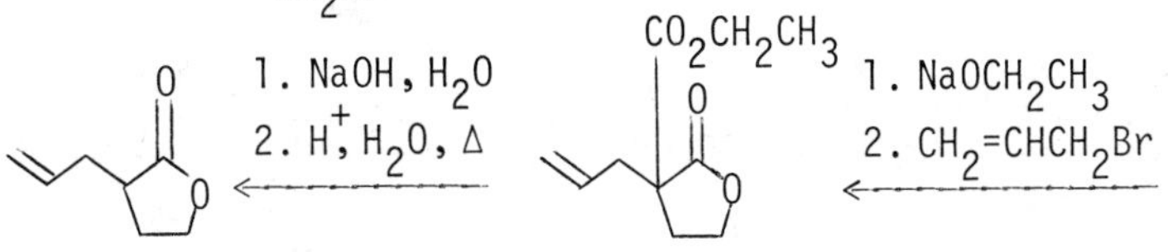

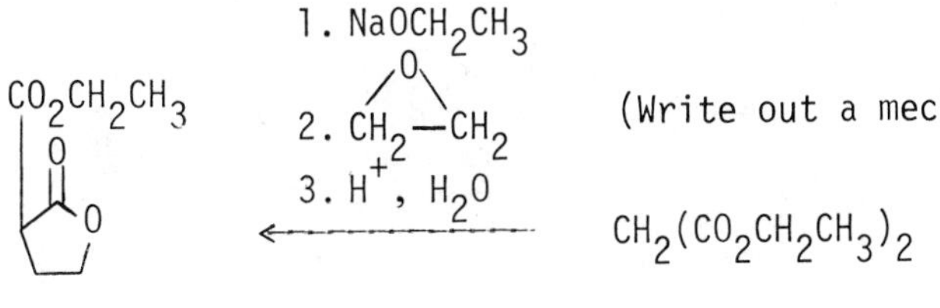

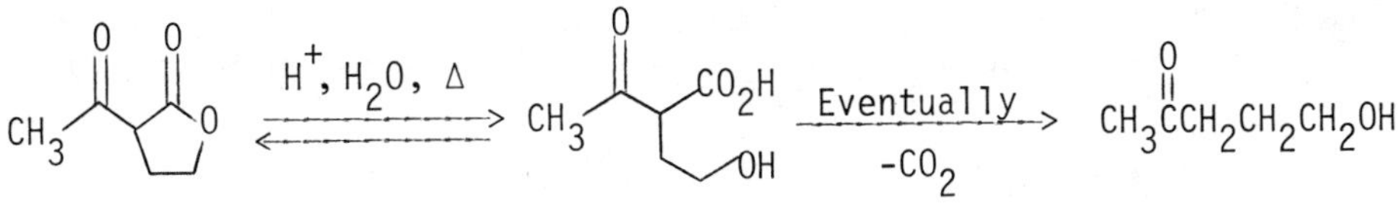

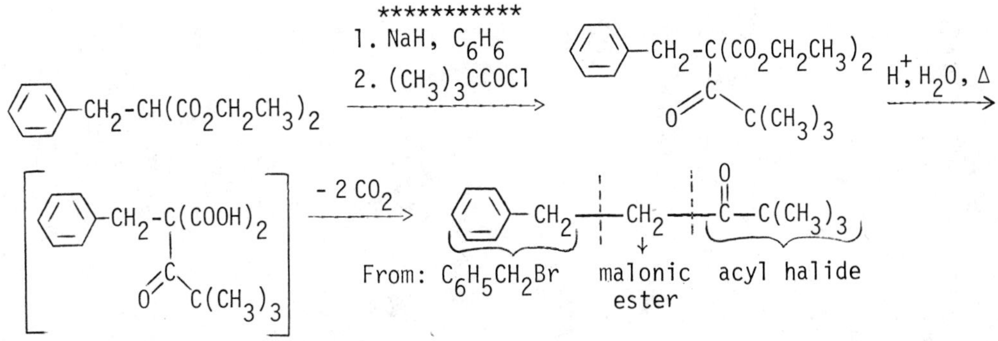

<u>Both</u> COOH groups (in brackets on previous page) are 3-keto acid groups due to additional carbonyl, so <u>both</u> decarboxylate.

****

23. $CH_3(CH_2)_n\overset{O}{\overset{||}{C}}$-S-(protein) + HO$\overset{O}{\overset{||}{C}}$-CH=C-S-(protein) $\longrightarrow$

Nucleophilic enol
(or, perhaps, enolate)

$CH_3(CH_2)_n\overset{O^-}{\underset{S-(protein)}{C}}$-CH—$\overset{CO_2H}{\underset{}{C}}\overset{OH}{\overset{||}{}}$-S-(protein) $\xrightarrow[\text{- S-(protein)}]{-H^+}$ $CH_3(CH_2)_n\overset{O}{\overset{||}{C}}$-CH—$\overset{CO_2H}{\underset{}{C}}\overset{O}{\overset{||}{}}$-S-(protein)

$\longrightarrow$ CO_2 + product

****

24. (a) (cyclohexanone)=O + $CH_2(CO_2CH_2CH_3)_2$ $\xrightarrow{(CH_3CH_2)_2NH, \Delta}$ product (Knoevenagel condensation)

(b) (1,3-cyclohexanedione) + $H\overset{O}{\overset{||}{C}}(CH_2)_3CH_3$ $\xrightarrow{(CH_3CH_2)_2NH, \Delta}$ product

(c) $CH_3\overset{O}{\overset{||}{C}}CH_3$ + $CH_2\overset{CN}{\underset{CO_2CH_2CH_3}{<}}$ $\xrightarrow{(CH_3CH_2)_2NH, \Delta}$ product

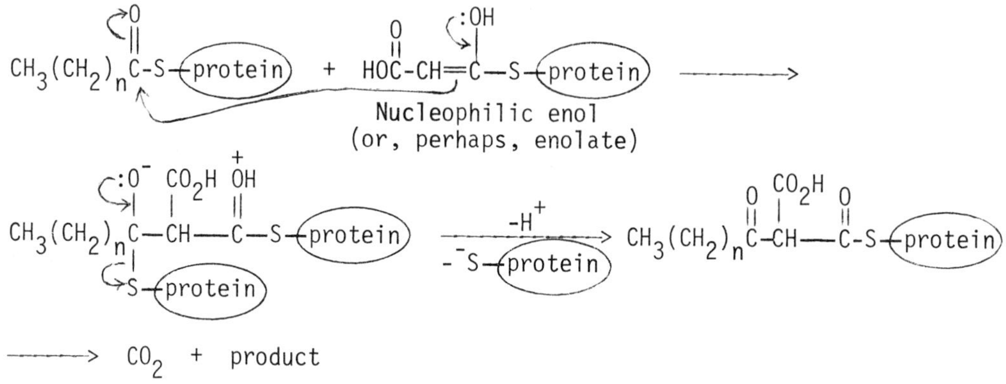

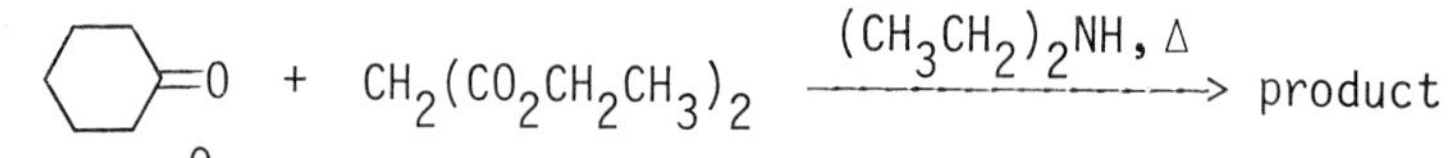

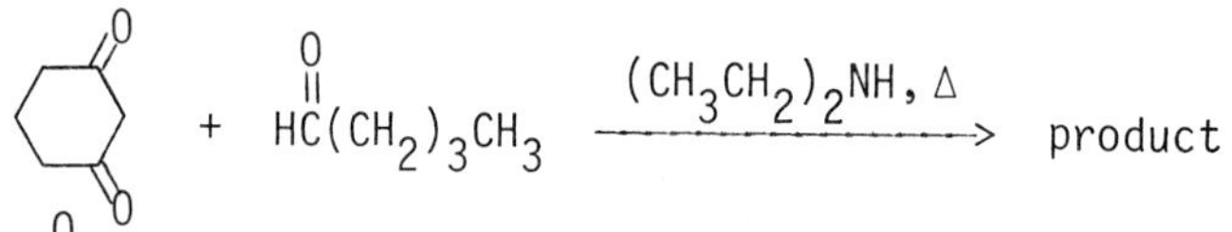

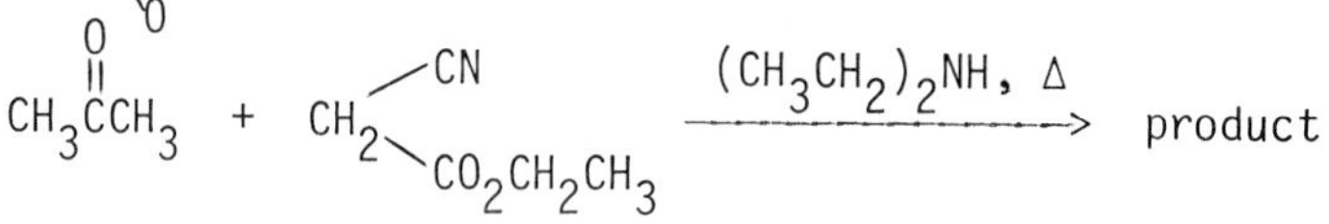

(very much like a β-dicarbonyl compound)

(d) (1,3-cyclopentanedione) + $CH_2=CH\overset{O}{\overset{||}{C}}CH_3$ $\xrightarrow{\text{cat. NaOCH}_2CH_3}$ product (Michael addition)

(e) (2-cycloheptenone) + $CH_2(CO_2CH_2CH_3)_2$ $\xrightarrow{\text{cat. NaOCH}_2CH_3}$ product

(f) (2-cyclopentenone) + $CH_3\overset{O}{\overset{||}{C}}CH_2CO_2CH_2CH_3$ $\xrightarrow[\text{(Michael)}]{\text{cat.} \\ \text{NaOCH}_2CH_3}$ (structure) $\xrightarrow[\text{-CO}_2]{\text{1. NaOH, H}_2O \\ \text{2. H}^+, H_2O, \Delta}$ product

****

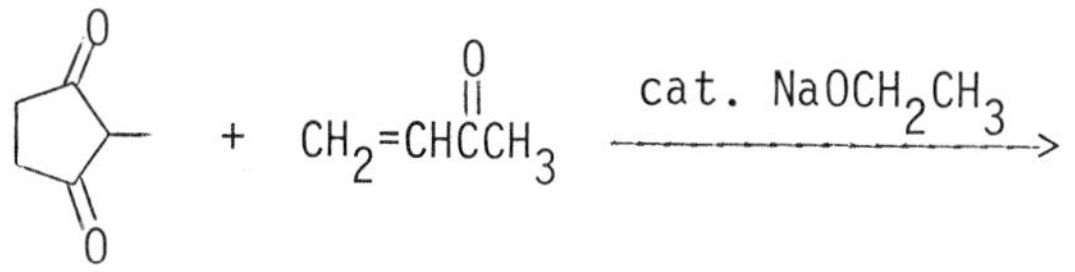

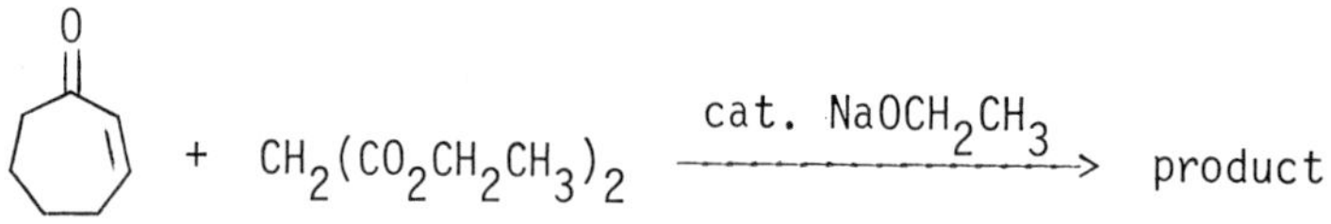

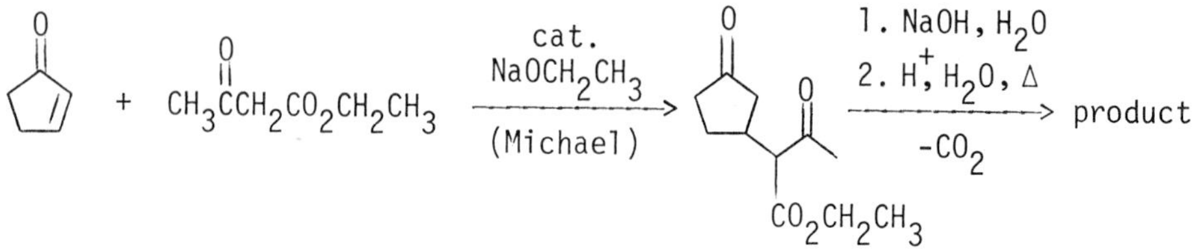

25. $(CH_3CH_2O_2C)_2CH\text{—}H \xrightarrow[-CH_3CH_2OH]{^{-}\ddot{O}CH_2CH_3} (CH_3CH_2O_2C)_2\ddot{C}H^{-} + CH_2{=}CHCCH_3$ (C=O) $\overset{*}{\rightleftharpoons}$

$(CH_3CH_2O_2C)_2CHCH_2\ddot{C}^{-}HCOCH_3 \xrightarrow{H\text{—}CH(CO_2CH_2CH_3)_2} (CH_3CH_2O_2C)_2CHCH_2CH_2COCH_3$

(product)

$+ \ \ddot{C}^{-}H(CO_2CH_2CH_3)_2$ regenerated to continue on.

The step marked with a star(*) is reversible and, in fact, is an unfavorable equilibrium since the product (a simple ketone enolate) is a less stable anion than is the doubly-stabilized malonate anion. However, the next step, reaction with more malonic ester to make a new malonate anion, drives the equilibrium to product. The reaction is catalytic in base since malonate is regenerated in this last step.

****

26. Cyclopentanone:

$HCO_2CH_2CH_3 + CH_3CO_2CH_2CH_3 \xrightarrow{\text{Claisen}} HCCH_2CO_2CH_2CH_3$ (HC=O)

CH_3CCH_3 (C=O) $\xrightarrow{Br_2,\ CH_3CO_2H} BrCH_2CCH_3$ (C=O)

$HCCH_2CO_2CH_2CH_3$ (HC=O) $\xrightarrow{\text{1. } NaOCH_2CH_3 \text{ 2. } BrCH_2COCH_3} HCCHCH_2CCH_3$ (both C=O; $CO_2CH_2CH_3$ on CH) $\xrightarrow{H^+,\ H_2O,\ \Delta} HCCH_2CH_2CCH_3$ (both C=O)

$\xrightarrow[\text{aldol}]{NaOH,\ H_2O,\ \Delta}$ 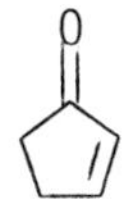 $\xrightarrow{H_2,\ Pd\text{-}C}$ 

Cyclohexanone:

CH_3CCH_3 (C=O) $+ CH_2{=}O \xrightarrow[\text{aldol}]{NaOH,\ H_2O} CH_3CCH_2CH_2OH$ (C=O) $\xrightarrow{H^+,\ \Delta} CH_3CCH{=}CH_2$ (C=O)

$HCCH_2CO_2CH_2CH_3$ (HC=O) from above $\xrightarrow[\text{Michael}]{\text{1. } NaOCH_2CH_3 \text{ 2. } CH_3COCH{=}CH_2} HCCHCH_2CH_2CCH_3$ (both C=O; $CO_2CH_2CH_3$ on CH) $\xrightarrow[\text{as above}]{\text{same steps}}$ 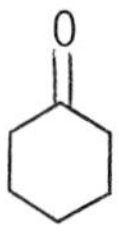

****

27. Work backwards. Note carbon-carbon bonds being formed (arrows).

(a)

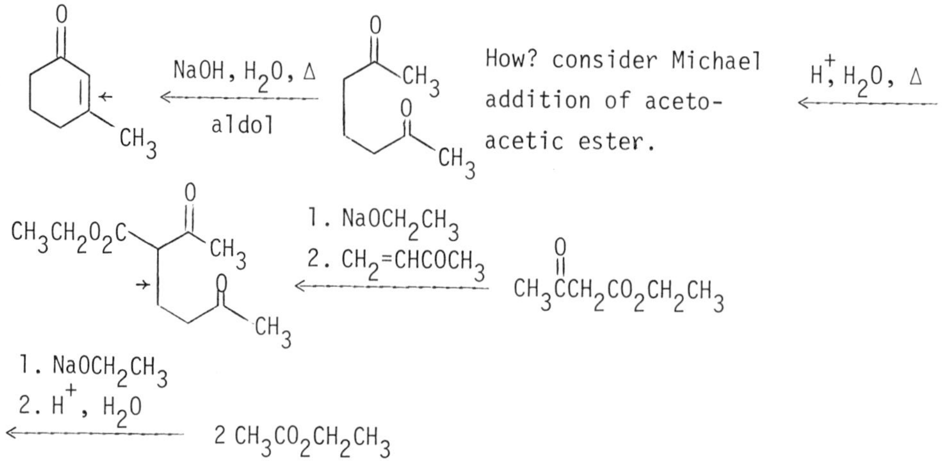

(b)

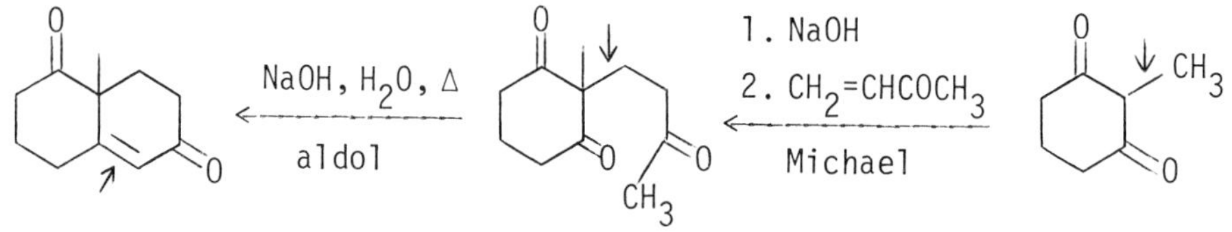

(A Robinson annelation sequence)

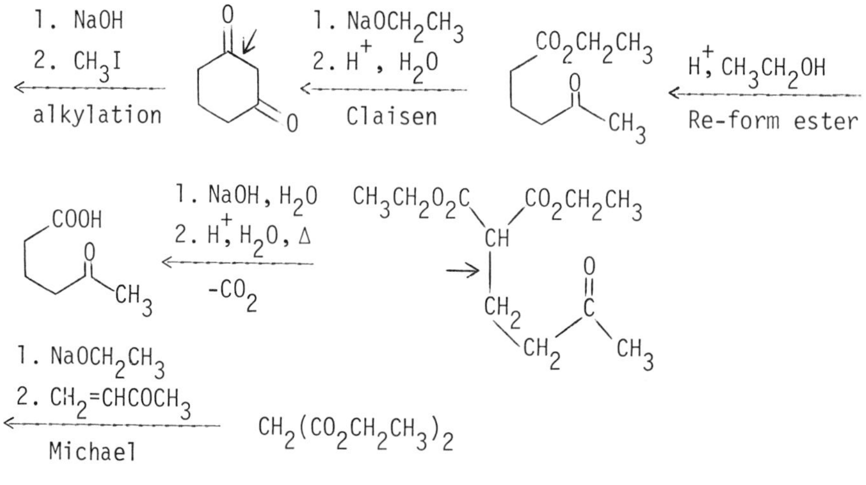

(c) Identical sequence to (b), but substitute two alkylations with $BrCH_2COCH_3$ for the two Michael additions to CH_2=$CHCOCH_3$.

****

28. Without details:

(a) $\underset{CH_2COOH}{\overset{CH_2COOH}{|}}$ $\Rightarrow$ $BrCH_2CO_2R + CH_2(CO_2R)_2$ Alkylation, then hydrolysis/decarboxylation.

(Problem 20, part b)

(b) $\underset{CH_2COOH}{\overset{CH_2COR'}{|}}$ $\Rightarrow$ $BrCH_2COR' + CH_2(CO_2R)_2$ or $R'\overset{O}{\overset{\|}{C}}CH_2CO_2R + BrCH_2CO_2R$ Similar.

(c) $\underset{CH_2COR''}{\overset{CH_2COR'}{|}}$ $\Rightarrow$ $BrCH_2COR' + R''\underset{O}{\underset{\|}{C}}CH_2CO_2R$ Again.

(d) $\underset{CH_2COOH}{\overset{CH_2CH_2COOH}{|}}$ $\Rightarrow$ $CH_2{=}CHCO_2R + CH_2(CO_2R)_2$ Michael addn., then hydrolysis/decarboxylation.

(e) $\underset{CH_2COOH}{\overset{CH_2CH_2COR'}{|}}$ $\Rightarrow$ $CH_2{=}CHCOR' + CH_2(CO_2R)_2$ or $R'\overset{O}{\overset{\|}{C}}CH_2CO_2R + CH_2{=}CHCO_2R$ Similar.

(f) $\underset{CH_2COR''}{\overset{CH_2CH_2COR'}{|}}$ $\Rightarrow$ $CH_2{=}CHCOR' + R''\underset{O}{\underset{\|}{C}}CH_2CO_2R$ Again.

****

29.

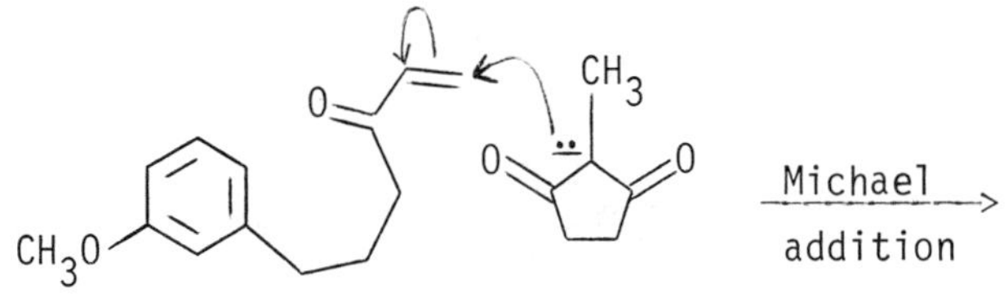

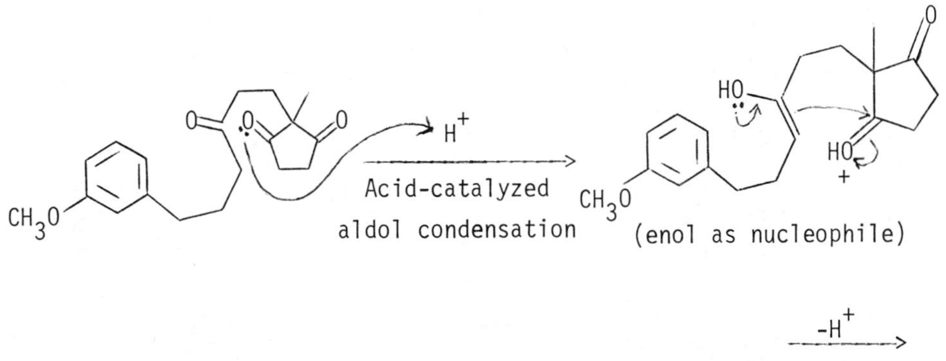

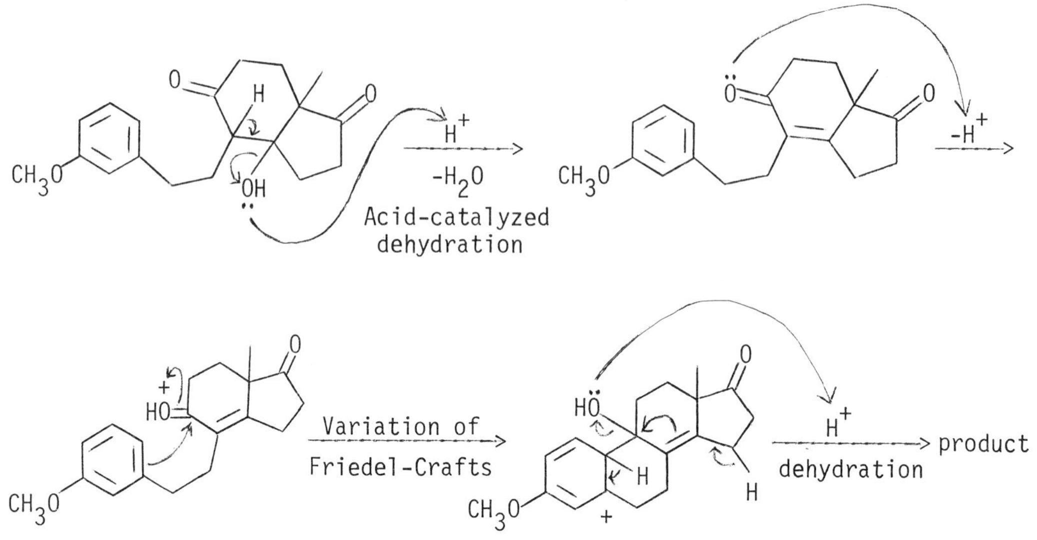

Acid-catalyzed dehydration

Variation of Friedel-Crafts

dehydration → product

****

30. (a)

$\bigcirc$—CHO + $CH_2(CO_2CH_2CH_3)_2$

1. $(CH_3CH_2)_2NH$, Δ
2. H^+, H_2O, Δ
$\longrightarrow$
$\bigcirc$—CH=CHCOOH

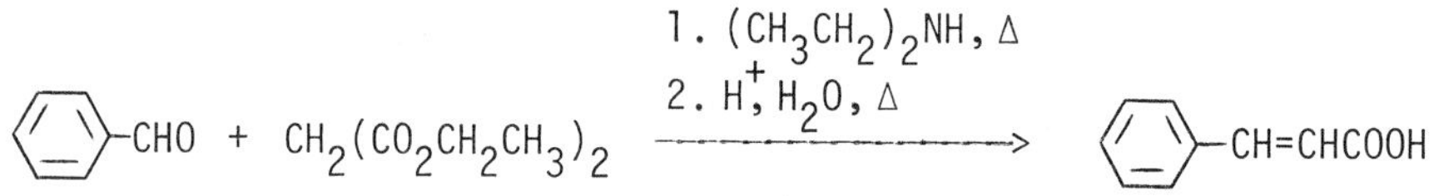

Note: there is a similar but shorter method, the "Perkin condensation," which accomplishes the same synthesis as follows:

$\bigcirc$—CHO + $CH_3\overset{O}{\overset{\|}{C}}\overset{O}{\overset{\|}{C}}CH_3$ $\xrightarrow{Na^+\ {}^-\overset{O}{\overset{\|}{O}}CCH_3}$ $\bigcirc$—CH=CHCOOH

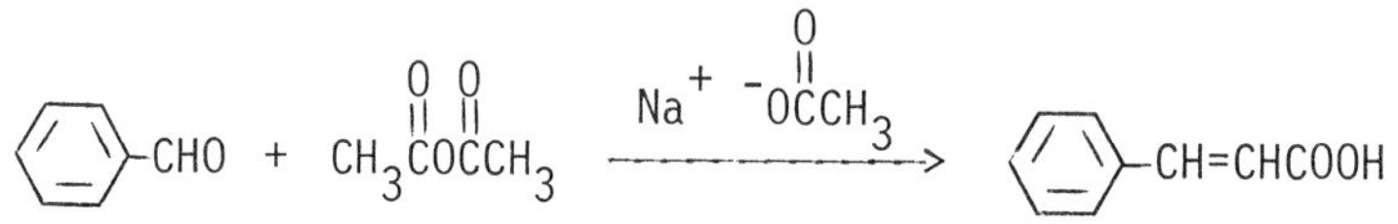

You might try formulating a mechanism, based on the principles in this and earlier chapters.

(b) $\bigcirc$—CHO + $H\overset{O}{\overset{\|}{C}}CH_2CO_2CH_2CH_3$

1. $(CH_3CH_2)_2NH$, Δ
2. H^+, H_2O, Δ
$\longrightarrow$
$\bigcirc$—CH=CHCHO

(c) $\bigcirc$—CHO + $N\equiv CCH_2CO_2CH_2CH_3$

1. $(CH_3CH_2)_2NH$, Δ
2. H^+, H_2O, Δ
$\longrightarrow$
$\bigcirc$—CH=CHC≡N

****

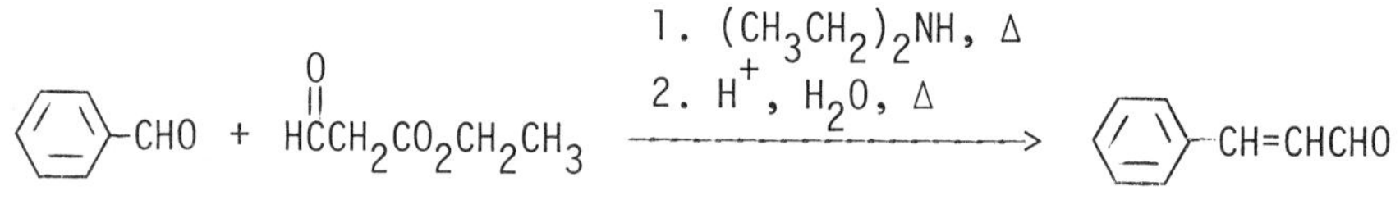

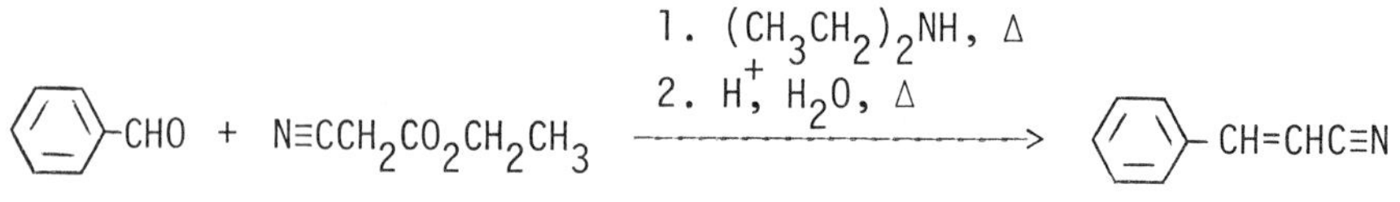

CHAPTER 23

Carbohydrates: Polyfunctional Compounds in Nature

General Introduction

In this chapter we'll begin to apply the material you've just seen to a major class of "real world" molecules, carbohydrates (sugars). For a change, nomenclature will play a more central role: the names of sugars and sugar derivatives follow their own kind of independent system, which includes some special stereochemical terms. On the other hand, most of the reactions are old ones, and most of them are needed for only a limited number of purposes such as structure determination, interconversion of derivatives, or (occasionally) synthesis of one sugar from another. You need to be good at deductive reasoning so you can solve the puzzles posed by some of the problems. If you can, then this chapter should not be too hard for you.

Outline of the Chapter

23-1. The Names and Structures of Carbohydrates.

Be prepared for a lot of new terminology.

23-2. The Polyfunctional Chemistry of Sugars.

The basics: mostly (but not entirely) review material.

23-3. The Stepwise Build-Up and Degradation of Sugars.

Application in synthesis and structure determination.

23-4. Disaccharides, Polysaccharides, and Sugars in Nature.

Keys to the Chapter

23-1. The Names and Structures of Carbohydrates.

The naming system presented in this section comes from an assortment of historically-derived trivial names organized into a semi-official framework that is universally used. So, sugars are all ketones or aldehydes containing alcohol groups, and their names all end in "-ose". Most all of them have stereocenters, and they are usually drawn in Fischer projections with the carbon chain vertical and the carbonyl group nearest the top. If the stereocenter nearest the bottom of the Fischer projection has the -OH on the right, it has an "*R*" configuration, and the sugar is said to belong to the "D" family. If this -OH is on the left, we have an "*S*" configuration, and an "L" sugar. Look at Figures 23-1 and 23-2. Each horizontal row contains structures that are all diastereomers of each other. None of the mirror-image structures (enantiomers) of any of these are illustrated; the mirror image of any D-sugar is just an L-sugar with the same name.

Since sugars contain alcohols and carbonyl groups, they can (and usually do) form cyclic hemiacetals, typically with either five- or six-membered rings. Translating an open-chain structure into a picture of the cyclic hemiacetal is tricky: here's a step-by-step way to do it.

1. Write in wedges and dotted lines and (for a D-series sugar) lay the structure on its side, with the top moved down to the right. Then, locate the -OH group that you will use to form the cyclic hemiacetal with the carbonyl group:

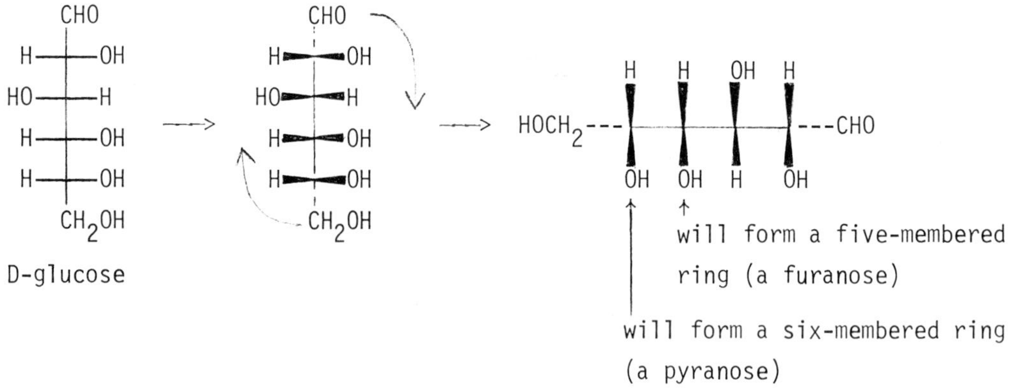

2. Rotate around the C-C bond to the right of the -OH group you picked out until the -OH is horizontal and pointing away from you (make a model!). Then wrap this left-hand end of the chain behind the plane of the paper to put the -OH near to the carbonyl carbon. Finally, make the hemiacetal bond (this sequence is shown step-by-step on the following page - 433).

By convention the procedure for L-series sugars is modified such that the top of the structure is rotated down *to the left* when it is laid on its side. That allows the L and D structures to look like mirror images when placed side-by-side:

β-D-glucopyranose β-L-glucopyranose

For a furanose:

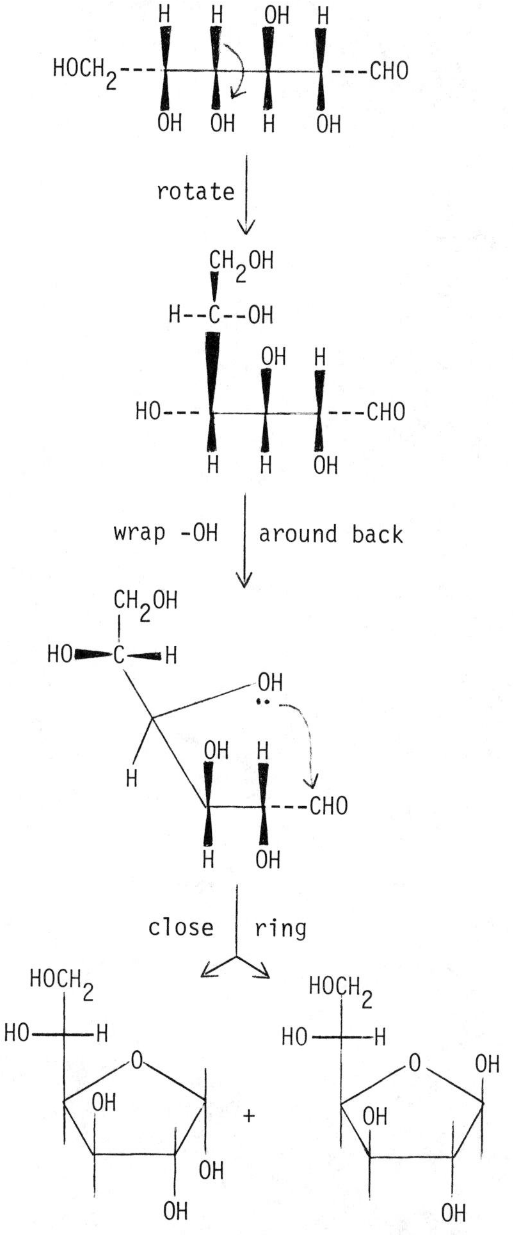

α-D-glucofuranose β-D-glucofuranose

anomers

For a pyranose:

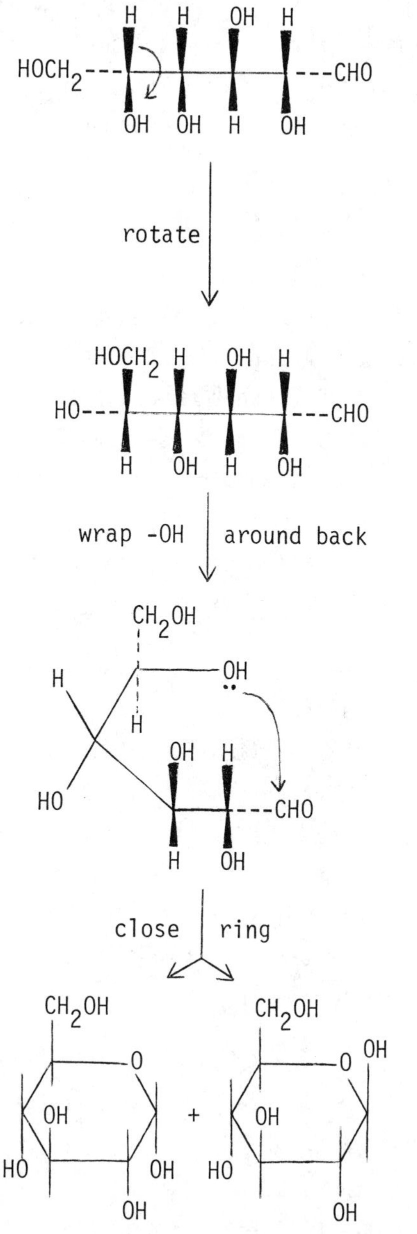

α-D-glucopyranose β-D-glucopyranose

anomers

If you like, you can derive the cyclic structure of an L-sugar by doing the D-sugar first, and then writing its mirror image.

Remember, sugars in solution typically exist as equilibrium mixtures of open chain plus cyclic hemiacetal structures. For glucose, this equilibrium mixture contains 63.6% β-pyranose, 36.4% α-pyranose, together with just traces of open chain and furanose structures. The interconversion of β and α anomers is called mutarotation.

23-2. The Polyfunctional Chemistry of Sugars.

Although most of the reactions in this section are old ones, typical of either alcohol or aldehyde/ketone chemistry, a couple of new reagents are introduced. These mainly allow selective reactions to be carried out on the multifunctional sugar molecule. Examples are Br_2 in H_2O which oxidizes only the aldehyde of an aldose to $-CO_2H$, and HNO_3 which oxidizes both the end carbons of an aldose, forming a dicarboxylic acid. The reactions in this section have been chosen for their importance in practical aspects of sugar chemistry, the material in the latter half of this chapter.

23-3. The Stepwise Build-Up and Degradation of Sugars.

Determining sugar structures was a major effort involving development of reaction sequences to lengthen or shorten sugar chains, and use of some very clever logic dealing with the consequences of the stereochemistry of sugars and sugar derivatives. The "Fischer proof" illustrates the main techniques used. Note that the process repeatedly makes use of the synthesis of dicarboxylic acids which are tested for the presence or absence of optical activity. An optically inactive diacid is assumed to be a meso compound, containing a plane of symmetry, and this kind of information is used to narrow down possible structures for unknown sugars.

23-4. Disaccharides, Polysaccharides, and Sugars in Nature.

This section presents simple extensions of the material just completed. Mother Nature has developed a convenient method for linking sugar molecules together: an alcohol group of one sugar forms an acetal by reactions with the hemiacetal group of another. This connection, called a "glycoside" linkage, is just a fancier version of a simple acetal formed by reaction of a sugar with an ordinary alcohol, like methanol (to form a "methyl glycoside," as in the previous section). Again, the determination of unknown structures represents a common type of problem. There are two important features that distinguish sugars containing free hemiacetal groups from those lacking them. In solution, hemiacetals are always in equilibrium with aldehydes. So, hemiacetal-containing sugars

(1) undergo mutarotation and (2) are readily oxidized by mild oxidants like Ag$^+$. The latter feature is the basis for the "Tollens test" for "reducing" (that is, oxidizable) sugars. Some of the sugars in this section contain acetal but not hemiacetal groups. Find them! These are examples of "non-reducing" sugars.

Solutions to Chapter 23 Problems

1. (a) D-aldopentose (Note: only one stereocenter!); (b) L-aldopentose;

    (c) D-ketoheptose.

****

2. You get

$$
\begin{array}{c}
\text{CHO} \\
\text{H}-\!\!\!-\text{OH} \\
\text{H}-\!\!\!-\text{OH} \\
\text{HO}-\!\!\!-\text{H} \\
\text{CH}_2\text{OH}
\end{array}
$$

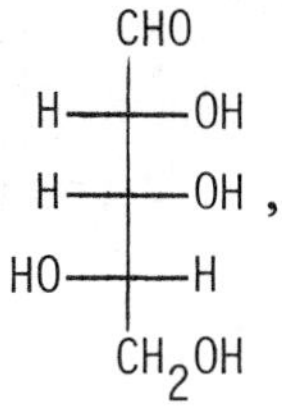

, the mirror image (enantiomer) of D-lyxose (Figure 23-1). Therefore this sugar is L-lyxose, a diasteriomer of D-ribose.

****

3.

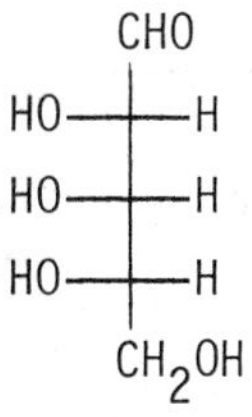

CHO	Systematic name:
HO——H	(2S,3S,4S)-2,3,4,5-
HO——H	tetrahydroxypentanal
HO——H	
CH$_2$OH	

L-ribose

CHO	Systematic name:
HO——H	(2S,3R,4S,5S)-2,3,4,5,6-
H——OH	pentahydroxyhexanal
HO——H	
HO——H	
CH$_2$OH	

L-glucose

****

4. I know it sounds like an awful thing to make you do, but you might just have to review sections 5-4 and 5-5 for this one. The Study Guide text for these sections may also help.

    (a) L-glyceraldehyde; (b) D-erythrulose; (c) just D-glucose (upside down!);

    (d) D-threose; (e) L-xylose.

****

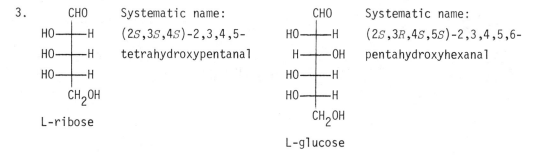

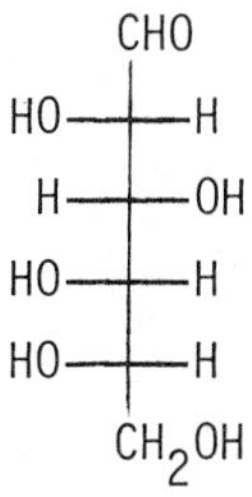

5. Make models if you need to!!

(a) 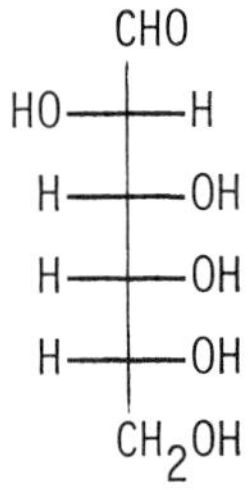

D-altrose

(b) 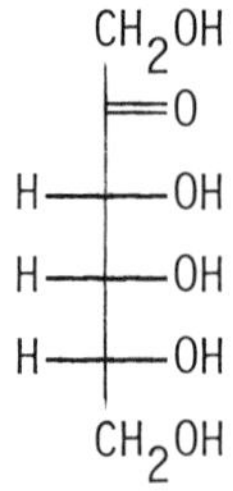

D-psicose

(c) 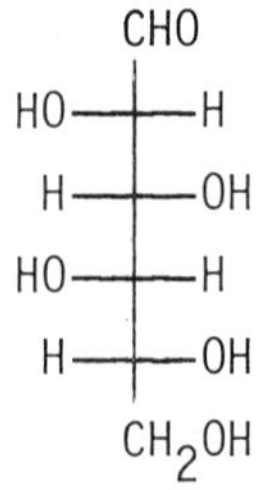

D-idose

(d) 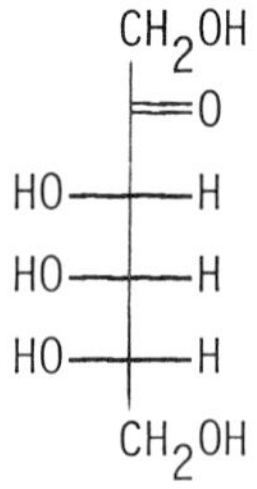

L-psicose

****

6. See procedure in the Study Guide text for this chapter. Careful: (b) and (c) are L-sugars.

(a) 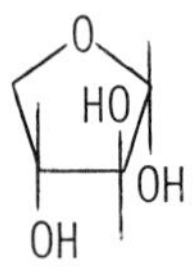 and 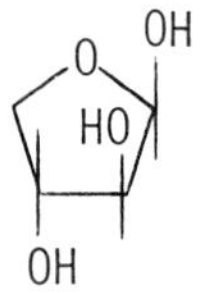 ;

α-furanose β-furanose

(b) 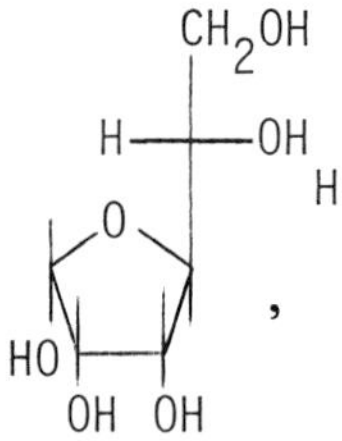 ,  , 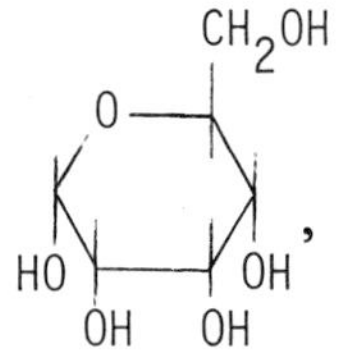 , and  ,

α-furanose β α-pyranose β

(c) 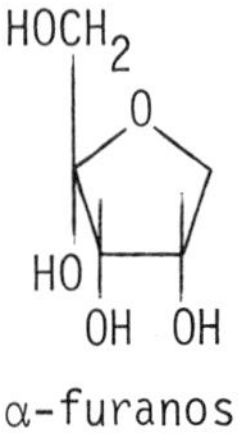 and  ;

α-furanose β

(d) 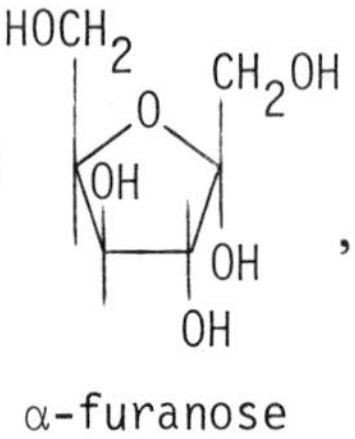 , 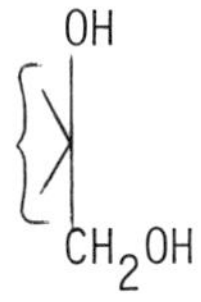 , 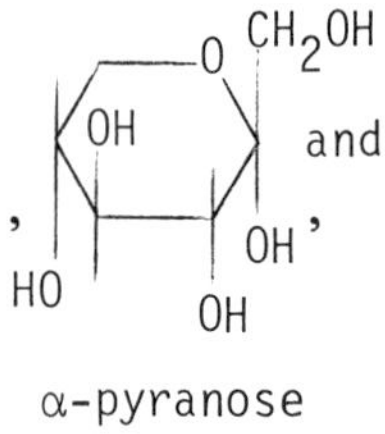 , and 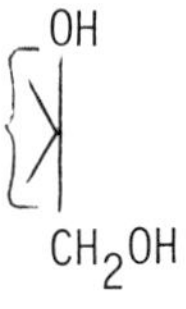

α-furanose β α-pyranose β

(e) 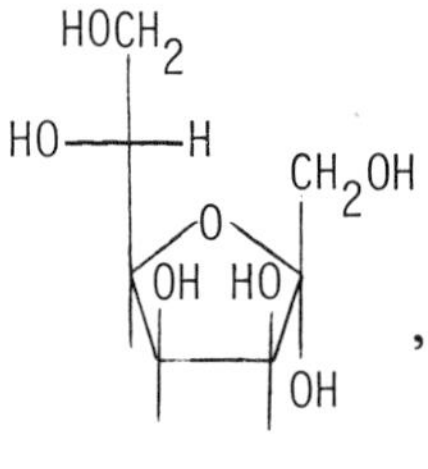 , 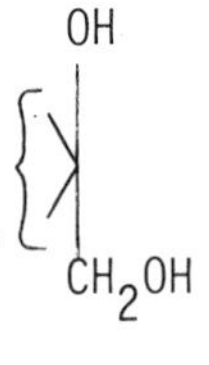 , 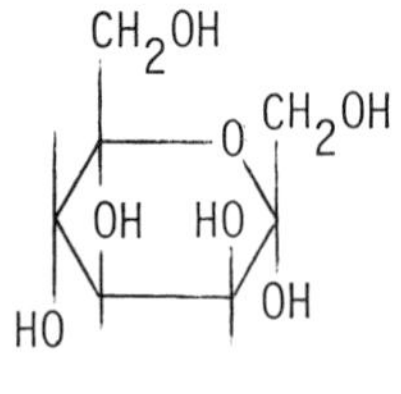 , and 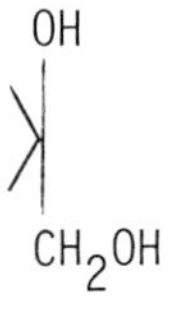

α-furanose β α-pyranose β

****

7. No. They are all hemiacetals and therefore are capable of readily interconverting their α and β anomers.

****

8. (a) 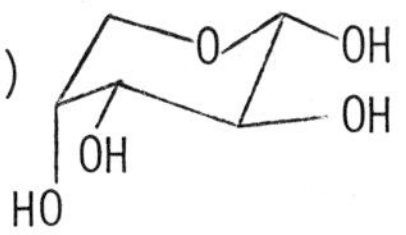 ; (b) 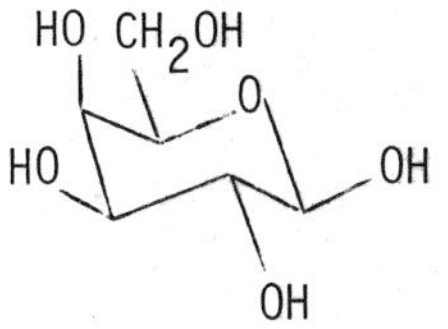 ; (c) 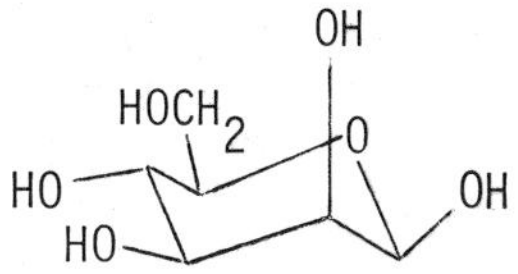 ;

(d) 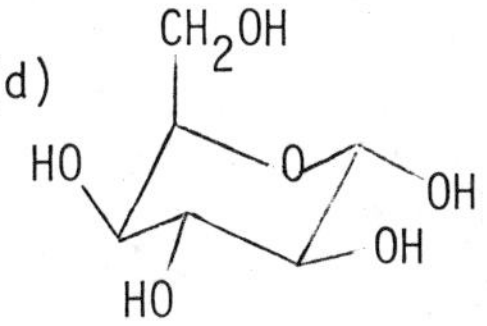

(An unusual case where the $-CH_2OH$ is forced to be axial to allow all four -OH's to be equatorial.)

****

9. (i) (ii) (iii) (iv)

(a)

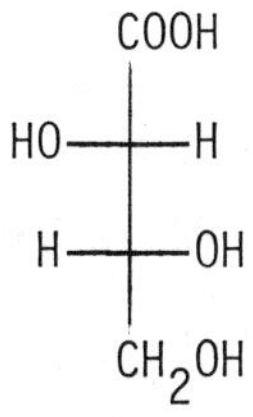

D-threonic acid

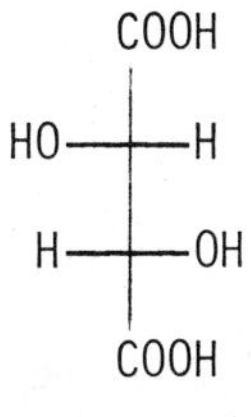

D-tartaric acid

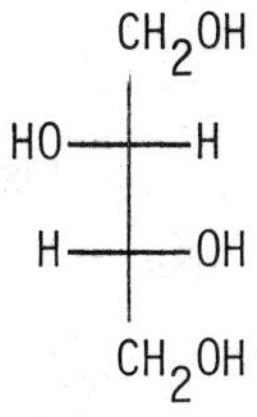

D-threitol

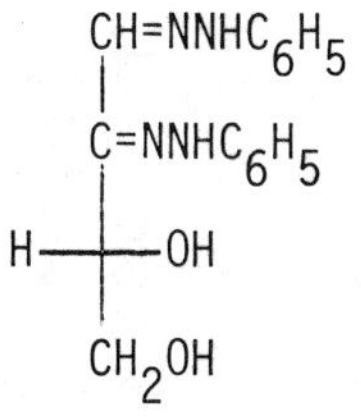

D-threose phenylosazone*

(b)

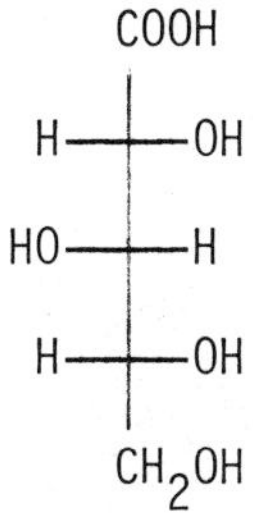

D-xylonic acid

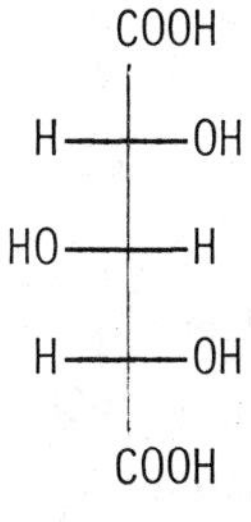

D-xylaric acid

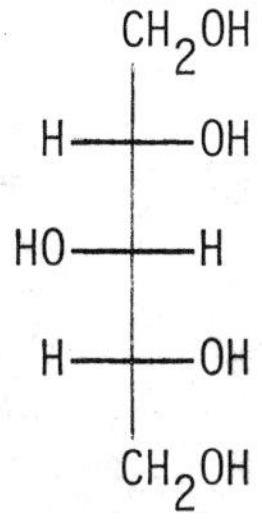

D-xylitol

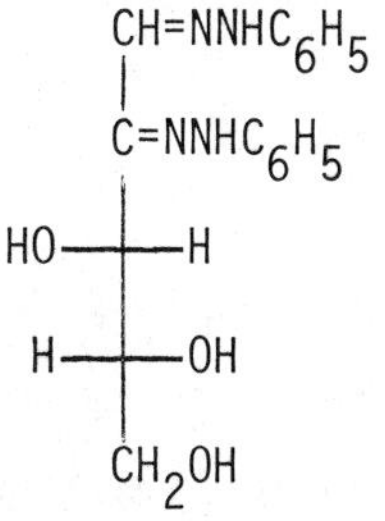

D-xylose phenylosazone**

(c)

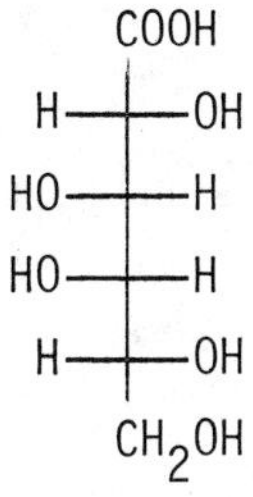

D-galactonic acid

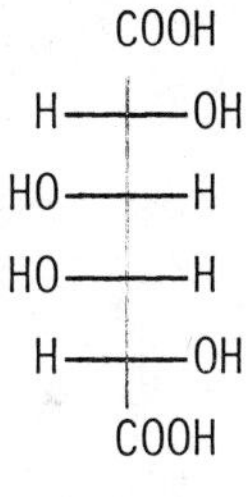

D-galactaric acid

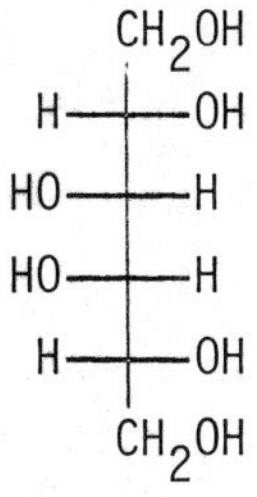

D-galactitol

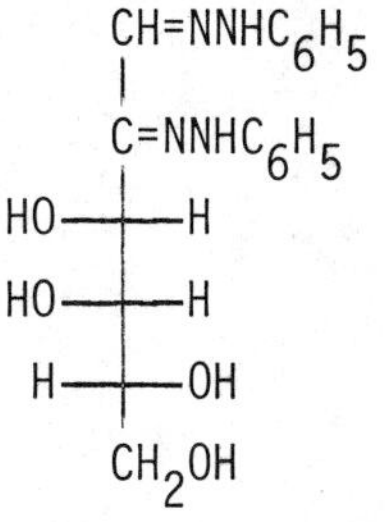

***

D-galactose phenylosazone

*Same as D-erythrose phenylosazone. **Same as D-lyxose phenylosazone.

***Same as D-talose phenylosazone.

****

10. (a) D-glucose (Figure 23-1); (b) L-allose (all OH's on left side)

****

11. (a) Arabinose and lyxose. Ribitol and xylitol are meso compounds.

(b)

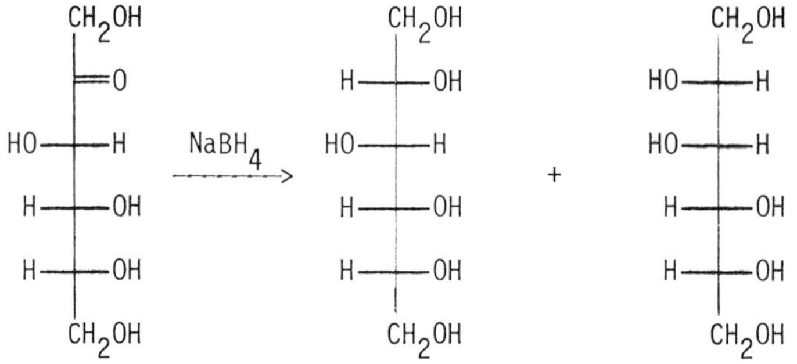

D-fructose D-glucitol D-mannitol

A new stereocenter is generated at C-2, so two diastereomeric alditols are produced. In contrast, reduction of any aldose will be simpler, as no new stereocenter will be generated, so only a single product can form.

****

12. (a) and (d), since they still possess hemiacetal functionality. In (b) and (c) the -OH at C-1 in glucose has become $-OCH_3$, and the molecule is now an acetal, incapable of mutarotation.

(e) is 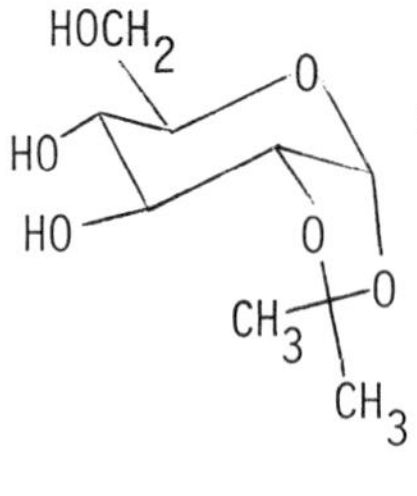 , also with an acetal, not a hemiacetal, at C-1.

****

13. (a) The oxygen at C-1 of an aldopyranose is a hemiacetal oxygen, not a simple alcohol oxygen. It can therefore be methylated the same way a hemiacetal may be converted to an acetal: with methanol and acid via a stabilized carbocation.

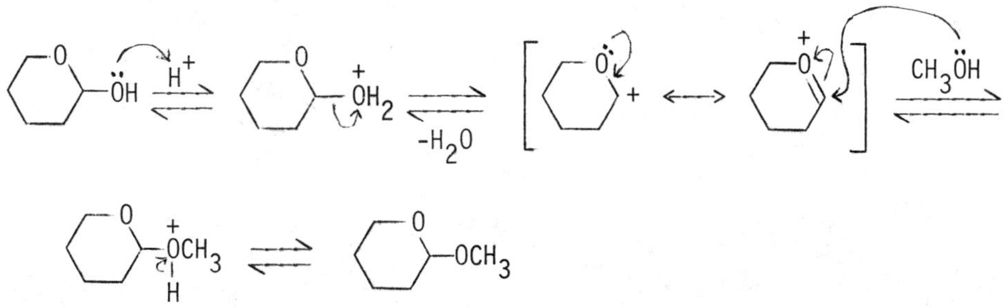

(b) The oxygen at C-1 in this case is an acetal oxygen, not a simple methyl ether. Similar to the case in part (a), mild aqueous acid is sufficient for hydrolysis due to the same stabilized carbocation intermediate shown above (the mechanism is just the reverse of the one shown).

(c) Four methyl glycosides are possible (refer to the structures for fructofuranose and fructopyranose in section 23-1):

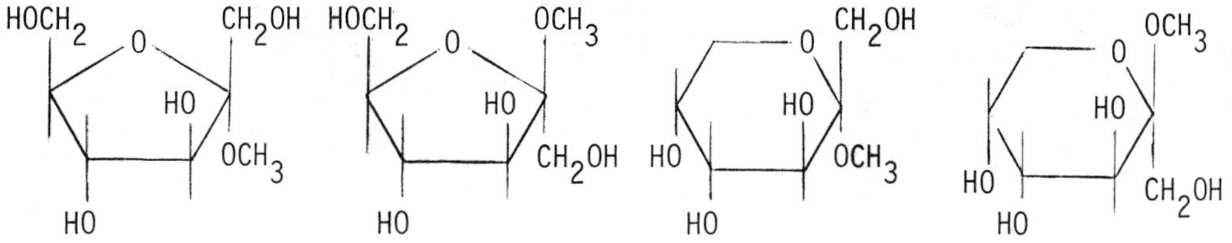

methyl α-D-fructofuranoside | β | methyl α-D-fructopyranoside | β

****

14. Arabinose (as a β-pyranose) forms a double acetal (section 23-2). So does ribose, since in its α-pyranose form all four hydroxy groups are cis:

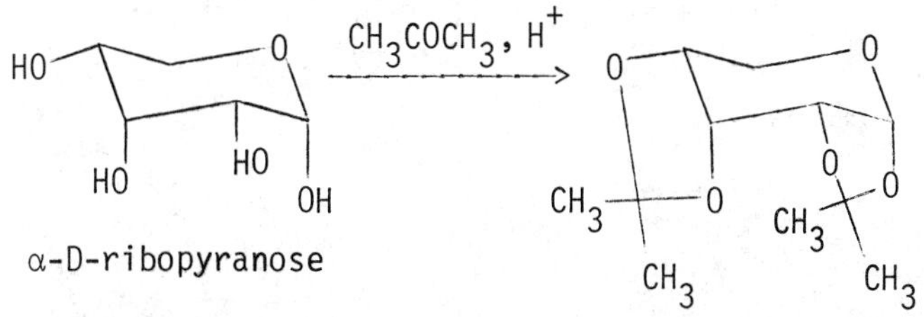

α-D-ribopyranose

The best xylose and lyxose can do is have only one pair of adjacent cis hydroxy groups, so these readily form only monoacetals:

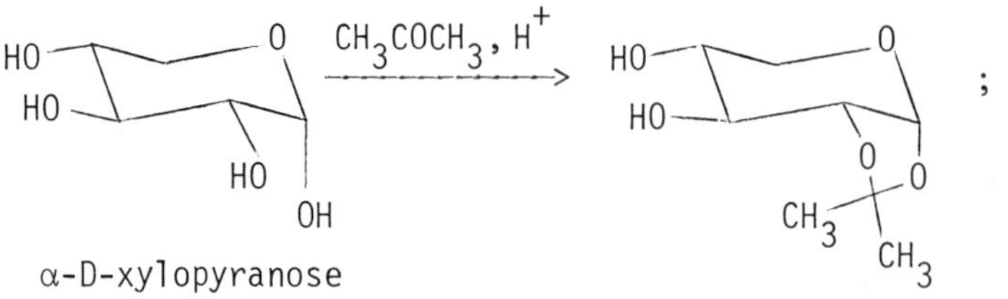

α-D-xylopyranose

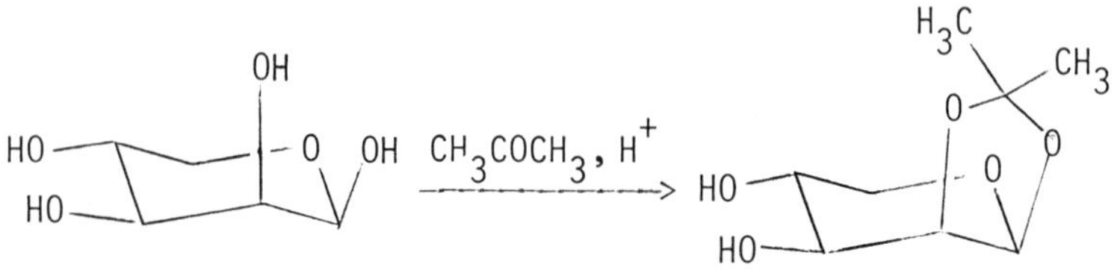

β-D-lyxopyranose

****

15. (a) Aldol condensations! Abbreviated mechanisms are shown below. Refer to section 16-3 for more details if necessary.

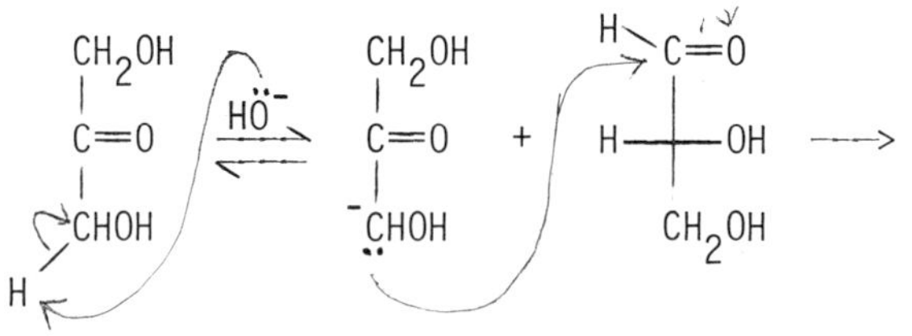

D-sorbose and D-fructose (epimeric at C-4, the newly generated stereocenter)

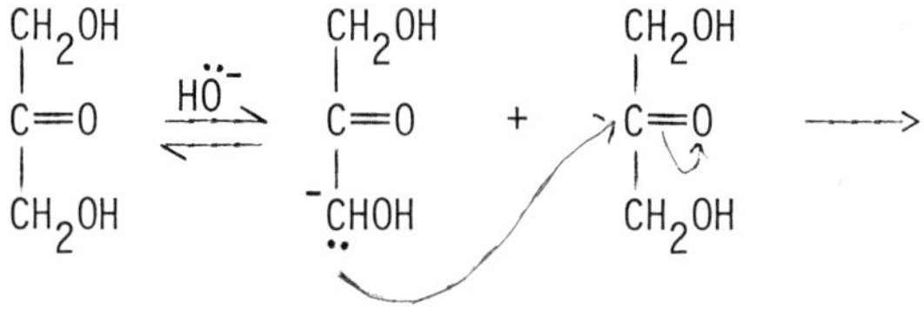

dendroketose

(b) The hint is supposed to make you think about enolate anions. Glyceraldehyde and 1,3-dihydroxypropanone are readily interconverted in aqueous basic solution via enolates and enols:

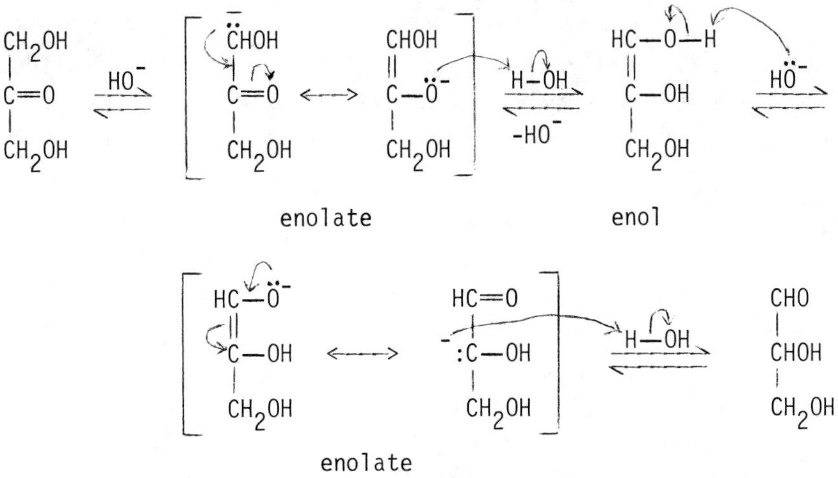

So a basic solution of either one rapidly becomes a mixture of the two, and the reactions in part (a) can then occur. This aldose ⇌ ketose interconversion is general. Glucose and fructose are interconverted by aqueous base, for example.

****

16. This is a retro-aldol reaction, the reverse of the chemistry in problem 15:

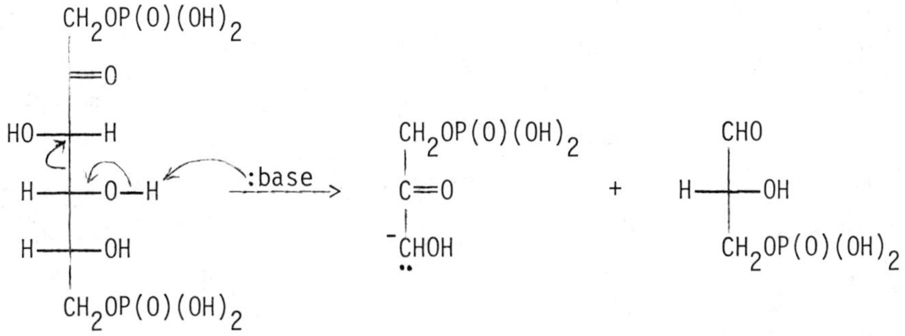

****

17. (a) Br_2, H_2O; (b) see answer to problem 9b; (c) CH_3OH, H^+; (d) ester of acid in part b: $-COOCH_3$ at the top; (e) forms the amide: $-CONH_2$ at the top. Then:

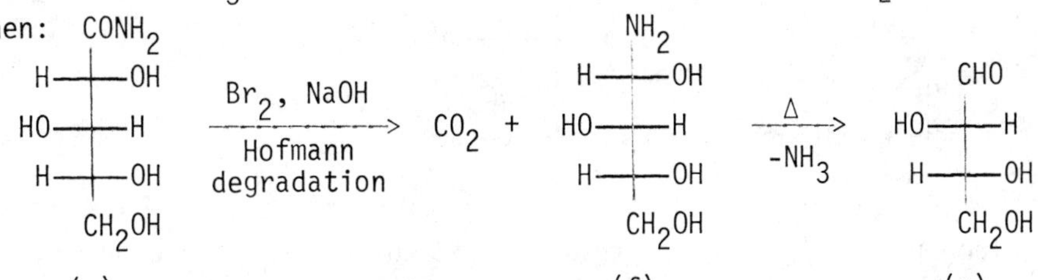

(e) (f) (g)

The hydroxyamine (f) readily loses NH_3 on heating to give the aldehyde. This sequence achieves the removal of C-1 from an aldose to form a new aldose with one less carbon, just like the Wohl and Ruff degradations.

****

18. (i) The sugar has 7 carbons and is a <u>ketose</u> since HIO_4 treatment produces a mole of CO_2 (see similar reaction of D-fructose, section 23-2). The sugar has two $-CH_2OH$ groups (leading to 2 methanals) and four $-CHOH$ groups (leading to 4 moles of methanoic acid).

(ii) Since the sugar forms the same osazone as an <u>aldose</u>, its ketone must be at C-2. So far, therefore, we have the following partial structure:

```
        CH2OH
         |
         C=O
         |
        CHOH  ⎤
         |    ⎥
        CHOH  ⎬  stereochemistry
         |    ⎥     unknown
        CHOH  ⎦
         |
    H—C—OH  ← 'D' sugar
         |
        CH2OH
```

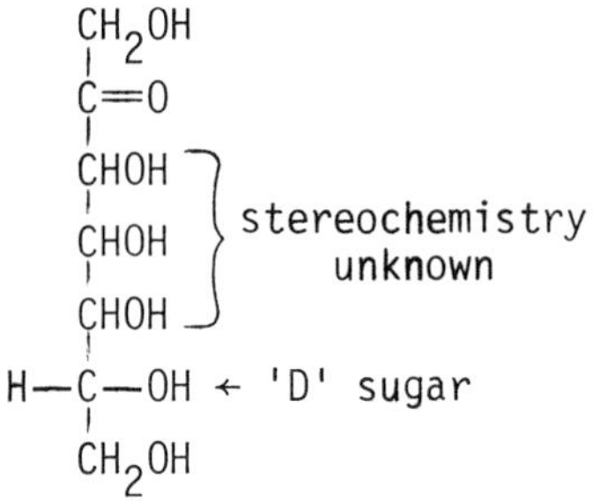

(iii) and (v) tell us the following:

```
   CHO                    CHO                 CHO
    |                      |                   |
   CHOH                   CHOH            H——————OH  ←⎤  we now know these
    |                      |                   |      ⎥  carbons are 'R' in
   CHOH        Ruff       CHOH     Ruff   H——————OH  ←⎦  sugars B, A, and
    |        ———————>      |      ———————>      |        D-sedoheptulose as
   CHOH                   CHOH            H——————OH       well.
    |                      |                   |
   CHOH                   CHOH               CH2OH
    |                      |
  H—C—OH                 H—C—OH
    |                      |
   CH2OH                  CH2OH
```

  aldoheptose 'A'   aldoheptose 'B'   D-ribose

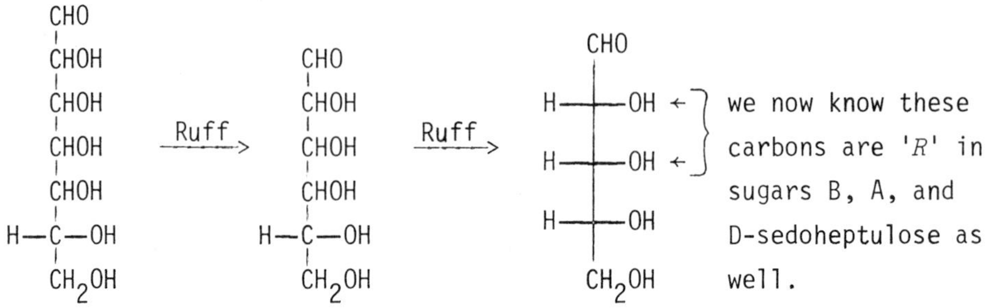

Next, (iv) tells us this:

```
   CHO                        COOH                              COOH
    |                          |                                 |
   CHOH                       CHOH  ← this carbon must be 'S' → HO——————H
    |          HNO3, H2O, Δ    |                                 |
  H—C—OH      ——————————>    H—C—OH                          H——————OH
    |                          |                                 |
  H—C—OH                     H—C—OH                          H——————OH
    |                          |                                 |
  H—C—OH                     H—C—OH                          H——————OH
    |                          |                                 |
   CH2OH                      COOH                              COOH
```

  aldoheptose 'B'   this is said to be   otherwise the product
                           optically <u>active</u>   would be <u>meso</u>

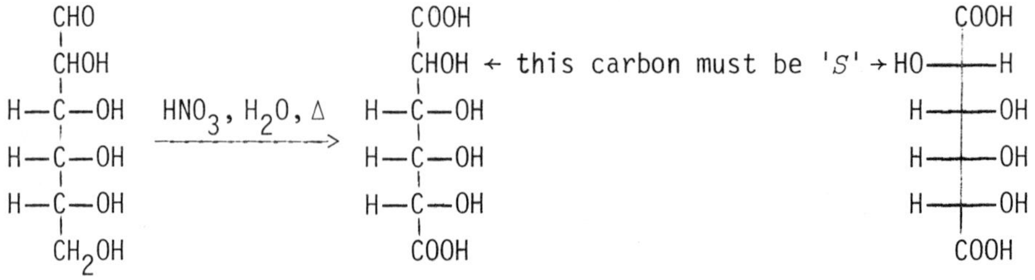

From this information we now can work
backwards towards the unknown: the
stereocenters in D-sedoheptulose
must be 3*S*, 4*R*, 5*R*, and 6*R*.

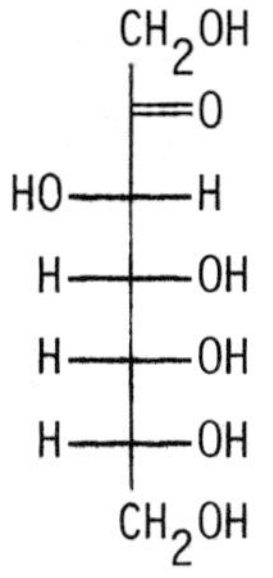

D-sedoheptulose

****

19. Two aldoheptoses are formed. Upon HNO_3 treatment one gives an optically
active diacid, the other an inactive mesocompound:

	CHO			COOH				CHO			COOH	
HO—		—H	HO—		—H		H—		—OH	H—		—OH
HO—		—H	HO—		—H		HO—		—H	HO—		—H
HO—		—H	HO—		—H	$\xrightarrow{HNO_3}$;	HO—		—H	$\xrightarrow{HNO_3}$	HO—		—H
HO—		—H	HO—		—H		HO—		—H	HO—		—H
H—		—OH	H—		—OH		H—		—OH	H—		—OH
	CH_2OH			COOH				CH_2OH			COOH	
				active							meso	

****

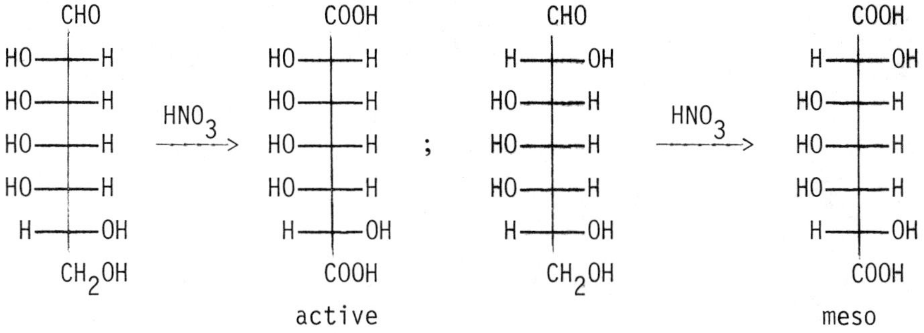

20. The presence of Fe^{3+} and H_2O_2, both <u>oxidizing agents</u>, should help get you
started. Referring to the material in section 17-11, the Hunsdiecker
decarboxylation also involves an oxidation. So:

$$
\begin{array}{c}
CO_2H \\
H\!-\!\!\!-\!OH \\
\end{array}
\xrightarrow{\text{oxidation}} H^+ +
\begin{array}{c}
H\!-\!\!\!-\!OH \\
\end{array}
\xrightarrow{-CO_2}
\begin{array}{c}
H\!-\!\overset{\bullet}{}\!-\!OH \\
\end{array}
\xrightarrow{\text{oxidation}}
$$

$$
\begin{array}{c}
H\!-\!\overset{+}{}\!O\!-\!H \\
\end{array}
\longrightarrow H^+ +
\begin{array}{c}
H\!-\!C\!\!\overset{O}{=}\\
\end{array}
$$

****

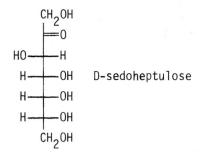

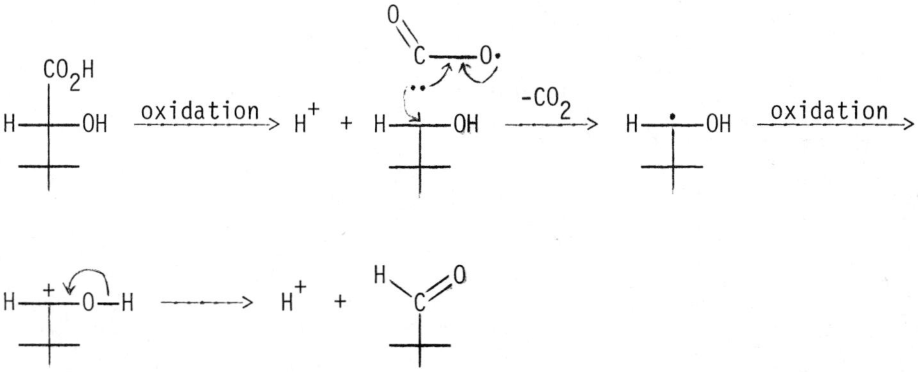

21. (a) CH_3OH, H^+; (b) 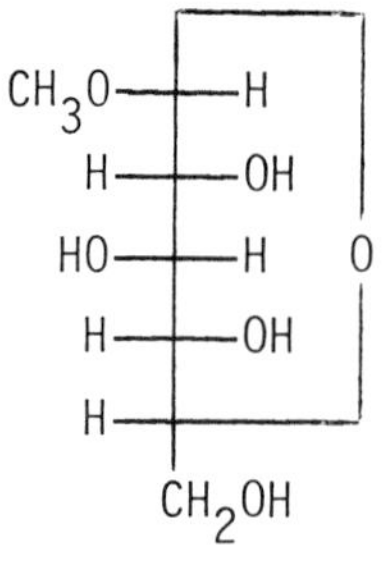 ; (c) 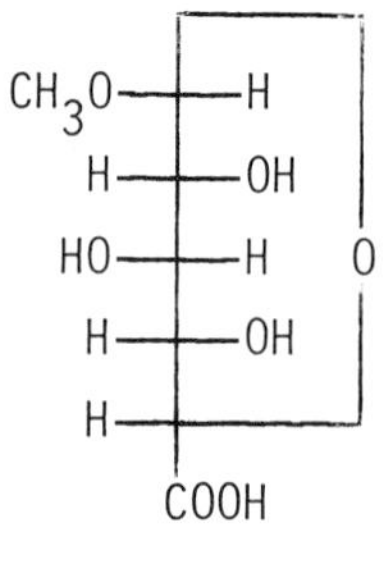 (d) 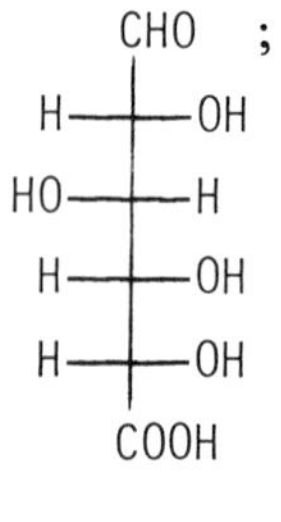

(e) 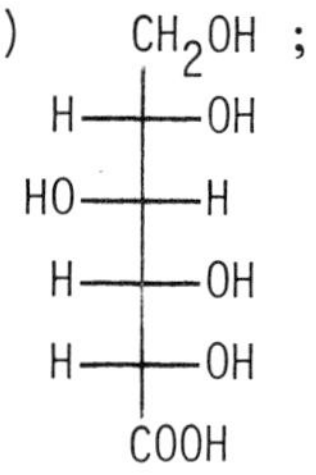 (f) 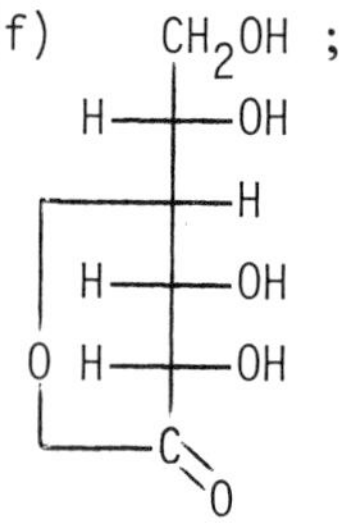 (g) 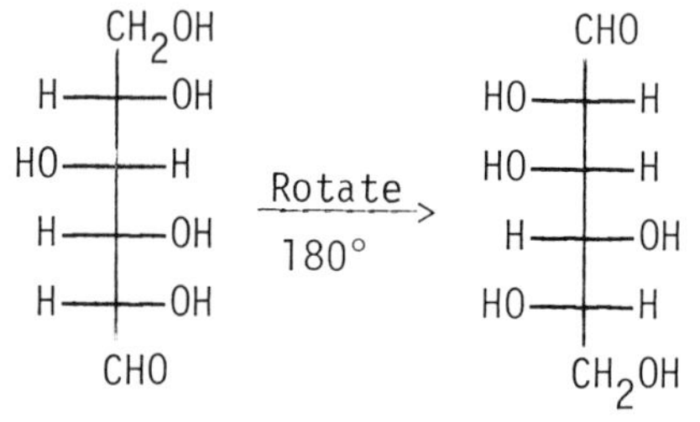

As you can see, the gulose Fischer synthesized was the L-enantiomer (hydroxy group on C-5 is on the left).

****

22. (a) 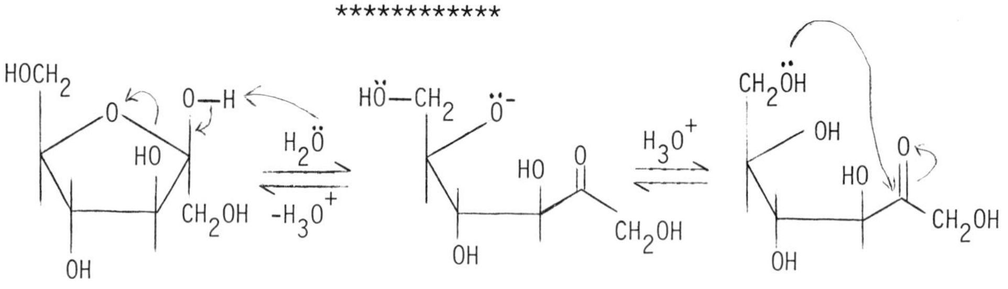

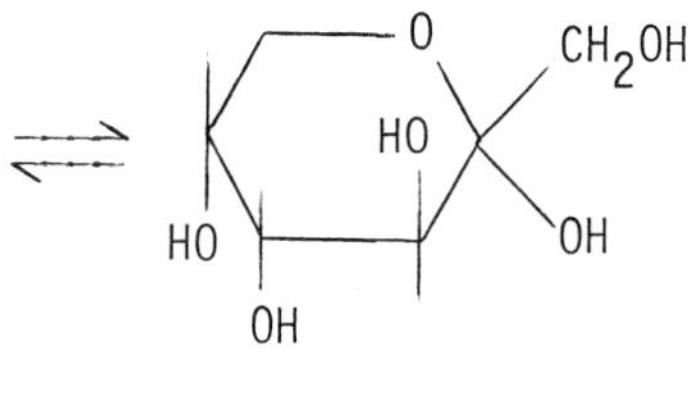 after protonation (both anomers)

(b) 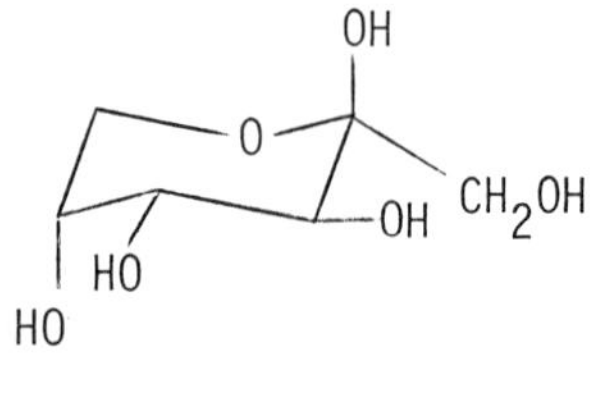 (three equatorial and two axial substituents)

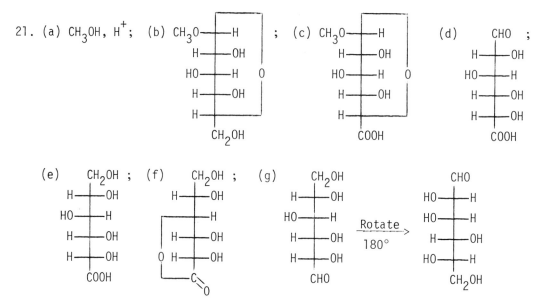

(c) 0.82 kcal/mole (Table 2-7)

(d) Common sense: $[\alpha]_{mixture} = X_A[\alpha]_A + X_B[\alpha]_B$ where X = mole fraction for each component. Let A = pyranose and B = furanose. So:

$-92° = (.8)(-132°) + (.2)[\alpha]_B$, and $[\alpha]_B = +68°$.

****

23. Reducing: (a), (b), (c), (e), (f), (h), (i), and (j) (all have hemiacetal groups).

****

24. The glycoside linkages tie up all three of the original monosaccharide carbonyl groups as acetals. No hemiacetals are present.

****

25. Yes. At the lower right of the formula (section 23-4) is a hemiacetal group:

****

26. Trehalose must be (d), the only non-reducing sugar illustrated.

Turanose is (b), the only one containing a ketose (the bottom half).

Sophorose is (a) (top half is an α anomer and bottom half is a β anomer).

Sugar (c) is composed of two aldoses that are epimers of each other at C-4.

****

27. (a) Sugar 'C':

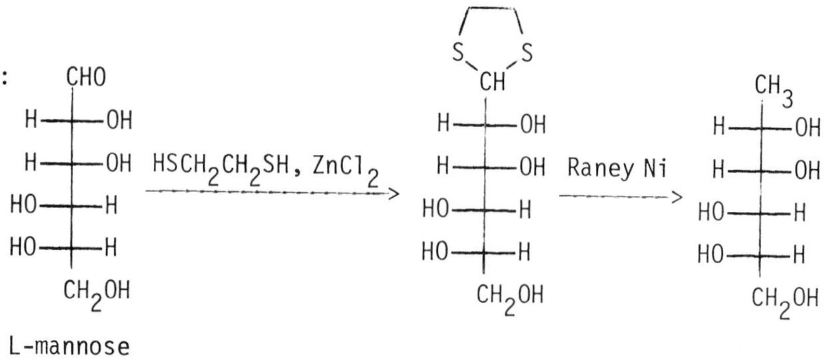

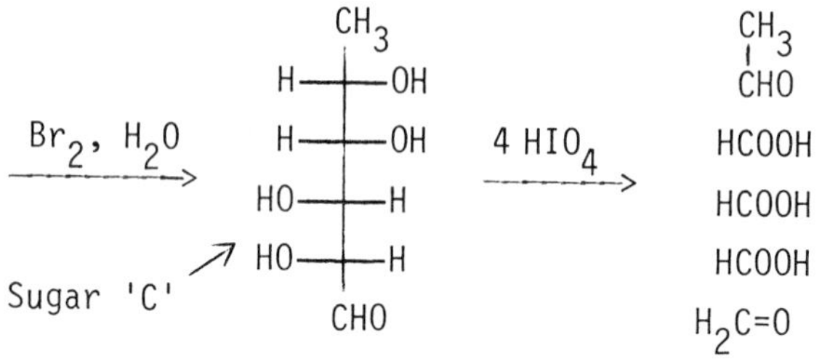

(b) This procedure attaches methyl groups to all hydroxy oxygens in the disaccharide. After hydrolyzing the glycosidic linkage between the monosaccharides, the oxygens involved in the linkage are released as free hydroxy groups. So, since the oxygen at C-6 of the methyl glucoside does not bear a methyl group, it must have been involved in the glycosidic linkage. The same goes for the oxygen at C-1 of sugar 'C'. (In both cases the oxygen at C-5 must be contained in a pyranose ring.) So, for rutinose, connect C-6 of glucose and C-1 or sugar 'C' by a glycosidic oxygen. The two anomeric carbons could each have either α or β configurations. So:

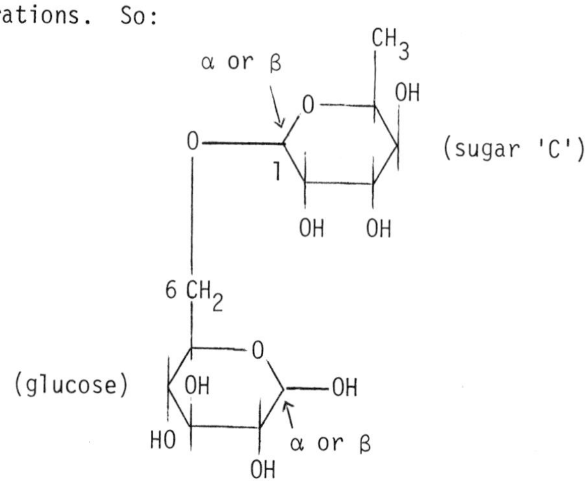

****

28. First, D-glucuronic acid γ-lactone is 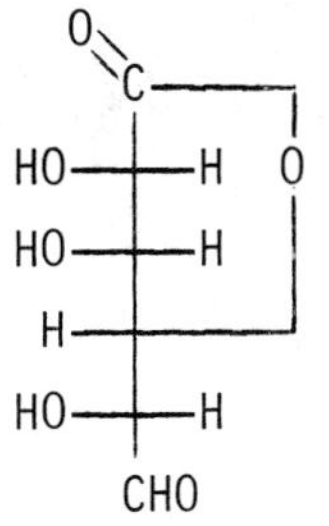 , and L-gulonic acid γ-lactone has already been illustrated (answer to part f of problem 21).

(a) $NaBH_4$; (b) 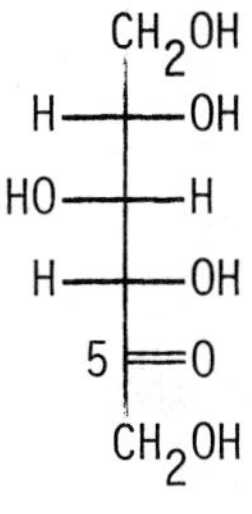 ; (c) 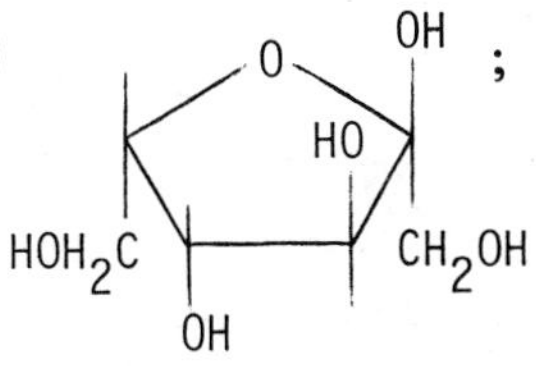 ;

(d) 1. 2 CH_3COCH_3, H^+; 2. $KMnO_4$ to oxidize unprotected primary alcohol to carboxylic acid; (e) H_2O, H^+ (hydrolyze acetals); (f) Δ ($-H_2O$).

****

CHAPTER 24

Substituted Benzenes

General Introduction

In this and the next two chapters the chemistry of aromatic compounds will be continued. In this chapter you will find out about reactions at a carbon attached to a benzene ring (a "benzyl" carbon) and about more reactions of benzenes containing either hydroxy or amino groups attached directly to the ring. All of these areas represent situations where the interaction of the benzene ring with the attached group modifies its chemistry in important ways. So this chapter also continues the general topic of molecules with multiple functional groups.

Outline of the Chapter

24-1. Benzylic Resonance Stabilization.

Carbons attached to benzene rings display enhanced reactivity.

24-2. Oxidation and Reduction of Benzene and Its Derivatives.

Including one especially useful oxidation of alkyl side chains.

24-3. The Naming and Preparation of Benzenols (Phenols).

24-4. The Reactivity of Benzenols.

24-5. The Oxidation of Benzenols: Cyclohexadiendiones (Quinones).

Aromatic alcohols: how the functional groups affect each other.

24-6. Arenediazonium Salts--Useful Synthetic Intermediates.

Using aromatic amines to synthesize substituted benzenes.

Keys to the Chapter

24-1. Benzylic Resonance Stabilization.

Chemical reactivity at a saturated carbon atom attached to a benzene ring is greatly enhanced over that of ordinary alkyl carbons due to resonance stabilization of both reaction transition states and intermediates. After reading this section once, go back and take a good look at the sets of resonance forms for the phenylmethyl (benzyl) radical, cation, and anion. Notice the four resonance forms for each one, leading to enhanced stability and ease of formation. Most often encountered is nucleophilic substitution on compounds containing potential leaving groups on the benzylic carbon. Both the carbocation intermediate for an S_N1 mechanism and the transition state for the S_N2 mechanism are stabilized, so both processes can occur. Just as you saw a long time ago with secondary haloalkanes (Section 7-3), and more recently with allyl systems (Sections 14-1 and 14-2), the choice of mechanism is determined by the specific conditions and reagents. Also, by analogy with allyl compounds, both free radical and anionic reactions occur at benzyl carbons as well. Notice, though, that the products of these reactions never involve attachment of groups to the benzene ring itself: double bond migrations which often occur with allyl systems do not occur with benzyls, because the aromaticity of the benzene ring would be lost (see Problem 2).

24-2. Oxidation and Reduction of Benzene and Its Derivatives.

Of the several reactions in this section, the one you are most likely to encounter is the oxidation of alkyl side chains on benzene rings with, typically, Mn^{VII} or Cr^{VI} reagents, forming benzenecarboxylic acids. Notice two features: first, all carbons but the benzylic carbon are chewed off by the reagent and disappear, and second, an o,p-directing alkyl group is converted into an m-directing -COOH group.

24-3, 24-4, and 24-5. Naming, Preparation, and Reactions of Benzenols.

Aromatic alcohols are sufficiently different in their behavior compared with ordinary alcohols that they merit special coverage of their properties. Most of the differences are due to the ability of the benzene ring to delocalize a lone pair of electrons from the benzenol (or "phenol") oxygen. The immediate result is that benzenols are more acidic and less basic than ordinary alcohols. One consequence is that the conjugate bases of benzenols, phenoxide ions, are much less basic than alkoxide ions, and can therefore be generated by reaction of benzenols with HO^-. Being less basic, phenoxide ions are much better leaving groups than hydroxide or alkoxide (see problem 18 for a practical consequence of this), but they are still good nucleophiles, especially useful in ether syntheses via S_N2 reaction.

The resonance between benzenol oxygen and the benzene ring also has consequences on benzene reactivity. The extra electron density in the ring makes it susceptible to electrophilic attack by even rather weak electrophiles: reactions with methanal and CO_2 in the presence of base are examples.

24-6. Arenediazonium Salts--Useful Synthetic Intermediates.

Like aromatic alcohols, aromatic amines are also special. In particular, resonance of the lone pair on nitrogen with the benzene ring makes aromatic amines much less basic than their alkyl relatives. Most of the reactions of aromatic amines are similar enough qualitatively to those af alkanamines, though, that there's really no need to rehash all that stuff. Instead, this section presents just one class of reactions of these compounds, chosen because of its special versatility in synthesis. Diazotization of a primary benzenamine produces an arenediazonium salt containing an $-N_2^+$ substituent on the benzene ring. The value of these salts lies in the ease of replacement of this group by any of the following (reagents are given in parentheses):

$-H(H_3PO_2)$	$-F(BF_4^-, \Delta)$	$-Cl, Br\ (CuX, \Delta)$
$-I\ (I^-, \Delta)$	$-OH\ (H_2O, \Delta)$	$-CN\ (CuCN, CN^-, \Delta)$

Arenediazonium salts are also electrophilic enough to react with benzenols or benzenamines to form so-called "azo dyes" via the diazo coupling process.

Solutions to Chapter 24 Problems

1. (a) 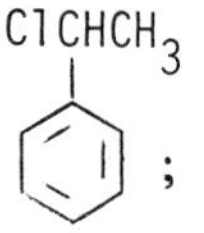

; (b) 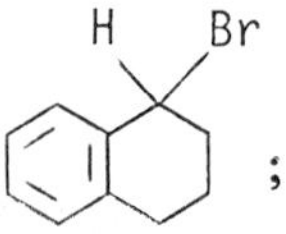

; (c) 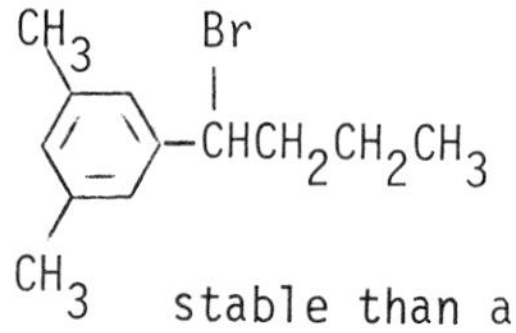

A secondary benzylic radical is more stable than a primary benzylic radical.

****

2. 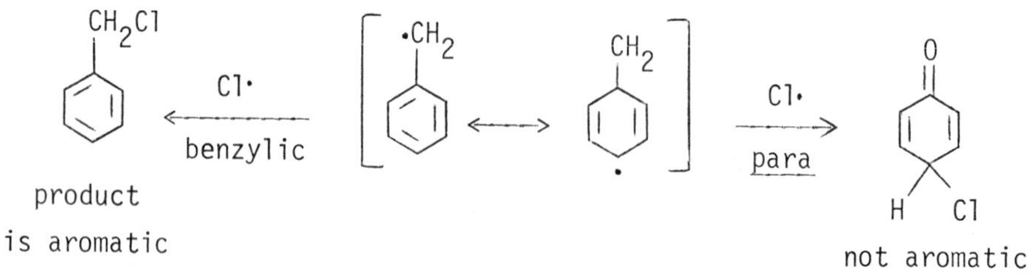

****

3. Yes to the first question: a benzylic carbon is oxidized. No to the second for two reasons. First, the amine is a reactive and oxidizable

functional group, and would have to be protected. Second, generation of a new stereocenter in exclusively the proper configuration would be difficult, although resolution of a racemic product mixture into its enantiomers would be straightforward.

****

4. (a) $BrCH_2CH_2CH_2$––CH_2OH (benzylic position is most reactive in a solvolyses via S_N1 mechanism); (b) 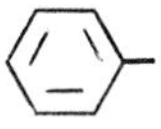–CH_2COOH;

(c) 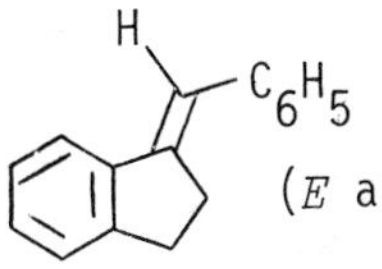

(*E* and *Z*), via 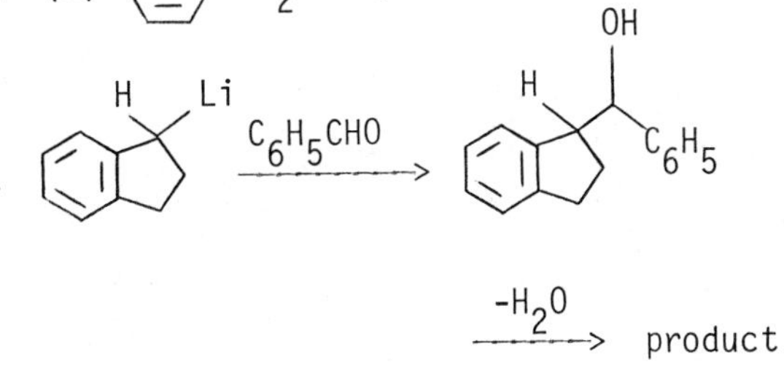

****

5. 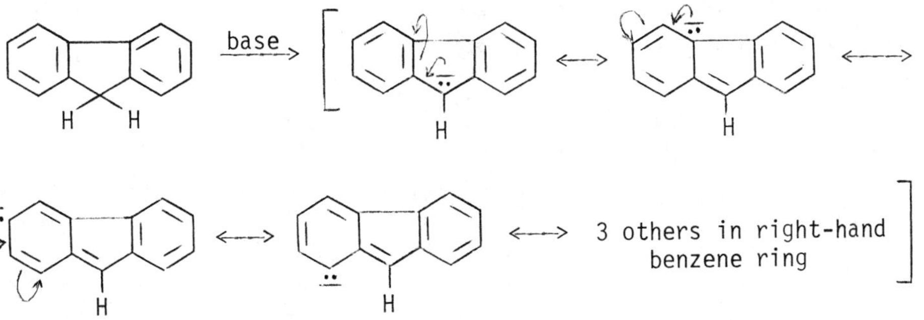

Seven resonance forms make this carbanion especially stable.

****

6. Recall (Section 14-2) that the amine in these reactions is a good solvating agent, especially good at activating alkyllithium reagents as bases by complexing to lithium.

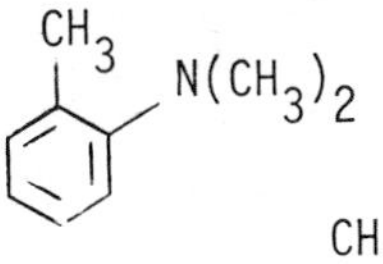

contains its own, internal amine, and therefore an external one doesn't need to be added:

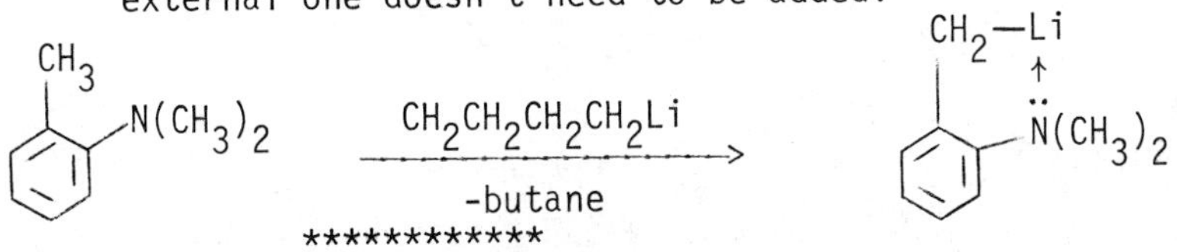

****

7. (a) Ortho:

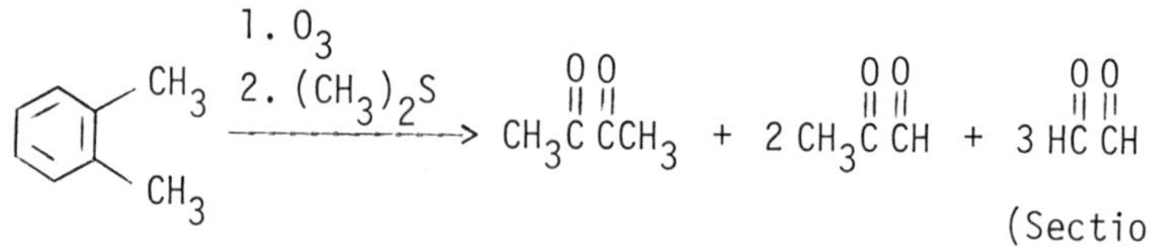

$$\xrightarrow[\text{2. }(CH_3)_2S]{\text{1. }O_3} \quad CH_3\overset{O}{\overset{||}{C}}\overset{O}{\overset{||}{C}}CH_3 \;+\; 2\;CH_3\overset{O}{\overset{||}{C}}\overset{O}{\overset{||}{C}}H \;+\; 3\;H\overset{O}{\overset{||}{C}}\overset{O}{\overset{||}{C}}H$$

(Section 24-2)

Meta:

$$\xrightarrow[\text{2. }(CH_3)_2S]{\text{1. }O_3} \quad 4\;CH_3\overset{O}{\overset{||}{C}}\overset{O}{\overset{||}{C}}H \;+\; 2\;H\overset{O}{\overset{||}{C}}\overset{O}{\overset{||}{C}}H$$

Para:

$$\xrightarrow[\text{2. }(CH_3)_2S]{\text{1. }O_3} \quad 4\;CH_3\overset{O}{\overset{||}{C}}\overset{O}{\overset{||}{C}}H \;+\; 2\;H\overset{O}{\overset{||}{C}}\overset{O}{\overset{||}{C}}H$$

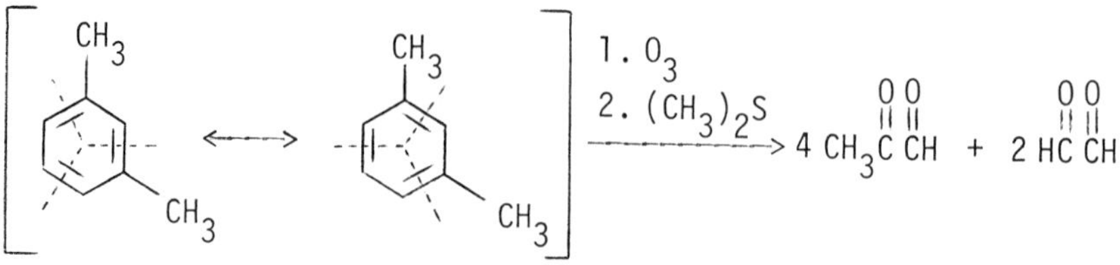

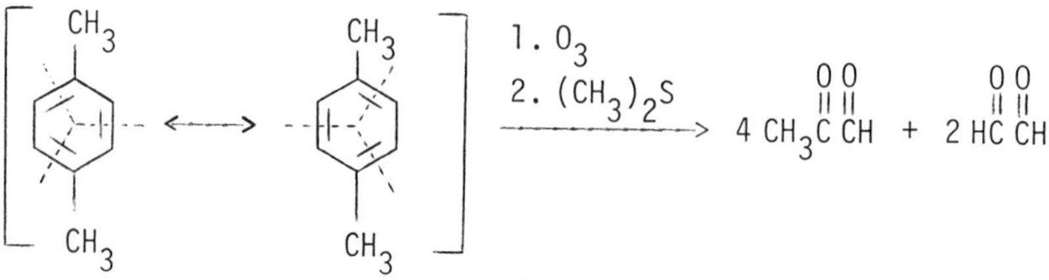

No. The *meta* and *para* isomers give the same result, a 2:1 mixture of 2-oxopropanal and ethanedial.

(b) The compound is a <u>hydrocarbon</u>, and the two products are formed in <u>equimolar</u> quantities. Work backwards: how can these two be put together?

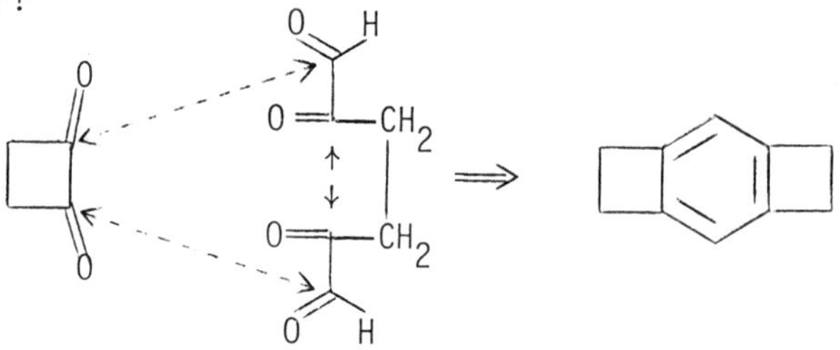

is the most straightforward answer

****

8. Birch reduction: refer to example involving in Section 24-2.

****

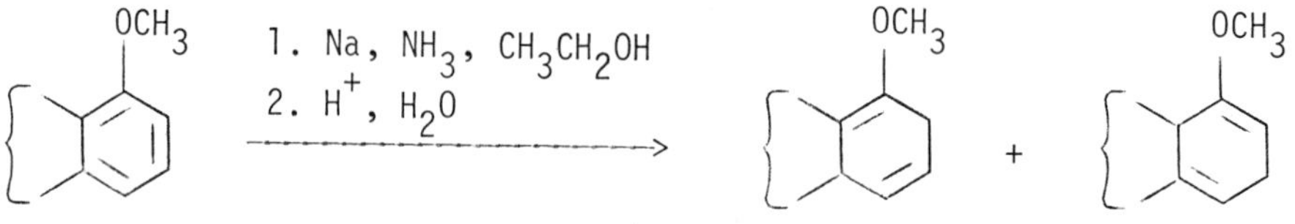

9. (a) On solution, perhaps a bit roundabout: 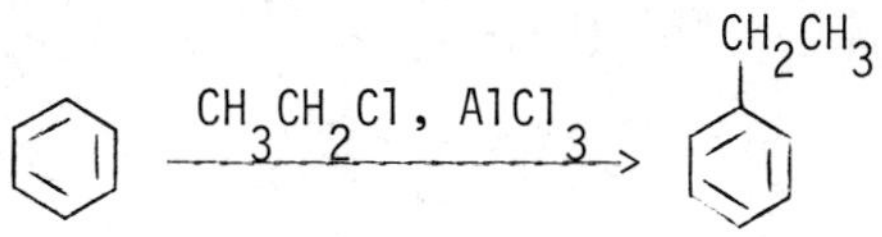

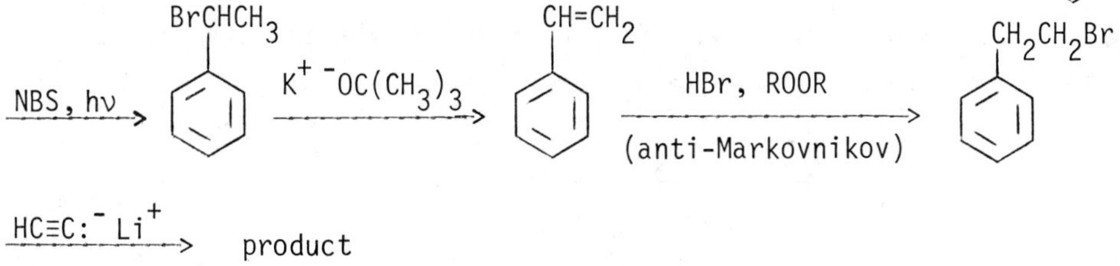

(b) 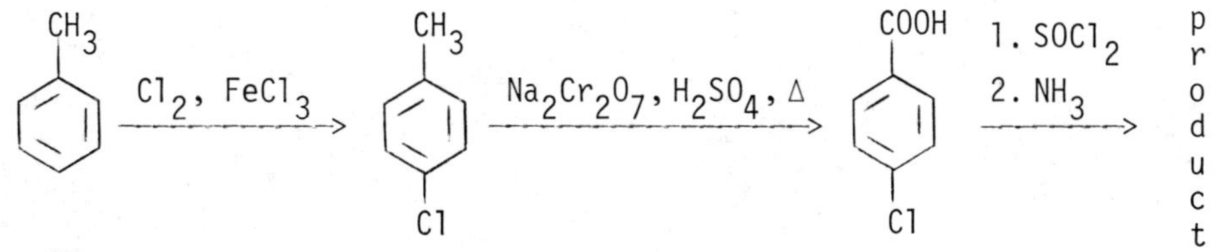

(c) 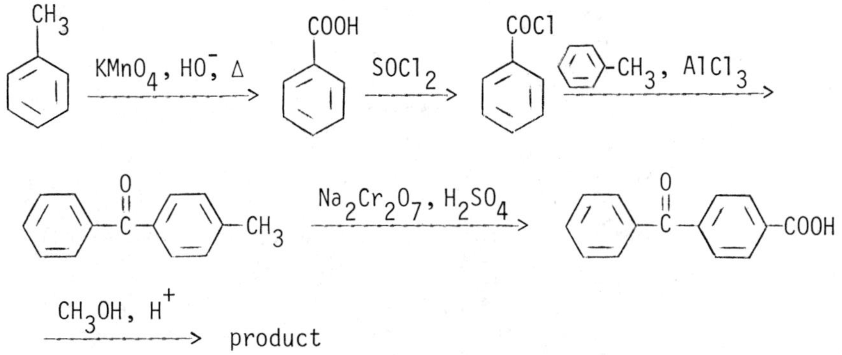

(d) 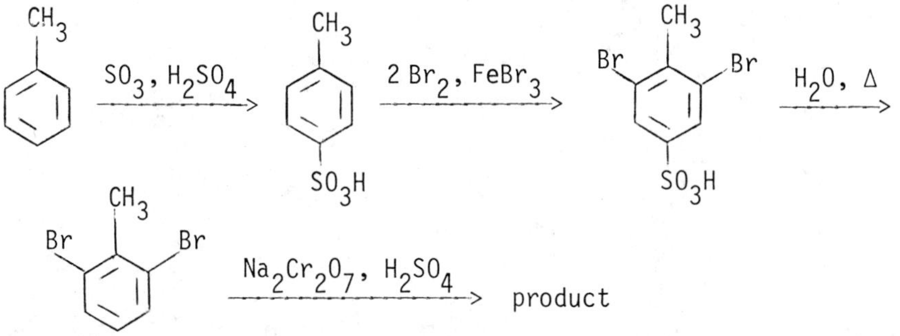

****

10. (a) 1. 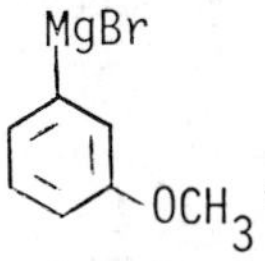, 2. H^+, H_2O; (b) H_2, Pd/C (cleaves all <u>benzylic</u> C-O bonds); (c) 1. CrO_3, pyridine (makes ketone), 2. H_3PO_4, Δ (Friedel-Crafts: Problem 16 of Chapter 19); (d) 1. H_2, PtO_2 (hydrogenates alkene), 2. Na, NH_3, CH_3CH_2OH, 3. H^+, H_2O (Birch reduction sequence - see Exercise 24-8);

(e) $(CH_3)_2CuLi$.

****

11. The two alkyl groups on C-6 make aromatization impossible. At least one hydrogen there is necessary to permit enolization.

****

12. (a) 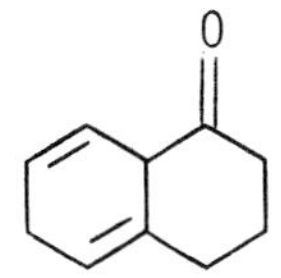 ; (b) 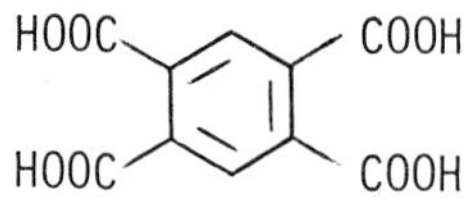

; (c) 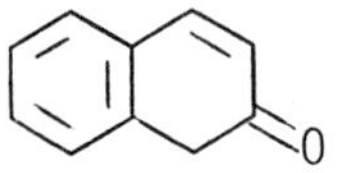 (via aldol condensation of 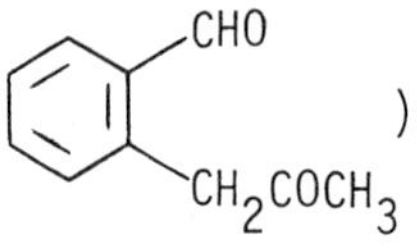

); (d) 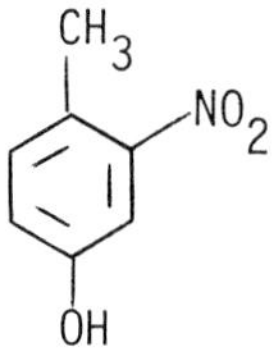

****

13. (c) (The $-SO_3H$ group is a very strong acid) > (b) > (e) > (f) > (d) > (a). Carboxylic acids are more acidic than most benzenols, and electron withdrawing groups increase the acidity of benzenols.

****

14. (a) 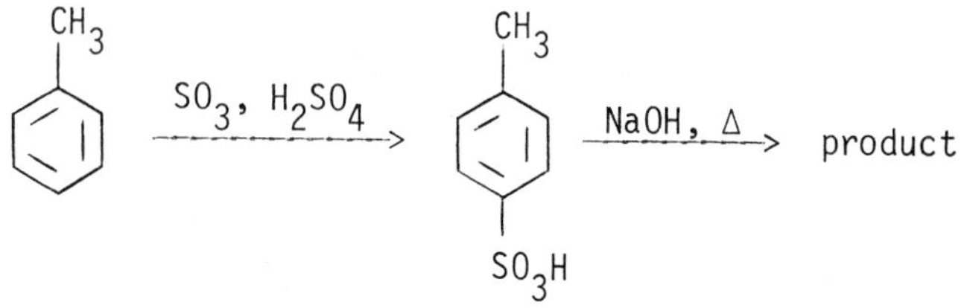

(b) 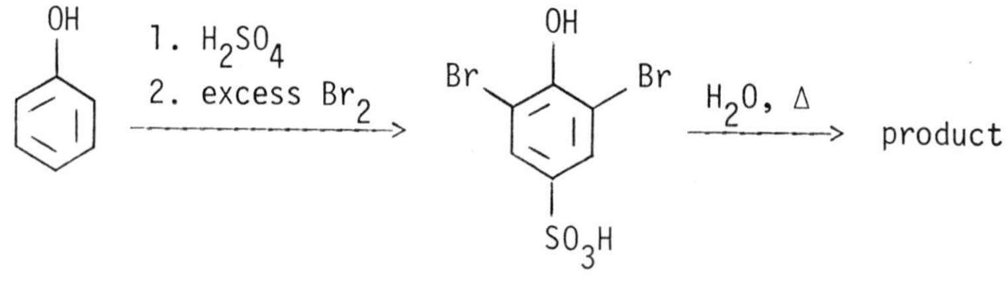

(c) 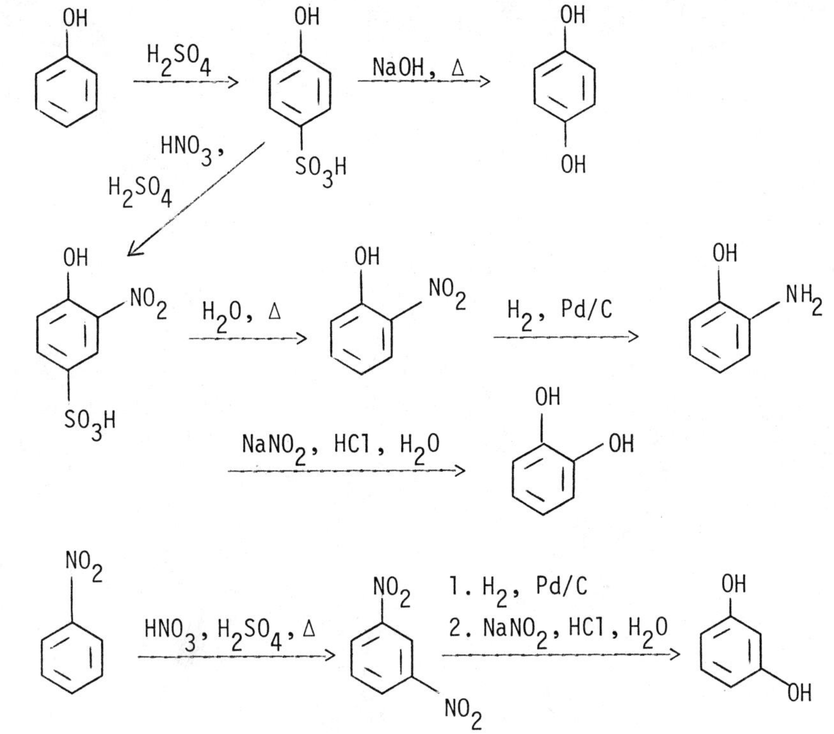
OH
H_2SO_4
OH
NaOH, Δ
OH
OH
SO_3H
HNO_3,
H_2SO_4
OH
NO_2
SO_3H
H_2O, Δ
OH
NO_2
H_2, Pd/C
OH
NH_2
$NaNO_2$, HCl, H_2O
OH
OH
NO_2
HNO_3, H_2SO_4, Δ
NO_2
NO_2
1. H_2, Pd/C
2. $NaNO_2$, HCl, H_2O
OH
OH

(d) 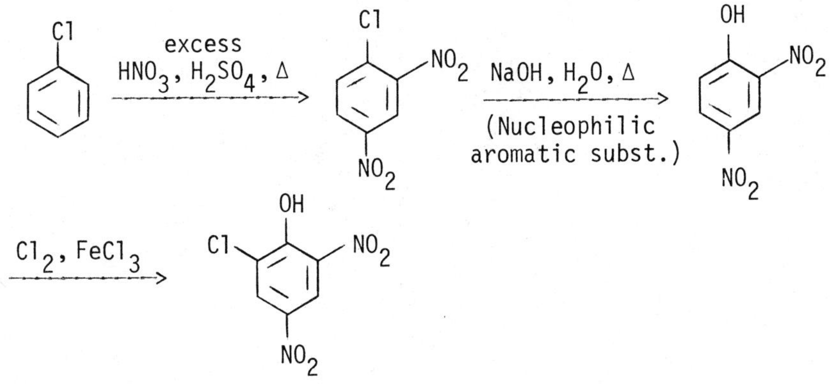
Cl
excess
HNO_3, H_2SO_4, Δ
Cl
NO_2
NO_2
NaOH, H_2O, Δ
(Nucleophilic
aromatic subst.)
OH
NO_2
NO_2
Cl_2, $FeCl_3$
OH
Cl
NO_2
NO_2

****

15. (a) 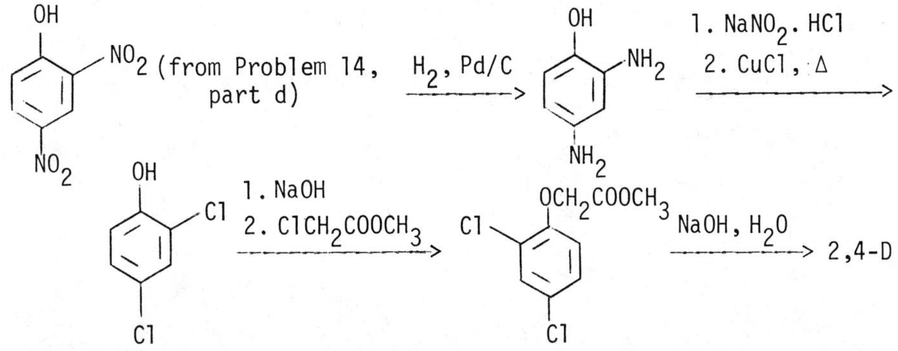
OH
NO_2
(from Problem 14,
part d)
NO_2
H_2, Pd/C
OH
NH_2
NH_2
1. $NaNO_2$. HCl
2. CuCl, Δ
OH
Cl
Cl
1. NaOH
2. $ClCH_2COOCH_3$
OCH_2COOCH_3
Cl
Cl
NaOH, H_2O
2,4-D

(b)

$$\text{benzene} \xrightarrow[\text{2. NaOH, } \Delta]{\text{1. SO}_3, \text{H}_2\text{SO}_4} \text{(phenol, OH)} \xrightarrow[\text{2. CH}_3\text{CH}_2\text{Br}]{\text{1. NaOH}} \text{(OCH}_2\text{CH}_3) \xrightarrow[\text{2. H}_2, \text{Pd/C}]{\text{1. HNO}_3, \text{H}_2\text{SO}_4}$$

4-ethoxyaniline (OCH$_2$CH$_3$ / NH$_2$)

$$\xrightarrow[\Delta]{\overset{\text{O O}}{\underset{}{\text{CH}_3\text{C}\text{O}\text{C}\text{CH}_3}}} \text{product}$$

(c)

$$\text{benzene} \xrightarrow[\text{2. Br}_2, \text{FeBr}_3]{\text{1. SO}_3, \text{H}_2\text{SO}_4} \text{(SO}_3\text{H / Br)} \xrightarrow[\text{2. Br}_2, \text{CCl}_4]{\text{1. NaOH, } \Delta} \text{(OH / Br / Br)} \xrightarrow[\text{KHCO}_3, \text{H}_2\text{O}]{\text{CO}_2, \text{pressure,}}$$

(OH, OH / Br / Br)

$$\xrightarrow[\text{H}^+, \Delta]{\overset{\text{O O}}{\underset{}{\text{CH}_3\text{C}\text{O}\text{C}\text{CH}_3}}} \text{product}$$

****

16. (a)

$$\text{CH}_3\text{O:} \text{(benzene)} \xrightarrow{\text{AlCl}_3} \text{CH}_3\overset{+}{-}\text{O}-\text{AlCl}_2^- \rightleftharpoons \ddot{\text{Cl}}^- + \text{CH}_3\overset{+}{-}\text{O}-\text{AlCl}_2 \longrightarrow \text{CH}_3\text{Cl} +$$

(OAlCl$_2$) $\xrightarrow{\text{H}^+, \text{H}_2\text{O}}$ (OH)

(b)

$$\text{CH}_3\overset{\text{O}}{\text{C}}\text{O:} \text{(benzene)} \xrightarrow[-\text{Cl}^-]{\text{AlCl}_3} \text{CH}_3\overset{\text{O}}{\text{C}}\overset{+}{-}\text{O}-\text{AlCl}_2 \rightleftharpoons \text{CH}_3\overset{+}{\text{C}}=\text{O} + \text{(OAlCl}_2) \xrightarrow[\text{Friedel-Crafts}]{\text{normal}}$$

<u>o</u> and <u>p</u> products

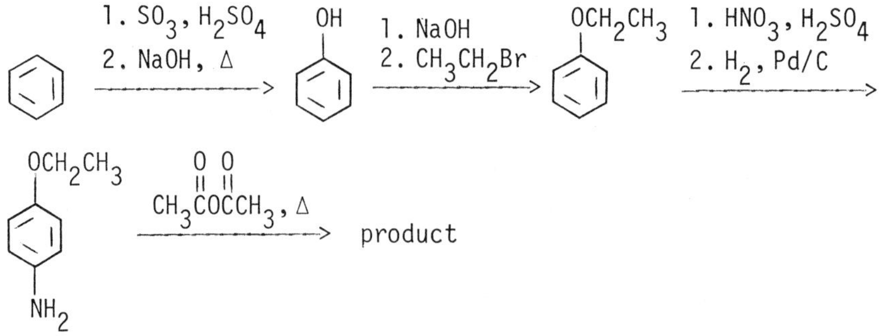

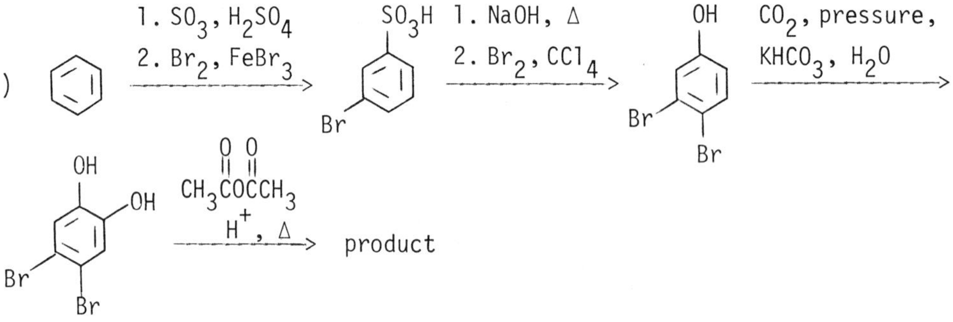

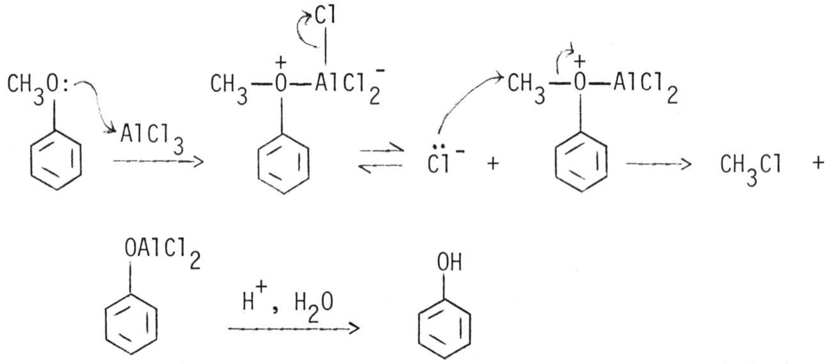

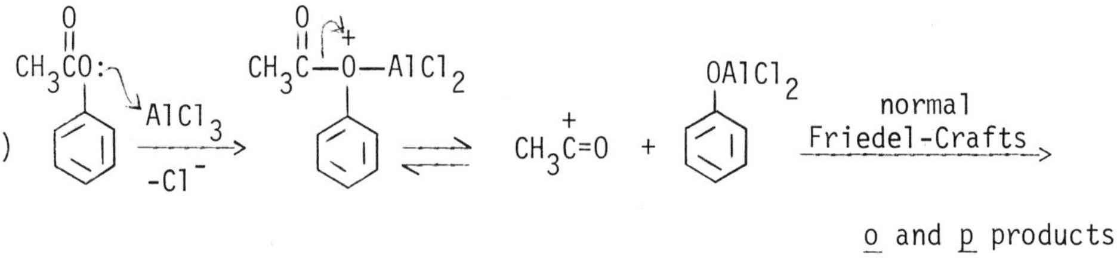

(c) 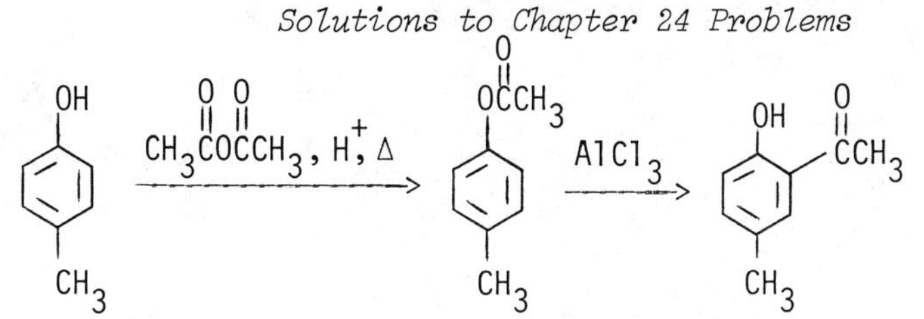 $\underline{o}$ product is only one possible since $\underline{p}$ position is blocked

****

17. (a) 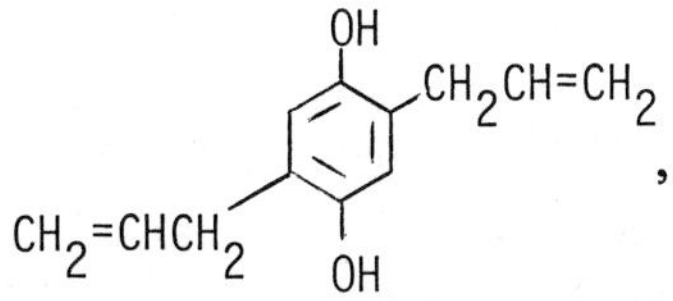, via double Claisen rearrangement of 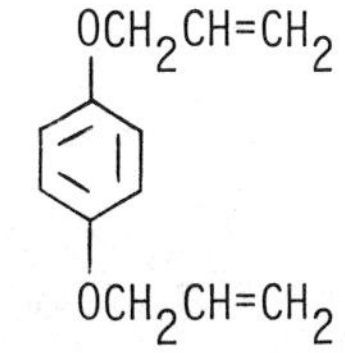;

(b) Step-by-step, 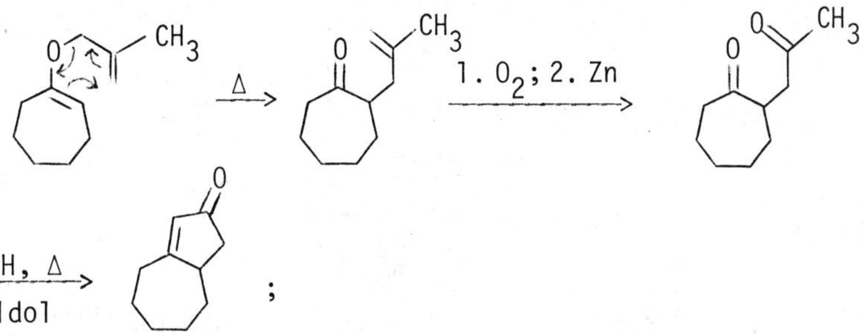;

(c) Cope rearrangement:  (the need for "heat" is exaggerated here; this rearrangement occurs well below room temperature)

(d) 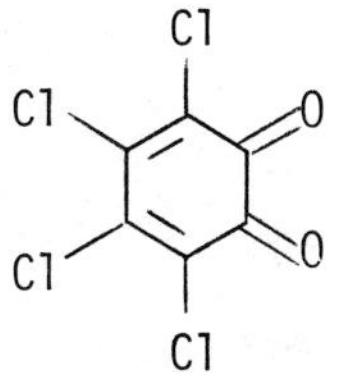; (e) 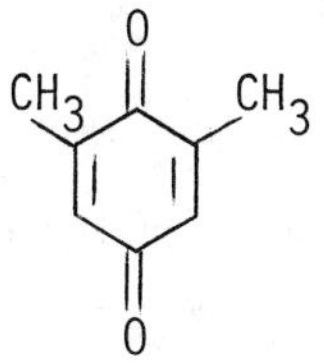; (f) The thiol is readily oxidized, so one likely reaction is redox ⟶  + $CH_3CH_2SSCH_2CH_3$;

conjugate addition is another possibility ⟶ 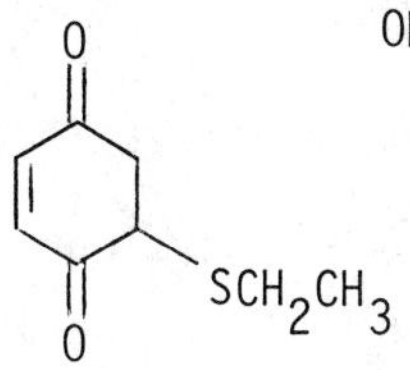:

(g) 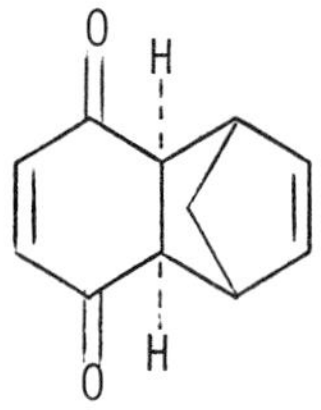 ; (h) 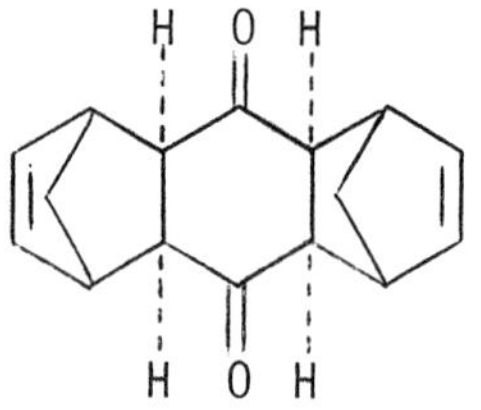 (one and two Diels-Alder cyclizations, respectively).

****

18. Aspirin is a phenyl ester, and the equilibrium benzenol + carboxylic acid $\rightleftharpoons$ phenyl ester is <u>endothermic</u> as written. So, aqueous solutions of aspirin are thermodynamically unstable, and hydrolyze rather readily to give salicylic acid and ethanoic acid:

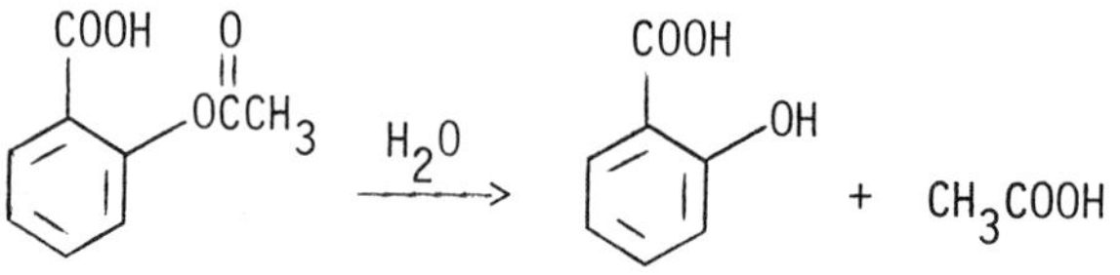

****

19. (a) CH_3CH_2Cl, $AlCl_3$; (b) 1. $CH_3CH_2CH_2CH_2Li$, TMEDA, 2. $HC(=O)C(=O)OCH_2CH_3$ (makes 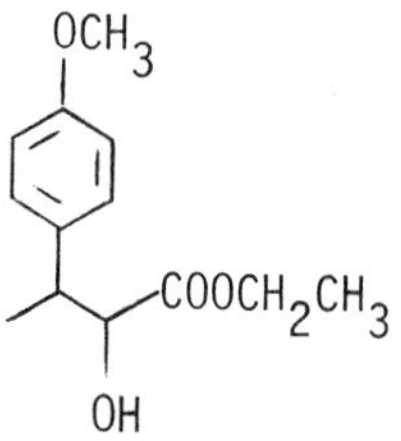), 3. H^+, H_2O, Δ, 4. H_2, Pd/C;

(c) 1. $HAl[CH_2CH(CH_3)_2]_2$, 2. $(CH_3)_2CHCH_2MgCl$, 3. H^+, H_2O; (d) 1. Na, NH_3, CH_3CH_2OH, 2. H^+, H_2O, 3. H_2, Pd/C; (e) See problem 25 of Chapter 18, then the last step is CrO_3, pyridine.

****

20. (a) (1) Electrophilic attack is the only reasonable choice.

(b) Formation of the oxacyclopropane probably involves electrophilic attack of a reagent like H_2O_2 (derived from O_2) on the benzene ring, catalyzed by acid:

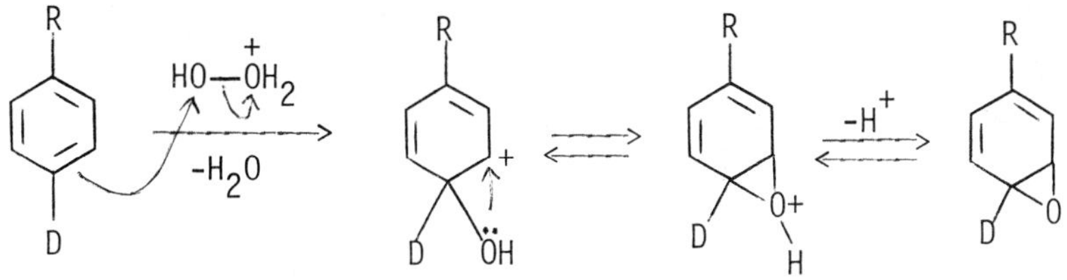

The final phenol probably arises from reversal of the last two steps. The oxacyclopropane ring can always close again, but eventually the carbocation reacts via an alternative pathway, involving D migration to give the rearranged aromatic product:

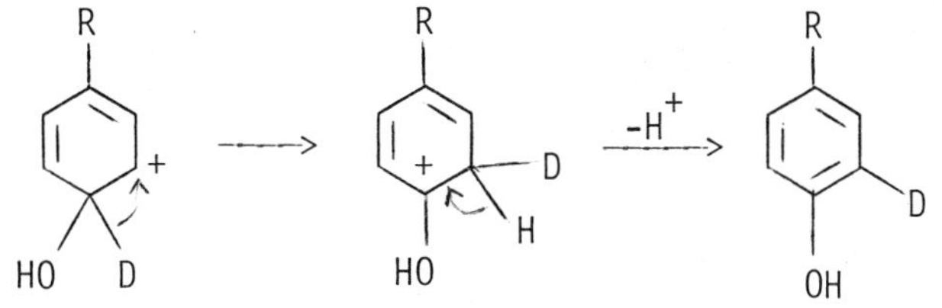

Obviously, D^+ can also be lost in the final step, giving the phenol lacking deuterium.

****

21. 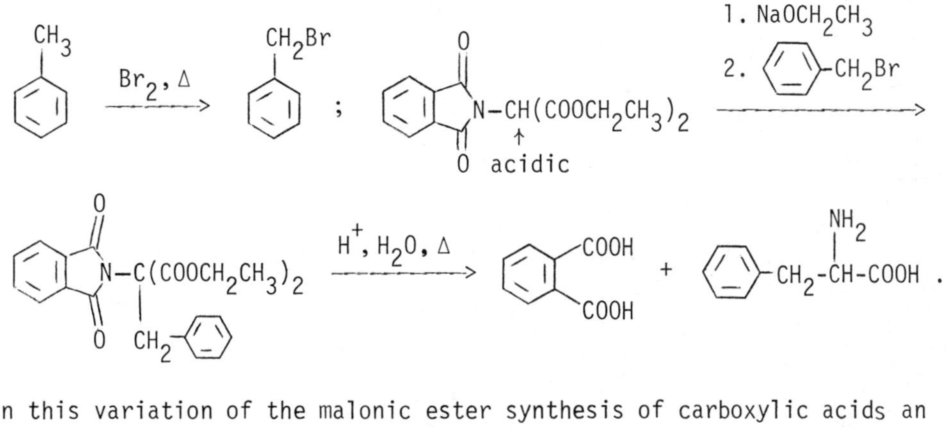

In this variation of the malonic ester synthesis of carboxylic acids an amino group is also introduced at the α-carbon using a version of the Gabriel synthesis (Section 21-4).

****

22. (a) Prepare 1,3-diketones using mixed ketone-ester Claisen condensation (Section 22-3): 1. *trans*-$CH_3CH{=}CHCOOCH_2CH_3$, $NaOCH_2CH_3$, CH_3CH_2OH, 2. H^+, H_2O.

(b) There actually are two: 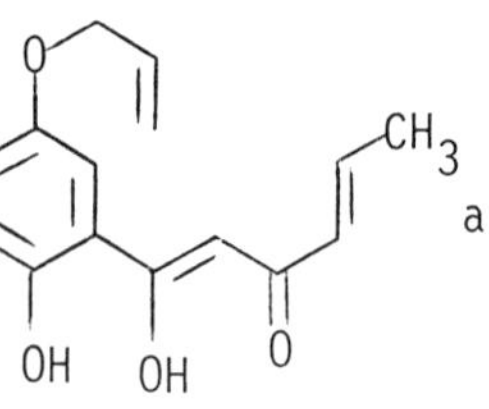 and 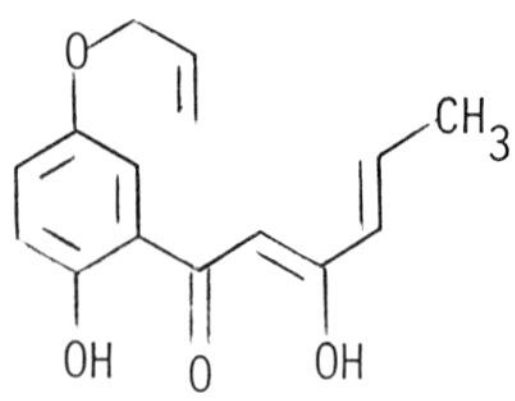

(c) 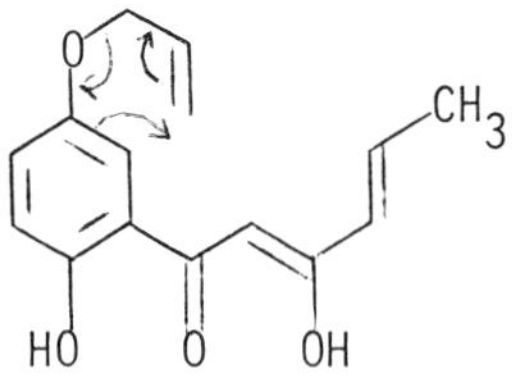 Claisen rearrangement → 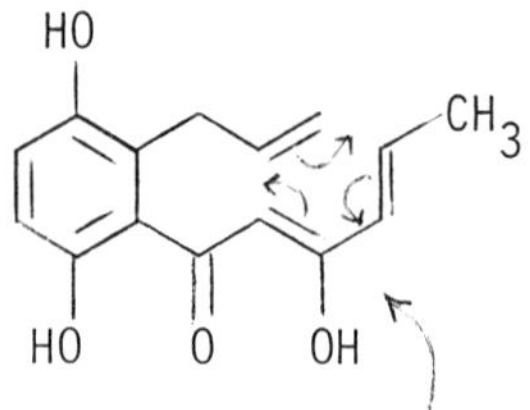

Note diene tautomer

intramolecular Diels-Alder → 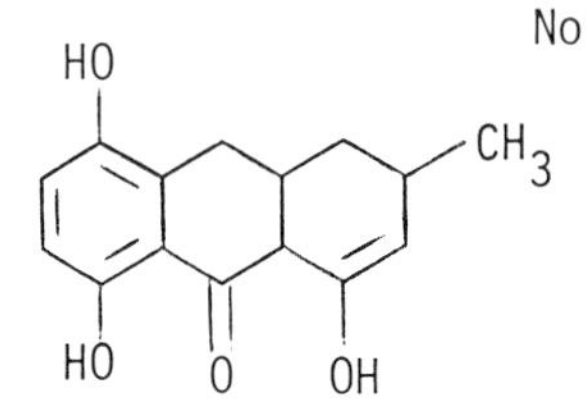

(d) How: enol-keto tautomerism. Why: product is a more stable enol (with double bond and ketone carbonyl conjugated).

****

23. (a) 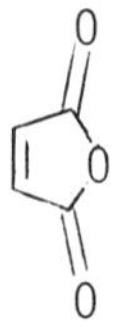, Δ (Diels-Alder); (b) H_2, Pd/C; (c) 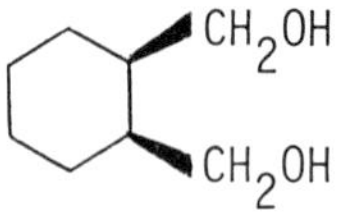 ;

(d) 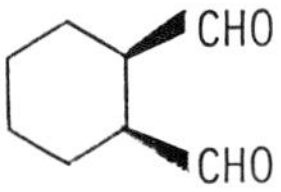 . Now what? Work <u>backwards</u> from the product:

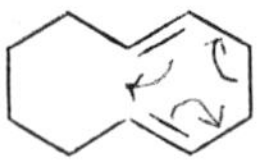 ← Δ, Cope rearrangement — 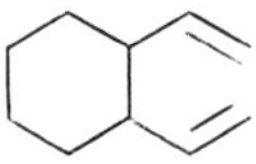 ← $2\ CH_2{=}P(C_6H_5)_3$, Wittig twice — 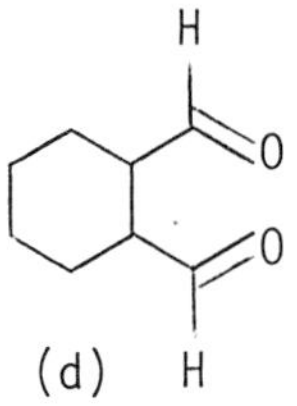 .

(f) (e) (d)

****

24. In (ii) the $-OCH_3$ group preferentially stabilizes the dione (quinone):

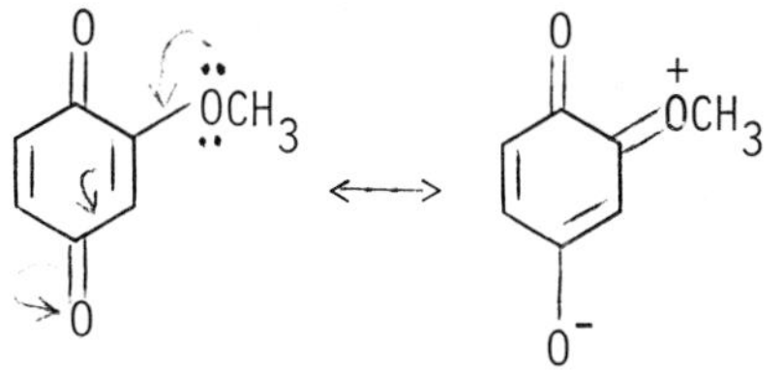

In (iii) the -CN group preferentially stabilizes the diol:

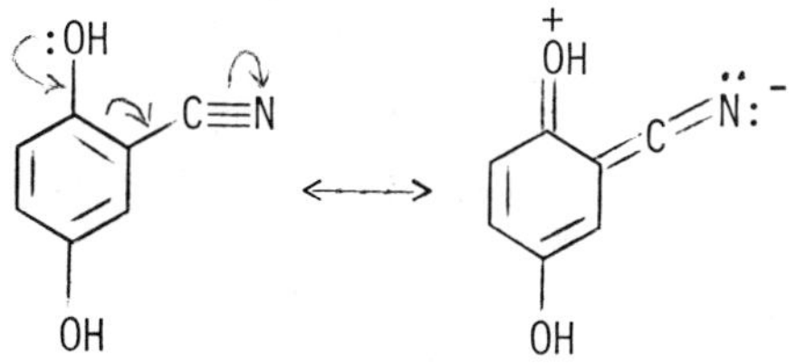

So, relative to (i), equilibrium (ii) lies further to the right and equilibrium (iii) lies further to the left.

****

25. 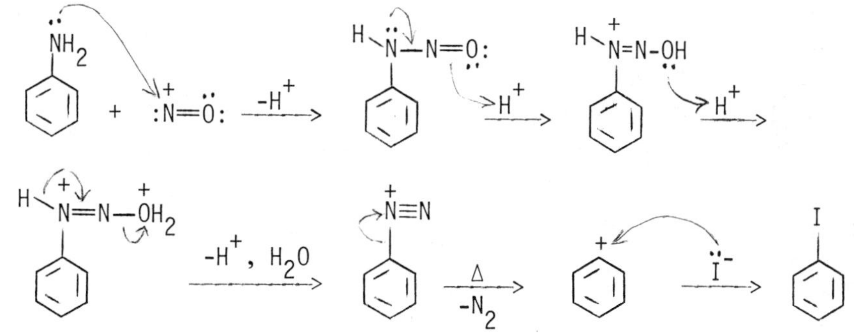

(one possibility)

There is some question whether a phenyl cation is actually involved in reactions such as this.

****

26. Think about benzenediazonium salts as intermediates likely to be useful in these.

(a) 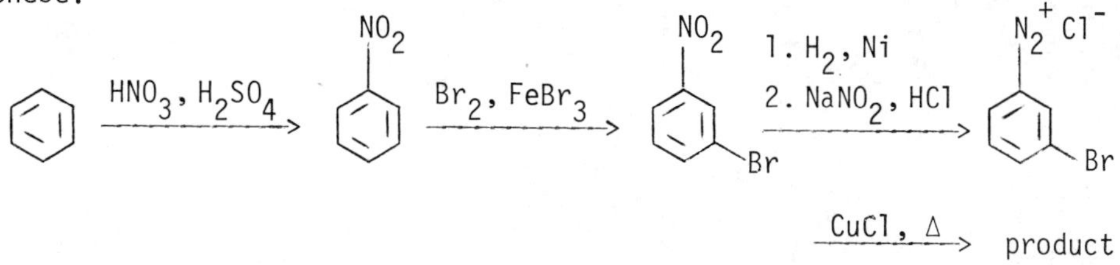

(b) 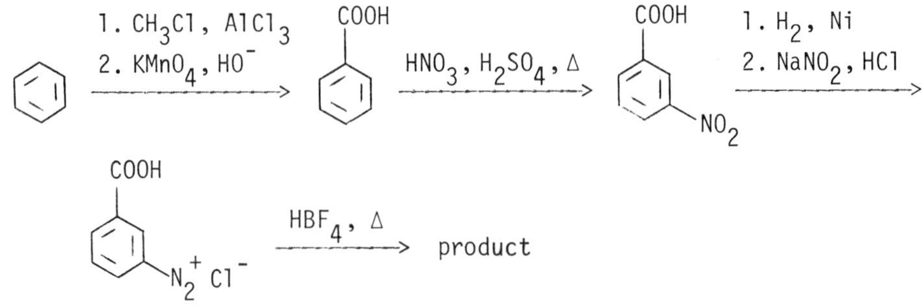
1. CH3Cl, AlCl3
2. KMnO4, HO-
COOH
HNO3, H2SO4, Δ
COOH
NO2
1. H2, Ni
2. NaNO2, HCl
COOH
N2+ Cl-
HBF4, Δ
product

(c) 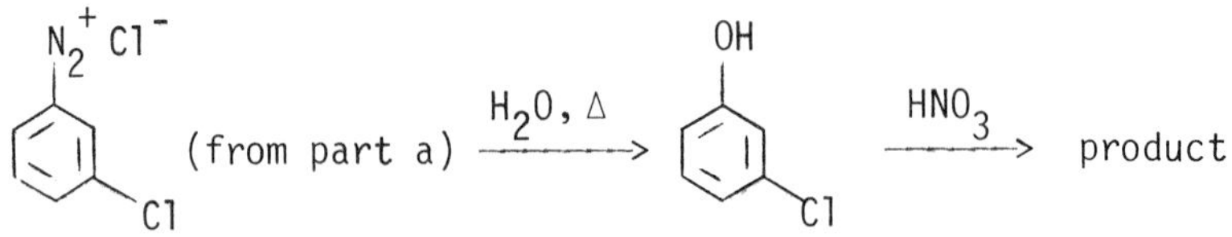
N2+ Cl-
Cl
(from part a)
H2O, Δ
OH
Cl
HNO3
product

(d) 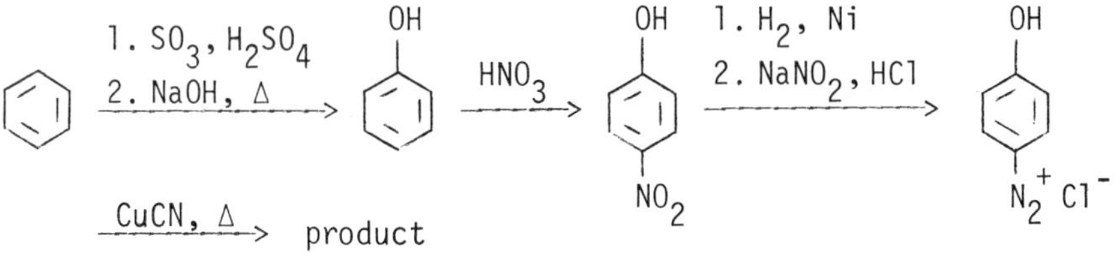
1. SO3, H2SO4
2. NaOH, Δ
OH
HNO3
OH
NO2
1. H2, Ni
2. NaNO2, HCl
OH
N2+ Cl-
CuCN, Δ
product

(e) 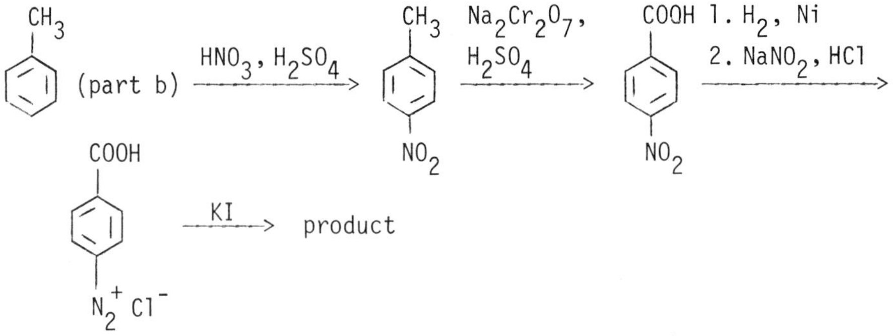
CH3
(part b)
HNO3, H2SO4
CH3
NO2
Na2Cr2O7, H2SO4
COOH
NO2
1. H2, Ni
2. NaNO2, HCl
COOH
N2+ Cl-
KI
product

(f) 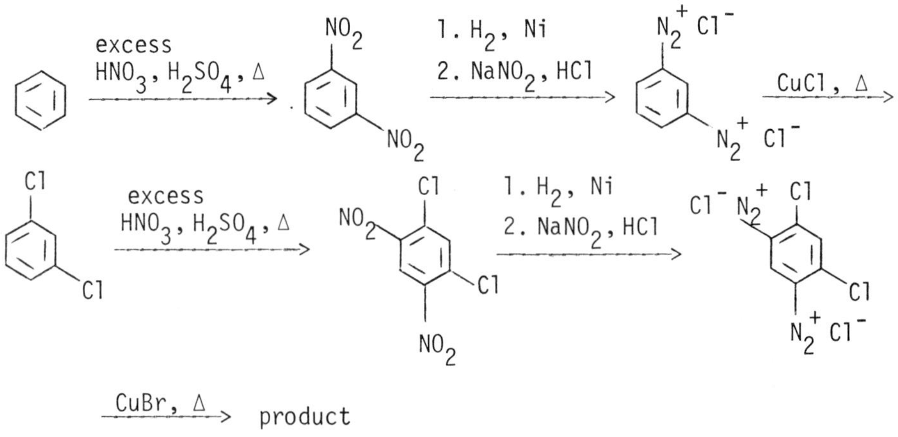
excess HNO3, H2SO4, Δ
NO2
NO2
1. H2, Ni
2. NaNO2, HCl
N2+ Cl-
N2+ Cl-
CuCl, Δ
Cl
Cl
excess HNO3, H2SO4, Δ
NO2
Cl
Cl
NO2
1. H2, Ni
2. NaNO2, HCl
Cl- N2+
Cl
Cl
N2+ Cl-
CuBr, Δ
product

(g) (part a) $\xrightarrow{Br_2, H_2O}$ $\xrightarrow{NaNO_2, HCl}$

1. CuCN, Δ
2. H^+, H_2O, Δ
$\longrightarrow$ product

(h) (part d) $\xrightarrow{CH_3COCCH_3}$ $\xrightarrow{\text{excess } HNO_3}$ $\xrightarrow{KOH, H_2O, \Delta}$

1. $NaNO_2$, HCl
2. H_3PO_2
$\longrightarrow$ product

****

27. (a) HO—⟨⟩—N≡N—⟨⟩—SO_3H ; (b) ⟨⟩—N≡N—⟨⟩—NH—⟨⟩
    OH SO_3H

(c) HO—⟨naphthyl⟩—N≡N—⟨⟩—SO_3H Diazo coupling is generally <u>para</u> to the
                                     activating group, if possible.

****

28. (a) $(CH_3)_2N$—⟨⟩ + $^+N_2$—⟨⟩—SO_3^- ;   Note how the benzene ring
                                                     in the coupling reaction
    SO_3^- Na^+ is always strongly activated
(b) 2 ⟨naphthyl⟩ + $^+N_2$—⟨⟩—⟨⟩—N_2^+ ;   by -OH, -NH_2, or related
    NH_2 groups.

(c) H_2N—⟨⟩ + $^+N_2$—⟨⟩—SO_2NH_2
         NH_2

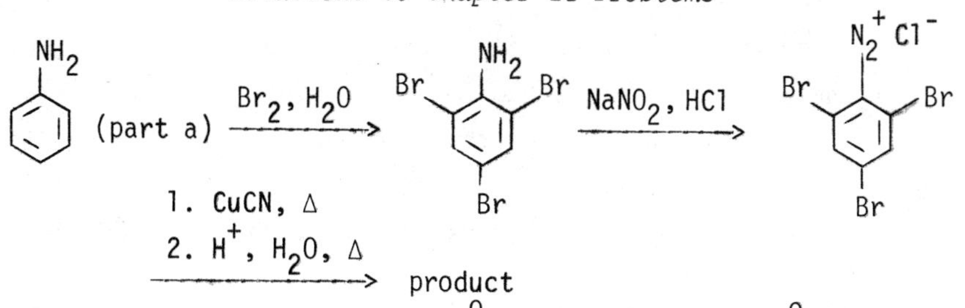

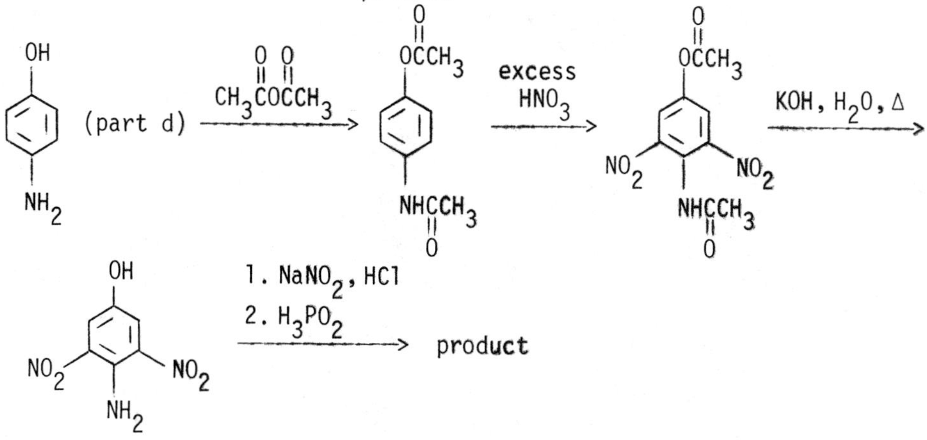

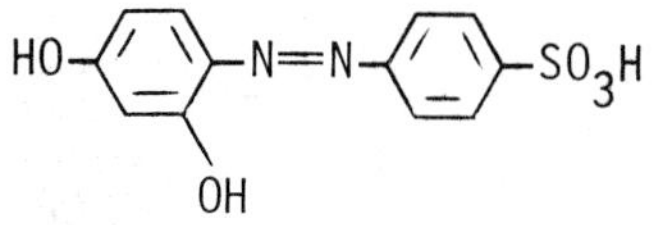

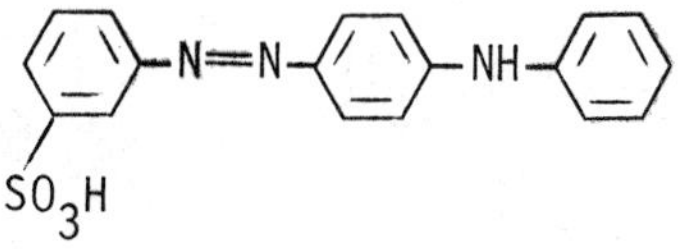

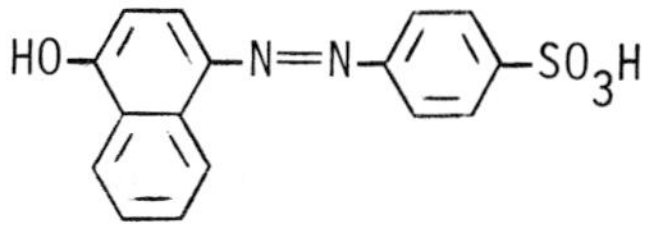

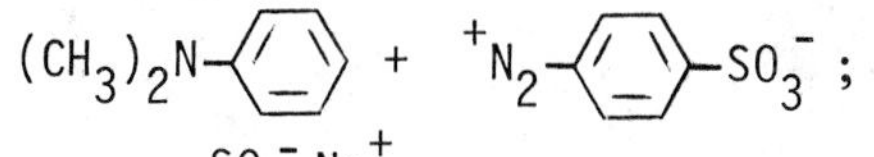

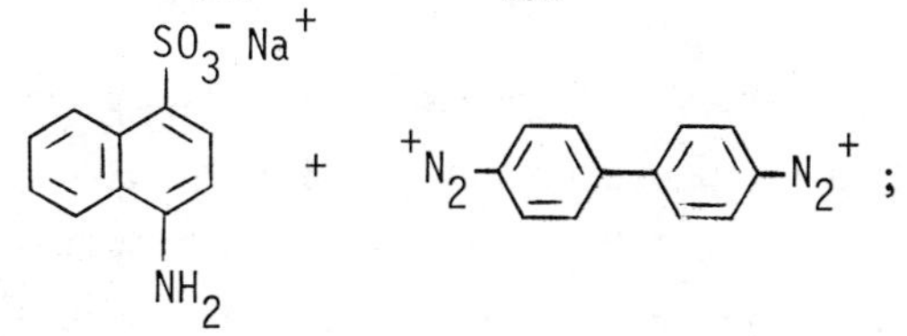

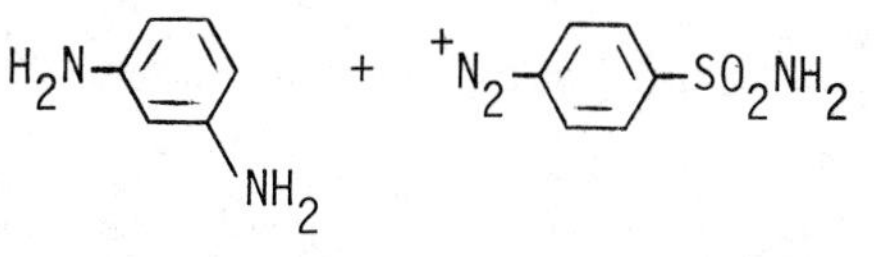

29. (a) You can begin either with the spectra or the reaction scheme. Starting with the reaction scheme is probably easier, but let's do it the hard way here and see what we come up with. Formula of B (degrees of unsaturation, Study Guide Chapter 11): $H_{sat'd} = 16 + 2 = 18$; deg. unsat'n. $= \frac{18-8}{2} = 5$ π bonds and/or rings. ^1H NMR indicates the presence of CH_3O- (δ 3.9), $-\overset{O}{\overset{\|}{C}}H$ (δ 9.8), and four other hydrogens. One of the latter has a very broad signal (δ 6.7), a possible -OH. The other three are probably attached to a benzene ring. IR and ^{13}C NMR confirm the aldehyde, six benzene carbons (three attached to H), and the methyl, giving these pieces:

CH_3O- , $H\overset{O}{\overset{\|}{C}}-$, HO- , and  with 3H's on it = $C_8H_8O_3$.

What we don't know is the *arrangement* of these groups around the ring in unknown B.

So, on to the reaction scheme. Here are the answers:

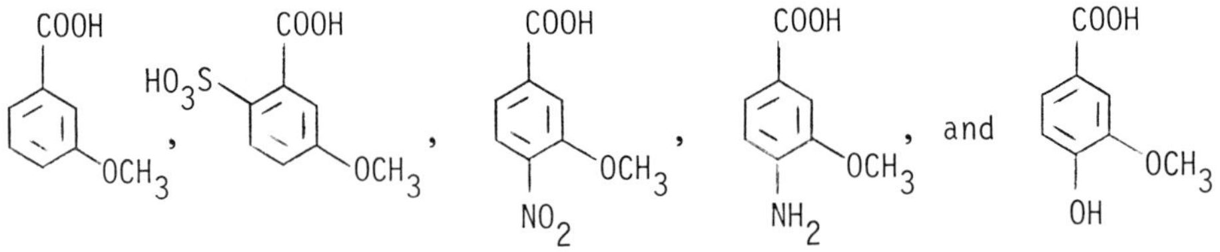

D E F G C

Since treatment of B with Ag_2O (an oxidizing agent) gives C (and we know that B is an aldehyde), B must have the same arrangement of groups as C, except with -CHO instead of -COOH:

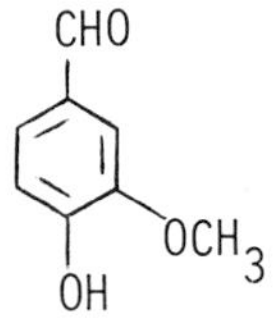

(b) Last part: What is A? Methylation before hydrolysis attaches methyl groups to all oxygens of the glucose except for those at C-5 (part of pyranose ring) and at C-1. So the O at C-1 of glucose must link it to compound B. Where is the attachment point on B? The logical place is the benzenol oxygen, and this is consistent with this oxygen not being methylated by this process, too. So, A is either the α or β anomer of this structure:

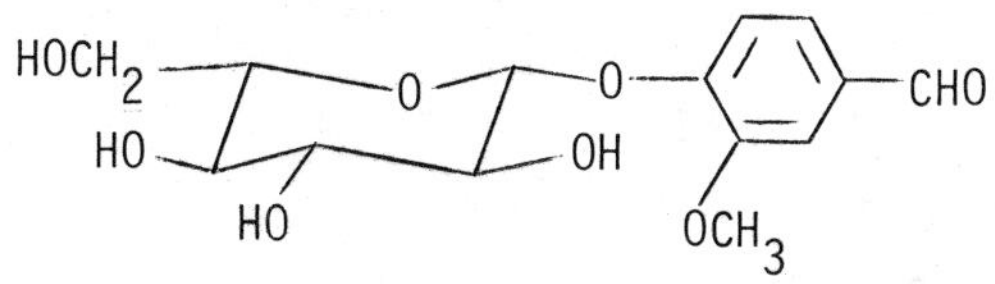

This is the naturally-occurring form of vanillin, the flavor of vanilla.

****

30. Again, several places to start; let's go step-by-step.

(i) Degrees of unsaturation (Study Guide Chapter 11):
Urushiol I, $H_{sat'd} = 42 + 2 = 44$; deg. unsat'n. - $\frac{44-36}{2} = 4$ π bonds and/or rings.
Urushiol II, deg unsat'n. $= \frac{44-34}{2} = 5$ π bonds and/or rings.

(ii) Urushiol II contains only one double bond that is easily hydrogenated. The 4 degrees of unsaturation in urushiol I must either be rings, or hard-to-hydrogenate π bonds (like in a benzene ring).

(iii) Urushiol II contains the piece $CH_3CH_2CH_2CH_2CH_2CH_2CH{=}CHR$ (the CH=CHR portion: part of aldehyde 'H')

(iv) Synthesis of aldehyde 'H' is presented. Here are the structures of the intermediates:

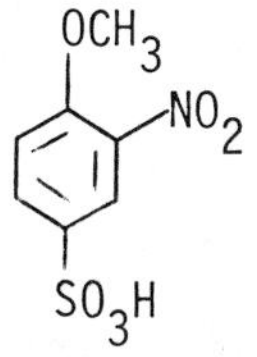

I

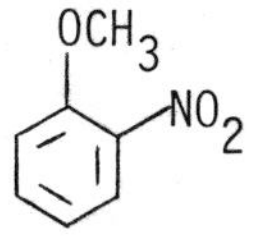

J

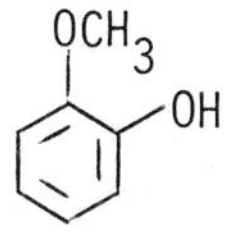

K

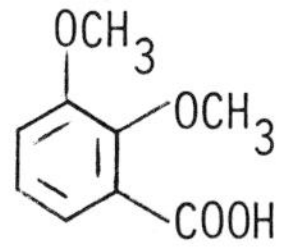

L

(-COOH attached via Kolbe reaction)

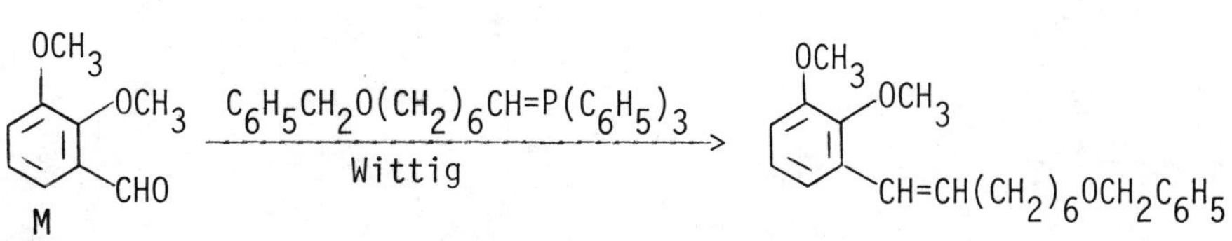

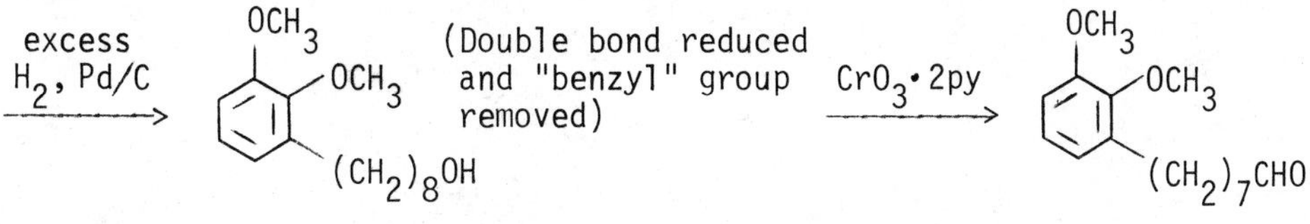

aldehyde H

Going back to part (iii), we can now work backwards to the structure of urushiol II:

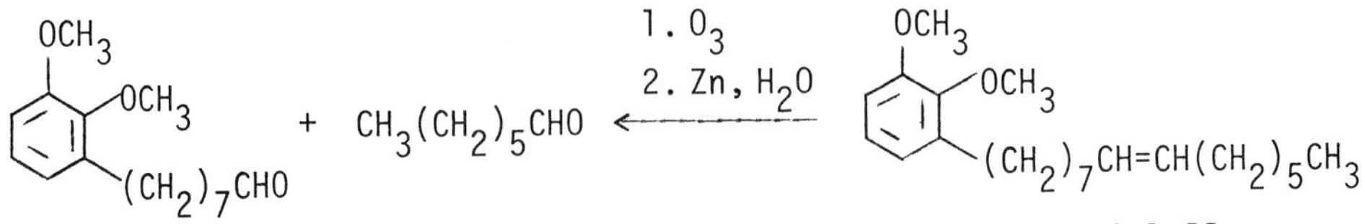

dimethylurushiol II

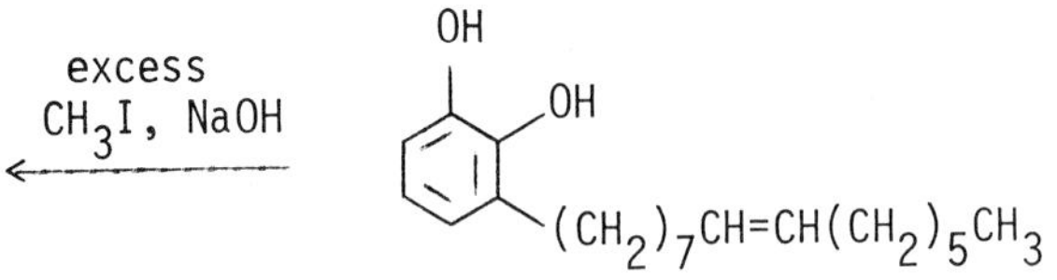

is urushiol II.

Returning to part (ii), urushiol I must be 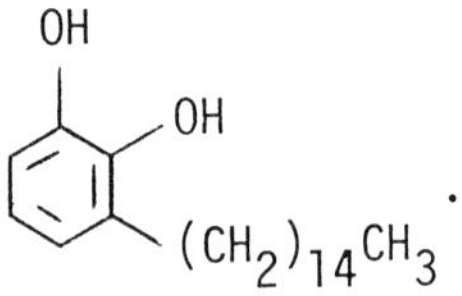 .

****

CHAPTER 25

Polycyclic Benzenoid Hydrocarbons and Other Cyclic Polyenes

General Introduction

Other kinds of aromatic compounds exist besides simple benzene derivatives. Two common types will be covered in this chapter: polycyclic fused benzenoid hydrocarbons, and other cyclic polyenes with either more or less than six carbons in the ring. In Chapter 26 a third common class, heterocyclic aromatic compounds, will be presented. You will see that many of these compounds resemble benzene in some of their physical and chemical properties, but each will have its own special features as well. For example, addition reactions occur much more readily to some of the polycyclic benzenoid hydrocarbons than is the case with benzene itself, a result of the smaller relative amounts of aromatic stabilization associated with these compounds.

Outline of the Chapter

25-1. The Naming of Fused Benzenes: Polycyclic Benzenoid Hydrocarbons.

Common names in universal use.

25-2. The Physical Properties of Naphthalene.

25-3. The Synthesis and Reactions of Naphthalene.

What happens when two benzene rings are fused together.

25-4. The Tricyclic Benzenoid Hydrocarbons: Anthracene and Phenanthiene.

The importance of addition reactions increases with these.

25-5. Other Cyclic Polyenes: Hückel's Rule.

Getting to the heart of the matter: whence aromaticity?

Keys to the Chapter

25-1 through 25-4. Polycyclic Benzenoid Hydrocarbons.

The fusion of benzene rings leads to a large class of polycyclic hydrocarbons beginning with naphthalene as the simplest (and only bicyclic) example.

These are all aromatic, but as examination of their properties shows, their aromaticity is not as great, relatively speaking, as that in benzene. There are two consequences of this. First, electrophilic substitutions on fused polycyclics are generally easier, proceeding with milder reagents, than with benzene. This is because the activation energies for electrophilic attack are reduced due to the small amount of aromatic stabilization being disrupted. If the rings are not equally substituted, reaction occurs at the most activated ring, and substituents have the same directing and activating/deactivating effects, as you saw with benzene.

The second consequence of reduced relative aromaticity is the increased tendency of fused polycyclics to undergo addition reactions, which are rare for benzene itself. As a general rule of thumb, additions occur in such a way as to preserve intact benzene rings as much as possible, since simple benzenes have the highest relative aromaticity. So (Section 25-4), additions to anthracene and phenanthiene occur at the 9,10 positions, in each preserving intact two simple benzene rings. Alternative additions across, say, the 1,2 or 1,4 positions are almost never seen; these would leave intact a naphthalene-like product, which is not as good as two benzenes:

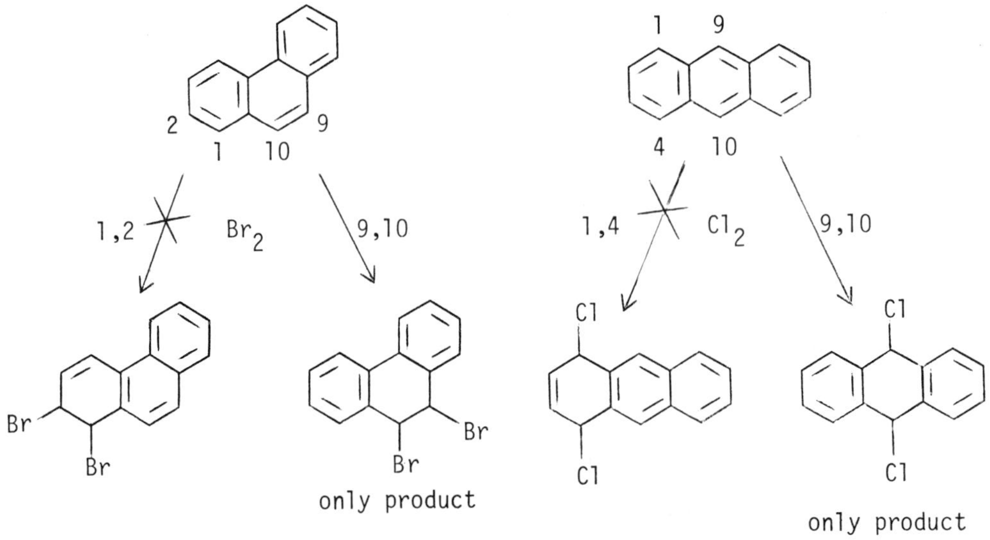

25-5. Other Cyclic Polyenes: Hückel's Rule.

Really very simple. For a molecule to be aromatic, it must have (1) $4n + 2$ π electrons contained in (2) a complete, unbroken circle of p orbitals. A whole molecule may be aromatic, or one or more portions of it may be aromatic separately. Sometimes a molecule may prefer an otherwise unorthodox resonance form or an atom may adopt an unexpected hybridization if in doing so, an aromatic structure results. Examples are given in problems 17-22.

Solutions for Chapter 25 Problems

1. 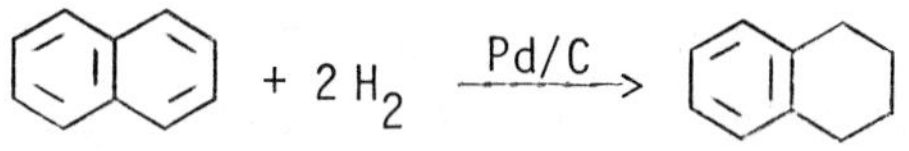

Although aromatic, naphthalene does undergo some addition reactions like this one. Addition occurs in such a way that one aromatic benzene ring is left fully intact.

****

2. 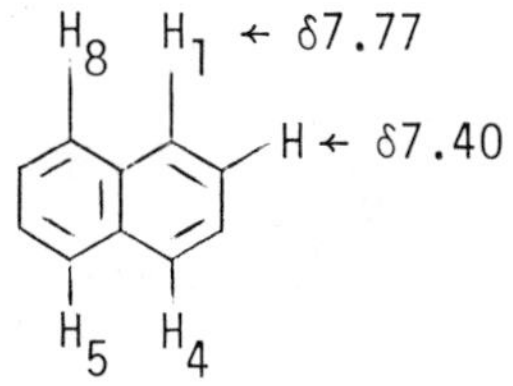

The hydrogens at C-1,4,5, and 8 are deshielded because they are closer to the <u>other</u> benzene ring in the molecule. They feel the deshielding effects of π-electron ring currents three ways: the ring current around the whole molecule (i), the ring current of their own benzene ring (ii), and the ring current of the <u>adjacent</u> benzene ring (iii):

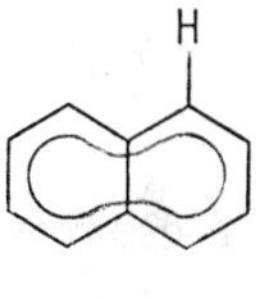

(i)

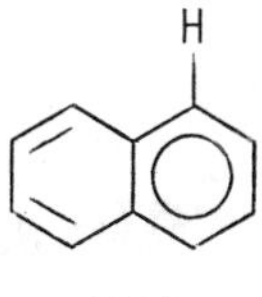

(ii)

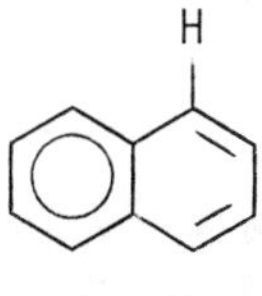

(iii)

The hydrogens at C-2,3,6, and 7 are too far away to feel a significant amount of the ring current of the other benzene ring.

****

3. Since there are 10 signals in the aromatic region of the ^{13}C NMR, let's guess that the molecule is related to naphthalene. The ^{1}H NMR shows a 1H signal at δ7.25 (the hint), another 1H signal (broad) at δ5.3, and signals for 6 other aromatic H's, for a total of 8 hydrogens. $C_{10}H_8$ adds up to a molecular weight of 128, so 16 more mass units are needed to give the *m/z* of 144. The IR seems to indicate the presence of an -OH, so an oxygen supplies the rest of the molecular weight of the molecule, $C_{10}H_8O$. The ^{1}H NMR signal at δ5.3 is probably the -O<u>H</u>. If this is a naphthalene, then we have 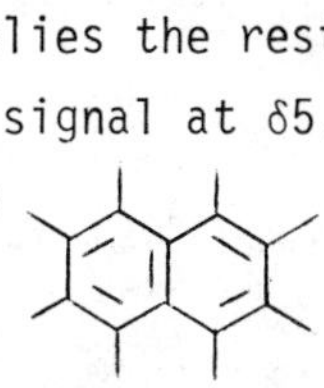 attached to an -OH and 7 -H's. There are only two

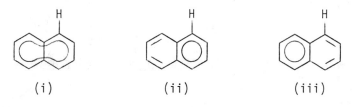

possibilities: 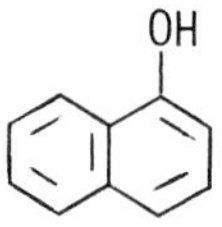 and 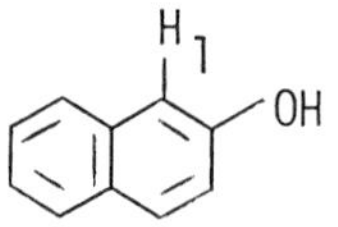 .

Can we distinguish them? In the first compound (1-naphthalenol), all ring hydrogens have neighbors, and so they should all show splitting in the ^1H NMR. In the second compound (2-naphthalenol), the H at C-1 (shown) has <u>no neighbors</u>, and should be a <u>singlet</u>, consistent with the signal at $\delta 7.25$. This is the answer.

****

4. 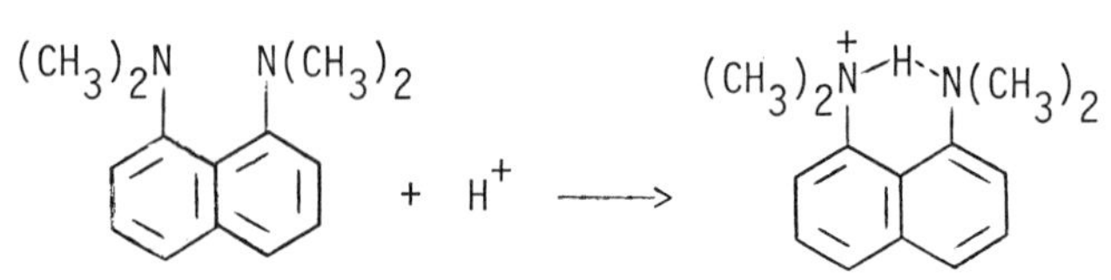

When a proton attaches to one of the nitrogens it is also firmly attracted to the lone pair of the other via a very strong hydrogen bond. This six-membered ring is quite stable, so the proton goes in very readily, and is very hard to remove.

****

5. Reaction should occur on the most activated (or least deactivated) ring, directed by the groups present.

(a) 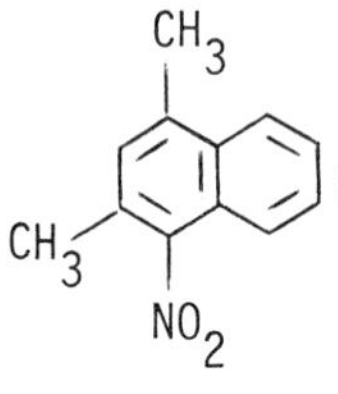 ; (b) 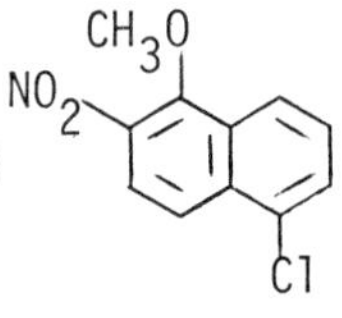 (major; 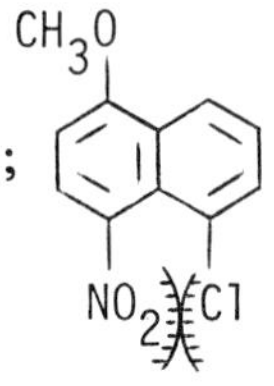 is sterically hindered);

(c) 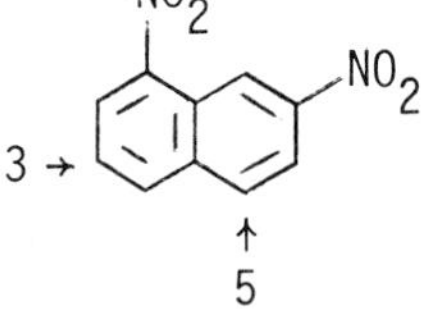

Two choices: C-3 (<u>meta</u> to C-1 NO_2) and C-5 (<u>meta</u> to C-7 NO_2). If all other factors are equal, substitution next to a ring fusion is preferred since one benzene ring is left intact in the intermediate (see "Activating Substituent at C-2", Section 25-3). So nitration occurs at C-5.

(d) 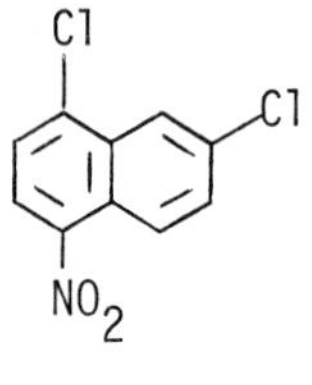

Reasons: *para* to a Cl, next to a ring fusion, and relatively unhindered.

****

6. (a) 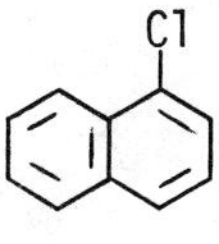

; (b) 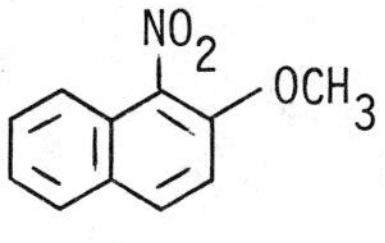

; (c) 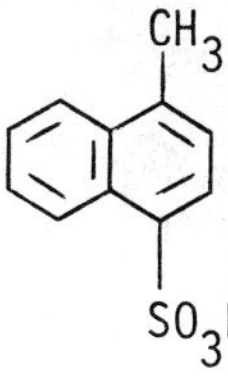

; (d) 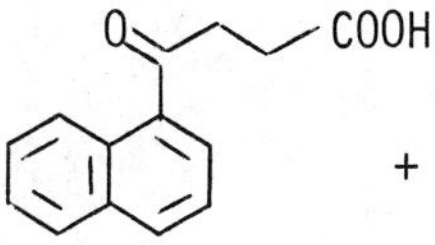

\+ 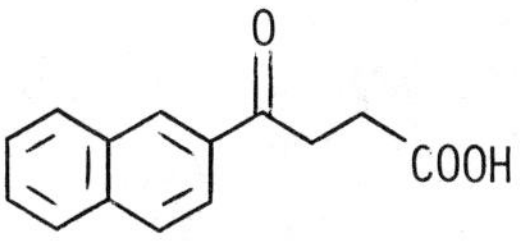

; (e) 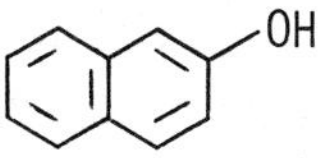

; (f) 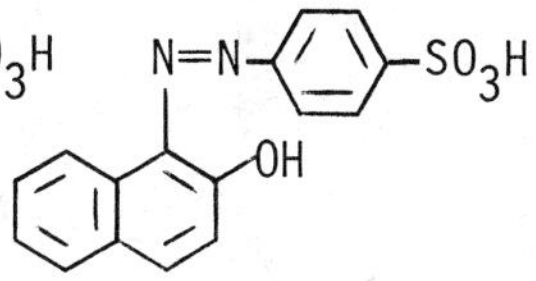

;

(g) 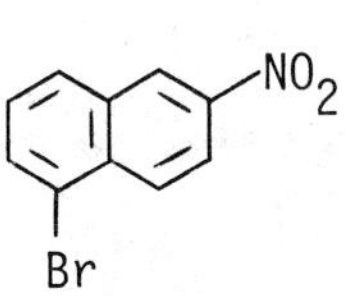

\+ 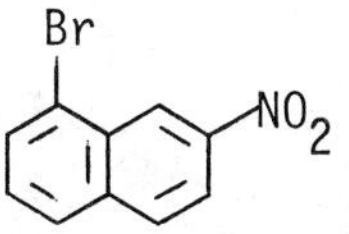

; (h) 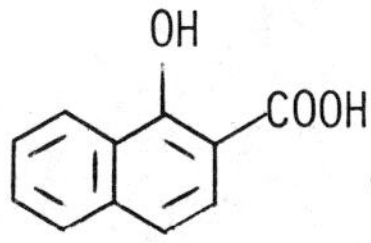

after acidification.

****

7. 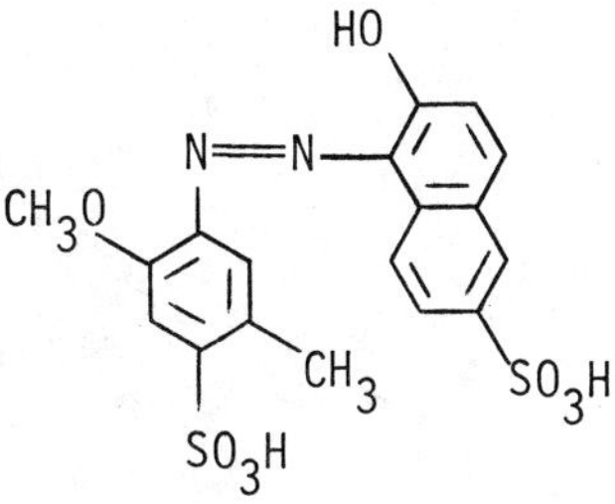

****

8. Use a Diels-Alder cycloaddition to make the second ring:

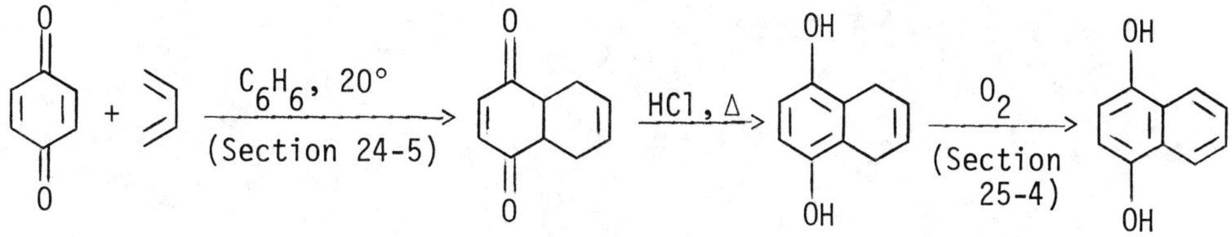

****

9. Work backwards: 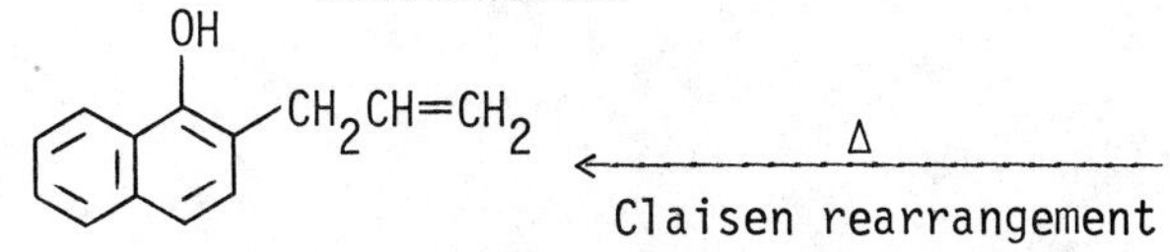

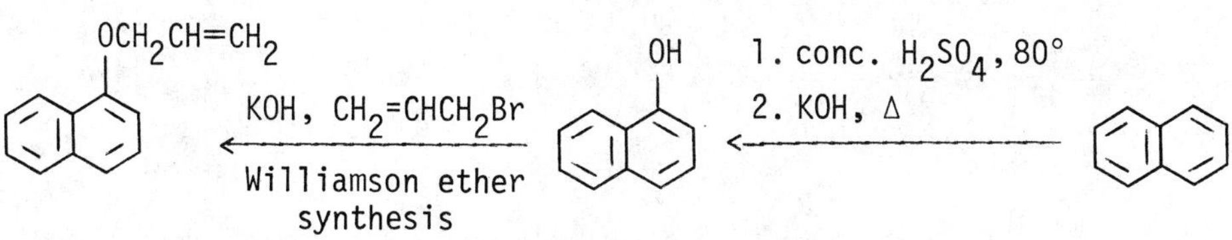

****

10.

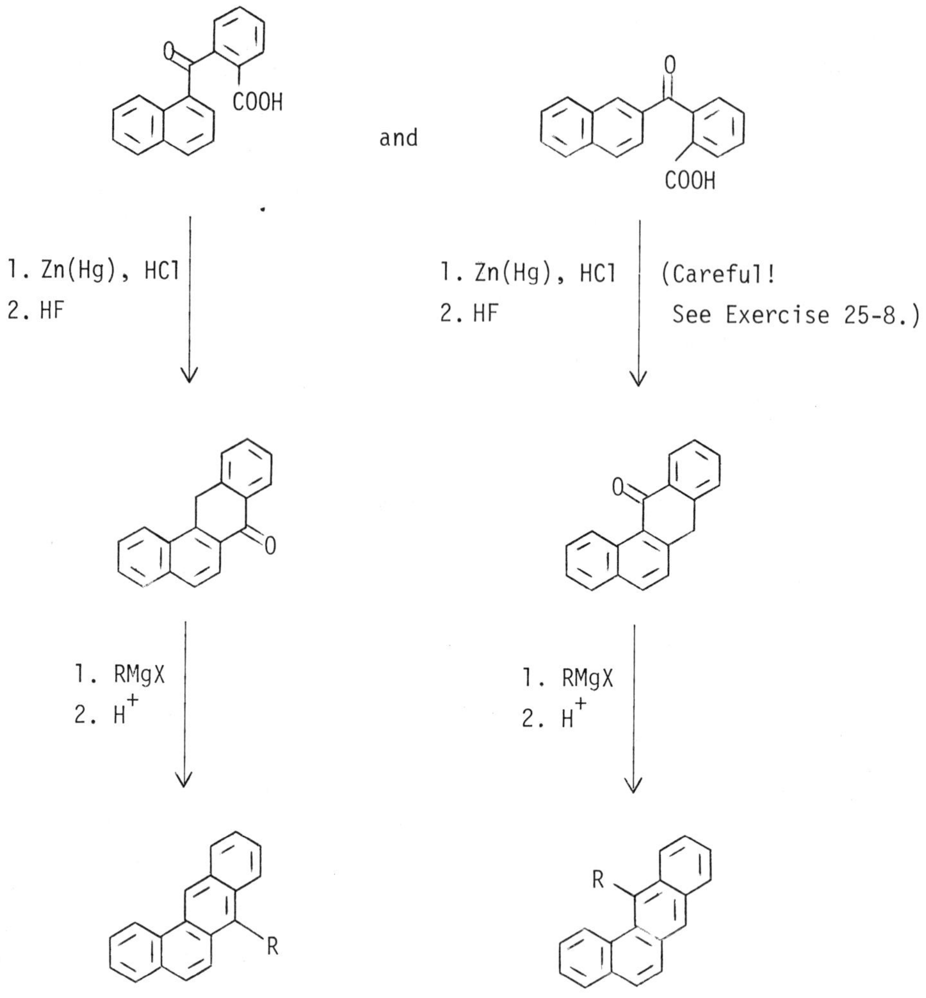

****

11. (a) 1. HNO_3, CH_3COOH, Δ, 2. SO_3, H_2SO_4 (makes 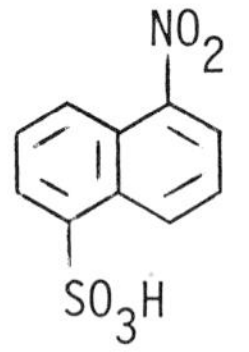), 3. Strong heating (isomerizes $-SO_3H$ group to 1,6-isomer), 4. H_2, Pd/C; (b) 1. NaOH, Δ, 2. $CH_3\overset{O}{\overset{\|}{C}}O\overset{O}{\overset{\|}{C}}CH_3$ (alkanoylates both -OH and $-NH_2$), 3. NaOH, H_2O (hydrolyzes ester back to free -OH); (c) 1. KOH, CH_3I, 2. NaOH, H_2O, Δ (hydrolyzes amide to free $-NH_2$), 3. $NaNO_2$, HCl, 4. KI; (d) 1. Mg, 2. $H\overset{O}{\overset{\|}{C}}CH_2CH_2\overset{O}{\overset{\|}{C}}O^-$, 3. H^+, H_2O (makes 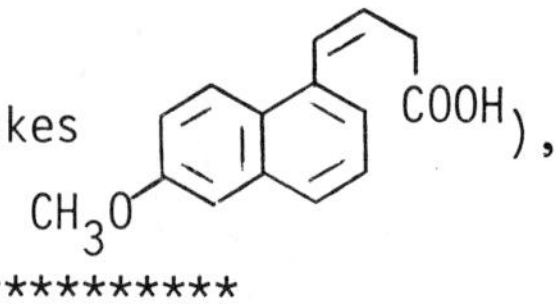), 4. H_2, Pd/C; (e) 1. $SOCl_2$, 2. $AlCl_3$.

****

12. 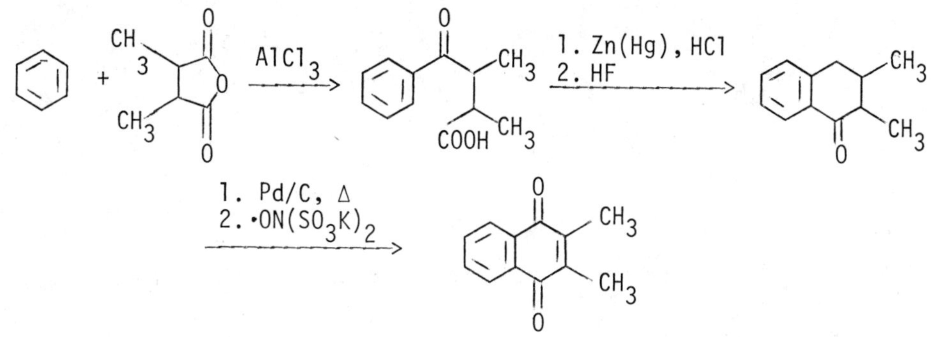

****

13. (a) 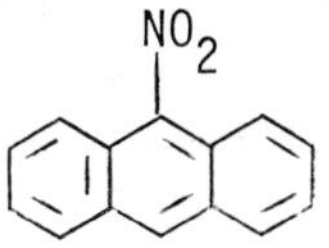 ; (b) 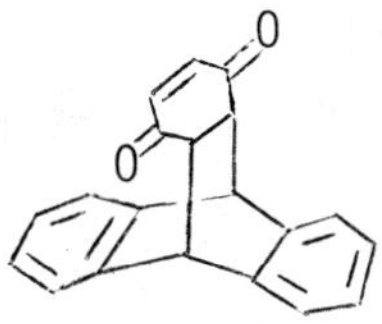 ; (c) 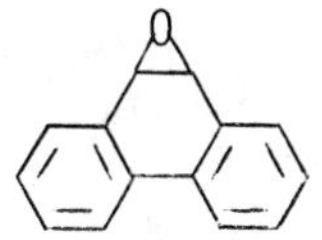 ;

(d) 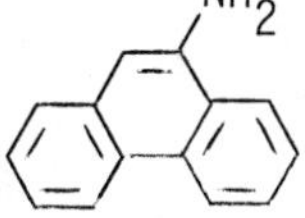 ("benzyne"-type reaction, Section 20-6)

****

14. 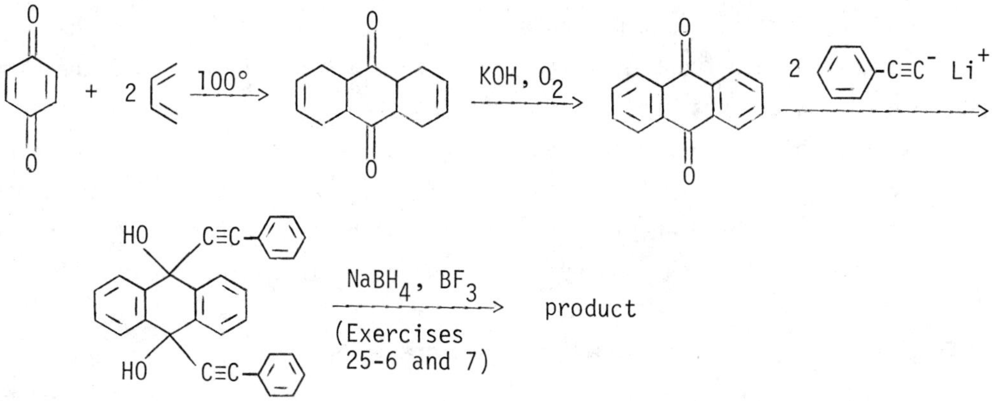

****

15. All positions in the end benzene rings of phenanthrene are either o or p to either the 9,10-double bond substituent or the other benzene ring. The 9,10-double bond will act electronically as the better activating group because resonance involving it does not disrupt the other benzne ring. So the 1 (o to double bond) and 3 (p to double bond) positions are most activated electronically:

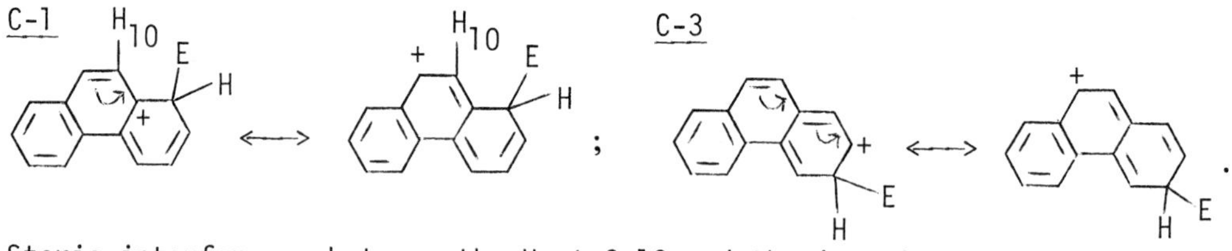

Steric interference between the H at C-10 and the incoming electrophile at C-1 (see above) causes the final choice to be substitution at C-3.

****

16. 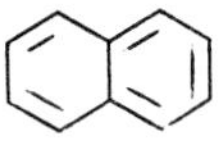 (10 e^-); 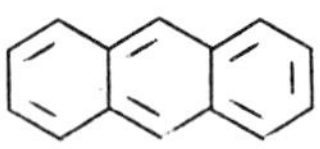 (14 e^-); 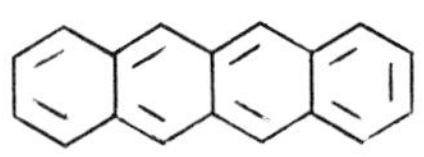 (18 e^-);

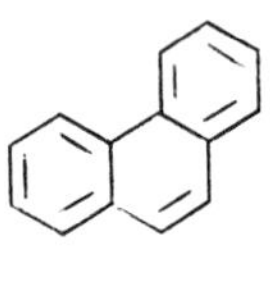 (14 e^-); 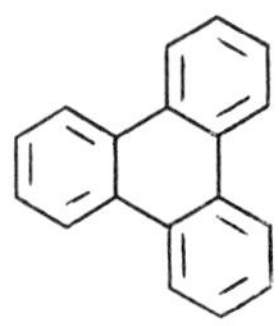 (18 e^-); 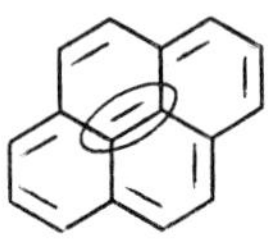 Pyrene is unusual: it has 7 double bonds around the periphery of the molecule in the resonance form shown, for 14 π electrons. It also has an extra double bond in the middle (circled)! The molecule is still aromatic, though: in this resonance form, the 2 electrons of this extra π bond are not in the annulene circle, and do not disrupt the aromaticity. Another way to look at pyrene is via its resemblance to phenanthrene in the structure given at the beginning of Chapter 25 in the text: it just has an extra alkene bridge between positions 4 and 5 of phenanthrene. Two intact benzene rings are present in both the phenanthrene and pyrene resonance forms shown.

****

17. Rule: aromaticity requires (1) 4n + 2 π electrons contained in (2) a complete, unbroken circle of p orbitals.

(a) No (3 π electrons); (b) Yes (benzene is intact; extra double bond is an irrelevant substituent, not being part of the circle); (c) No (the saturated carbon is sp^3, breaking the circle of p orbitals; without that the number of π electrons is irrelevant); (d) Yes (10 π electrons; the sp^3 carbon here is bridging, and does not interrupt the p orbital circle); (e) No (12 π electrons: wrong number); (f) No (9 π bonds = 18 π electrons which would be fine, except that the 2- charge adds 2 more for a total of 20 electrons: wrong number); (g) No (saturated ring fusion carbons interrupt circle); (h) Yes, via a trick:

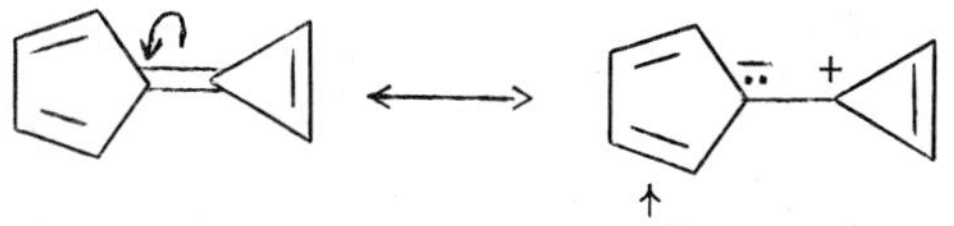

← 2 e^- aromatic cyclopropenyl cation

6 e^- cyclopentadienide ring, also aromatic

****

18. Structure (i) contains 4 *cis* and 3 *trans* double bonds; structure (ii) contains 3 *cis* and 4 *trans* double bonds. The NMR indicates the presence of 4 "inside" and 10 "outside" hydrogens (see Exercise 25-11), consistent with structure (ii) only:

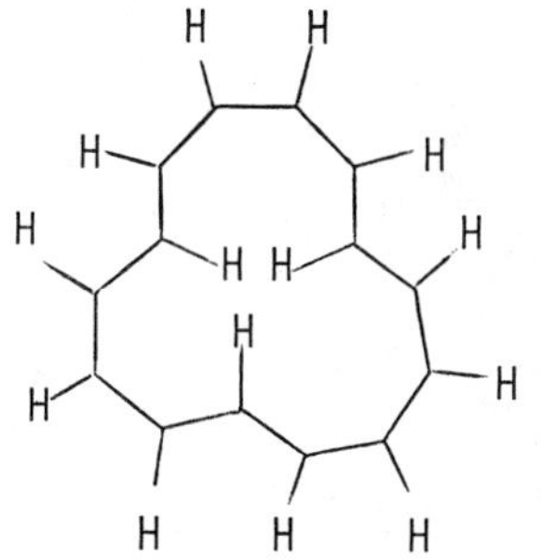

(i), 3 "inside" and 11 "outside" H's

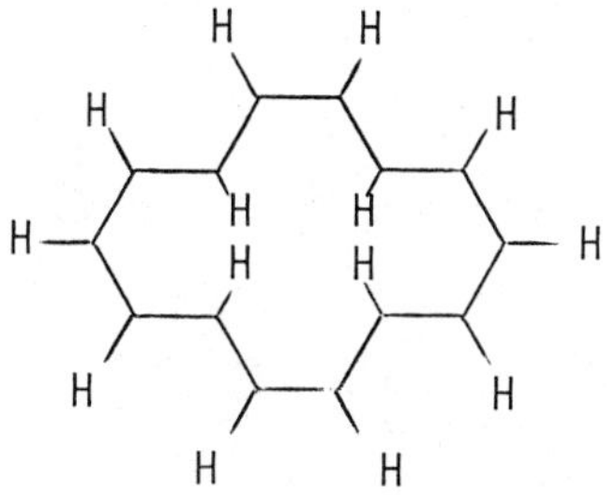

(ii), 4 "inside" and 10 "outside" H's

****

19. The conjugate base of fluorene is aromatic: 14 π electrons in a circle of p orbitals which is completed by rehybridizing the negatively charged carbon to sp^2.

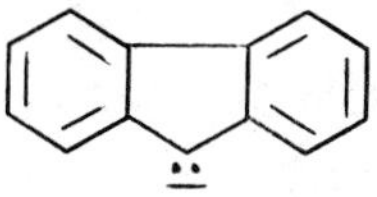

****

20.

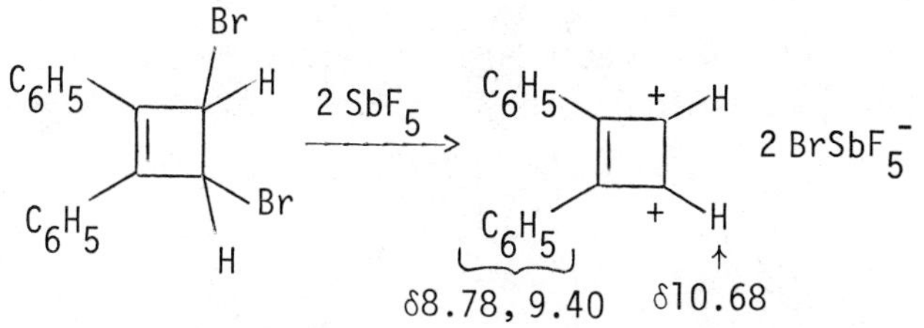

2 $BrSbF_5^-$ Aromatic 2 e^- dication.

****

21. Since the two π bonds of a triple bond are in <u>perpendicular planes</u> (Section 13-2), only one of them can be part of the circle of p orbitals. So the triple bond contributes only 2 of its π electrons to the ring, just like a double bond. The compound illustrated therefore contains 14 π electrons in the circle (counting <u>2</u> from the triple bond) and is aromatic.

****

22. (a)

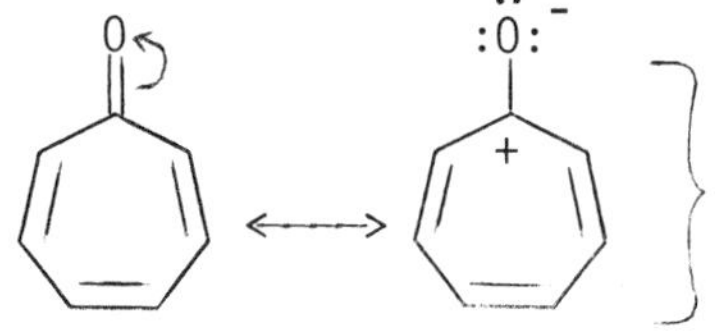

6 π electrons = aromatic

But

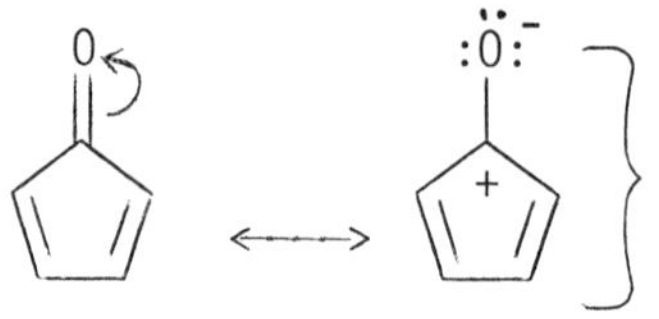

4 π electrons = not aromatic, very unstable like cyclobutadiene

(b) As seen in part a, the "normal" $\overset{+}{C}-\overset{-}{O}$ polarization of the carbonyl group is disfavored in cyclopentadienone (and its derivatives). The reaction shown pictures a nucleophilic alkyllithium adding to *oxygen*, followed by attachment of the electrophilic carbon of CH_3I to a ring *carbon*:

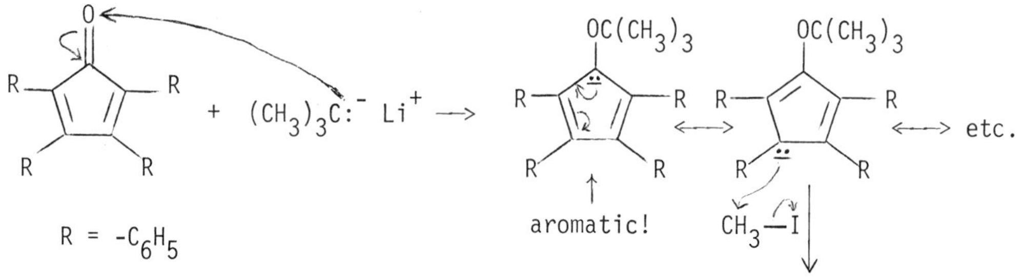

This is quite bizarre-looking until you realize that the intermediate is a 6 π electron aromatic anion.

****

23. The compound present after the second treatment with aqueous Ag_2O, but before heating (step 4) is the following:

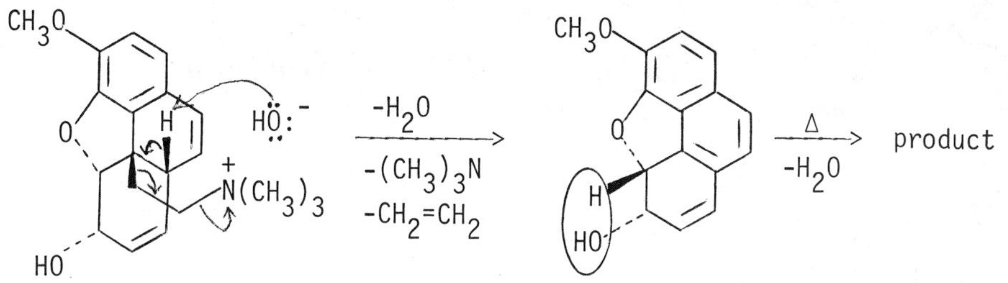

Instead of ordinary Hofmann elimination on heating, the alternative process shown takes place, which allows formation of the *fully aromatic* phenanthrene derivative as the final product.

****

24. Look at (iii), noting especially the two carbon-carbon bonds that need to be formed. Then proceed, using the functional groups in (i) and (ii) in logical ways.

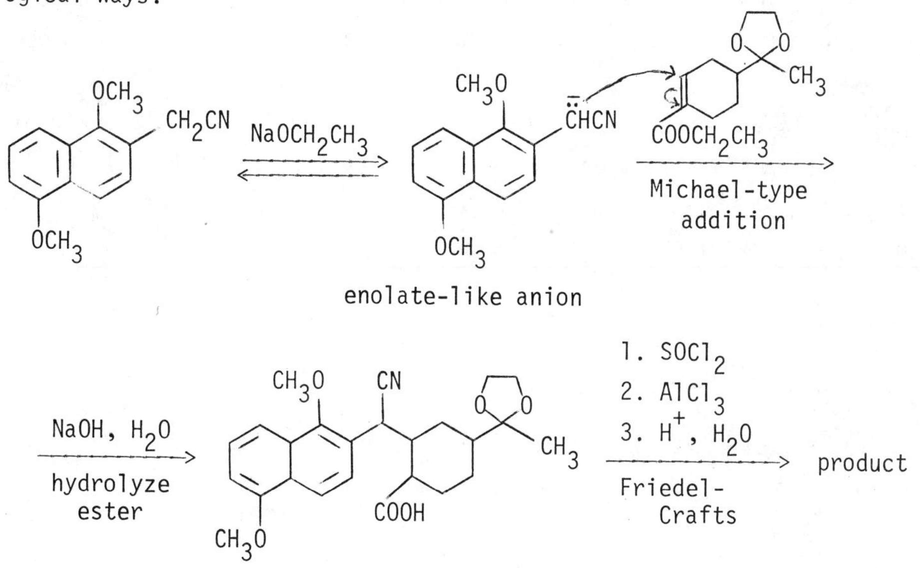

****

CHAPTER 26

Heterocycles: Heteroatoms in Cyclic Organic Compounds

General Introduction

The material in this chapter really falls into two broad categories: non-aromatic and aromatic heterocycles. You have already seen many examples of non-aromatic heterocycles (see the section references at the start of the text chapter). There will be new ones, especially containing nitrogen atoms in three-, four-, or five-membered rings.

Heteroatoms may also be present in aromatic rings, and compounds with this feature are the subject of the last four sections of the chapter. In general, the properties of these compounds will be predictable from principles you've already seen: they will be similar to acyclic compounds with similar heteroatoms unless (1) the ring is strained or (2) the ring is aromatic. When the ring is aromatic, the effect of the heteroatom on its chemistry will be important, and this will be a new topic to which you will need to apply your knowledge of inductive and resonance effects.

Outline of the Chapter

26-1. The Naming of Heterocycles.

26-2. The Three-membered Heterocycles: Strain Imparts Reactivity.

26-3. Four- and Five-membered Heterocycloalkanes.

Direct extrapolations of lots of things you've already learned about.

26-4. The Aromatic Heterocyclopentadienes: Pyrrole, Furan, and Thiophene.

26-5. Pyridine, an Azabenzene.

The most common monocyclic heteroaromatic compounds.

26-6. Quinoline and Isoquinoline: the Benzpyridines.

26-7. Nitrogen Heterocycles in Nature: Alkaloids.

Even more rings!

Keys to the Chapter

26-1. The Naming of Heterocycles.

Note simply that the text will stick to strict systematic nomenclature for non-aromatic heterocycles, but will use the universally accepted common names for the aromatic system.

26-2 and 26-3. Three-, Four-, and Five-membered Heterocycles.

These two sections generalize what you have learned before concerning the preparation and reactions of cyclic ethers. Rings containing nitrogen and sulfur illustrate two principal similarities with their oxygen relatives: preparation methods again make considerable use of intramolecular S_N2 ring-closure reactions, and ring opening to relieve strain governs the reactivity of the smaller rings (three or four atoms). The section stops with five-membered rings since the properties of heterocycloalkanes of this size or larger closely resemble those of their acyclic analogues (ethers, thioethers, and amines).

26-4, 26-5, and 26-6. The Aromatic Heterocycles.

Five- and six-membered heterocyclic compounds make up the vast majority of aromatic heteroatom-containing systems. Counting electrons in the π systems of these rings is occasionally confusing. Here is a simple way to determine if a lone pair of a heteroatom is part of the cyclic π system: if only single bonds link the heteroatom to its neighbors in the ring, then *one* lone pair from the heteroatom may be in a p orbital and become part of the cyclic π system. Examples are pyrrole, furan, and thiophene. Notice that in the latter two, only one of the two lone pairs on the heteroatom is part of the π system; the other is in an sp^2 orbital and has nothing to do with the molecule's aromaticity at all. If the heteroatom is doubly bonded to another ring atom, as is the case with pyridine, a lone pair on it will be in an sp^2 orbital, and will *never* count towards the cyclic π system in the molecule. Try to apply these rules to as many structures illustrated in these sections as you can; they are all aromatic, so you know what the answers should be.

Typically, syntheses of the aromatic heterocycles utilize combinations of carbonyl condensation reactions and 1,2- or 1,4-additions of enolate and heteroatom nucleophiles to α,β-unsaturated carbonyl compounds: no fundamentally new chemistry here. Reactions of these systems show a blending of benzene/aromatic chemistry and the chemistry of non-aromatic analogues with the same heteroatom. Furan is a good example: it undergoes electrophilic substitution (aromatic chemistry), ring cleavage in acid (ether chemistry), and Diels-Alder cycloaddition (diene chemistry). Putting the large number of reactions here into their appropriate compartments should help you organize them for study and problem-solving.

Solutions to Chapter 26 Problems

1\. (a) 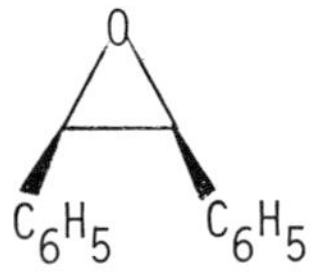

; (b) 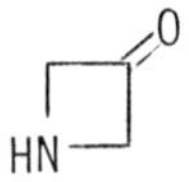

: (c) 

; (d) 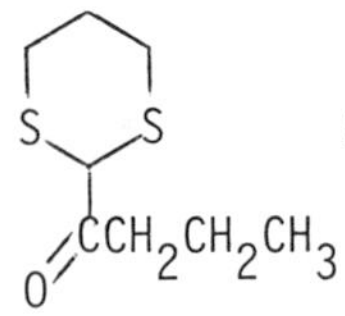

;

(e) 2-methanoylfuran or furan-2-carbaldehyde; (f) N-methylpyrrole or 1-methylpyrrole; (g) quinoline-4-carboxylic acid; (h) 2,3-dimethylthiophene.

****

2\. (a) *anti*-addition: 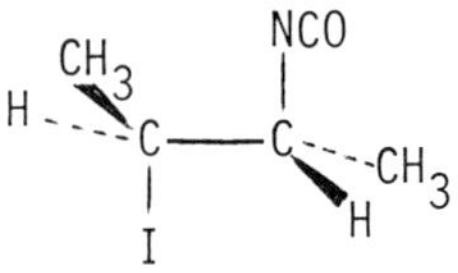

; (b) 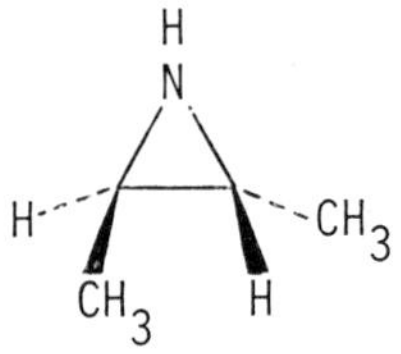

(c) $I-N=\overset{+}{N}=\overset{-}{\ddot{N}}:$, isoelectronic with INCO and similar in reactivity: 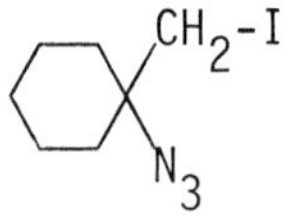

(d) 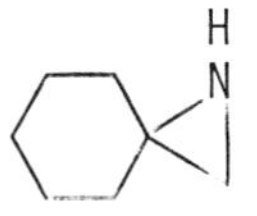

.

****

3\. (a) 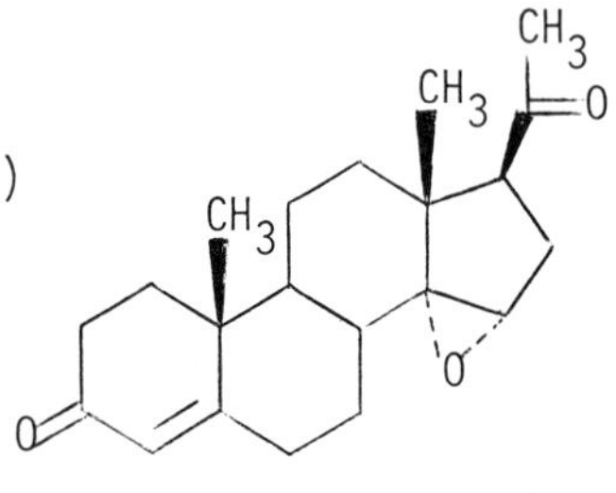

Electrophilic attack by peracid on a normal, electron-rich double bond.

(b) 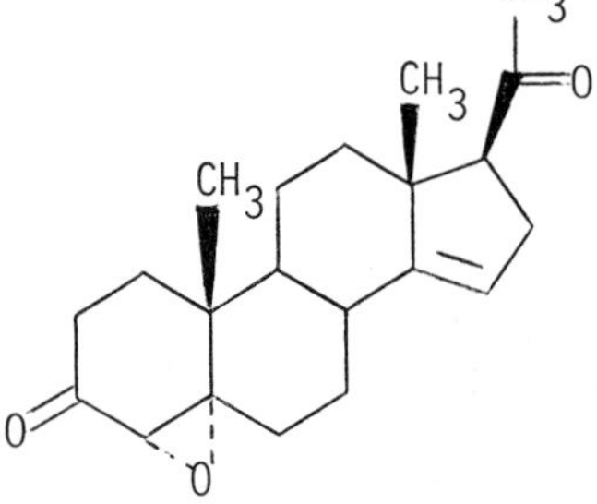

Nucleophilic 1,4- attack by HOO^- on an α,β-unsaturated ketone (an electron-poor double bond).

****

4. This is a severely folded ring system: . The "top" face of the
    double bond ("inside" the fold) is $\overset{H}{\underset{H}{\quad}}$ severely hindered.
    Electrophiles are limited to attack only at the less-hindered bottom face:

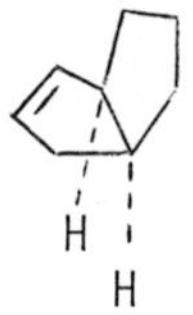

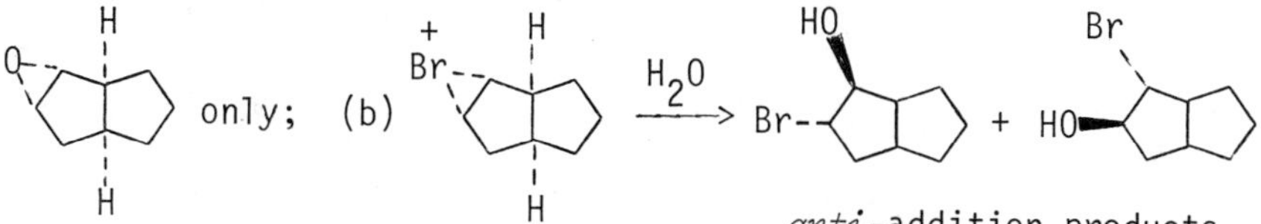

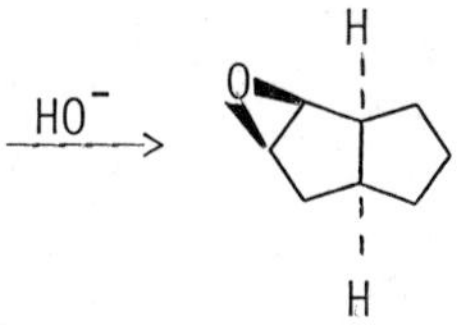

(a) only; (b) $\xrightarrow{H_2O}$ Br— + HO—

anti-addition products

intermediate

$\xrightarrow{HO^-}$ only.

****

5. (a) C_6H_5CH + $C_6H_5CCOOCH_2CH_3$ $\longrightarrow$ $C_6H_5CH-\overset{\overset{O^-}{\parallel}}{C}COOCH_2CH_3$ $\xrightarrow{-Cl^-}$ product

$\overset{|}{C_6H_5}$

(b) C_6H_5CH + $Cl\overset{..}{\underset{..}{C}}HCOOCH_2CH_3$ $\longrightarrow$ $C_6H_5CH-\overset{\overset{:N^-C_6H_5}{|}}{C}HCOOCH_2CH_3$ $\xrightarrow{-Cl^-}$ product

****

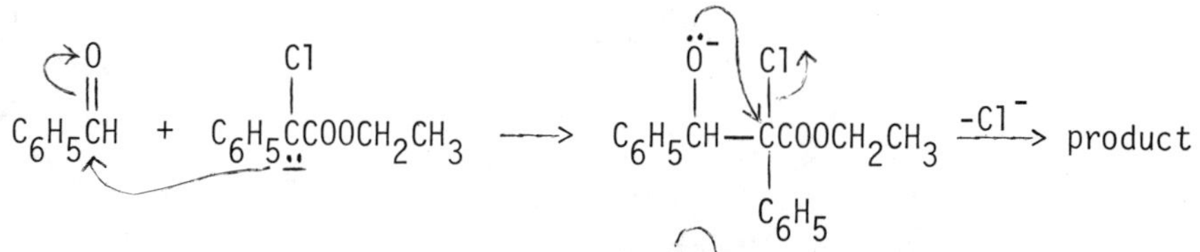

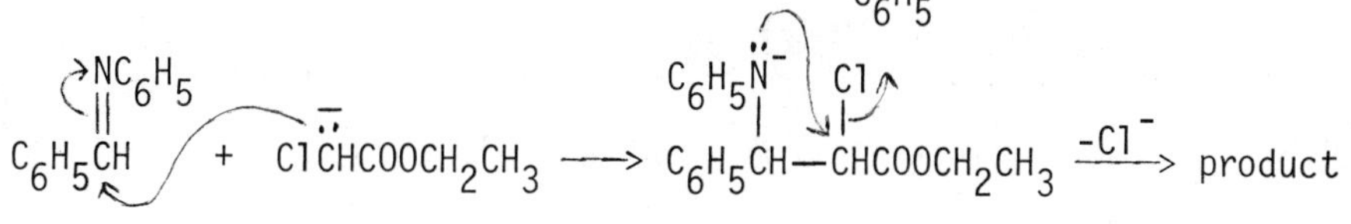

6. (a) $CH_3CH=CH_2$ $\xrightarrow[\text{2. }CH_3OH]{\text{1. INCO}}$ $\overset{\overset{NHCOOCH_3}{|}}{CH_3CHCH_2I}$ $\xrightarrow[\text{(Section 18-5)}]{LiAlH_4}$ $\left[\overset{\overset{\overset{..}{N}CH_3}{|}}{CH_3CHCH_2I} \right]$

$\downarrow$

product ;

(b) $\xrightarrow[\text{3. KOH, }H_2O]{\overset{\text{1. INCO}}{\text{2. }CH_3OH}}$ product; (c) phenanthrene + MCPBA $\longrightarrow$ product;

(d) + H_2O_2, NaOH, CH_3OH $\longrightarrow$ product.

****

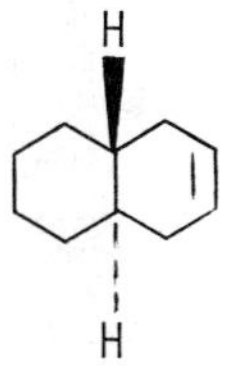

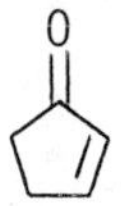

7. (a) 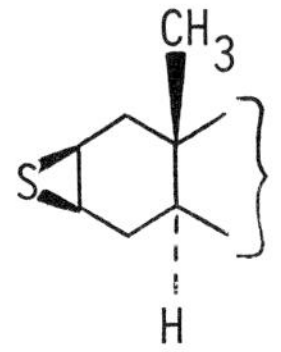 ; (b) 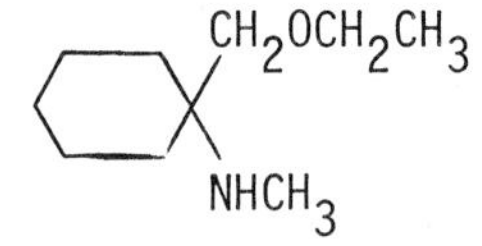 ; (c) 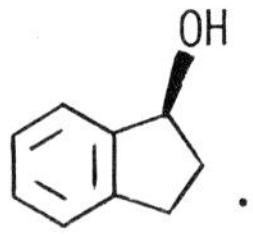 .

****

8. 1. one equivalent CH_3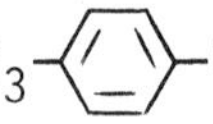SO_2Cl, pyridine (reacts with secondary -OH preferentially); 2. NaOH, CH_3OH (deprotonates tertiary -OH leading to internal S_N2).

****

9. 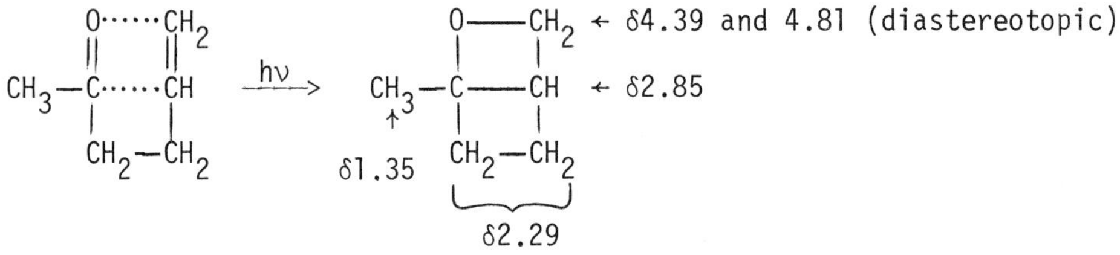

****

10. (a) 1,3-dibromo-5,5-dimethyl-1,3-diaza-2,4-cyclopentanedione.

(b) Thinking mechanistically we have the following:

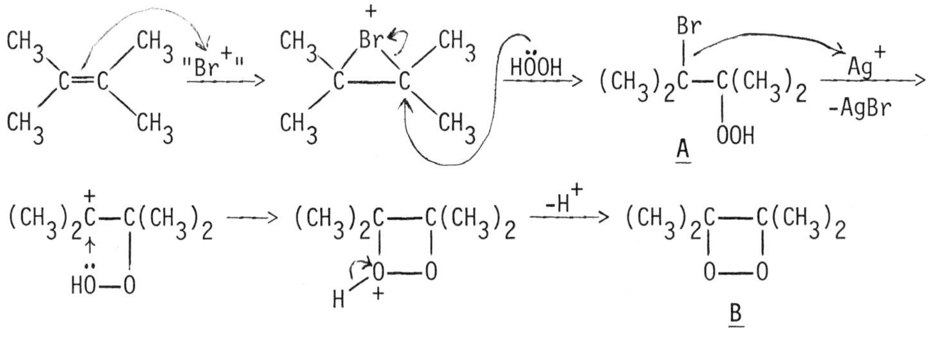

B is 3,3,4,4-tetramethyl-1,2-dioxacyclobutane.

****

11. (a)

most reactive
towards
nucleophiles

Protein-N̈H₂

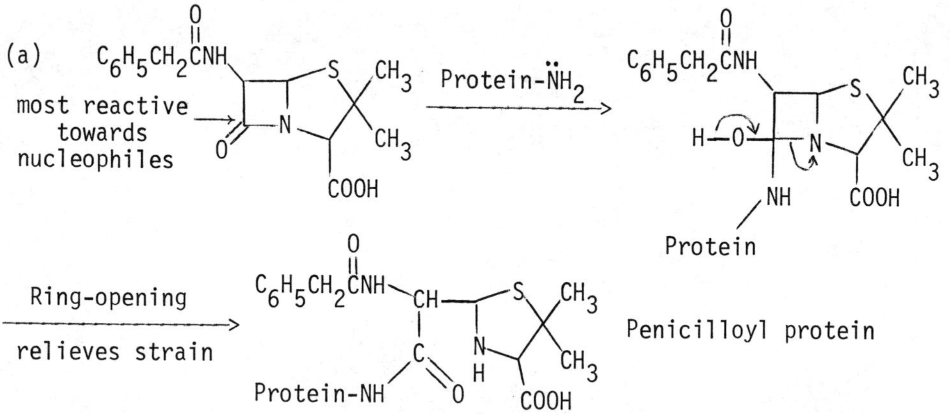

Penicilloyl protein

Ring-opening
relieves strain

(b)

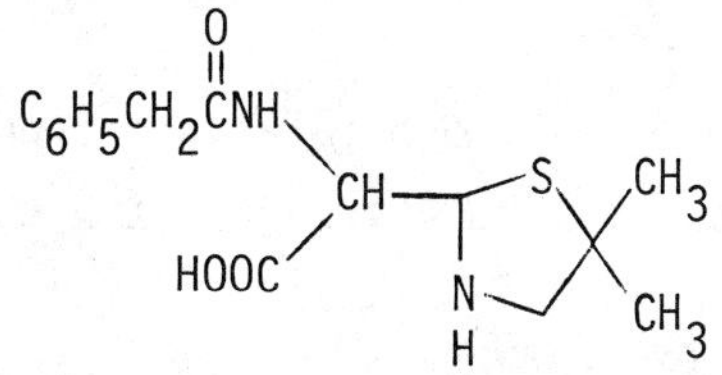

via a parallel mechanism with H_2O
as the nucleophile. This product,
penicilloic acid, no longer possesses
the necessary strained azacyclobutanone ring for reaction with bacterial
protein. It therefore lacks any antibiotic properties.

****

12. Abbreviated mechanism (note the "double" Michael addition):

$(CH_3)_2C$=$CHCCH$=$C(CH_3)_2$ + $\ddot{N}H_3$ $\xrightarrow{\text{1,4-addition}}$ $(CH_3)_2C$=$CHCCH_2C(CH_3)_2$

$\xrightarrow{\text{again}}$ product

****

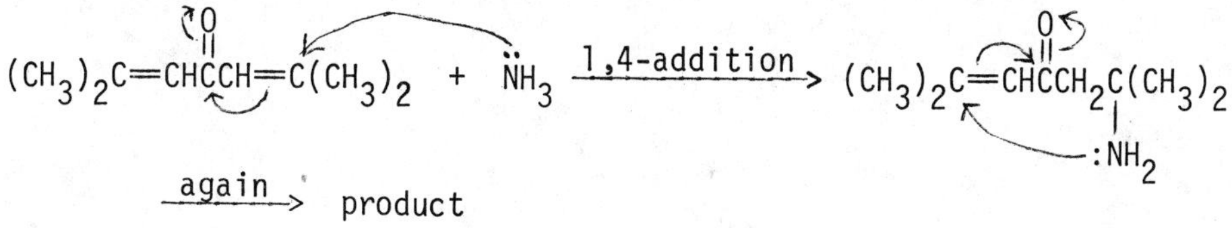

13. Degrees of unsaturation (Study Guide, Chapter 11): $H_{sat'd}$ = 16 + 2 = 18;
deg. unsat'n. = $\frac{18-8}{2}$ = 5 π bonds and/or rings. NMR: C_6H_5 group is present,
accounting for 4 degrees of unsaturation. No alkene C-H signals, so the
last degree of unsaturation is probably a ring. So far: C_6H_5-, 2C, 3H, O
present, adding up to C_8H_8O. The three H's all couple to each other (all 3
signals are split), so an -OH is unlikely. Therefore, the O is an ether
oxygen, giving as the only possible answer

diastereotopic

C_6H_5, 2-phenyloxacyclopropane.

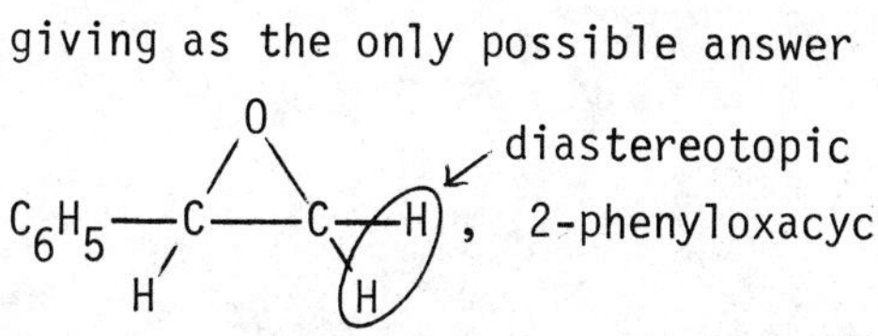

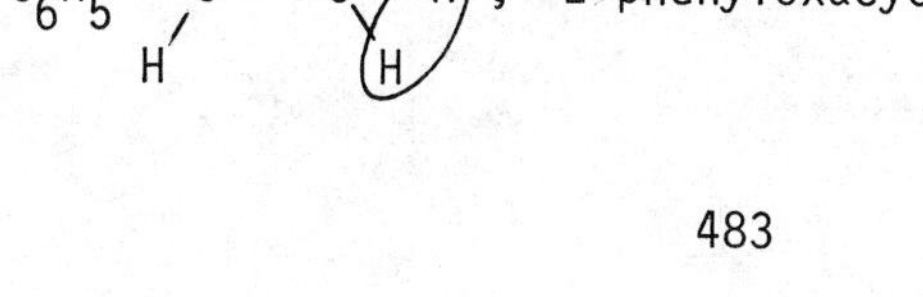

Conc. aq. HCl causes ring opening to 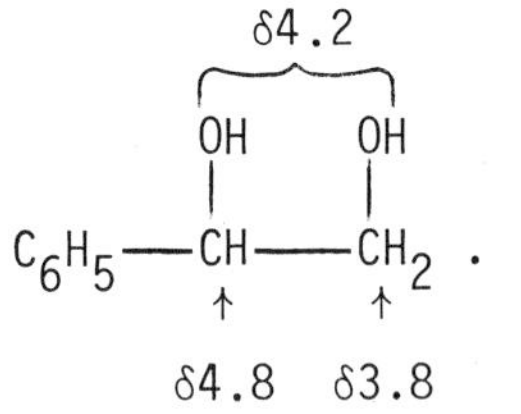

****

14. 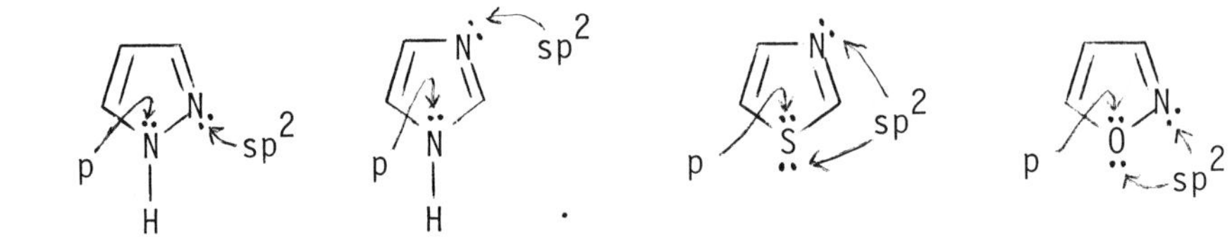

All have 2 double bonds plus one lone pair in a p orbital = 6 π electrons, so all are aromatic. All have sp^2-hybridized lone pairs on nitrogen, not tied up in the aromatic π system, and therefore available to act in a Lewis-base manner. Pyrrole lacks an sp^2-hybridized lone pair; therefore all the compounds above are stronger bases than pyrrole.

****

15. (a) 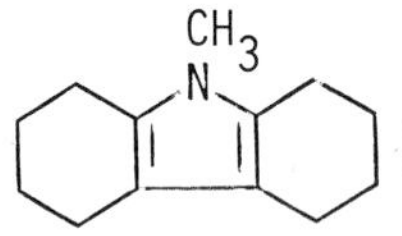

; (b) 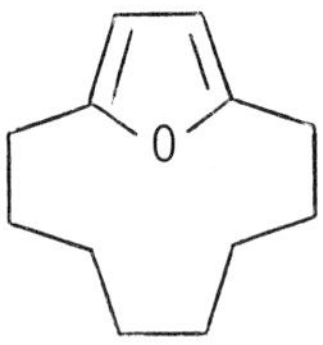

****

16. Abbreviated mechanism:

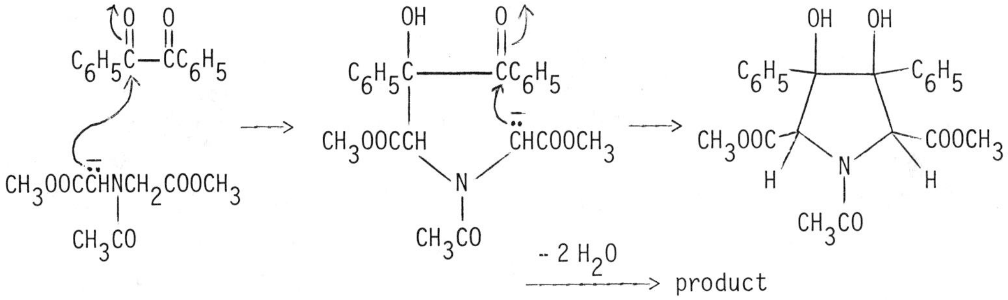

Synthesis: 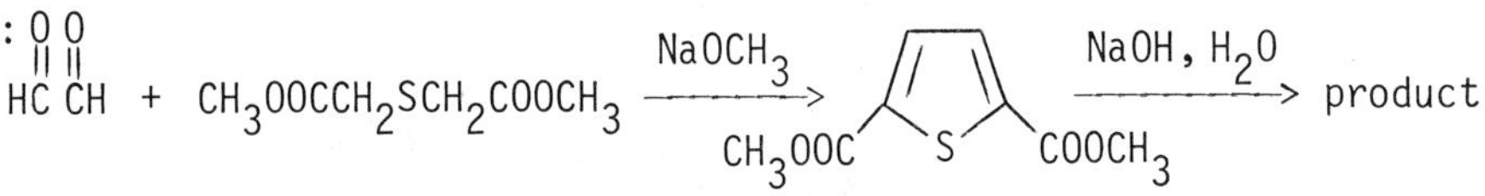

****

17. There are three factors to keep in mind: (1) the inherent preference of these compounds for substitution at C-2 over C-3, (2) the much greater reactivity of all of them compared with benzene, and (3) directing effects of substituent groups (which work the same way as in benzene). These are toughies!

(a) Two conflicting preferences: m-directing group → ; preference of ring →

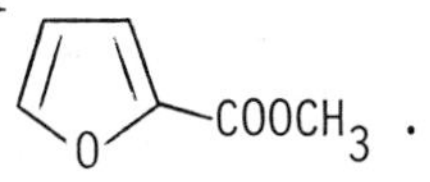

In this case
a mixture might be expected:

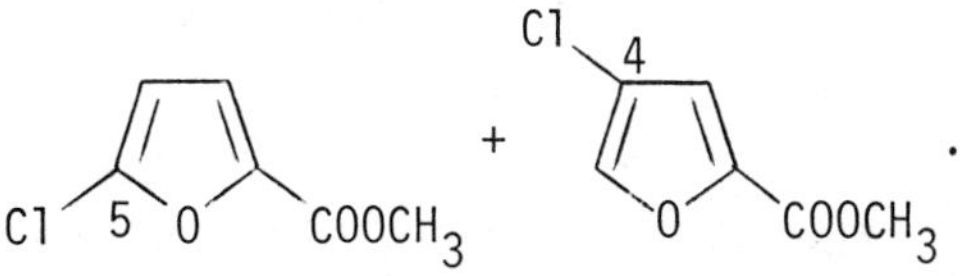

The first is actually the major product; the directing effect of the activating ring oxygen to C-5 wins out over that of the moderately deactivating $-COOCH_3$ group to C-4.

(b) Easier:

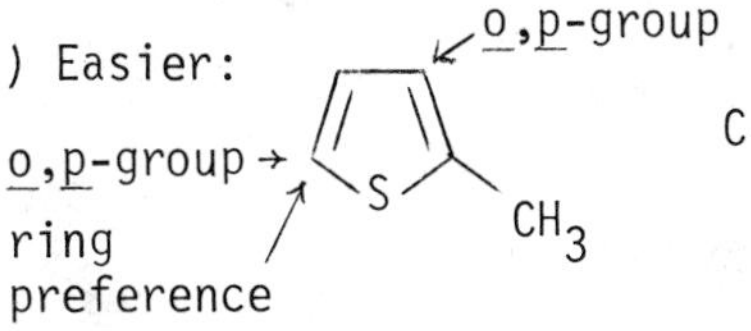

C-5 is strongly activated:

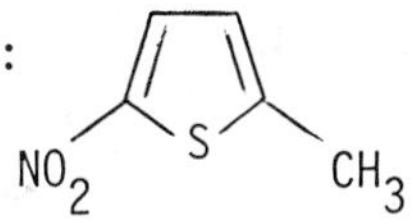

(c) Tricky. If this were benzene, the Friedel-Crafts reaction would not work at all due to the presence of the $-COCH_3$ group. It does proceed here, since the heterocycle is much more reactive. The ketone substituent is complexed by $AlCl_3$ during the reaction, making it even more strongly deactivating and meta-directing, however. The overall result is slow formation of

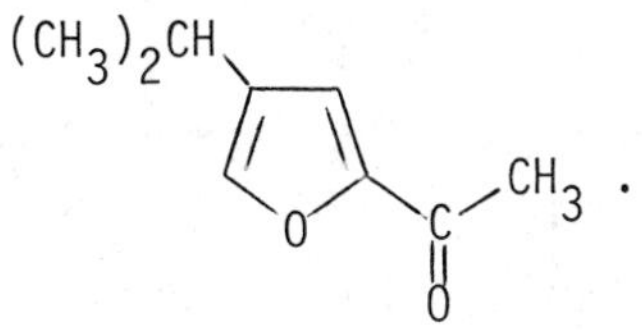

(d) Easy:

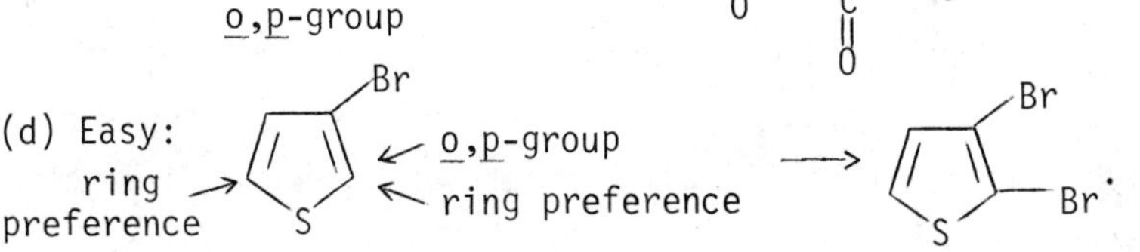

C-1 is doubly preferred.

(e) Now you have to work from scratch! Compare attack at:

C-2

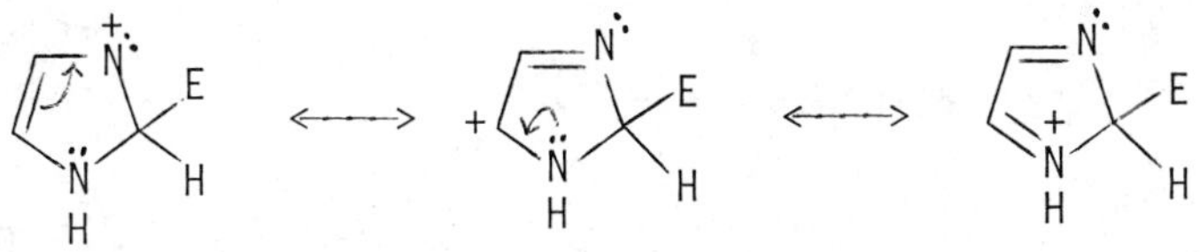

C-4

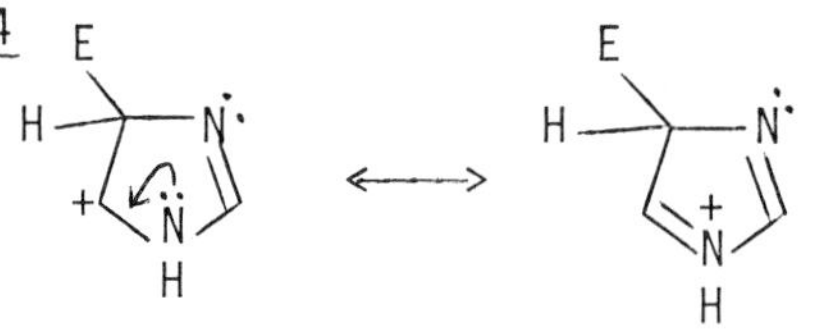

C-5

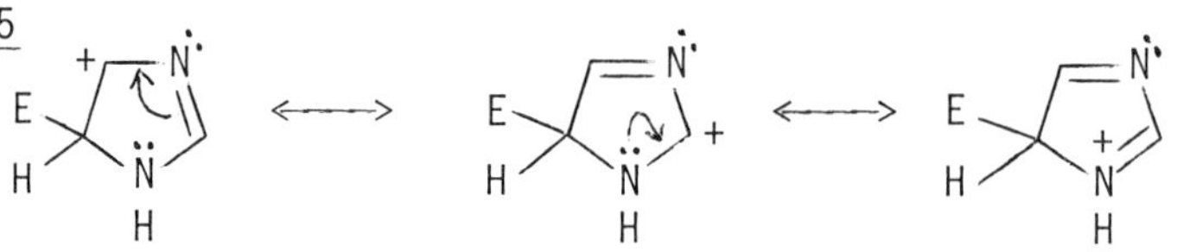

Rule out C-4 (only two resonance forms for cation). Choose C-5 over C-2 (avoids placing electron sextet and a positive charge on electronegative N at upper right). Thus C-5 is the site of attack by typical electrophiles. In this particular example, though, the major product is due to diazo coupling at C-2, since under the basic conditions the imidazole *anion* is attacked, and reaction at C-2 gives a symmetrical intermediate with two equivalent resonance forms:

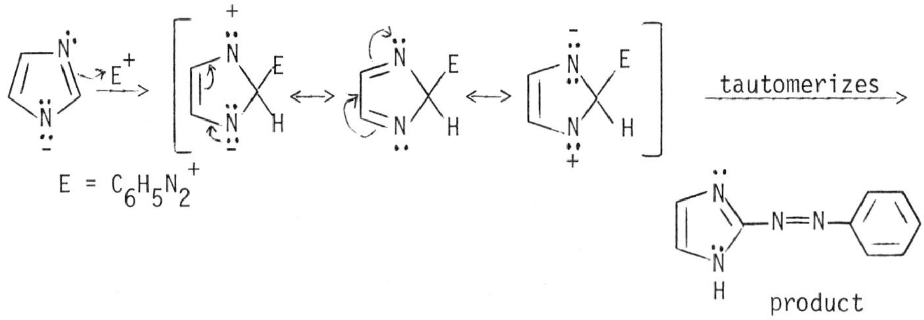

****

18. Selenophene is more reactive. The Se lone pair required to complete the aromatic 6 π electron system is in a 4 p orbital, which overlaps less well with the carbon 2 p orbitals (compared with the 3p orbital of S in thiophene). The result is that selenophene is less aromatic, and the activation energy for an electrophile attacking its π electrons is correspondingly lower.

****

19. (a) 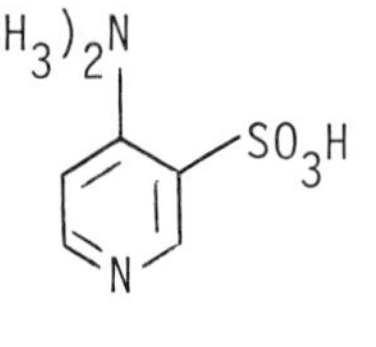 ; (b) Diels-Alder: 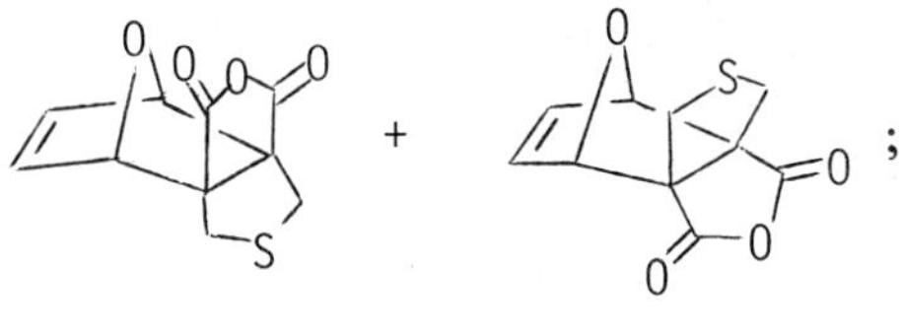 ;

(c) 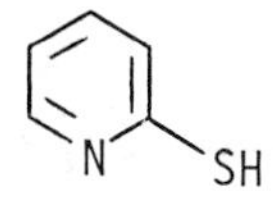 : (d) $CH_3CH_2CH_2CH_2\overset{O}{\overset{\|}{C}}C_6H_5$ (via 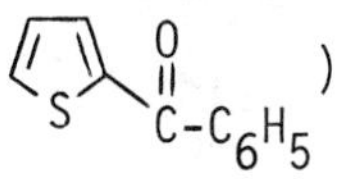); (e) 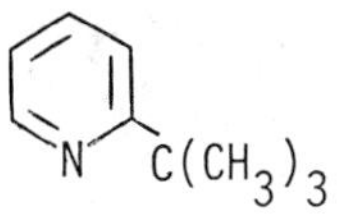

****

20. (a) Friedländer: 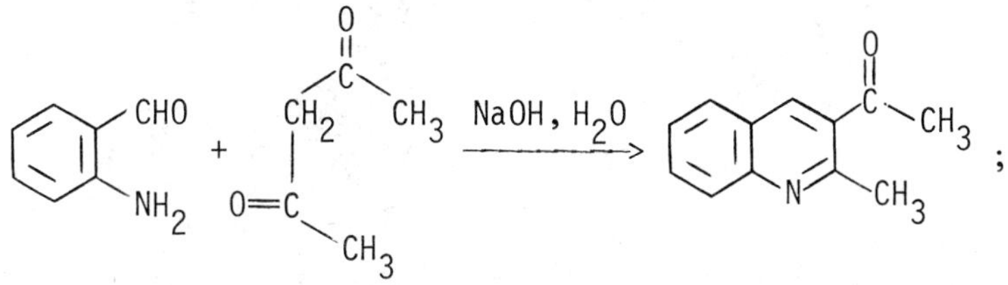

(b) Hantzsch: $C_6H_5\overset{O}{\overset{\|}{C}}CH_2\overset{O}{\overset{\|}{C}}OCH_2CH_3 \xrightarrow{H_2C=O,\ NH_3}$ 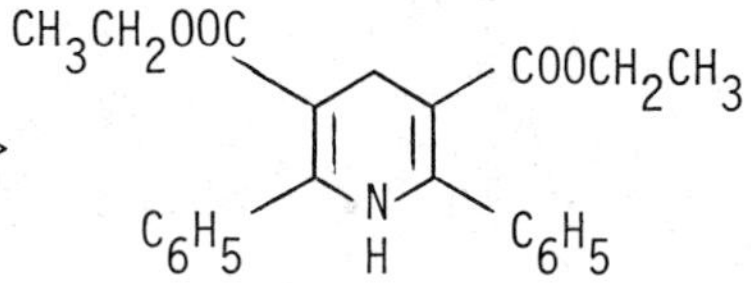

1. HNO_3, H_2SO_4
2. KOH, CH_3CH_2OH
3. CaO, Δ

⟶ product ;

(c) Paal-Knorr: $H\overset{O}{\overset{\|}{C}}\underset{CH_3}{\underset{|}{C}H}-\underset{CH_3}{\underset{|}{C}H}\overset{O}{\overset{\|}{C}}H \xrightarrow{NH_3}$ product;

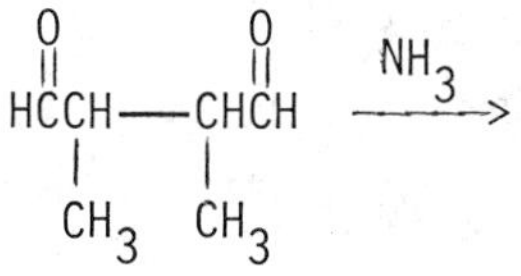

(d) Fischer: 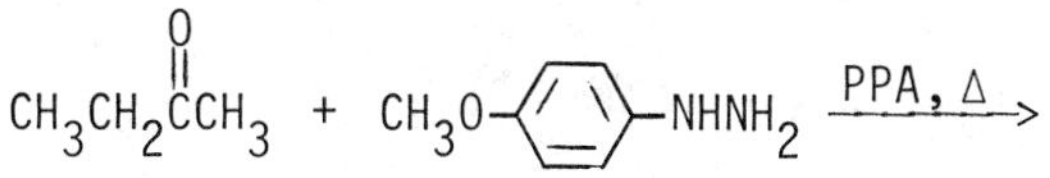

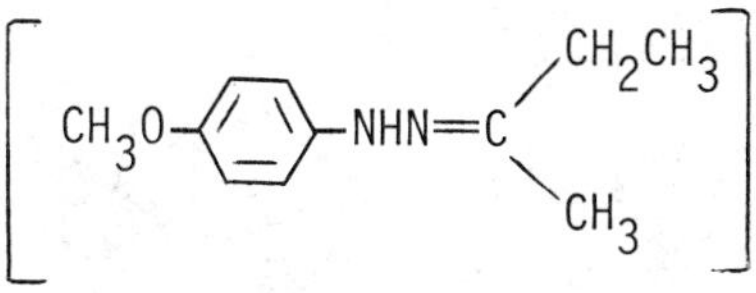 ⟶ product.

****

21. $H_{sat'd} = 10 + 2 = 12$; deg. unsat'n. $= \frac{12-6}{2} = 3$ π bonds and/or rings in 'E'. 'F' has 1 π bond or ring. Result of H_2 addition to 'E' suggests that it has 2 π bonds and 1 ring, and the π bonds are gone in 'F'.

NMR of E: CH_3- (δ2.3), perhaps 3 CH's, leaving one C and one O. No evidence for an alcohol, so assume the O is an ether. Some possibilities:

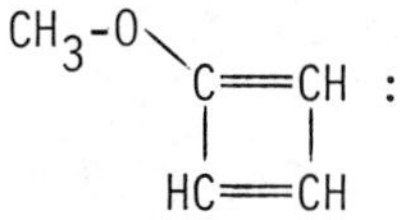 : unreasonable: CH_3- signal should be further downfield, and the ring would be very unstable (Section 25-5).

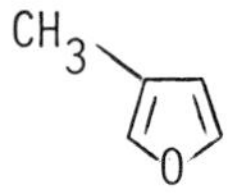 and 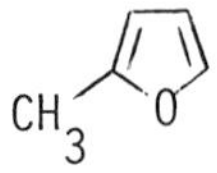: both reasonable possibilities at this stage.

NMR of F: complicated, but two pieces of information are extractable. First, the CH_3- is upfield (δ1.2) and a doublet, consistent with either

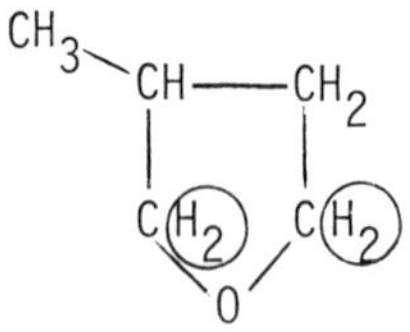

4H near O

or

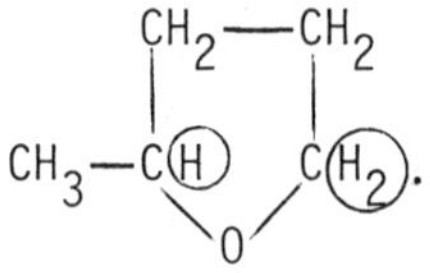

3H near O

Second, the signal between δ3.4 and 4.0 for H's on carbons next to O integrates to 3H, consistent only with the second structure. So E is 2-methylfuran and F is 2-methyloxacyclopentane.

****

22. $H_{sat'd} = 10 + 2 = 12$; deg. unsat'n. $= \frac{12-4}{2} = 4$ π bonds and/or rings.

NMR: δ9.7 suggests aldehyde (supported by IR), together with 3 CH's. Similar to problem 21, try furans as possibilities:

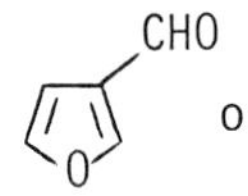 or 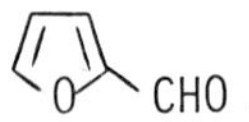.

How to choose? Which is more likely to come from an aldopentose? A possible (abbreviated) mechanism:

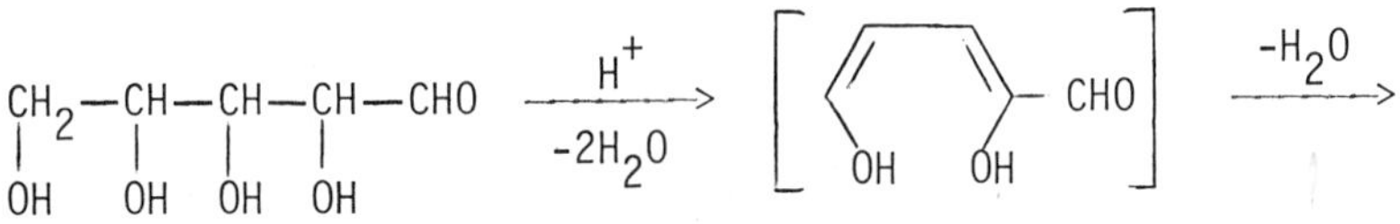

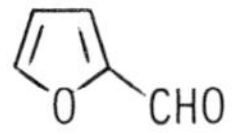 is G.

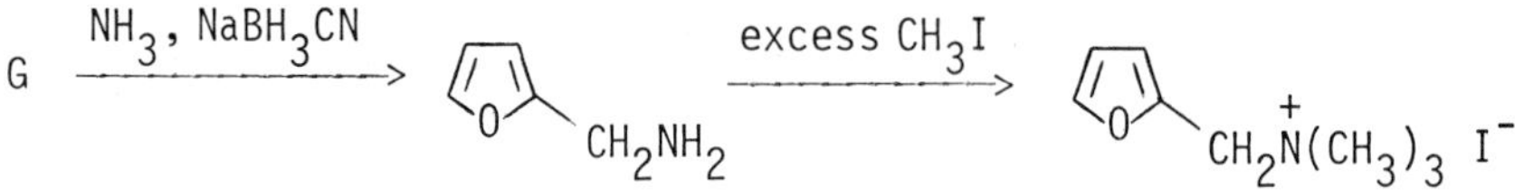

furethonium

****

23. 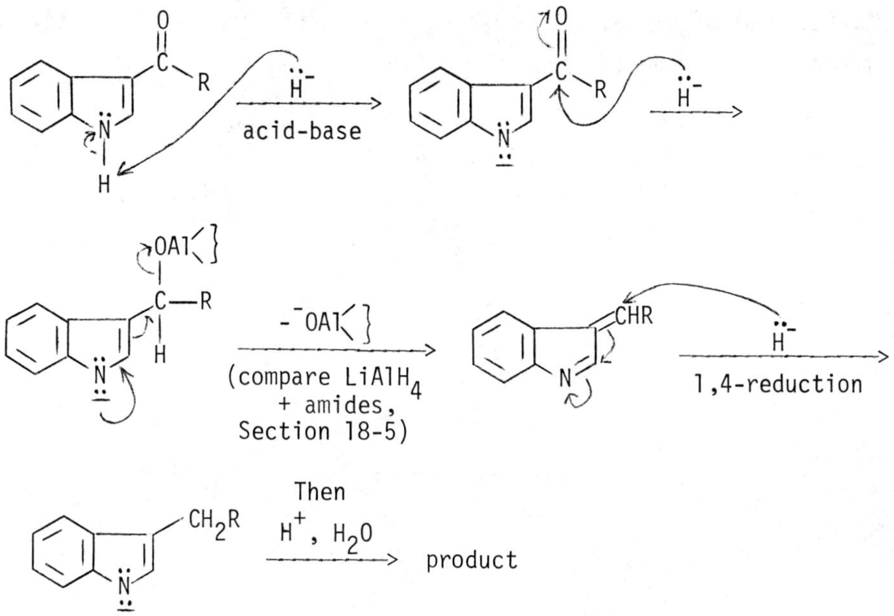

****

24. 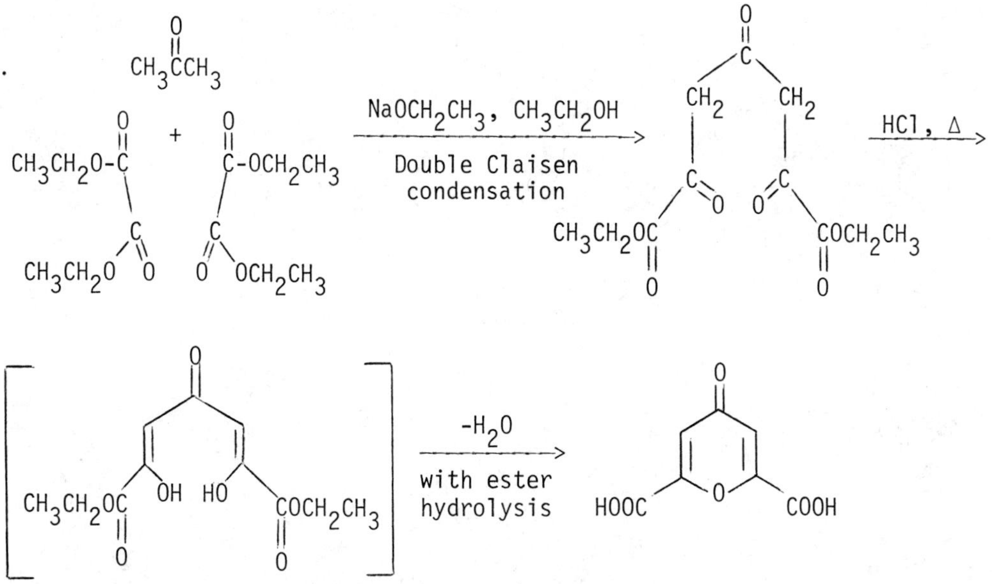

Bis-enol: compare synthesis
of furans, etc., from 1,4-diketones.

****

25. (a) H_2, Pt; (b) Stepwise, ring opening of azacyclopropane first, followed by intramolecular amide (lactam) formation:

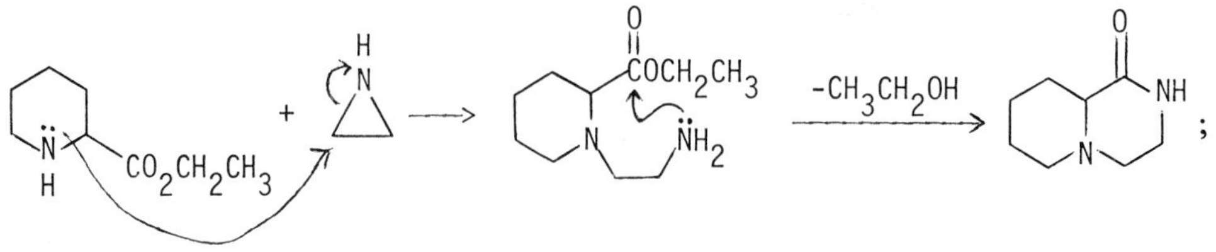

(c) 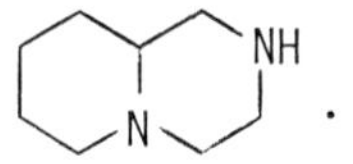

****

26. 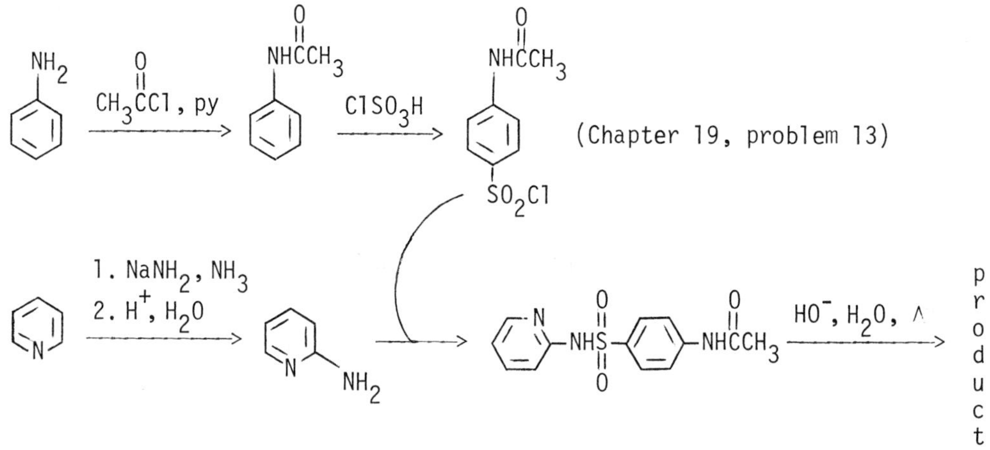

****

27. 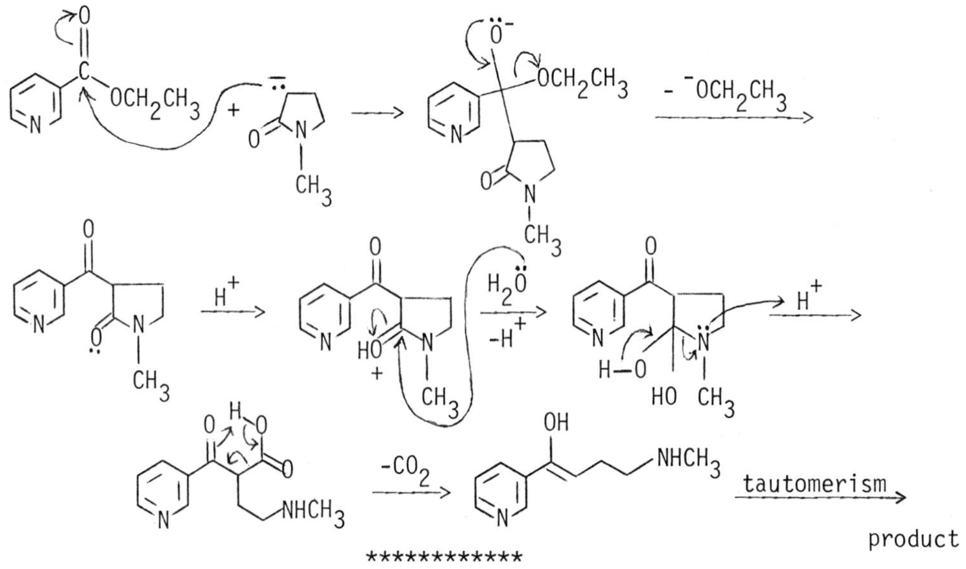

****

28. Reaction with an activated derivative of ethanoic acid such as the anhydride would provide the product:

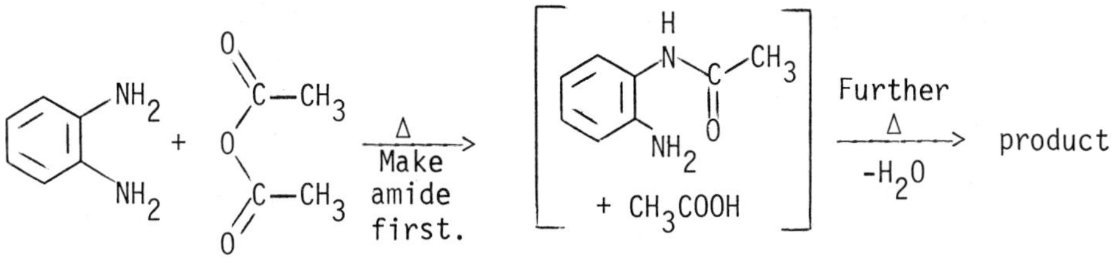

****

29. Double imine formation:

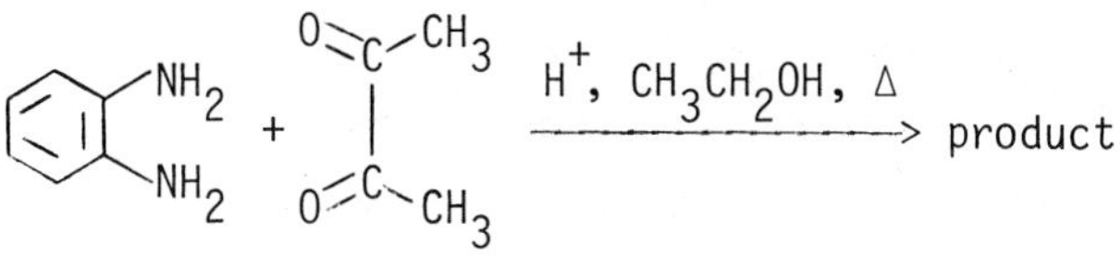

****

30. Stepwise:

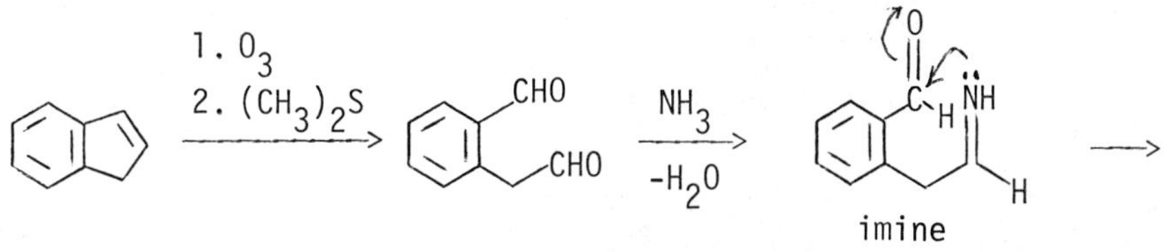

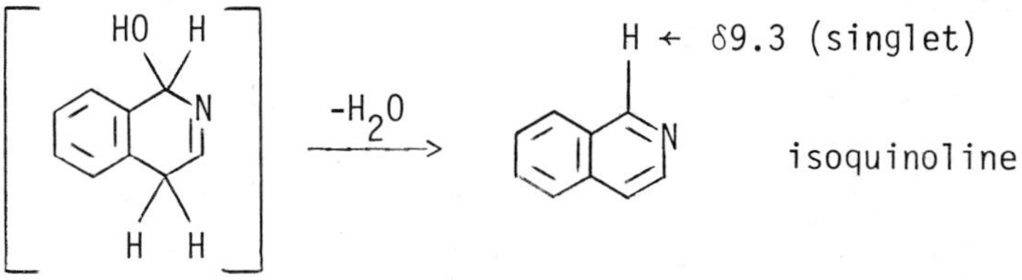

****

CHAPTER 27

Amino Acids, Peptides, and Proteins: Nitrogen-containing Monomers and Polymers in Nature

General Introduction

Here it is: the last chapter! It is, however, as much a beginning as an end. Chemistry in general, and organic chemistry in particular, are not isolated fields. Organic chemistry is the basic stuff of biology, and this chapter is the bridge between the two. The basic principles that govern the behaviour of organic molecules in general are shown here to be directly applicable to molecules of greater and greater complexity. You will see here some of the most fundamental molecules of life viewed from the organic chemist's point of view. The next step in this direction is biochemistry.

Outline of the Chapter

27-1. The Structure and Acid-Base Properties of Amino Acids.

Nature's most versatile building blocks.

27-2. The Preparation of Amino Acids.

Fancy footwork involving two very different functional groups.

27-3. Amino Acid Oligomers and Polymers: Peptides and Proteins.

The whole is greater than the sum of its parts.

27-4. The Determination of Polypeptide Primary Structure: Sequencing.

Exercises in logic, plus a lot of hard work.

27-5. The Synthesis of Polypeptides: a Protecting Group Challenge.

Even fancier footwork; how does Nature do it so easily??!!

27-6. Polypeptides in Nature: the Proteins Myoglobin and Hemoglobin.

27-7. The Biosynthesis of Proteins: Nucleic Acids.

How Nature *appears* to do it so easily.

Keys to the Chapter

27-1. The Structure and Acid-Base Properties of Amino Acids.

Read the introduction to the chapter and this text section, and then come back here. All done? O.K., here's the big picture. The chemistry of life is complicated. Structures have to be built to hold things together, and a lot of chemical reactions have to be going on to maintain the various functions that maintain life, such as energy storage and utilization. These all have to occur under a very constrained set of conditions: water is the only available solvent, and in general only very narrow ranges of temperature and pH are acceptible. Otherwise everything falls apart. So how is it done? The answer begins with the amino acids.

Look first at the structures of the twenty most common examples: Table 27-1. They differ only in the group attached to the α-carbon. The variety in these groups establishes the versatility of amino acids. There are nonpolar groups, both small and large, capable of varying degrees of steric interaction. There are uncharged but polar groups, capable of hydrogen bonding. There are nitrogen-containing groups of varying base strengths, some of which will be protonated and positively charged at pH 7. There are oxygen and sulfur groups of varying acid strengths, some of which will be deprotonated and negatively charged at pH 7. Because of this variety, Nature can choose from among these twenty compounds just the right one to fill any of a number of chemical needs. One feature that is emphasized in this section is the acid-base behaviour of the amino acids as a function of pH. Table 27-1 lists pK_a values for all relevant groups. Notice, for one thing, that the way we have drawn amino acids up to now, H_2N-CHR-COOH, is *wrong*. Amino acids in fact *never* exist to any significant extent in this form, with neutral amino and carboxylic acid groups present at the same time. Depending on the pH, one or both of these groups is always charged, with the pH 7 structure being ^+H_3N-CHR-COO^-. This feature has two immediate consequences: amino acids can interact well with polar molecules, including water, and amino acids are very good *buffers* at a variety of different pH's, depending on R. Obviously the effects of pH on amino acid structure are important, and problem 3 will give you several examples to work on so you can get the feel for it.

27-2. The Preparation of Amino Acids.

Although none of the individual reactions in this section are new, the sequences present them in clever combinations aimed at solving the problem of introducing basic and acidic groups into the same molecule.

27-3 and 27-4. The Structure of Peptides and Proteins.

Techniques for determining this information are extremely well worked out (and problems 16-23 will give you plenty of chances to try them for yourself). The results, especially in the subtleties of folding of these polymeric chains, reveal the true extent to which the characteristics of the different amino acids are combined and used in nature to generate large molecular assemblies perfectly suited for very specific biological roles. Problems 11-15 are intended to give you something to think about in this regard.

27-5. The Synthesis of Polypeptides: a Protecting Group Challenge.

Don't ever lose sight of the fact that the linkage between amino acids is nothing more than a simple amide bond: -HN—CO-. Nonetheless, the construction of peptide chains from simple amino acids is a major challenge for the same reasons that, say, mixed aldol or Claisen condensations (Sections 16-3 and 18-4) are tricky things to do: each amino acid involved has <u>both</u> a potentially nucleophilic atom (the N) and a potentially electrophilic one (the carboxyl C). Thus, an attempt at linking, say, the amine of amino acid 1 with the carboxyl of amino acid 2 is going to be complicated by the need to *prevent* the simultaneous linkage of either two molecules of a.a.1 to each other, two molecules of a.a.2 to each other, or a.a.1 to a.a.2 in the *wrong sense*: carboxyl of 1 to amine of 2. The solution to the problem lies in, again, a very well worked out array of functional group protection-deprotection procedures, the simplest of which are presented here. Problems 24-26 will let you try them for yourself.

27-6 and 27-7. Proteins in Operation; Biosynthesis.

Obviously only a tiny taste of what's involved with these topics can be presented in the space of two chapter sections. Nonetheless, you should be able to sense the remarkable way in which the linkage of relatively small units gives rise to structures of such highly elaborate function. This stuff is really neat. You might like to read more about it some time.

Solutions to Chapter 27 Problems

1.

$$
\begin{array}{cc}
\begin{array}{c}
\text{COOH} \\
\text{H}_2\text{N} \!-\!\!\!\!-\! \text{H} \quad S \\
\text{H}_3\text{C} \!-\!\!\!\!-\! \text{H} \quad S \\
\text{CH}_2\text{CH}_3
\end{array}
\text{L-isoleucine ;}
&
\begin{array}{c}
\text{COOH} \\
\text{H}_2\text{N} \!-\!\!\!\!-\! \text{H} \quad S \\
\text{H} \!-\!\!\!\!-\! \text{OH} \quad R \\
\text{CH}_3
\end{array}
\text{L-threonine}
\end{array}
$$

****

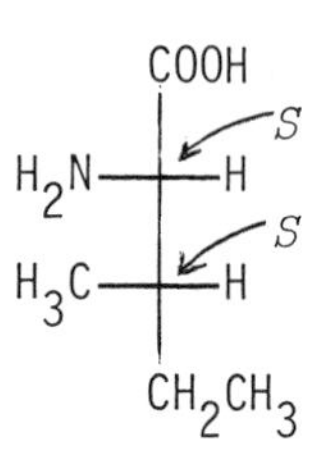

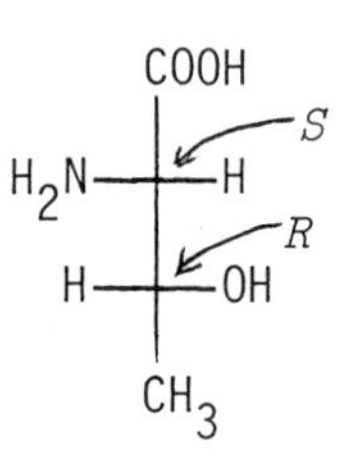

2. 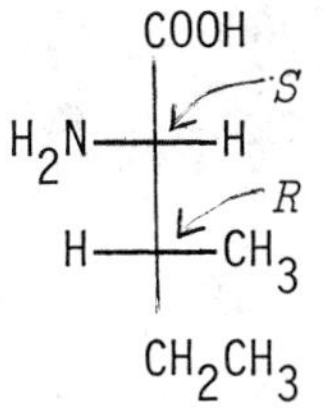 allo-L-isoleucine

****

3. Structures are presented in order of increasing pH (value in parentheses).

(a) 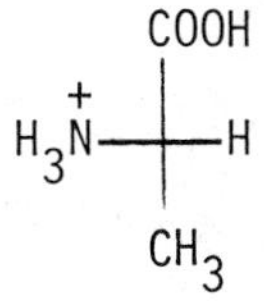 (1), 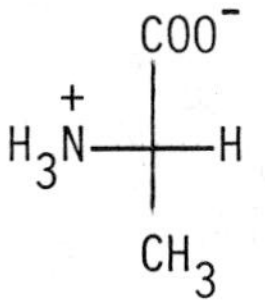 (7), 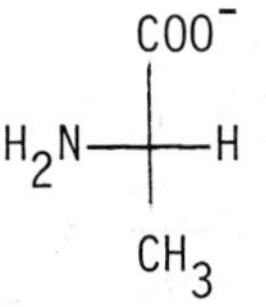 (12)

Isoelectric point, $pI = \frac{2.4+9.9}{2} = 6.2$

(b) 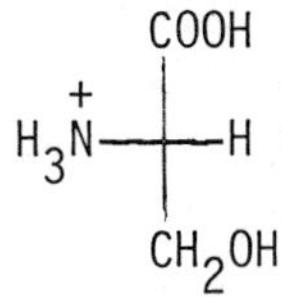 (1), 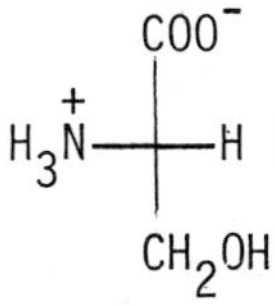 (7), 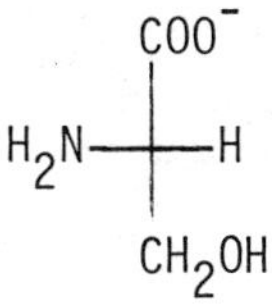 (12) $pI = \frac{2.2+9.4}{2} = 5.8$

(c) 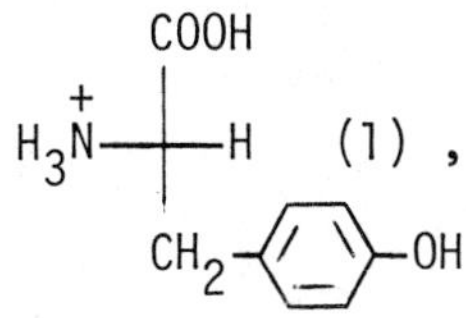 (1), 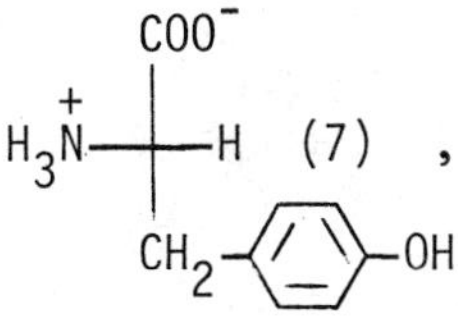 (7), 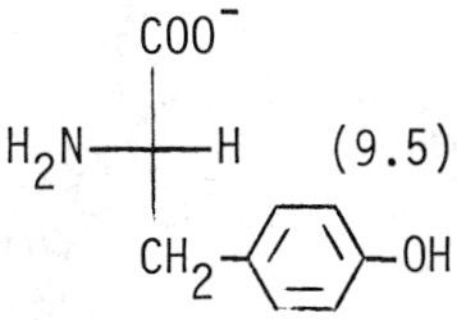 (9.5)

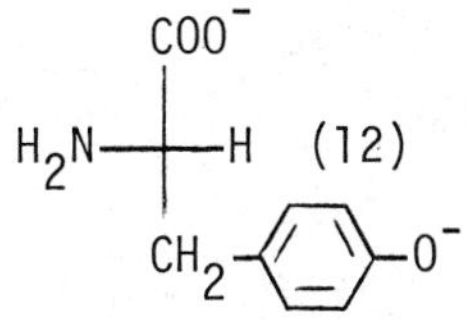 (12) $pI = \frac{2.2+9.1}{2} = 5.7$

(d) 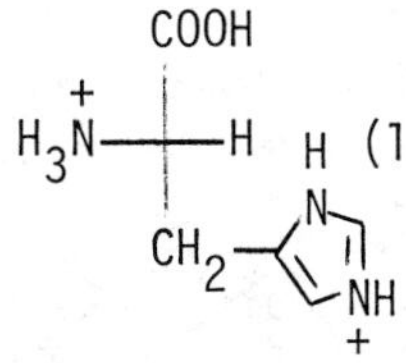 (1), 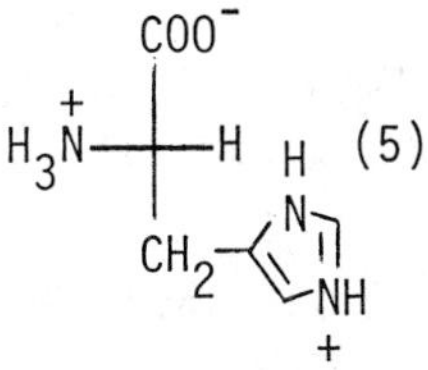 (5), 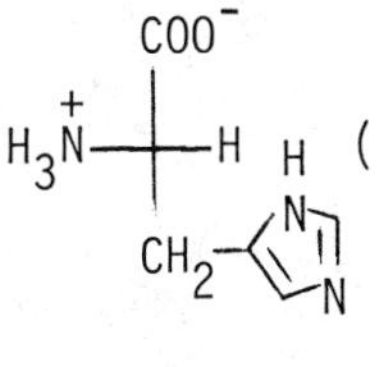 (7),

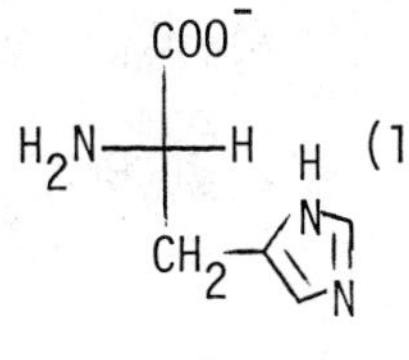 (12) $pI = \frac{6.1+9.2}{2} = 7.7$

(e) 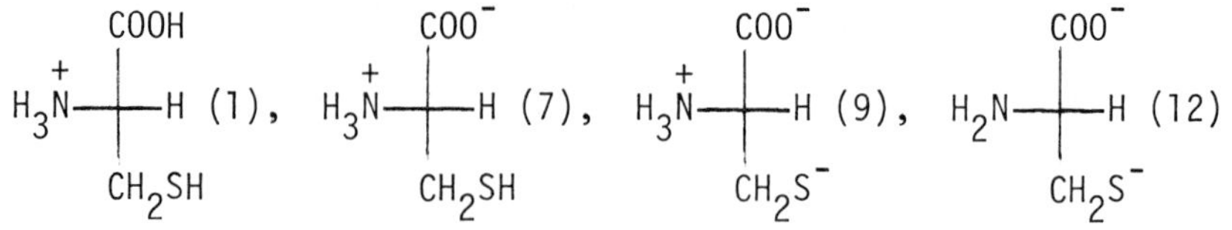

$$pI = \frac{1.9+8.4}{2} = 5.2$$

Note in the cases where more than two p$\underline{K}$ values exist that the p$\underline{I}$ is calculated using the p$\underline{K}$'s of the groups that react <u>first</u> upon treatment of the charge-neutralized zwitterionic form with acid and base, respectively.

(f) 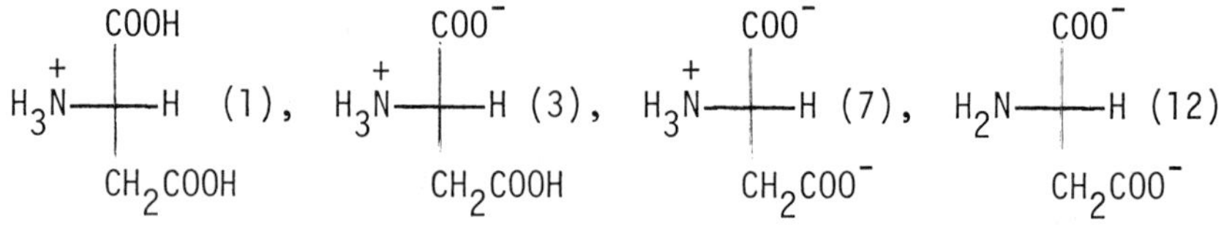

$$pI = \frac{2.0+3.9}{2} = 3.0$$

(g) 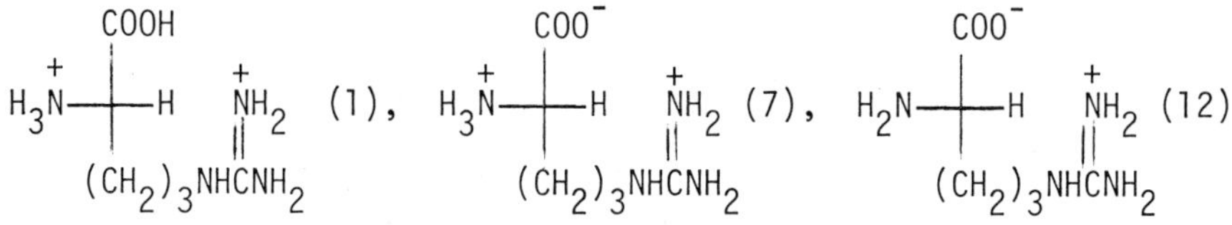

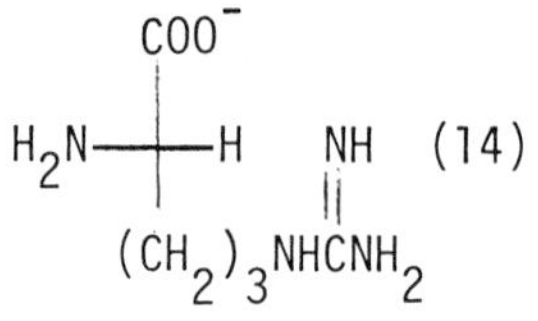

$$pI = \frac{9.0+13.2}{2} = 11.1$$

****

4. (a) Arg; (b) Ala, Ser, Tyr, His, Cys; (c) Asp.

****

5. (a) Since the R group is secondary, alkylation routes should be avoided. Use Strecker:

$$(CH_3)_2CHCHO \xrightarrow[2.\ HCN]{1.\ NH_3} (CH_3)_2CHCH(NH_2)CN \xrightarrow{H^+,\ H_2O} (CH_3)_2CHCH(\overset{+}{N}H_3)COO^-$$

(b) The R group is primary; now we have a choice. Either Strecker synthesis starting with $(CH_3)_2CHCH_2CHO$, or a Gabriel based method will do:

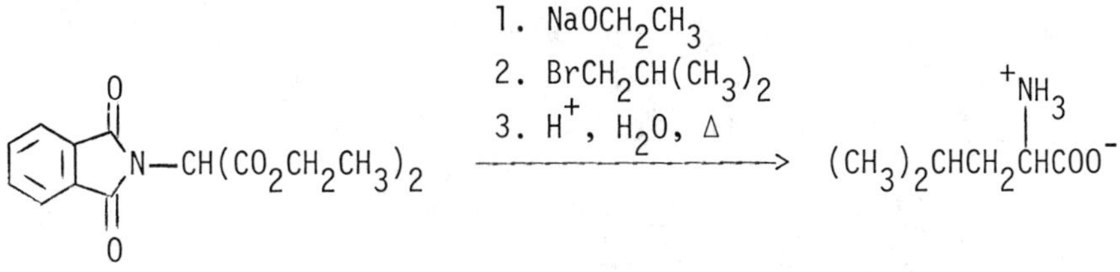

Even the (Hell-Volhardt-Zelinsky)-Amination sequence works just fine here:

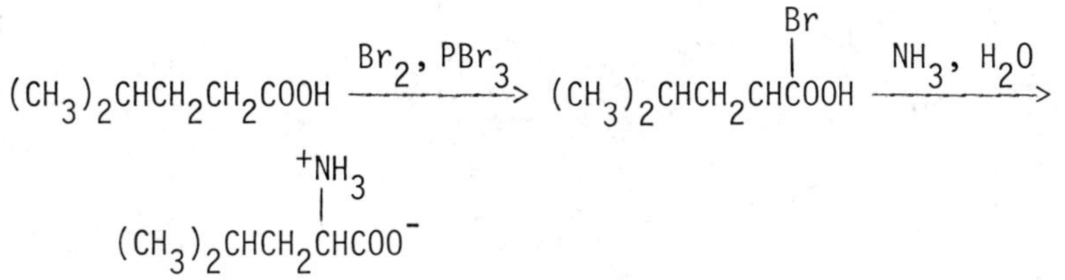

(c) Several ways to go, but you have to first recognize the need for a three-carbon building block with leaving groups at each end to allow linkage to both the α-carbon and the amine nitrogen to form the ring. The acetamido malonic ester method is illustrative:

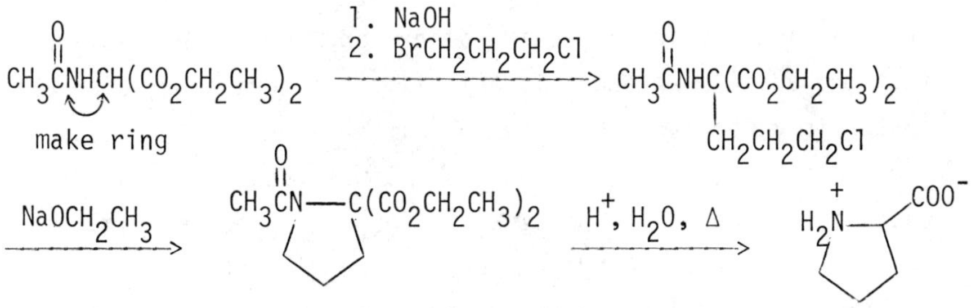

(d) Use the acetamidomalonic ester method again, replacing the $CH_2{=}O$ (used to synthesize serine) with CH_3CHO:

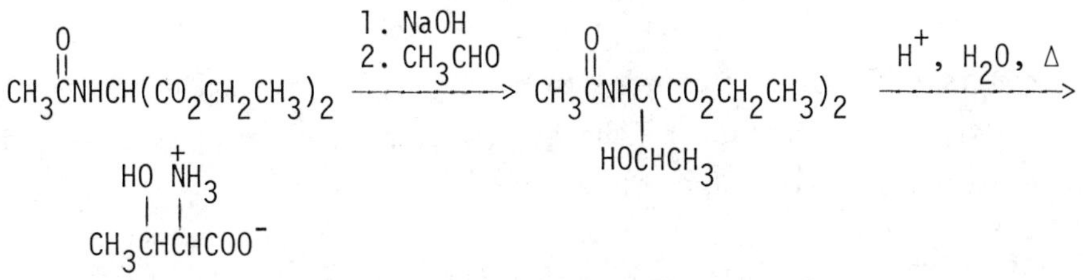

(e) The extra amine group must be present in protected form, irrespective of the method used. Here's a Gabriel-type sequence:

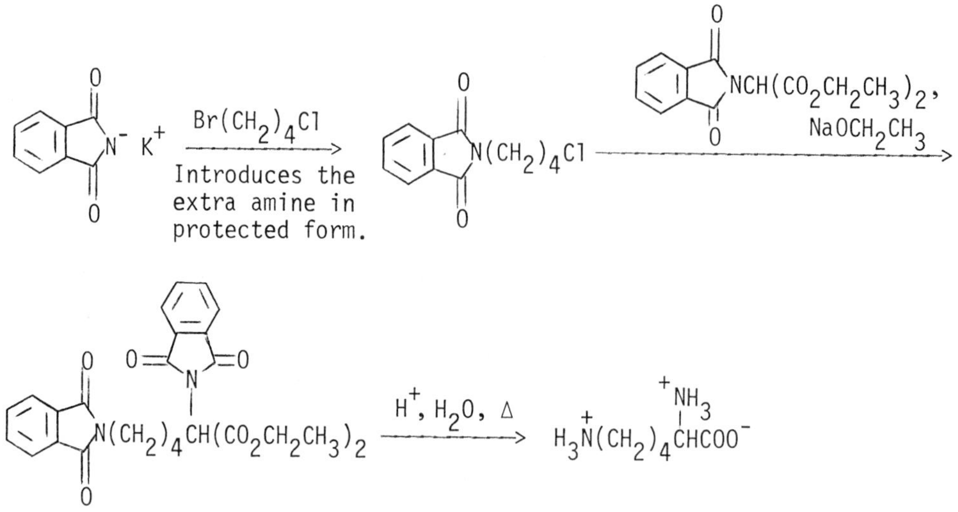

$$\text{Br(CH}_2)_4\text{Cl}$$

Introduces the extra amine in protected form.

$$\xrightarrow{\text{NaOCH}_2\text{CH}_3}$$

$$\xrightarrow{\text{H}^+,\ \text{H}_2\text{O},\ \Delta} \quad \text{H}_3\overset{+}{\text{N}}(\text{CH}_2)_4\overset{\overset{+}{\text{NH}_3}}{\underset{|}{\text{CH}}}\text{COO}^-$$

****

6. (a)
$$\xrightarrow[\substack{\text{3. H}^+,\ \text{H}_2\text{O}}]{\substack{\text{1. NH}_3 \\ \text{2. HCN}}}$$

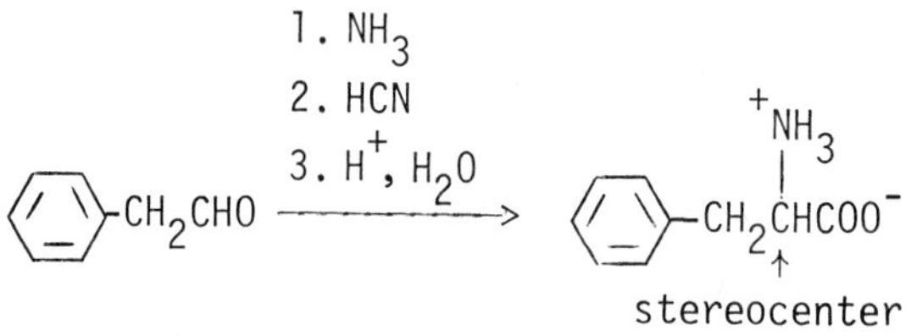

Chiral, but racemic (i.e., not optically active).

stereocenter

(b) The use of an optically active amine (an *S* enantiomer is shown) means that the addition product is actually a mixture since a second stere- center is generated, which can be either *R* or *S*. This is, therefore, a mixture of *R,S* and *S,S* products. Since these are <u>diastereomers</u> of each other, they don't necessarily form in identical yields. In fact, the *S,S* product (illustrated) greatly predominates, and, after hydroly- sis and removal of the phenylmethyl group in H_2, mainly *S* amino acid is obtained.

****

7. Allicin is structurally related to cysteine, which should be readily avail- able using a modification in the acetamidomalonic ester synthesis of serine by the sequence -OH → -Br → SH:

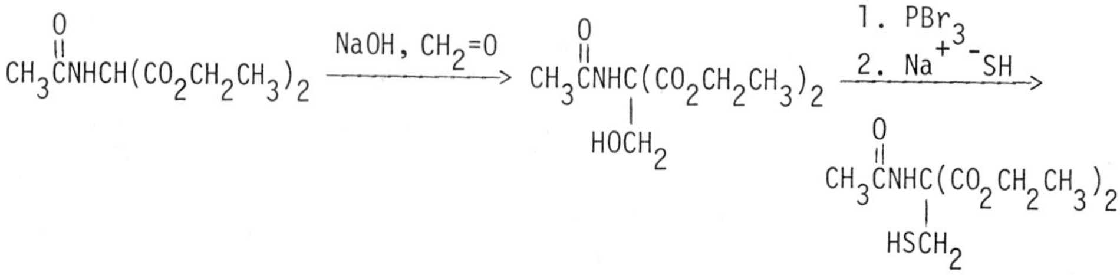

Treatment of this product with hot aqueous acid gives cysteine directly. Otherwise:

1. NaOH
2. $CH_2=CHCH_2Br$ $\longrightarrow$ $CH_3\overset{O}{\overset{||}{C}}NHC(CO_2CH_2CH_3)_2$

$CH_2=CHCH_2SCH_2$

1. H_2O_2
2. H^+, H_2O, Δ $\longrightarrow$ $CH_2=CHCH_2SCH_2\overset{O}{\overset{||}{C}}\overset{\overset{+NH_3}{|}}{C}HCOO^-$

****

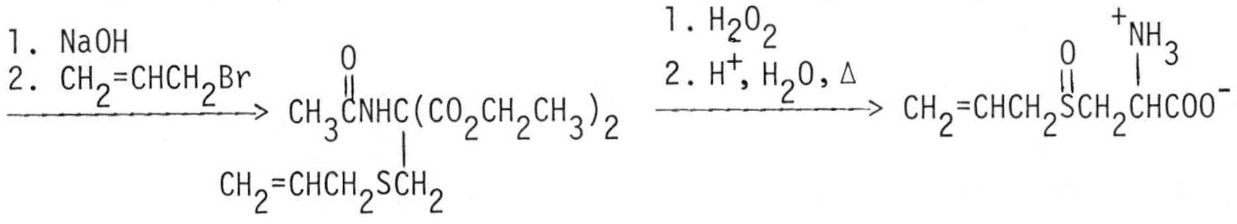

8. The alloisoleucines are diastereomers of the isoleucines, so simple recrystallization will separate them:

    mixture
    1. Dissolve in hot 80% ethanol
    2. Cool to 0°
    — crystals → (+)- and (-)-isoleucine
    — solution → (+)- and (-)- alloisoleucine

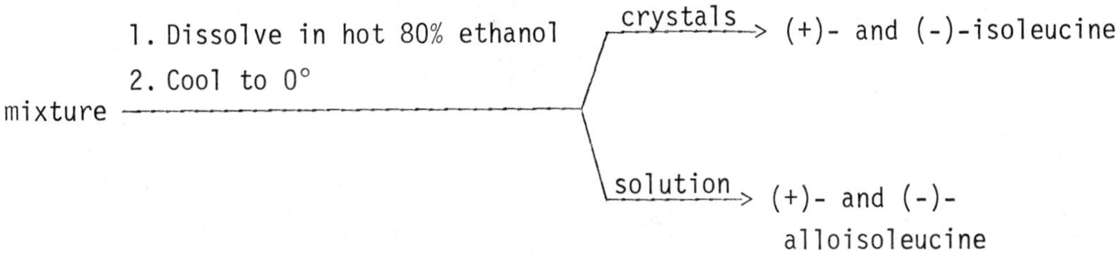

Continue with __each__ mixture of enantiomers separately, making use of brucine as a resolving agent as follows:

$CH_3CH_2CH(CH_3)\overset{\overset{+NH_3}{|}}{C}HCOO^-$
(+)/(-) mixture
$\xrightarrow[\text{(e.g. R = C}_6\text{H}_5)]{\overset{O\ O}{\overset{||\ ||}{RCOCR, \Delta}}}$ $CH_3CH_2CH(CH_3)\overset{\overset{\overset{O}{||}}{RCNH}}{\underset{|}{C}}HCOOH$
(+)/(-)

1. brucine, CH_3OH, 0°
2. separate (crystallization)

salt of (-)-acid   salt of (+)-acid

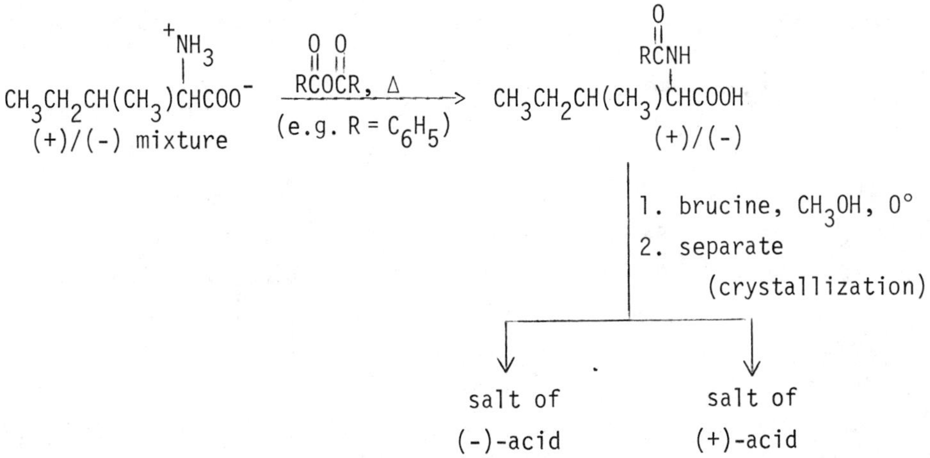

Finally, H^+, H_2O treatment releases each pure amino acid enantiomer in turn.

****

9. (a) tripeptide; (b) dipeptide; (c) tetrapeptide; (d) pentapeptide. The peptide bonds are simply the amide linkages, $-\overset{O}{\overset{||}{C}}-NH-$
    ↑

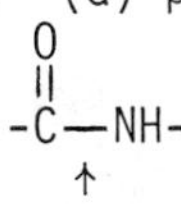

For example, in tripeptide (a):

$$(CH_3)_2CH \quad\quad CH_3 \quad\quad HSCH_2$$

$$\overset{+}{H_3}N-CH-\overset{\overset{O}{\|}}{C}-NH-CH-\overset{\overset{O}{\|}}{C}-NH-CH-COO^-$$

****

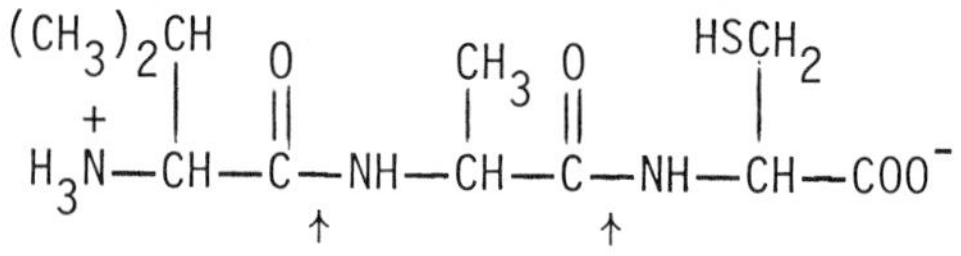

10. By convention, the short notation format always begins with the end of the peptide chain with the amino group (the "N-terminal" or "amino-terminal" end).

    (a) Val-Ala-Cys; (b) Ser-Asp; (c) His-Thr-Pro-Lys;

    (d) Tyr-Gly-Gly-Phe-Leu.

****

11. Determine the net charge on the amino acid or peptide at pH 7, and then recall that negative species migrate to the anode (A), positive to the cathode (C), and neutrals do not migrate at all (N).
    Amino acids (problem 3): (a)-(e) N, (f) A, (g) C.
    Peptides (problem 9): (a) N, (b) A, (c) C, (d) N.

****

12. The side chains are all small ($-H$, $-CH_3$, or $-CH_2OH$), and mostly non-polar. In the illustrations, especially Figure 27-4(b), note that the sheet structure packs the R groups into small channels between layers of sheets, where only small groups will fit easily. The non-polar nature of five of the six groups is also compatible with their location, a relatively non-polar region with few hydrogen-bonding groups in the vicinity.

****

13. The α-helix stretches are fairly noticeable by their spiral shape [compare Figure 27-4(c)]. Myoglobin in fact contains eight significant α-helical stretches which are labeled by the letters A-H (see following page - 501):

α-helix	amino acid numbers	α-helix	amino acid numbers
A	3-18	E	58-77
B	20-35	F	86-94
C	36-42	G	100-118
D	51-57	H	125-148

In the figure all but α-helix D (which is viewed on-end from this perspective) are fairly easy to pick out.

The four prolines are located at or near the ends of α-helixes, and coincide with "kinks" in the overall tertiary structure of the molecule; a result of the conformational characteristics of the five-membered ring:

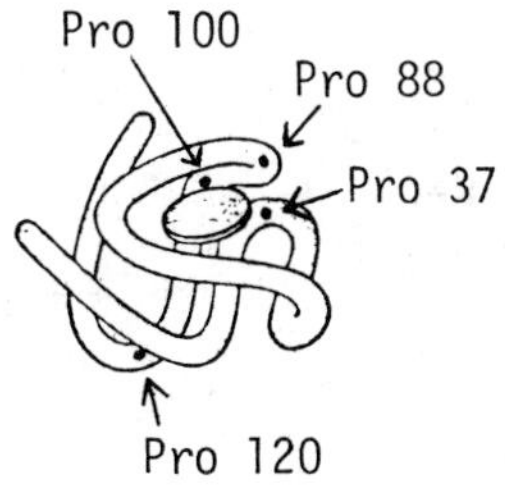

****

14. Except for the two histidines associated with the heme-bound iron atom, all the polar side chains are well-positioned for hydrogen bonding with solvent molecules (water). In contrast, all the non-polar side chains adopt interior positions, avoiding contact with polar solvent molecules.

****

15. (a) The sheet structure is favored by amino acids with small, non-polar side chains, and has very little ability to hydrogen bond to a polar solvent like water (problem 12).

(b) In globular proteins the polar side chains are exposed to the solvent, solubilizing the entire molecule (problem 14). Similar effects are seen in micelles formed by soap molecules, in which polar groups are located on the surface, facilitating water solubility, while non-polar groups are buried in the inside (Figure 17-16, Section 17-12).

(c) If the tertiary structure of a globular protein is disrupted, its non-polar amino acid side chains become exposed to the polar solvent, greatly reducing the overall solubility of the protein molecule.

****

16. (1) Treat with HCO_3H to cleave disulfide bridge. (2) On a portion of the sample, degrade the entire chain by amide hydrolysis (6N HCl, 110°C, 24h) to determine amino acid composition using amino acid analyzer. (3) On another portion of material apply repetitive Edman degradation to determine the sequence of amino acids. Since only nine are present, the entire chain may be sequenced in this way.

****

17. (a) 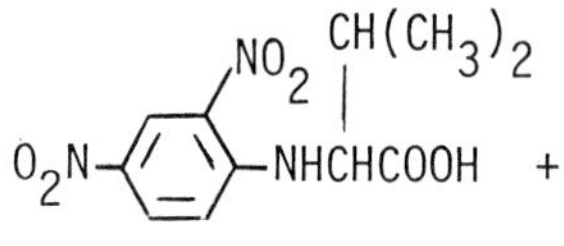 + Ala, Cys ; (b) 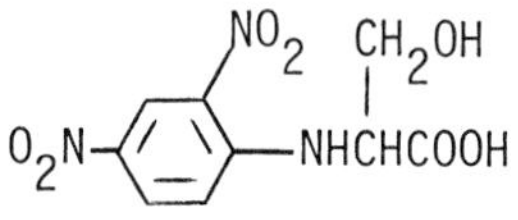 + Asp ;

(c) 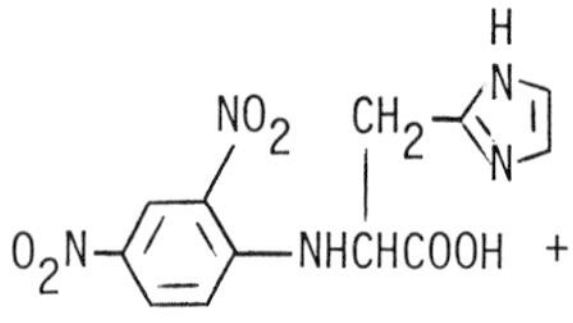 + Thr, Pro, Lys ;

(d) 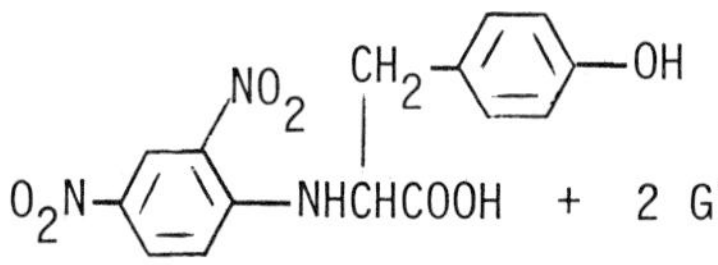 + 2 Gly, Phe, Leu.

****

18. Since the peptide is cyclic, neither process will give a normal result. Sanger's reagent will react with the "extra" amino groups of the two ornithines. After hydrolysis the products will be 2 moles of

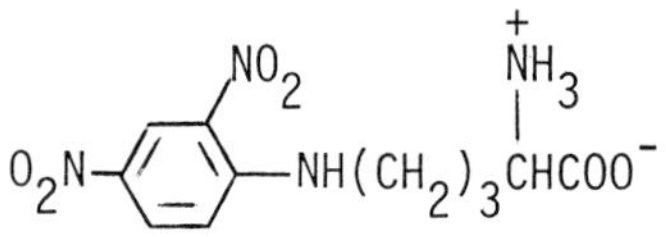 and 2 moles each of Leu, *R*-Phe, Pro, and Val.

The Edman procedure will simply form thiourea derivatives at the two Orn amino groups: 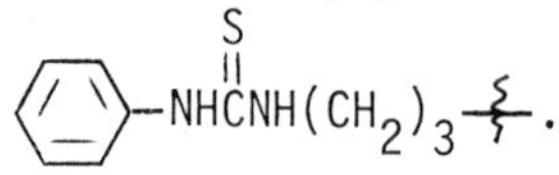. Since there is no α-amino group available to react, mild acid treatment will not cleave any bonds in the product at all, and the cyclic polypeptide structure will remain intact.

****

19. Sanger's reagent reveals the "first" (N-terminal) amino acid to be Arg. Complete hydrolysis indicates a total of nine amino acid units are present. Using the four fragments of incomplete hydrolysis, we know that the peptide begins with Arg (above) so the fragment Arg-Pro-Pro-Gly must be first. There is only one Gly present, so the last Gly of this tetrapeptide must be the same one that is at the start of the tripeptide fragment Gly-Phe-Ser. We can use the same logic to start overlapping all the pieces to generate the whole solution. So, since only one Ser is present, the last Ser in the above tripeptide must be the same as the first one in Ser-Pro-Phe. We have so far:

1 2 3 4 5 6 7 8

Arg-Pro-Pro-Gly

Gly-Phe-Ser

Ser-Pro-Phe

The final fragment, Phe-Arg, clearly is at the end, overlapping the Phe in position 8. So the answer is:

Arg-Pro-Pro-Gly-Phe-Ser-Pro-Phe-Arg.

****

20. (a) If cleavage of an S-S bridge does not separate a peptide into two chains, then obviously the two sulfurs must be contained in two Cys units within a single peptide chain:

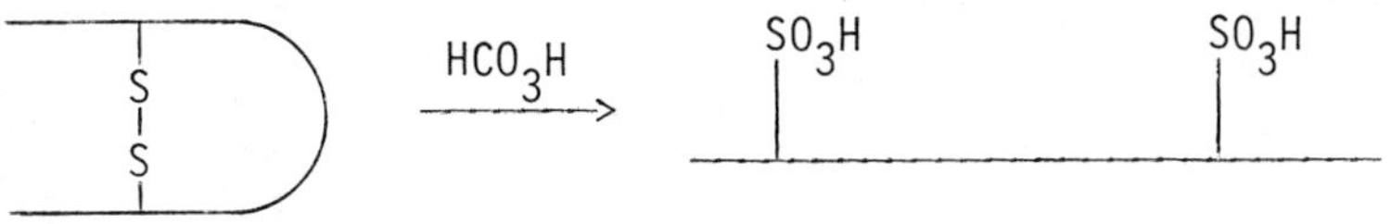

(b) Trypsin cleaves only after Arg or Lys. The first and third peptides end in Lys, but the second ends in Cys(SO_3H). Since trypsin should not cleave after Cys(SO_3H) the only way to get a piece with Cys(SO_3H) at the end is if the whole peptide ends in Cys(SO_3H):

cleave ↓ after each Lys:

—Lys—Lys—Cys(SO_3H) $\xrightarrow{\text{trypsin}}$ —Lys + —Lys + —Cys(SO_3H).

So the peptide ends with Thr-Phe-Thr-Ser-Cys.

(c) Chymotrypsin cleaves after Phe, Trp, and Tyr, giving a different assortment of peptide fragments. The job now is to overlap the fragments from trypsin and chymotrypsin hydrolyses:

This overlap is the key to the solution.

	Thr-Phe-Thr-Ser-Cys	(trypsin piece)
Ala-Gly-Cys-Lys-Asn-Phe	Lys-Thr-Phe Thr-Ser-Cys	(chymo trypsin)
Ala-Gly-Cys-Lys Asn-Phe-Phe-Trp-Lys		(trypsin again)

So the answer is:

Ala-Gly-Cys-Lys-Asn-Phe-Phe-Trp-Lys-Thr-Phe-Thr-Ser-Cys.
(S—S bridge between the two Cys)

****

21. In order of appearance, 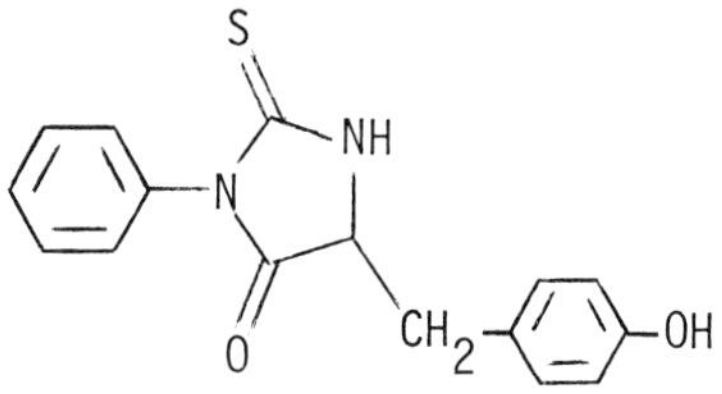 , 2 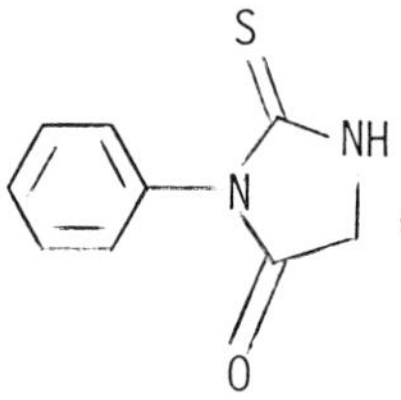 ,

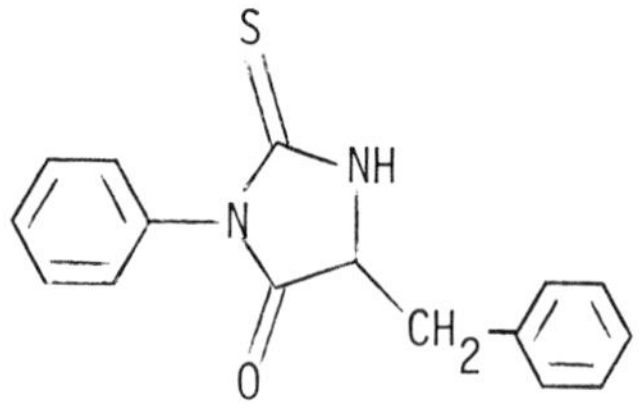 , and 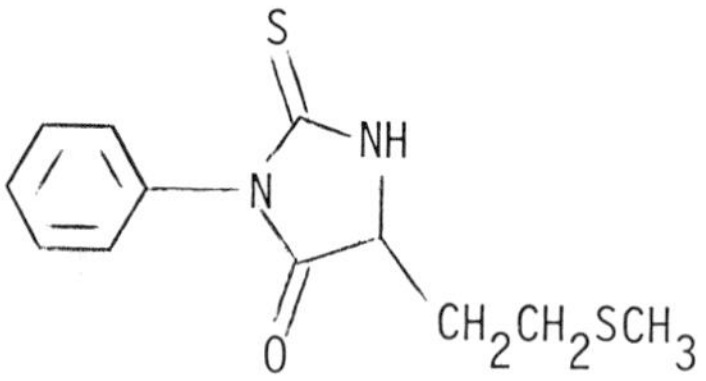 .

The last product to appear from leu-enkephalin would be 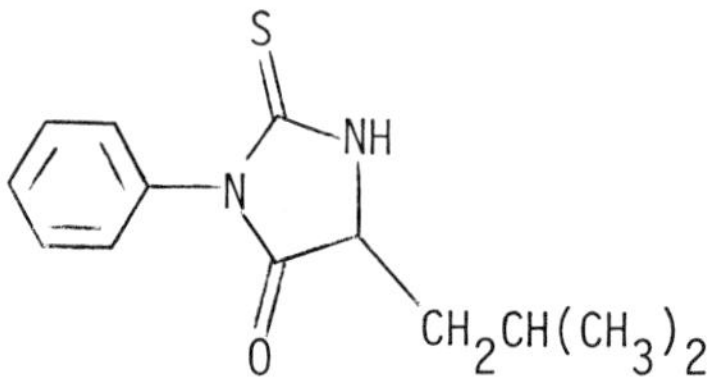 .

****

22. As in problem 20, look first for a piece that ends with an amino acid that should not be a site of cleavage by one of the enzymes. All the chymotrypsin fragments end in Phe, Trp, or Tyr, so that's no help. The trypsin results are more useful: it only cleaves after Arg or Lys, so the 18-amino acid fragment ending in Phe must be at the end of the intact hormone as well: Now it's a matter of matching up all the pieces. Start with this end piece from trypsin hydrolysis and overlap it with chymotrypsin fragments:

(trypsin piece) Val-Tyr-Pro-Asp-Ala-Gly-Glu-Asp-Gln-Ser-Ala-Glu-Ala-Phe-Pro-Leu-Glu-Phe
(chymotrypsin pieces) Pro-Asp-Ala-Gly-Glu-Asp-Gln-Ser-Ala-Glu-Ala-Phe Pro-Leu-Glu-Phe

Now identify a chymotrypsin piece to overlap with the Val-Tyr- front end of the trypsin piece, and then continue the process, all the way to the N-terminal end (the "beginning") of the entire hormone:

Ser-Tyr-Ser-Met-Glu-His-Phe-Arg Trp-Gly-Lys Pro-Val-Gly-Lys Pro-Val-Lys Val-Tyr-
Ser-Tyr Ser-Met-Glu-His-Phe Arg-Trp Gly-Lys-Pro-Val-Gly-Lys-Lys-Arg-Arg-Pro-Val-Lys-Val-Tyr

The complete answer is read directly, starting at Ser-Tyr- just above, overlapping Val-Tyr with the large trypsin piece, and then on to the end:

Ser-Tyr-Ser-Met-Gln-His-Phe-Arg-Trp-Gly-Lys-Pro-Val-Gly-Lys-Lys-Arg-Arg-Pro-Val-Lys-Val-Tyr-Pro-Asp-Ala-Gly-Glu-Asp-Gln-Ser-Ala-Glu-Ala-Phe-Pro-Leu-Glu-Phe

****

23. (a) Thermolysin cleaves before Leu, Ile, and Val, so chain 'B' beginning with His, must be at the beginning of the entire hormone.

Chymotrypsin does not cleave peptide 'A', so the Phe in it must be at its end (otherwise chymotrypsin would have cleaved it after the Phe). We know from Sanger degradation that 'A' starts with Leu. We can therefore put together the clostripain pieces and get the entire structure of peptide 'A':

Sanger ↓ Must be at end. ↓
Leu-Asp-Ser-Arg Arg Ala-Gln-Asp-Phe (clostripain fragments)
so Leu-Asp-Ser-Arg-Arg-Ala-Gln-Asp-Phe is peptide 'A'.

Since 'B' begins with His (Sanger), the chymotrypsin results extend our knowledge this far:

His-Ser-Gln-Gly-Thr-Phe-(Ser-Lys-Tyr / Thr-Ser-Asp-Tyr) peptide 'B'.
↑ order unknown

(b) The trypsin piece overlaps with the first four amino acids of peptide 'A', so it tells us that the amino acid immediately preceding the beginning of peptide 'A' is Tyr. Since this is a piece derived from trypsin hydrolysis, this Tyr must follow either a Lys or an Arg (these are the sties of trypsin hydrolysis). Now we are cooking: look for Tyr's at the ends of other fragments to find one that follows a Lys or an Arg. The <u>only one</u> is the Tyr that follows a Lys in one of the pieces of peptide 'B'. This must obviously be at the end of peptide 'B', attaching to the beginning of peptide 'A', so now we know the correct order of peptide 'B':

His-Ser-Gln-Gly-Thr-Phe-Thr-Ser-Asp-Tyr-Ser-Lys-Tyr is peptide 'B'.

So now we know this much about the hormone:

His-····-Tyr-Leu-····-Phe- (Val-Gln-Tyr / Leu-Met-Asn-Thr)

His-····-Tyr = peptide 'B'; Leu-····-Phe = peptide 'A'; (Val-Gln-Tyr, Leu-Met-Asn-Thr) ↑ order unknown

(c) Since chymotrypsin releases Leu-Met-Asn-Thr from the hormone, and chymotrypsin is <u>not</u> supposed to cleave after Thr, this piece must be at the end of the entire molecule.

So the answer is:

His-Ser-Gln-Gly-Thr-Phe-Thr-Ser-Asp-Tyr-Ser-Lys-Tyr-Leu-Asp-Ser-Arg-Arg-Ala-Gln-Asp-Phe-Val-Gln-Tyr-Leu-Met-Asn-Thr.

****

24. Follow the lead of Exercise 27-10, and start at the carboxy-terminal end:

1. Phe + $(CH_3)_3C\overset{O}{\overset{\|}{C}}O\overset{O}{\overset{\|}{C}}OC(CH_3)_3 \longrightarrow$ Boc-Phe (N-protected Phe)

2. Leu $\xrightarrow{CH_3OH,\ H^+}$ Leu-OCH_3 (methyl ester: carboxy-protected Leu)

3. Boc-Phe + Leu-OCH_3 $\xrightarrow{DCC}$ Boc-Phe-Leu-OCH_3 $\xrightarrow{dil.\ H^+}$ Phe-Leu-OCH_3

4. Gly + $(CH_3)_3C\overset{O}{\overset{\|}{C}}O\overset{O}{\overset{\|}{C}}OC(CH_3)_3 \longrightarrow$ Boc-Gly (N-protected Gly)

5. Boc-Gly + Phe-Leu-OCH_3 $\xrightarrow{DCC}$ Boc-Gly-Phe-Leu-OCH_3 $\xrightarrow{dil.\ H^+}$ Gly-Phe-Leu-OCH_3

6. Boc-Gly again + Gly-Phe-Leu-OCH_3 $\xrightarrow{DCC}$ Boc-Gly-Gly-Phe-Leu-OCH_3 $\xrightarrow{dil.\ H^+}$ Gly-Gly-Phe-Leu-OCH_3

7. Tyr + excess $(CH_3)_3COC(=O)OC(=O)OC(CH_3)_3$ $\rightarrow$ Boc-Tyr (N- and phenolic O-protected Tyr)

8. Boc-Tyr + Gly-Gly-Phe-Leu-OCH_3 $\xrightarrow{DCC}$ Boc-Tyr-Gly-Gly-Phe-Leu-OCH_3 $\xrightarrow{1.\ H^+,\ H_2O;\ 2.\ HO^-,\ H_2O}$ Tyr-Gly-Gly-Phe-Leu (= Leu-enkephalin)

****

25. 1. His $\xrightarrow{Cbz\text{-}Cl}$ ring N-protected (Cbz)His $\xrightarrow{(CH_3)_3COC(=O)OC(=O)OC(CH_3)_3}$ amine N-protected Boc-(Cbz)His

The purpose here is to block <u>both</u> reactive nitrogens of His differently. The Boc group will be later removed by acid to allow a peptide bond to be formed, while the ring N remains Cbz protected.

2. Pro $\xrightarrow{CH_3OH,\ H^+}$ Pro-OCH_3 (carboxy-protected Pro)

3. Boc-(Cbz)His + Pro-OCH_3 $\xrightarrow{DCC}$ Boc-(Cbz)His-Pro-OCH_3 $\xrightarrow{dil.\ H^+}$ (Cbz)His-Pro-OCH_3

4. Glu $\xrightarrow{135\text{-}140°}$ pyroglutamic acid (amine group now an amide - so no further protection is necessary)

5. pyroglutamic acid + (Cbz)His-Pro-OCH_3 $\xrightarrow{DCC}$ pyroglutamoyl-(Cbz)His-Pro-OCH_3 $\xrightarrow{1.\ HO^-,\ H_2O;\ 2.\ DCC;\ 3.\ NH_3}$ pyroglutamoyl-(Cbz)His-Pro-NH_2 $\xrightarrow{H_2,\ Pd}$ TRH

****

26. Yes: the second carboxylic acid group in Asp will be a problem. A way must be devised to selectively protect this "extra" -COOH group, leaving the other -COOH free to form the peptide linkage. Other amino acids that cause problems are Glu, for the same reason, and Lys, due to its "extra" $-NH_2$,

which likewise requires selective protection in any peptide synthesis.

****

27. (a) C: 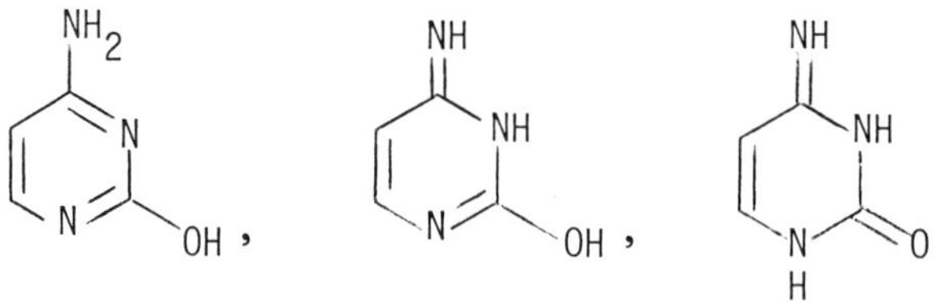

T: 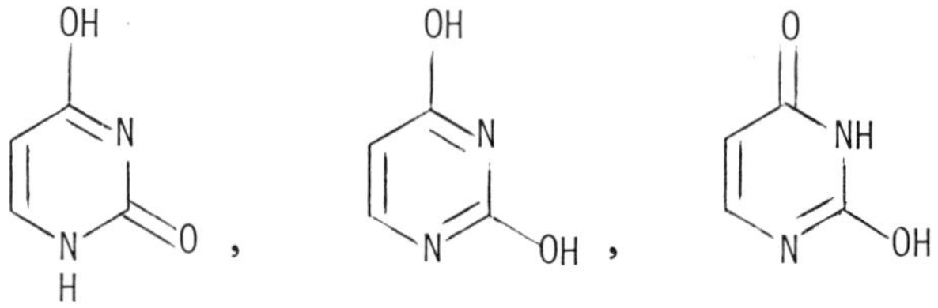

A: 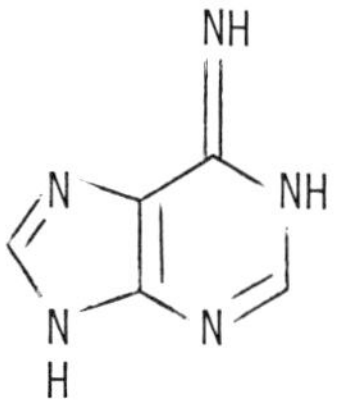

G: 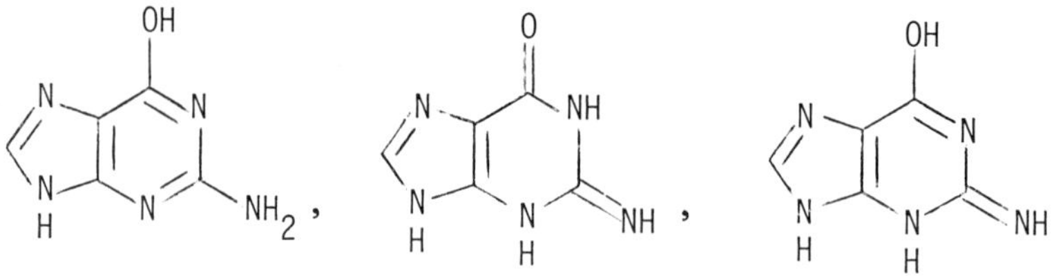

(b) 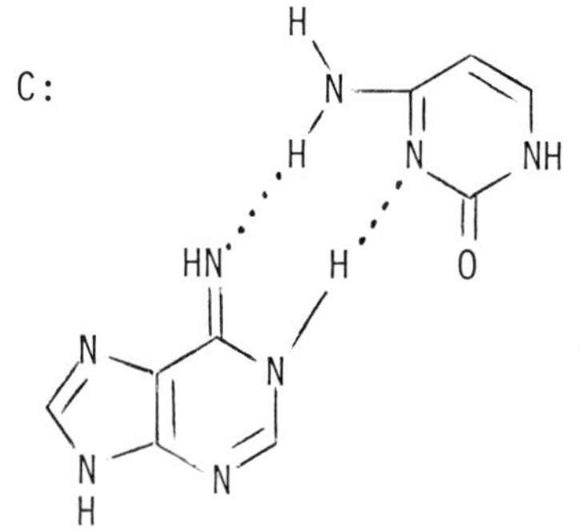

This mispairing makes the A look like a G (it pairs with C instead of a U).

(c) Amino acids: Tyr-Gly-Gly-Phe-Met.

Possible codons: AUG-UAC-GGA-GGA-UUU-AUG-UGA.

If an A in the DNA strand were to mis-pair with C instead of U in the synthesis of this m-RNA at the circled position, the result would be

CAC instead of UAC, which codes for His instead of Tyr. So the peptide ultimately synthesized would be His-Gly-Gly-Phe-Met.

****

28. 2332 X 3 + 3 (initiation codon) + 3 (termination codon) = 7002.

****

29. (a) 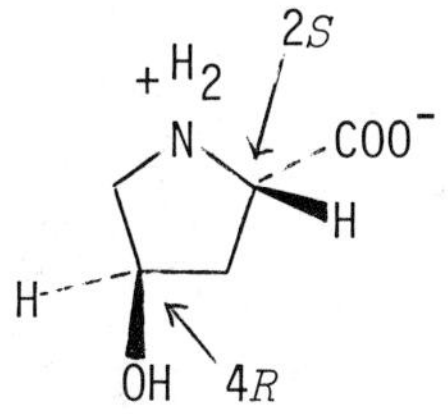

(b) (i) 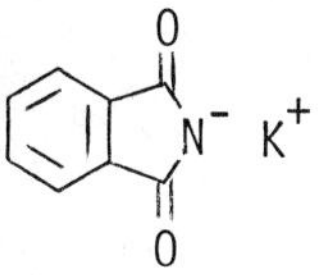 ; (ii) 1. H^+, H_2O, Δ; 2. HO^-, H_2O, Δ. Mechanisms:

(i) 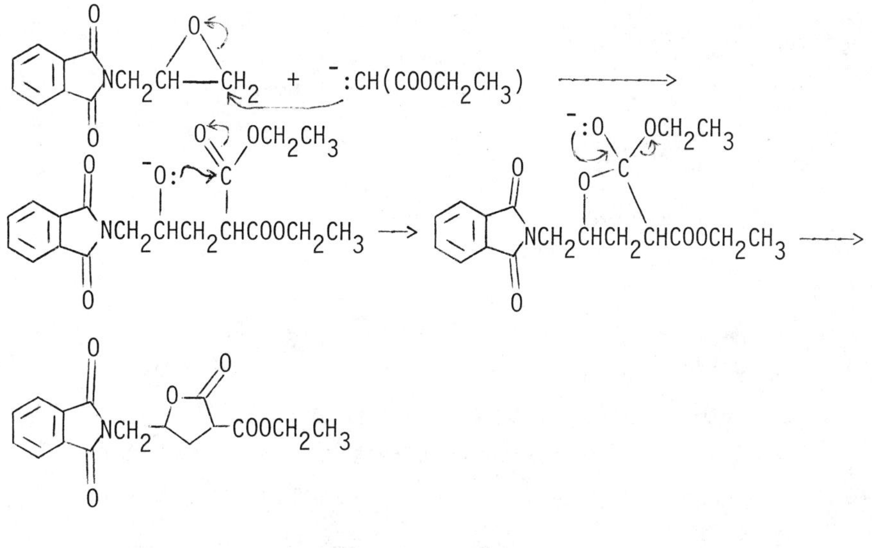

(ii)

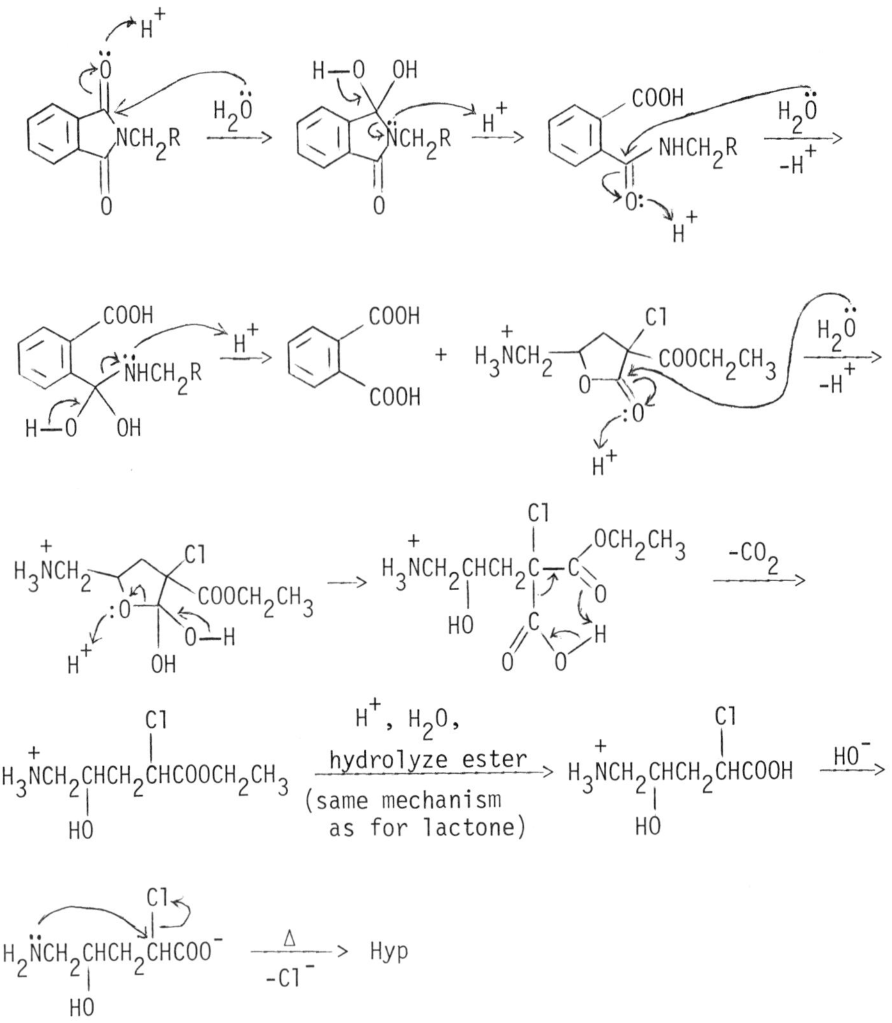

(c) There is no codon for Hyp in the table. Free Hyp is of no use to the body in the synthesis of collagen, since the body has no way of incorporating free Hyp into peptide chains. Gelatin does supply a lot of Pro, so it is useful in that regard, but it does not replace the indispensable need for vitamin C in collagen biosynthesis.

****

30. (a) AUG-GUG-CAC-CUG-ACU-CCU-GAG-GAG-AAG-etc.

initiation ↗ Val-His-Leu-Thr-Pro-Glu-Glu-Lys-etc.

(b) GAG → GUG, now codes for Val.

(c) Replacement of Glu, a polar (anionic at pH 7) amino acid, by Val, a non-polar (neutral at pH 7) one, reduces the overall polarity of the molecule, making it less water soluble. Since the non-polar Val will prefer to reside in the interior of the molecule (and it replaces an amino acid which preferred to stick out into the water), the overall shape of the molecule (i.e., the tertiary structure) is changed. This change is especially disastrous since this substitution occurs very near the beginning of the first long stretch of α-helix in the molecule. The result is a defective hemoglobin that tends to aggregate into insoluble clumps that can block blood vessels and generally reduce the blood's capability to transport oxygen.

****